17th EDITION

OCEAN SHIPS

17th EDITION

OCEAN SHIPS

ALLAN RYSZKA-ONIONS

Ian Allan
PUBLISHING

Contents

Front cover: **Norweigian Getaway :** Genting Hong Kong : *Chris Brooks*
Half title: **Anthem of the Seas :** Royal Caribbean Intl. : *ARO*
Title page: **Britannia :** Carnival Corp - P&O Cruises : *Chris Brooks*
Back cover: **Atlantic Star :** Grimaldi - Atlantic Container Line : *Atlantic Container Line*

First published 2016

ISBN 978 0 7110 3848 6

All rights reserved. No part of this book may be reproduced or
transmitted in any form or by any means, electronic or mechanical,
including photocopying, recording, scanning or by any information
storage and retrieval system, on the internet or elsewhere, without
permission from the Publisher in writing.

© Allan Ryszka-Onions 2016

Published by Ian Allan Publishing

an imprint of Ian Allan Publishing Ltd, Addlestone, Surrey KT15 2SF.
Printed in Malta.

Visit the Ian Allan Publishing website at www.ianallanpublishing.com

Preface

I would like to welcome you to *Ocean Ships* 2016 and to celebrate the fact that it is now over 50 years since the first edition was published. This, the 17th edition, retains the format of recent editions and is again in two sections: the first providing details of the major cruise ships operating world-wide and the second the fleets of major shipping companies operating deep-sea routes to Northern European ports. As in the previous edition, all illustrations are in colour and the additional information, IMO numbers, expanded vessel descriptions and cargo capacities, have been retained. Additionally, in many cases, details of vessels known to be on order have also been included.

In the three years since the previous edition, the quest for cost effectiveness has seen the size of container ships continue to grow, the largest now in the region of 20,000teu. In order to maximise the benefits, new alliances have been formed – the largest of these has been the 2M Alliance between Maersk and MSC, whilst the Ocean 3 Alliance, CMA CGM, UASC and China Shipping Container Line, remains in second place. Following pressure from the Chinese Government, COSCO and CSCL have merged and the new entity, China COSCO Shipping Corp, (COSCOCS) was officially born on 18 February 2016; how this will affect the Ocean 3 Alliance is not known. CMA CGM is likely to complete its acquisition of APL during 2016 and commercial pressures have re-opened the possibility of Hyundai Merchant Marine and Hanjin forming a working partnership. With sanctions against Iran being lifted, there are rumours that the state shipping line, IRISL, will be placing a significant order for mega box boats and it will no doubt be courted by the various Alliances.

Other major changes to reduce costs have been introduced. One of these is operating at lower steaming speeds, and hull forms of new-build box boats have been specifically designed to give optimum performance at around 20–22 knots. Many older vessels are having their bulbous bows replaced with designs that are more effective at these lower speeds. Companies have also looked at ways of increasing the capacity of existing vessels, Maersk in particular has raised the superstructure on a number of vessels to permit loading extra tiers of boxes, and, although lengthening is a well established practice, NSC has had three vessels widened from 32m to 37m, the first time such a novel approach has been attempted.

Perhaps not surprisingly, the large number of new mega container carriers entering service has led to a huge overcapacity in the market. Freight rates have fallen to record lows and a large number of older, smaller vessels placed in lay-up – at the turn of 2016 exceeding 1 million teu of capacity. Many of these vessels are destined for the breaker's torch, but with scrap prices falling due to the surfeit of cheap Chinese steel on the market, owners are reticent to sell until scrap rates recover.

But others see opportunities, and the surfeit of vessels 'for sale' has seen Greek shipowners entering the container market, firstly acquiring second hand tonnage, often followed by orders for new-builds.

The period has almost certainly seen the beginning of the end for conventional reefers. Many new large container ships are being built with additional reefer plugs and some existing reefer services have already gone over to full containerisation. It should be noted that both SeaTrade and Dole have fully cellular container vessels either in service or on order.

Vehicle carriers have also increased in size to over 70,000gt and capable of carrying 8,500ceu. They are generally fitted with movable decks, giving additional flexibility to handle large items. In many cases, the additional volume is achieved by utilising a broader beam, up to the new Panama Canal limit of 37m, whilst retaining a length of 200m, a favoured length in many ports. Some recently delivered vessels have also been fitted with an array of solar cells on the top deck, producing sufficient electricity to supply the ship's energy requirements whilst alongside.

Bulk carriers continue to be built at an alarming rate in China, again causing an overcapacity that has brought the Baltic Dry Index down to record lows. Most of these vessels are being built to standardised eco-friendly designs.

The move to natural gas as a major fuel source has brought about a huge increase in the number of large LNG carriers, capable of carrying around 175,000m³, being built. A considerable number of smaller LPG carriers are also being built to cater for the export of fracked gas from USA.

The other major change in industry operation is the introduction of emission limits in northern Europe. Shipping companies have been faced with a choice of either using higher cost, low-sulphur fuels or having scrubbers fitted to the exhaust systems of their vessels. Although the bolt-on efficiency of these units is unquestionable, they do little for the aesthetics of the ship's design, and many new vessels are now being built with scrubbers incorporated at the design stage.

The popularity of cruising seems to be showing no slow-down and most of the major operators have new tonnage on order, generally for mega-carriers catering for upwards of 4,000 passengers, although there has also been an increase in the number of small companies offering 'expedition' cruises particularly to the North and South Poles. The other interesting aspect of the cruise industry is that companies are tapping into the growing market for Chinese cruisers and are basing vessels in Shanghai to service this potentially lucrative new market. But speed is of the essence as the Chinese are already building their own cruise ships.

Following comments received after the previous edition, I have listed more tanker fleets whose vessels are regularly seen in Northern European ports. This has meant that in order to keep the book to an acceptable size something had to go. In this case I have removed most Far Eastern owned bulkers and VLCCs that largely trade between Japan and Australia or the Middle East. I have also removed most of the smaller Far Eastern owned container vessels that only trade locally and do not visit Europe.

In order to keep the book as up to date as possible, I have included, where possible, names and/or IMO numbers of a number of vessels on order with major operators, together with shipyard, yard number and expected delivery date where known, but it should be remembered that on occasion orders can be cancelled or delayed for a variety of reasons, vessels sold prior to delivery or possibly exchanged depending on market conditions, ie bulkers swapped for tankers as recently seen with the Scorpio Group.

I would like to express my thanks to all who have provided their excellent photographs for this edition and to my many friends, acquaintances and correspondents for their interest, comments and information. I would also like to thank my wife Roz, and daughter Natasha, for putting up with my incarceration in my office for many, many hours, particularly as deadline day drew nearer.

Allan Ryszka-Onions
Havant, England
April 2016

Disclaimer

The publishers, the shipping companies and the author accept no liability for any loss or damage caused by any error, inaccuracy or omission in the information published in this edition of *Ocean Ships*.

Maersk Niteroi : Cie. Maritime Belge - Delphis n.v. : *Hans Kraijenbosch*

Glossary

The companies in each section are listed in alphabetical order under the main company name, followed by the country of origin. Individual 'one-ship' owning companies are not given, but in some cases subsidiary fleets are separately listed. Other variations in ownership, joint ownership, management or charter are generally covered by footnotes. Funnel and hull colours are those normally used by the companies, although these may vary when a vessel is operating on a particular service, or on charter to another operator. Where both owners and operators are listed the vessel will generally appear in the owners list,

name registered name
eng. all vessels are single screw motorships unless indicated after the name as having more than one screw or other types of main propulsive machinery as follows

as	sail with auxiliary engines
df	dual fuel diesel electric
tf	trifuel diesel electric
me	diesel with electric drive
gm	combined gas turbine and diesel with electric drive
gt	gas turbine with electric drive
st	steam turbine
p	directional pod propulsion system

flags

Are	United Arab Emirates	Cni	Canary Islands	Isr	Israel	Pmd	Madeira
Arg	Argentina	Cuw	Curaçao	Ita	Italy	Prt	Portugal
Atf	Kerguelen Islands	Cym	Cayman Islands	Jpn	Japan	Qat	Qatar
Atg	Antigua and Barbuda	Cyp	Cyprus	Kor	South Korea	Rif	French International
Aus	Australia	Deu	Germany	Kwt	Kuwait	Rus	Russia
Bel	Belgium	Dis	Danish International	Lbr	Liberia	Sau	Saudi Arabia
Bgr	Bulgaria	Dnk	Denmark	Lux	Luxembourg	Sey	Seychelles
Bhr	Bahrain	Egy	Egypt	Lva	Latvia	Sgp	Singapore
Bhs	Bahamas	Eth	Ethiopia	Mex	Mexico	Swe	Sweden
Bmu	Bermuda	Fin	Finland	Mhl	Marshall Islands	Tha	Thailand
Bra	Brazil	Fra	France	Mlt	Malta	Twn	Taiwan
Brb	Barbados	Gbr	United Kingdom	Mys	Malaysia	Usa	United States of America
Brn	Brunei Darussalam	Gib	Gibraltar	Nis	Norwegian International	Vct	St. Vincent and
Can	Canada	Grc	Greece	Nld	Netherlands		Grenadines
Che	Switzerland	Hkg	Hong Kong (China)	Nor	Norway	Ven	Venezuela
Chl	Chile	Hrv	Croatia	Pan	Panama	Zaf	South Africa
Chn	China	Iom	Isle of Man (British)	Phl	Philippines		

year year of completion - not necessarily of launching or commissioning.
gt gross tonnage – not weight, but volume of hull and enclosed space measured under 1969 International Tonnage Convention
dwt deadweight tonnes – maximum weight of cargo, stores, fuel etc – one tonne (1000 kg) equals 0.984 ton (British)
loa overall length (metres); (- -) length between perpendiculars
bm overall breadth of hull (metres) – some vessels have greater width to superstructure/bridge etc.
kts service speed in normal weather and at normal service draught – one knot equals 6,050ft per hour or 1.146 mph.
type general description of type of vessel
pass maximum number of passengers in lower and upper berths or (——) in lower berths only

vessel types :

bbu	bulk carrier	gpc	cargo/part container	tco	tanker – oil products
bbp	bulk - pitch carrier	gmp	cargo/multipurpose	tcr	tanker – crude oil
bcb	bulk/container	goh	cargo – open hatch	tcs	tanker – shuttle
bce	cement carrier	grf	refrigerated cargo	tfj	tanker – fruit juice
bor	ore carrier	lng	liquefied natural gas	tms	tanker – molten sulphur
brs	refined sugar carrier	lpg	liquefied petroleum gas	mve	vehicle carrier
bsd	bulk - self discharging	mlv	livestock carrier	ucc	cellular container
bwc	bulk woodchip carrier	ocl	cable layer	urc	ro-ro/container
cbo	ore/bulk/oil carrier	ohl	heavy-lift/semi-submersible	urh	ro-ro/heavy lift
ggc	general cargo	tci	tanker – icebreaker	urr	roll-on, roll-off
ghl	heavy-lift vessel	tch	tanker – chemical		

remarks:

conv	converted from other ship type (with date where known)	wid	date hull widened
ex:	previous names followed by year of change to subsequent name	NE	date re-engined
		teu	twenty-foot equivalent unit (one teu equals about 14 tonnes deadweight)
c/a	name as completed		
l/a	name at launch or 'float-out' prior to completion	ceu	car equivalent units (based on typical family car of 1,500kg)
l/d	name allocated when laid-down at commencement of construction	cr(x)	number of cranes on heavy lift and multipurpose vessels and their maximum safe working load (swl), only those over 100t lift included – NB, in many cases the cranes can be used in tandem
pt:	part of ship		
len	date hull lengthened		
rbt	rebuilt	m^3	cargo capacity of gas carriers in cubic metres
sht	date hull shortened		

tankers:

ULCC	crude tankers 300,000-500,000 dwt	
VLCC	crude tankers 200,000-299,999 dwt	
Malaccamax	draft constraint of 25m	largest vessel capable of navigating Strait of Malacca
Suezmax	draft constraint of 20m	largest vessel capable of navigating the Suez Canal
Aframax	80,000-120,000dwt	largest vessel in the Average Freight Rate Assessment Scale

Bulkers:

Handysize	15,000-50,000 dwt	
Handymax	35,000-50,000 dwt	
Panamax *	65,000-80,000 dwt	limited by maximum width 32m (37m, when new locks opened)
Capesize	100,000-180,000 dwt	vessel too large to navigate the Suez Canal

* term can be applied to all vessel types

Explorer of the Seas : Royal Caribbean Intl. : *Chris Brooks*

Part One
Passenger Liners and Cruise Ships

Marco Polo : Cruise & Maritime Voyages : *ARO*

All Leisure Holidays Ltd.   **U.K.**

Voyages of Discovery, U.K.
funnel: *white with narrow turquoise band below blue top or with pale/dark blue wave symbol.* **hull:** *white with blue or red boot-topping.*
history: *commenced cruises in 1984 with chartered ships until acquiring vessel in 2004.* **web:** *www.voyagesofdiscovery.com*

8709573	Voyager	(2)	Bhs	1990	15,271	153	20	18	556	ex Alexander von Humboldt-12, Alexander von Humboldt II-08, Jules Verne-08, Walrus-07, Nautican-96, Crown Monarch-94

Swan Hellenic, U.K.
funnel: *dark blue with gold swan symbol.* **hull:** *Dark blue with red boot-topping.* **history:** *commenced operations in 1954 as Swan's Hellenic Cruises by Swan travel agency using chartered ships. Acquired 1983 by P&O, but closed by Carnival acquisition in 2007, when brand acquired by Lord Sterling and 2008 recommenced operations after acquisition by All Leisure.* **web:** *www.swanhellenic.com*

9144196	Minerva	(2)	Bhs	1996	12,449	133	20	14	350	ex Explorer II-08, Alexander von Humboldt-05, Explorer II-05, Saga Pearl-05, Minerva-03, l/a Okean

Hebridean International Cruises Ltd., U.K.
funnel: *red with narrow black top.* **hull:** *black with narrow white line above red boot-topping.* **history:** *founded 1988 as Hebridean Island Cruises to 2006.* **web:** *www.hebridean.co.uk*

6409351	Hebridean Princess	(2)	Gbr	1964	2,112	72	14	14	49	ex Columba-89

Carnival Corporation   **U.S.A.**

funnel: *red forward, blue aft, separated by vertical curved white arc.* **hull:** *white with narrow red band, blue boot-topping.* **history:** *founded 1972 as Carnival Cruise Lines Inc until 1993. Between 1989 and 2001 acquired numerous other operators to become the largest cruising company with many brands aimed at different markets. The expansion continued with joint venture with TUI in 2006 and a joint venture with Iberojet in 2007, the same year as Swan Hellenic was closed down and Windstar Cruises was sold.* **web:** *www.carnivalplc.com or www.carnivalcorp.com*

9555723	Carnival Breeze	(me2p)	Pan	2012	128,500	304	37	22	3,652	
9198355	Carnival Conquest	(me2p)	Pan	2002	110,239	290	36	19	3,700	
9378474	Carnival Dream	(me2p)	Pan	2009	128,251	304	37	22	3,646	
8711344	Carnival Ecstasy	(me2)	Pan	1991	70,526	262	32	18	2,634	ex Ecstasy-07
9118721	Carnival Elation	(me2)	Pan	1998	70,390	262	32	20	2,634	ex Elation-07
8700773	Carnival Fantasy	(me2)	Pan	1990	70,367	261	32	18	2,634	ex Fantasy-07
9041253	Carnival Fascination	(me2)	Bhs	1994	70,538	262	32	18	2,624	ex Fascination-07
9333149	Carnival Freedom	(me2)	Pan	2007	110,320	290	36	21	3,783	
9198367	Carnival Glory	(me2)	Pan	2003	110,239	290	36	22	3,700	
9053878	Carnival Imagination	(me2)	Bhs	1995	70,367	262	32	18	2,624	ex Imagination-07
9187489	Carnival Inspiration	(me2)	Bhs	1996	70,367	262	32	18	2,634	ex Inspiration-07
9224726	Carnival Legend	(me2p)	Pan	2002	85,942	293	32	22	2,680	
9278181	Carnival Liberty	(me2)	Pan	2005	110,320	285	32	22	3,700	
9378486	Carnival Magic	(me2p)	Pan	2011	128,048	304	37	22	3,652	
9237357	Carnival Miracle	(me2p)	Pan	2004	85,942	293	32	22	2,680	
9120877	Carnival Paradise	(me2p)	Pan	1998	70,390	262	32	21	2,634	ex Paradise-07
9223954	Carnival Pride	(me2p)	Pan	2001	85,920	293	32	22	2,680	
8711356	Carnival Sensation	(me2)	Bhs	1993	70,538	262	32	20	2,634	ex Sensation-07
9188647	Carnival Spirit	(me2p)	Pan	2001	85,920	293	32	22	2,680	
9333163	Carnival Splendor	(me2)	Pan	2008	113,323	290	36	22	3,540	
9070058	Carnival Sunshine	(me2)	Bhs	1996	103,881	272	36	18	3,006	ex Carnival Destiny-13 (rbt. 2013)
9138850	Carnival Triumph	(me2)	Bhs	1999	101,509	272	36	21	3,470	
9236389	Carnival Valor	(me2)	Pan	2004	110,239	290	36	22	3,710	
9172648	Carnival Victory	(me2)	Pan	2000	101,509	272	36	22	3,470	
9692569	Carnival Vista		Bmu	2016	135,000	322			3,954	

newbuildings:

9767091				2018	135,000				3,954	Fincantieri 6243

Aida Cruises, Germany
funnel: *white with 'AIDA' (letters in blue, red, yellow and green respectively).* **hull:** *white with red 'lips' and 'eye' and blue wave symbols on bows.* **history:** *originally founded 1999 as joint venture between by P&O and Arkona Touristik which merged with Seetours International in 2000.* **web:** *www.aida.de*

9221566	AIDAaura *	(me2)	Ita	2003	42,289	203	28	19	1,582	
9362542	AIDAbella	(me2)	Ita	2008	69,203	249	32	21	2,030	
9398888	AIDAblu	(me2)	Ita	2010	71,304	252	32	21	2,174	
9112789	AIDAcara	(2)	Ita	1996	38,557	193	28	18	1,186	ex Aida-01
9334856	AIDAdiva	(me2)	Ita	2007	69,203	252	32	21	2,030	
9334868	AIDAluna	(me2)	Ita	2010	69,203	252	32	21	2,030	
9490052	AIDAmar *	(me2)	Ita	2012	71,304	249	32	21	2,174	
9636955	AIDAprima *	(me2p)	Ita	2016	125,572	300	38	21	3,250	

Minerva : All Leisure Holidays - Swan Hellenic : *Mike Lennon*

Carnival Legend : Carnival Corp : *F. de Vries*

IMO#	name	screws	flag	year	gt	loa	bm	kts	pass	comments
9490040	AIDAsol *	(me2)	Ita	2011	71,304	252	32	21	2,174	
9601132	AIDAstella	(me2)	Ita	2013	71,304	253	32	21	2,050	
9221554	AIDAvita *	(me2)	Ita	2002	42,289	203	28	19	1,582	
newbuildings:										
9636967	*AIDAperla*				125.500	300	38	21	3,250	[Hyperion 2] MHI Nagasaki 2301
					183,200				6,600	[Helios 1 – LNG fuel] Meyer Werft
					183,200				6,600	[Helios 3 – LNG fuel] Meyer Werft

* owned by Costa Crociere SpA

Costa Crociere SpA, Italy

funnel: *yellow with blue 'C' and black top.* **hull:** *white with blue boot-topping.* **history:** *founded 1924 and entered passenger shipping 1947. Acquired by Airtours and Carnival joint venture in 1997, Carnival acquiring complete control in 2001.* **web:** *www.costacruise.com or www.costacruises.co.uk*

IMO#	name	screws	flag	year	gt	loa	bm	kts	pass	comments
9187796	Costa Atlantica	(me2p)	Ita	2000	85,619	293	32	22	2,680	
9398917	Costa Deliziosa	(me2p)	Ita	2010	92,720	294	32		2,828	
9636888	Costa Diadema	(me2p)	Ita	2014	132,500	306	37	21	4,977	
9479864	Costa Fascinosa	(me2)	Ita	2012	113,216	290	36	21	3,780	
9479852	Costa Favolosa	(me2?)	Ita	2011	113,216	290	36	21	3,780	
9239783	Costa Fortuna	(me2)	Ita	2003	102,587	272	36	20	3,470	
9239795	Costa Magica	(me2)	Ita	2004	102,587	272	36	20	3,470	
9398905	Costa Luminosa	(me2p)	Ita	2009	92,720	294	32		2,828	
9237345	Costa Mediterranea	(me2p)	Ita	2003	85,619	293	32	22	2,680	
8716502	Costa neoClassica	(2)	Ita	1991	52,926	221	31	19	1,766	ex Costa Classica-14
9172777	Costa neoRiviera	(me2)	Ita	1999	48,200	216	29	19	1,667	ex Grand Mistral-13, Mistral-05
8821046	Costa neoRomantica	(2)	Ita	1993	57,150	230	40	19	1,782	ex Costa Romantica-12 (rbt 2011)
9378498	Costa Pacifica	(me2)	Ita	2009	114,288	290	36	21	3,780	
9343132	Costa Serena	(me2)	Ita	2007	114,147	290	36	21	3,780	
9109031	Costa Victoria	(me2)	Ita	1996	75,166	253	32	23	2,200	
newbuildings:										
				2019	183,200				6,600	[Helios 2 – LNG fuel] Meyer Turku
				2020	183,200				6,600	[Helios 4 – LNG fuel] Meyer Turku

*managed by Polaris Shipping Co.,Seoul, S. Korea

AIDAstella : Carnival Corp - AIDA Cruises : *Nico Kemps*

IMO#	name	screws	flag	year	gt	loa	bm	kts	pass	comments

Cunard Line Ltd., U.K.

funnel: *red with two narrow black rings and black top.* **hull:** *charcoal grey with red boot-topping.* **history:** *founded 1840 as British and North American RMSP Co by Samuel Cunard, becoming Cunard Steam-Ship Co Ltd in 1878. Merged with White Star Line in 1930's. Company acquired by Trafalgar House Investments in 1971 and acquired Norwegian America Cruises in 1983. Trafalgar acquired by Kvaerner in 1996 and Cunard sold to Carnival in 1998.* **web:** *www.cunard.com or www.cunard.co.uk*

IMO#	name	screws	flag	year	gt	loa	bm	kts	pass	comments
9477438	Queen Elizabeth	(me2p)	Bmu	2010	90,901	294	32	23	2,092	
9421061	Queen Mary 2	(gme4p)	Bmu	2003	148,528	345	41	29	2,620	
9320556	Queen Victoria	(me2p)	Bmu	2007	90,049	294	32	23	2,014	

Holland-America Line, Netherlands

funnel: *white with black/white ship symbol within double black ring, narrow black top or vents.* **hull:** *black with red boot-topping.* **history:** *founded 1873 as Nederlandsch Amerikaansche Stoomvaart Maatschappij. Later Holland America Cruises Inc until 1983 merger with Westours Inc to form Holland America Westours Inc to 2002. Acquired 50% share in Windstar Cruises in 1987 and acquired Home Lines in 1988. Acquired by Carnival in 1989.* **Web:** *www.hollandamerica.com*

IMO#	name	screws	flag	year	gt	loa	bm	kts	pass	comments
9188037	Amsterdam	(me2p)	Nld	2000	62,735	238	32	21	1,738	
9378448	Eurodam	(me2p)	Nld	2008	86,273	285	32	22	2,104	
9692557	Koningsdam	(me2p)	Nld	2016	99,836	296	38	21	2,648	
8919257	Maasdam	(me2)	Nld	1993	55,575	219	31	20	1,629	
9378450	Nieuw Amsterdam	(me2p)	Nld	2010	86,273	290	32	24	2,106	
9230115	Noordam	(gme2p)	Nld	2006	82,318	290	32	24	1,800	
9221281	Oosterdam	(gme2p)	Nld	2003	82,305	285	32	22	2,388	
8700280	Prinsendam	(2)	Nld	1988	38,848	204	29	21	837	ex Seabourn Sun-02, Royal Viking Sun-99
9122552	Rotterdam	(me2)	Nld	1997	61,849	238	32	22	1,620	
9102992	Veendam	(me2)	Nld	1996	57,092	219	31	20	1,629	
9156515	Volendam	(me2)	Nld	1999	61,214	237	32	22	1,824	
9226891	Westerdam	(gme2p)	Nld	2004	82,348	285	32	22	1,800	
9156527	Zaandam	(me2)	Nld	2000	61,396	237	32	22	2,272	
9221279	Zuiderdam	(gme2p)	Nld	2002	82,305	285	32	22	1,848	
newbuilding:										
				2018	99,500				2,650	Fincantieri [Pinnacle class]

Costa Deliziosa : Carnival Corp - Costa Cruise Line : *Mike Lennon*

Rotterdam : Carnival Corp - Holland Amerika Linie : *Roy Fenton*

Azura : Carnival Corp - P&O Cruises : *Mike Lennon*

Royal Princess : Carnival Corp - Princess Cruises : *Chris Brooks*

IMO#	name	screws	flag	year	gt	loa	bm	kts	pass	comments

P&O Cruises Ltd., U.K.

funnel: *blue with gold rising sun logo.* **hull:** *white with partial Union Flag at bow, red boot-topping.* **history:** *founded 1837 as Peninsular Steam Navigation Co, becoming Peninsular & Oriental Steam Navigation Co in 1840. P&P-Orient Lines formed 1961 when remaining Orient Lines shares acquired. Princess Cruises acquired 1974. P&O Princess Cruises remerged from P&O in 2000. Acquired by Carnival in 2003.* **web:** *www.pocruises.co.uk*

IMO#	name	screws	flag	year	gt	loa	bm	kts	pass	comments
9210220	Adonia *	(me2)	Bmu	2001	30,277	181	25	18	777	ex Royal Princess-11, Minerva II-07, R Eight-03
9226906	Arcadia	(me2p)	Bmu	2005	83,781	285	32	22	2,556	l/dn Queen Victoria
9169524	Aurora	(me2)	Bmu	2000	76,152	270	32	24	1,878	
9424883	Azura	(me2)	Bmu	2010	115,055	290	36	22	3,076	
9614036	Britannia	(me2p)	Bmu	2015	143,730	330	44	21	3,647	
9169550	Oceana	(me2)	Bmu	1999	77,499	261	32	21	2,272	ex Ocean Princess-02
9050137	Oriana	(2)	Bmu	1995	69,840	260	32	24	2,108	
9333175	Ventura	(me2)	Bmu	2008	116,017	290	36	22	3,100	

* *in April 2016 Adonia will transfer within the Carnival Corporation to a new brand called Fathom Travel, operating out of Miami and catering for those who wish to work alongside local communities in the Dominican Republic*

P&O Cruises Australia Ltd., Australia

funnel: *blue with small white 'Pacific' and large yellow 'Star or Sun'.* **hull:**. *white with broad blue above narrow yellow bands.* **history:** *formed 1987 as P&O Resorts Pty Ltd to 1998, then as P&O Australian Resorts Pty Ltd to 2004* **web:** *www.pocruises.com.au*

IMO#	name	screws	flag	year	gt	loa	bm	kts	pass	comments
8919269	Pacific Aria	(me2)	Gbr	1994	55,819	219	31	20	1,629	ex Ryndam-15
8521232	Pacific Dawn	(me2)	Gbr	1991	70,285	245	32	19	1,900	ex Regal Princess-07
8919245	Pacific Eden	(me2)	Gbr	1993	55,819	219	31	20	1,629	ex Statendam-15
8521220	Pacific Jewel	(me2)	Gbr	1990	70,310	245	32	19	1,900	ex Ocean Village Two-09, AIDAblu-07, A'Rosa Blu-04, Crown Princess-02
8611398	Pacific Pearl *	(me2)	Gbr	1989	63,786	246	32	19	1,692	ex Ocean Village-10, Arcadia-03, Star Princess-97, Sitmar Fairmajesty-89

* *to be transferred to Cruise & Maritime Voyages in March 2017, to be renamed Columbus*

Princess Cruises Inc., U.S.A.

funnel: *white funnel with blue/white 'Princess' flowing hair insignia,* **hull:** *white with green boot-topping.* **history:** *founded 1965 and acquired by P&O in 1974. Acquired Sitmar in 1988. Demerged as P&O-Princess Cruises in 2000 and acquired by Carnival in 2003.* **web:** *www.princesscruises.com*

IMO#	name	screws	flag	year	gt	loa	bm	kts	pass	comments
9215490	Caribbean Princess *	(me2)	Bmu	2004	112,894	290	36	22	3,798	l/dn Crown Princess
9229659	Coral Princess	(gme2)	Bmu	2002	91,627	294	32	21	2,581	
9293399	Crown Princess	(me2)	Bmu	2006	113,561	290	36	22	3,599	
9103996	Dawn Princess	(me2)	Bmu	1997	77,441	261	32	21	1,950	
9228198	Diamond Princess *	(me2)	Bmu	2004	115,875	290	38	23	2,600	l/dn Sapphire Princess
9333151	Emerald Princess	(gme2)	Bmu	2007	113,561	290	36	22	3,599	
9192351	Golden Princess	(me2)	Bmu	2001	108,865	290	36	22	3,300	
9104005	Grand Princess	(me2)	Bmu	1998	108,806	290	36	22	3,300	
9230402	Island Princess	(gme2)	Bmu	2003	91,627	294	32	24	2,581	
9187887	Pacific Princess	(me2)	Bmu	1999	30,277	181	25	18	688	ex R Three-02
9584724	Regal Princess	(me2)	Bmu	2014	142,714	330	38	22	3,600	
9584712	Royal Princess	(me2)	Bmu	2013	142,714	330	38	22	3,600	
9378462	Ruby Princess	(me2)	Bmu	2008	113,561	290	36	22	3,599	
9228186	Sapphire Princess *	(me2)	Bmu	2004	115,875	290	38	23	3,078	l/dn Diamond Princess
9150913	Sea Princess	(me2)	Bmu	1998	77,499	261	32	19	2,342	ex Adonia-05, Sea Princess-03
9192363	Star Princess	(me2)	Bmu	2002	108,977	290	36	22	3,211	
9000259	Sun Princess	(me2)	Bmu	1995	77,441	261	32	21	2,342	
newbuilding:										
9614141	Majestic Princess **		Bmu	2017	143,000	330	38		3,560	Fincantieri

* *owned by Princess Cruise Lines, Bermuda.,* ** *to be based Shanghai, also carries name Sheng Shi Gong Zhu Hao*
Dawn Pricesss to be renamed Pacific Explorer in 2017

Seabourn Cruises Inc., U.S.A.

funnel: *white with three narrow white lines forming 'S' on blue shield and blue top.* **hull:** *white with pale blue band and blue boot-topping.* **history:** *founded 1987 by Norwegian industrialist. Carnival acquired 25% in 1991, a further 25% in 1996 and the balance in 1998.* **web:** *www.seabourn.com*

IMO#	name	screws	flag	year	gt	loa	bm	kts	pass	comments
9417086	Seabourn Odyssey	(me2)	Bhs	2009	32,346	198	26	19	450	
9483126	Seabourn Quest	(me2)	Bhs	2011	32,346	198	26	19	450	
9417098	Seabourn Sojourn	(me2)	Bhs	2010	32,346	198	26	19	450	
newbuildings:										
9731171	Seabourn Encore		Bhs	2016	40,350	210	28	18	604	Fincantieri
9764958	Seabourn Ovation		Bhs	2018	40,350	210	28	18	604	

Celestyal Cruises   Cyprus

funnel: *white with red sun/wave symbol above dark blue 'L', black top.* **hull:** *white with red or dark blue boot-topping.* **history:** *founded 1935 and commenced shipping owning in 1987, trading as Louis Cruise Line until September 2014 when restyled to present name.* **web:** *www.louisgroup.com or www.celestyalcruises.com*

IMO#	name	screws	flag	year	gt	loa	bm	kts	pass	comments
7827213	Celestyal Cristal *	(2)	Mlt	1980	25,611	159	25	21	1,452	ex Louis Cristal-15, Cristal-11, Opera-07, Silja Opera-06, Superstar Taurus-02, Leeward-00, Sally Albatross-95, Viking Saga-86
9183518	Celestyal Odyssey	(2)	Bhs	2001	24,318	178	26	27	836	ex Explorer-15, Olympia Explorer-04, I/a Olympic Explorer
7927984	Celestyal Olympia *	(2)	Cyp	1982	37,773	215	28	20	1,664	ex Louis Olympia-15, Thomson Destiny-12, Sunbird-05, Song of America-99
6821080	Louis Aura *	(2)	Mlt	1968	15,781	160	23	20	928	ex Orient Queen-13, Bolero-04, Starward-95

* owned by Louis plc

Cruise & Maritime Voyages   U.K.

funnel: *white with dark blue 'CMV' below sail symbol or dark blue with symbols on white disc.* **hull:** *white with red boot-topping* **history:** *founded 2010.* **web:** *www.cruiseandmaritime.com*

IMO#	name	screws	flag	year	gt	loa	bm	kts	pass	comments
8506373	Astor *	(2)	Bhs	1987	20,606	176	23	18	620	ex Fedor Dostoevskiy-95, Astor-88
5383304	Azores **	(2)	Pmd	1948	16,144	160	21	18	566	Athena-13, Caribe-05, Valtur Prima-03, Italia Prima-00, Italia I-93, Fridtjof Nansen-93, Volker-86, Volkerfreundschaft-85, Stockholm-60
8217881	Magellan *	(2)	Pmd	1985	46,052	222	28	22	1,794	ex Grand Holiday-15, Holiday-09
6417097	Marco Polo *		Bhs	1965	22,080	176	24	16	850	ex Aleksandr-91, Aleksandr Pushkin-91

chartered from * Global Cruise Lines Ltd., Greece; ** Cale Sgps SA (Island Cruises Transportes), Portugal

Disney Cruise Line   U.S.A.

funnel: *red with white 'Mickey Mouse' symbol over three black waves, black top.* **hull:** *black with white band above red boot-topping.* **history:** *founded 1995 as a subsidiary of Walt Disney World Corp.* **web:** *www-disneycruise.com*

IMO#	name	screws	flag	year	gt	loa	bm	kts	pass	comments
8434254	Disney Dream	(me2p)	Bhs	2010	129,690	340	38		4,000	
9445590	Disney Fantasy	(me2p)	Bhs	2012	129,750	340	38		4,000	
9126807	Disney Magic	(me2)	Bhs	1998	83,338	294	32	21	2,500	
9126819	Disney Wonder	(me2)	Bhs	1999	83,308	294	32	21	2,500	

Genting Hong Kong Ltd.   Hong Kong

Crystal Cruises Inc., U.S.A.

funnel: *black, large white side panels with blue symbol.* **hull:** *white with narrow blue band.* **history:** *formed 1988 by NYK (founded 1885 – see cargo section), sold to Genting Hong Kong in May 2015.* **web:** *www.crystalcruises.com*

IMO#	name	screws	flag	year	gt	loa	bm	kts	pass	comments
8705266	Crystal Esprit	(2)	Pan	1991	3,341	82	14	16	82	ex MegaStar Taurus-15, Aurora I-94, Lady D-91, I/a Lady Diana
9243667	Crystal Serenity	(me2p)	Bhs	2003	68,870	250	32	23	1,080	
9066667	Crystal Symphony	(me2)	Bhs	1995	51,044	238	31	21	975	

newbuildings:

IMO#	name	screws	flag	year	gt	loa	bm	kts	pass	comments
	Crystal Exclusive			2018	100,000				1,000	Lloyd Werft, Bremerhaven

Also 2 further 100,000gt, 1,000px ice-class [Lloyd Werft (2019/20)]

Dream Cruises, Hong Kong
newbuildings:

IMO#	name	screws	flag	year	gt	loa	bm	kts	pass	comments
9733105	Genting Dream		Hkg	2016	150,000	330			3,364	Meyer Werft 711
9733117	World Dream		Hkg	2017	150,000	330			3,364	Meyer Werft 712

Norwegian Cruise Line, U.S.A.

funnel: *dark blue with gold 'NCL' within gold square outline.* **hull:** *white, many with multi-coloured artwork) blue boot-topping.* **history:** *founded in 1967 as Norwegian Caribbean Lines by Klosters Rederi, becoming Kloster Cruise AS in 1987 and Norwegian Cruise Line in 1996. Acquired Royal Viking Line in 1984 and Royal Cruise Line in 1989. Aquired Prestige Cruises Gp, Oceania Cruises and Regent Seven Seas Cruises in 2014 - www.ncl.com*

IMO#	name	screws	flag	year	gt	loa	bm	kts	pass	comments
9606912	Norwegian Breakaway	(me2p)	Bhs	2013	144,017	354	43	21	4,000	
9195169	Norwegian Dawn	(me2)	Bhs	2002	92,250	292	32	25	2,500	I/dn SuperStar Sagittarius
9410569	Norwegian Epic	(me2)	Bhs	2010	155,873	325	40	21	4,200	
9677076	Norwegian Escape	(me2p)	Bhs	2015	165,167	335	42	21	4,248	
9355733	Norwegian Gem	(me2)	Bhs	2007	93,000	294	32	24	2,384	
9606924	Norwegian Getaway	(me2p)	Bhs	2014	144,017	354	43	21	4,000	
9304057	Norwegian Jade	(me2p)	Bhs	2006	92,250	294	32	24	2,400	ex Pride of Hawaii-08

Seabourn Odyssey : Carnival Corp - Seabourn Cruises : *Chris Brooks*

Louis Aura : Celestyal Cruises : *F. de Vries*

Magellan : Cruise & Maritime Voyages : *Nico Kemps*

Crystal Symphony : Genting Hong Kong - Crystal Cruises : *F. de Vries*

Norwegian Breakaway : Genting Hong Kong - Norwegian Cruise Line : *Mike Lennon*

Norwegian Getaway : Genting Hong Kong - Norwegian Cruise Line : *Chris Brooks*

IMO#	name	screws	flag	year	gt	loa	bm	kts	pass	comments
9304045	Norwegian Jewel	(me2p)	Bhs	2005	91,740	294	32	24	2,400	
9342281	Norwegian Pearl	(me2)	Bhs	2006	93,500	294	32	24	2,400	
9128532	Norwegian Sky	(me2p)	Bhs	1999	77,104	260	32	20	2,450	ex Pride of Aloha-08, Norwegian Sky-04, l/dn Costa Olympia
9141065	Norwegian Spirit	(me2)	Bhs	1998	75,338	269	32	24	2,975	ex SuperStar Leo-04
9195157	Norwegian Star	(me2p)	Bhs	2001	91,740	294	32	24	2,500	l/dn SuperStar Libra
9218131	Norwegian Sun	(me2)	Bhs	2001	78,309	258	32	20	2,359	
9209221	Pride of America	(me2p)	Usa	2005	80,439	276	32	22	2,146	
newbuildings:										
9703796	*Norwegian Bliss*			2017	165,000	335	42	21	4,248	[Breakaway Plus 2] Meyer Werft 694
9751509				2018	164,000	335	42	21	4,248	[Breakaway Plus 3] Meyer Werft
9751511										[Breakaway Plus 4] Meyer Werft

2 further Breakaway Plus 335m 4,200px [2018-2019]

Oceania Cruises, U.S.A.

funnel: *white with blue 'O' symbol.* **hull:** *white.* **history:** *founded 2002, the three original ships being chartered until purchased in 2006. Private equity firm acquired majority stake in 2007.* **web:** *www.oceaniacruiseline.com*

IMO#	name	screws	flag	year	gt	loa	bm	kts	pass	comments
9156462	Insignia	(me2)	Mhl	1998	30,277	181	25	18	684	ex Columbus 2-14, Insignia-12, R One-03
9438066	Marina	(me2)	Mhl	2011	66,084	252	32	20	1,260	
9200938	Nautica	(me2)	Mhl	2000	30,277	181	25	18	684	ex Blue Star-05, R Five-04
9156474	Regatta	(me2)	Mhl	1998	30,277	181	25	18	684	ex Insignia-03, R Two-03
9438078	Riviera	(me2)	Mhl	2012	66,172	252	32	20	1,260	
9187899	Sirena	(me2)	Bmu	1999	30,277	181	25	18	684	ex Ocean Princess-16, Tahitian Princess-09, R Four-02

Managed by V. Ships Leisure SAM, Monaco

Regent Seven Seas Cruises Inc., U.S.A.

funnel: *white with purple 'Regent'.* **hull:** *white with blue band and blue waterline above red boot-topping.* **history:** *originally founded 1992 as Diamond Cruise Line, later becoming Radisson Seven Seas Cruises to 2006. Acquired by Apollo Management equity group in 2008.* **web:** *www.rssc.com*

IMO#	name	screws	flag	year	gt	loa	bm	kts	pass	comments
9210139	Seven Seas Mariner	(me2p)	Wlf	2001	48,075	216	29	19	769	
9064126	Seven Seas Navigator	(2)	Bhs	1999	28,550	171	24	17	542	l/dn Akademik Nikolay Pilyugin (1991)

Marina : Genting Hong Kong - Oceania Cruises : *Mike Lennon*

Seven Seas Voyager : Genting Hong Kong - Regent Seven Seas Cruises : *F. de Vries*

Fram : Hurtigruten : *ARO*

MSC Sinfonia : MSC Cruises : *Nico Kemps*

IMO#	name	screws	flag	year	gt	loa	bm	kts	pass	comments
9247144	Seven Seas Voyager	(me2p)	Bhs	2003	41,500	207	29	20	769	
newbuildings:										
9703150	*Seven Seas Explorer*		Bhs	2016	54,000				750	

Star Cruise AS Sendirian Berhad, Malaysia

funnel: *dark blue with yellow eight-pointed star on broad red band.* **hull:** *white with red band and blue boot-topping.*
history: *formed 1993 and acquired Norwegian Cruise Line in 2000.* **web:** *www.starcruises.com*

IMO#	name	screws	flag	year	gt	loa	bm	kts	pass	comments
8314122	Henna *	(2)	Mlt	1986	47,262	225	28	19	1,800	ex Pacific Sun-12, Jubilee-04
8705278	MegaStar Aries	(2)	Pan	1991	3,264	82	14	16	82	ex Aurora II-94, l/a Lady Sarah
8710857	Star Pisces	(2)	Pan	1990	40,053	177	30	22	2,165	ex Kalypso-93
9008421	SuperStar Aquarius	(2)	Bhs	1993	51,309	230	32	18	2,100	ex Norwegian Wind-07, Windward-98 (len-98)
9008419	SuperStar Gemini	(2)	Bhs	1992	50,764	230	32	18	2,100	ex Norwegian Dream-12, Dreamward-98 (len-98)
8612134	SuperStar Libra	(2)	Bhs	1988	42,276	216	32	20	1,798	ex Norwegian Sea-05, Seaward-97
9141077	SuperStar Virgo	(me2)	Pan	1999	75,338	269	32	24	2,975	

Hurtigruten Group   Norway

funnel: *black with white 'H' symbol above white wave on red disc or black with broad white band edged with narrow red bands.*
hull: *black with broad red band.* **history:** *service commenced 1893 by Vesteraalens Dampskibs, alter being joined by Bergenske Dampskibs and Nordenfjeldske Dampskibs in 1894 and by Ofotens Dampskibs in 1936.* **web:** *www.hurtigruten.co.uk*

IMO#	name	screws	flag	year	gt	loa	bm	kts	pass	comments
9231951	Finnmarken	(2)	Nor	2002	15,000	139	22	15	638	
9370018	Fram	(me2p)	Nor	2007	12,700	110	20	16	382	
9039119	Kong Harald	(2)	Nor	1993	11,200	122	19	15	490	
5424562	Lofoten		Nor	1964	2,621	87	13	16	147	
9247728	Midnatsol	(2)	Nor	2003	16,151	136	22	15	652	
9107772	Nordkapp	(2)	Nor	1996	11,386	123	20	15	464	
9048914	Nordlys	(2)	Nor	1994	11,200	122	19	15	482	
9107784	Nordnorge	(2)	Nor	1997	11,384	123	20	18	455	
9107796	Polarlys	(2)	Nor	1996	12,000	123	20	15	479	
9040429	Richard With	(2)	Nor	1993	11,205	122	19	15	483	
9233258	Trollfjord	(2)	Nor	2002	15,000	136	22	15	648	
8019368	Vesteralen	(2)	Nor	1983	6,261	109	17	15	316	

operating Norwegian Coastal voyages and seasonal voyages to Alaska, Antarctica and Central America.
* owned by Karlson Shipping, Norway.

Majestic International Cruises Inc.   Greece

Mediterranean Classic Cruises

funnel: *white with blue swan symbol on yellow disc or* charterers colours. **hull:** *white or dark blue with red boot-topping.*
history: *founded 2002.* **web:** *www.mccruises.gr*

IMO#	name	screws	flag	year	gt	loa	bm	kts	pass	comments
6602898	Ocean Majesty	(2)	Prt	1966	10,417	131	19	20	613	ex Homeric-95, Ocean Majesty-95, Olympic-95, Ocean Majesty-94, Kypros Star-89, Sol Christiana-86, Juan March-85

Mitsui-OSK Lines K.K.   Japan

funnel: *light red.* **hull:** *white.* **history:** *see part 2.* **web:** *www.mopas.co.jp*

IMO#	name	screws	flag	year	gt	loa	bm	kts	pass	comments
8700474	Fuji Maru	(2)	Jpn	1989	23,235	167	27	20	603	
8817631	Nippon Maru	(2)	Jpn	1990	22,472	167	24	18	607	

MSC Crociere S.A.   Italy

funnel: *white with 'M' over 'SC'.* **hull:** *white with narrow blue band, blue boot-topping.* **history:** *formed 1986 as Mediterranean Shipping Cruises, a subsidiary of Mediterranean Shipping Co. (formed 1970) and renamed in 2002.* **web:** *www.msccruises.com*

IMO#	name	screws	flag	year	gt	loa	bm	kts	pass	comments
7902295	Melody	(2)	Pan	1982	35,143	205	27	20	1,492	ex Starship Atlantic-97, Atlantic-88
9210141	MSC Armonia	(me2p)	Pan	2001	65,542	275	29	21	2,680	ex European Vision-04 (len-08 &14)
9585285	MSC Divina	(me2)	Pan	2012	139,072	333	38	22	3,887	l/d MSC Fantastica
9359791	MSC Fantasia	(me2)	Pan	2008	137,936	333	38	22	3,887	
9246102	MSC Lirica	(me2p)	Pan	2003	65,591	275	29	20	2,680	(len-08 &15)
9387085	MSC Magnifica	(me2p)	Pan	2010	95,128	294	32	22	3,013	
9320087	MSC Musica	(me2p)	Pan	2006	92,409	294	32	22	3,013	
9250464	MSC Opera	(me2p)	Pan	2004	65,591	275	29	20	2,680	(len-05 &15)
9320099	MSC Orchestra	(me2p)	Pan	2007	92,409	294	32	22	3,013	
9387073	MSC Poesia	(me2p)	Pan	2008	92,627	294	32	22	3,013	
9595321	MSC Preziosa	(me2)	Pan	2013	139,072	333	38	22	3,887	l/d Phoenicia
9210153	MSC Sinfonia	(me2p)	Pan	2002	65,542	275	29	21	2,680	ex European Stars-04, l/a European Dream (len-03 &15)

IMO#	name	screws	flag	year	gt	loa	bm	kts	pass	comments
9359806	MSC Splendida	(me2)	Pan	2009	137,936	333	38	22	3,887	l/d as MSC Seranata
newbuildings:										
9745366	MSC Seaside		Pan	2017	154,000	323	41		5,179	[Seaside 1] Fincantieri 6256
9745378			Pan	2018	154,000	323	41		5,179	[Seaside 2] Fincantieri 6257
9760512	MSC Meraviglia		Pan	2017	167,600	315			4,500	[Vista 1] STX St. Nazaire E34
9760524				2019	167,600	315			4,500	[Vista 2] STX St. Nazaire F34

NB, MSC Preziosa, MSC take over of vessel originally ordered by Libyan Govt.
also holds options for Vista 3 and 4 (2020, 2022) and Seaside 3 (2021)

Noble Caledonia   U.K.

funnel: *owners colours* hull: *various.* history : *non-owing operator, founded 1991, using seasonally chartered vessels for adventure, educational and expedition cruises. The company operates worldwide but only vessels operating in Europe/Mediterranean are listed* **web:** *www.noble-caledonia.co.uk*

8802870	Caledonian Sky		Bhs	1991	4,200	90	15	15	114	ex Sunrise-11, Hebridean Spirit-09, Capri-01, Megastar Capricorn-01, Sun Viva 2-00 Renaissance Six-98

Sea Explorer I : Noble Caledonia : *Mike Lennon*

Braemar : Fred Olsen Cruise Line : *Nico Kemps*

22

IMO#	name	screws	flag	year	gt	loa	bm	kts	pass	comments
8802882	Hebridean Sky **	2)	Mhl	1991	4,200	91	15	15	114	ex Sea Explorer I-16, Sea Explorer-14,Corinthian II-13, Island Sun-05, Sun-04, Renai I-03, Renaissance Seven-01, Regina Renaissance-98, Renaissance Seven-92
8802894	Island Sky	(2)	Bhs	1992	4,200	90	15	15	114	ex Sky-04, Renai II-03, Renaissance Eight-01
5142657	Serenissima *		Vct	1960	2,598	87		13	107	ex Andrea-12, Harald Jarl-02

owned by Premier Cruises Ltd., Split, HRV   ** *owned by Fleetpro Ocean Inc.*

NYK Line   Japan

NYK Cruises Co. Ltd., Japan
funnel: *white with two red bands and black top.* **hull:** *white with blue boot-topping.* **web:** *www.asukacruise.co.jp*

8806204	Asuka II	(me2)	Bhs	1990	50,142	241	30	22	960	ex Crystal Harmony-06

Jointly owned by Asuka Ship Co., Japan

Fred Olsen Cruise Lines Ltd.   U.K.
funnel: *red with white/blue houseflag, narrow black top.* **hull:** *dark grey with thin red line on white upperworks, red boot-topping.*
history: company originally founded 1848 in Norway and UK cruise subsidiary formed in 1997. **web:** *www.fredolsencruises.com*

8506294	Balmoral	(2)	Bhs	1988	43,537	218	32	22	1,240	ex Norwegian Crown-07, Crown Odyssey-03, Norwegian Crown-00, Crown Odyssey-96 (len-07)
7108930	Black Watch	(2)	Bhs	1972	28,670	205	25	18	902	ex Star Odyssey-96, Westward-94, Royal Viking Star-91 (NE-05)(len-81)
7217395	Boudicca	(2)	Pan	1973	28,388	205	25	18	1,022	ex Grand Latino-05, SuperStar Capricorn-04, Hyundai Kumgang-01, SuperStar Capricorn-98, Golden Princess-96, Sunward-93, Birka Queen-92, Sunward-92, Royal Viking Sky-91 (NE)(leng-83)
9000699	Braemar	(2)	Pan	1993	24,344	196	23	18	1,116	ex Crown Dynasty-01, Norwegian Dynasty-99, Crown Majesty-97, Crown Dynasty-97, Cunard Dynasty-97, Crown Dynasty-95 (len-08)

Paul Gauguin Cruises   U.S.A.
funnel: white **hull:** white boot topping. **history:** *formerly owned by Grand Circle Line, company sold in 2010 to Pacific Beachcomber Crocieres, Washington* **web:** *www.pgcruises.com*

9111319	Paul Gauguin	(me2)	Bhs	1997	19,170	154	22	18	320	
9159830	Tere Moana	(2)	Wlf	1990	3,504	100	14	16	90	ex Le Levant-12

Amadea : Phoenix Reisen : *Chris Brooks*

IMO#	name	screws	flag	year	gt	loa	bm	kts	pass	comments

Phoenix Reisen   Germany

funnel: *turquoise with white seagull in flight over yellow sun.* **hull:** *white with turquoise band, blue boot-topping.* **history:** *German tour operator entered cruise business in 1988 by chartering the Maksim Gorkiy.* **web:** *www.phoenixreisen.com*

IMO#	name	screws	flag	year	gt	loa	bm	kts	pass	comments
7304314	Albatros	(2)	Bhs	1973	29,518	205	25	18	812	ex Crown-04, Norwegian Star I-02, Norwegian Star-01, Royal Odyssey-97, Royal Viking Sea-91 (len-83)
8913162	Amadea	(2)	Bhs	1991	29,008	190	25	21	604	ex Asuka-06
8201480	Artania	(2)	Bmu	1984	44,588	231	29	21	1,260	ex Artemis-11, Royal Princess-05

managed by V. Ships Leisure SAM, also operates seasonal cruises with Deutschland, see Absolute Nevada LLC, p33

Compagnie du Ponant   France

funnel: *black louvers with three white sail symbol.* **hull:** *dark grey with red boot-topping.* **history:** *Founded in 1988, formerly Cie. des Isles du Ponant until 2009.* **web:** *www.ponant.com*

IMO#	name	screws	flag	year	gt	loa	bm	kts	pass	comments
9502518	L'Austral		Wlf	2010	10,944	142	18	16	264	
9502506	Le Boréal		Wlf	2010	10,944	142	18	16	264	
9704130	Le Lyrial		Wlf	2015	10,992	142	18	16	244	
9641675	Le Soléal		Wlf	2013	10,950	142	18	16	264	

newbuildings : 4 x 10,000gt, 128 x 18m, 180px cruise ships [Fincantieri Varda (2018/9)]
also operates small sail-cruise vessel Le Ponant.

Royal Caribbean International   Norway

funnel: *white with blue crown and anchor symbol.* **hull:** *white or pale blue, blue boot-topping.* **history:** *founded 1969 as Royal Caribbean Cruises Ltd by Norwegian shipowners Anders Wilhelmsen, I M Skaugen & Co and Gotaas-Larsen being renamed in 1997, when Celebrity Cruises was acquired.* **web:** *www.royalcaribbean.com*

IMO#	name	screws	flag	year	gt	loa	bm	kts	pass	comments
9167227	Adventure of the Seas	(me3p)	Bhs	2001	137,276	311	39	23	3,840	
9383948	Allure of the Seas	(me3p)	Bhs	2010	225,282	360	61	22	6,318	
9656101	Anthem of the Seas	(me2p)	Bhs	2015	158,350	347	50	22	4,180	
9195200	Brilliance of the Seas	(gt2p)	Bhs	2002	90,090	294	32	24	2,500	
9111802	Enchantment of the Seas	(me2)	Bhs	1997	82,910	301	32	22	2,730	(len-05)
9228368	Xpedition *		Ecu	2001	2,842	89	14	13	96	ex Sun Bay-04
9161728	Explorer of the Seas	(me3p)	Bhs	2000	137,308	311	39	23	3,840	
9304033	Freedom of the Seas	(me3p)	Bhs	2006	154,407	339	39	22	4,375	
9102978	Grandeur of the Seas	(me2)	Bhs	1996	73,817	279	32	22	2,440	
9349681	Independence of the Seas	(me3p)	Bhs	2008	154,407	339	39	21	4,375	
9228356	Jewel of the Seas	(gt2p)	Bhs	2004	90,090	293	32	24	2,500	
9070620	Legend of the Seas	(me2)	Bhs	1995	69,490	264	32	24	2,060	
9330032	Liberty of the Seas	(me3p)	Bhs	2007	154,407	339	39	21	4,375	
8819512	Majesty of the Seas	(2)	Bhs	1992	73,937	268	32	20	2,744	
9227510	Mariner of the Seas	(me3p)	Bhs	2004	138,279	311	39	22	3,807	
9227508	Navigator of the Seas	(me3p)	Bhs	2003	138,279	311	39	22	3,807	
9383936	Oasis of the Seas	(me3p)	Bhs	2009	225,282	360	61	22	6,360	
9697753	Ovation of the Seas	(me2p)	Bhs	2016	158,350	348	50	22	4,100	
9549463	Quantum of the Seas	(me2p)	Bhs	2014	158,350	347	50	22	4,180	
9195195	Radiance of the Seas	(gt2p)	Bhs	2001	90,090	293	32	24	2,500	
9116864	Rhapsody of the Seas	(me2)	Nis	1997	78,491	279	32	22	2,416	
9228344	Serenade of the Seas	(gt2p)	Bhs	2003	90,090	293	32	24	2,501	
9116876	Vision of the Seas	(me2)	Bhs	1998	78,340	279	32	22	2,416	
9161716	Voyager of the Seas	(me3p)	Bhs	1999	137,276	311	39	22	3,840	
newbuildings:										
9682875	Harmony of the Seas	(me3p)	Bhs	2016	225,282	362	66	22	6,360	[Oasis 3] STX St. Nazaire A34
9744001				2018	227,000				6,360	[Oasis 4] STX St. Nazaire B34
			Bhs	2019	158,350	347	50	22	4,100	[Quantum4] Meyer Werft
			Bhs	2020						[Quantum5] Meyer Werft

* *managed for Islas Galapagos Tourismo*

Azamara Club Cruises, U.S.A.

funnel: *white with blue globe logo.* hull: *black with blue globe logo and small 'AZAMARA over CLUB CRUISES' towards stern.* **history:** *founded as Azamara Cruises in 2007, rebranded 2009.* **web:** *www.azamaraclubcruises.co.uk*

IMO#	name	screws	flag	year	gt	loa	bm	kts	pass	comments
9200940	Azamara Journey	(me2)	Mlt	2000	30,277	181	25	18	777	ex Blue Dream-07, R Six-05
9210218	Azamara Quest	(me2)	Mhl	2000	30,277	181	25	18	702	ex Blue Moon-07, Delphin Renaissance-06, R Seven-03

Celebrity Cruises, U.S.A.

funnel: *black or black/white horizontal striped with large white diagonal cross (edged yellow on later vessels).* **hull:** *white with broad black bands at lifeboat level and waterline.* **history:** *founded 1989 by Chandris and acquired 1997. Formed Celebrity Expeditions in 2004.* **web:** *www.celebritycruises.com*

Ovation of the Seas : Royal Caribbean Intl. : *ARO*

Azamara Quest : Royal Caribbean Intl. - Azamara Cruises : *Mike Lennon*

IMO#	name	screws	flag	year	gt	loa	bm	kts	pass	comments
9192399	Celebrity Constellation	(gt2p)	Mlt	2002	90,280	294	32	24	2,449	ex Constellation-07
9404314	Celebrity Eclipse	(me2p)	Mlt	2010	121,878	317	37	24	2,850	
9372456	Celebrity Equinox	(me2p)	Mlt	2009	121,878	317	37	24	2,850	
9189421	Celebrity Infinity	(gt2p)	Mlt	2001	90,228	294	32	24	2,449	ex Infinity-07
9189419	Celebrity Millennium	(gt2p)	Mlt	2000	90,963	294	32	24	2,449	ex Millennium-09
9506459	Celebrity Reflection	(me2p)	Mlt	2012	125,366	315	37	24	3,030	
9451094	Celebrity Silhouette	(me2p)	Mlt	2011	122,210	317	37	24	2,850	
9362530	Celebrity Solstice	(me2p)	Mlt	2008	121,878	317	37	24	2,850	l/a Solstice
9192387	Celebrity Summit	(gt2p)	Mlt	2001	90,280	294	32	24	2,449	ex Summit-08
newbuildings:										
				2018	117,000				2,900	[project Edge 1] STX St. Nazaire
				2020	117,000				2,900	[project Edge 2] STX St. Nazaire

also see TUI Cruises joint venture.

Celebrity Reflection : Royal Caribbean Intl - Celebrity Cruises : *Chris Brooks*

Zenith : Royal Caribbean - Pullmantur/Crocieres de France : *Mike Lennon*

IMO#	name		screws	flag	year		gt	loa	bm	kts	pass	comments

Pullmantur Cruises, Spain

funnel: *dark blue with four 'waves' in turquoise.* **hull:** *dark blue topped with turquoise line which towards the stern incorporates the first of four 'waves' over 'Pullmantur' in white* **history:** *Formed 2000 by established Spanish travel company, acquired by Royal Caribbean in 2006. CDF Crosières de France set up in 2008 to cater for French market.* **web:** *www.pullmantur.es*

IMO#	name	screws	flag	year	gt	loa	bm	kts	pass	comments
8716899	Empress **	(2)	Mlt	1990	48,563	211	31	19	2,020	ex Empress of the Seas-08, Nordic Empress-04
8807088	Horizon *	(2)	Mlt	1990	47,427	208	29	19	1,798	ex Pacific Dream-10, Island Star-09 Horizon-05
8819500	Monarch	(2)	Bhs	1991	73,937	268	32	20	2,744	ex Monarch of the Seas-13
8512281	Sovereign	(2)	Mlt	1987	73,529	268	32	21	2,524	ex Sovereign of the Seas-08
8918136	Zenith *	(2)	Mlt	1992	47,413	208	29	21	1,774	

** operates seasonally for CDF Crosières de France ** expected to transfer to Royal Caribbean Intl. during 2016*

Saga Group   U.K.

funnel: *yellow with narrow white band below narrow dark blue top.* **hull:** *dark blue with red boot-topping or white with black boot-topping (Spirit).* **history:** *parent company founded in 1950's and entered shipping owning in 1997. Spirit of Adventure subsidiary formed 2005.* **web:** *www.saga.co.uk/cruising*

IMO#	name	screws	flag	year	gt	loa	bm	kts	pass	comments
8000214	Saga Pearl II	(2)	Mlt	1981	18,591	164	23	18	446	ex Quest for Adventure-13, Saga Pearl II-12, Astoria-09, Arkona-02, Astor-85
7822457	Saga Sapphire	(2)	Bhs	1981	37,301	200	29	21	706	ex Bleu de France-12, Holiday Dream-08, SuperStar Aries-04, SuperStar Europe-99, Europa-99

newbuilding:

				2019	55,900	234	31		1,000	Meyer Werft

holds options for 2 further newbuilds at Meyer

Sea Cloud Cruises   Germany

hull: *white.* **history:** *founded about 1994 by subsidiary of Hansa Treuhand Group.* **web:** *www.seacloud.com*

IMO#	name	screws	flag	year	gt	loa	bm	kts	pass	comments
8843446	Sea Cloud	(as2)	Mlt	1931	2,532	110	15	12	68	ex Sea Cloud of Grand Cayman-87, Sea Cloud-80, Antarna-79, Patria-64, Angelita-61, Sea Cloud-52, Hussar-35
9171292	Sea Cloud II	(as2)	Mlt	2000	3,849	117	16	14	96	

Sea Cloud II : Sea Cloud Cruises : *ARO*

Silver Whisper : Silver Sea Cruises : *F. de Vries*

Mein Schiff 1 : TUI Cruises : *F. de Vries*

IMO#	name	screws	flag	year	gt	loa	bm	kts	pass	comments

Silversea Cruises U.S.A.

funnel: *white with blue 'SS' symbol.* **hull:** *white.* **history:** *founded by former owners of Sitmar after 1988 sale to P&O.*

web: *www.silversea.com*

IMO#	name	screws	flag	year	gt	loa	bm	kts	pass	comments
8903923	Silver Cloud	(2)	Bhs	1994	16,927	156	21	17	314	
8806747	Silver Explorer	(2)	Gbr	1969	6,072	108	16	15	140	ex Prince Albert II-11, World Discoverer-08, Dream 21-01, Delfin Star-97, Baltic Clipper-92, Sally Clipper-92, Delfin Clipper-90
9192167	Silver Shadow	(2)	Bhs	2000	28,258	182	25	21	388	
9437866	Silver Spirit	(2)	Bhs	2009	36,009	199	26	19	540	
9192179	Silver Whisper	(2)	Bhs	2001	28,258	182	25	21	388	l/dn Silver Mirage
8903935	Silver Wind	(2)	Bhs	1995	16,927	156	21	17	296	
newbuildings:										
9784350	Silver Muse		Bhs	2017	40,700	212			596	Fincantieri, Genoa

Also 2 further Silver Muse class on order [Fincantieri]

Star Clippers Ltd. Monaco

funnel: *none.* **hull:** *white.* **history:** *founded 1991 as Star Clippers Inc. to 2000.* **web:** *www.starclippers.com*

IMO#	name	screws	flag	year	gt	loa	bm	kts	pass	comments
8712178	Royal Clipper	(as)	Lux	2000	4,425	133	16	13	224	l/a Gwarek (1991), (len-91)
8915445	Star Clipper	(as)	Lux	1992	2,298	112	15	12	194	
8915433	Star Flyer	(as)	Lux	1991	2,298	112	15	12	194	l/a Star Clipper
newbuilding:										
9793545					8,770	162	19	16	300	Brodosplit yard # 483 5-mast barque

TUI Cruises GmbH Germany

funnel: *white with red 'tui' logo..* **hull:** *dark blue with large white 'Mein Schiff' and light blue German phrases, red boot-topping.*
history: *TUI dates back to 1968 and has undergone many changes since. TUI Cruises was formed 2009, as a joint venture between TUI and Royal Caribbean.* **web:** *www.tuicruises.com*

IMO#	name	screws	flag	year	gt	loa	bm	kts	pass	comments
9106297	Mein Schiff 1	(2)	Mlt	1996	76,998	264	32	21	1,896	ex Mein Schiff-10, Celebrity Galaxy-09, Galaxy-08
9106302	Mein Schiff 2	(2)	Mlt	1997	77,302	264	32	21	1,896	ex Celebrity Mercury-11, Mercury-08
9641730	Mein Schiff 3	(2)	Mlt	2014	99,526	295	36	21	2,506	
9678408	Mein Schiff 4	(2)	Mlt	2015	99,430	295	36	21	2,506	
newbuildings:										
9753193	Mein Schiff 5		Mlt	2016	97.000	295	36	21	2,506	Meyer Turku 1389
9753208	Mein Schiff 6		Mlt	2017	97.000	295	36	21	2,506	Meyer Turku 1390
	Mein Schiff 7			2018	97.000	295	36	21	2,860	Meyer Turku 1392
	Mein Schiff 8			2019	97.000	295	36	21	2,860	Meyer Turku 1393

Europa 2 : TUI Cruises - Hapag-Lloyd : *ARO*

IMO#	name	screws	flag	year	gt	loa	bm	kts	pass	comments

Hapag-Lloyd Cruises, Germany

funnel: *orange with blue 'HL'.* **hull:** *white with orange/blue band, red boot-topping.* **history:** *formed by 1970 merger of the long-established Hamburg America and Norddeutscher Lloyd lines. Control acquired by Preussag group in 1997 and Hapag-Lloyd acquired control of travel group TUI in 1998.* **web:** *www.hl-cruises.com*

IMO#	name	screws	flag	year	gt	loa	bm	kts	pass	comments
8907424	Bremen	(2)	Bhs	1990	6,752	112	17	16	184	ex Frontier Spirit-93
9183855	Europa	(me2p)	Bhs	1999	28,437	199	24	21	408	
9616230	Europa 2	(me2p)	Mlt	2013	42,830	225	27	21	516	
9138329	Hamburg **	(2)	Bhs	1997	15,067	145	22	18	423	ex C. Columbus-12
9000168	Hanseatic *	(2)	Bhs	1991	8,378	123	18	14	188	ex Society Adventurer-92

** chartered from Hanseatic Cruises GmbH until 2008 and ** operated by Plantours.*

Quark Expeditions, U.S.A.

funnel: *chartered ships with various owners colours..* **hull:** *owners colours.* **history:** *TUI merged its expedition cruising subsidiaries in 2008, including Clipper Cruise Line (founded 1982, sold to Kuoni in 1999 and acquired by First Choice in 2006), Peregrine Adventures (formed 1977 as part of First Choice), Quark Expeditions (formed 1991) and First Choice Expeditions.* **web:** *www.quarkexpeditions.com*

IMO#	name	screws	flag	year	gt	loa	bm	kts	pass	comments
7325629	Ocean Diamond	(2)	Wlf	1974	8,282	124	16	16	265	ex Le Diamant-12, Song of Flower-04, Explorer Starship-89, Begonia-87, Fernhill-74
7625811	Ocean Endeavour		Mhl	1982	12,907	137	21	17	500	ex Kristina Katarina-14, The Iris-10, Francesca-00, Konstantin Simonov-96
8913916	Ocean Nova		Bhs	1992	2,183	73	12	16	78	ex Sarpik Ittuk-07
7391422	Sea Adventurer	(2)	Bhs	1975	4,376	100	16	17	116	ex Clipper Adventurer-12, Alla Tarasova-97
9152959	50 Let Pobedy *	(2)	Rus	2007	23,439	160	30	21	128	

* chartered from 'Atomflot' Federal State Unitary Enterprise, Russia. Also operates a number of smaller expedition ships including Kapitan Khlebnikov

Thomson Cruises, U.K.

funnel: *pale blue with red 'tui' logo.* **hull:** *white with blue over yellow over red bands, blue or red boot-topping.* **history:** *long established holiday operator acquired by TUI in 2000. Island Cruises subsidiary formed 2002 as joint venture between Royal Caribbean and First Choice (control acquired by TUI in 2007) was closed early in 2009.* **web:** *www.thomson-cruises.co.uk*

IMO#	name	screws	flag	year	gt	loa	bm	kts	pass	comments
8027298	Thomson Celebration	(2)	Mlt	1984	33,933	215	27	21	1,340	ex Noordam-05
8407735	Thomson Dream	(2)	Mlt	1986	54,763	243	29	19	1,773	ex Costa Europa-10, Westerdam-02, Homeric-88 (len-90)
8814744	Thomson Majesty *	(2)	Mlt	1992	40,876	207	33	31	1,460	ex Louis Majesty-12, Norwegian Majesty-09, Royal Majesty-97
8024014	Thomson Spirit *	(2)	Mlt	1983	33,930	215	27	21	1,374	ex Spirit-03, Nieuw Amsterdam-02, Patriot-02, Nieuw Amsterdam-00

acquisition:

IMO#	name	screws	flag	year	gt	loa	bm	kts	pass	comments
9070632	Thomson Discovery	(me2)	Bhs	1996	69,130	264	32	24	1,833	Splendour of the Seas-16

* managed by Core Marine Ltd.,

Viking Ocean Cruises

funnel: *white with red and white sailed viking longship symbol.* **hull:** *white, dark blue boot topping.* **history:** *founded in 2013 as deep-sea sister company to Viking River Cruises.* **web:** *vikingcruises.co.uk*

IMO#	name	screws	flag	year	gt	loa	bm	kts	pass	comments
9725421	Viking Sea	(2)	Nis	2016	47,842	227	29	20	930	
9650418	Viking Star	(2)	Nis	2015	47,842	227	29	20	930	

newbuildings:

IMO#	name	screws	flag	year	gt	loa	bm	kts	pass	comments
9725433	Viking Sky		Nis	2017	47,800	227	29	20	930	Fincantieri 6245
9725433	Viking Sun		Nis	2018	47,800	227	29	20	930	Fincantieri 6246
	Viking		Nis	2018	47,800				930	Fincantieri
	Viking			2020	47,800				930	Fincantieri

Windstar Cruises Ltd.   U.S.A.

funnel: *white with turquoise symbol.* **hull:** *white with turquoise band and blue boot-topping.* **history:** *founded 1984 as Windstar Sail Cruises Ltd. Holland America acquired a 50% share in 1987 and the balance in 1988, before being taken over by Carnival Corp. Sold to Ambassadors International Inc in 2007. Ambassadors Intl. filed for Chapter 11 bankruptcy in 2011 and was taken over by Anschultz Corp. operating through their subsidiary Xanterra Parks & Resorts.* **web:** *www.windstarcruises.com*

IMO#	name	screws	flag	year	gt	loa	bm	kts	pass	comments
8807997	Star Breeze	(2)	Bhs	1989	9,975	134	19	16	212	ex Seabourn Spirit-15
9008598	Star Legend	(2)	Bhs	1992	9,961	135	19	16	212	ex Seabourn Legend-15, Queen Odyssey-96, Royal Viking Queen-94, l/dn Seabourn Legend
8707343	Star Pride	(2)	Bhs	1988	9,975	134	19	16	212	ex Seabourn Pride -14
8603509	Wind Spirit	(as/me)	Bhs	1988	5,736	134	16	11	150	
8420878	Wind Star	(as/me)	Bhs	1986	5,307	134	16	11	150	

Ocean Nova : TUI Cruises - Quark Expeditions : *Mike Lennon*

Thomson Celebration : TUI Cruises - Thomson Cruises : *Mike Lennon*

Viking Star : Viking Cruise Line : *Simon Olsen colln*

Funchal : Soc. de Consultores Maritimos (Portuscale Cruises) : *Chris Brooks*

IMO#	name	screws	flag	year	gt	loa	bm	kts	pass	comments
8700785	Wind Surf	(as/me2)	Bhs	1989	14,745	187	20	15	453	ex Club Med 1-97, l/a La Fayette

other cruise ships

Absolute Nevada LLC, U.S.A.
9141807	Deutschland	(2)	Deu	1998	22,496	175	23	20	600	ex World Odyssey-16, Deutschland-15

operates seasonal cruises for Pheonix Reisen and at other times operates as World Odyssey *for Institute for Shipboard Education (Semester at Sea)*

Aegean Experience Maritime, Greece
7225910	Aegean Odyssey	(2)	Mlt	1973	11,906	141	21	17	350	ex Aegean 1-10, Aegean Dolphin-96, Dolphin-90, Aegean Dolphin-89, Alkyon-86, Narcis-85 (conv.urr/rbt-85-88)

chartered to Voyages to Antiquity, U.K.

Bahamas Paradise Cruise Line, USA
8314134	Grand Celebration	(2)	Bhs	1987	47,263	223	28	19	1,896	ex Celebration-08

Soc. de Consultores Maritimos, Portugal
funnel: *yellow with black top.* **hull:** *black with boot-topping.* **history:** *Portuscale Cruises, founded 2013, with the purchase of the former vessels of Classic International Cruises, vessels managed by SDCM,* . **web:** *www.portuscalecruises.pt*

5124162	Funchal	(2)	Pmd	1961	9,563	153	19	14	442	
6419057	Porto	(2)	Pmd	1965	5,888	117	17	18	312	ex Arion-13, Nautilus 2000-99, Astra I-99, Astra-96, Istra-91

both vessels currently laid up, Lisbon

Clipper Group, Denmark
9000687	Gemini		Bhs	1992	19,093	164	23	19	800	ex Vision Star-09, Superstar Gemini-09, Crown Jewel-95
9213129	Saint Laurent		Bhs	2001	4,954	91	15	10	202	ex Sea Voyager-15, Cape May Light-09
9213131	Sea Discoverer		Bhs	2004	4,954	91	15	10	294	ex Clipper Discoverer-09, Coastal Queen 2-09, Cape Cod Light-07
8800195	Silver Discoverer		Bhs	1989	5,218	103	15	18	128	ex Clipper Odyssey-13, Oceanic Odyssey-98, Oceanic Grace-97

G Adventures, Canada
7211074	Expedition		Lbr	1972	6,334	105	18	14	124	ex Alandsfarjan-08, Tiger-86, N.F.Tiger-85, Kattegat-78, (rbt-08)

Japan Cruise Line, Japan
9160011	Pacific Venus	(2)	Jpn	1998	26,518	183	25	20	720	

Fleetpro Ocean Inc., U.S.A.
7214715	Oasia	(2)	Gbr	1973	24,492	191	25	21	670	ex Saga Ruby-14, Caronia-05, Vistafjord-99
8802868	Sea Spirit		Bhs	1991	4,200	91	15	15	112	ex Spirit of Oceanus-10, Megastar Sagittarius-01

vessels chartered to operating companies such as Noble Caledonia, Quark Expeditions etc

Lindblad Expeditions, U.S.A.
8019356	National Geographic Explorer	(2)	Bhs	1982	6,100	109	17	17	148	ex Lyngen-08, Midnatsol II-05, Midnatsol-03
6611863	National Geographic Endeavour		Ecu	1966	3,132	89	14	15	110	ex Endeavour-05, Caledonian Star-01, North Star-89, Lindmar-83, Marburg-82 (conv fff-83)
9273076	National Geographic Orion		Bhs	2003	3,986	103	14		102	ex Orion-14

also operates the small National Geographic Sea Bird and National Geographic Sea Lion (both 630gt), National Geographic Islander (1,021gt) and National Geographic Polaris (2,138gt). Acquired Orion Expeditions of Australia during 2013 and will rename their vessel National Geographic Orion (3,984gt) in March 2014

Mano Maritime, Israel
7358573	Golden Iris	(2)	Ita	1977	16,852	164	23	19	812	ex Rhapsody-09, Cunard Princess-95, l/a Cunard Conquest

IMO#	name	screws	flag	year	gt	loa	bm	kts	pass	comments
7032997	Royal Iris		Pan	1971	9,159	142	22	21	1,000	ex Eloise-04, The Azur-87, Azur-87, Eagle-75 (conv: ofy-82)

Oceanwide Expeditions b.v., Netherlands

IMO#	name	screws	flag	year	gt	loa	bm	kts	pass	comments
8509181	Ortelius	(2)	Cyp	1989	4,575	91	17	12	106	ex Marina Tsvetayeva-11
7432044	Plancius		Nld	1976	3,434	144	17		114	ex Tydeman A906 - 09

Orion Expedition Cruises, Australia

IMO#	name	screws	flag	year	gt	loa	bm	kts	pass	comments
9273076	Orion		Bhs	2003	3,984	103	14	16	130	ex Sun Explorer-03
8708672	Orion II	(2)	Mlt	1990	4,077	88	15	15	100	ex Clelia II-11, Renaissance Four-96

ResidenSea Ltd., Norway

IMO#	name	screws	flag	year	gt	loa	bm	kts	pass	comments
9219331	The World	(2)	Bhs	2002	43,188	196	29	18	656	

operated by Silversea Cruises Ltd. with accommodation comprising 110 privately owned apartments and 88 guest suites

SeaDream Yacht Club, Norway

IMO#	name	screws	flag	year	gt	loa	bm	kts	pass	comments
8203438	SeaDream I	(2)	Bhs	1984	4,333	105	15	17	116	ex Seabourn Goddess I-01, Sea Goddess I-00
8203440	SeaDream II	(2)	Bhs	1985	4,333	105	15	17	116	ex Seabourn Goddess II-01, Sea Goddess II-00

chartered from Stella Maritime, Bahamas for use as a floating University

Sete Yacht Management, Greece

IMO#	name	screws	flag	year	gt	loa	bm	kts	pass	comments
8907216	Turama	(2)	Sau	1990	8,343	116	17	18	229	ex Columbus Caravelle-04, Sally Caravelle-91, Delfin Caravelle-91

Société Services et Transports, Monaco

IMO#	name	screws	flag	year	gt	loa	bm	kts	pass	comments
9007491	Club Med 2	(as/me2)	Fra	1992	14,983	187	20	15	392	

operated by Club Méditerranée and managed by V. Ships Leisure

The Peace Boat, Japan

operating world cruises on charter to non-governmental organisation as 'The Peace Boat'. GP Cruise Inc.

IMO#	name	screws	flag	year	gt	loa	bm	kts	pass	comments
7915096	Ocean Dream		Pan	1981	35,265	205			1,422	ex Pacific Star-08, Costa Tropicale-05

Pacific Naval Register Ltd. (Adriana Shipping Ltd.), U.K.

IMO#	name	screws	flag	year	gt	loa	bm	kts	pass	comments
7118404	Adriana	(2)	Skn	1972	4,490	104	14	16	312	ex Adriana III-10, Adriana-08, Aquarius-87

Vishal Cruises Pvt. Ltd., Mauritius

funnel: *white with light blue dolphin on dark blue disc interrupting three narrow dark blue bands.* **hull:** *white with red or blue boot-topping.* **history :** *purchased vessel from Delphin Cruises 2011 and chartered to Passat Kreuzfahrten until they filed for bankruptcy in 12:2014.* **web:** *none found*

IMO#	name	screws	flag	year	gt	loa	bm	kts	pass	comments
7347536	Delphin	(2)	Bhs	1975	16,214	156	22	21	554	ex Kazakhstan II-96, Byelorussiya-93

currently being used as accommodation ship for US military at Rijeka

Part Two
Cargo Vessels and Tankers

Mathilde Maersk : A. P. Møller-Maersk A/S : *ARO*

Agelef Shipping Co. (London) Ltd.   U.K.

Agelef Shipping Co (London) Ltd. founded 1968 to act as shipbrokers and agents for Alpha Bulkers Shipmanagement, formerly Alpha Tankers and Freighters Intl, Amethyst Management Ltd., Anangel Maritime Services and Maran Tankers Management Ltd.

Alpha Bulkers Shipmanagement., Greece

funnel: *white with green 'A' between narrow red bands below black top.* **hull:** *blue with red boot-topping.* **history:** *related family company founded 1991.* **Web:** *www.alphatankers.com*

IMO	name	flag	year	gt	dwt	loa	bm	kts	type	comments
9221853	Alpha Afovos	Grc	2001	39,941	74,428	225	32	15	bbu	ex Anangel Afovos-01
9527910	Alpha Bravery	Grc	2011	93,715	179,398	292	45	24	bbu	ex Cassiopeia Bulker-14
9226530	Alpha Century	Grc	2000	87,407	170,415	289	45	14	bbu	ex Anangel Century-02
9455040	Alpha Confidence	Mlt	2011	89,991	177,830	292	45	15	bbu	
9221009	Alpha Cosmos	Grc	2001	87,378	169,770	289	45	15	bbu	ex Mineral York-02, Mineral Trader-01
9462811	Alpha Dignity	Mlt	2011	89,991	176,296	292	45	15	bbu	
9189081	Alpha Effort	Grc	1999	38,564	72,844	225	32	15	bbu	
9220990	Alpha Era	Grc	2000	87,407	170,387	289	45	14	bbu	ex Mineral Sakura-02
9423774	Alpha Faith	Grc	2008	91,373	178.104	292	45	14	bbu	
9185774	Alpha Flame	Grc	1999	38,852	74,545	225	32	14	bbu	ex United Support-04
9722364	Alpha Freedom	Grc	2015	92,531	179,258	292	45	15	bbu	
9189108	Alpha Happiness	Grc	1999	38,564	72,800	225	32	15	bbu	
9221865	Alpha Harmony	Grc	2001	39,941	74,492	225	32	14	bbu	ex Alpha Harmony I-02, Alpha Harmony-01
9722376	Alpha Honesty	Grc	2016	92,531	179,258	292	45	15	bbu	
9446582	Alpha Hope	Mhl	2011	92,758	181,433	292	45	14	bbu	ex Obelix-16, Orient Vega-12
9590709	Alpha Liberty	Grc	2011	93,274	179,276	292	45	15	bbu	ex Blue Manaslu-14
9311177	Alpha Loyalty	Mlt	2007	40,033	75,949	225	32	14	bbu	ex Perla Bulker-13
9221889	Alpha Melody	Grc	2002	39,941	74,374	225	32	15	bbu	l/a Anangel Melody
9212058	Alpha Millennium	Grc	2000	87,407	170,415	280	45	15	bbu	ex Anangel Millennium-02
9597214	Alpha Progress	Grc	2012	43,721	81,251	229	32	14	bbu	
9423762	Alpha Prudence	Grc	2008	91,373	178,002	292	45	14	bbu	
9597202	Alpha Vision	Grc	2012	43,721	81,254	229	32	14	bbu	
9423918	Antonis Angelicoussis	Grc	2007	91,373	177,855	292	45	14	bbu	
9457012	Brave Sailor	Mlt	2011	89,991	176,283	292	45	15	bbu	
9189093	Future *	Grc	1999	38,564	72,893	225	32	15	bbu	ex Alpha Future-10
9605700	Herodotus	Grc	2012	89,991	176,000	292	45	14	bbu	
9233703	Maria A. Angelicoussi	Grc	2001	86,201	169,163	289	45	15	bbu	l/a Fabulous
9213375	Marvellous *	Grc	2000	86,201	169,150	289	45	15	bbu	ex Mineral Marvel-04, Marvel-04
9423920	Skythia	Mlt	2010	89,990	177,830	292	45	15	bbu	
9597238	Transatlantic	Mlt	2012	43,721	81,250	229	32	13	bbu	
9597226	Transpacific	Mlt	2012	43,721	82,000	229	32	14	bbu	

newbuildings:

IMO	name	flag	year	gt	dwt	loa	bm	kts	type	comments
9722388	Alpha Optimism	Mlt	2016	92,531	179,258	292	45	15	bbu	Hyundai Samho S765

* managed by associated company Amethyst Management Ltd,, Athens

Anangel Maritime Services Inc., Greece

funnel: *white with green 'trefilli' between two narrow red bands beneath narrow black top.* **hull**: *light grey, dark grey or blue with red boot-topping.* **history**: *Anangel Shipping Company founded 1971, formerly trading since 1947 as A Angelicoussis and D Efthimiou, who had been shipowners since 1947, Anangel Maritime Services formed as management company in 1991* **web**: *www.agelef.co.uk*

IMO	name	flag	year	gt	dwt	loa	bm	kts	type	comments
9428463	Anangel Argonaut	Grc	2009	89,990	177,835	292	45	14	bbu	
9581681	Anangel Aspiration	Grc	2012	61,504	114,013	250	43	15	bbu	
9581239	Anangel Astronomer	Grc	2012	89,891	179,719	292	45	15	bbu	
9581241	Anangel Conqueror	Grc	2012	89,891	179,719	292	45	14	bbu	
9593218	Anangel Courage	Grc	2013	106,884	205,888	300	50	15	bbu	
9455533	Anangel Dawn	Grc	2011	61,504	114,091	250	43	15	bbu	
9179593	Anangel Destiny	Grc	1999	87,523	171,997	289	45	15	bbu	
9169603	Anangel Dynasty	Grc	1999	86,600	171,101	289	45	14	bbu	ex Yangtze Ore-02
9648295	Anangel Elegance	Grc	2014	106,727	205,960	300	50	14	bbu	
9176644	Anangel Eternity	Grc	1999	86,600	171,176	289	45	14	bbu	ex Virginie Venture-02
9295012	Anangel Explorer	Grc	2007	87,582	171,927	289	45	14	bbu	
9329459	Anangel Fortune	Grc	2005	87,820	174,272	289	45	14	bbu	
9739240	Anangel Future	Grc	2015	93,490	179,318	292	45	14	bbu	l/a SBI Camacho
9434383	Anangel Glory	Grc	2012	91,656	180,391	292	45	14	bbu	
9440320	Anangel Grace	Grc	2011	91,656	180,391	292	45	14	bbu	
9434369	Anangel Guardian	Grc	2010	89,891	179,718	292	45	14	bbu	
9082350	Anangel Haili	Grc	1995	147,812	260,723	322	58	15	bor	ex Astro Luna-09, Tango-02, Diamond Iris-01 (conv tcr-09)
9470923	Anangel Happiness	Grc	2008	89,565	177,720	292	45	14	bbu	
9434412	Anangel Harmony	Grc	2010	91,656	180,055	292	45	14	bbu	
9702687	Anangel Hero	Grc	2016	94,385	180,000	292	45	14	bbo	l/a Bruno Marks
9729178	Anangel Hope	Grc	2015	93,488	179,445	292	45	14	bbu	ex SBI Magnum-16

IMO	name	flag	year	gt	dwt	loa	bm	kts	type	comments
9702699	Anangel Horizon	Mlt	2016	94,385	180,000	292	45	14	bbu	l/a Jenmark
9286798	Anangel Innovation	Grc	2004	87,050	171,681	289	45	15	bbu	
9439072	Anangel Mariner	Grc	2011	89,891	179,700	292	45	14	bbu	
9458590	Anangel Merchant	Grc	2010	89,891	179,718	292	45	14	bbu	
9593220	Anangel Nobility	Grc	2013	106,727	205,938	300	50	14	bbu	
9455569	Anangel Ocean	Grc	2011	61,504	114,007	250	43	15	bbu	
9332523	Anangel Odyssey	Grc	2006	87,485	171,660	289	45	14	bbu	
9606754	Anangel Progress	Grc	2014	61,504	114,047	250	43	14	bbu	c/a Lomar Progress
9347176	Anangel Prosperity	Grc	2006	88,853	174,240	289	45	14	bbu	
9345764	Anangel Sailor	Grc	2006	87,050	171,681	289	45	14	bbu	
9434371	Anangel Seafarer	Mlt	2011	94,082	179,754	292	45	14	bbu	
9004786	Anangel Shagang	Grc	1992	154,532	277,218	328	57	15	bor	ex Astro Leon-09, Ambon-00; (conv tcr-09)
9455545	Anangel Sky	Grc	2011	61,504	114,078	250	43	15	bbu	
9721011	Anangel Spirit	Grc	2016	92,916	179,129	292	45	14	bbu	l/d SBI Churchill
9455557	Anangel Sun	Grc	2011	61,504	114,078	250	43	15	bbu	
9439060	Anangel Transporter	Grc	2010	89,891	179,718	292	45	14	bbu	
9434400	Anangel Trust	Grc	2012	91,656	180,391	292	45	14	bbu	
9729166	Anangel Unity	Grc	2015	93,464	179,405	292	45	14	bbu	ex SBI Montesino-16
9703239	Anangel Venture	Grc	2016	94,385	180,000	292	45	14	bbu	l/a Star Aries
9434395	Anangel Vigour	Grc	2012	91,566	180,391	292	45	14	bbu	
9440332	Anangel Virtue	Grc	2012	91,566	180,391	292	45	14	bbu	
9332951	Anangel Vision	Grc	2007	87,485	171,810	289	45	14	bbu	
9458688	Anangel Voyager	Grc	2010	89,891	179,718	292	45	14	bbu	
9606766	Anangel Wisdom	Grc	2014	61,504	114,046	250	43	14	bbu	
9581708	Anangel Zenith	Grc	2013	61,504	114,037	250	43	14	bbu	
8812667	Anangel Zhongte	Grc	1989	138,648	246,732	321	57	15	bor	ex Astro Lupus-09, Navix Seibu-00; (conv tcr-09)
9000986	Ore Sudbury	Grc	1992	154,552	276,599	328	57	15	bor	ex Astro Libra-10, Irian-00; (conv tcr-10)
9286803	Pioneer	Grc	2004	87,050	171,681	289	45	15	bbu	

newbuildings:

IMO	name	flag	year	gt	dwt	loa	bm	kts	type	comments
9721023	Anangel Victory	Grc	2016	94,000	180,000	292	45	14	bbu	l/d SBI Presidente Daewoo Mangalia
9721035			2016	94,000	180,000	292	45	14	bbu	l/d SBI Prefecto Daewoo Mangalia
9703241			2016	94,000	180,000	292	45	14	bbu	l/a Star Taurus SWS 1339

Maran Tankers Management Inc., Greece

funnel: *dark blue with 'MTM in dark blue disc on broad light blue band.* **hull:** *black with red boot-topping.* **history:** *founded 1992 as Kristen Navigation Inc being renamed in 2009.* **web:** *www.agelef.co.uk* or *www.maranuk,co.uk*

IMO	name	flag	year	gt	dwt	loa	bm	kts	type	comments
9216717	Antonis I. Angelicoussis	Bhs	2000	156,758	306,085	332	58	15	tcr	
9122916	Astro Arcturus	Grc	1997	53,074	98,805	248	43	15	tcr	
9235244	Astro Chorus	Grc	2001	159,016	305,704	332	58	16	tcr	ex Zeeland-03
9257149	Elizabeth I. A.	Grc	2004	153,911	306,229	332	58	15	tcr	ex Elizabeth I. Angelicoussi-09
9414022	Maran Atlas	Grc	2009	56,957	105,096	244	42	15	tco	
9171448	Maran Callisto	Grc	1999	157,833	299,167	332	58	15	tcr	ex Astro Callisto-09, Picardie-03

Alfa Era : Agelef Shipping Co - Anangel Shg. Enterprises : *Chris Brooks*

IMO	name	flag	year	gt	dwt	loa	bm	kts	type	comments
9330563	Maran Canopus	Grc	2007	158,970	320,472	333	60	15	tcr	ex Astro Canopus-09
9174660	Maran Capella	Mlt	1998	79,714	159,713	274	48	15	tcr	ex Astro Capella-09
9389019	Maran Capricorn	Grc	2008	158,970	320,513	333	60	15	tcr	ex Astro Capricorn-09
9240512	Maran Carina	Grc	2003	153,911	306,314	332	58	15	tcr	ex Astro Carina-09
9257137	Maran Cassiopeia	Grc	2003	82,982	158,553	274	48	15	tcr	ex Astro Cassiopeia-09
9194127	Maran Castor	Grc	2001	153,911	306,344	332	58	16	tcr	ex Astro Castor-09
9073050	Maran Centaurus	Grc	1995	156,565	300,294	332	58	15	tcr	ex Astro Centaurus-09, Mindoro-00
9593191	Maran Cleo	Grc	2013	164,364	318,000	333	60	15	tcr	
9252333	Maran Corona	Grc	2003	153,911	306,092	332	58	16	tcr	ex Astro Corona-09
9227479	Maran Cygnus	Grc	2001	153,911	306,344	332	58	16	tcr	ex Astro Cygnus-09
9174218	Maran Gemini	Bhs	1999	160,036	301,139	333	58	16	tcr	ex Gemini Voyager-13, Richard H. Matzke-03
9042063	Maran Lyra	Grc	1995	153,429	286,120	328	57	15	tcr	ex Astro Lyra-09, Flores-00
9402914	Maran Penelope	Grc	2009	79,890	158,267	274	48	16	tcr	
9399507	Maran Plato	Grc	2009	79,890	158,267	274	48	16	tcr	l/a Astro Plato
9402926	Maran Poseidon	Grc	2009	79,890	158,267	274	48	16	tcr	
9402902	Maran Pythia	Grc	2009	79,890	158,267	274	48	16	tcr	l/a Astro Pythia
9174220	Maran Regulus	Grc	2000	160,036	310,106	333	60	15	tcr	Regulus Voyager-14, Chang-Lin Tien-03
9414034	Maran Sagitta	Grc	2009	56,957	105,071	244	38	16	tco	
9519494	Maran Taurus	Grc	2011	162,330	321,052	333	60	15	tcr	ex Blue Garnet-15
9527295	Maran Thaleia	Grc	2011	162,330	321,335	333	60	15	tcr	ex Blue Aquamarine-15
9421247	Maran Thetis	Grc	2012	161,969	320,105	333	60	15	tcr	ex Blue Jade-14, G Elephant-13
9237632	Maran Triton	Grc	2003	160,889	318,809	333	60	15	tcr	ex Samco Asia-13
9216705	Maria A. Angelicoussis	Grc	2000	153,911	306,283	332	58	15	tcr	
newbuildings:										
9752993	Maran Apollo	Grc	2016	170,000	320,000	333	60	15	tcr	Daewoo 5413 04.2016
9753002	Maran Artemis				319,000	333	60	15	tcr	Daewoo 5414 04.2016
9753014					319,000	333	60	15	tcr	Daewoo 5415 09.2016
9753026					319,000	333	60	15	tcr	Daewoo 5416 11.2016
					319,000	333	60	15	tcr	Daewoo 5425 10.2016
					319,000	333	60	15	tcr	Daewoo 5426 12.2016
					157,000					Daewoo 5427 02.2017
					157,000					Daewoo 5428 04.2017

Maran Carina : Agelef Shipping Co - Maran Tankers Mgmt. : *Mike Lennon*

IMO	name	flag	year	gt	dwt	loa	bm	kts	type	comments
					157,000					Daewoo Mangalia 5019 03.2017
					157,000					Daewoo Mangalia 5020 06.2017
					157,000					Daewoo Mangalia 5021 09.2017
					157,000					Daewoo Mangalia 5022 12.2017

:

Maran Gas Maritime Inc., Greece

IMO	name	flag	year	gt	dwt	loa	bm	kts	type	comments
9324435	Al Jassasiya (st) *	Grc	2007	97,496	84,554	285	43	19	lng	145,800 m³
9682588	Maran Gas Achilles	Grc	2016	113,502	92,713	289	45	19	lng	174,000 m³
9650054	Maran Gas Alexandria [tf]	Grc	2015	105,773	90,494	289	45	19	lng	161,870 m³
9633422	Maran Gas Apollonia	Grc	2014	105,773	90,434	289	45	19	lng	161,870 m³
9302499	Maran Gas Asclepius (st)	Grc	2005	97,496	84,659	285	43	19	lng	145,800 m³ ex Rasgas Asclepius-14, Maran Gas Asclepius-10
9331048	Maran Gas Coronis	Grc	2007	97,491	84,823	285	43	19	lng	145,700 m³
9633173	Maran Gas Delphi	Grc	2014	103,928	89,671	294	44	19	lng	159,800 m³
9627497	Maran Gas Efessos	Grc	2014	103.928	89.711	294	44	19	lng	159,800 m³
9627502	Maran Gas Lindos	Grc	2015	103,893	89,343	294	44	19	lng	159,800 m³
9658238	Maran Gas Mystras	Grc	2015	103,893	89,269	294	45	19	lng	159,800 m³
9633434	Maran Gas Posidonia	Grc	2014	105,773	90,349	289	45	19	lng	161,870 m³
9650042	Maran Gas Sparta	Grc	2015	105,773	90,392	289	45	19	lng	161,870 m³
9658240	Maran Gas Troy	Grc	2015	103,893	89,240	289	45	19	lng	159,800 m³
9320386	Simaisma (st) *	Grc	2006	97,496	84,500	285	43	19	lng	145,700 m³
9308431	Umm Bab (st) *	Grc	2005	97,496	84,659	285	43	19	lng	145,700 m³
9682576	Woodside Chaney (tf)	Grc	2016	113,502	85,000	289	45	19	lng	174,000 m³ l/a Maran Gas Ajax
9633161	Woodside Goode (df)	Grc	2013	103,928	90,125	294	44	19	lng	159,800 m³
9627485	Woodside Rogers (df)	Grc	2013	103,928	90,327	294	44	19	lng	159,800 m³ l/a Maran Gas Olympia

newbuildings:

IMO	name	flag	year	gt	dwt	loa	bm	kts	type	comments
9682590	Maran Gas Agamemnon	Grc	2016	110,000	85,000	289	45	19	lng	174,000 m³ Hyundai Samho S690
9682605	*Maran Gas Pericles*	Grc	2016	110,000	85,000	289	45	19	lng	174,000 m³ Hyundai Samho S691
9709489		Grc	2016	110,000	85,000	289	45	19	lng	174,000 m³ H Samho S734 07.2016
9709491		Grc	2016	110,000	85,000	289	45	19	lng	174,000 m³ H. Samho S735 09.2016
9701217	*Maran Gas Amphipolis*	Grc	2016	110,920	83,000	289	45		lng	173,400 m³ Daewoo 2412 03.2016
9701229			2016						lng	173,400 m³ Daewoo 2413 10.2016
9732369	*Maran Gas Vergina*	Grc	2016	110,920	83,000	289	45		lng	173,400 m³ Daewoo 2414 08.2016
9732371			2016						lng	173,400 m³ Daewoo 2415 11.2016
			2019						lng	173,400 m³ Daewoo 2456 01.2019
			2019						lng	173,400 m³ Daewoo 2457 04.2019
			2018						lng	173,400 m³ Daewoo 2458 06.2018
			2019						lng	173,400 m³ Daewoo 2459 01.2019

* up to 30% owned by Qatar Gas Transport Co and on 20-year charter to Ras Laffan Qatar-Mobil QM Gas project formed by subsidiaries of Qatar Petroleum and ExxonMobil

Pantheon Tankers Management, Greece

funnel: *dark green with dark blue PTM on broad light blue band.* **hull**: *black with red boot-topping.* **history**: *group tankers management company founded 2013.* **web**: *www.*

IMO	name	flag	year	gt	dwt	loa	bm	kts	type	comments
9237072	Astro Challenge	Grc	2002	157,878	299,222	332	58	15	tcr	ex Maia-04, l/a Uvas
9389253	Astro Chloe	Grc	2009	158,327	320,000	333	60	15	tcr	
9280873	Astro Perseus	Grc	2004	80,620	159,116	274	48	15	tcr	
9280885	Astro Phoenix	Grc	2004	80,620	159,055	274	48	15	tcr	
9281151	Astro Polaris	Grc	2004	80,620	159,074	274	48	15	tcr	
9235725	Astro Saturn	Grc	2003	57,022	105,166	248	43	15	tcr	
9235713	Astro Sculptor	Grc	2003	57,022	105,109	248	43	15	tco	
9389265	Caesar	Mlt	2009	158,327	318,441	333	60	15	tcr	ex Astro Caesar-09
9413834	Patroclus	Grc	2009	79,890	158,267	274	48	16	tcr	ex Astro Patroclus-09
9412103	Pegasus	Grc	2009	79,890	158,267	274	48	16	tcr	ex Astro Pegasus-09
9412098	Phaethon	Grc	2009	79,890	158,267	274	48	16	tcr	ex Astro Phaethon-09
9346859	Sea Falcon	Grc	2007	59,611	110,295	245	42	15	tcr	ex Mare Italicum-14
9237620	Sea Lion	Grc	2003	160,889	318,778	333	40	15	tcr	ex Samco America-13
9290775	Sea Lynx	Grc	2004	161,223	318,306	333	40	15	tcr	ex Eagle Vienna-13.

Aggregate Industries U.K. Ltd.   U.K.

funnel: *blue with white Aggregate Industries logo above white 'YEOMAN' and 'GLENSANDA'.* **hull:** *red with red boot-topping.* **history:** *founded 1923 as Foster Yeoman Ltd and acquired by Aggregate Industries UK Ltd in 2006.* **web:** *www.aggregate-uk.com*

IMO	name	flag	year	gt	dwt	loa	bm	kts	type	comments
7422881	Yeoman Bank	Lbr	1982	24,870	38,997	205	27	15	bsd	ex Salmonpool-90
8912297	Yeoman Bontrup	Bhs	1991	55,695	96,725	250	38	15	bsd	ex Western Bridge-02
8912302	Yeoman Bridge	Bhs	1991	55,695	96,772	250	38	15	bsd	ex Eastern Bridge-00

Alpha Ship GmbH   Germany

funnel: *green with wide light green and narrow light blue 'darts' on broad cream band or charterers colours.* **hull:** *green, brown or red with red boot-topping.* **history:** *founded 1992 as Jan R. Freese, later Reederei J. Freese & Partner to 1994.* **web:** *www.alphaship.de*

IMO	name	flag	year	gt	dwt	loa	bm	kts	type	comments
9225421	AS Aries **	Lbr	2000	23,722	29,240	194	28	21	ucc	1,804 teu: ex Aries-15, Maersk Itajai-08, Aries-01
9127526	AS Castor	Mhl	1997	14,241	18,445	159	24	19	ucc	1,129 teu: ex Cap Matatula-08, Castor-05, TMM Guadalajara-99, Castor-97
9127502	AS Mars	Mhl	1996	14,241	18,449	159	24	19	ucc	1,129 teu: ex Mars-07, Safmarine Emonti-01, Mars-00, Sea Viking-99, CMBT Mars-97, CGM La Bourdonnais-97, Mars-96
9127514	AS Venus *	Mhl	1996	14,241	18,400	159	24	19	ucc	1,129 teu: ex Venus-07, DAL Karoo-02, Venus-00, CMBT Encounter-97, Venus-96
9127784	Nadir *	Mhl	1997	21,199	25,039	178	28	21	ucc	1,606 teu: ex Maersk Hong Kong-10, Nadir-98
9127796	Orion	Mhl	1997	21,199	25,107	178	28	21	ucc	1,606 teu: ex Maersk Lima-99, Orion-98, TNX Mercury-98, I/a Orion
9127538	Pollux	Mhl	1997	14,241	18,400	159	24	18	ucc	1,129 teu: ex Lykes Pelican-01, Pollux-00
9396634	Saturn	Atg	2008	16,162	17,350	161	25	19	ucc	953 teu: ex Montego-13, I/a Rickmers Vietnam
9127801	Sirius *	Mhl	1998	21,199	25,107	183	28	21	ucc	1,606 teu:
9134593	Taurus	Mhl	1998	23,722	29,260	194	28	21	ucc	1,804 teu: ex CMA CGM Castilla-09, Cap Victor-06, Columbus Waikato-06, Taurus-02, Kota Perabu-01, Taurus-99

* owned by GHF GmbH, Bremen: vesselsmanaged by Alpha Shipmanagement GmbH & Co KG
** managed by Ahrenkiel Steamship

Arcadia Shipmanagement Co. Ltd.   Greece

funnel: *dark blue with blue/white house flag on broad red band, narrow black top,* **hull:** *red with 'ARCADIA HELLAS' in white, red boot topping,* **history:** *established Athens, 1998,* **web:** *www.arcadiasm.gr*

IMO	name	flag	year	gt	dwt	loa	bm	kts	type	comments
9290323	Aegean Angel	Grc	2004	81,074	159,092	274	48	15	tcr	
9346720	Aegean Blue	Grc	2007	61,473	115,878	274	48	15	tcr	
9290335	Aegean Dignity	Grc	2004	81,074	159,100	274	48	15	tcr	
9232888	Aegean Faith	Grc	2003	57,171	106,074	244	42	15	tcr	
9232876	Aegean Freedom	Grc	2003	57,171	106,074	244	42	15	tcr	
9338917	Aegean Harmony	Grc	2007	61,473	115,824	249	44	15	tcr	
9326811	Aegean Horizon	Grc	2007	81,084	158,738	274	48	15	tcr	
9200964	Aegean Legend	Grc	2000	58,243	105,278	244	42	15	tcr	
9348479	Aegean Myth	Grc	2005	61,473	115,838	249	44	14	tcr	
9326809	Aegean Navigator	Grc	2007	81,084	159,040	274	48	15	tcr	
9345441	Aegean Nobility	Grc	2007	61,473	115,814	249	44	15	tcr	
9338905	Aegean Power	Grc	2007	61,473	115,754	249	44	15	tcr	
9200952	Aegean Pride	Grc	1999	58,243	105,302	244	42	15	tcr	
9252371	Maratha	Grc	2003	57,171	105,995	244	42	15	tcr	

Arklow Shipping Ltd.   Ireland

funnel: *white with coat or arms on white shield.* **hull:** *light green, red boot topping.* **history:** *founded 1966 and in 2000 acquired Hamno Shipping b.v. (founded 1900 as Heinich Hamno & Co. b.v.).* **web:** *www.asl.ie*

IMO	name	flag	year	gt	dwt	loa	bm	kts	type	comments
9649536	Arklow Spirit	Irl	2013	22,868	34,905	182	30	14	bbu	
9649548	Arklow Spray	Irl	2014	22,868	34,919	182	30	14	bbu	

also operates a large fleet of smaller vessels

Atlanship S.A.   Switzerland

funnel: *white with narrow red diagonal line aft of blue triangle.* **hull:** *stone or white with red boot-topping.* **history:** *founded 1982.* **web:** *www.atlanship.nl*

IMO	name	flag	year	gt	dwt	loa	bm	kts	type	comments
9304758	Chiquita Express *	Lbr	2005	27,059	34,426	212	30	22	ucc	2,492 teu: ex Coral Bay-15, Maersk Narbonne-11, I/a Caroline E, I/dn Coral Bay
9304760	Chiquita Trader *	Lbr	2005	27,059	34,393	212	30	22	ucc	2,492 teu: ex Crystal Bay-16, Maersk Nashville-11, I/a Andres E, I/dn Crystal Bay
9675406	Orange Blossom 2	Lbr	2014	22,687	23,874	170	26	15	tfj	
9675391	Orange Ocean	Lbr	2014	22,687	22,918	170	26	15	tfj	
9228370	Orange Sky	Lbr	2000	22,063	26,863	172	27	14	tfj	I/a May Oldendorff-01 (conv. bbu-02)
9564384	Orange Star	Lbr	2011	34,432	36,994	190	32	14	tfj	
9342580	Orange Sun	Lbr	2007	33,070	43,420	205	32	17	tfj	

Phaethon : Agelef Shipping Co - Pantheon Tkrs. Mgmt : *Hans Kraijenbosch*

Aegean Horizon : Arcadia Shipmanagement : *Chris Brooks*

Orange Ocean : Atlanship A.S. : *Hans Kraijenbosch*

IMO	name	flag	year	gt	dwt	loa	bm	kts	type	comments
9057123	Orange Wave	Lbr	1993	13,444	16,700	157	26	18	tfj	

* managed by NSC Shipping GmbH & Cie, Hamburg

Bahri   Saudi Arabia

funnel: *white with blue logo,* **hull:** *blue with white 'Bahri', Arabic symbols and logo and grey boot topping, replacing green or red some with red or blue boot-topping.* **history:** *formed 1979 as Saudi National Shipping Co. with 25% owned by Saudi government. Acquired 30% share of Petredec in 2005. Operated as National Shipping Co. of Saudi Arabia until restyled as Bahri during 2012.*
web: *www.bahri.sa*

IMO	name	flag	year	gt	dwt	loa	bm	kts	type	comments
9247182	Abqaiq	Bhs	2002	159,990	302,986	333	58	16	tcr	
9421415	Arsan	Mhl	2010	161,969	314,000	333	60	15	tcr	ex Voss Spirit-16, B Elephant-14
9519717	Awtad	Lbr	2011	160,493	317,660	333	60	16	tcr	ex Hanjin Ras Tanura-16
9620944	Bahri Abha	Sau	2013	50,714	25,957	223	32	17	urc	364 teu
9620956	Bahri Hofuf	Sau	2013	50,714	25,901	223	32	17	urc	364 teu
9292826	Bahri Iris	Lbr	2004	32,083	49,000	200	32	14	tco	ex Altair Star-14
9292838	Bahri Jasmine	Lbr	2005	32,083	49,000	200	32	14	tco	ex Alnasl Star-14
9620970	Bahri Jazan	Sau	2013	50,714	25,901	223	32	17	urc	364 teu
9626522	Bahri Jeddah	Sau	2014	50,714	26,000	223	32	17	urc	364 teu
9323596	Bahri Rose	Lbr	2006	32,083	49,000	200	32	14	tco	ex Altarf Star-14
9620968	Bahri Tabuk	Sau	2013	50,714	25,957	223	32	17	urc	364 teu
9324497	Bahri Tulip	Lbr	2006	32,083	49,000	200	32	14	tco	ex Zaurak Star-14
9626534	Bahri Yanbu	Sau	2014	50,714	26,000	223	32	17	urc	364 teu
9448700	Dilam	Mhl	2010	161,969	314,000	333	60	15	tcr	ex Hemsedal Spirit-16, A Elephant-14, l/a D Elephant
9386964	Dorra	Bhs	2009	160,782	317,458	333	60	15	tcr	
9484742	Farhah	Lbr	2010	162,863	319,302	333	60	15	tcr	ex Homam Star-14
9102241	Ghawar	Bhs	1996	163,882	300,361	340	56	15	tcr	
9387009	Ghazal	Sau	2009	160,782	317,664	333	60	15	tcr	
9484728	Ghinah	Lbr	2010	162,863	319,141	333	60	15	tcr	ex Virgo Star-14
9386940	Habari	Bhs	2008	160,782	317,693	333	60	15	tcr	
9220952	Harad	Bhs	2001	159,990	303,115	333	58	17	tcr	l/a Hellespont Burnside
9102265	Hawtah	Bhs	1996	163,882	300,361	340	56	15	tcr	ex TI Hawtah-11, Hawtah-07
9237773	Hilwah	Lbr	2002	164,292	316,808	333	60	15	tcr	ex Pisces Star-14
9378541	Jaham	Lbr	2008	162,252	319,430	333	60	15	tcr	ex Albutain Star-14
9384227	Jaladi	Lbr	2008	162,252	319,464	333	60	15	tcr	ex Janah Star-14
9386938	Jana	Bhs	2007	160,782	317,693	333	60	15	tcr	
9386952	Kahla	Bhs	2009	160,782	317,521	333	60	15	tcr	
9384239	Karan	Lbr	2009	162,252	319,410	333	60	15	tcr	ex Saiph Star-14
9251274	Khafji	Lbr	2003	60,387	115,999	248	43	15	tco	ex Aldebaran Star-14
9384215	Khuzama	Lbr	2008	162,252	319,423	333	60	15	tcr	ex Almizan Star-14
9519482	Kidan	Lbr	2010	162,330	321,050	333	60	15	tcr	ex Blue Pearl-15
9330698	Layla	Bhs	2007	160,782	317,788	333	60	15	tcr	
9237797	Lulu	Lbr	2003	164,292	316,507	333	60	15	tcr	ex Capricorn Star-14
9384198	Manifah	Lbr	2008	162,252	319,430	333	60	15	tcr	ex Sirius Star-14

Ghazal : BAHRI : *Hans Kraijenbosch*

IMO	name	flag	year	gt	dwt	loa	bm	kts	type	comments
9220964	Marjan	Bhs	2002	159,990	303,115	333	58	17	tcr	
9484716	Niban	Lbr	2010	162,863	319,285	333	60	15	tcr	ex Antares Star-14
9484730	Nisalah	Lbr	2010	162,863	319,287	333	60	15	tcr	ex Matar Star-14
9102239	Ramlah	Bhs	1996	163,882	300,361	340	56	15	tcr	
9102277	Safaniyah	Bhs	1997	163,882	300,361	340	56	15	tcr	
9223887	Safwa	Bhs	2002	159,990	302,977	333	58	16	tcr	
9388273	Sahba	Bhs	2009	160,782	317,563	333	60	15	tcr	
9384203	Shaybah	Lbr	2008	162,252	319,429	333	60	15	tcr	ex Vega Star-14
9237785	Shiblah	Lbr	2003	164,292	316,478	333	60	15	tcr	ex Aries Star-14
9237761	Tinat	Lbr	2002	164,292	316,501	333	60	15	tcr	ex Leo Star-14
9102253	Watban	Bhs	1996	163,882	300,361	340	56	15	tcr	ex TI Watban-11, Watban-07
9332535	Wafrah	Bhs	2007	160,782	317,788	333	60	15	tcr	
9524970	Weydan	Lbr	2010	162,330	321,234	333	60	15	tcr	ex Blue Topaz-16
newbuildings:										
9779800		Lbr	2017	160,000	320,000	333	60	15	tcr	Hyundai Samho S842
9779812		Lbr	2017	160,000	320,000	333	60	15	tcr	Hyundai Samho S843
9779824		Lbr	2017	160,000	320,000	333	60	15	tcr	Hyundai Samho S844
9779836		Lbr	2017	160,000	320,000	333	60	15	tcr	Hyundai Samho S845
9779848		Lbr	2017	160,000	320,000	333	60	15	tcr	Hyundai Samho S846

also 5 options confirmed, 300,000 dwt tcr [Hyundai Samho yard # S847 - S851 (2018)]
managed by Mideast Ship Management Ltd, UAE (formed 1996 jointly by NSCSA and V.Ships (UK) Ltd – www.msml.com)

Bahri Dry Bulk, Saudi Arabia
funnel: *White with blue logo* **hull:** *blue with Bahri logo and Bahri in white, grey boot-topping.* **history:** *formed 2013 as j/v between Bahri (60%) and ARASCO (40%)*

IMO	name	flag	year	gt	dwt	loa	bm	kts	type	comments
9660516	Bahri Arasco	Sau	2013	43,894	81,855	229	32	14	bbu	
9660528	Bahri Grain	Sau	2014	43,894	81,855	229	32	14	bbu	
9660530	Bahri Bulk	Sau	2014	43,894	81,864	229	32	14	bbu	
9660542	Bahri Wafi	Sau	2014	43,894	81,855	229	32	14	bbu	
9660554	Bahri Trader	Sau	2014	43,894	81,855	229	32	14	bbu	

Bahri Chemicals, (National Chemical Carriers), Saudi Arabia
funnel: *white with 'NCC' in green, between two narrow green bands, narrow black top* **hull:** *red with red boot-topping,*
history: *company, 80% owned by NSCSA,20% by SABIC, formed 1990 J/V pool with Odfjell dissolved 2013.* **web:** ncc-riyadh.com

IMO	name	flag	year	gt	dwt	loa	bm	kts	type	comments
9087025	Bow Jubail *	Nis	1996	23,197	37,449	183	32	16	tco	ex NCC Jubail-09
9047752	Bow Mekka *	Nis	1995	23,197	37,272	183	32	16	tco	ex NCC Mekka-09
9047506	Bow Riyad *	Nis	1994	23,197	37,252	183	32	16	tco	ex NCC Riyad-09
9295282	NCC Abha	Sau	2006	29,575	45,958	183	32	14	tco	
9411317	NCC Amal	Sau	2011	29,168	45,544	183	32	14	tco	
9335056	NCC Dammam	Sau	2008	29,575	45,965	183	32	14	tco	
9419541	NCC Danah	Sau	2011	29,168	45,579	183	32	14	tco	
9595644	NCC Fajr	Sau	2013	45,452	81,336	228	37	14	tco	l/a Saudi Arabia
9335068	NCC Haiel	Sau	2008	29,575	45,953	183	32	14	tco	
9399272	NCC Huda	Sau	2011	29,168	45,459	183	32	14	tco	
9299886	NCC Hijaz	Sau	2005	29,575	45,956	183	32	14	tco	
9681405	NCC Jood	Sau	2014	29,785	49,990	183	32	14	tco	ex STI Mythos-16
9387683	NCC Maha	Sau	2009	29,644	46,265	183	32	14	tco	ex Brimanger-15
9688336	NCC Masa	Sau	2014	29,785	49,990	183	32	14	tco	ex STI Chelsea-16
9299874	NCC Najd	Sau	2005	29,575	45,998	183	32	14	tco	
9459022	NCC Najem	Sau	2012	28,300	45,499	183	32	14	tco	
9459008	NCC Nasma	Sau	2011	29,168	45,550	183	32	14	tco	
9399260	NCC Noor	Sau	2011	29,165	45,565	183	32	14	tco	
9387671	NCC Qamar	Sau	2009	29,644	46,195	183	32	14	tco	ex Berganger-15
9306811	NCC Qassim	Sau	2008	29,575	46,038	183	32	14	tco	
9335032	NCC Rabigh	Sau	2006	29,575	46,038	183	32	14	tco	
9459034	NCC Reem	Sau	2012	28,300	45,498	183	32	14	tco	
9411329	NCC Safa	Sau	2011	29,168	45,471	183	32	14	tco	
9480150	NCC Sama	Sau	2012	29,168	45,471	183	32	14	tco	
9459010	NCC Shams	Sau	2012	29,168	45,468	183	32	14	tco	
9335044	NCC Sudair	Sau	2007	29,575	46,012	183	32	14	tco	
9306809	NCC Tabuk	Sau	2006	29,575	45,963	183	32	14	tco	
9295270	NCC Tihama	Sau	2005	29,575	45,948	183	32	14	tco	
9688348	NCC Wafa	Sau	2014	29,785	49,990	183	32	14	tco	ex STI Lexington-16
aquisitions:										
9685205			2014	29,785	49,990	183	32	14	tco	ex STI Olivia-16
9685190			2014	29,785	49,990	183	32	14	tco	ex STI Powai-16

* bareboat chartered to Odfjell SE, Norway (www.odfjell.com) until 2019, other vessels commercially operated by NCC Odfjell Chemical Tankers JLT, Dubai managed by Mideast Ship Management Ltd, UAE (formed 1996 jointly by NSCSA and V.Ships (UK) Ltd – www.msml.com)

IMO	name	flag	year	gt	dwt	loa	bm	kts	type	comments

Baltmed Reefer Services Ltd. (Laskaridis Gp.)   Greece

funnel: *blue with blue 3 light blue wavy lines on broad white band* **hull:** *white with red boot-topping.* **history:** *Laskaridis Gp. founded 1977.* **web:** *none found*

IMO	name	flag	year	gt	dwt	loa	bm	kts	type	comments
9017276	Crystal Reefer	Lbr	1993	10,629	10,620	150	23	21	grf	ex Chile Star-15, Polar Chile-05, Trajan-96
9184536	Frio Chikuma	Pan	1998	7,367	8,097	134	20	20	grf	ex Chikuma Reefer-12
8908193	Frio Las Palmas	Lbr	1990	9,070	11,595	149	21	17	grf	ex Himalaya Bay-14, Amer Himalaya-08
9184548	Frio Mogami	Pan	1998	7,367	8,077	134	20	20	grf	ex Mogami Reefer-12
8801814	Frio Oceanic	Bhs	1988	8,487	9,727	141	21	21	grf	ex Changuinola Bay-14, Sun Rosie-06, Cap Changuinola-00
8906975	Shandong Reefer	Lbr	1992	10,629	10,593	150	23	21	grf	ex Honduras Star-15, Polar Colombia-05, Appian-95
9017264	Uruguay Reefer	Lbr	1993	10,629	10,593	150	23	21	grf	ex Uruguay Star-15, Polar Uruguay-05, Hadrian-96

Belships ASA   Norway

funnel: *blue with blue 'S' inside 'C' above blue anchor within narrow blue ring on white disc.* **hull:** *blue, dark grey or red with red boot-topping.* **history:** *founded 1918 as Christen Smith & Co and 1926 as Skibs A/S Belships.* **web:** *www.belships.com*

IMO	name	flag	year	gt	dwt	loa	bm	kts	type	comments
9698185	Belforest	Pan	2015	34,773	61,252	200	32	14	bbu	
9490703	Belnor	Sgp	2010	32,837	58,018	190	32	14	bbu	
9490818	Belocean	Sgp	2011	32,839	58,018	190	32	14	bbu	
9490648	Belstar	Sgp	2009	32,837	58,018	190	32	14	bbu	
9140530	Super Challenge *	Pan	1996	17,977	28,581	172	27	14	bbu	ex IVS Super Challenge-03, Super Challenge-02

newbuildings:

IMO	name	flag	year	gt	dwt	loa	bm	kts	type	comments
9698197	Belisland		2016	34,773	61,252	200	32	14	bbu	Shin Kasado Dockyard S-K086

*owned by Belships Supramax Singapore : * time chartered and managed by Belships Tianjin Shipmanagement*
Jointly owns Elkem Chartering, operating 13 'handymax' bulkers on time charter

Bergshav Shipholding AS   Norway

funnel: *white with white 'B' symbol on broad red band, separated by narrow white band from black top.* **hull:** *brown with black 'BERGSHAV', red or grey boot-topping.* **history:** *formed 1988 as Bergshav A/S and company now over 60% owned by Frontline.* **web:** *www.bergshav.com*

IMO	name	flag	year	gt	dwt	loa	bm	kts	type	comments
9336414	Bergina	Bhs	2007	57,657	105,786	241	42	15	tcr	ex SPT Conqueror-14
9336426	Bergitta	Bhs	2007	57,657	105,850	241	42	15	tcr	ex SPT Crusader-14
9336402	Grimstad	Bhs	2007	57,657	105,786	241	42	15	tcr	ex SPT Challenger-14
9307346	Larvik	Bhs	2006	35,711	61,213	213	32	14	tco	
9336397	Lillesand	Bhs	2007	57,657	105,786	241	42	15	tcr	ex SPT Champion-14

Frio Chikuma : Baltmed Reefer Services : *Chris Brooks*

IMO	name	flag	year	gt	dwt	loa	bm	kts	type	comments
9306641	Ocean Dignity *	Iom	2006	22,184	34,663	171	27	14	tco	
9167162	Ocean Quest *	Iom	2000	22,181	34,999	171	27	14	tco	ex Maersk Rochester-05
9306665	Ocean Spirit *	Iom	2005	22,184	34,603	171	27	14	tco	

* owned by Ocean Product Tankers DIS, (20% owned by Bergshav Mgmt.) and bare-boat chartered to Roxana Shipping, Greece

F. H. Bertling Reederei GmbH   Germany

funnel: *blue with 3 blue '~' on white square* **hull:** *blue with red boot-toping.* **history:** *founded 1865* **web:** *www.bertling.com*

IMO	name	flag	year	gt	dwt	loa	bm	kts	type	comments
9626118	Alentejo +	Sgp	2013	24,166	34,845	180	30	13	bbu	
9611278	Aquitania +	Sgp	2012	24,166	34,845	180	30	13	bbu	
9262572	Atacama	Mlt	2004	24,960	35,015	188	28	17	gpc	1,874 teu
9262546	Caledonia	Mlt	2002	24,918	35,079	188	28	14	ggc	
9309526	Catalonia	Mlt	2005	24,960	35,200	188	28	14	ggc	
9626120	Dalarna +	Sgp	2014	24,166	34,845	180	30	13	bbu	
9548835	Dalmatia +	Sgp	2011	33,601	51,624	200	32	14	ggc	
9262560	Diamond Land	Mlt	2004	24,918	35,079	188	28	14	ggc	ex Calabria-16
9601902	Istria +	Sgp	2013	43,951	81,699	229	32	14	bbu	
9291987	Levante	Mlt	2005	24,960	35,200	188	28	14	ggc	
9309514	Lombardia	Mlt	2005	24,960	35,200	188	28	14	ggc	
9126003	Nasca *	Per	1997	29,289	45,750	183	32	14	tco	ex Iver Excel-14
9548823	Navarra +	Sgp	2010	33,601	51,624	200	32	14	ggc	
9170640	Normandie	Mlt	1999	25,719	36,120	190	28	14	ggc	
9611280	Patagonia +	Sgp	2012	24,166	34,845	180	30	13	bbu	
9226322	Solent	Mlt	2002	24,918	35,079	188	28	14	ggc	
9262558	Valdivia	Mlt	2003	24,918	35,079	188	28	14	ggc	

* operated by Transgas International, USA + managed by Bertling Chartering & Ship, Singapore

Bidsted & Co. A/S   Norway

funnel: *buff with large blue 'B' or black with broad red band with large black 'D'* **hull:** *black or red wih red boot-toping.*
history: *formed 1940* **web:** *www.bidsted.dk*

IMO	name	flag	year	gt	dwt	loa	bm	kts	type	comments
9284489	Bianco Dan *	Pan	2004	30,619	55,628	190	32	14	bbu	ex Pescadores Bulker-06
9608702	Bianco Olivia Bulker *†	Mlt	2013	20,928	32,500	180	28	13	bbu	
9278739	Bianco Venture * †	Pan	2004	19,828	33,773	175	28	14	bbu	
9608697	Bianco Victoria Bulker * †	Mlt	2012	20,928	32,178	180	28	13	bbu	
9124146	Caribbean ID †	Pan	1996	18,108	27,940	169	27	14	bbu	ex Mount Cook-08, Shinyo Challenge-06, Admire-03
9515682	Danship Bulker †	Mlt	2009	17,025	28,291	169	27	14	bbu	
9624328	ID Copenhagen †	Pan	2012	17,027	28,206	169	27	14	bbu	
9223825	ID Mermaid	Hkg	2001	17,944	27,105	178	26	14	bbu	ex Clipper Mermaid-10

ID Copenhagen : Bidsted A/S : *Chris Brooks*

IMO	name	flag	year	gt	dwt	loa	bm	kts	type	comments
9464546	Idship Bulker †	Hkg	2008	17,018	28,361	169	27	14	bbu	
9519195	Poavosa Brave †	Mlt	2009	17,018	28,367	169	27	14	bbu	ex ID North Sea-15

* owned by Dansk Rederi AS,   † on charter to Lauritzen Bulkers

Reederei Blue Star Holding GmbH **Germany**

E.R. Schiffahrts GmbH & Cie. KG

funnel: *black with white 'ER' on broad blue band edged with narrow white bands or charterers colours.* **hull:** *dark blue with pink boot-topping or charterers colours.* **history:** *Nordcapital Holdings formed 1992 by Bertram and Erck Rickmers, in 1996 brothers split and company became E.R Capital Holdings,which is now the sole shareholder of Nordcapital and major shareholder of Blue Star Holdings, formed July 2012 after merger with Komrowski.* **web:** *www.er-ship.com*

IMO	name	flag	year	gt	dwt	loa	bm	kts	type	comments
9358890	Balkan **	Mlt	2007	15,633	17,005	161	25	19	ucc	1,304 teu: ex CSAV Caribe-08
9275062	Cap Beatrice	Lbr	2004	26,833	33,315	210	32	19	ucc	2,556 teu: ex Nedlloyd Valentina-14, P&O Nedlloyd Valentina-06, I/dn Valentina Star
9275024	Cap Beaufort	Lbr	2003	26,833	34,567	210	30	22	ucc	2,556 teu: ex Nedlloyd Adriana-14, P&O Nedlloyd Adriana-05, Adriana Star-03
9483231	Clarke Quay	Lbr	2010	32,672	55,618	188	32	14	bbu	ex E.R. Brest-15
9318046	CMA CGM Carmen	Lbr	2006	91,649	100,680	334	43	25	ucc	8,204 teu: I/a E.R. Tokyo
9305491	CMA CGM Don Carlos	Lbr	2006	91,649	101,496	334	43	25	ucc	8,204 teu: I/a E.R.Toulouse
9305506	CMA CGM Don Giovanni	Lbr	2006	91,649	100,680	334	43	25	ucc	8,204 teu: ex E.R.Toronto-06
9318101	CMA CGM Don Pascuale	Lbr	2007	91,649	101,477	334	43	25	ucc	8,204 teu: ex Don Pascuale-14, CMA CGM Don Pascuale-12, MSC Xian-09, I/a E.R. Trieste
9318058	CMA CGM Faust	Lbr	2006	91,649	100,680	334	43	25	ucc	8,204 teu: ex Faust-14, CMA CGM Faust-12, MSC Bengal-09, I/a E.R. Texas
9314973	CMA CGM Lavender	Lbr	2006	27,779	39,418	222	30	23	ucc	2,824 teu: ex E.R. Montpellier-06
9314961	CMA CGM Mimosa	Lbr	2006	27,779	39,200	222	30	23	ucc	2,824 teu: ex E.R. Monaco-06
9318060	CMA CGM Parsifal	Lbr	2006	91,649	101,505	335	43	25	ucc	8,204 teu: ex Parsifal-14, CMA CGM Parsifal-12, I/a E.R. Toulon
9305477	Cosco Germany	Pmd	2006	91,649	101,532	335	43	25	ucc	8,204 teu: I/a E.R. Tianshan
9305489	Cosco Napoli	Pmd	2006	91,649	101,491	335	43	25	ucc	8,204 teu: I/a E.R. Tianping
9213571	E.R. Amsterdam	Lux	2000	66,289	67,557	277	40	26	ucc	5,762 teu: ex MSC Antares-16, E.R. Amsterdam-08, P&O Nedlloyd Magellan-05, I/a E.R. Amsterdam
9483217	E.R. Barcelona	Lbr	2010	32,672	55,783	188	32	14	bbu	
9483243	E.R. Basel	Lbr	2011	32,672	55,800	188	32	14	bbu	
9519066	E.R. Bavaria	Lbr	2010	93,186	179,436	292	45	15	bbu	
9507893	E.R. Bayern	Lbr	2010	93,186	178,978	292	45	15	bbu	
9507520	E.R. Bayonne	Lbr	2010	93,186	178,978	292	45	15	bbu	

E.R. Bayern : Blue Star Reederei - E.R. Schiffahrts : *Hans Kraijenbosch*

IMO	name	flag	year	gt	dwt	loa	bm	kts	type	comments
9483188	E.R. Bergamo	Lbr	2009	32,672	55,783	188	32	14	bbu	
9214214	E.R. Berlin	Lbr	2000	66,289	67,660	277	40	26	ucc	5,762 teu: ex OOCL Germany-10, E.R. Berlin-01
9483205	E.R. Bilbao	Lbr	2010	32,672	55,783	188	32	14	bbu	
9483229	E.R. Bordeaux	Lbr	2010	32,672	55,800	188	32	14	bbu	
9507519	E.R. Borneo	Lbr	2010	93,186	178,978	292	45	15	bbu	
9483267	E.R. Bornholm	Lbr	2011	32,672	55,800	188	32	14	bbu	
9507881	E.R. Boston	Lbr	2010	93,186	178,978	292	45	15	bbu	
9519078	E.R. Bourgogne	Lbr	2010	93,186	178,906	292	45	15	bbu	
9505833	E.R. Brandenburg	Lbr	2010	93,186	179,436	292	45	15	bbu	
9507788	E.R. Brighton	Lbr	2010	32,672	55,783	188	32	14	bbu	
9507790	E.R. Bristol	Lbr	2011	32,672	55,800	188	32	14	bbu	
9507544	E.R. Buenos Aires	Lbr	2010	93,186	178,978	292	45	15	bbu	
9301433	E.R. Caen	Lbr	2004	26,836	34,289	210	30	21	ucc	2,556 teu: ex CMA CGM Jaguar-09, E.R. Caen-04
9301445	E.R. Calais	Lbr	2005	26,718	34,567	210	30	21	ucc	2,556 teu: ex CMA CGM l'Astrolabe-10
9231236	E.R. Canada	Lbr	2001	65,792	68,025	277	40	26	ucc	5,762 teu: ex APL Canada-14, E.R. Canada-01
9275048	E.R. Cape Town	Lbr	2003	26,833	34,295	210	30	22	ucc	2,556 teu: ex Cap Bonavista-16, Nedlloyd Marita-14, P&O Nedlloyd Marita-06, Marita Star-03
9239903	E.R. Cuxhaven	Lbr	2002	26,200	33,800	212	30	22	ucc	2,496 teu: ex Maersk Newark-09, E.R. Cuxhaven-02
9231250	E.R. Denmark	Lbr	2002	65,792	67,935	277	40	26	ucc	5,762 teu: ex APL Denmark-12, E.R. Denmark-02
9246346	E.R. Elsfleth	Lbr	2003	26,200	33,800	212	30	22	ucc	2,496 teu: ex Andes Bridge-08, Maersk Newcastle-07, E.R. Elsfleth-03
9213583	E.R. Felixstowe	Lux	2000	66,289	67,564	277	40	26	ucc	5,762 teu; ex MSC Mira-16, E.R. Felixstowe-08, P&O Nedlloyd Torres-06, l/a E.R. Felixstowe
9214226	E.R. France	Deu	2001	66,289	67,591	277	40	26	ucc	5,762 teu; ex MSC Adriatic-15, OOCL France-09, E.R. Paris-01
9160425	E.R. Hamburg	Lbr	1998	26,125	30,721	196	30	19	ucc	2,226 teu: ex Safmarine Niger-12, E.R. Hamburg-09, CSAV Shanghai-07, Las Americas Bridge-03, CSAV Shanghai-01, Aconcagua-99, l/a E.R. Hamburg
9239898	E.R. Helgoland	Lbr	2002	27,322	34,608	212	30	22	ucc	2,496 teu: ex Safmarine Zambezi-12, E.R. Helgoland-02
9231248	E.R. India	Lbr	2002	65,792	68,025	277	40	26	ucc	5,762 teu: ex APL India-14, E.R. India-02
9222974	E.R. Kobe	Lbr	2001	66,289	68,196	277	40	26	ucc	5,762 teu: ex Suape Express-15, E.R. Kobe-11, CSCL Kobe-11, l/a E.R. Kobe
9214202	E.R. London	Deu	2000	66,289	67,566	277	40	26	ucc	5,762 teu: ex MSC Gemma-16, E.R. London-09, P&O Nedlloyd Vespucci-05, l/a E.R. London
9222986	E.R. Los Angeles	Lbr	2001	66,289	68,196	277	40	26	ucc	5,762 teu: ex Montevideo Express-15, E.R. Los Angeles-11, MSC Los Angeles-10, CSCL Los Angeles-08, l/a E.R. Los Angeles
9314985	E.R. Martinique	Lbr	2007	27,927	39,200	222	30	23	ucc	2,824 teu: ex ANL Burilla-12, CMA CGM Anemone-11 Anemone-10, CMA CGM Anemone-09, E.R. Martinique-07
9211169	E.R. Pusan	Deu	2000	66,289	67,737	277	40	26	ucc	5,762 teu: ex OOCL Los Angeles-10, l/a E.R. Pusan
9448669	E.R. Riga	Lbr	2010	12,514	14,236	158	24	19	ucc	1,084 teu: ex Leguan-12
9160437	E.R. Santiago	Lbr	1998	26,125	30,720	196	30	19	ucc	2,226 teu: ex Safmarine Nyanga-12, E.R. Santiago-09, CSAV Ningbo-07, Copiapo-04, l/a E.R. Santiago
9208021	E.R. Seoul	Lux	2000	66,289	66,298	277	40	26	ucc	5,762 teu: ex CSAV Houston-15, E.R. Seoul-11, OOCL Malaysia-09, E.R. Seoul-00
9231262	E.R. Sweden	Lbr	2002	65,792	68,025	277	40	26	ucc	5,762 teu: ex APL Sweden, E.R. Sweden-02
9448671	E.R. Tallinn	Lbr	2011	12,514	14,230	158	24	19	ucc	1,084 teu: ex Ossian-12
9305465	E.R. Tianan	Pmd	2005	91,649	101,570	335	43	25	ucc	8,204 teu: ex Cosco China-16, l/a E.R. Tianan
9448683	E.R. Turku	Lbr	2011	12,514	14,292	158	24	19	ucc	1,084 teu: ex Montan-12
9448695	E.R. Visby	Lbr`	2012	12,514	14,236	158	24	19	ucc	1,084 teu: ex Titian-13
9285665	E.R. Yokohama	Lbr	2004	83,133	93,659	300	43	25	ucc	7,488 teu: ex MSC Yokohama-15, Cosco Yokohama -13, l/a E.R. Yokohama
9358905	Heluan **	Lbr	2007	15,633	16,960	161	25	19	ucc	1,304 teu

IMO	name	flag	year	gt	dwt	loa	bm	kts	type	comments
9273210	Julian **	Lbr	2004	40,160	73,513	225	32	14	bbu	ex Lowlands Julian-11, Bonanza-09
9303534	Maersk Saigon	Lbr	2006	94,483	108,251	332	43	24	ucc	8,452 teu: ex P&O Nedlloyd Maria-06
9289922	Maersk Sana *	Lbr	2004	94,724	94,724	335	43	24	ucc	8,452 teu: ex P&O Nedlloyd Mondriaan-06, Mondriaan Star-04
9289934	Maersk Santana *	Lbr	2005	94,724	94,724	335	43	24	ucc	8,452 teu: ex P&O Nedlloyd Manet-06, Manet Star-05
9289946	Maersk Sarnia *	Lbr	2005	94,724	94,724	335	43	24	ucc	8,452 teu; ex P&O Nedlloyd Michelangelo-06, Michelangelo Star-05
9306550	Maersk Seoul	Lbr	2006	94,483	108,343	332	43	25	ucc	8,402 teu: I/a Marlene Star
9299927	Maersk Seville *	Lbr	2006	94,724	97,552	335	43	24	ucc	8,452 teu: ex Mahler Star-06, P&O Nedlloyd Mahler-05
9299939	Maersk Sheerness *	Lux	2006	94,724	97,536	335	43	24	ucc	8,452 teu: ex P&O Nedlloyd Mendelssohn-06
9308649	Maersk Singapore *	Lbr	2007	94,724	97,552	335	43	24	ucc	8,452 teu: I/a P&O Nedlloyd Montevideo
9308637	Maersk Sofia *	Lux	2007	94,724	97,549	332	43	24	ucc	8,452 teu: I/a Menotti Star
9303522	Maersk Stralsund *	Lbr	2005	94,493	108,212	332	43	25	ucc	8,402 teu: ex P&O Nedlloyd Marilyn-05
9289958	Maersk Sydney *	Lbr	2005	93,511	97,535	335	43	24	ucc	7,500 teu: ex P&O Nedlloyd Miro-06, I/a Miro Star
9337274	Mozart	Lbr	2007	28,616	39,339	222	30	21	ucc	2,824 teu: ex Sofia Schulte-13, Cap Cleveland-12, Sofia Schulte-08
9465277	MSC Altair †	Lbr	2012	141,635	141,051	366	48	24	ucc	13,092 teu
9465253	MSC Benedetta	Deu	2011	141,635	140,991	366	48	24	ucc	13,092 teu: I/a E.R. Benedetta
9465318	MSC Margrit	Lbr	2012	141,635	141,141	366	48	24	ucc	13,092 teu: ex CMA CGM Margrit-15, MSC Margrit-12, I/a E.R. Castor
9285677	MSC Ningbo	Lux	2004	83,133	93,572	300	43	25	ucc	7,488 teu: ex Cosco Long Beach-15, I/a E.R. Shenzhen
9465306	MSC Renee	Lbr	2012	141,635	140,958	366	48	24	ucc	13,092 teu: I/a E.R. Pollux
9285689	MSC Seattle	Lux	2004	83,133	93,728	300	43	25	ucc	7,488 teu: ex Cosco Seattle-13, I/a E.R. Seattle
9285653	MSC Shenzen	Lux	2004	83,133	93,643	300	43	25	ucc	7,488 teu: Cosco Shenzen-13, I/dn E.R. Long Beach
9285691	MSC Vancouver	Lux	2004	83,133	93,638	300	43	25	ucc	7,488 teu: ex Cosco Vancouver-13, I/a E.R. Vancouver
9465265	MSC Vega	Lbr	2012	141,635	148,580	366	48	24	ucc	13,092 teu
9246322	Puccini	Lbr	2003	27,322	34,418	212	30	22	ucc	2,496 teu: ex E.R. Bremen-13, CCNI Manzanillo-10, Maersk Norfolk-07, E.R. Bremen-03
9238806	Queens Quay	Lbr	2003	39,941	50,900	264	32	24	ucc	4,253 teu: ex E.R. Kingston-14, CMA CGM Kingston-11, E.R. Kingston-04, CMA CGM Kingston-03, I/a E.R. Kingston
9452646	Salford Quay	Lbr	2011	33,036	56,956	190	32	14	bbu	ex Conti Pyrit-14

managed for * MPC Group   ** Ernst Komrowski Reederei KG   † managed for SinOceanic II AS, Norway

Arne Blystad A/S   Norway

funnel: *yellow with red 'B' on broad white band edged with narrow blue bands, narrow black top.*   **hull:** *black or red wih red boot-topping.*   **history:** *formed 1989 as Blystad Shipping (USA) Inc. to 2003. Saga Tankers inc. 2010 30% owned, 100% of Offshore Heavy Lift purchased in 2008 by Albatross Investerings AS, part of Blystad Group. Also owns 40% of Gram Car Carriers with P. D. Gram & Co..*   **web:** *www.blystad.no*

IMO	name	flag	year	gt	dwt	loa	bm	kts	type	comments
9310707	Challenge Passage	Pan	2008	28,823	48,658	180	32	15	tco	
9423645	Songa Breeze **	Mhl	2009	11,919	19,999	146	24	14	tco	ex Clipper Makishio-14
9409510	Songa Challenge **	Mhl	2009	11,623	19,993	146	24	14	tco	ex Global Challenge-13
9314105	Songa Coral	Mhl	2005	58,099	107,081	247	42	14	tcr	ex Al Muminah-15, Forward Pioneer-13
9378321	Songa Crystal **	Mhl	2006	8,485	12,926	127	20	14	tco	ex Samho Crystal-06
9460459	Songa Diamond **	Mhl	2009	11,259	17,543	144	23	14	tco	
9461714	Songa Eagle **	Mhl	2009	8,505	13,250	128	20	14	tco	
9473937	Songa Emerald **	Mhl	2009	11,259	17,567	144	23	14	tco	
9482653	Songa Falcon *	Mhl	2009	8,505	13,224	128	20	14	tco	
9693812	Songa Fortune	Mhl	2015	28,326	49,718	184	32	14	tco	
9482665	Songa Hawk **	Mhl	2009	8,505	13,265	128	20	14	tco	
9473925	Songa Jade **	Mhl	2009	11,259	17,604	144	23	14	tco	
9473913	Songa Opal **	Mhl	2009	11,259	17,588	144	23	14	tco	
9409522	Songa Peace **	Mhl	2009	11,623	19,992	146	24	14	tco	ex Global Peace-13
9444455	Songa Pearl **	Mhl	2008	11,259	17,539	144	23	14	tco	
9444479	Songa Ruby **	Mhl	2008	11,259	17,604	144	23	14	tco	
9444467	Songa Sapphire **	Mhl	2008	11,259	17,539	144	23	14	tco	
9460461	Songa Topaz **	Mhl	2009	11,259	17,596	144	23	14	tco	
9416109	Songa Winds **	Pan	2009	11,662	19,954	144	24	14	tco	

IMO	name	flag	year	gt	dwt	loa	bm	kts	type	comments
newbuilding:										
9693824	Songa Pride			29.000	49.000	183	32	14	tco	Brodotrogir 326

*managed by Songa Shipmanagement, Singapore or by * Laurentzens Skibs Management, or ** Navig8 Chemicals Inc*

Gram Car Carriers AS, Norway

funnel: black with dark blue 'G' in a white diamond outlined with dark blue on a broad light blue band or charterers colours
hull: dark blue wih red boot-topping. *history:* P.D. Gram began car carrier operations in 1974, now 40% owned by Blystad

IMO	name	flag	year	gt	dwt	loa	bm	kts	type	comments
9407677	City of Oslo	Sgp	2010	20,209	4,693	140	22	18	mve	2,000 ceu
9209934	Eishun	Sgp	1999	33,854	8,531	173	27	20	mve	3,500 ceu
9407665	Höegh Caribia	Sgp	2010	20,209	4,693	140	22	18	mve	2,000 ceu
9318462	Höegh Delhi	Sgp	2007	55,775	16,890	200	32	20	mve	6,500 ceu
9673018	Viking Adventure	Sgp	2015	62,106	18,372	200	32	19	mve	6,700 ceu
9481049	Viking Amber	Sgp	2010	39,362	12,471	167	28	18	mve	4,200 ceu

Songa Ruby : Arne Blystad A/S : *Mike Lennon*

Viking Amber : Arne Blystad A/S - Gram Car Carriers : *Mike Lennon*

IMO	name	flag	year	gt	dwt	loa	bm	kts	type	comments
9673020	Viking Bravery	Sgp	2015	62,106	19,000	200	32	19	mve	6,700 ceu
9188790	Viking Chance	Sgp	1999	33,863	10,834	164	28	18	mve	4,300 ceu: ex Modern Chance-11
9407689	Viking Constanza	Sgp	2010	20,209	4,696	140	22	18	mve	2,000 ceu
9481051	Viking Coral	Sgp	2011	39,362	12,588	167	28	18	mve	4,200 ceu
9481075	Viking Diamond	Sgp	2011	39,362	12,572	167	28	18	mve	4,200 ceu
9188817	Viking Drive	Sgp	2000	33,831	10,817	164	28	18	mve	4,300 ceu: ex Modern Drive-10
9514987	Viking Emerald	Sgp	2012	39,362	12,500	167	28	18	mve	4,200 ceu
9514999	Viking Ocean	Sgp	2012	39,362	12,500	167	28	18	mve	4,200 ceu
9398876	Viking Odessa	Sgp	2009	20,216	4,693	140	22	18	mve	2,000 ceu
9515008	Viking Sea	Sgp	2012	39,362	12,500	167	28	18	mve	4,200 ceu
newbuildings:										
9728851		Sgp	2017	62,100	19,000	200	32	19	mve	6,700 ceu JLZ8120436
9728863		Sgp	2017	62,100	19,000	200	32	19	mve	6,700 ceu JLZ8120437

vessels managed by OSM Ship Management, Singapore

Offshore Heavy Transport A/S, Norway
funnel: blue with company logo on broad white band or yellow with red 'B' on broad white band edged with narrow blue bands, narrow black top   hull: blue with 'Offshore Heavy Transport' in white at stern. history: founded 2008 after restructuring with 100% shares since 2012 owned by Albatross Investering AS, part of Blystad Group web: www.oht.no

IMO	name	flag	year	gt	dwt	loa	bm	kts	type	comments
9032496	Albatross	Mhl	1993	34,925	34,797	265	43	14	ohl	ex Tordis Knutsen-13 (conv tcs-14)
8616568	Osprey	Nis	1989	38,722	53,000	223	45	15	ohl	ex Heavylift Ancora-09, Ancora-08, Songa Ancora-08, Ancora-05, Leon Spirit-04, Borja Tapias-04 (conv tcr/sht-08)
7931454	Eagle	Nis	1981	31,021	31,809	199	42	14	ohl	ex Heavylift Eagle-09, Willift Eagle-08, Willift Lady-06, Lucky Lady-06, Albe-94, World Cliff-90, Cliff-84, World Cliff-83 (conv tcr/sht-06)
7915278	Falcon	Nis	1981	31,027	31,908	199	42	14	ohl	ex Heavylift Falcon-09, Willift Falcon-08, Nilos-08, Nile-95, World Zeal-90 (conv tcr/sht-07)
8616556	Hawk	Nis	1989	38,722	54,000	223	45	15	ohl	ex Heavylift Hawk-09, Hawk-08, Hawker-08, Front Transporter-07, Genmar Transporter-04, Crude Transporter-03, Nord-Jahre Transporter-00, Jahre Transporter-93 (conv tcr/sht-08)

Aug. Bolten Wm. Miller's Nachfolger (GmbH & Co.)KG
Germany
funnel: black with black 'B' inside red rectangle outline and diagonal cross on white houseflag or (*) black 'L' on blue-edged white disc at centre of blue diagonal crossed and edged houseflag on broad white band. hull: black with red boot-topping. history: parent originally founded 1801 and shipping company formed in 1906. Joint owners of Eurasia Shipping & Management with B Schulte to 1988. web: www.aug-bolten.de

IMO	name	flag	year	gt	dwt	loa	bm	kts	type	comments
9655212	Abtenauer	Mhl	2014	24,163	36,056	180	30	14	bbu	
9646728	Abyssinian	Mhl	2014	24,247	36,063	180	30	14	bbu	
9238313	Antonia	Lbr	2002	22,072	34,655	179	28	14	bbu	ex Aquila Voyager-12, Valiant-08, Austyn Oldendorff-06, IVS Valiant-03
9646704	Appaloosa	Mhl	2013	24,247	36,053	180	30	14	bbu	
9646699	Ardennes	Mhl	2013	24,247	36,062	180	30	14	bbu	
9646730	Asturcon	Mhl	2014	24,247	36,071	180	30	14	bbu	
9427392	Callisto	Lbr	2010	15,861	25,009	157	27	14	ggc	
9718442	Carlota Bolten	Pmd	2015	24,198	37,500	180	30	14	bbu	I/a Nordic Weihei
9718454	Carolina Bolten	Pmd	2015	24,198	37,500	180	30	14	bbu	I/a Nordic Qingdao
9574042	Diana Bolten	Lbr	2011	23,264	38,273	180	30	14	bbu	
9483451	Franziska Bolten	Lbr	2008	18,493	29,234	170	27	14	bbu	ex Western Wave-09, Yahua No.1-08
9427380	Helen Bolten	Lbr	2009	15,861	24,979	157	27	14	ggc	
9406063	Lilly Bolten	Lbr	2009	19,972	30,760	179	28	14	bbu	
9406049	Louisa Bolten	Lbr	2009	19,972	30,522	179	28	14	bbu	
9149653	Marielle Bolten	Lbr	1997	19,354	29,534	181	26	14	ggc	
9138458	Paros	Lbr	1997	14,397	23,984	154	26	14	bbu	ex Pacific Bridge-03
9149665	Sigrun Bolten	Lbr	1997	19,354	29,534	181	26	14	ggc	ex Cielo di Savona-01, Sigrun Bolten-97

Lydia Mar Shipping Co. S.A., Greece
funnel: black with house flag hull: black with red boot-topping history: Bolten subsidiary founded 1981 web: www.lydiamar.gr

IMO	name	flag	year	gt	dwt	loa	bm	kts	type	comments
9646716	Amorgos	Mhl	2014	24,210	36,063	180	30	14	bbu	
9691632	Ithaki	Mhl	2014	23,268	38,060	180	30	14	bbu	

IMO	name	flag	year	gt	dwt	loa	bm	kts	type	comments
9449780	Kefalonia	Mhl	2009	18,096	28,742	170	27	14	bbu	
9138446	Milos	Mlt	1997	14,397	24,045	154	26	14	bbu	ex Arwad Island-14, Milos-09
9449792	Paxi	Mhl	2010	18,096	28,734	170	27	14	bbu	
9177985	Skyros	Cyp	1998	14,781	24,128	154	26	14	bbu	ex Diamond Star-03
9181493	Tala	Mhl	1998	15,349	24,175	159	26	14	ggc	ex Bright Sky-11
newbuilding:										
		Mhl	2016	24,000	38,273	180	30	14	bbu	Japanese yard

Borealis Maritime Ltd. U.K.

funnel: *black* **hull:** *various* **history:** *company founded 2010. Joined O&S Chartering (formed 2013 by Reederei Nord and Bernhard Schulte) in September 2015 which then became Hanseatic Unity Chartering* **web:** *www.borealismaritime.com*

IMO	name	flag	year	gt	dwt	loa	bm	kts	type	comments
9506382	Beethoven *	Lbr	2012	26,374	34,116	209	30	22	ucc	2,546 teu: ex Rio Anna-13
9510371	Bomar Amber	Lbr	2012	32,305	58,110	190	32	14	bbu	ex Sandra-16
9330525	Bomar Hamburg	Mlt	2006	28,616	39,359	222	30	23	ucc	2,824 teu: ex Santa Belina-16, Maersk Jamestown-11, I/a Santa Belina
9275036	Bomar Juliana	Lbr	2003	26,833	34,273	210	30	22	ucc	2,556 teu: ex NileDutch Oryx-15, Nedlloyd Juliana-14, P&O Nedlloyd Juliana-06, Juliana Star-03
9391610	Bomar Oyster	Lbr	2012	31,670	58,110	190	32	14	bbu	ex Selecta-16
9376892	Bomar Regent	Mhl	2007	16,162	16,509	161	24	19	ucc	1,338 teu, ex Montana-14, Mell Sayang-13, Montana-12, Rickmers China-07
9240873	Bomar Resilient	Cyp	2002	27,093	34,638	210	30	22	ucc	2,520 teu: ex Annabelle Schulte-14, P&O Nedlloyf Barossa Valley-05, P&O Nedlloyd Barossa-02, I/a Kynouria
9408774	Bomar Resolute	Lbr	2007	35,991	42,074	231	32	23	ucc	3,554 teu: ex Gabriel Schulte-15, Cap Moreton-14, Maruba Cristina-09, Cap Moreton-07, I/a Gabriel Schulte
9204489	Bomar Rissen	Atg	2010	16,802	23,028	185	25	19	ucc	1,730 teu: ex Rissen-14, Wehr Rissen-13, MOL Utility-09, Wehr Rissen-08, Delmas Mascareignes-07, CMA CGM Bourgainville-04, Wehr Rissen-99
9316359	Bomar Spring	Lbr	2006	32,214	39,063	211	32	22	ucc	2,732 teu: ex Passat Spring-15
9242637	Bomar Valour	Mhl	2002	17,189	22,300	180	28	19	ucc	1,700 teu: ex Maersk Valletta-14, I/a Amadeus I

Bomar Juliana : Borealis Maritime : *Hans Kraijenbosch*

IMO	name	flag	year	gt	dwt	loa	bm	kts	type	comments
9242625	Bomar Vanquish	Mhl	2002	17,189	22,308	180	28	19	ucc	1,700 teu: ex Maersk Vancouver-14, l/a Aquarius
9242649	Bomar Victory	Mhl	2002	17,189	22,200	180	28		ucc	1,700 teu: ex Maersk Vigo-14, Starlight
9473327	Brahms +	Mlt	2011	41,074	75,200	225	32	14	bbu	ex Conti Serpentin-14
9344679	Cap Palliser **	Lbr	2007	22,914	28,219	186	28	21	ucc	1,819 teu: l/a San Alfredo
9344655	Cap Pasley **	Lbr	2007	22,914	28,142	186	28	21	ucc	1,819 teu: l/a San Allessandro
9344631	Cap Portland **	Lbr	2007	22,914	28,142	186	28	21	ucc	1,819 teu: l/a San Albano
9275050	Maersk Nottingham	Lbr	2004	26,833	34,300	210	32	21	ucc	ex P&O Nedlloyd Regina-06, l/dn Regina Star
9235402	Northern Enterprise	Lbr	2001	25,713	33,836	208	30	21	ucc	2,456 teu: ex Cap Salinas-08, NYK Freesia-05, Cap Salinas-04, Northern Enterprise-03, Andhika Lourdes-02
9347279	San Adriano **	Lbr	2008	22,914	28,300	186	28	21	ucc	1,819 teu: ex Ibn Qutaibah-09, l/a San Adriano
9347293	San Alessio **	Lbr	2008	22,914	28,142	186	28	21	ucc	1,819 teu
9347255	San Andres **	Lbr	2008	22,914	28,300	186	28	21	ucc	1,819 teu

*managed by Laeisz Reederei ** managed by CPO Containerschiffreederei + managed by Nord Reederei*

BP Shipping Ltd.   U.K.

funnel: red with green band on broad white band beneath black top. **hull:** black with red boot-topping. **history:** subsidiary of BP plc. Shipping company formed 1915 as British Tanker Shipping to carry oil for Anglo-Persian Oil Co., the forerunner of BP. 1956 renamed BP Tanker Co. Ltd. and in 1981 BP Shipping Ltd. **web:** www.bp.com/shipping

IMO	name	flag	year	gt	dwt	loa	bm	kts	type	comments
9266841	British Beech	Iom	2003	58,070	106,138	241	42	15	tcr	
9288760	British Chivalry *	Iom	2005	29,335	46,803	183	32	15	tco	
9307750	British Commerce (st)	Iom	2006	48,772	54,478	230	37	17	lpg	83,270 m³
9282493	British Cormorant	Iom	2005	63,661	113,782	250	44	15	tcr	
9307762	British Councillor (st)	Gbr	2007	48,772	54,450	230	37	18	lpg	83,270 m³
9307748	British Courage (st)	Iom	2006	48,772	54,533	230	37	18	lpg	83,270 m³
9288825	British Courtesy	Iom	2005	29,214	47,210	183	32	14	tco	
9258894	British Curlew	Iom	2004	63,661	114,809	250	44	15	tcr	
9297345	British Cygnet	Iom	2005	63,462	113,782	250	44	15	tcr	
9333620	British Diamond (df)	Iom	2008	102,064	84,553	288	44	20	lng	151,945 m³
9297371	British Eagle	Iom	2006	63,462	113,553	250	44	15	tcr	
9333591	British Emerald (df)	Iom	2007	102,064	84,303	282	44	20	lng	151,945 m³
9251573	British Esteem	Gbr	2003	23,235	37,220	183	27	15	tco	
9251561	British Explorer	Gbr	2003	23,235	37,321	183	27	15	tco	
9297369	British Falcon	Iom	2006	63,462	113,553	250	44	15	tcr	
9285744	British Fidelity	Iom	2004	29,335	46,803	183	32	14	tco	
9282481	British Gannet	Iom	2005	63,661	114,809	250	44	15	tcr	
9288813	British Harmony *	Iom	2005	29,335	46,803	183	32	14	tco	
9266853	British Hazel	Iom	2004	58,070	106,085	241	42	15	tcr	
9266865	British Holly	Iom	2004	58,070	106,085	241	42	15	tcr	
9238040	British Innovator (st)	Iom	2002	93,498	75,074	279	43	19	lng	138,000 m³
9277858	British Integrity	Iom	2004	29,335	46,803	183	32	15	tco	
9397357	British Kestrel	Iom	2006	63,462	113,553	250	44	15	tcr	
9285756	British Liberty	Iom	2004	29,335	46,803	183	32	14	tco	
9285720	British Loyalty	Iom	2004	29,335	46,803	183	32	14	tco	
9282479	British Mallard	Iom	2005	63,661	114,809	250	44	15	tcr	
9250191	British Merchant (st)	Iom	2003	93,498	75,059	279	43	19	lng	138,000 m³
9258870	British Merlin	Iom	2003	63,661	114,761	250	44	15	tcr	
9247792	British Oak	Iom	2003	57,567	106,500	241	42	15	tcr	
9683013	British Renown [K]	Iom	2016	64,309	109.258	250	44	14	tcr	
9683001	British Respect [K]	Iom	2016	64,309	109,258	250	44	14	tcr	
9282508	British Robin	Iom	2005	63,462	113,782	250	44	15	tcr	
9333606	British Ruby (df)	Iom	2008	102,064	84,491	282	44	20	lng	151,945 m³
9333618	British Sapphire (df)	Iom	2008	102,064	84,455	282	44	20	lng	151,945 m³
9285718	British Security	Iom	2004	29,335	46,803	183	32	14	tco	
9288837	British Serenity	Iom	2005	29,214	47,210	183	32	14	tco	
9285706	British Tenacity	Iom	2004	29,335	46,080	183	32	14	tco	
9238038	British Trader (st)	Iom	2003	93,498	75,109	279	43	19	lng	138,000 m³
9288849	British Tranquility	Iom	2005	29,214	47,210	183	32	14	tco	
9285732	British Unity	Iom	2004	29,335	46,080	183	32	14	tco	
9597276	British Vantage **	Iom	2013	161,833	320,278	333	60	15	tcr	c/a Eagle Versailles
9597264	British Venture **	Iom	2013	161,833	320,122	333	60	16	tcr	c/a Eagle Verona
9266877	British Vine	Iom	2004	58,070	106,021	241	42	15	tcr	

newbuildings:

IMO	name	flag	year	gt	dwt	loa	bm	kts	type	comments
9683025	British Reliance [K]	Iom	2016	64,300	109,258	250	44	14	tcr	STX Jinhae 1613 03.2016
9683037	British Resource [K]	Iom	2016	64,300	109,258	250	44	14	tcr	STX Jinhae 1614 03.2016
9683049	British Rigour [K]	Iom	2016	64,300	109,258	250	44	14	tcr	STX Jinhae 1615 04.2016
9683051	British Resolution [K]	Iom	2016	64,300	109,258	250	44	14	tcr	STX Jinhae 1616 06.2016
9683063	British Regard [K]	Iom	2016	64,300	109,258	250	44	14	tcr	STX Jinhae 1617 08.2016

IMO	name	flag	year	gt	dwt	loa	bm	kts	type	comments
9683075	British Restraint [K]	Iom	2016	64,300	109,258	250	44	14	tcr	STX Jinhae 1618 10.2016
9683087	British Reason [K]	Iom	2016	64,300	109,258	250	44	14	tcr	STX Jinhae 1619 11.2016
9683099	British Resolve [K]	Iom	2017	64,300	109,258	250	44	14	tcr	STX Jinhae 1620 01.2017
9682967	British Century [IC]	Iom	2016	81,000	157,000	274	49	14	tcr	STX 1631 06.2016
9682980	British Heritage [IC]	Iom	2016	81,000	157,000	274	49	14	tcr	STX 1632 07.2016
9682992	British Tradition [IC]	Iom	2016	81,000	157,000	274	49	14	tcr	STX 1633 09.2016
9734288	British Legacy [IC]	Iom	2016	81,000	157,000	274	49	14	tcr	STX 1635 11.2016
9724532	British Cumulus [IC]	Iom	2016	26,000	40,000	183	32	14	tco	Hyundai Mipo 2494 09.3016
9724544	British Nimbus [IC]	Iom	2016	26,000	40,000	183	32	14	tco	Hyundai Mipo 2495 11.2016
9724556	British Stratus [IC]	Iom	2016	26,000	40,000	183	32	14	tco	Hyundai Mipo 2496 12.2016
9724568	British Cirrus [IC]	Iom	2017	26,000	40,000	183	32	14	tco	Hyundai Mipo 2497 01.2017
9724570	British Altus [IC]	Iom	2017	26,000	40,000	183	32	14	tco	Hyundai Mipo 2498 03.2017
9724582	British Mariner [IC]	Iom	2016	29,700	45,000	183	32	14	tco	Hyundai Mipo 2575 03.2016
9724594	British Navigator [IC]	Iom	2016	29,700	45,000	183	32	14	tco	Hyundai Mipo 2576 04.2018
9724609	British Seafarer [IC]	Iom	2016	29,700	45,000	183	32	14	tco	Hyundai Mipo 2577 08:2016
9724673	British Sailor [IC]	Iom	2016	29,700	45,000	183	32	14	tco	Hyundai Mipo 2578 10.2016
9724685	British Captain [IC]	Iom	2016	29,700	45,000	183	32	14	tco	Hyundai Mipo 2579 12.2016
9724697	British Officer [IC]	Iom	2017	29,700	45,000	183	32	14	tco	Hyundai Mipo 2580 02.2017
9724702	British Engineer [IC]	Iom	2017	29,700	45,000	183	32	14	tco	Hyundai Mipo 2581 04.2017
9724714	British Cadet [IC]	Iom	2017	29,700	45,000	183	32	14	tco	Hyundai Mipo 2582 05.2017
9724726	British Chief [IC]	Iom	2017	29,700	45,000	183	32	14	tco	Hyundai Mipo 2583 07.2017

additionally holds 9 unspecified options with STX : also on order : 6 lng 174,000 m³ Daewoo
* owned by MSEA Tankers LLC,   ** owned by AET Inc. Ltd., Bermuda
[K] leased from Kmarin, Seoul : [IC] leased from Industrial & Commercial Bank of China for 10 years
also see Alaska Tanker Co LLC, USA (formed 1999 jointly with Overseas Shipholding Group Inc and Keystone Shipping Group) under OSG

Briese Schiffahrts GmbH & Co. KG   Germany

funnel: *white with company logo.* **hull:** *blue or grey with green boot-topping.* **history:** *founded 1983.* **web:** *www.briese.de*

IMO	name	flag	year	gt	dwt	loa	bm	kts	type	comments
9303302	BBC Amazon	Atg	2007	12,936	17,300	143	23	15	ggc	l/a Hatzum
9563706	BBC Amber	Atg	2011	12,838	14,403	153	23	15	ghl	cr: 2(400)
9504724	BBC Amethyst *	Atg	2012	12,838	14,452	153	23	15	ghl	cr: 2(400)
9504736	BBC Aquamarine *	Atg	2012	12,838	14,465	153	23	15	ghl	cr: 2(400): c/a North Sea Commander
9504748	BBC Citrine *	Atg	2012	12,838	14,387	153	23	15	ghl	cr: 2(400): c/a North Sea Trader
9436331	BBC Congo	Atg	2010	12,974	16,936	143	23	15	ghl	cr: 2(250) 1(80): l/a Strong Breeze
9563720	BBC Coral	Atg	2012	12,838	14,487	153	23	15	ghl	cr: 2(400): c/a North Sea Bird
9571399	BBC Danube	Atg	2012	12,936	16,949	143	23	15	ghl	cr: 2(250) 1(80)

BBC Danube : Briese Schiffahrts : *Chris Brooks*

IMO	name	flag	year	gt	dwt	loa	bm	kts	type	comments
9347059	BBC Elbe	Atg	2006	12,936	17,349	143	23	15	ggc	ex Hornumersiel-06
9504750	BBC Emerald *	Atg	2013	12,838	14,731	153	23	15	ggc	cr: 2(400): c/a North Sea Favour
9347035	BBC Ems	Atg	2006	12,936	17,349	143	23	15	ggc	ex Suderdamm-06
9508304	BBC Ganges	Atg	2010	12,974	16,944	143	23	15	ghl	cr: 2(250) 1(80):
9435868	BBC Hudson	Atg	2010	12,874	16,944	143	23	15	ghl	cr: 2(250) 1(80): ex Dornumersiel-09
9347061	BBC Mississippi	Atg	2006	12,936	17,349	143	23	15	ggc	ex Greetsiel-07
9563732	BBC Moonstone	Atg	2013	12,838	14,338	153	23	15	ghl	cr: 2(400): l/a North Sea Moon
9571375	BBC Nile	Atg	2011	12,980	16,991	143	23	15	ghl	cr: 2(250) 1(80): l/a Osterbur
9161182	BBC Ostfriesland	Lbr	1998	13,066	20,567	153	24	17	ggc	ex Delmas Nigeria-07, BBC Ostfriesland-06, Germana-06, BBC Argentina-04, Cielo di Caracas-02, Lily Oldendorff-01, Libra Chile-00, CSAV Genoa-00, Lily Oldendorff-99, Barrister-99, Lily Oldendorff-98
9537264	BBC Neptune	Lbr	2010	24,050	37,506	190	28	14	bbu	
9508316	BBC Oder	Atg	2010	12,974	16,953	143	23	15	ghl	cr: 2(250) 1(80)
9571387	BBC Parana	Atg	2012	12,980	16,953	143	24	15	ghl	cr: 2(250) 1(80)
9504786	BBC Pearl	Atg	2012	12,838	14,418	153	23	15	ghl	cr: 2(400): l/a North Sea Carrier
9537276	BBC Pluto	Lbr	2010	24,050	37,495	190	28	14	bbu	
9202041	BBC Rheiderland	Lbr	2000	13,066	20,144	153	24	17	ggc	ex Delmas Ghana-07, BBC Rheiderland-06, Paul Oldendorff-02
9563744	BBC Ruby	Atg	2016	12,838	14,310	153	23	15	ghl	cr: 2(400): l/a North Sea Sun
9504798	BBC Sapphire	Atg	2012	12,838	14,356	153	23	15	ghl	cr: 2(400): l/a North Sea Island
9508380	BBC Seine	Atg	2010	12,974	16,967	143	23	15	ghl	cr: 2(250) 1(80): l/a Pilsum
9418999	BBC Spring	Atg	2010	15,377	16,523	166	23	17	ghl	cr: 2(400) 1(120): ex HHL Bilbao-12, Beluga Sao Paulo-12, l/a Beluga Participation
9436329	BBC Volga	Gib	2009	12,936	17,302	143	23	15	ggc	cr: 2(250) 1(80): l/a Ocean Breeze
9347047	BBC Weser	Atg	2006	12,936	17,290	143	23	15	ggc	ex STX Bright-12, BBC Weser-10, Westerdamm-06
9301122	Hooge	Gib	2005	15,633	16,921	161	25	19	ucc	1,402 teu
9435856	Kurt Paul	Atg	2009	12,936	17,354	143	23	15	ggc	
9301134	Langenes	Gib	2006	15,633	16,921	161	25	19	ucc	1,402 teu
9256315	Norderoog	Gib	2004	15,633	16,921	161	25	19	ucc	1,402 teu: ex Syms Peonia-08, Norderoog-04
9386988	Petkum	Deu	2008	15,633	16,921	161	25	19	ucc	1,402 teu
9303314	Sjard	Atg	2007	12,936	17,305	143	23	15	ggc	
9256327	Süderoog	Gib	2005	15,633	16,921	161	25	19	ucc	1,402 teu: ex Syms Bohenia-06, l/a Suderoog
9386976	Wybelsum	Gib	2008	15,597	16,921	161	25	19	ucc	1,402 teu
newbuildings:										
9504803	BBC Tourmaline *	Atg	2016	12,838	14,350	153	23	15	ghl	cr: 2(400): l/a North Sea Cruiser
9504815	BBC Topaz *	Atg	2016	12,838	14,350	153	23	15	ghl	cr: 2(400): l/a North Sea Steamer

*vessels operated by Briese Chartering: also operates numerous smaller vessels,   * owned by W. Bockstiegel Reederei*

British Marine plc U.K.

funnel: *black with company logo on broad white band.* **hull:** *black with 'British Marine' in white, red topping.* **history:** *established 1999 as Verney Services, operated within Ocean Bulk group until 2007 when took control of OBC fleet and restyled British Marine plc.* **web:** *www.britmarine.co.uk*

IMO	name	flag	year	gt	dwt	loa	bm	kts	type	comments
9300491	Aquitania	Gbr	2006	31,238	55,932	190	32	14	bbu	
9266205	Clementine	Gbr	2004	27,985	50,238	190	32	14	bbu	
9514377	Diamond Jubilee	Gbr	2015	31,748	56,172	190	32	15	bbu	
9211121	Gloriana	Gbr	2000	29,499	52,068	190	32	14	bbu	ex Trident Destiny-07, Navios Aegean-03, Agios Andreas-03
9220718	Marylebone	Gbr	2001	27,581	48,377	187	32	14	bbu	ex Ocean Mariner-03
9220706	Primrose	Gbr	2001	27,581	48,377	187	32	14	bbu	ex Britannia-14
newbuildings:										
9765706	RB Jake	Mhl	2016	43,278	82,000	229	32	14	bbu	JMU Maizuru 5091
9730816	RB Jordana	Mhl	2016	44,000	82,000	229	32	14	bbu	Sungdong 1224

also operates chartered tonnage

Hermann Buss GmbH & Cie. KG Germany

funnel: *white with blue outlined 'H' interlinked with blue 'B' narrow blue/red/blue band or charterers colours.* **hull:** *green with red or black boot-topping or charterers colours.* **history:** *family commenced ship-owning in Leer, during 1838 and as Reederei Hermann Buss from 1967 to 1988. Acquired 50% share in Schulte & Bruns in 2005. Received regulatory approval during 2015 for take over by Döhle but in January 2016 formed j/v with Liberty One Shipping., Bremen.* **web:** *www.reederei-buss.de*

IMO	name	flag	year	gt	dwt	loa	bm	kts	type	comments
9138317	Baltrum Trader	Atg	1999	25,361	34,017	207	30	21	ucc	2,470 teu: ex Clan Challenger-09, Baltrum Trader-07, P&O Nedlloyd Fremantle-00, Baltrum Trader-99
9509683	Berlin Trader	Lbr	2010	22,863	33,248	180	28	15	ggc	ex Opal Brilliance-11

IMO	name	flag	year	gt	dwt	loa	bm	kts	type	comments
9213105	Ems Trader	Pmd	2000	25,535	33,917	200	30	21	ucc	2,452 teu: ex Alemania Express-05, Sea Cheetah-02, l/a Ems Trader
9138290	Juist Trader	Atg	1998	25,361	34,041	207	30	20	ucc	2,470 teu: ex Maruba Orion-10, Juist Trader-07, CP Canada-06, Cielo del Canada-05, Juist Trader-99
9158496	Jümme Trader	Atg	1998	25,355	33,987	207	30	21	ucc	2,474 teu: ex Monteverde-10, l/a Jumme Trader
9213117	Leda Trader	Lbr	2000	25,535	33,917	200	30	22	ucc	2,452 teu: ex MOL Sunshine-09, Leda Trader-07, Cap Castillo-05, l/a Leda Trader
9509607	Lisbon Trader	Lbr	2009	22,863	31,182	179	28	15	ggc	ex Medamur-09
9594470	Madrid Trader	Lbr	2011	22,863	33,217	179	28	15	ggc	
9377561	Main Trader	Lbr	2008	28,048	37,950	215	30	21	ucc	2,700 teu: ex TS Qingdao-09, l/dn Main Trader
9437139	Michigan Trader	Atg	2008	15,334	18,414	166	25	19	ucc	1,284 teu: ex Medmichigan-08
9377573	Mosel Trader	Atg	2009	28,048	37,968	215	30	21	ucc	2,700 teu
9509700	Oslo Trader	Lbr	2011	22,863	33,210	179	28	15	ggc	
9509645	Rome Trader	Lbr	2010	22,863	33,175	179	28	15	ggc	
9509621	San Marino Trader	Lbr	2010	22,863	33,217	179	28	15	ggc	
9130121	Szczecin Trader	Lbr	1998	16,803	22,990	185	25	19	ucc	1,730 teu: ex MOL Honesty-09, CMA CGM Kiwi-08, Maruba Trader-04, l/a Szczecin Trader
9437189	Victoria Trader	Lbr	2008	15,334	18,471	166	25	19	ucc	1,284 teu
9509671	Warnow Moon	Lbr	2010	22,863	31,264	179	28	15	ggc	

Carl Büttner-Bremen GmbH & Co. KG Tankreederei   Germany

funnel: *yellow with white 'CB' and four corner stars on red houseflag, narrow black top.* **hull:** *black with red boot-topping.*
history: *formed 1856 as Carl Büttner GmbH to 2003.* **web:** *www.carlbuettner.de*

IMO	name	flag	year	gt	dwt	loa	bm	kts	type
9234616	Admiral	Gib	2002	16,914	23,998	168	26	15	tco
9258624	Apatura	Gib	2004	16,901	24,064	168	26	15	tco
9234628	Apollo	Gib	2003	16,914	24,028	169	26	15	tco

Clementine : British Marine plc : *ARO*

IMO	name	flag	year	gt	dwt	loa	bm	kts	type	comments
9327102	Aurelia	Gib	2006	16,683	24,017	168	26	15	tco	
9327097	Avalon	Gib	2006	16,683	23,434	168	26	15	tco	

managed by Carl Büttner Shipmanagement GmbH. Also operates smaller chemical tankers

BW Shipping Group   Norway

history: *founded 1887 by Berge Bergesen and shipping company formed 1918 as Sigval Bergesen, then A/S Sig. Bergesen d.y. & Co to 1986, which merged in 1996 with A/S Havtor Management the gas tanker subsidiary of Kvaerner Shipping AS (formerly P Meyer to 1981 and Rederiet Helge R Meyer A/S to 1992 when merged with Irgens-Larsen A/S) as Bergesen dy ASA. In 2003 acquired by Sohmen family controlled World-Wide Shipping Group, Hong Kong (formed 1951), company being renamed Bergesen Worldwide ASA from 2005*

Berge Bulk Ltd, Bermuda

funnel: *green base with white 'B' on dark blue rectangle above green hull section on broad white band, dark blue top.* **hull:** *red with dark blue 'BERGE BULK' and logo, black or red boot-topping.* **history:** *subsidiary formed in 2007* **web:** *www.bwbulk.com*

IMO	name	flag	year	gt	dwt	loa	bm	kts	type	comments
9447548	Berge Aconcagua	Iom	2012	195,911	388,139	361	65	14	bor	
9713193	Berge Annupuri	Iom	2016	21,530	34,536	180	30	14	bbu	
9223590	Berge Aoraki	Iom	2000	87,322	172,502	289	45	14	bbu	ex Cape Camellia-12, Cape Daisy-04
9233337	Berge Apo	Iom	2000	85,888	171,012	287	45	14	bbu	ex Mona River-13
9221906	Berge Arctic	Pan	2001	91,563	174,285	292	48	15	bor	ex BW Arctic-10, Berge Arctic-06
9713181	Berge Asahidake	Iom	2016	21,550	34,534	180	30	14	bbu	
9164184	Berge Atlantic	Nis	1998	91,962	172,704	292	48	16	bbu	
9439113	Berge Atlas	Pan	2008	90,092	180,180	289	45	15	bbu	ex BW Atlas-10
9531882	Berge Blanc	Iom	2012	151,073	297,160	327	55	15	bor	
9036454	Berge Bureya	Pan	1993	153,506	293,239	332	57	15	bor	ex BW Bureya-10, BW Bandeira-07, Sebu-07, Seki-94 (conv tcr-07)
9713179	Berge Daisetsu	Iom	2015	21,530	34,533	180	30	14	bbu	
9000998	Berge Denali	Pan	1992	155,656	286,006	328	57	14	bor	ex BW Denali-10, BW Noto-08, Noto-06, Argo Thetis-00 (conv tcr-09)
9201695	Berge Eiger	Pan	2000	83,849	170,780	289	45	16	bor	ex Cape Lotus-13
8902424	Berge Elbrus	Pan	1991	155,626	285,739	328	57	15	bor	ex BW Nile-09, Nile-06, Argo Pallas-00 (conv tcr-10)
9112090	Berge Enterprise	Iom	1997	108,083	211,485	312	51	14	bbu	ex SG Enterprise-12, Jedforest-00, SG Enterprise-98
9447536	Berge Everest	Pan	2011	195,199	388,133	361	65	14	bor	
8314471	Berge Fjord	Pan	1986	159,534	310,698	332	57	13	bor	ex BW Fjord-10, Berge Fjord-06, Docefjord-00 (conv. cbo-02)
9122590	Berge Fuji	Iom	1996	145,963	268,025	324	57	14	bor	ex Navix Astral-12
9713167	Berge Hakodate	Iom	2015	21,530	34,534	180	30	14	bbu	
9675949	Berge Heng Shan	Iom	2015	116,760	216,461	305	52	14	bbu	
9035450	Berge Hua Shan	Iom	1993	150,170	268,011	332	50	14	bor	ex Zheng Hao-13, Crystal Beauty-10, Front Tobago-06, Toba-00
9447550	Berge Jaya	Iom	2012	195,011	388,079	361	65	14	bor	
9709506	Berge K2	Iom	2015	134,693	262,583	327	57	14	bor	
9073438	Berge Kangchenjunga	Iom	1994	148,159	264,158	322	58	15	bor	ex Pacific Crystal-13, Diamond Falcon-03 (conv tcr-10)
9036442	Berge Kibo	Iom	1993	155,823	279,989	328	58	15	bor	ex BW Kibo-10, Sala-08 (conv. tcr-09)
9271391	Berge Kinabalu	Iom	2003	89,529	177,173	289	45	14	bor	ex Cape Glory-13
9083964	Berge Lhotse	Iom	1995	146,393	257,616	326	57	14	bor	Oriental Beauty-12, Shinyo Sawako-10, Golden Stream-06
9709518	Berge Makalu	Iom	2016	134,693	262,500	327	57	14	bor	
9000352	Berge Manaslu	Pan	1992	146,817	269,101	338	58	14	bor	ex Zheng Jie-13, Pacific Courage-10, Stena Comfort-00, Wisteria-97
9738868	Berge Mawson	Pan	2015	92,732	181,160	292	45	14	bbu	
9447562	Berge Neblina	Iom	2013	195,911	388,079	361	65	14	bor	
9406544	Berge Odel	Pan	2007	104,721	206,330	300	50	15	bbu	ex BW Odel-12
8420804	Berge Stahl	Iom	1986	175,720	364,767	343	64	13	bor	
9675937	Berge Tai Shan	Iom	2015	117,760	216,656	305	52	14	bbu	
9567063	Berge Townsend	Iom	2012	91,971	175,588	292	45	14	bbu	
8800286	Berge Vinson	Pan	1990	155,708	290,160	327	57	15	bor	ex BW Vinson-09, Grand King-08, Ness-04, Argo Hebe-00 (conv tcr-10)
9161508	Berge Yotei	Iom	1997	87,322	172,846	289	45	14	bbu	ex Cape Wisteria-12, Cape Rosa-04
9750919	Berge Zugspitze	Iom	2016	109,716	211,182	300	49	14	bbu	
newbuildings:										
9709520		Iom	2016	134,693	250,000	327	57	14	bor	Guangzhou Longxue 1312100 10
9709532		Iom	2016	134,693	250,000	327	57	14	bor	Guangzhou Longxue 1312100 11
9744374			2017		262,000				bor	Guangzhou Longxue 1312100 12
9744386			2017		262,000				bor	Guangzhou Longxue 1312100 13
9744398					262,000				bor	Guangzhou Longxue 1312100 15
9713208	*Berge Shari*	Iom	2016	21,530	34,534	180	30	14	bbu	Hakodate 5/6

Berge Neblina : BW Shg. Gp. - Berge Bulk : *Hans Kraijenbosch*

Berge Yotei : BW Shg. Gp. - Berge Bulk : *Nico Kemps*

IMO	name	flag	year	gt	dwt	loa	bm	kts	type	comments
9713222	*Berge Rishiri*	Iom	2016	21,530	34,534	180	30	14	bbu	Hakodate 6/6
9750921	*Berge Grossglockner*	Iom	2016	109,700	210,000	300	49	14	bbu	Bohai 424-4 04.2016
9750933	*Berge Toubkal*	Iom	2016	109,700	210,000	300	49	14	bbu	Bohai 424-5 06.2016
9750945	*Berge Mulhacen*	Iom	2016	109,700	210,000	300	49	14	bbu	Bohai 424-6 08.2016
9713210	*Berge Bandai*		2016	21,550	39,000				bbu	Hakodate 875 05.2016

vessels managed by Berge Bulk Maritime Pte. Singapore .

BW Maritime Pte., Singapore

funnel: blue with white 'B' above white 'W'. **hull:** black or red with red boot-toppin or light green with white 'BW' on dark blue diagonal stripe. **history:** formed 2005 after reorganisation of BW business **web:** www.bwmaritime.com

IMO	name	flag	year	gt	dwt	loa	bm	kts	type	comments
9324289	BW Amazon	Pan	2006	43,815	76,565	229	32	15	tco	ex Amazon-06
9716004	BW Argon	Iom	2016	11,918	19,993	147	24	14	tch	
9315070	BW Bauhinia	Hkg	2007	156,569	301,019	332	58	14	tcr	
9694476	BW Bobcat	Sgp	2014	29,737	49,999	183	32	15	tco	
9269245	BW Clyde	Sgp	2004	42,011	73,400	229	32	15	tco	ex BW Isis-14, Avra-13, Newlead Avra-11, Altius-10, Michele Iuliano-04
9324291	BW Columbia	Sgp	2007	43,797	76,604	229	32	15	tco	
9675494	BW Cougar	Sgp	2014	29,737	49,999	183	32	14	tct	ex Elandra Cougar-14
9365001	BW Danube	Sgp	2007	43,797	76,543	229	32	15	tco	
9708071	BW Eagle	Sgp	2015	29,562	49,999	183	32	14	tco	
9315082	BW Edelweiss	Hkg	2008	158,569	301,021	332	58	14	tcr	
9607174	BW Egret	Sgp	2014	29,768	50,237	183	32	14	tco	
9607186	BW Falcon	Sgp	2015	29,768	49,999	183	32	15	tco	
9607198	BW Hawk	Sgp	2015	29,768	49,999	183	32	15	tco	
9324306	BW Hudson	Sgp	2007	43,797	76,574	229	32	15	tco	
9635858	BW Jaguar	Sgp	2014	29,737	49,999	183	32	14	tco	ex Elandra Jaguar-14
9607203	BW Kestrel	Sgp	2015	29,768	49,999	183	32	15	tco	
9307786	BW Kronborg	Sgp	2007	42,048	73,708	229	32	15	tco	ex Torm Ugland-12
9258521	BW Lake	Hkg	2004	158,557	298,564	332	58	15	tcr	ex World Lake-09
9269257	BW Lara	Sgp	2004	42,011	73,495	229	32	15	tco	ex Fortune-13, Newlead Fortune-11, Fortius-10, c/a Altius
9324318	BW Lena	Sgp	2007	43,797	76,578	229	32	15	tco	
9635822	BW Leopard	Sgp	2014	29,737	49,999	183	32	14	tco	l/a Elandra Leopard

BW Kronborg : BW Shg. Gp. - BW Maritime : *Chris Brooks*

IMO	name	flag	year	gt	dwt	loa	bm	kts	type	comments
9258519	BW Lion	Hkg	2004	158,557	298,563	332	58	15	tcr	ex World Lion-09
9675509	BW Lioness	Sgp	2014	29,737	49,999	183	32	14	tco	ex Elandra Lion-14
9385037	BW Lotus	Hkg	2011	166,414	320,142	332	60	15	tcr	
9635808	BW Lynx	Sgp	2013	29,737	49,999	183	32	15	tcr	ex Elandra Lynx-14
9682239	BW Merlin	Sgp	2015	29,768	49,999	183	32	15	tco	
9407093	BW Mia	Iom	2008	11,645	19,702	144	24	14	tch	ex Stream Mia-14, Golden Mia-11
9708083	BW Myna	Sgp	2015	29,562	49,999	183	32	14	tco	
9455662	BW Opal	Iom	2012	161,969	320,105	333	60	15	tcr	ex Blue Opal-14, H Elephant-13
9324320	BW Orinoco	Sgp	2008	43,797	76,580	229	32	15	tco	
9682241	BW Osprey	Sgp	2015	29,768	49,999	183	32	15	tco	
9694464	BW Panther	Sgp	2014	29,737	49,999	183	32	15	tco	l/a Elandra Panther
9385843	BW Peony	Hkg	2011	166,414	320,014	332	60	15	tcr	
9706073	BW Petrel	Sgp	2016	29,751	49,999	183	32	15	tco	
9479929	BW Pine	Iom	2011	45,812	53,028	226	37	18	lpg	80,156 m³: ex Maersk Tuas-13, Derby-13
9635810	BW Puma	Sgp	2013	29,737	49,999	183	32	14	tco	ex Elandra Puma-14
9706061	BW Raven	Sgp	2015	29,751	49,999	183	32	15	tco	
9341940	BW Rhine	Sgp	2008	43,815	76,578	229	32	15	tco	
9342217	BW Seine	Sgp	2008	43,797	76,578	229	32	15	tco	
9506069	BW Shinano	Sgp	2008	43,797	76,594	229	32	15	tco	
9479979	BW Stream	Iom	2010	11,757	19,998	136	24	14	tch	ex Stream Luna-14, Pacific Luna – 11
9713844	BW Swift	Sgp	2016	29,751	49,999	183	32	15	tco	
9393084	BW Thames	Sgp	2008	43,797	76,586	229	32	15	tco	
9635846	BW Tiger	Sgp	2014	29,737	49,999	183	32	24	tco	ex Elandra Tiger-14
9181649	BW Ulan	Pan	2000	157,814	299,325	332	58	15	tcr	ex Ulan-06
9221918	BW Utah	Pan	2001	157,814	299,498	332	58	15	tcr	ex Utah-08
9227948	BW Utik	Pan	2001	157,814	299,450	332	58	15	tcr	ex Utik-06
9713856	BW Wren	Sgp	2016	29,751	50,237	183	32	15	tco	
9393096	BW Yangtze	Sgp	2009	43,797	76,579	229	32	15	tco	
9393101	BW Zambeze	Sgp	2010	43,797	76,578	229	32	15	tco	
9274094	Compass	Sgp	2006	41,589	72,735	229	32	15	tco	ex Newlead Compass-12, Stena Compass-10
9295036	Compassion	Sgp	2006	41,589	72,782	229	32	15	tco	ex Newlead Compassion-12, Stena Compassion-10
newbuildings :										
9766190		Bmu	2016	42,500	85,000	219	38	14	tco	STX 1694
9766205			2016	42,500	85,000	219	38	14	tco	STX 1695
9755217			2017	42,500	85,000	219	38	14	tco	STX 1696
9766229			2017	42,500	85,000	219	38	14	tco	STX 1697
9774525			2017	42,500	85,000	219	38	14	tco	STX 1698
9774537			2017	42,500	85,000	219	38	14	tco	STX 1699
9716016	BW Boron	Iom	2016	11,918	19,900	147	24	14	tch	Shitanoe 7060
9740770	BW Cobalt		2016	12,000	19,900	147	24	14	tch	Shitanoe 7061
9740782	BW Helium		2017	12,000	19,900	147	24	14	tch	Shitanoe 7062
9749685	BW Iridium		2017	12,000	19,900	147	24	14	tch	Shitanoe 7063
	BW Lithium		2017	12,000	19,900	147	24	14	tch	
	BW Mercury		2018	12,000	19,900	147	24	14	tch	
	BW Neon		2018	12,000	19,900	147	24	14	tch	
			2018		19,000				tch	Fukuoka F-1323
			2018		19,900				tch	Fukuoka F-1324

BW Gas ASA, Norway

funnel: *blue with white 'B' above white 'W'.* **hull:** *light green or red with white 'BW' on dark blue diagonal stripe, red boot-topping.*
history: *formed 2005 after reorganisation of BW business* **web:** *www.bwgas.com*

IMO	name	flag	year	gt	dwt	loa	bm	kts	type	comments
9256597	Berge Arzew (st)	Bhs	2004	93,844	77,470	277	43	19	lng	138,089 m³
9317987	Berge Nantong *	Hkg	2006	47,012	58,757	225	37	16	lpg	82,244 m³
9308493	Berge Ningbo *	Hkg	2006	47,012	58,899	225	37	16	lpg	82,252 m³
8902371	Berge Summit	Bhs	1990	44,690	50,748	230	37	15	lpg	78,488 m³ ex Sunny Hope-04
9701786	BW Aries	Iom	2014	47,342	54,561	225	37	15	lpg	84,000 m³
9370537	BW Austria	Nor	2009	48,502	54,707	226	37	16	lpg	84,603 m³ ex BW Duke-09, l/a Apollonia Gas
9320740	BW Birch	Iom	2007	47,386	58,123	225	37	16	lpg	80,656 m³ ex Maersk Virtue-13
9208227	BW Borg	Bhs	2001	47,156	54,826	230	36	16	lpg	84,333 m³ ex Formosagas Apollo-07
9208239	BW Boss	Bhs	2001	47,156	54,586	230	36	16	lpg	84,301 m³ ex Formosagas Bright-07
9377781	BW Broker	Lbr	2007	45,805	53,600	227	36	16	lpg	80,138 m³
9701798	BW Carina	Iom	2015	47,342	54,561	225	37	15	lpg	84,000 m³
9320738	BW Cedar	Iom	2007	47,386	58,063	225	37	16	lpg	80,656 m³ ex Maersk Visual-13
9307736	BW Confidence	Iom	2006	48,772	54,492	230	36	16	lpg	81,604 m³ ex British Confidence-12
9193733	BW Denise	Nis	2001	49,292	56,745	226	36	17	lpg	78,637 m³ ex Berge Denise-06
9232515	BW Energy	Iom	2002	46,506	53,556	227	36	17	lpg	82,488 m³ ex Dynamic Energy-12

IMO	name	flag	year	gt	dwt	loa	bm	kts	type	comments
9230062	BW GDF Suez Boston (st)	Nis	2003	93,844	77,410	277	43	19	lng	138,059 m³ ex BW Suez Boston-12, Berge Boston-07
9368314	BW GDF Suez Brussels (df)	Bmu	2009	103,670	89,452	295	43	19	lng	162,514 m³ ex BW Suez Brussels-09
9243148	BW GDF Suez Everett (st)	Nis	2003	93,844	77,410	277	43	19	lng	138,028 m³ ex BW Suez Everett-13, Berge Everett-08
9368302	BW GDF Suez Paris (df)	Bmu	2009	103,670	89,556	295	43	19	lng	162,524 m³ ex BW Suez Paris-09
9703007	BW Gemini	Iom	2015	47,342	54,651	225	37	15	lpg	84,000 m³
8814768	BW Havfrost	Nis	1991	34,946	44,995	205	32	15	lpg	57,180 m³ ex Havfrost-07
9009023	BW Havis	Nis	1993	34,951	49,513	205	32	15	lpg	57,139 m³ ex Havis-08
8912182	BW Helios	Nis	1992	34,974	49,513	205	32	15	lpg	57,160 m³ ex Helios-07
9703019	BW Leo	Iom	2015	47,342	54,561	225	37	15	lpg	84,000 m³
9350288	BW Liberty	Nis	2007	48,456	55,056	226	37	15	lpg	84,529 m³ ex Flanders Liberty-11
9719496	BW Libra	Iom	2015	47,342	54,561	225	37	15	lpg	84,000 m³
9350604	BW Lord	Nis	2008	48,502	54,691	226	37	17	lpg	84,615 m³ ex Olympia Gas-08
9350290	BW Loyalty	Nis	2008	48,456	55,056	226	37	15	lpg	84,501 m³ ex Flanders Loyalty-12
9320752	BW Maple	Iom	2008	47,386	59,423	225	37	16	lpg	80,645 m³ ex Maersk Value-13
9253818	BW Nantes	Bmu	2003	35,190	44,773	216	32	17	lpg	59,399 m³ ex Berge Nantes-07
9247819	BW Nice	Bmu	2003	35,346	44,639	216	32	17	lpg	59,375 m³ ex Berge Nice-07
9320764	BW Oak	Iom	2008	47,386	58,159	225	37	16	lpg	80,606 m³ ex Maersk Venture-13
9719501	BW Orion	Iom	2015	47,342	54,561	225	37	15	lpg	84,000 m³
9350422	BW Prince	Nis	2007	47,194	54,368	225	37	15	lpg	82,383 m³
9353242	BW Princess	Nis	2008	47,194	53,500	225	37	15	lpg	82,383 m³
9640437	BW Pavilion Vanda	Sgp	2015	105,945	91,515	289	46	19	lng	162,000 m³ I/d BW Dover
9640645	BW Pavilion Leeara	Sgp	2015	105,945	91,496	289	46	19	lng	162,000 m³ I/d BW Malacca
9397080	BW Sakura	Iom	2010	46,025	49,999	230	37	19	lpg	77,324 m³ ex Vermilion First-15
9306548	BW Trader	Sgp	2006	46,632	53,151	225	36	17	lpg	78,631 m³ ex Berge Trader-07
9735658	BW Tucana	Iom	2016	47,342	54,600	225	37	15	lpg	84,000 m³
9232503	BW Vision	Bhs	2001	46,506	53,503	227	36	17	lpg	82,488 m³ ex Dynamic Vision-11
9267015	LNG Benue (st)	Bmu	2005	97,561	82,971	285	43	20	lng	145,952 m³
9266994	LNG Enugu (st)	Bmu	2005	97,561	83,160	285	43	20	lng	145,926 m³
9311581	LNG Imo (st)	Bmu	2008	98,798	83,688	288	43	19	lng	148,452 m³

LNG Enugu : BW Shg. Gp. - BW Gas ARA : *Chris Brooks*

IMO	name	flag	year	gt	dwt	loa	bm	kts	type	comments
9311567	LNG Kano (st)	Bmu	2007	98,798	83,961	288	43	19	lng	148,565 m³
9269960	LNG Lokoja (st)	Bmu	2006	98,798	83,965	288	43	19	lng	148,471 m³
9311579	LNG Ondo (st)	Bmu	2007	98,798	83,688	288	43	19	lng	148,478 m³
9267003	LNG Oyo (st)	Bmu	2005	97,561	83,068	285	43	20	lng	145,842 m³
9266982	LNG River Orashi (st)	Bmu	2004	97,561	83,068	285	43	20	lng	145,914 m³
newbuildings:										
9735660	BW Volans	Iom	2016	47,342	54,600	225	37	15	lpg	84,000 m³ Hyundai Ulsan 2737
	BW Magellan									84,000 m³ Daewoo 2351 09.16
9640465	BW Malacca									84,000 m³ Daewoo 2352 12.16
	BW Mindoro									84,000 m³ Daewoo 2353 12.16
	BW Messina									84,000 m³ Daewoo 2354 10.16

4 x 173,300m³ lng [Daewoo 2435 (2017), 2436, 2488 (2018) 2489 (2019)], 1 x 170,000m³ lng [Samsung 2118 (2016)]

Neu Seeschiffahrt GmbH, Germany

funnel: *turquoise with 'NEU' houseflag on white rectangle.* **hull:** *red with red boot-topping.* **history:** *formed 1958 as Krupp Seeschiffahrt GmbH to 1965, then other Krupp names until 1988, then Krupp-Lonrho GmbH Seeschiffahrt partnership to 1993, then Krupp Seeschiffahrt GmbH (part of ThyssenKrupp AG after 1997 merger) to 2001, when Bergesen acquired 51% control. Vessels managed by General Ore International Corp. Ltd., Isle of Man.* **web:** *www.neusee.com or www.goicl.com*

IMO	name	flag	year	gt	dwt	loa	bm	kts	type	comments
9334882	Abigail N	Lbr	2009	151,448	297,430	327	55	15	bor	
9002776	Bing N	Lbr	1992	154,030	322,941	339	55	14	bor	ex Bergeland-08
9398175	Daniel N	Lbr	2011	151,448	297,359	327	55	15	bor	
9597185	Edward N	Lbr	2011	91,374	176,000	292	45	15	bbu	
9127150	Eva N	Lbr	1997	107,512	218,283	305	53	15	bor	ex Berge Nord-08
9597197	Harriette N	Lbr	2011	91,374	176,000	292	45	15	bbu	
9479163	Helen N	Lbr	2011	151,448	297,000	327	55	15	bor	
9398096	Hugo N	Lbr	2011	151,448	297,000	327	55	15	bor	
9084190	Janice N	Lbr	1995	148,533	264,340	322	58	15	bor	ex Diamond Hope-08 (conv tcr-11)
9479369	Julia N	Lbr	2012	151,200	297,077	327	55	15	bor	
9374088	Regena N	Lbr	2006	90,091	180,277	289	45	15	bor	
9377406	Steven N	Lbr	2010	151,448	297,462	327	55	15	bor	

Neu Gas Shipping

funnel: *turquoise with 'NEU' houseflag on white rectangle.* **hull:** *turquoise with 'LPG' in white, red boot-topping.* **web:** *neugasshipping.com or goicl.com*

IMO	name	flag	year	gt	dwt	loa	bm	kts	type	comments
9377236	Ernest N	Lbr	2009	36,459	43,563	205	32	16	lpg	60,243 m³
9407122	Fritzi N	Lbr	2009	47,141	58,448	225	37	16	lpg	82,322 m³
9377224	George N.	Lbr	2009	36,459	43,601	205	32	16	lpg	60,243 m³
9377248	Jenny N	Lbr	2009	36,459	43,538	205	32	16	lpg	60,243 m³
9386299	Karoline N	Lbr	2009	42,897	54,004	227	32	16	lpg	75,000 m³
9386304	Ronald N	Lbr	2008	42,897	54,004	227	32	16	lpg	75,000 m³

Campbell Shipping Co. Ltd.   Bahamas

funnel: *buff with device and Campbell banner.* **hull:** *green with white 'CAMPBELL' red boot topping* **history:** *founded 2006 by Campbell Gp. following sale of Dockendale Shipping.* **web:** *www.campbellshipping.com*

IMO	name	flag	year	gt	dwt	loa	bm	kts	type	comments
9542520	CS Calla	Bhs	2011	24,065	37,479	189	28	14	bbu	
9542532	CS Calvina	Bhs	2011	24,065	37,456	189	28	14	bbu	
9542544	CS Candy	Bhs	2012	24,065	37,459	189	28	14	bbu	
9406104	CS Caprice	Bhs	2010	19,972	30,465	178	28	14	bbu	ex Clipper Anemone-10, l/d Clipper Taurus
9406087	CS Caroline	Bhs	2010	19,972	30,420	178	29	14	bbu	l/a Clipper Tango
9320295	CS Chara	Bhs	2006	19,918	30,634	179	28	14	bbu	ex Bossclip Trader-09
9406128	CS Crystal	Bhs	2010	19,972	30,478	179	28	14	bbu	l/a Clipper Terra
9660061	CS Jaden	Bhs	2013	23,268	38,101	180	30	14	bbu	
9748409	CS Jenna	Bhs	2015	23,269	37,713	180	30	14	bbu	
9300192	CS Salina	Bhs	2004	20,225	32,355	177	28	14	bbu	ex Angel Rainbow-09
9635468	CS Sarafina	Bhs	2014	24,793	37,693	180	30	14	bbu	
9635456	CS Satira	Bhs	2013	24,793	37,650	180	30	14	bbu	
9569944	CS Sonoma	Bhs	2010	32,982	56,704	190	32	14	bbu	
9569932	CS Soraya	Bhs	2010	32,984	56,700	190	32	14	bbu	
9285419	CS Vanguard	Bhs	2004	22,072	34,812	179	28	14	bbu	ex DS Vanguard-09

Capital Ship Management Corp.   Greece

funnel: *white with blue, red, & green chevrons over 'CAPITAL' in red* **hull:** *blue with 'CAPITAL' in white, red boot topping* **history:** *Marinakis owned company, formed?* **web:** *www.capitalship.gr*

IMO	name	flag	year	gt	dwt	loa	bm	kts	type	comments
9354662	A. Idefix	Mlt	2008	18,263	23,623	182	25	21	ucc	1,702 teu: ex Convent-15, Cassandra B-10, l/s Convent
9354674	A. Obelix	Atg	2008	18,199	23,831	182	25	21	ucc	1,702 teu: ex Clipper-15
9398072	Achilleas	Lbr	2010	156,915	297,863	330	60	15	tcr	

IMO	name	flag	year	gt	dwt	loa	bm	kts	type	comments
9700342	Active	Lbr	2015	29,770	50,135	183	32	15	tco	
9315381	Agamemnon	Lbr	2007	89,776	103,772	318	43	25	ucc	7,920 teu : ex Bunga Seroja Dua-12
9315745	Agisilaos	Mhl	2006	23,270	36,760	184	27	14	tco	
9337004	Aias	Lbr	2008	78,809	150,096	274	48	14	tcr	
9328297	Akeraios	Lbr	2007	27,916	47,781	185	32	14	tco	
9377418	Alexander the Great	Lbr	2010	156,915	297,958	330	60	15	tcr	
9384021	Alexandros II	Mhl	2008	30,010	51,257	183	32	14	tco	ex Overseas Serifos-13, l/a Alexandros II
9427376	Alterego II	Lbr	2002	83,616	159,924	274	48	14	tcr	c/a Yannis P.
9327437	Alkiviadis	Mhl	2006	23,270	36,623	184	27	14	tco	
9700469	Amadeus	Lbr	2015	29,770	50,108	183	32	14	tco	
9700471	Amor	Lbr	2015	29,770	50,072	183	32	14	tco	
9226968	Amore Mio II	Lbr	2001	83,616	159,982	274	48	14	tcr	ex Giorgios S-07
9337016	Amoureux	Lbr	2008	78,809	150,393	274	48	14	tcr	ex Tango-10
9327463	Anemos I	Lbr	2007	27,916	47,782	181	32	14	tco	
9733806	Apollonas	Mhl	2016	157,169	299,999	333	60	15	tcr	
9327451	Apostolos	Lbr	2007	27,916	47,782	181	32	14	tco	
9260158	Apostolos II	Mhl	2003	22,082	34,676	179	28	14	bbu	ex IVS Viscount-04
9315379	Archimidis	Lbr	2006	89,776	103,717	318	43	25	ucc	7,920 teu : ex Bunga Seroja Satu-12
9315757	Arionas	Mhl	2006	23,270	36,725	184	27	14	tco	
9327413	Aristidis	Mhl	2006	23,270	36,582	184	27	14	tco	
9571416	Aristos II	Lbr	2011	22,927	32,474	181	30	14	bbu	
9633501	Aristotelis	Lbr	2013	29,877	51,604	183	32	14	tco	
9700483	Athlos	Lbr	2016	29,770	50,034	183	32	15	tco	
9389899	Atlantas	Mhl	2010	162,198	319,300	333	60	14	tcr	
9354648	Atout	Lbr	2010	18,199	23,978	182	25	20	ucc	1,702 teu: ex Miltiadis Junior III-13, Driever-10, Cypria-10
9315939	Avax	Lbr	2007	27,916	47,834	181	32	14	tco	
9315941	Axios	Lbr	2007	27,916	47,781	181	32	14	tco	
9410014	Ayrton II	Lbr	2009	30,010	51,260	183	32	14	tco	
9315769	British Emissary *	Iom	2007	23,270	37,651	184	27	15	tco	ex Aiolos-07, l/dn Alkiviadis
9312913	British Ensign *	Iom	2006	23,270	36,713	184	27	15	tco	ex Atlantas-06
9312925	British Envoy *	Iom	2006	23,270	37,582	184	27	15	tco	l/a Aktoras
9451264	Cape Agamemnon	Lbr	2010	92,744	179,221	292	45	15	bbu	
9706308	CMA CGM Amazon	Lbr	2015	96,424	115,145	300	48	22	ucc	9,162 teu: l/a Akadimos

Aias : Capital Ship Management : *Chris Brooks*

IMO	name	flag	year	gt	dwt	loa	bm	kts	type	comments
9724049	CMA CGM Magdalena	Lbr	2016	96,424	115,145	300	48	22	ucc	9,162 teu: l/a Anaxagoras
9706310	CMA CGM Uruguay	Lbr	2015	96,424	115,145	300	48	22	ucc	9,162 teu: l/a Adonis
9317119	Crown Princess	Pan	2005	30,046	52,347	190	32	14	bbu	ex Irika-07
9328285	El Pipila **	Mex	2007	27,916	47,786	183	32	14	tco	ex Atrotos-09
9637155	Hyundai Platinum	Lbr	2013	52,447	62,335	255	37	22	ucc	5,023 teu: l/a Aktor
9625542	Hyundai Paramount	Lbr	2013	52,447	62,335	255	37	22	ucc	5,023 teu: l/a Attalos
9625530	Hyundai Premium	Lbr	2013	52,447	62,335	255	37	22	ucc	5,023 teu: ex CCNI Shanghai-13, Hyundai Premium-13, l/a Aristotelis
9625528	Hyundai Prestige	Lbr	2013	52,447	62,335	255	37	22	ucc	5,023 teu: ex CCNI Angol-14, Hyundai Prestige-13, l/a Alexandros
9625554	Hyundai Privilege	Lbr	2013	52,447	62,335	255	37	22	ucc	5,023 teu: c/a Appolonos II
9327449	Insurgentes **	Mex	2006	27,916	47,872	183	32	14	tco	ex Assos-09
9693745	Miltiadis Junior	Lbr	2014	166,308	320,926	333	60	14	tcr	
9311610	Miltiadis M II	Lbr	2006	87,146	162,397	280	50	14	tcr	l/a Eton
9384033	Overseas Sifnos +	Mhl	2008	30,109	51,225	183	32	14	tco	l/a Aristotelis II
newbuildings:										
9761449	Attalos I	Lbr	2016	17,674	21,900	172	27	18	ucc	1,700 teu GWS486
9733818	Atromitos	Mhl	2016	154,000	300,000	333	60	15	tcr	Daewoo 5412
9710488	Anikitos	Lbr	2016	29,770	50,000	183	32	15	tco	Samsung (Ningbo)
9710490	Alkaios	Lbr	2016	29,770	50,000	183	32	14	tco	Samsung (Ningbo)
9724611	Archon	Lbr	2016	29,770	50,000	183	32	14	tco	Samsung (Ningbo)
9724623	Amfitrion	Lbr	2016	29,770	50,137	183	32	14	tco	Samsung (Ningbo)
	Aison		2017		50,000			14	tco	Samsung (Ningbo)
	Agon		2017		50,000			14	tco	Samsung (Ningbo)
	Aristaios		2016		112,800			15	tco	Daehan
	Aristoklis		2016		112,800			15	tco	Daehan
	Asklipios II		2017		112,800			15	tco	Daehan
	Aristomenis II		2017		112,800			15	tco	Daehan
			2017		112,800					
			2017		112,800					
			2017		112,800					
			2017		112,800					

* bareboat chartered to BP Shipping extended until 2016/2018,
** bareboat chartered to PEMEX,   + bareboat chartered to Overseas Shipholding Gp.

CMA CGM Amazon : Capital Ship Management : *Chris Brooks*

Cardiff Marine Inc.   Greece

funnel: *black with blue band edged with yellow bands, black top.* **hull:** *black or grey with red boot-topping.* **history:** *formed 1986, 70% owned by Economou family, and now run as three operating divisions.* **web:** *www.cardiff.gr*

Dryships Inc. TMS Dry

history: formed 2004 as management subsidiary of Cardiff Marine Inc.

IMO	name	flag	year	gt	dwt	loa	bm	kts	type	comments
9228174	Alameda	Mlt	2001	86,743	170,726	290	45	14	bbu	ex Cape Araxos-05
9493016	Alona	Mlt	2009	91,373	177,944	292	45	14	bbu	
9480526	Andama	Mlt	2010	91,373	178,064	292	45	14	bbu	ex Parramatta-14
9587269	Cancun	Mlt	2014	106,847	206,097	300	50	14	bbu	
9248526	Capri	Mlt	2001	87,390	172,529	289	45	15	bbu	ex Gran Trader-08
9308869	Cohiba	Mlt	2006	88,930	174,234	289	45	14	bbu	ex Mineral Hong Kong-09
9353620	Fernandina	Mlt	2006	88,853	174,204	289	45	14	bbu	
9587257	Huahine	Mlt	2013	106,847	206,037	300	50	14	bbu	
9355161	Madeira	Mlt	2007	91,373	178,198	292	45	14	bbu	
9363015	Malindi	Mlt	2008	91,373	177,987	292	45	14	bbu	
9275957	Manasota	Mlt	2004	88,129	171,061	289	45	14	bbu	ex Katerina V-05
9465708	Milagro	Mlt	2009	40,170	75,205	225	32	14	bbu	
9409182	Miramarin	Mlt	2010	73,779	85,523	300	40	25	ucc	6,572 teu: ex APL Dubai-12, Miramarin-11, CMA CGM Kessel-10
9325025	Montecristo	Mlt	2005	90,091	180,263	289	45	15	bbu	ex Mineral Monaco-09
9363041	Omaha	Mlt	2008	91,407	177,805	292	45	14	bbu	
9480538	Panormos	Mlt	2009	91,373	178,006	292	45	14	bbu	
9272345	Partagas	Mlt	2004	88,930	173,880	289	45	14	bbu	ex Jin Tai-09, Mineral Shanghai-07
9363065	Petani	Mlt	2008	40,170	75,528	225	32	14	bbu	
9346768	Pompano	Mlt	2006	88,853	174,240	289	45	14	bbu	
9493028	Pounda	Mlt	2009	91,373	177,897	292	45	14	bbu	
9580376	Raiatea	Mhl	2011	92,924	179,078	292	45	14	bbu	ex Conches-14
9386512	Robusto	Mlt	2006	88,930	173,949	289	45	15	bbu	ex Mineral London-09
9268992	Saldanha	Mlt	2004	38,886	75,707	225	32	14	bbu	ex Shinyo Brilliance-07
9408085	Shibumi	Mlt	2010	91,373	178,090	292	45	14	bbu	
9363053	Sidari	Mlt	2007	40,170	75,204	225	32	14	bbu	
9363039	Sivota	Mlt	2008	91,373	177,804	292	45	14	bbu	
9465710	Striggla	Mlt	2009	40,170	75,196	225	32	14	bbu	
9363027	Tampa	Mlt	2008	91,373	177,987	292	45	14	bbu	
9346756	Ventura	Mlt	2006	88,930	174,316	289	45	14	bbu	

Pounda : Cardiff Marine Inc. - Dryships : *Chris Brooks*

IMO	name	flag	year	gt	dwt	loa	bm	kts	type	comments
9584499	Woolloomooloo	Mlt	2011	41,254	76,064	225	32	14	bbu	
newbuildings:										
9724635	Conquistador	Mlt	2016	102,000	208,000	300	50	14	bbu	Jiangsu YZJ 2013-1130
9724647	Pink Sands	Mlt	2016	102,000	208,000	300	50	14	bbu	Jiangsu YZJ 2013-1131
9724659				102,000	208,000	300	50	14	bbu	Jiangsu YZJ 2013-1132
9724661				102,000	208,000	300	50	14	bbu	Jiangsu YZJ 2013-1133
9773478									bbu	Shanghai Waigaoxiao 1352
9773521										

also 4 + 2 208,000 dwt Newcastle-max bulkers (2016)SWS

TMS Bulkers Ltd.

IMO	name	flag	year	gt	dwt	loa	bm	kts	type	comments
9465801	Amalfi	Mlt	2009	40,170	75,206	225	32	14	bbu	
9261360	Bargara	Mlt	2001	40,437	74,500	225	32	14	bbu	ex Songa Hua-07, De Hua Hai-06
9260122	Capitola	Mlt	2001	40,437	74,816	225	32	14	bbu	ex Songa Hui-07, De Hui Hai-06
9299604	Catalina	Mlt	2005	40,485	74,432	225	32	14	bbu	
9200562	Coronado	Mlt	2000	38,818	75,706	225	32	14	bbu	ex Seafarer II-05, Seafarer-04
9216391	Ecola	Mlt	2001	39,893	73,931	225	32	14	bbu	ex Zella Oldendorff-07, Trave River-01
9634701	Fakarava	Mlt	2012	106,847	206,160	300	50	15	bbu	
9284570	Flecha	Mlt	2004	87,440	170,012	289	45	14	bbu	ex Nightflight-08, Cape Kassos-07
9185736	Helena	Mhl	1999	38,364	73,744	225	32	14	bbu	ex Rule-07
]9216406	Levanto	Mlt	2001	39,893	73,926	225	32	14	bbu	ex Heinrich Oldendorff-09, l/a Elbe River
9279513	Ligari *	Mlt	2004	38,851	75,845	225	32	14	bbu	ex Star of Emirates-06, l/a Hamburg Harmony
9223497	Maganari	Mlt	2001	39,126	75,941	225	32	14	bbu	ex Atacama-06, Semeli-05, Lowlands Kamsar-04
9294109	Majorca	Mlt	2005	40,485	74,477	225	32	13	bbu	ex Maria G.O.-07
9189782	Marbella	Mlt	2000	37,831	72,561	225	32	14	bbu	Restless-07, Ayrton II-06, Millenniu Venture-05
9231298	Mendocino	Mlt	2002	39,727	76,623	225	32	14	bbu	ex Conrad Oldendorff-06
9421831	Mystic	Mlt	2008	89,510	170,102	291	45	14	bbu	ex Golden Nassim-08
9587245	Negonego	Mlt	2013	106,847	206,100	300	50	14	bor	
9180786	Ocean Crystal	Mlt	1999	38,372	73,688	225	32	14	bbu	ex Samsara-05, Ocean Crystal-05
9214123	Oregon	Mlt	2002	38,727	74,204	225	32	14	bbu	ex Athina Zafirakis-07, Jin Tai-04, Jin Hui-02
9634713	Rangiroa	Mlt	2013	106,847	206,026	300	50	14	bbu	
9413690	Rapallo	Mlt	2009	40,170	75,123	225	32	15	bbu	
9584504	Raraka	Mlt	2012	41,254	76,064	225	32	15	bbu	
9211597	Redondo	Mlt	2000	40,562	74,500	225	32	14	bbu	ex Liberty One-06, Alessandra d'Amato-06
9236171	Samatan	Mlt	2001	40,437	74,823	225	32	14	bbu	ex Trans Atlantic-07, Yong Ler-05
9236195	Sonoma	Mlt	2001	40,437	74,786	225	32	14	bbu	ex Yong Kang-05
9310408	Sorrento	Mlt	2004	39,736	76,633	225	32	15	bbu	ex Federal Maple-08, Maple Ridge-07
9211585	Topeka	Mlt	2000	40,562	74,716	225	32	14	bbu	ex Gianfranca d'Amato-07

TMS Cardiff Gas Ltd.

IMO	name	flag	year	gt	dwt	loa	bm	kts	type	comments
9636711	Corcovado LNG	Mlt	2014	103,905	77,440	294	44	21	lng	160,106 m³
9275359	Fuji LNG [st]	Mlt	2004	118,219	77,351	290	49	21	lng	147,895 m³ : ex Muscat LNG-12
9636723	Kita LNG	Mlt	2014	103,902	89,752	294	44	21	lng	160,118 m³
9636735	Palu LNG	Mlt	2014	103,885	89,874	294	44	21	lng	160,000 m³
9636747	Yari LNG	Mlt	2014	103,885	89,804	294	44	21	lng	160,000 m³

all TFDE except Fuji LNG

newbuildings: 4 x 78,780 m³ lng [Hyundai HI (Q2/3 2017)]

TMS Tankers Ltd.

IMO	name	flag	year	gt	dwt	loa	bm	kts	type	comments
9389083	Agrari	Grc	2009	58,428	107,009	244	42	14	tcr	
9527855	Alicante	Mlt	2013	61,332	115,707	249	44	14	tcr	
9516959	Belmar	Mlt	2011	61,332	115,903	249	44	14	tcr	
9297541	Bonita	Grc	2006	57,711	108,386	247	42	14	tcr	
9621596	Bora Bora	Mlt	2016	30,100	50,300	183	32	14	tco	SPP 1179 ex Roxana Shg.
9529499	Bordeira	Mlt	2013	81,380	158.513	274	48	14	tcr	
9395329	Botafogo	Grc	2010	58,418	106,892	244	42	14	tcr	
9522128	Calida	Mlt	2012	61,332	115,812	249	44	14	tcr	
9308857	Carmel	Grc	2006	58,418	104,493	244	42	14	tcr	
9528043	Daytona	Mlt	2011	61,332	115,896	249	44	14	tcr	
9395305	Desimi	Mlt	2011	156,651	296,865	330	50	14	tcr	
9395331	Corossol	Grc	2010	58,418	106,897	244	42	14	tcr	
9529487	Lipari	Mlt	2012	81,380	158,425	274	48	14	tcr	
9208833	Lovina	Grc	2005	58,418	104,493	244	42	14	tcr	
9537927	Mareta	Mlt	2013	61,332	115,795	249	44	14	tcr	

Lovina : Cardiff Marine Inc - TMS Tankers : *ARO*

Yari LNG : Cardiff Marine Inc - TMS Cardiff Gas : *ARO*

Champion Tide : Champion Tankers : *Hans Kraijenbosch*

IMO	name	flag	year	gt	dwt	loa	bm	kts	type	comments
9389095	Mindoro	Grc	2009	58,418	106,850	244	42	14	tcr	
9297553	Montego	Grc	2006	57,711	108,402	247	42	14	tcr	
9377779	Monterey	Grc	2007	58,418	105,009	244	42	14	tcr	
9389100	Myrtos	Grc	2009	58,418	106,750	244	42	14	tcr	
9600865	Nantucket	Mlt	2014	81,670	156,902	275	48	14	tcr	
9178317	Oriental Green	Mlt	1998	56,955	99,991	244	42	14	tcr	
9529475	Petalidi	Mlt	2012	81,380	158,532	274	48	14	tcr	
9384069	Saetta	Grc	2009	58,418	107,023	245	42	14	tcr	
9528031	Saga	Mlt	2011	61,332	115,739	249	44	14	tcr	
9383869	Sarasota	Grc	2008	58,418	104,856	244	42	14	tcr	
9389071	Scorpio	Grc	2009	58,418	107,157	245	42	14	tcr	
9436006	Signal Cheetah *	Mlt	2009	62,775	112,984	250	44	14	tcr	ex Ghibli-14, Stealth Chios-09, l/a Cape Anglia
9395317	Solana	Mlt	2010	156,651	296,790	330	60	15	tcr	
9600877	Tahiti	Mlt	2014	83,816	157,022	275	48	14	tcr	
9600889	Tamara	Mlt	2015	81,670	157,016	275	48	14	tcr	
9158874	Universal Brave	Mlt	1997	156,692	301,242	331	58	15	tcr	
9283306	Venice	Grc	2004	61,764	109,637	245	42	14	tcr	ex Maersk Pristine-07
9529293	Vilamoura	Mlt	2011	81,380	158,621	275	48	14	tcr	
9308821	Zuma	Grc	2005	58,418	105,188	244	42	14	tcr	ex Corcovado-06
newbuildings:										
9621601	Lacerta	Mlt	2016	30,100	50,300	183	32	14	tco	SPP 1180 ex Roxana Shg.
9776731		Grc	2016	81,000	158,000	279	49	14	tcr	Samsung 2161
9776743		Grc	2016	81,000	158,000	279	49	14	tcr	Samsung 2162
9776755		Mlt	2016	61,000	115,000	250	44	14	tcr	Samsung 2163
9776767		Mlt	2017	61,000	115,000	250	44	14	tcr	Samsung 2164
9777931		Mlt	2017	61,000	115,000	250	44	14	tcr	Samsung 2165
9777943		Mlt	2017	61,000	115,000	250	44	14	tcr	Samsung 2166
			2017	81,000	158,000	274	48		tcr	Shanghai Waigaoqiao 1392
			2017		114,000	250	44		tcr	Jiangsu Hantong 001
			2017		114,000	250	44		tcr	Jiangsu Hantong 002
			2017		114,000	250	44		tcr	Jiangsu Hantong 003
			2017		114,000	250	44		tcr	Jiangsu Hantong 004

4 (+2 options) 115,000dwt Aframax [Nantong H.I. (2017)] announced 08:2015
* managed by Thenamaris

Champion Tankers AS   Norway

funnel: *dark blue with white 'CT'.* hull: *black with red boot-topping.* history: *founded 1994.* web: *www.champion-tankers.no*

IMO	name	flag	year	gt	dwt	loa	bm	kts	type	comments
9113147	Champion Cornelia	Nis	1996	28,337	44,999	183	32	14	tco	ex-Cariad-11, Libertad-01
9290608	Champion Ebony	Nis	2004	27,547	46,938	182	32	14	tco	ex Ebony-12, Ebony Point-10
9143697	Champion Express	Lbr	1999	22,680	43,157	192	29	14	tco	ex Isola Gialla-08
9489209	Champion Istra	Hrv	2012	30,638	52,610	195	32	14	tco	ex Istra-15
9341146	Champion Pula	Mhl	2006	27,547	46,927	182	32	15	tco	ex Pula-15
9155767	Champion Tern	Lbr	1999	27,526	47,363	182	32	15	tco	ex Okhotsk Sea-13
9112117	Champion Tide	Nis	1996	26,218	46,166	181	32	14	tco	ex-Tikhvin-10
9127667	Champion Trader	Lbr	1997	21,897	40,727	188	29	14	tco	ex Isola Rossa-08
9080493	Champion Trust	Nis	1995	26,218	46,166	181	32	14	tco	ex Trogir-10
9105085	Emma Victory **	Nis	1996	26,218	46,144	181	32	14	tco	ex Troitsk-10
9105102	Lynda Victory **	Nis	1996	26,218	46,087	181	32	14	tco	ex Timoshevsk-11
9105114	Nina Victory **	Nis	1996	26,218	46,144	181	32	14	tco	ex Tula-11
9185499	Susanne Victory	Nis	2000	27,185	48,309	182	32	14	tco	ex Siteam Neptun-14, Team Neptun-08
9258612	Thelma Victory	Nis	2004	27,357	47,171	183	32	14	tco	ex Gener8 Consul-16, Genmar Consul-15, Stena Consul-10

acquisition:
| 9455739 | | Hrv | 2011 | 30,638 | 52,579 | 195 | 32 | 14 | tco | ex Pomer |

managed by Genoa Maritime S.A., Greece or by Thome Ship Management Pte Ltd, Singapore. * owned by Champion Shipping A/S, Norway
** managed by Timur Ship Mgmt. Pte..

Chandris Group   Greece

funnel: *dark blue with large white 'X'.* hull: *dark blue with red boot-topping.* history: *founded 1911 as John D Chandris to 1942.*
web: *www.chandris-hellas.gr*

IMO	name	flag	year	gt	dwt	loa	bm	kts	type	comments
9379612	Aegea	Grc	2009	61,303	115,878	249	44	14	tco	
9291236	Aktea	Grc	2005	60,007	107,091	248	43	15	tcr	
8705618	Al Nabila 5 *	Egy	1993	18,106	29,027	175	26	13	tco	ex Nordpolen-09, Chem Lily-08, Sun-06, Andrea-00
8906822	Alexia 2 *	Egy	1990	53,724	94,603	232	42	15	tco	ex Meribel-08, Atalandi-04, Glory Central-97
9173733	Althea	Grc	1999	56,841	105,401	248	43	15	tco	
9216248	Amira *	Mhl	2001	39,818	74,401	225	32	14	bbu	
9379624	Amorea	Grc	2009	61,303	115,760	249	44	14	tco	

IMO	name	flag	year	gt	dwt	loa	bm	kts	type	comments
9711456	Aretea	Grc	2015	62,394	113,969	251	44	15	tcr	
9173721	Astrea	Grc	1999	56,841	84,999	248	43	15	tco	
9291248	Athinea	Grc	2006	60,007	107,160	248	43	14	tco	
9284926	Australis	Grc	2003	156,914	299,095	330	60	16	tcr	ex Saga-04, I/a Front Saga
9227481	Britanis	Grc	2002	157,581	304,732	332	58	16	tcr	
9381172	Chris *	Mhl	2006	39,736	76,629	225	32	14	bbu	
9600619	Dona Bibi	Pan	2012	44,130	81,966	229	32	14	bbu	ex Asita Sun-15
9597812	Dona Tara	Pan	2011	44,130	81,323	229	32	14	bbu	ex Orion Pride-15
9322267	Ellinis	Grc	2007	157,844	306,507	332	58	15	tcr	
9316672	Maribella	Mlt	2004	39,736	76,629	225	32	15	bbu	
9218789	Marichristina	Mlt	2001	40,121	74,410	225	32	15	bbu	ex SA Warrior-03
9281437	Marietta	Mlt	2004	40,135	73,880	225	32	15	bbu	ex World Prosperity-04
9434565	Marijeannie	Pan	2009	94,232	179,759	292	45	15	bbu	
9434553	Mariloula	Pan	2008	94,232	179,759	292	45	15	bbu	
9325063	Marinicki	Mlt	2005	39,738	76,629	225	32	15	bbu	
9447017	Mariperla	Mlt	2009	94,232	179,759	292	45	15	bbu	
9484493	Marivictoria	Grc	2009	94,232	179,759	292	45	15	bbu	
9532757	Oceanis	Grc	2011	161,273	320,780	330	60	14	tcr	
9405423	Serenea	Grc	2009	81,502	158,583	274	48	15	tcr	
9406659	Sestrea	Lbr	2009	81,502	158,518	274	48	15	tcr	
9083287	Sharifa 4 *	Egy	1995	52,875	95,416	244	42	15	tcr	ex Falster Spirit-10, Bona Rover-00, Vendonna-96

newbuildings : 2 x LNG 73,400 m³ [Daewoo (2018)] to be managed by 'K' Line and operated by BP
*operated by independent subsidiary Chandris (Hellas) Inc, Greece (founded 1988). * owned by Pyramid Navigation Co.*

Chartworld Shipping Corp. Greece

funnel: black with white K in blue circle in centre of white cross on broad blue band, black top, or operators colours. **hull:** black or red with red boot topping or operators colours. **history:** Kollakis family company established over 40 years ago. **web:** www.chartworld.gr

IMO	name	flag	year	gt	dwt	loa	bm	kts	type	comments
9217929	Aifanourios	Bhs	2002	28,693	50,220	190	32	14	bbu	
9216494	Aigeorgis	Bhs	2001	28,693	50,354	190	32	14	bbu	
9492074	Anastasia K	Bhs	2011	43,830	79,500	229	32	14	bbu	
9189897	Atlantic Acanthus	Bhs	1999	9,649	11,793	145	22	21	grf	ex Atlantic Iris-11
8300365	Belgian Reefer **	Bhs	1983	12,383	14,786	145	24	18	grf	ex Anne B-92
8300377	Brazilian Reefer **	Bhs	1984	12,383	14,786	145	24	16	grf	ex Betty B-92
9258882	British Osprey	Iom	2003	63,661	114,809	250	44	15	tcr	
9258868	British Swift	Iom	2003	63,661	114,809	250	44	15	tcr	
9227194	Capt. Stefanos	Bhs	2002	39,035	74,077	225	32	14	bbu	
8700230	Chaiten **	Bhs	1991	14,406	16,950	164	24	19	grf	ex Knud Lauritzen-11
8917546	Chilean Reefer ***	Bhs	1992	7,944	11,095	141	20	22	grf	ex Carelian Reefer-97
9014755	Chiquita Bremen *	Bhs	1992	10,842	12,890	157	23	21	grf	
9014767	Chiquita Rostock *	Bhs	1993	10,842	12,850	157	24	21	grf	
9492086	Diane	Bhs	2011	43,830	78,992	229	32	14	bbu	
8819926	Ditlev Reefer **	Bhs	1990	14,406	16,950	164	24	20	grf	ex Ditlev Lauritzen-11
8819938	Ivar Reefer **	Bhs	1990	14,406	16,950	165	24	19	grf	ex Ivar Lauritzen-11
9007489	Jorgen Reefer **	Bhs	1991	14,406	16,950	164	24	19	grf	ex Jorgen Lauritzen-11
8903167	Knud Reefer **	Bhd	1991	14,406	16,950	164	24	19	grf	ex Knud Lauritzen-11
9121003	Limar	Mhl	1996	28,357	46,170	183	32	14	tco	ex Overseas Limar-13, Limar-05, Osprey Lyra-01
9242651	MSC Amy	Mlt	2002	17,189	22,308	179	28	20	ucc	ex Maersk Venice-14, Landstar-02
9169122	MSC Annick	Pan	1998	40,306	52,329	261	32	24	ucc	4,038 teu: ex Mare Superum-13, Maersk Tirana-09, Dalian Express-07, Maersk Tirana-06, P&O Nedlloyd Cartagena-05, Elbe Bridge-04, Mare Superum-98
9154220	MSC Capri	Deu	1998	25,713	34,051	206	30	21	ucc	2,460 teu: ex Conti Valencia-14, MSC Malaga-08, Conti Valencia-06, MSC Spain-05, Conti Valencia-03, Lykes Hunter-01, Ivaran Hunter-99, Sea Tiger-98, Conti Valencia-98
9124512	MSC Carla 3	Deu	1997	31,730	34,954	193	32	22	ucc	2,507 teu: Hansa Century-15, ex Kota Perdana-04, Zim Pusan I-02, Hansa Century-98, Ibn Duraid-98, Hansa Century-97
9123221	MSC Elsa 3	Lbr	1997	16,799	22,994	184	25	19	ucc	1,730 teu: ex Alexandra N-15, Adrian -14, TMM Hidaldo-08, Delmas Tourville-06, Adrian-02, Ivory Star-02, TMM Manzanillo-01, Adrian-01, CSAV Barcelona-00, Adrian-00, Santa Paula-98, Adrian-97, Jan Ritscher-97

IMO	name	flag	year	gt	dwt	loa	bm	kts	type	comments
9152856	MSC Gianna	Pan	1998	30,280	35,848	202	32	22	ucc	2,825 teu: ex E.R. Fremantle-13, CMA CGM Turkey-08, CSCL Indus-03, Indus-02, Hyundai Infinity-01
9062984	MSC Hina	Lbr	1994	23,540	30,621	187	30	19	ucc	2,074 teu: ex Sydney Express-15, CP Dynasty-06, CanMar Dynasty-05, TMM Guadalajara-03, P&O Nedlloyd Melbourne-01, Coral Seatel-98, Contship Sydney-98, Coral Seatel-94
9124366	MSC Imma	Pan	1996	30,280	35,966	202	32	22	ucc	2,825 teu: ex E.R. Darwin-13, Suzhou Dragon-11, E.R. Darwin-10, China Star-09, E.R. Darwin-02, Ganges-02, Hanjin Genoa-00
9000742	MSC Jenny	Pmd	1994	28,397	32,984	200	32	18	ucc	2,303 teu: ex Alianca Europa-15
9193719	MSC Lana	Mhl	1999	23,722	29,240	194	28	21	ucc	1,804 teu: ex AS Poseidon-14. Safmarine Memling-09, SCL Memling-02, Poseidon-99
9062996	MSC Mila 3	Gbr	1995	23,540	30,645	187	30	19	ucc	2,074 teu: ex Fremantle Express-15, CP Voyager-06, Lykes Voyager-05, P&O Nedlloyd Bandar Abbas-01, P&O Nedlloyd Yafo-99, Pax-98, CMBT Melbourne-97, Contship Melbourne-97, I/a Pax
9149328	MSC Nadriely	Lbr	1998	25,608	34,015	208	30	21	ucc	2,468 teu: ex Helvetia-14, CCNI Guayas-12, Alianca Hong Kong-06, Columbus Chile-04, Alianca Rotterdam-02, Lykes Traveler-01, CMA CGM Gaugain-01, CGM Gaugin-00, Charlotta-98
9163207	MSC Nora	Mhl	1999	23,722	29,210	194	28	21	ucc	1,804 teu: ex Uranus-14, Cap van Diemen-09, Uranus-06, Alianca Antuerpia-03, Uranus-01
9038907	MSC Roberta	Lbr	1993	53,815	67,640	294	32	23	ucc	4,639 teu: ex Stuttgart Express-15
9116369	MSC Sena	Pan	1996	30,280	35,966	202	32	22	ucc	2,825 teu: ex E.R. Albany-13, MacAndrews America-07, CMA CGM Egypt-06, E.R. Albany-04, Rhein-02, Zim Sydney-00
9036002	MSC Shaula	Pan	1992	51,836	61,153	275	37	26	ucc	4,651 teu: ex MSC Idil-12, Hyundai Emperor-11, APL Emperor-08
9193680	MSC Tia	Mhl	1999	23,722	29,210	194	28	21	ucc	1,804 teu: ex Pluto-14
9163192	MSC Uma	Mhl	1998	23,722	29,233	194	28	21	ucc	1,804 teu: ex Neptun-14, CMA CGM Cortes-12, Cap Vincent-06, Neptun-02, Kota Perdana-00, Neptun-99
9207417	Ocean Spirit	Bhs	1999	38,526	73,807	225	32	14	bbu	ex Lucia Bulker-09, Santa Lucia-05
8917572	Peruvian Reefer ***	Bhs	1992	7,944	11,092	141	20	22	grf	ex Savonian Reefer-97
9129952	Rimar	Bhs	1998	28,357	45,999	183	32	14	tco	ex Overseas Rimar-13, Rimar-05, Petrobulk Sirius-01
9523512	Ruby Star	Bhs	2011	43,753	79,200	229	32	14	bbu	ex Newlead Gujarat-12
8917560	Scandinavian Reefer ***	Bhs	1992	7,944	11,054	141	20	22	grf	
9589683	Star Betty	Bhs	2011	44,232	81,168	229	32	14	bbu	ex Prabhu Mohini-15
9316036	Star Planet	Bhs	2005	40,041	76,812	225	32	14	bbu	ex Ocean Planet-13
9296200	Star Princess	Bhs	2003	90,091	180,202	289	45	15	bbu	ex Atlantic Princess-13
9461142	Star Trader	Pan	2010	43,012	82,181	229	32	14	bbu	ex Torm Trader-15
8413019	Summer Flower *	Bhs	1984	12,659	13,584	169	24	22	grf	ex Chiquita Baru-96, Vivian M-90
8407814	Summer Meadow *	Bhs	1985	12,659	13,584	169	24	22	grf	ex Chiquita Bocas-96, Irma M-90
8907876	Swan Chacabuco **	Bhs	1990	13,099	12,974	152	24	18	grf	ex Chacabuco-97

*operated by SeaTrade, ** operated by Cool Carriers, *** Chiquita Brands*

Chemikalien Seetransport GmbH　　　　　　　　　　　　Germany

funnel: blue with white 'ST' inside large white outlined 'C' on blue square on broad white band. **hull:** black, blue or red with blue or red boot-topping. **history:** formed 1989. **web:** www.cst-hamburg.de

IMO	name	flag	year	gt	dwt	loa	bm	kts	type	comments
9298313	Athens Star	Lbr	2005	41,966	71,869	229	32	14	tco	
9270488	Chemtrans Moon	Lbr	2004	40,763	72,296	229	32	14	tco	I/a Silver Dolphin
9182667	Chemtrans Ray	Lbr	2000	40,516	71,637	227	32	15	tco	ex Emerald Ray-03
9214745	Chemtrans Riga *	Lbr	2001	22,184	34,810	171	27	14	tco	ex Maersk Riga-11. Roy Maersk-03
9167174	Chemtrans Rouen	Lbr	2000	22,181	34,860	171	27	15	tco	ex Maersk Rouen-10, Maersk Rye-03
9167186	Chemtrans Rugen *	Lbr	2001	22,181	34,861	171	27	14	tco	ex Maersk Rugen-10, Maersk Ramsey-03
9270490	Chemtrans Sea	Lbr	2004	40,764	72,365	229	32	14	tco	ex Red Dolphin-04
9185504	Chemtrans Sky	Lbr	2000	37,033	63,381	229	32	14	tco	ex Asopos-04
9185516	Chemtrans Star	Lbr	2000	37,033	63.331	229	32	15	tco	ex Aliakmon-03

IMO	name	flag	year	gt	dwt	loa	bm	kts	type	comments
9323560	Gandhi *	Lbr	2008	25,400	40,165	176	31	14	tco	
9259886	Green Point	Lbr	2003	29,982	49,511	183	32	14	tco	
9298325	Hamburg Star	Lbr	2005	41,966	73,869	229	32	14	tco	
9247508	Hans Scholl	Lbr	2004	25,399	40,250	176	31	15	tco	
9330343	London Star	Lbr	2006	41,966	73,869	229	32	14	tco	
9247493	MS Simon	Lbr	2004	25,399	37,247	176	31	15	tco	
9241798	MS Sophie	Lbr	2004	25,399	37,247	176	31	15	tco	l/a Chemtrans Sophie
9330355	New York Star	Lbr	2006	41,966	73,869	229	32	14	tco	
9298818	Revel	Lbr	2004	22,184	35,187	171	27	14	tco	ex Maersk Radiant-11
9496680	Trans Nanjiang *	Lbr	2011	51,255	93,226	230	38	14	bbu	
9283643	Trans Pacific *	Lbr	2004	40,485	74,403	225	32	14	bbu	ex CMB Eline-05
9496678	Trans Shanghai	Lbr	2010	51,255	93,260	230	38	14	bbu	ex RBD Shanghai-12

managed by subsidiary Chemkalian Seetransport Cyprus Ltd., operates in Klaveness Baumarine Pool
partner in Star Tankers Pool with Heidmar Inc and in Baumarine Pool. Also see Team Tankers Pool under Blystad Shipmanagement Ltd.

Chevron Corp U.S.A.

Chevron Shipping Co. LLC, U.S.A.

funnel: white with three narrow blue bands, narrow black top. **hull:** black with red boot-topping. **history:** formed 2005 as successor to ChevronTexaco Corp formed by 2001 by merger of Chevron Corp (founded 1906 as Standard Oil Co of California, merged 1926 with Pacific Oil Co (founded 1879) and acquired Gulf Oil Corp in 1984) and Texaco Inc (founded 1901 as The Texas Co to 1926, The Texas Corp to 1941 and The Texas Co to 1959). Subsidiary formed 1957 as California Shipping Co to 1965, then Chevron Shipping Co to 2001 and ChevronTexaco Shipping Co LLC to 2006. **web:** www.chevron.com or www.chevrontexaco.com

IMO	name	flag	year	gt	dwt	loa	bm	kts	type	comments
9125736	Aberdeen	Bhs	1996	47,274	87,055	222	37	14	tcs	
9288875	Andromeda Voyager	Bhs	2005	160,808	320,472	333	60	15	tcr	
9581203	Antares Voyager	Bhs	2012	161,535	317,052	333	60	15	tcr	
9289491	Aquarius Voyager	Bhs	2006	161,331	320,821	333	60	15	tcr	
9588299	Arcturus Voyager	Bhs	2010	161,535	317,052	333	60	15	tcr	
9295000	Aries Voyager	Bhs	2006	160,808	320,870	332	58	15	tcr	
9610779	Asia Endeavour (df)	Bhs	2015	101,427	82,434	285	43	19	lng	160,000 m³
9606950	Asia Energy (df)	Bhs	2014	101,427	82,424	285	43	10	lng	160,000 m³
9610767	Asia Excellence (df)	Bhs	2015	101,427	82,721	285	43	19	lng	160,000 m³
9606948	Asia Vision (df)	Bhs	2014	101,427	82,487	285	43	19	lng	160,000 m³
9637777	Brasil Voyager	Bhs	2013	83,942	153,684	282	49	15	tcs	
9144926	California Voyager	Usa	1999	30,770	45,656	190	32	15	tco	ex HMI Brenton Reef-08
9330604	Capricorn Voyager +	Bhs	2007	58,442	104,610	244	42	14	tcr	
9330599	Castor Voyager	Bhs	2006	58,088	104,866	244	42	14	tcr	
9035060	Cygnus Voyager	Bhs	1993	88,919	156,835	275	50	15	tcr	ex Samuel Ginn-03
9118630	Florida Voyager	Usa	1998	30,415	46,094	183	32	14	tco	
9583732	Hercules Voyager	Bhs	2014	161,692	319,359	333	60	15	tcr	
9583720	Hydra Voyager	Bhs	2013	161,692	319,357	333	60	15	tcr	
9602473	Leo Voyager	Bhs	2014	164,511	319,450	333	60	15	tcr	
9693206	Libra Voyager	Bhs	2014	164,511	319,431	333	60	15	tcr	
9131369	Mississippi Voyager	Usa	1998	30,415	46,069	183	32	14	tco	
9249178	Neptune Voyager	Bhs	2003	58,088	104,875	244	42	14	tcr	
9250725	Northwest Swan (st)	Bmu	2004	96,165	73,676	280	43	19	lng	137,000 m³
9144194	Oregon Voyager	Usa	1999	30,770	45,671	190	32	15	tco	ex Seabulk Energy-10, S/R Bristol Bay-02
9665736	Pegasus Voyager	Bhs	2014	85,147	155,374	276	48	15	tcr	
9665748	Polaris Voyager	Bhs	2014	85,147	155,415	276	48	15	tcr	
9482304	Sonangol Benguela (st) *	Bhs	2011	104,537	89,806	291	43	19	lng	160,500 m³
9482299	Sonangol Etosha (st) *	Bhs	2011	104,537	89,932	291	43	19	lng	160,500 m³
9475600	Sonangol Sambizanga (st) *	Bhs	2011	104,537	89,742	291	43	19	lng	160,500 m³
9249180	Stellar Voyager	Bhs	2003	58,088	104,801	244	42	15	tcr	
9256468	Vega Voyager	Bhs	2003	58,088	104,864	244	42	15	tcr	

newbuildings: 2 x 160,000 m³ lng Samsung
* managed for Sonangol Shipping, Angola, + chartered from Mitsui Soko Co Ltd, Japan
see also Angelicoussis Shipping Group Ltd.

China COSCO Shipping Corp. (COSCOCS) China

funnel:. **hull:.** **history:** founded Feb 18th 2016 by merger of COSCO, parent founded April 1961 as China Ocean Shipping Co to 1993. Container subsidiary formed 1997 by amalgamation with Shanghai Ocean Shipping Co. and CSCL, government controlled company formed 1997 by merging of various government shipping Bureau and Administrations. COSCOCS now regarded as the largest shipping company in the world. The ramifications of the merger, new corporate identity etc., are not clear at the time of publication, so the ships are still listed under individual companies **web:** www.coscon.com

IMO	name	flag	year	gt	dwt	loa	bm	kts	type	comments
9345439	Cosco Africa	Pan	2008	114,394	110,038	349	46	25	ucc	10,046 teu
9345427	Cosco America	Pan	2008	114,394	109,950	349	46	25	ucc	10,046 teu

IMO	name	flag	year	gt	dwt	loa	bm	kts	type	comments
9345403	Cosco Asia	Pan	2007	114,394	109,968	349	46	25	ucc	10,046 teu: ex Hanjin Fuzhou-11, Cosco Asia-09
9516404	Cosco Belgium	Hkg	2013	153,666	156,605	366	51	24	ucc	13,386 teu
9516478	Cosco Denmark	Hkg	2014	153,666	156,600	366	51	24	ucc	13,386 teu
9516428	Cosco England	Hkg	2013	153,666	156,618	366	51	24	ucc	13,386 teu
9345415	Cosco Europe	Pan	2008	114,394	109,968	349	46	25	ucc	10,046 teu
9516416	Cosco France	Hkg	2013	153,666	156,596	366	51	24	ucc	13,386 teu
9516454	Cosco Italy	Hkg	2014	153,666	156,610	366	51	24	ucc	13,386 teu
9355563	Cosco Kaohsiung	Hkg	2008	115,776	111,414	349	46	25	ucc	10,020 teu: ex Cosco Indian Ocean-10
9516430	Cosco Netherlands	Hkg	2013	153,666	156,549	366	51	24	ucc	13,386 teu
9334923	Cosco Oceania	Hkg	2008	115,776	111,385	349	46	25	ucc	10,020 teu
9355551	Cosco Pacific	Hkg	2008	115,776	111,315	349	46	25	ucc	10,020 teu: ex Hanjin Bilbao-11, Cosco Pacific-09
9516466	Cosco Portugal	Hkg	2014	153,666	156,605	366	51	24	ucc	13.386 teu
9516442	Cosco Spain	Hkg	2014	153,666	156,572	366	51	24	ucc	13,386 teu
9355575	Cosco Taicang	Hkg	2009	115,993	111,499	349	46	25	ucc	10,046 teu: l/a Cosco Atlantic

newbuildings:

name									type	comments
Cosco Creation									ucc	20,000 teu SWS 02.2018
Cosco Wisdom									ucc	20,000 teu SWS 05.2018
Cosco Explorer									ucc	20,000 teu SWS 07.2018
Cosco Valiance									ucc	20,000 teu Nantong 02.2018
Cosco Achievement									ucc	20,000 teu Nantong 04.2018
Cosco Endeavour									ucc	20,000 teu Nantong 06.2018
Cosco Legend									ucc	20,000 teu Nantong 08.2018
Cosco Luck									ucc	20,000 teu Dalian SY 02.2018
Cosco Happiness									ucc	20,000 teu Dalian SY 05:2018
Cosco Grand									ucc	20,000 teu Dalian SY 02:2018
Cosco Magnificence									ucc	20,000 teu Dalian SY 05.2018
									ucc	14,500 teu Jiangnan 3020 2017
									ucc	14,500 teu Jiangnan 3021 2017
									ucc	14,500 teu Jiangnan 3022 2018
									ucc	14,500 teu Jiangnan 3023 2018
									ucc	14,500 teu Jiangnan 3012 2018

also reported: 5 x 9,400 teu ucc [Jiangnan Changxing (2016/7), 5 x 14,500 teu ucc [Shanghai Jiangnan Changxing SB (2017-8))
3 x 20,000teu [Shanghai Waigaoqiao SY (2018)]
operates many smaller container vessels on coastal services, see also other vessels with Cosco prefix

COSCO England : China COSCO Shipping Co. : *Roy Fenton*

COSCO Tengfei : China COSCO Shipping Co. : *Chris Brooks*

CSCL Arctic Ocean : China COSCO Shipping Co. : *Hans Kraijenbosch*

CSCL Mercury : China COSCO Shipping Co. : *Hans Kraijenbosch*

IMO	name	flag	year	gt	dwt	loa	bm	kts	type	comments

COSCO Guangzhou, China

funnel: blue with white vertical line through white ring above white 'COSCO', broad yellow base and narrow black top. **hull:** *grey or black with blue 'COSCO', green or red boot-topping.*

IMO	name	flag	year	gt	dwt	loa	bm	kts	type	comments
9454711	Cosco Shengshi	Pan	2011	51,671	14,868	183	32	20	mve	5,000 ceu
9454723	Cosco Tengfei	Pan	2011	51,671	14,759	183	32	20	mve	5,000 ceu

China Shipping Container Lines Co. Ltd.

funnel: blue with blue 'CIS' on broad white/yellow band. **hull:** *green with white 'CHINA SHIPPING LINE', red boot-topping.* **history:***.Government controlled company founded 1997* **web:** *www.cnshippingdev.com*

IMO	name	flag	year	gt	dwt	loa	bm	kts	type	comments
9695169	CSCL Arctic Ocean	Hkg	2015	187,541	184,320	400	59	22	ucc	18,982 teu
9285976	CSCL Asia	Hkg	2004	90,645	101,612	334	43	25	ucc	8,468 teu
9695145	CSCL Atlantic Ocean	Hkg	2015	187,541	184,320	400	59	22	ucc	18,982 teu
9695121	CSCL Globe	Hkg	2014	187,541	184,320	400	59	22	ucc	18,982 teu
9695157	CSCL Indian Ocean	Hkg	2015	187,541	184,320	400	59	22	ucc	18,982 teu
9467263	CSCL Jupiter	Hkg	2011	150,853	155,480	366	51	26	ucc	14,074 teu
9467287	CSCL Mars	Hkg	2011	150,853	155,467	366	51	26	ucc	14,074 teu
9467265	CSCL Mercury	Hkg	2011	150,853	155,374	366	51	26	ucc	14,074 teu
9467316	CSCL Neptune	Hkg	2011	150,853	155,264	366	51	26	ucc	14,074 teu
9695133	CSCL Pacific Ocean	Hkg	2014	187,541	184,320	400	59	22	ucc	18,982 teu
9467299	CSCL Saturn	Hkg	2011	150,853	155,426	366	51	26	ucc	14,074 teu
9645853	CSCL Spring	Hkg	2014	116,603	121,849	335	49	22	ucc	10,036 teu
9466867	CSCL Star	Hkg	2011	150,853	155,470	366	51	26	ucc	14,074 teu
9645865	CSCL Summer	Hkg	2014	116,603	121,805	335	49	22	ucc	10,036 teu
9645877	CSCL Winter	Hkg	2014	116,603	121,839	335	49	22	ucc	10,036 teu
9645889	CSCL Bohai Sea	Hkg	2014	116,603	121,824	335	49	22	ucc	10,036 teu
9645891	CSCL Autumn	Hkg	2014	116,568	121,270	335	49	22	ucc	10,036 teu
9645906	CSCL Yellow Sea	Hkg	2014	116,568	121,194	335	49	22	ucc	10,036 teu
9645918	CSCL East China Sea	Hkg	2014	116,568	121,186	335	49	22	ucc	10,036 teu
9645920	CSCL South China Sea	Hkg	2014	116,568	121,147	335	49	22	ucc	10,036 teu
9467304	CSCL Uranus	Hkg	2012	150,853	155,300	366	51	26	ucc	14,074 teu
9467251	CSCL Venus	Hkg	2011	150,853	155,470	366	51	26	ucc	14,074 teu
9314246	Xin Beijing *	Hkg	2007	108,069	111,571	337	46	25	ucc	9,580 teu: l/d Xin Hamburg
9337949	Xin Da Yang Zhou	Chn	2009	90,757	102,418	335	43	25	ucc	8,530 teu
9337937	Xin Fei Zhou	Chn	2008	90,757	102,379	335	43	25	ucc	8,530 teu
9314222	Xin Hong Kong *	Hkg	2007	108,069	111,746	337	46	25	ucc	9,580 teu
9307217	Xin Los Angeles *	Hkg	2006	108,069	111,889	337	46	25	ucc	9,580 teu
9337925	Xin Mei Zhou	Chn	2008	90,757	102,453	335	43	25	ucc	8,530 teu
9337913	Xin Ou Zhou	Chn	2007	90,757	102,460	335	43	25	ucc	8,530 teu
9307231	Xin Shanghai *	Hkg	2006	108,089	111,889	337	46	25	ucc	9,580 teu
9334935	Xin Ya Zhou	Chn	2007	90,757	102,395	335	43	25	ucc	8,530 teu

newbuildings:

IMO	name	flag	year	gt	dwt	loa	bm	kts	type	comments
9731913				91,800	110,000				ucc	10,600 teu Jiangnan Changxing
9731925				91,800	110,000				ucc	10,600 teu Jiangnan Changxing
9731937				91,800	110,000				ucc	10,600 teu Jiangnan Changxing
9731949				91,800	110,000				ucc	10,600 teu Jiangnan Changxing
9731951				91,800	110,000				ucc	10,600 teu Jiangnan Changxing

see other chartered vessels with 'CSCL' prefix in index.

Chinese-Polish Joint Stock Shipping Co.   China/Poland

funnel: cream with cream 'C' and white 'P' on broad red band, narrow black top. **hull:** *light grey with blue 'CHIPOLBROK', green over black boot-topping.* **history:** *formed jointly by the governments of China and Poland on 15th June 1951.* **web:** *www.chipolbrok.com.cn or www.chipolbrok.com.pl*

IMO	name	flag	year	gt	dwt	loa	bm	kts	type	comments
9432115	Adam Asnyk	Cyp	2009	24,115	30,346	200	28	19	ggc	
9432165	Chipolbrok Cosmos	Hkg	2011	24,142	30,281	200	28	19	ggc	
9432141	Chipolbrok Galaxy	Hkg	2010	24,142	30,330	200	28	19	ggc	
9272216	Chipolbrok Moon	Hkg	2004	24,167	30,460	200	28	19	ggc	
9710177	Chipolbrok Pacific	Cyp	2015	24,778	32,000	200	28	19	ghl	cr :3(350)
9432147	Chipolbrok Star	Hkg	2010	24,142	30,346	200	28	19	ggc	
9272230	Chipolbrok Sun	Hkg	2004	24,167	30,396	200	28	19	ggc	
8821943	Chongming	Hkg	1993	18,177	22,109	170	28	16	ggc	
9133410	Hong Xing	Chn	1997	18,207	22,271	170	28	16	ggc	ex Taixing-12
8821955	Jia Xing	Hkg	1992	18,177	22,109	170	28	16	ggc	ex Bao Zheng-92
9432153	Kraszewski	Cyp	2011	24,221	30,435	200	28	19	ggc	
9272228	Leopold Staff	Cyp	2004	24,167	30,469	200	28	19	ggc	
9133422	Norwid	Mlt	1998	18,202	22,258	170	28	16	ggc	
9432139	Parandowski	Cyp	2010	24,115	30,346	200	28	19	ggc	
8821929	Szymanowski	Cyp	1991	18,252	22,313	170	28	16	ggc	
8821931	Wieniawski	Mlt	1992	18,208	22,130	170	28	16	ggc	

IMO	name	flag	year	gt	dwt	loa	bm	kts	type	comments
9271925	Wladyslaw Orkan	Cyp	2003	24,167	30,435	200	28	19	ggc	
9150303	Yongxing	Hkg	1998	18,207	22,309	170	28	16	ggc	
newbuildings:										
9710189	Nowowiejski	Cyp	2016	24,778	32,000	200	28	19	ghl	cr: 3(350) Shanghai Shipyard 1225
9731377	Chipolbrok Atlantic	Hkg	2016	24,000	32,000	200	28	19	ghl	cr: 3(350) Shanghai Shipyard 1226
9731389	Paderewski	Cyp	2016	24,000	32,000	200	28	19	ghl	cr: 3(350) Shanghai Shipyard 1227

Cido Shipping (H.K.) Co. Ltd.   Hong Kong (China)

funnel: charterers colours. **hull:** black or blue or long-term charterers colours with red boot-topping. **history:** founded 1993 as Cido Maritime Corp and Cido Shipping Co Ltd, which were merged in 2004. **web:** www.cidoship.com

IMO	name	flag	year	gt	dwt	loa	bm	kts	type	comments
9383974	Atlantic Canyon	Hkg	2009	23,342	36,677	184	27	15	tco	
9374272	Atlantic Hope	Hkg	2008	29,266	47,128	183	32	14	tco	
9455052	Atlantic Sirius	Hkg	2010	23,342	36,677	184	27	14	tco	
9464560	Atlantic Symphony	Hkg	2009	23,342	36,677	184	27	15	tco	
9279331	CCNI Andino *	Pan	2004	59,217	18,381	200	32	18	mve	6,500 ceu: ex Höegh Durban-12, Hual Durban-07
9303156	Dream Angel	Pan	2006	41,662	15,089	186	28	19	mve	4,075 ceu
9303168	Dream Beauty	Pan	2006	41,662	15,119	186	28	19	mve	4,075 ceu
9325788	Dream Diamond	Pan	2007	41,662	15,069	186	28	20	mve	4,113 ceu
9325790	Dream Diva	Pan	2007	41,662	15,068	186	28	20	mve	4,113 ceu
9334246	Dream Jasmine	Pan	2008	41,662	15.068	186	28	20	mve	4.113 ceu
9360568	Dream Orchid	Pan	2009	41,662	15,097	186	28	20	mve	4,113 ceu
9340570	Grand Champion	Pan	2008	59,217	18,262	200	32	19	mve	6,400 ceu
9169316	Grand Choice	Pan	1999	50,309	16,669	179	32	19	mve	4,373 ceu
9303182	Grand Cosmo	Pan	2006	59,217	17,750	200	32	20	mve	6,502 ceu
9355238	Grand Dahlia	Pan	2009	59,217	18,054	200	32	20	mve	6,502 ceu
9303223	Grand Diamond +	Pan	2007	59,217	18,058	200	32	19	mve	6,502 ceu
9279329	Grand Dolphin	Pan	2004	58,947	18,369	200	32	19	mve	6,501 ceu: ex Höegh Dubai-14, Hual Dubai-06
9303170	Grand Duke	Pan	2005	59,217	18,315	200	32	20	mve	6,502 ceu
9267663	Grand Eagle	Pan	2003	58,947	19,048	200	32	19	mve	6,500 ceu: ex Höegh Oceania-14, Hual Oceania-05
9339806	Grand Hero +	Pan	2007	59,217	18,085	200	32	19	mve	6,502 ceu
9355240	Grand Legacy	Pan	2009	59,217	17,550	200	32	19	mve	6,502 ceu
9228306	Grand Mark	Pan	2000	50,310	16,681	179	32	19	mve	4,373 ceu
9247584	Grand Mercury +	Pan	2002	58,947	19,121	200	32	20	mve	6,501 ceu
9303209	Grand Neptune	Pan	2006	59,217	17,550	200	32	20	mve	6,400 ceu
9303194	Grand Orion	Pan	2006	59,217	18,312	200	32	20	mve	6,400 ceu
9169328	Grand Pace	Pan	1999	50,309	16,714	179	32	19	mve	5,100 ceu
9284776	Grand Pavo	Pan	2005	59,217	18,376	200	32	20	mve	6,502 ceu
9339844	Grand Pearl +	Pan	2008	59,217	18,090	200	32	19	mve	6,502 ceu
9284764	Grand Phoenix	Pan	2005	59,217	18,383	200	32	20	mve	6,400 ceu
9247572	Grand Pioneer	Pan	2002	58,947	19,120	200	32	20	mve	6,500 ceu
9181479	Grand Quest	Pan	2000	50,309	16,702	179	32	19	mve	5,100 ceu
9184940	Grand Race	Pan	2000	50,309	16,689	179	32	19	mve	4,373 ceu
9325221	Grand Ruby	Pan	2007	59,217	18,117	200	32	19	mve	6,400 ceu
9325233	Grand Sapphire +	Pan	2007	59,217	18,099	200	32	19	mve	6,400 ceu
9472206	Grand Uranus	Sgp	2014	72,408	26,985	232	32	19	mve	7,600 ceu: ex D Ladybug-14
9355252	Grand Vega	Pan	2009	59,217	18,049	200	32	19	mve	6,400 ceu
9303211	Grand Venus	Pan	2006	59,217	13,500	200	32	20	mve	6,400 ceu
9334234	Grand Victory +	Pan	2007	59,217	18,299	200	32	19	mve	6.400 ceu
9378618	LR2 Pioneer †	Pan	2008	59,172	115,273	244	42	15	tco	
9378620	LR2 Polaris †	Pan	2008	59,172	115,273	244	42	15	tco	
9378632	LR2 Poseidon †	Pan	2009	59,172	109,996	244	42	15	tco	
9395290	Maersk Hayama	Sgp	2011	156,915	297,221	330	60	14	tcr	
9410301	Maersk Wolgast	Hkg	2010	18,123	22,314	173	27	19	ucc	1,805 teu
9231688	Modern Express	Pan	2001	33,831	10,817	164	28	21	mve	3,060 ceu
9188829	Modern Link	Pan	2000	33,831	10,419	164	28	18	mve	3,000 ceu
9188805	Modern Peak	Pan	1999	33,831	10,817	164	28	18	mve	3,000 ceu
9332810	Pacific Apollo	Hkg	2007	59,164	115,577	244	42	15	tcr	
9270749	Pacific Oasis	Pan	2004	28,799	47,999	180	32	14	tco	
9270737	Pacific Polaris	Pan	2004	28,799	47,999	180	32	14	tco	
9427550	Spring Sky	Hkg	2010	25,745	9,301	165	26	20	mve	2,520 ceu
9427562	Spring Wind	Hkg	2010	25,745	9,274	165	26	20	mve	2,520 ceu
9077836	Topaz Ace *	Pan	1995	48,210	14,696	180	32	18	mve	5,317 ceu

chartered out to * CCNI , + Eukor Car Carriers Inc., † to Torm LR2 Pool or to other owners.

Clipper Group Management Ltd.   Bahamas

Clipper Marine Services A/S, Denmark

funnel: *black with white 'C' symbol.* **hull:** *black or green with white 'CLIPPER', red boot-topping.* **history:** *formed 1972, acquired Lasco Shipping in 2003, in 2010 divested its tanker interests and became major shareholder in Nordic Tankers.* **web:** *www.clipper-group.com*

IMO	name	flag	year	gt	dwt	loa	bm	kts	type	comments
9713480	Clipper Amsterdam +	Pan	2015	34,810	61,268	200	32	14	bbu	
9615119	Clipper Belle +	Pan	2012	23,264	38,204	180	30	14	bbu	
9605102	Clipper Bettina +	Pan	2012	23,264	38,221	180	30	14	bbu	
9636450	Clipper Excalibur +	Pan	2013	38,203	66,721	200	36	14	bbu	
9636462	Clipper Excelsior +	Pan	2013	38,203	66,684	200	36	14	bbu	
9660085	Clipper I-Star +	Sgp	2013	34,815	61,403	200	32	14	bbu	
9605073	Clipper Ise +	Pan	2012	17,027	28,227	169	27	14	bbu	
9663128	Clipper Kalavryta	Mhl	2015	36,294	63,325	200	32	14	bbu	ex Sainty Virtue-15, l/a Taxiarchos
9663116	Clipper Kythira	Mhl	2015	36,294	63,273	200	32	14	bbu	ex Sainty Voyager-15, l/a Michail
9283837	Clipper Lasco *	Bhs	2004	16,954	28,200	169	27	14	bbu	
9151723	Clipper Lis	Bhs	2009	17,018	28,321	169	27	14	bbu	
9551375	Clipper Lotus	Bhs	2010	17,019	28,331	169	27	14	bbu	
9478743	Clipper Phoenix +	Pan	2011	31,230	55,636	190	32	14	bbu	
9524542	Clipper Polaris +	Pan	2009	31,236	55,691	190	32	14	bbu	
9406075	Clipper Talent	Bhs	2009	19,972	30,475	179	28	14	bbu	
9320300	Clipper Target	Bhs	2006	19,918	30,587	179	29	14	bbu	
9406099	Clipper Tarpon	Bhs	2009	19,972	30,427	179	28	14	bbu	
9406116	Clipper Terminus	Bhs	2010	19,972	30,425	179	28	14	bbu	
9320348	Clipper Tenacious	Bhs	2007	19,918	30,634	179	29	14	bbu	ex Kent Tenacious-12, Clipper Tenacious-10
9406037	Clipper Titan	Bhs	2009	19,972	30,439	179	28	14	bbu	
9375953	Clipper Trader	Bhs	2008	19,972	30,487	179	28	14	bbu	ex Clipper Tsuji-09
9406051	Clipper Tradition	Bhs	2009	19,972	30,465	179	28	14	bbu	
9667447	Clipper Triton +	Pan	2013	34,800	61,448	200	32	14	bbu	
9406024	Clipper Triumph	Bhs	2009	19,972	30,472	179	28	14	bbu	
9320312	Clipper Trust	Bhs	2007	19,918	30,611	179	29	14	bbu	
9285407	Clipper Valour	Bhs	2003	22,072	34,790	179	28	14	bbu	
9738789	Clipper Victory +	Sgp	2015	40,937	77,119	225	32	14	bbu	
9727326	Clipper Viking +	Sgp	2015	40,937	77,111	225	32	14	bbu	
9713428	Clipper Vision +	Mhl	2015	40,937	77,154	225	32	14	bbu	

newbuildings:
2 further 61,000dwt bbu, and 7 further bbu from 38,000 to 76,000dwt
vessels managed by Clipper Bulk Shipping Ltd., Bahamas ** by Clipper Bulk (Singapore) Pte Ltd (founded 2007 – www.clipper-bulk.com)*
+ chartered vessels: see also Shoei Kisen Kaisha

CMA CGM Holding & Co. S.A.   France

funnel: *red 'CMA and blue 'CGM' on white band between blue base and red top.* **hull:** *blue with white 'CMA CGM', red boot-topping.* **history:** *amalgamation in 1999 of Cie. Maritime d'Affretement (founded 1978) and Cie. Generale Transatlantique SA (founded 1854 and state-controlled from 1933), which itself was a 1977 merger of CGT and Cie. des Messageries Maritimes (founded 1948). ANL name acquired 1998 (formed 1956 as Australian Coastal Shipping Commission, becoming Australian Shipping Commission in 1974 and Australian National Line in 1989. Cheng Lie Navigation Co Ltd acquired 2007 (founded 1971).* **web:** *www.cma-cgm.com*

IMO	name	flag	year	gt	dwt	loa	bm	kts	type	comments
9334167	ANL Wangaratta †	Gbr	2008	39,906	50,596	260	32	24	ucc	4,250 teu: l/d Sui An Rickmers
9334155	ANL Wyong †	Gbr	2008	39,906	52,000	261	32	24	ucc	4,250 teu: l/d Olympia Rickmers
9451965	CMA CGM Africa Four	Bhs	2010	40,827	51,619	228	37	21	ucc	3,718 teu
9451905	CMA CGM Africa One	Bhs	2010	40,827	51,634	228	37	21	ucc	3,718 teu
9451939	CMA CGM Africa Three	Bhs	2010	40,827	51,604	228	37	21	ucc	3.718 teu
9451927	CMA CGM Africa Two	Bhs	2010	40,827	51,608	228	37	21	ucc	3,718 teu
9335197	CMA CGM Alcazar +	Pan	2007	54,778	68,282	294	32	25	ucc	5,060 teu
9454448	CMA CGM Alexander von Humboldt	Gbr	2013	175,343	186,470	396	54	24	ucc	16,020 teu: l/d CMA CGM Vasco da Gama
9450648	CMA CGM Almaviva	Fra	2011	89,787	107,000	334	43	25	ucc	8,465 teu
9350381	CMA CGM Amber	Gbr	2008	49,810	50,200	282	32	24	ucc	4,389 teu
9295971	CMA CGM America +	Cyp	2006	42,382	52,683	268	32	25	ucc	4,043 teu: ex Laja-06, l/dn Conti Nantes
9454395	CMA CGM Amerigo Vespucci	Fra	2010	152,991	156,887	366	51	24	ucc	13,344 teu
9410727	CMA CGM Andromeda	Gbr	2009	131,332	128,760	363	46	24	ucc	11,356 teu
9410741	CMA CGM Aquila	Gbr	2009	131,332	128,550	363	46	24	ucc	11,356 teu
9360154	CMA CGM Aristote	Gbr	2007	17,594	21,267	170	27	21	ucc	1,713 teu

IMO	name	flag	year	gt	dwt	loa	bm	kts	type	comments
9722651	CMA CGM Arkansas [H]	Mlt	2015	94,440	104,236	300	48	22	ucc	10,034 teu
9280598	CMA CGM Bellini *	Bhs	2004	65,247	72,500	277	40	24	ucc	5,770 teu
9706891	CMA CGM Benjamin Franklin	Gbr	2015	178,228	185,000	399	54	22	ucc	17,859 teu
9222297	CMA CGM Berlioz *	Fra	2001	73,157	80,250	300	40	25	ucc	6,628 teu
9317963	CMA CGM Blue Whale *	Gbr	2007	54,309	65,892	294	32	25	ucc	5.040 teu
9702156	CMA CGM Bougainville	Fra	2015	175.688	186,528	398	54	23	ucc	17,722 teu
9410753	CMA CGM Callisto	Gbr	2010	131,332	128,550	363	46	24	ucc	11,356 teu
9410765	CMA CGM Cassiopeia	Gbr	2011	131,332	128,550	363	46	24	ucc	11,356 teu
9709192	CMA CGM Cayenne	Gbr	2015	26,645	27,322	190	30	19	ucc	2,140 teu
9449819	CMA CGM Cendrillon	Gbr	2010	90,931	109,021	334	43	25	ucc	8,465 teu
9410777	CMA CGM Centaurus	Gbr	2011	131,332	128,550	363	46	24	ucc	11,356 teu
9335202	CMA CGM Chateau d'If +	Cyp	2007	54,778	68,281	294	32	25	ucc	5,060 teu: l/a Cosco Norfolk
9280603	CMA CGM Chopin *	Fra	2004	69,022	73,235	277	40	24	ucc	5,770 teu
9453559	CMA CGM Christophe Colomb	Fra	2009	153,022	157,092	366	51	24	ucc	13,344 teu
9410789	CMA CGM Columba	Gbr	2011	131,332	128,760	363	46	25	ucc	11,356 teu
9722663	CMA CGM Columbia [H]	Mlt	2015	94,440	110,525	300	48	22	ucc	10,034 teu
9350393	CMA CGM Coral	Gbr	2008	49,810	50,200	282	32	24	ucc	4,389 teu
9454400	CMA CGM Corte Real +	Gbr	2010	150,269	156,898	366	51	24	ucc	13,344 teu
9450624	CMA CGM Dahlia	Fra	2011	90,931	109,021	334	43	25	ucc	8,465 teu
9674517	CMA CGM Danube [C]	Mlt	2014	95,366	112,580	300	49	23	ucc	9,289 teu
9248112	CMA CGM Eiffel *	Bhs	2002	49,855	58,344	282	32	26	ucc	4,367 teu
9674529	CMA CGM Elbe [C]	Mlt	2014	95,366	112,576	300	49	23	ucc	9,289 teu
9299642	CMA CGM Fidelio	Fra	2006	107,898	113,964	334	43	24	ucc	9,415 teu: l/a CMA CGM Othello
9450600	CMA CGM Figaro	Fra	2010	90,931	109,021	334	43	25	ucc	8,465 teu
9348704	CMA CGM Florida	Gbr	2008	54,309	65,800	294	32	25	ucc	5,042 teu
9261918	CMA CGM Fort St. Georges	Fra	2003	26,342	30,450	198	30	21	ucc	2,226 teu
9261889	CMA CGM Fort St. Louis	Fra	2003	26,342	30,804	198	30	21	ucc	2,226 teu
9261891	CMA CGM Fort St. Pierre	Fra	2003	26,342	30,804	198	30	21	ucc	2,226 teu
9261906	CMA CGM Fort Ste. Marie	Fra	2003	26,342	30,804	198	30	21	ucc	2,226 teu
9410791	CMA CGM Gemini	Gbr	2011	131,332	128,550	363	46	24	ucc	11,356 teu
9702144	CMA CGM Georg Forster	Gbr	2015	175,688	186,745	398	54	23	ucc	17,722 teu: l/a CMA CGM James Cook
9351127	CMA CGM Georgia	Gbr	2008	54,309	65,890	294	32	25	ucc	5,042 teu
9360142	CMA CGM Herodote	Gbr	2007	17,594	18,860	170	27	21	ucc	1,713 teu
9362322	CMA CGM Homere	Gbr	2007	17,594	21,264	170	27	21	ucc	1,713 teu
9356309	CMA CGM Hydra +	Gbr	2009	128,600	131,831	347	46	24	ucc	11,038 teu
9134646	CMA CGM Impala	Gbr	1996	16,803	22,990	185	25	19	ucc	1,728 teu: ex Semira-03, P&O Nedlloyd Amado-03, Semira-02, CGM Seville-02, Semira-97
9722716	CMA CGM Jacques Junior [M]	Mlt	2016	94,400	110,569	300	48	22	ucc	10,034 teu l/d CMA CGM Tennessee
9454450	CMA CGM Jules Verne	Fra	2013	175,368	186,470	396	54	24	ucc	16,020 teu: l/d CMA CGM Zheng He
9326770	CMA CGM Jamaica +	Cyp	2006	41,899	53,663	264	32	23	ucc	4,298 teu
9339545	CMA CGM Kailas	Pan	2006	21,971	24,279	196	28	22	ucc	1,850 teu
9702132	CMA CGM Kerguelen	Gbr	2015	175,688	186,745	398	54	23	ucc	17,722 teu
9450612	CMA CGM La Scala	Gbr	2010	90,931	109,021	334	43	25	ucc	8,465 teu
9224946	CMA CGM La Tour +	Bhs	2001	26,050	30,442	196	30	22	ucc	2,226 teu
9299795	CMA CGM La Traviata	Atf	2006	91,410	101,779	334	43	25	ucc	8,204 teu
9409194	CMA CGM Lamartine	Gbr	2010	73,779	85,446	300	40	25	ucc	6,572 teu
9454412	CMA CGM Laperouse	Gbr	2010	150,269	57,092	366	51	24	ucc	13,344 teu
9399208	CMA CGM Leo	Mlt	2010	131,332	131,236	366	46	25	ucc	11,312 teu
9399193	CMA CGM Libra	Mlt	2009	131,332	131,325	366	46	25	ucc	11,312 teu
9314923	CMA CGM Lilac	Hkg	2005	28,927	39,262	222	30	23	ucc	2,824 teu
9705055	CMA CGM Litani [C]	Mlt	2014	95,793	112,063	300	49	22	ucc	10,622 teu
9674531	CMA CGM Loire [C]	Mlt	2015	95,263	112,729	300	48	22	ucc	9,365 teu

IMO	name	flag	year	gt	dwt	loa	bm	kts	type	comments
9410806	CMA CGM Lyra	Gbr	2011	131,332	131,266	363	46	25	ucc	11,356 teu
9454424	CMA CGM Magellan +	Gbr	2010	150,269	157,254	366	51	24	ucc	13,344 teu
9224958	CMA CGM Manet +	Cyp	2001	26,050	30,442	196	30	21	ucc	2,226 teu
9454436	CMA CGM Marco Polo	Gbr	2012	175,343	187,625	396	54	22	ucc	16,020 teu
9709207	CMA CGM Marseille	Gbr	2015	26,645	27,322	190	30	19	ucc	2,140 teu
9192428	CMA CGM Matisse +	Cyp	1999	25,777	32,274	196	30	21	ucc	2,226 teu
9409209	CMA CGM Maupassant	Gbr	2010	73,779	85,450	300	40	25	ucc	6,572 teu
9299800	CMA CGM Medea	Fra	2006	107,711	113,964	334	43	24	ucc	9,415 teu
9280615	CMA CGM Mozart	Fra	2004	69,247	72,500	277	40	24	ucc	5,770 teu
9356311	CMA CGM Musca +	Gbr	2009	128,600	131,830	347	46	24	ucc	11,038 teu
9299630	CMA CGM Nabucco	Fra	2006	91,410	101,810	334	43	24	ucc	8,204 teu
9351141	CMA CGM New Jersey	Bhs	2008	54,309	65,890	294	32	25	ucc	5,042 teu
9722675	CMA CGM Niagara [S]	Mlt	2015	94,440	110,482	300	48	22	ucc	10,034 teu
9299812	CMA CGM Norma	Fra	2006	107,711	113,909	334	43	24	ucc	9,415 teu
9722687	CMA CGM Ohio [H]	Mlt	2015	94,440	110,552	300	48	22	ucc	10,034 teu
9189160	CMA CGM Okapi	Gbr	2000	16,803	22,900	185	25	19	ucc	1,748 teu: ex Mina K-03, CMA CGM Seville-03, Mina K-02, Alianca Hamburgo-01, l/a Mina K
9299628	CMA CGM Otello	Rif	2005	91,410	101,810	334	43	24	ucc	8,204 teu: l/a CMA CGM Fidelio
9399010	CMA CGM Pegasus	Mlt	2010	131,332	131,268	366	46	24	ucc	11,312 teu
9362437	CMA CGM Platon	Gbr	2007	17,594	21,263	170	27	24	ucc	1,713 teu
9280627	CMA CGM Puccini	Fra	2004	69,022	73,234	277	40	24	ucc	5,770 teu
9248124	CMA CGM Puget	Bhs	2002	49,855	58,548	282	32	24	ucc	4,367 teu
9674543	CMA CGM Rhone [C]	Mlt	2015	95,263	113,800	300	48	22	ucc	9,365 teu
9299654	CMA CGM Rigoletto	Fra	2006	107,711	114,004	334	43	24	ucc	9,415 teu
9722699	CMA CGM Rio Grande [H]	Mlt	2016	94,449	110,521	300	48	22	ucc	10,034 teu
9280637	CMA CGM Rossini	Fra	2004	65,730	73,235	277	40	24	ucc	5,770 teu
9709219	CMA CGM Saint Laurent	Gbr	2015	26,645	27,322	190	30	19	ucc	2,140 teu
9295969	CMA CGM Sambhar +	Cyp	2006	42,382	51,870	268	32	25	ucc	4,043 teu: ex Lontue-06, Araya-04, l/dn Conti Nice
9072111	CMA CGM Simba	Gbr	1994	11,062	15,166	158	23	18	ucc	1,049 teu: ex TMM Durango-05, MSC Nigeria-04, P&O Nedlloyd San Pedro-01, Kent Merchant-99, Maersk Libreville-98, Antje-97, Lanka Amila-97, Antje-94

CMA CGM Georg Forster : CMA CGM : *ARO*

IMO	name	flag	year	gt	dwt	loa	bm	kts	type	comments
9331000	CMA CGM Swordfish	Gbr	2007	54,309	65,987	294	32	25	ucc	5,052 teu
9674555	CMA CGM Tage [C]	Mlt	2015	95,263	113,800	300	48	22	ucc	9,365 teu
9722704	CMA CGM Tanya [M]	Mlt	2016	108,000	104,236	300	48	22	ucc	10,034 teu: l/d CMA CGM Saint Lawrence
9331012	CMA CGM Tarpon	Gbr	2007	54,309	65,903	294	32	25	ucc	5,042 teu
9356294	CMA CGM Thalassa +	Cyp	2008	128,600	131,938	347	46	24	ucc	11,038 teu
9674567	CMA CGM Thames [C]	Mlt	2015	95,263	113,800	300	48	22	ucc	9,365 teu
9705067	CMA CGM Tigris	Mlt	2014	95,793	113,800	300	49	22	ucc	10,622 teu
9399222	CMA CGM Titan	Mlt	2011	131,332	128,550	366	46	24	ucc	11,312 teu
9450636	CMA CGM Titus	Gbr	2011	90,931	109,021	334	43	25	ucc	8,465 teu
9199783	CMA CGM Tosca	Bhs	2006	91,410	101,818	334	43	24	ucc	8,204 teu
9705079	CMA CGM Ural [C]	Mlt	2015	95,793	113,800	300	48	22	ucc	10,622 teu
9192430	CMA CGM Utrillo *	Cyp	1999	25,777	32,274	196	30	21	ucc	2,226 teu
9706889	CMA CGM Vasco De Gama	Gbr	2015	178,228	184,700	399	54	22	ucc	17,859 teu: l/d CMA CGM Benjamin Franklin
9351139	CMA CGM Virginia	Gbr	2008	54.309	65,890	294	32	25	ucc	5,042 teu
9705081	CMA CGM Volga [C]	Mlt	2015	95.793	113,800	300	48	22	ucc	10,622 teu
9317975	CMA CGM White Shark	Gbr	2007	54,309	53,790	294	32	25	ucc	5,040 teu
9706906	CMA CGM Zheng He	Gbr	2015	178,228	185,000	399	54	22	ucc	17,859 teu
9072094	Delmas Swala	Gbr	1994	11,062	15,166	158	23	18	ucc	1,049 teu: ex Macandrews Swala-08, CMA CGM Swala-06, Elbstrom-05, Cala Puebla-04, Elbstrom-02, P&O Nedlloyd Dakar-01, Urundi-99, Elbstrom-98, UB Lion-98, Lanka Ruwan-97, Elbstrom-95
newbuildings:										
9780847		Mlt	2016			400	51		ucc	20,000 teu Hyundai Ulsan 2855 12.2016
9780859		Mlt	2016			400	51		ucc	20,000 teu Hyundai Ulsan 2856 12.2016

CMA CGM Thames : CMA CGM : *Chris Brooks*

IMO	name	flag	year	gt	dwt	loa	bm	kts	type	comments	
9780861		Nlt	2017			400	51		ucc	20,000 teu	Hyundai Ulsan 2857 02.2017
9780873		Mlt	2017			400	51		ucc	20,000 teu	Hyundai Ulsan 2858 04.2017
9780885		Mlt	2017			400	51		ucc	20,000 teu	Hyundai Ulsan 2859 05.2017
9780897		Mlt	2017			400	51		ucc	20,000 teu	Hyundai Ulsan 2860 06.2017
9776418		Mlt	2017			400	51		ucc	20,000 teu	HHIC-Phil 149 07.2017
9776420		Mlt	2017			400	51		ucc	20,000 teu	HHIC-Phil 150 11.2017
9776432		Mlt	2017			400	51		ucc	20,000 teu	HHIC-Phil 151 12.2017

* owned by subsidiary CMA Ships UK Ltd (formed 1990 as Donrich Ltd, later CMA UK Ltd to 1999, then CMA CGM UK Ltd to 2003 and CMA CGM (UK) Shipping Ltd to 2007)   + various finance houses   † chartered to Australian National Lines
[C] leased from China International Marine Containers Gp.
[H] leased from Bank of Communications/Hanyuen
[S] leased from Bank of Communications Shanghai.
[M] leased from Minsheng Financial Leasing Co., Beijing
subsidiary Cheng Lie Navigation Co Ltd, Taiwan owns six 15,000 grt container ships operating in Far East.
also see other vessels with 'CMA CGM' prefixes in index

Delmas Armement, France

funnel: *blue with white waterwheel device.* **hull:** *black with white 'DELMAS' or 'OTAL', red boot-topping.* **history:** *formed 1864 as Société Navale Delmas-Vieljeux until 1971. Acquired Navale et Commerciale Havraise Peninsulaire from CNN-Worms Group (1986), Chargeurs Réunis (1988) and amalgamated with L Martin & Cie in 1991. Later 1991 taken over by SCAC (Bollore Group) as SCAC-Delmas-Vieljeux. Acquired by CMA-CGM in 2006.* **web:** *www.delmas.com*

IMO	name	flag	year	gt	dwt	loa	bm	kts	type	comments
9225782	Delmas Keta *	Bhs	2003	26,047	30,450	196	30	21	ucc	2,226 teu: ex MOL Rainbow-08. Louis Delmas-03
9239850	Elisa Delmas **	Bhs	2002	16,916	20,979	169	27	20	ucc	1,641 teu
9239862	Flora Delmas **	Bhs	2002	16,916	21,420	169	27	20	ucc	1,641 teu
9225770	Julie Delmas *	Bhs	2002	26,047	30,453	196	30	21	ucc	2,226 teu
9220859	Kumasi *	Bhs	2001	26,061	30,450	196	30	21	ucc	2,226 teu: ex WAL Ubangi-04, Catherine Delmas-03
9220847	Marie Delmas *	Bhs	2001	26,061	30,450	196	30	21	ucc	2,226 teu
9239874	Nala Delmas **	Bhs	2002	16,916	20,944	169	27	20	ucc	1,641 teu: ex Gaby Delmas-06
9220861	Nicolas Delmas **	Bhs	2002	26,061	30,450	196	30	21	ucc	2,226 teu
7724306	Saint Roch **	Bhs	1980	16,744	24,260	187	32	18	urc	1,183 teu: ex Höegh Belle-81

* managed by CMA Ships UK Ltd or ** by Midocean (IOM) Ltd, Isle of Man

Cie. Maritime Belge S.A. Belgium

Bocimar International N.V., Belgium

funnel: *blue with blue 'B' on broad yellow band.* **hull:** *black, blue or orange with blue or red boot-topping, some with 'Bocimar' in white.*
history: *parent founded 1895 and formed from 1930 merger of Cie Belge Maritime du Congo SA and Lloyd Royal Belge SA. Armement Deppe (founded 1863) merged 1984. Acquired Merzario in 1989 and Woermann from Essberger (Deutsche Afrika-Linien) in 1990. Group taken over by Savery family in 1991. 43% share of Canmar (formed 1984) sold to CP Ships in 1993. Bocimar formed 1970.*
web: *www.cmb.be*

IMO	name	flag	year	gt	dwt	loa	bm	kts	type	comments
9737565	Bochem Luxembourg	Hkg	2015	19,950	19,950	145	24	15	tco	
9597991	CMB Adrien *	Hkg	2011	20,846	32,663	180	30	14	bbu	
9474254	CMB Ariane *	Hkg	2011	23,432	33,660	180	30	14	bbu	
9474228	CMB Boris *	Hkg	2011	23,432	33,716	180	28	14	bbu	
9597977	CMB Catrine *	Hkg	2012	20,846	32,618	180	28	14	bbu	
9559705	CMB Charlotte *	Hkg	2010	20,846	32,646	180	28	14	bbu	
9701190	CMB Chikako +	Pan	2014	34,810	61,299	200	32	14	bbu	
9457309	CMB Coralie **	Hkg	2009	32,505	53,463	190	32	14	bbu	
9559690	CMB Edouard *	Hkg	2010	20,846	32,648	180	28	14	bbu	
9588419	CMB Giulia *	Hkg	2012	22,137	23,500	180	28	14	bbu	
9474230	CMB Julliette *	Hkg	2011	23,432	33,683	180	30	14	bbu	
9474278	CMB Kristine *	Hkg	2011	23,432	33,684	180	30	14	bbu	
9474266	CMB Liliane *	Hkg	2011	23,432	33,674	180	30	14	bbu	
9474216	CMB Maé *	Hkg	2010	23,432	33,694	180	30	14	bbu	
9615171	CMB Medoc +	Pan	2012	50,633	95,746	235	38	14	bbu	
9498937	CMB Mistral *	Hkg	2009	18,499	29,130	170	27	14	bbu	ex JBU Mistral-10
9615183	CMB Pauillac *	Hkg	2012	50,625	95,707	235	38	14	bbu	
9474280	CMB Paule *	Hkg	2011	23,432	33,717	180	30	14	bbu	
9598335	CMB Pomerol +	Pan	2012	50,617	95,731	235	38	14	bbu	
9316854	CMB Sakura	Pan	2006	38,891	75,765	225	32	14	bbu	
9597989	CMB Virginie *	Hkg	2011	20,846	32,519	180	28	14	bbu	
9474199	CMB Weihei *	Hkg	2010	23,432	33,716	180	30	14	bbu	
9474242	CMB Yasmine *	Hkg	2011	23,432	33,647	180	30	14	bbu	
9558713	FMG Cloudbreak **	Hkg	2012	106,952	205,097	300	50	14	bbu	I/a Mineral Queensland
9528196	FMG Grace	Hkg	2012	106,952	205,236	300	50	14	bbu	I/a Mineral Pilbara
9528201	FMG Matilda	Hkg	2012	106,952	205,203	300	50	14	bbu	

IMO	name	flag	year	gt	dwt	loa	bm	kts	type	comments
9456680	Lake Dolphin	Bel	2011	93,695	179,418	292	45	14	bbu	
9224740	Mineral Antwerpen ‡	Pan	2003	87,495	172,424	289	45	15	bbu	
9272383	Mineral Beijing	Bel	2004	88,930	174,083	289	45	15	bbu	
9309021	Mineral Belgium	Bel	2005	88,930	173,806	289	45	14	bbu	
9264790	Mineral China	Bel	2003	88,292	171,128	289	45	14	bbu	l/a CIC Oslo
9474137	Mineral Dalian	Bel	2009	94,863	180,171	295	46	14	bbu	ex FMG Cloudbreak-12
9508392	Mineral Dragon	Bel	2008	91,373	178,062	292	45	14	bbu	
9727352	Mineral Edo +	Pan	2015	107,514	207,219	300	50	14	bbu	
9314090	Mineral Energy	Sgp	2004	90,085	180,319	289	45	14	bbu	ex Nord-Energy-16
9575668	Mineral Faith **	Hkg	2012	91,971	175,620	292	45	14	bbu	c/a Bulk Majesty
9489845	Mineral Haiku *	Pan	2010	90,423	180,242	289	45	15	bbu	
9384954	Mineral Hokkaido +	Pan	2008	90,423	180,159	289	45	15	bbu	
9748095	Mineral Hokusai +	Pan	2015	107,514	207,219	300	50	14	bbu	
9614892	Mineral Honshu **	Hkg	2012	92,727	181,408	292	45	15	bbu	
9567025	Mineral Hope **	Hkg	2012	91,971	175,591	292	45	15	bbu	c/a Bulk Charity
9314064	Mineral Kyoto	Bel	2004	90,398	180,310	289	45	15	bbu	
9345366	Mineral Kyushu	Pan	2006	90,091	180,211	289	45	14	bbu	
9374040	Mineral Shikoku *	Pan	2006	104,727	206,312	300	50	14	bbu	
9519767	Mineral New York	Bel	2010	91,971	175,841	292	45	15	bbu	
9336945	Mineral Nippon	Pan	2007	101,933	203,275	300	50	14	bbu	
9416848	Mineral Ningbo	Bel	2009	91,373	178,120	292	45	15	bbu	
9283681	Mineral Noble	Bel	2004	88,179	170,649	289	45	15	bbu	ex Mineral Kiwi-04
9413717	Mineral Oak	Hkg	2010	91,373	177,921	292	45	15	bbu	
9748100	Mineral Utamaro+	Pan	2016	107,222	207,469	300	50	14	bbu	
9519779	Mineral Stonehenge	Bel	2010	91,971	175,713	292	45	15	bbu	l/a Mineral Zhoushan
9456678	Mineral Subic	Hkg	2011	93,695	179,397	292	45	15	bbu	
9292565	Mineral Tianjin	Bel	2004	88,930	174,096	289	45	15	bbu	
newbuilding:										
9757838	Mineral Yarden		2016	90,000	180,600	292	45	14	bbu	Imabari, Hiroshima 2560

partner in Cape International Pool formed jointly with Ofer (Zodiac), Belships, Moller, Torvald Klaveness and Overseas Shipholding Corp.
* owned by Bohandymar Ltd. ** owned by Bocimar Hong Kong + chartered vessels
vessels managed by Anglo-Eastern (Antwerp) NV or Anglo-Eastern Ship Management Ltd, Hong Kong.
† managed by 28% owned Wah Kwong Ship Management, Hong Kong or ‡ by Oak Maritime (Canada) Ltd., Canada

Delphis n.v., Belgium

funnel: *blue with blue and white circle and dolphin logo on white panel or charterers colours,* **hull:** *blue with red boot topping,*
history: *founded 2004, as subsidiary of Saverco n.v., a holding company of CMB.* **web:** *www.delphis.be*

IMO	name	flag	year	gt	dwt	loa	bm	kts	type	comments
9292254	Bear Hunter	Hkg	2004	54,519	65,006	294	32	23	ucc	4,738 teu: ex Valencia Bridge-15
9293466	Buffalo Hunter	Pan	2005	54,519	64,986	294	32	23	ucc	4,738 teu: ex Victoria Bridge-15
9292242	Bull Hunter	Pan	2004	54,519	64,990	294	32	23	ucc	4,738 teu: ex Virginia Bridge-15
9439498	Cap Hamilton	Lbr	2009	41,358	51,745	262	32	24	ucc	4,255 teu: l/a CPO Boston
9440784	Cap Harriett	Lbr	2009	41,358	51,780	262	32	24	ucc	4,255 teu: l/a CPO Philadelphia
9440801	Cap Harvey	Lbr	2009	41,358	51,744	262	32	24	ucc	4,255 teu: l/a CPO Richmond
9238789	Cuckoo Hunter	Lbr	2003	39,941	50,900	264	32	24	ucc	4,253 teu: ex E.R. New York-15, CMA CGM Nilgai-11, ANL Pacific-04, CMA CGM New York-04, l/a E.R. New York
9280809	Duck Hunter	Bhs	2004	40,952	55,461	261	32	24	ucc	4,130 teu: ex RDO Harmony-15, CSAV Lirquen-14, APL Brazil-11, l/a RDO Harmony
9305635	Grouse Hunter	Hkg	2006	40,952	55,483	261	32	24	ucc	4,130 teu: ex RDO Honour-15, NYK Cosmos-14, l/a RDO Honour
9491836	Hermes Arrow	Hkg	2009	26,195	34,966	210	30	21	ucc	2,478 teu
9434905	Maersk Niagara	Hkg	2008	26,836	33,434	210	30	21	ucc	2,550 teu: l/a Poseidon Hope
9434917	Maersk Niamey	Hkg	2009	26,836	33,413	210	30	21	ucc	2,550 teu: l/a Poseidon Hero
9434929	Maersk Nejmegen	Hkg	2009	26,836	33,450	210	30	21	ucc	2,550 teu: l/a Poseidon Glory
9434931	Maersk Nimes	Hkg	2009	26,836	33,447	210	30	21	ucc	2,550 teu: l/a Poseidon Goal
9434943	Maersk Niteroi	Hkg	2009	26,836	33,411	210	30	21	ucc	2,550 teu: l/a Poseidon Faith
9446104	Maersk Nienburg	Hkg	2010	26,836	34,966	210	30	21	ucc	2,550 teu: l/a Poseidon Fame
9610157	MOL Nabila	Hkg	2014	41,286	51,916	228	37	21	ucc	3,836 teu: l/a Believer
9610169	MOL Naima	Hkg	2014	41,286	52,033	228	37	21	ucc	3,836 teu: l/a Achiever
9626041	MOL Naja	Hkg	2014	41,286	52,038	228	37	21	ucc	3,836 teu: l/a Conceiver
9626053	MOL Nala	Hkg	2014	41,286	51,950	228	37	21	ucc	3,836 teu: l/a Perceiver
9293167	Mongoose Hunter	Lbr	2005	58,289	64,519	294	32	25	ucc	4,922 teu: ex Santa Regina-15, MOL Cullinan-14, P&O Nedlloyd Heemskerck-06
9293179	Moose Hunter	Lbr	2005	58,289	64,519	294	32	25	ucc	4,922 teu: ex Santa Regula-15, MOL Caledon-14, P&O Nedlloyd Livingstone-06, l/a Santa Regula
9282974	Zim Savannah	Lbr	2004	54,626	67,170	294	32	25	ucc	5,075 teu: l/a E.R. Savannah
newbuildings:										
9763710	Delphis Bothnia	Hkg	2016	25,000	24,700	177	31	19	occ	1,900 teu Hanjin N263

CMB Virginie : Cie. Maritime Belge - Bocimar : *Chris Brooks*

Mineral Ningbo : Cie. Maritime Belge - Bocimar : *Hans Kraijenbosch*

IMO	name	flag	year	gt	dwt	loa	bm	kts	type	comments
9763722	Delphis Finland	Hkg	2016	25,000	24,700	177	31	19	occ	1,900 teu Hanjin N264
9780653	Delphis Gdansk	Hkg	2016	25,000	24,700	177	31	19	occ	1,900 teu Hanjin N265
9780665	Delphis Riga	Hkg	2016	25,000	24,700	177	31	19	occ	1,900 teu Hanjin N266

also operates small feeder, El Toro, SCI Kamal and A La Marine

Euronav N.V., Belgium

funnel: *Black, white flag with narrow red horizontal cross on broad white cross on blue disc or ** blue with gold overlapping 'GO'.*
hull: *black with white 'EURONAV', with red boot-topping.* **history:** *formed 1989 by Compagnie Nationale de Navigation (acquired 1986 by Worms Group from Elf Oil), France and Mercurius Group, Sweden. By 1995 jointly owned by CMB and CNN as Euronav Luxembourg SA. In 1998 CMB acquired 90% share of CNN, which was sold in 1999 and later demerged from CMB.*
web: *www.euronav.com*

IMO	name	flag	year	gt	dwt	loa	bm	kts	type	comments
9722924	Alex	Bel	2016	154,379	299,446	333	60	16	tcr	l/d Crude Sun
9530905	Alsace *	Grc	2012	161,177	320,350	333	60	16	tcr	
9709087	Alice	Bel	2016	154,379	299,320	333	60	15	tcr	l/d Crude Sky
9709075	Antigone	Grc	2015	154,379	299,421	330	60	15	tcr	l/a Crude Star
9290347	Ardennes Venture	Hkg	2004	161,045	318,000	333	60	16	tcr	
9230969	Artois	Atf	2001	159,456	298,330	334	60	16	tcr	
9321706	Cap Charles *	Grc	2006	81,324	158,880	274	48	14	tcr	
9229295	Cap Diamant *	Grc	2001	94,729	160,044	277	53	14	tcr	
9380738	Cap Felix	Bel	2008	81,324	158,765	274	48	14	tcr	
9128283	Cap Georges *	Grc	1998	81,148	147,443	274	48	14	tcr	
9321691	Cap Guillaume *	Grc	2006	81,324	158,889	274	48	14	tcr	
9158147	Cap Jean *	Grc	1998	81,148	146,439	274	48	14	tcr	
9330874	Cap Lara *	Grc	2007	81,324	158,826	274	48	14	tcr	
9274434	Cap Leon *	Grc	2003	81,328	159,048	274	48	14	tcr	
9321718	Cap Philippe *	Grc	2006	81,324	158,880	274	48	14	tcr	
9274446	Cap Pierre *	Grc	2004	81,328	159,048	274	48	14	tcr	
9160229	Cap Romuald *	Grc	1998	81,148	146,639	274	48	14	tcr	
9380740	Cap Theodora	Grc	2008	81,324	158,819	274	48	14	tcr	
9321720	Cap Victor *	Grc	2007	81,324	158,880	274	48	14	tcr	
9541380	Captain Michael *	Grc	2012	81,427	157,648	275	48	14	tcr	
9516117	Devon *	Grc	2011	81,427	157,642	275	48	14	tcr	
9516105	Eugenie *	Grc	2011	81,427	157,672	275	48	14	tcr	
9416692	Felicity	Bel	2009	81,247	157,667	275	48	14	tcr	
9236004	Filikon *	Grc	2002	78,845	149,989	274	48	15	tcr	ex Paros-04
9236016	Finesse *	Grc	2003	78,845	150,709	274	48	15	tcr	ex Anafi-04
9235256	Flandre	Atf	2004	159,016	305,704	332	58	15	tcr	
9416733	Fraternity	Bel	2009	81,427	157,667	275	48	14	tcr	
9457952	Hakata	Atf	2010	159,806	302,550	333	60	16	tcr	ex Maersk Hakata-15
9398084	Hakone *	Grc	2010	159,806	302,624	333	60	14	tcr	ex Maersk Hakone-14
9377420	Hirado	Grc	2011	159,806	302,550	333	60	14	tcr	ex Maersk Hirado-15
9457543	Hojo	Bel	2013	156,990	302,965	330	60	14	tcr	ex Maersk Hojo-14
9588392	Ilma	Bel	2012	160,716	318,477	333	60	14	tcr	ex Maersk Ilma-14, l/a Vasant J. Sheth
9529956	Ingrid	Bel	2012	160,716	318,478	333	60	14	tcr	ex Maersk Ingrid-14, l/a Maneklal Ujamshi Sheth
9529968	Iris	Bel	2012	160,716	318,478	333	60	14	tcr	ex Maersk Isabella-14, l/a Ardeshir H. Bhiwandiwalla-14,
9530890	Maria *	Grc	2012	81,427	157,523	275	48	15	tcr	
9323948	Nautic	Sgp	2008	159,911	307,284	333	58	16	tcr	ex Maersk Nautica-14
9312494	Nautilus	Mhl	2006	159,911	307,284	333	58	16	tcr	ex Maersk Nautilus-14
9312509	Navarin	Mhl	2007	159,911	307,284	333	58	16	tcr	ex Maersk Navarin-14
9323936	Nectar	Sgp	2008	159,911	307,284	333	58	16	tcr	ex Maersk Nectar-14
9312511	Neptun	Sgp	2007	159,911	307,284	333	58	16	tcr	ex Maersk Neptune-14
9358292	Newton	Bel	2009	159,911	307,284	333	58	16	tcr	ex Maersk Newton-14
9358280	Noble	Bel	2008	159,911	307,284	333	58	16	tcr	ex Maersk Noble-14
9322293	Nucleus	Mhl	2007	159,911	307,284	333	58	16	tcr	ex Maersk Nucleus-14
9537757	Sandra	Rif	2011	164,641	323,183	332	60	14	tcr	ex Maersk Sandra-14
9537745	Sara	Fra	2011	164,641	323,182	332	60	14	tcr	ex Maersk Sara-14
9537769	Simone	Bel	2012	164,641	323,182	332	60	14	tcr	ex Maersk Simone-14
9537771	Sonia	Bel	2012	164,641	322,200	332	60	14	tcr	ex Maersk Sonia-14
9235268	TI Europe	Bel	2002	234,006	441,561	380	68	16	tcr	ex Hellespont Tara-04
9290086	TI Hellas	Bel	2005	161,127	319,254	333	60	16	tcr	ex Chrysanthemum-05
9230907	TI Topaz	Bel	2002	161,135	319,430	333	60	16	tcr	ex Crude Topaz-05, Oriental Topaz-05

newbuildings:

IMO	name	flag	year	gt	dwt	loa	bm	kts	type	comments
9722936		Bel	2016	154,000	308,000	333	60	16	tcr	l/d Crude Gulf Hyundai Gunsan 2728

*vessels managed by Euronav Ship Management SAS, France or * by Euronav Ship Management (Hellas) Ltd, Greece and operating mainly in Tankers International Pool formed jointly with Klaus Oldendorff, Sanko, Overseas Shipholding Group, Shinyo, Petronas, Oak Maritime, Wah Kwong and Essar Shipping.*

IMO	name	flag	year	gt	dwt	loa	bm	kts	type	comments

Cobelfret N.V.   Belgium

funnel: *yellow with red 'C' on white diamond on blue band.* **hull:** *black, grey or red with green or red boot-topping.* **history:** *formed 1928.* **web:** *www.cobelfret.com*

IMO	name	flag	year	gt	dwt	loa	bm	kts	type	comments
9738947	Lowlands Amstel *	Pan	2015	34,810	61,117	200	32	14	bbu	
9705134	Lowlands Audacity *	Mhl	2016	94,000	180,000	292	45	14	bbu	l/a Glory Max
9609665	Lowlands Boreas	Mlt	2013	24,177	37,144	180	30	14	bbu	
9400916	Lowlands Brabo *	Pan	2010	20,238	32,280	178	28	14	bbu	
9660097	Lowlands Breeze *	Pan	2013	34,815	61,430	200	32	14	bbu	
9227003	Lowlands Brilliance	Mlt	2002	85,906	169,631	289	45	14	bbu	
9304289	Lowlands Camellia *	Pan	2006	40,042	76,807	225	32	14	bbu	
9728136	Lowlands Comfort *	Pan	2016	43,013	81,845	229	32	14	bbu	
9345611	Lowlands Erica *	Pan	2007	89,603	176,862	289	45	16	bbu	
9461154	Lowlands Kamsar *	Pan	2010	43,012	82,206	229	32	14	bbu	

TI Hellas : Cie. Maritime Belge - Euronav : *ARO*

Lowlands Amstel : Cobelfret n.v. : *Nico Kemps*

IMO	name	flag	year	gt	dwt	loa	bm	kts	type	comments
9218777	Lowlands Longevity	Bel	2001	86,848	173,018	289	45	15	bbu	
9304239	Lowlands Maine *	Pan	2005	40,039	76,784	225	32	14	bbu	
9724192	Lowlands Nello	Mlt	2015	43,439	82,014	229	32	14	bbu	
9317559	Lowlands Opal *	Pan	2007	30,678	55,381	190	32	14	bbu	
9271614	Lowlands Orchid *	Pan	2005	88,594	176,193	289	45	15	bbu	
9520675	Lowlands Patrasche *	Mhl	2013	32.365	58,108	190	32	14	bbu	
9303845	Lowlands Phoenix *	Pan	2004	89,543	177,036	289	45	14	bbu	
9586813	Lowlands Prosperity	Sgp	2012	93,684	279,895	292	45	14	bbu	ex Houheng 3-14
9609653	Lowlands Saguenay	Mlt	2013	24,177	37,150	180	30	14	bbu	
9491587	Lowlands Scheldt	Pan	2011	21,483	33,178	177	29	14	bbu	
9581758	Lowlands Serenity *	Pan	2011	92,752	181,458	292	45	15	bbu	
9590826	Lowlands Sunrise *	Pan	2011	92,752	181,458	292	45	15	bbu	
9586801	Lowlands Tenacity	Mlt	2011	93,684	179,929	292	45	14	bbu	ex Houheng 2-15
newbuilding:										
9705134	Lowlands Audacity	Mhl	2016	94,000	180,000	292	45	14	bbu	l/a Glory Max

operated by Cobelfret Bulk Carriers NV, Belgium. * *on time-charter from various Philippine, Singapore and Japanese owners.*

ConocoPhillips Polar Tankers Inc. U.S.A.

funnel: *polar bear and red sun logo on broad white band over narrow black band over vertical black & white stripes., narrow black top.*
hull: *blue with red or grey boot-topping.* **history:** *founded as Continental Oil Co in 1875 on merger of Marland Oil Co and Continental Oil and Transportation Co until renamed Conoco Inc in 1979 and amalgamated with Phillips Petroleum Co in 2002.*
web: *www.polartankers.conocophillips.com*

IMO	name		flag	year	gt	dwt	loa	bm	kts	type	comments
9244063	Polar Adventure (2)		Usa	2004	85,387	141,739	273	46	16	tcr	
9206114	Polar Discovery (2)		Usa	2003	85,387	140,320	273	46	16	tcr	
9193551	Polar Endeavour (2)		Usa	2001	85,387	141,740	273	46	16	tcr	l/a Arco Endeavour
9250660	Polar Enterprise (2)		Usa	2005	85,387	141,739	273	46	16	tcr	
9193563	Polar Resolution (2)		Usa	2002	85,387	141,737	273	46	16	tcr	

vessels owned and managed by subsidiary Polar Tankers Inc. (formed 1980 as ARCO Marine Inc until 2000 when acquired by Phillips Petroleum

Conti Reederei GmbH Germany

history: *founded 1970 as Cosima Reederei, restyled Conti Reederei in 1979. Holds 67.5% shares of BBG-Bremer and 45% of NSB Niederelbe; these companies have the management responsibility of owned vessels*

BBG-Bremer Bereederungs GmbH & Co. KG, Germany

funnel: *White with blue 'BBG' on white diamond on blue band or charterers colours.* **hull:** *blue or black with red boot-topping.* **history:** *founded 1984 as Frigomaris Shipping GmbH, taking over Ganymed Schiffahrts in 1985, renamed Frigomaris Reefer Schiffahrt to 1990, then Ganymed Shipping GmbH to 2003. Associated with Conti Holdings* **web:** *www.bbg-shipmanagement.com*

IMO	name		flag	year	gt	dwt	loa	bm	kts	type	comments
9519286	Achat *		Lbr	2010	32,987	56,969	190	32	14	bbu	ex Pos Achat -13
9519298	Alexandrit *		Lbr	2010	32,987	57,015	190	32	14	bbu	ex Pos Alexandrit-13
9519303	Almandin		Lbr	2010	32,987	56,988	190	32	14	bbu	ex Pos Almandin-13

Lowlands Sunrise : Cobelfret n.v. : *Chris Brooks*

IMO	name	flag	year	gt	dwt	loa	bm	kts	type	comments
9519315	Amazonit	Lbr	2010	32,987	57,015	190	32	14	bbu	ex Pos Amazonit-13
9519339	Amethyst	Lbr	2011	32,987	56,889	190	32	14	bbu	ex Pos Amethyst
9519341	Ametrin	Lbr	2010	32,987	56,855	190	32	14	bbu	ex Pos Ametrin-13
9551674	Aquamarin	Lbr	2011	32,987	56,969	190	32	14	bbu	ex Pos Aquamarin-13
9551686	Aragonit	Lbr	2012	32,987	56,757	190	32	14	bbu	ex Pos Aragonit-13 , l/a Conti Aragonit
9551698	Aventurin	Lbr	2012	32,987	56,778	190	32	14	bbu	ex Pos Aventurin-13
9551703	Azurit	Lbr	2012	32,987	56,771	190	32	14	bbu	ex Pos Azurit-13
9503275	Conti Flint	Lbr	2012	33,044	57,000	190	32	14	bbu	
9503287	Conti Fuchsit	Lbr	2012	33,044	57,000	190	32	14	bbu	
9476525	Conti Jade	Lbr	2012	51,265	93,252	229	38	15	bbu	
9476537	Conti Japsis	Lbr	2012	51,265	93,266	229	38	15	bbu	
9452634	Conti Peridot	Lbr	2011	33,036	57,001	190	32	14	bbu	
9452658	Conti Lapislazuli	Lbr	2011	33,036	57,001	190	32	14	bbu	
9452660	Conti Larimar	Lbr	2011	33,036	57,075	190	32	14	bbu	
9473274	Conti Saphir *	Lbr	2010	41,074	75,200	225	32	14	bbu	
9473315	Conti Selenit *	Lbr	2010	41,074	75,200	225	32	14	bbu	
9473341	Conti Spinell	Lbr	2011	41,074	75,200	225	32	14	bbu	
9474620	Tansanit	Lbr	2011	51,195	92,776	229	38	15	bbu	ex Pos Tansanit-13, c/a Conti Tansanit
9474632	Topas	Lbr	2011	51,195	92,655	229	38	15	bbu	ex Pos Topas-13, l/a Conti Topas
9474618	Tuerkis	Lbr	2012	51,195	92,759	229	38	15	bbu	ex Pos Tuerkis-13, l/a Conti Tuerkis
9474644	Turmalin	Lbr	2012	51,195	92,750	229	38	15	bbu	ex Pos Turmalin-13, l/a Conti Turmalin
9699347	Nautical Elizabeth **	Lbr	2015	36,324	63,537	200	32	14	bbu	
9699036	Nautical Hilary **	Lbr	2015	36,324	63,531	200	32	14	bbu	
9699359	Nautical Jennifer **	Lbr	2015	36,324	63,495	200	32	14	bbu	
9699311	Nautical Loredana **	Lbr	2015	36,324	63,556	200	32	14	bbu	
9699361	Nautical Lucia **	Lbr	2016	36,324	63,548	200	32	14	bbu	
9699373	Nautical Marie **	Lbr	2015	36,324	63,529	200	32	14	bbu	
9699335	Nautical Runi **	Lbr	2015	36,324	63,577	200	32	14	bbu	
9699323	Nautical Sif **	Lbr	2015	36,324	63,549	200	32	14	bbu	

*managed for Conti Reederei (Conti Holding GmbH) : ** managed for Nautical Bulk Holding Ltd., Bermuda*

NSB Niederelbe Schiffahrts GmbH & Co. KG, Germany

funnel: *blue with blue 'NSB' on white diamond or blue 'N' on square on broad white band or charterers colours.* **hull:** *black, dark blue or dark grey with red boot-topping.* **history:** *formed 1982 and associated with W. Harms GmbH & Co KG and Conti Holding GmbH & Co KG.* **web:** *www.reederei-nsb.com*

IMO	name	flag	year	gt	dwt	loa	bm	kts	type	comments
9221815	Buxcliff **	Pmd	2001	72,760	79,501	300	40	26	ucc	6,456 teu: ex CMA CGM Verlaine-12, l/a Buxcliff
9221827	Buxcoast **	Pmd	2001	72,760	79,559	300	40	26	ucc	6,546 teu: CMA CGM Voltaire-12, l/a Buxcoast
9235828	Buxcontact	Deu	2002	25,375	33,864	207	30	21	ucc	2,478 teu: ex CMA CGM Pacifico-11, APL Osaka-08, Cap Ferrato-06
9150212	Buxfavourite **	Lbr	1997	25,713	34,083	206	30	21	ucc	2,468 teu: ex CSCL Yingkou-03, Sea Puma-01, Buxfavourite-98
9150195	Buxhansa **	Lbr	1998	25,713	33,995	206	30	21	ucc	2,468 teu: ex ANL Esprit-09, CMA CGM Falcon-04, CSCL Nantong-03, Sea Leopard-01, Buxhansa-98
9377133	Buxharmony *	Lbr	2007	28,050	38,070	215	30	22	ucc	2,702 teu: ex Maruba Europa-07, l/a Buxharmony
9235816	Buxlink	Lbr	2002	25,375	33,817	207	30	23	ucc	2,470 teu: ex APL Jebel Ali-08, Buxlink-06, P&O Nedlloyd Hunter Valley-05
9377145	Buxmelody **	Lbr	2008	28,050	38,092	215	30	22	ucc	2,702 teu: Maruba Maxima-10, l/a Buxmelody
9248162	Chicago	Deu	2003	65,918	68,037	278	40	26	ucc	5,752 teu: ex Hanjin Chicago-14
9354923	CMA CGM Vela *	Deu	2008	128,600	131,831	347	46	24	ucc	10,960 teu: l/a Conti Jupiter
9391361	Conti Agulhas	Lbr	2008	23,403	37,606	184	27	15	tco	
9286255	Conti Annapurna *	Mlt	2004	90,745	101,906	334	43	25	ucc	8,238 teu: ex Pacific Link-16
9357119	Conti Arabella *	Lbr	2007	22,801	30,562	204	28	22	ucc	2,710 teu: ex CMA CGM Fortuna-12, l/a Conti Arabella
9248136	Conti Basel	Deu	2003	65,918	68,200	279	40	26	ucc	5,752 teu: ex Hanjin Basel-13, Hanjin Lisbon-03
9391373	Conti Benguela	Lbr	2008	23,403	37,606	184	27	15	tco	
9200677	Conti Canberra	Deu	1999	66,278	68,824	279	40	26	ucc	5,618 teu: ex Hanjin Amsterdam-15, l/a Conti Canberra
9200689	Conti Darwin	Deu	1999	66,278	68,996	279	40	26	ucc	5,618 teu: ex Hanjin Copenhagen-16, Conti Darwin-99
9357092	Conti Elektra	Lbr	2007	22,801	30,607	204	28	21	ucc	2,127 teu: ex Maruba Africa-10, l/a Conti Elektra
9391385	Conti Equator	Lbr	2008	23,403	37,527	184	27	15	tco	
9286231	Conti Everest *	Mlt	2004	90,745	101,662	334	43	25	ucc	8,238 teu: ex CMA CGM Hugo-15, l/a Conti Everest

IMO	name	flag	year	gt	dwt	loa	bm	kts	type	comments
9235103	Conti Gothenburg	Pmd	2002	65,131	68,063	275	40	25	ucc	5,551 teu: ex Hanjin Gothenburg-15, CMA CGM Seattle-09, I/a Conti Gothenburg
9391397	Conti Greenland	Lbr	2008	23,403	37,606	184	27	15	tco	
9391402	Conti Guinea	Lbr	2008	23,403	37,554	184	27	15	tco	
9235098	Conti Helsinki *	Pmd	2002	65,131	68,045	275	40	25	ucc	5,551 teu: ex Hanjin Helsinki-15, Helsinki-12, Hanjin Helsinki-11
9391414	Conti Humboldt	Lbr	2008	23,403	37,602	184	27	15	tco	
9222285	Conti Lyon	Deu	2001	73,172	77,946	300	40	26	ucc	6,627 teu: ex CMA CGM Baudelaire-15, Conti Lyon-01
9248150	Conti Madrid *	Pmd	2003	65,918	67,979	279	40	26	ucc	5,752 teu: ex Hanjin Madrid-14
9200718	Conti Melbourne *	Deu	2000	66,278	68,834	278	40	26	ucc	5,618 teu: ex Hanjin Ottawa-15, Conti Melbourne-00
9222273	Conti Paris	Deu	2001	73,172	77,941	300	40	26	ucc	6,627 teu: ex CMA CGM Balzac-15, Conti Paris-01
9357080	Conti Salome	Lbr	2007	22,801	30,573	204	28	21	ucc	2,127 teu
9200706	Conti Stockholm	Deu	2000	66,278	68,819	279	40	26	ucc	5,618 teu: ex Hanjin Athens-14, YM Athens-05, Hanjin Athens-03, Conti Fremantle-00
9293765	Ever Champion *	Deu	2005	90,449	100,949	334	43	25	ucc	8,073 teu
9293777	Ever Charming *	Deu	2005	90,465	100,887	334	43	25	ucc	8,073 teu
9293791	Ever Chilvary *	Deu	2006	90,465	100,902	334	43	25	ucc	8,073 teu
9293818	Ever Conquest *	Deu	2006	90,465	100,909	334	43	25	ucc	8,073 teu
8614194	Frontier	Lbr	1987	10,811	13,464	147	23	15	ucc	1,022 teu: ex Doria-07, ANL Pioneer-04, MSC Kiwi-02, Everett Express-01, Doria-00, OOCL Admiral-98, Doria-97, Sea-Land Mexico-94, Doria-94, Contship Asia-91, Ocean Asia-88, Doria-88
9402562	Gaschem Nordsee	Deu	2009	13,878	18,846	156	23	17	lpg	17,000 m³
9402574	Gaschem Pacific	Deu	2009	13,879	18,919	156	23	17	lpg	17,000 m³
9290488	Hanjin Baltimore *	Deu	2005	83,133	92,964	300	43	24	ucc	7,471 teu
9290464	Hanjin Boston *	Deu	2005	83,133	92,964	300	43	24	ucc	7,471 teu
9295220	Hanjin Dallas *	Deu	2005	83,133	92,964	300	43	24	ucc	7,471 teu
9215646	Hanjin Geneva *	Deu	2000	65,918	68,263	279	40	26	ucc	5,752 teu: ex Cosco Tianjin-05, Hanjin Geneva-03, Conti Porto-00
9290476	Hanjin Miami *	Deu	2005	83,133	92,964	300	43	24	ucc	7,471 teu
9215634	Hanjin Vienna *	Deu	2000	65,918	68,263	279	40	26	ucc	5,752 teu: ex CMA CGM Vancouver-09, Hanjin Vienna-09, Conti Lissabon-00
9295218	Hanjin Yantian *	Deu	2005	82,794	92,964	300	43	24	ucc	7,471 teu
9293789	Hatsu Courage *	Deu	2005	90,449	100,936	334	43	25	ucc	8,073 teu
9293820	Hatsu Crystal *	Deu	2006	90,449	100,882	334	43	25	ucc	8,073 teu
9293806	Ital Contessa *	Deu	2006	90,465	101,007	334	43	25	ucc	8,073 teu: I/a LT Contessa
9248148	Lisbon	Pmd	2003	65,918	67,979	279	40	26	ucc	5,752 teu: ex Hanjin Lisbon-14
9293753	LT Cortesia *	Deu	2005	90,449	100,863	334	43	25	ucc	8,073 teu
9225653	MSC Alessia	Deu	2001	75,590	85,891	304	40	25	ucc	6,732 teu
9320441	MSC Carouge	Pmd	2007	62,700	79,403	283	40	24	ucc	6,336 teu: ex Buxwind-16, MSC Carouge-14, I/a Buxpost: wid-16
9349801	MSC Cordoba	Lbr	2008	50,963	63,428	275	32	24	ucc	4,860 teu: I/a Conti Cordoba
9225615	MSC Flaminia	Mlt	2001	75,590	85,823	304	40	24	ucc	6,732 teu: rbt 2014, I/a Buxclipper
9320427	MSC Geneva	Pmd	2006	62,702	79,403	283	40	24	ucc	6,336 teu: I/a Buxsong: wid-15
9225641	MSC Ilona	Deu	2001	75,590	85,890	304	40	25	ucc	6,732 teu: I/a Buxcomet
9320398	MSC Lausanne **	Mlt	2005	62,702	79,403	283	40	24	ucc	6,336 teu: ex Buxhai-15, MSC Lausanne-13, I/a Buxhai, wid-15
9349796	MSC Monterey	Lbr	2007	50,963	63,300	283	32	24	ucc	4,860 teu: I/a Buxvillage
9150183	MSC Natalia **	Lbr	1997	40,465	49,238	259	32	23	ucc	3,961 teu: ex Buxtaurus-14, Kohala-11, Buxtaurus-10, Ville de Taurus-10
9150200	MSC Patricia **	Lbr	1997	40,465	49,308	259	32	23	ucc	3,962 teu: ex Buxstar-14, ANL Georgia-06, Ville de Mimosa-04
9286243	MSC Texas *	Mlt	2004	90,745	101,898	334	43	25	ucc	8,238 teu
9256535	Queen Zenobia	Lbr	2002	16,770	19,621	156	25	19	lpg	22,952 m³
9410648	Sigma Integrity †	Lbr	2010	57,221	105,291	244	42	15	tco	ex Alpine Alaska-14, I/d Conti Alaska
9410650	Sigma Triumph †	Lbr	2010	57,221	105,291	244	42	15	tco	ex Alpine Athelia-14 I/d Conti Madagaskar
9200691	X-Press Annapurna **	Deu	2000	66,278	68,790	279	40	26	ucc	5,618 teu: ex Hanjin Brussels-15
9400112	Zim San Francisco	Mlt	2009	50,963	63,355	275	32	24	ucc	4,860 teu
9400136	Zim Ontario	Mlt	2009	50,963	63,350	275	32	24	ucc	4,860 teu

newbuildings: 4 x 5,000teu df ucc [Jiangsu Sainty (2016 – 2017)] + 5 options [announced 08:2014], 3 x 74,000dwt LR1 tco
* managed for associated Conti Reederei (Conti Holding GmbH & Co KG – www.conti-grupp.de) or ** for Gebab Konzeptions-und Emissions
† managed by Heidmar Inc. (Sigma Pool)
* GmbH. Also see United Product Tanker (UPT) pool (under Schoeller Holdings), BBG-Bremer GmbH & Co KG and Martime–Gesellschaft GmbH*

IMO	name	flag	year	gt	dwt	loa	bm	kts	type	comments

Costamare Shipping Co. S.A.

Greece

funnel: *blue with black top or charterers colours.* **hull:** *grey or black with red boot-topping.* **history:** *formed 1975. subsidiary, Ciel Shipmanagement S.A. founded 2001.* **web:** *www.costamare.com*

IMO	name	flag	year	gt	dwt	loa	bm	kts	type	comments
9222467	Areopolis	Lbr	2000	25,630	33,694	208	30	21	ucc	2,474 teu: ex E.R. Lubeck-14, CSCL Fuzhou-08, I/a E.R. Lubeck
9226815	Arkadia	Lbr	2001	15,988	20,700	170	25	16	ucc	1,262 teu: ex Hansa Kristiansand-15, Zim Santos-11, MOL Focus-08, Hansa Kristiansand-07, Kota Machan-03, Hansa Kristiansand-02
9308508	Cosco Beijing	Mlt	2006	109,149	107,504	351	43	25	ucc	9,383 teu
9305570	Cosco Guangzhou	Mlt	2006	109,149	107,526	351	43	25	ucc	9,383 teu
9308510	Cosco Hellas	Mlt	2006	109,149	107,483	351	43	25	ucc	9,383 teu
9305582	Cosco Ningbo	Mlt	2006	109,149	107,492	351	43	25	ucc	9,383 teu
9305594	Cosco Yantian	Mlt	2006	109,149	107,498	351	43	25	ucc	9,383 teu
9179816	Elafonisos	Lbr	1999	25,705	33,843	208	30	21	ucc	2,526 teu: ex Spirit of Luck-14, Estebroker-13, CSAV Trinidad-08, Hanjin Dubai-07, Trade Bravery-05, TPL Merchant-02, Lykes Crusader-01, TMM Quetzel-01, I/a Widukind
9247546	Ensenada	Lbr	2001	66,332	67,170	279	40	25	ucc	5,576 teu: ex Ensenada Express-15, Bremen Bridge-13, YM Bridge-06, Bremen Bridge-04
9200823	Halifax Express **	Hkg	2000	54,437	66,818	294	32	24	ucc	4,843 teu; ex New York Express-12
9157698	Itea	Lbr	1998	39,582	48,304	258	32	24	ucc	3,842 teu: ex MSC Itea-16, Kyparissia-14, Bunga Raya Satu-12
8906731	Karmen *	Lbr	1991	37,209	47,230	236	32	21	ucc	3,029 teu: ex Japan Sea-10, Zim Japan-07, Japan Sea-04, Zim Japan-04
9248679	Lakonia **	Hkg	2004	28,270	33,282	213	32	23	ucc	2,586 teu: ex Theodor Storm-14, TS Nagoya,12, Theodor Storm-10
9107887	Maersk Kawasaki	Grc	1997	81,488	90,456	318	43	25	ucc	7,908 teu: ex Kirsten Maersk-07
9196840	Maersk Kobe	Grc	2000	74,661	81,584	304	40	25	ucc	6,252 teu: ex Safmarine Himalaya-07, Sealand Virginia-03
9085560	Maersk Kokura	Grc	1997	81,488	84,900	318	43	25	ucc	7,908 teu: ex Katrine Maersk-08
9085522	Maersk Kure	Grc	1996	81,488	82,135	318	43	25	ucc	7,908 teu: ex Regina Maersk-07
8906743	Marina *	Mlt	1992	37,209	47,230	236	32	21	ucc	2,402 teu: ex Zim Hong Kong-11
9142942	Messini	Lbr	1997	25,499	34,167	200	30	21	ucc	2,458 teu: ex Pembroke-12, Kota Pahlawan-09, CMA CGM Emerald-04, Pembroke Senator-03, P&O Nedlloyd Fos-01, ECL Europa-99, Pembroke Senator-99
9605267	MSC Ajaccio	Grc	2014	94,402	112,230	300	48	22	ucc	9,403 teu
9605279	MSC Amalfi	Grc	2014	94,402	112,359	300	48	22	ucc	9,403 teu
9618305	MSC Athens	Grc	2013	95,390	110,853	300	48	22	ucc	8,827 teu
9618317	MSC Athos	Grc	2013	95,390	110,875	300	48	22	ucc	8,827 teu

MSC Ajaccio : Costamare Shipping Co. : *ARO*

IMO	name	flag	year	gt	dwt	loa	bm	kts	type	comments
9605255	MSC Azov	Mlt	2014	94,402	112,434	300	48	22	ucc	9,403 teu
9244946	MSC Kalamata	Hkg	2003	74,656	81,094	304	40	25	ucc	6,246 teu: ex Maersk Kalamata-16
9244934	MSC Kingston	Hkg	2003	74,661	81,183	304	40	25	ucc	6,252 teu: ex Maersk Kingston-16, Safmarine Antwerp-08, l/a Maersk Kobe
9244922	MSC Kolkata	Hkg	2003	74,656	81,577	304	40	25	ucc	6,246 teu: Maersk Kolkata-16
9157703	MSC Koroni	Lbr	1998	39,582	48,244	258	32	24	ucc	3,842 teu: Koroni-14, Bunga Raya Dua-12
8613310	MSC Mandraki	Grc	1988	52,191	60,639	294	32	23	ucc	4,437 teu: ex Maersk Mandraki-08, Marit Maersk-04
9256755	MSC Methoni *	Lbr	2003	73,819	85,824	303	40	24	ucc	6,408 teu: ex MSC Viviana-11
8613308	MSC Mykonos	Grc	1988	52,191	60,639	294	32	23	ucc	4,437 teu: ex Maersk Mykonos-09, Marchen Maersk-05
9007817	MSC Namibia II *	Lbr	1991	23,953	31,829	181	31	18	ucc	1,928 teu: ex Maersk Vermont-11, Endeavour-06, Ibn Khaldoun-97, China Sea-94, CMB Drive-91
8907931	MSC Pylos *	Lbr	1991	27,103	29,651	178	32	18	ucc	1,848 teu: ex Oranje-11, Safmarine Oranje-11, Oranje-05, Safmarine Oranje-04, S.A. Oranje-00, Oranje-96, Afrika-91
9007831	MSC Reunion *	Lbr	1992	23,953	31,829	181	31	18	ucc	1,928 teu: ex MSC Sudan II-11, Maersk Maine-11, Enterprise-06, Ibn Zuhr-97, CMB Dawn-92
9275634	MSC Romanos **	Hkg	2003	54,881	68,209	294	32	23	ucc	5,048 teu: ex MSC Linzie-11
9007829	MSC Sierra II *	Lbr	1991	23,953	31,829	181	31	18	ucc	1,928 teu: ex Maersk Maryland-11, Endurance-06, Ibn Jubayr-97, CMB Dolphin-91
9243306	MSC Ulsan **	Hkg	2002	40,108	51,020	258	32	24	ucc	4,132 teu
9400289	Navarino	Mlt	2010	91,354	102,303	335	43	26	ucc	8,531 teu: ex Hyundai Navarino-12, MSC Navarino-11, l/a Carmen
9200811	Oakland Express **	Hkg	2000	54,437	66,781	294	32	24	ucc	4,843 teu: ex Kuala Lumpur Express-08
9152583	Padma **	Lbr	1998	16,927	21,563	168	27	19	ucc	1,645 teu; ex X-Press Padma-15,Hansa Caledonia-13, Maersk Malaga-07, Hansa Caledonia-03, CSAV Suape-98, Hansa Caledonia-98
9071272	Petalidi †	Lbr	1993	10,742	14,111	163	22	17	ucc	1,162 teu: ex Austria-13, Zim Houston III-08, Lukas-99, Kaedi-99, Kano-98, Lukas-98
9117181	Prosper **	Lbr	1996	17,287	22,183	175	27	20	ucc	1,684 teu: ex Forever Prosperity-11, Montania-09, YM Jakarta-06, Montania-06
9197545	Sealand Illinois	Mlt	2000	74,661	81,584	304	40	25	ucc	6,252 teu
9196864	Sealand Michigan	Mlt	2000	74,583	81,584	304	40	25	ucc	6,252 teu
9196838	Sealand New York	Mlt	2000	74,661	81,584	304	40	25	ucc	6,252 teu
9196852	Sealand Washington	Mlt	2000	74,661	81,584	304	40	25	ucc	6,252 teu
9200809	Singapore Express **	Hkg	2000	54,415	66,793	294	32	24	ucc	4,890 teu
9216092	Stadt Lübeck	Pan	2001	13,764	16,764	155	25	19	ucc	1,040 teu: ex New Confidence-10, l/a Stadt Lübeck
9628154	Valor	Mlt	2013	95,390	110,875	300	48	22	ucc	8,827 teu
9628166	Value	Mlt	2013	95,390	110,875	300	48	22	ucc	8,827 teu
9628178	Valiant	Mlt	2013	95,390	110,875	300	48	22	ucc	8,827 teu
9628180	Valence	Mlt	2013	95,390	110,875	300	48	22	ucc	8,827 teu
9628192	Vantage	Mlt	2013	95,390	110,857	300	48	22	ucc	8,827 teu
9260914	Venetiko	Lbr	2003	66,462	67,009	280	40	25	ucc	5,928 teu: ex Ace Ireland-13, APL Ireland-12
9111486	Zagora *	Mlt	1995	10,795	14,100	163	23	17	ucc	1,162 teu: ex CMA CGM Belem-04, Hasselwerder-02, CMBT Oceania-00, Hasselwerder-96
9231810	Zim New York **	Hkg	2002	53,453	62,740	294	32	24	ucc	4,839 teu: ex China Sea-06, Zim New York-04
9280847	Zim Piraeus **	Hkg	2004	53,453	62,740	294	32	24	ucc	5,042 teu: ex Yangtze Star-06, Zim Piraeus-05
9231822	Zim Shanghai **	Hkg	2002	53,453	66,597	294	32	24	ucc	4,839 teu

newbuildings:

IMO	name	flag	year	gt	dwt	loa	bm	kts	type	comments
9728916	Triton		2016	150,000	155,000	368	51	22	ucc	14,354 teu Samsung 2121 Q2 2016
9728928	Titan		2016	150,000	155,000	368	51	22	ucc	14,354 teu Samsung 2122 Q2 2016
9728930	Thalos		2016	150,000	155,000	368	51	22	ucc	14,354 teu Samsung 2123 Q3 2016
9728942	Tauros		2016	150,000	155,000	368	51	22	ucc	14,354 teu Samsung 2124 Q3 2016
9728954	Theseus		2016	150,000	155,000	368	51	22	ucc	14,354 teu Samsung 2125 Q3 2016
9706190				112,300	126,368				ucc	11,010 teu Hanjin Subic 113 Q2 2016

IMO	name	flag	year	gt	dwt	loa	bm	kts	type	comments
9706205				112,300	126,368				ucc	11,010 teu Hanjin Subic 114 Q2 2016
9727613				112,300	126,638				ucc	11,010 teu Hanjin Subic 115 Q2 2016
9727625				112,300	126,638				ucc	11,010 teu Hanjin Subic 116 Q2 2016
				112,300	126,638				ucc	11,010 teu Hanjin Subic 152 Q4 2016
									ucc	3,800 teu Jiangsu New Yangzi 1206
									ucc	3,800 teu Jiangsu New Yangzi 1207

new buildings Samsung and Hanjin vessels for Evergreen charter
2 x 3,800teu containerships [Jiangsu New Jiangzi SY. (2018)] for Hamburg-Süd 7-year charter [reported 11.2015] originally HS option
possibly ordering 20,000teu for MOL 2015
* owned or managed by associated Ciel Shipmanagement SA, Greece (formed 2001) or ** by Shanghai Costamare Ship Management Co Ltd,
China (founded 2005)

d'Amico Societa di Navigazione SpA　　　　　　　　Italy

funnel: *yellow with blue 8-pointed star.* **hull:** *grey or black with white or yellow 'd'AMICO', red boot-topping.* **history:** *origins date back to 1936, present company founded in Rome 1952.* **web:** *www.damicoship.com*

IMO	name	flag	year	gt	dwt	loa	bm	kts	type	comments
9585651	Cielo di Dublino	Ita	2011	23,758	37,064	183	28	14	bbu	
9341512	Cielo di Guangzhou	Ita	2006	25,507	38,875	168	29	14	tco	
9241803	Cielo di Roma	Ita	2003	25,382	40,096	176	31	15	tco	
9585663	Cielo di San									
	Francisco	Ita	2011	23,758	37,056	183	28	15	bbu	
9287168	Medi Baltimore	Ita	2005	39,976	76,469	225	32	14	bbu	
9377688	Medi Bangkok　*	Sgp	2006	29,986	53,466	189	32	14	bbu	
9279549	Medi Cagliari	Ita	2004	38,877	75,772	225	32	14	bbu	ex Medi Vancouver-07
9708746	Medi Hakata　+	Pan	2014	32,714	58,078	190	32	14	bbu	
9301043	Medi Hong Kong	Ita	2006	42,887	82,790	229	32	14	bbu	
9310642	Medi Lausanne　*	Sgp	2006	42,887	83,002	229	32	14	bbu	
9340491	Medi Lisbon	Sgp	2006	32,379	58,710	190	32	14	bbu	
9660607	Medi Manila　+	Pan	2014	32,370	57,903	190	32	14	bbu	
9189768	Medi Tokyo	Ita	1999	38,835	74,356	225	32	14	bbu	
9339480	Medi Valencia	Ita	2008	31,236	56,014	190	32	14	bbu	
9302774	Medi Venezia	Ita	2005	39,727	76,602	225	32	14	bbu	
9660592	Medi Yokohama　+	Pan	2014	32,370	57,905	190	32	14	bbu	

Cielo di Agadir : d'Amico Soc di Nav. : *Chris Brooks*

IMO	name	flag	year	gt	dwt	loa	bm	kts	type	comments
newbuildings:										
9735452		Mlt	2016	25,303	38,670			14	bbu	Yangfan Gp. Zhoushan Bc38k-Dm10
9735464				23,475	38,670			14	bbu	Yangfan Gp. Zhoushan
9735476				23,475	38,670			14	bbu	Yangfan Gp. Zhoushan
9735488				23,475	38,670			14	bbu	Yangfan Gp. Zhoushan
9539286	Cielo d'Europa +	Mlt	2016	65,000	119,000			14	bbu	Sanoyas 1316 L - 02.10.2015

also on order: 2 x 75,000dwt LR1 tco [Hyundai Mipo (2017)] :
* owned by d'Amico Shipping Singapore Pte.   + chartered vessels

d'Amico Dry Ltd., Ireland

IMO	name	flag	year	gt	dwt	loa	bm	kts	type	comments
9122045	Cielo di Agadir	Mar	1996	16,800	22,984	184	25	20	ucc	1,728 teu: ex CCNI Magallanes-11, Mercosul Pescada-07, Sofia Russ-01, CSAV Vancouver-00, Sofia Russ-00, Cielo del Venezuela-99, Sofia Russ-99, CSAV Rungue-98, Sofia Russ-96
9707742	Cielo di Angra	Lux	2015	25,303	39,202	180	30	14	bbu	
9595151	Cielo di Capalbio	Lbr	2012	23,790	36,699	183	28	14	bbu	
9695640	Cielo di Cartagena	Mlt	2015	25,303	39,202	180	30	14	bbu	
9143879	Cielo di Casablanca	Mar	1998	9,146	9,950	121	23	18	ucc	951 teu; ex Dartmoor-10, CMA CGM Estrella-08, Maersk Felixstowe-06, Ridvan Ozeler-03
9539274	Cielo d'Italia	Pan	2015	63,087	117,438	245	43	14	bbu	
9380829	Cielo di Livorno	Pan	2008	22,718	37,277	178	29	14	bbu	
9638147	Cielo di Monaco	Mlt	2014	25,303	39,202	180	30	14	bbu	
9141792	Cielo di Rabat	Mar	1997	21,531	30,202	182	30	20	ucc	2,061 teu: ex Santa Giorgina-15, CMA CGM Lagos-09, Canmar Promise-06, Santa Giorgina-03, P&O Nedlloyd Rio Grande-02, I/a Santa Giorgina
9638159	Cielo di Tocopilla	Mlt	2014	25,303	38,670	180	30	15	bbu	
9380817	Cielo di Tokyo +	Pan	2008	22,718	37,296	183	29	14	bbu	
9595149	Cielo di Vaiano	Lbr	2012	23,790	37,064	183	28	15	bbu	
9663776	Cielo di Valparaiso	Lbr	2015	25,303	39,232	180	30	15	bbu	
9663740	Cielo di Virgin Gorda	Lbr	2015	25,303	39,202	180	30	15	bbu	
9699177	DACC Egeo *	Mlt	2015	34,049	60,660	200	32	14	bbu	

Medi Nagasaki : d'Amico Soc. di Nav : *Chris Brooks*

IMO	name	flag	year	gt	dwt	loa	bm	kts	type	comments
9699165	DACC Tirreno *	Mlt	2015	34,049	60,550	200	32	14	bbu	
9638135	Giulia I	Mlt	2014	25,303	39,202	180	30	14	bbu	
9249271	Medi Nagasaki	Lbr	2003	29,295	53,098	189	32	14	bbu	
9514389	Medi Okinawa +	Pan	2011	31,754	56,118	190	32	14	bbu	
9403164	Medi Segesta +	Pan	2009	32,379	58,730	190	32	14	bbu	
9273818	Medi Vitoria	Lbr	2004	39,729	76,616	225	32	14	bbu	

owned by associated DACC Maritime Ltd, Dublin   *+ chartered vessels*

d'Amico Tankers, Ireland

IMO	name	flag	year	gt	dwt	loa	bm	kts	type	comments
9573684	Carina	Sgp	2010	28,813	47,962	183	32	14	tco	
9669653	Cielo di Gaeta	Mlt	2014	26,746	39,990	183	32	14	tco	
9241815	Cielo di Milano	Ita	2003	25,400	40,081	176	31	15	tco	
9669665	Cielo di New York	Mlt	2014	26,746	40,000	183	32	14	tco	
9717266	Cielo di Ulsan	Mlt	2015	24,184	39,060	184	27	14	tco	
9289740	High Courage	Lbr	2005	30,048	46,991	183	32	14	tco	
9674725	High Discovery	Mlt	2014	29,925	45,999	183	32	14	tco	
9424649	High Efficiency *	Pan	2009	28,231	46,547	183	32	15	tco	
9272391	High Endeavour	Lbr	2004	30,028	46,991	183	32	14	tco	ex High Star-04
9272929	High Endurance	Lbr	2004	30,028	46,991	183	32	14	tco	ex High Pearl-04
9689146	High Fidelity	Mlt	2014	29,935	50,000	183	32	14	tco	
9674713	High Freedom	Mlt	2014	29,935	49,990	183	32	14	tco	
9310812	High Glow +	Pan	2006	28,245	46,846	183	32	14	tco	
9681857	High Loyalty	Mlt	2015	29,935	49,990	183	32	14	tco	
9512747	High Pearl +	Sgp	2009	28,813	48,023	180	32	15	tco	
9301005	High Performance	Lbr	2005	30,081	51,303	183	32	15	tco	
9325324	High Presence	Sgp	2005	28,245	48,400	180	32	15	tco	
9282558	High Priority	Sgp	2005	28,245	46,847	180	32	15	tco	
9300996	High Progress	Lbr	2005	30,081	51,303	183	32	15	tco	
9292357	High Prosperity	Lbr	2006	28,794	48,711	183	32	15	tco	
9455703	High Seas	Lbr	2012	29,841	51,768	183	32	15	tco	
9424651	High Strength *	Pan	2009	28,231	46,592	183	32	15	tco	
9689134	High Sun	Mlt	2014	29,935	49,990	183	32	15	tco	
9455820	High Tide	Lbr	2012	29,841	51,768	183	32	15	tco	
9696242	High Trader	Lbr	2015	29,935	49,990	183	32	15	tco	
9289738	High Valor	Lbr	2005	30,048	46,991	183	32	15	tco	
9365817	High Venture	Lbr	2006	29,942	51,088	183	32	15	tco	
9681845	High Voyager	Mlt	2014	29,935	45,999	183	32	15	tco	

owned by associated DM Shipping Ltd. Dublin   *+ chartered vessels*

Thor Dahl Shipping AS   Norway

funnel: *white with Thor Dahl house flag or operators colours.* **hull:** *dark blue with red boot-topping.* **history:** *original company founded, Sandefjord, 1887.* **web:** *www.thordahl.no or www.tdman.no*

IMO	name	flag	year	gt	dwt	loa	bm	kts	type	comments
9148025	MSC Anahita	Cyp	1997	29,022	34,907	196	32	21	ucc	2,908 teu: ex Cape-13, Thorscape-13, Amasis-11, ANL Empress-03, Ibex Empress-02, Amasis-97
9135638	MSC Jeanne	Cyp	1996	29,022	35,021	196	32	21	ucc	2,959 teu: ex Wave-13, Thorswave-13, Eos I-08, Zim Mumbai-07, Eos I-06, Ming Dynasty-02, Hyundai Dynasty-98, Eos I-96
9162277	Thorsky *	Lbr	1999	21,583	30,135	183	30	20	ucc	2,168 teu: ex Santa Felicita P&O Nedlloyd Seoul-02, I/dn Santa Felicita
9253002	Thorstar	Lbr	2003	27,779	40,878	221	30	22	ucc	2,824 teu: ex Sils-15, Norasia Sils-06, Sils-03
9149873	Thorstream	Cyp	1998	16,803	23,007	185	25	20	ucc	1,730 teu: Nordstar-11, P&O Nedlloyd Pampas-02, Nordstar-01, Niver Austral-00, Nordstar-99, CSAV Rio Uruguay-99
9173135	Thorswind *	Lbr	1999	21,583	30,135	183	30	20	ucc	2,168 teu; ex Westwood Cascade-15, Santa Fabiola-11, CMA CGM Nyala-09, Santa Fabiola-08, P&O Nedlloyd Singapore-05, I/dn Santa Fabiola

owned by Thor Dahl Container AS (formed 1996 as Jahre Dahl Bergesen to 2005 and now owned by AS Thor Dahl Shipping (52.5%), Bulls Tankrederi AS (22.5%) and management)

Danaos Shipping Co. Ltd.   Greece

funnel: *blue or charterers colours.* **hull:** *black with red boot-topping or charterers colours.* **history:** *founded 1972 as successor to Roumeli Shipping formed in early 1970's when Dimitris Coustas bought out partners in joint venture (formed 1963).*
web: *www.danaosshipping.gr*

IMO	name	flag	year	gt	dwt	loa	bm	kts	type	comments
9166649	Amalia C	Mlt	1998	25,500	34,362	199	30	21	ucc	2,452 teu: ex Gemini-13, Cap Ortegal-09, CMA CGM Delacroix-02, Cap Ortegal-00, Gemini-98
9433793	CMA CGM Attila	Mlt	2011	91,498	101,474	335	43	25	ucc	8,533 teu
9436367	CMA CGM Bianca	Mlt	2011	91,498	101,433	335	43	25	ucc	8,533 teu
9473028	CMA CGM Melisande	Mlt	2012	91,498	101,376	335	43	25	ucc	8,530 teu
9401099	CMA CGM Moliere	Mlt	2009	72,884	83,293	300	40	25	ucc	6,540 teu
9406611	CMA CGM Musset	Mlt	2010	72,884	83,264	300	40	25	ucc	6,540 teu
9406623	CMA CGM Nerval	Mlt	2010	72,884	83,319	300	40	25	ucc	6,540 teu
9406635	CMA CGM Rabelais	Mlt	2010	72,884	83,318	300	40	25	ucc	6,540 teu
9406647	CMA CGM Racine	Mlt	2010	72,884	83,217	300	40	25	ucc	6,540 teu
9436379	CMA CGM Samson	Mlt	2011	91,498	100,383	335	43	25	ucc	8,533 teu
9436355	CMA CGM Tancredi	Mlt	2011	91,498	101,386	335	43	25	ucc	8,530 teu
9285990	CSCL America	Cyp	2004	90,645	101,612	334	43	25	ucc	8,468 teu: ex MSC Baltic-09, CSCL America-07
9285988	CSCL Europe	Cyp	2004	90,645	101,612	334	43	25	ucc	8,468 teu
9307243	CSCL Le Havre	Cyp	2006	108,069	111,790	337	46	26	ucc	9,580 teu
9307229	CSCL Pusan	Cyp	2006	108,069	111,889	337	46	26	ucc	9,580 teu
9226425	Danae C.	Mlt	2001	25,703	33,987	208	30	22	ucc	2,524 teu: ex NileDutch Palanca-15, Danae C-14, Wotan-13, CCNI Rimac-11, Wotan-06, MSC Venezuela-03, l/a Wotan
9278117	Derby D.	Cyp	2004	39,941	50,814	260	32	23	ucc	4,253 teu: ex Bunga Raya Tiga-11, Maersk Derby-09, P&O Nedlloyd Caracas-05
9278105	Deva	Cyp	2004	39,941	50,828	260	32	23	ucc	4,253 teu; ex Bunga Raya Tujah-10, Maersk Deva-09, Vancouver Express-08, Maersk Deva-06, P&O Nedlloyd Caribbean-06
9210074	Dimitris C	Mlt	2001	37,113	40,102	243	32	23	ucc	3,430 teu: ex Catalina Star-13, Santa Catalina-11, P&O Nedlloyd Dejima-05, l/a Santa Catalina
9267651	Genoa	Lbr	2002	66,292	67,197	279	40	25	ucc	5,570 teu: ex Genoa Bridge-15
9443047	Hanjin Algeciras	Mlt	2011	35,595	44,144	223	32	23	ucc	3,459 teu
9443011	Hanjin Buenos Aires	Mlt	2010	35,595	44,060	223	32	23	ucc	3,459 teu
9443059	Hanjin Constantza	Mlt	2011	35,595	44,012	223	32	23	ucc	3,459 teu
9484924	Hanjin Germany	Grc	2011	114,144	122,962	349	46	25	ucc	10,070 teu
9484948	Hanjin Greece	Lbr	2011	114,144	122,959	349	46	25	ucc	10,070 teu
9484936	Hanjin Italy	Lbr	2011	114,144	122,961	349	46	25	ucc	10,070 teu
9443023	Hanjin Santos	Mlt	2010	35,595	44,164	223	32	23	ucc	3,459 teu
9443035	Hanjin Versailles	Mlt	2010	35,595	44,080	223	32	23	ucc	3,459 teu

Danae C : Danaos Shg. Co. : *Mike Rhodes*

IMO	name	flag	year	gt	dwt	loa	bm	kts	type	comments
9149859	Hyundai Advance	Pan	1997	21,611	24,766	182	30	21	ucc	2,181 teu: ex Wan Hai 251-00, Hyundai Advance-98
9475703	Hyundai Ambition	Lbr	2012	140,979	140,565	367	48	24	ucc	12,562 teu
9158587	Hyundai Bridge	Pan	1998	21,611	24,766	182	30	21	ucc	2,181 teu
9149847	Hyundai Future	Pan	1997	21,611	24,799	182	30	21	ucc	2,181 teu
9158575	Hyundai Highway	Pan	1998	21,611	24,799	182	30	21	ucc	2,181 teu
9158563	Hyundai Progress	Pan	1997	21,611	24,766	182	30	22	ucc	2,181 teu: ex Wan Hai 252-00, Hyundai Progress-98
9475686	Hyundai Smart	Lbr	2012	141,770	141,458	367	48	24	ucc	12,562 teu
9475698	Hyundai Speed	Lbr	2012	140,979	141,356	367	48	24	ucc	12,562 teu
9149861	Hyundai Sprinter	Pan	1997	21,611	24,600	182	30	21	ucc	2,181 teu
9149835	Hyundai Stride	Pan	1997	21,611	24,777	182	30	21	ucc	2,181 teu
9475674	Hyundai Tenacity	Lbr	2012	141,770	140,565	366	48	24	ucc	12,562 teu
9473731	Hyundai Together	Lbr	2012	141,770	141,565	366	48	24	ucc	12,562 teu
9149823	Hyundai Vladivostok	Pan	1997	21,611	24,766	182	30	21	ucc	2,181 teu: ex CMA Oakland-01, Hyundai Vladivostok-99
9231157	MSC Zebra	Mlt	2001	27,093	33,220	210	30	22	ucc	2,622 teu: ex NileDutch Zebra-14, Marfret Sormiou-13, Sormiou-10, Rodin-07, CMA CGM Rodin-06, l/a Ansgaritor
9229302	NYK Leo	Pan	2002	75,201	77,900	300	40	27	ucc	6,178 teu
9229300	NYK Lodestar	Pan	2001	75,201	77,900	300	40	27	ucc	6,422 teu
9389693	OOCL Istanbul	Mlt	2008	40,030	50,550	260	32	24	ucc	4,526 teu: ex Zim Kingston-13
9391268	OOCL Novorossiysk	Mlt	2009	40,030	50,829	260	32	32	ucc	4,526 teu: ex Zim Dalian-13
9250971	Performance	Mlt	2001	74,071	74,453	294	40	27	ucc	6,402 teu: ex MOL Performance
9250995	Priority	Mlt	2002	74,071	74,453	294	40	26	ucc	6,402 teu: ex MOL Priority-14
9256212	SNL Colombo	Lbr	2004	41,855	53,610	264	32	24	ucc	4,334 teu: ex YM Colombo-12, Norasia Integra-07, E.R. Auckland-04, l/a E.R. Wellington
9230311	Suez Canal	Lbr	2002	68,687	71,359	285	40	25	ucc	5,610 teu: ex Suez Canal Bridge-15
9438523	YM Mandate	Lbr	2010	73,675	83,200	299	40	25	ucc	6,572 teu
9438535	YM Maturity	Lbr	2010	73,675	83,200	299	40	25	ucc	6,572 teu
9360910	YM Seattle	Cyp	2007	40,030	50,813	260	32	23	ucc	4,526 teu: ex Taiwan Express -12, YM Seattle-11
9256224	YM Singapore	Lbr	2004	41,855	53,611	264	32	24	ucc	4,334 teu; ex Norasia Atria-08, E.R. Wellington-04, l/a E.R. Auckland
9363364	YM Vancouver	Cyp	2007	40,030	50,632	260	32	23	ucc	4,253 teu
9403229	Zim Luanda	Mlt	2009	40,030	50,550	260	32	24	ucc	4,526 teu
9389708	Zim Monaco	Mlt	2009	40,030	50,842	260	32	24	ucc	4,526 teu
9363376	Zim Rio Grande	Mlt	2008	40,030	50,842	260	32	24	ucc	4,526 teu
9389681	Zim Sao Paolo	Mlt	2008	40,030	50,818	260	32	24	ucc	4,526 teu

Dannebrog Rederi A/S — Denmark

funnel: *yellow with houseflag, white cross on red penant flag, on broad blue band. Joint venture formed with Jutha Maritime (2006)*
hull: *grey with red boot-topping.* history: *formed 1883 as A/S Dannebrog to 1970.* web: *www.dannebrog.com*

IMO	name	flag	year	gt	dwt	loa	bm	kts	type	comments
9261657	Amalienborg *	Dnk	2004	24,663	40,059	175	31	15	tco	ex Southern Unity-08

Hyundai Smart : Danaos Shg. Co : *Chris Brooks*

IMO	name	flag	year	gt	dwt	loa	bm	kts	type	comments
9488047	Billesborg	Sgp	2011	9,627	12,696	139	21	15	ggc	ex Clipper Angela-12, Billesborg-11
9488061	Ellensborg	Sgp	2011	9,627	12,731	139	21	15	ggc	ex Clipper Amber-12, Ellensborg-12
9488059	Elsborg	Sgp	2011	9,627	12,671	139	21	15	ggc	
9465394	Fredensborg	Sgp	2011	9,627	12,667	139	21	15	ggc	
9316593	Kronborg *	Lbr	2007	25,400	40,208	176	31	15	tco	
9453793	Marselisborg	Lbr	2010	9,627	12,696	139	21	15	ggc	
8508369	Stjerneborg +	Sgp	1994	20,370	14,163	174	26	15	urc	ex Medcoa Lome-12, Frederiksborg-09, Global Africa-07 (len-12)
9687306	Wedellsborg	Ita	2014	21,801	11,630	180	26	18	urr	
newbuildings :										
9666089	*Stenaweco Impulse*	Bmu	2016	30,000	50,000	183	32	15	tco	

* owned by Difko Kronborg K/S, managed by Oceangold Tankers Inc., + owned by Nordana Shipping (Singapore), managed by Jutha Maritime see also Stena Weco

Herm Dauelsberg GmbH & Co. KG   Germany

funnel: *white with black 'D' on cream band between narrow blue bands, or charterers colours.* **hull:** *black or grey with red boot-topping.* **history:** *formed 1857 as shipbrokers and started shipowning in 1857, owned by Bunnemann family since 1887.* **web:** *www.dauelsberg.de*

9290440	Bellavia	Mhl	2005	53,807	66,501	294	32	25	ucc	5,117 teu
9064334	Bonavia	Lbr	1995	23,691	30,743	188	30	21	ucc	1,918 teu: ex CMA CGM Oryx-09, Bonavia-08, Cap Sunion-08, Bonavia-04, Safmarine Maluti-04, Maersk Algerciras-01, Contship Auckland-97, Bonavia-95
9570840	Elvia	Lbr	2010	50.697	92,500	230	38	14	bbu	
9570852	Fulvia	Lbr	2010	50.697	92,500	230	38	14	bbu	
9122435	Lindavia	Lbr	1996	23,825	30,615	188	30	21	ucc	2,078 teu: ex ACX Jasmine-10, Lindavia-06, Maersk Sydney-00, Lindavia-98, Sea Lindavia-98, Lindavia-96
9228576	Marivia	Lbr	2001	23,652	30,375	188	30	21	ucc	2,078 teu: ex SCI Trust-10, Marivia-09
9280811	Silvia	Mhl	2005	40,952	55,497	261	32	24	ucc	4,130 teu: ex YM Taichung-14, Chesapeake Bay Bridge-07, I/a Silvia

Asiatic Lloyd Shipping Pte. Ltd., Singapore

funnel: *white with white 'AL' on broad blue band between two narrow grey bands,* **hull:** *blue with red boot topping,* **history:** *company formed 2008 by Fredrich Brunneman, managing company of Herm Dauelsburg* **web:** *www.asiaticlloyd.com*

9261712	AL Encore	Sgp	2003	53,096	61,441	294	32	24	ucc	4,578 teu: ex MOL Encore-15
9261724	AL Endeavor	Sgp	2003	53,096	61,441	294	32	24	ucc	4,578 teu: ex MOL Endeavor-15
9261736	MOL Endurance	Sgp	2003	53,096	61,441	294	32	24	ucc	4,578 teu
9699115	UASC Umm Qasr	Sgp	2014	94,784	112,171	300	48	22	ucc	9,034 teu: ex Asiatic Spring-14
9699127	UASC Zamzam	Sgp	2014	94,784	112,171	300	48	22	ucc	9,034 teu: ex Asiatic Summer-14

also operates a fleet of 6 feeder container ships mainly in the Far East

Atlantic Lloyd GmbH & Co. KG, Germany

funnel: *white with white 'AL' on broad blue band between two narrow grey bands,* **hull:** *blue with red boot topping,* **history:** *company formed 2008 by Fredrich Brunneman, managing company of Herm Dauelsburg* **web:** *www.asiaticlloyd.com*

9261748	AL Enterprise	Lbr	2004	53,096	61,441	294	32	24	ucc	4,578 teu: ex MOL Enterprise-15
9289544	Atlantic Altair	Lbr	2005	54,626	66,939	294	32	25	ucc	5,075 teu: ex Zim Beijing-15, I/a E.R. Beijing sold Asiatic L 02:15
9570838	Cervia	Lbr	2010	50,697	92,500	230	38	14	bbu	
9295206	Clivia	Mhl	2005	40,952	55,490	261	32	24	ucc	4,130 teu: ex YM Ningbo-14, Cherokee Bridge-07, I/a Clivia
9228564	Lobivia	Lbr	2001	23,652	30,375	188	30	21	ucc	1,918 teu: ex Fathulkhair-09, Cala Pintada-08, Lobivia-04
9122447	Magnavia	Lbr	1996	23,825	30,743	188	30	21	ucc	2,078 teu: ex TS Incheon-09, Magnavia-08, MOL Waratah-02, Alligator Unity-01, Maersk Oceania-00, Magnavia-97
9290452	Octavia	Mhl	2005	53,807	66,501	294	32	25	ucc	5,117 teu
9579864	Piavia	Lbe	2011	50,697	92,500	230	38	14	bbu	

Delta Tankers   Greece

funnel: *white with blue triangle, narrow black top* **hull:** *black with 3 light blue 'waves' and 'Delta Tankers' in white, red boot topping* **history:** *established 2006* **web:** *www.deltatankers.gr*

9298753	Bouboulina	Grc	2006	84,844	163,759	276	50	14	tcr	
9299903	Deep Blue	Grc	2005	62,404	111,008	250	44	14	tcr	I/a Delta Blue
9288710	Delta Captain	Grc	2005	62,320	111,013	250	44	14	tcr	

IMO	name	flag	year	gt	dwt	loa	bm	kts	type	comments
9418157	Delta Commander	Grc	2010	81,360	157,477	274	48	14	tcr	
9700706	Delya Eurydice	Lbr	2015	81,293	149,990	274	48	14	tcr	
9408463	Delta Harmony	Grc	2009	81,360	157,410	274	48	14	tcr	
9406673	Delta Hellas	Grc	2009	81,360	157,583	274	48	14	tcr	
9406685	Delta Ios	Grc	2009	81,360	157,484	274	48	14	tcr	
9429015	Delta Kanaris	Grc	2010	81,360	157,563	274	48	14	tcr	
9700691	Delta Maria	Grc	2015	82,293	149,990	274	48	14	tcr	
9579573	Delta Mariner	Grc	2013	84,156	157,638	274	48	14	tcr	
9202716	Delta Millennium	Lbr	2000	157,093	301,930	333	60	15	tcr	ex Nordmillennium-08
9408475	Delta Ocean	Grc	2010	81,360	157,444	274	48	14	tcr	
9288693	Delta Pioneer	Grc	2004	62,320	111,013	250	44	14	tcr	
9468671	Delta Poseidon	Grc	2011	81,360	157,380	274	48	14	tcr	
9288722	Delta Sailor	Grc	2005	62,320	111,004	250	44	14	tcr	
9410181	Delta Sky	Lbr	2009	84,716	166,092	74	48	15	tcr	ex Ariadni-15
9458016	Delta Star	Grc	2013	61,314	109,990	249	44	14	tco	ex White Stars-13
9429027	Delta Tolmi	Grc	2010	81,360	157,486	274	48	14	tcr	
9288708	Delta Victory	Grc	2005	62,320	111,006	250	44	14	tcr	
9312133	Explorer	Grc	2006	84,844	163,759	276	50	14	tcr	
9298741	Meltemi	Grc	2006	84,844	163,759	276	50	15	tcr	
9298765	Nautilus	Grc	2006	84,844	163,927	276	50	15	tcr	
9299898	Pelagos	Grc	2005	62,404	111,775	250	44	14	tcr	
9312145	Sounion	Grc	2006	84,844	163,759	276	50	14	tcr	

DSS Holding LP   U.S.A.

Diamond S. Shipping Gp., U.S.A.
funnel: black with white 'S' in red diamond inside larger white diamond on broad red band between narrow white bands. **hull:** black or red with red boot topping. **history:** founded as partnership between Pecos Shipping and First Reserve Bank, 2008. purchased many product tankers from Cido Shipping (2011/12). **web:** www.diamondsshipping.com

9387918	Adriatic Wave	Hkg	2009	29,733	51,476	183	32	15	tco
9387920	Aegean Wave	Hkg	2009	29,733	51,510	183	32	15	tco
9392793	Alpine Magic	Hkg	2009	29,266	47,128	183	32	15	tco
9380506	Alpine Mathilde	Hkg	2008	29,266	47,128	183	32	14	tco

Delta Captain : Delta Tankers : *Hans Kraijenbosch*

IMO	name	flag	year	gt	dwt	loa	bm	kts	type	comments
9387932	Alpine Maya	Hkg	2010	29,733	51,149	183	32	15	tco	
9487944	Alpine Melina	Hkg	2010	29,733	51,483	183	32	15	tco	
9391440	Alpine Minute	Hkg	2009	29,266	47,128	183	32	15	tco	
9391438	Alpine Moment	Hkg	2009	29,266	47,128	183	32	15	tco	
9392808	Alpine Mystery	Hkg	2009	29,266	47,128	183	32	15	tco	
9381756	Atlantic Aquarius	Hkg	2008	29,266	47,128	183	32	15	tco	
9360336	Atlantic Breeze	Hkg	2007	29,266	47,128	183	32	15	tco	
9337511	Atlantic Grace	Hkg	2008	29,266	47,128	183	32	15	tco	
9381768	Atlantic Leo	Hkg	2008	29,266	47,128	183	32	15	tco	I/a Overseas Leo
9387138	Atlantic Mirage	Hkg	2009	29,733	51,476	183	32	15	tco	
9374301	Atlantic Muse	Hkg	2009	29,733	51,149	183	32	15	tco	
9354909	Atlantic Olive	Hkg	2008	29,266	47,128	183	32	15	tco	
9392799	Atlantic Polaris	Hkg	2009	29,266	47,128	183	32	15	tco	
9354911	Atlantic Rose	Hgk	2008	29,266	47,128	183	32	15	tco	
9337523	Atlantic Star	Hkg	2008	29,266	47,128	183	32	15	tco	
9594731	Brazos	Mhl	2012	81,341	158,582	274	48	15	tcr	
9594767	Colorado	Mhl	2012	81,341	158,615	274	48	15	tcr	
9596985	Frio	Mhl	2012	81,346	159,068	274	48	15	tcr	
9366299	High Jupiter	Hkg	2008	29,733	51,603	183	32	15	tco	
9366287	High Mercury	Hkg	2008	29,733	51,528	183	32	14	tco	
9413779	Pacific Jewel	Hkg	2009	28,754	48,012	183	32	14	tco	
9593743	Pecos	Mhl	2012	81,341	158,465	274	48	15	tcr	
9596573	Red	Mhl	2012	81,346	159,068	274	48	15	tcr	
9593438	Rio Grande	Mhl	2012	81,346	159,176	274	48	15	tcr	
9594755	Sabine	Mhl	2012	81,341	158,493	274	48	15	tcr	
9593426	San Saba	Mhl	2012	81,346	159,018	274	48	15	tcr	
9730361	Trinity	Mhl	2016	81,360	158,734	274	48	15	tcr	
newbuildings :										
9730373			2016	81,000	159,000	274	48	15	tcr	Hyundai Samho S788

see also Norient Product Pool

Diamond Ship Management N.V.   Belgium

funnel: *operators colours.* **hull:** *white with red boot-topping,* **history:** *founded 2007.* **web:** *www.diamondship.be*

9015204	Chiquita Belgie *	Bhs	1992	13,049	13,930	158	24	22	grf	
9015187	Hellas Reefer **	Bhs	1991	13,049	13,930	158	24	22	grf	ex Chiquita Deutschland-14
9030137	Italia Reefer **	Bhs	1992	13,049	13,930	158	24	22	grf	ex Chiquita Italia-14
9015199	Nederland Reefer **	Bhs	1991	13,049	13,930	158	24	21	grf	ex Chiquita Nederland-14
9015216	Schweiz Reefer **	Bhs	1992	13,049	13,930	158	24	22	grf	ex Chiquita Schweiz -14
9030149	Swedish Reefer **	Bhs	1992	13,049	13,930	159	24	21	grf	ex Chiquita Scandinavia-14

** operated by Chiquita Brands (successor to United Fruit Co.) ** managed by Chartworld Shipping Corp.,*

Diana Containerships Inc.   Greece

funnel: *white with red cross on white panel between narrow red bands.* **hull:** *blue or operators colours* **history:** *company founded 2010, associated with Diana Shipping Services which operates a large fleet of bulkers* **web:** *www.dcontainerships.com*

9215672	Cap Domingo	Mhl	2001	40,085	51,087	257	32	23	ucc	3,739 teu: ex Cap San Marco-12
9227285	Cap Doukato	Mhl	2002	40,085	51,059	257	32	22	ucc	3,739 teu: ex Cap San Raphael-12

Pecos : Diamond S Shipping : *Mike Rhodes*

IMO	name	flag	year	gt	dwt	loa	bm	kts	type	comments
9401178	Centaurus	Mhl	2010	36,087	42,604	229	32	23	ucc	3,414 teu: ex Frisia Cottbus-10
9267156	Great	Mhl	2004	66,332	67,270	279	40	26	ucc	5,576 teu: ex YM Great-15, l/a Ming Great
9332860	Hamburg	Mhl	2009	71,786	72,982	304	40	25	ucc	6,494 teu: ex APL Hamburg-14
9298997	March	Mhl	2004	66,332	67,270	279	40	25	ucc	5,576 teu: ex YM March-15, l/a Ming March
9326782	Pamina	Mhl	2005	54,809	67,247	295	32	25	ucc	4,839 teu: ex Santa Pamina-15, Maersk Dunedin-13, P&O Nedlloyd Detroit-05, l/a Santa Pamina
9306158	Pucon	Mhl	2006	73,934	81,099	304	40	25	ucc	6,541 teu: l/dn Paine
9306172	Puelo	Mhl	2006	73,934	81,250	304	40	25	ucc	6,541 teu
9401166	Sagitta	Mhl	2010	36,087	42,614	229	32	23	ucc	3,414 teu: ex Frisia Brussel-10
9332858	Rotterdam	Mhl	2008	71,786	72,982	304	40	25	ucc	6,494 teu: ex APL Rotterdam-13
9387102	YM Los Angeles	Mhl	2006	54,828	65,123	294	32	25	ucc	4,923 teu
9387097	YM New Jersey	Mhl	2006	54,828	65,123	294	32	23	ucc	4,923 teu

vessels managed by subsidiary Unitized Ocean Transport Ltd., Greece

Dioryx Maritime Corp.   Greece

funnel: *blue with blue 'P' on white band, or charterers colours.* **hull:** *blue or red with red boot topping.* **history:** *founded 1947*
web: *none found*

IMO	name	flag	year	gt	dwt	loa	bm	kts	type	comments
9397614	CMA CGM Jasper	Lbr	2009	40,560	52,427	259	32	24	ucc	4,308 teu
9386495	CMA CGM Lapis	Lbr	2009	40,560	52,513	259	32	24	ucc	4,308 teu
9386483	CMA CGM Opal	Lbr	2009	40,560	52,408	259	32	24	ucc	4,308 teu
9385611	CMA CGM Quartz	Lbr	2008	40,560	52,523	259	32	24	ucc	4,308 teu: ex Argolikos-08
9397602	CMA CGM Topaz	Lbr	2009	40,560	52,366	259	32	24	ucc	4,308 teu
9386471	CMA CGM Turquoise	Lbr	2009	40,560	52,513	259	32	24	ucc	4,308 teu: l/a Kossiakos
9444417	Corinthiakos	Lbr	2010	41,391	51,570	262	32	24	ucc	4,334 teu: ex STX Corinthiakos-13
9464247	Maliakos	Lbr	2012	41,391	51,310	262	32	24	ucc	4,400 teu: ex NileDutch Elephant-15, Maliakos-14, CCNI Austral-12, STX Maliakos-12
9442172	Patraikos	Lbr	2010	41,391	51,570	262	32	24	ucc	4,334 teu: ex STX Patraikos-13

Dockendale Ship Management DMC   Dubai

funnel: *white with red 'D' and 'S' above points of black anchor or operators colours.* **hull:** *black with red boot-topping, some with 'MUR' in white.* **history:** *founded 2006 after sale from Campbell organisation.* **web:** *www.dockendale.com*

IMO	name	flag	year	gt	dwt	loa	bm	kts	type	comments
9738753	African Baza *	Bhs	2015	34,815	61,313	200	32	14	bbu	
9351737	African Blue Crane *	Bhs	2007	31,328	55,970	190	32	14	bbu	

African Kite : Dockendale Ship Management - MUR Shipping : *Chris Brooks*

IMO	name	flag	year	gt	dwt	loa	bm	kts	type	comments
9682772	African Dove *	Bhs	2014	21,532	34,402	180	30	14	bbu	
9257046	African Eagle *	Bhs	2003	17,944	27,102	178	26	14	bbu	ex DS Mascot-03
9257058	African Falcon *	Bhs	2003	17,944	27,101	178	26	14	bbu	ex Clipper Majestic-03
9728485	African Goshawk *	Bhs	2016	21,521	34,370	180	30	14	bbu	
9701205	African Griffon *	Bhs	2014	34,815	61,286	200	32	14	bbu	
9755737	African Grouse *	Bhs	2015	23,750	37,700	183	30	14	bbu	
9343613	African Halcyon *	Bhs	2007	20,346	32,245	177	28	14	bbu	
9700794	African Harrier *	Bhs	2014	23,322	37,707	180	30	14	bbu	
9284362	African Hawk *	Bhs	2004	17,944	27,101	178	26	14	bbu	
9599779	African Hornbill *	Bhs	2011	34,795	61,440	200	32	14	bbu	
9295579	African Ibis *	Bhs	2004	20,211	32,347	177	28	14	bbu	
9737046	African Jay *	Bhs	2015	23,750	37,705	183	30	14	bbu	
9650937	African Kite *	Bhs	2013	34,800	61,413	200	32	14	bbu	
9682760	African Lark *	Bhs	2014	21,532	34,402	174	30	14	bbu	
9701267	African Merlin *	Bhs	2016	21,521	33,889	180	30	14	bbu	
9612143	African Osprey *	Bhs	2012	24,212	34,697	180	30	14	bbu	
9701255	African Owl *	Bhs	2016	21,421	34,382	180	30	14	bbu	
9692789	African Pelican *	Bhs	2015	21,532	34,365	180	30	14	bbu	
9692777	African Piper *	Bhs	2015	21,532	34,465	180	30	14	bbu	
9727405	African Raptor *	Bhs	2015	34,815	61,286	200	32	14	bbu	
9700287	African Raven *	Bhs	2014	23,753	37,711	183	31	14	bbu	
9317767	African Robin *	Bhs	2005	19,783	31,982	176	29	14	bbu	
9700299	African Rook *	Bhs	2015	23,750	37,686	180	30	14	bbu	
9403059	African Sanderling *	Bhs	2008	32,379	58,798	190	32	14	bbu	
9303364	African Swan *	Bhs	2005	19,887	32,776	177	28	14	bbu	
9649031	African Tern *	Bhs	2013	33,193	58,342	190	32	14	bbu	
9649043	African Wagtail *	Bhs	2013	33,193	58,340	190	32	14	bbu	
9728497	African Weaver *	Bhs	2016	21,521	34,369	180	30	14	bbu	
9271339	Carouge **	Bmu	2003	89,559	172,254	288	46	14	bbu	ex Azul Frontier-12
9182710	Certoux **	Bmu	2000	86,192	169,159	289	45	13	bbu	ex Daphne-12, Yue Shan-07
9269063	Chambesy **	Bmu	2004	88,292	171,995	289	45	14	bbu	ex Pacific Fortune
9726774	Chancy **	Bmu	2015	93,297	182,571	292	45	14	bbu	
9736925	Chevrier **	Bmu	2016	93,296	182,625	292	45	14	bbu	
9143051	Confignon **	Bmu	1997	85,437	170,896	289	45	13	bbu	ex Orchid River-12
9169378	Cornavin **	Bmu	1999	85,695	169,963	289	45	14	bbu	ex Gaia-12, Graceous-05
newbuilding:										
9736949	Choully **	Bmu	2016	93,500	182,000	292	45	14	bbu	JMU Tsu 5014

* owned and operated by Metall und Rohstoff (MUR) Shipping   ** operated by SwissMarine Services S.A.
see also Shoei Kisen Kaisha

Dockwise Shipping B.V.   Netherlands

funnel: *dark blue with black 'D' on white disc on light blue square on white band.* **hull:** *black, orange or green with 'DOCKWISE', red boot-topping.* **history:** *formed by 1994 merger of Wijsmuller Transport BV (formed 1914) with Dock Express Shipping BV (formed 1977) and owned by their respective parents Heerema (70%) and Royal Vopak (formerly Van Ommeren) (30%). Merged with Offshore Heavy Transport ASA, Norway (part owned by Wilh. Wilhelmsen and Dyvi) in 2001. Reported sold to equity group 3i in Jan.2007. All shares bought by Royal Boskalis Westminster N.V., April 2013* **web:** *www.dockwise.com*

IMO	name	flag	year	gt	dwt	loa	bm	kts	type	comments
9186326	Black Marlin *	Cuw	2000	37,938	57,021	218	42	14	ohl	
9186338	Blue Marlin *	Cuw	2000	51,821	76,051	218	63	14	ohl	(wid-03)
9618783	Dockwise Vanguard	Cuw	2012	91,784	116,173	275	79	14	ohl	
9670224	Dockwise White Marlin	Cuw	2015	51,065	72,148	216	63	14	ohl	l/a Fathom
9592850	Finesse	Cuw	2012	36,653	47,500	216	43	14	ohl	
9592848	Forte	Cuw	2012	36,653	48,164	217	43	14	ohl	
8766296	Fjell	Nld	2001	25,751	19,300	147	36	12	ohl	ex Fairmount Fjell-08, Boabarge 20-05 (conv: barge-09)
8636740	Fjord	Nld	2000	19,984	24,800	146	46	12	ohl	ex Fairmount Fjord-07, Boabarge 19-05 (conv. barge-09)
8130899	Mighty Servant 3 (me2)	Cuw	1984	22,123	27,720	181	40	14	ohl	(rbt-09 – following sinking off Luanda)
8025331	Super Servant 3 (2) **	Cuw	1982	10,224	14,138	140	32	13	ohl	
8001000	Swan	Cuw	1981	22,788	30,060	181	32	16	ohl	ex Sea Swan-96, Swan H.L.-89, Dyvi Swan-88
8113554	Swift *	Cuw	1983	22,835	32,187	183	32	15	ohl	ex Sea Swift-96, Swift H.L.-89, Dyvi Swift-88
8918942	Talisman *	Cuw	1993	42,515	53,000	216	45	14	ohl	ex Front Comor-08, Comor-99 (conv/sht tcr-08)
8617938	Target *	Cuw	1990	42,515	53,806	217	45	14	ohl	ex Front Target-07, Genmar Centaur-04, Crude Target-03, Nord-Jahre Target-00, Jahre Target-93 (conv/sht tcr-08)

IMO	name	flag	year	gt	dwt	loa	bm	kts	type	comments
8113566	Teal	Cuw	1984	22,835	32,101	181	32	15	ohl	ex Sea Teal-96, Teal H.L.-89, Dyvi Teal-88
8000977	Tern	Cuw	1982	22,788	30,060	181	32	16	ohl	ex Sea Tern-96, Tern H.L.-89, Dyvi Tern-88
8918930	Transporter	Cuw	1992	42,609	53,806	217	45	14	ohl	ex Front Sunda-08, Sunda-99 (conv/sht tcr-08)
8512279	Transshelf (me2)	Cuw	1987	26,547	34,030	173	40	15	ohl	
8617940	Treasure *	Cuw	1990	42,515	53,818	217	45	14	ohl	ex Front Traveller-08, GenmarTraveller-04, Crude Traveller-03, Nord-Jahre Traveller-00, Jahre Traveller-93 (conv/sht tcr-08)
8902967	Triumph *	Cuw	1992	42,515	53,818	269	45	14	ohl	ex Marble-08 (conv tcr-08)
8902955	Trustee *	Cuw	1991	42,515	54,013	269	45	14	ohl	ex Front Granite-08, Granite-01 (conv tcr-08)

* managed by Anglo-Eastern (UK) Ltd., UK (www.angloeasterngroup.com).

Peter Döhle Schiffahrts-KG   Germany

funnel: black with black 'PD' on white diamond on broad red band bordered by narrow white bands, black with yellow 'ICL' above yellow wave inside yellow rectangular outline (Independent) or charterers colours. **hull:** grey or dark blue with red boot-topping.
history: formed 1956 as Robert Bornhofen KG until 1962, then Peter Döhle to 1973. **web:** www.doehle.de

IMO	name	flag	year	gt	dwt	loa	bm	kts	type	comments
9306079	Adelina D.	Iom	2006	15,487	20,580	179	28	21	ucc	1,579 teu: ex TS Keelung-09, I/a Adeline
9400215	Aglaia	Lbr	2011	42,609	52,788	269	33	24	ucc	4,250 teu: ex UASC Zamzam-12, I/a Aglaia
9202481	Alidra	Pmd	2000	17,167	21,331	169	27	20	ucc	1,600 teu: ex Clou Island-13, MOL Amazonia-13, Clou Island-11, Mira-08, Cala Paestum-07, YM Hakata-04, P&O Nedlloyd Canterbury-03, Mira-02
9295945	Allegoria	Pmd	2006	66,280	68,228	276	40	25	ucc	5,527 teu: ex Anguila-13, Chaiten-12, I/dn Anguila
9217553	Altonia	Deu	2000	16,803	22,968	184	25	20	ucc	1,728 teu: ex MOL Ultimate-12, German Senator-08, Safmarine Mgeni-06, Altonia-04, Safmarine Buffalo-03, Maersk Felixstowe-01, CSAV Marsella-00, I/a Altonia
9397913	Amalthea	Mhl	2009	42,609	52,788	269	33	24	ucc	4,250 teu: ex UASC Sitrah-15, I/a Amalthea
9217565	Amanda D	Pmd	2000	16,803	22,967	184	25	19	ucc	1,728 teu: ex Amanda-15, NYK Lotus-12, Amanda-11, YM Santos-08, MOL Americas-06, Amanda-04, Libra Livorno-03, I/a Amanda
9219367	Anke	Atg	2002	35,824	42,200	220	32	22	ucc	3,104 teu: ex CSAV Moema-09, Norasia Makalu-06, APL Portugal-05, Antonia-02, I/a Chloe
9306201	Annaba	Lbr	2006	15,487	20,615	168	25	20	ucc	1,579 teu: TS Shenzhen-12, I/a Annaba

Choapa Trader : Peter Döhle Schiffahrts-KG : *ARO*

IMO	name	flag	year	gt	dwt	loa	bm	kts	type	comments
9360697	Apollon D	Lbr	2008	26,358	34,282	209	30	22	ucc	2,504 teu: ex TS Singapore-15, Apollon-08
9327671	Ariana	Lbr	2006	32,161	38,700	211	32	21	ucc	2,732 teu: ex CCNI Atenea-12, Ariana-12, l/a Amerigo Vespucci
9327669	Arosia	Lbr	2006	32,161	39,600	212	32	21	ucc	2,732 teu: ex MSC Davos-13, Vasco da Gama-06, Arosia-06, l/a Vasco da Gama
9339595	Artemis	Lbr	2008	26,358	34,439	209	30	22	ucc	2,504 teu: ex TS Korea-15 Artemis-08
9306225	Ava D.	Lbr	2007	15,487	20,647	168	25	20	ucc	1,579 teu: ex TS Hochiminh-12, l/a Ava
9437050	Barbara	Pmd	2010	52,726	65,741	294	32	24	ucc	5,303 teu: ex CSAV Recife-15, l/a Mederie
9306067	Calisto	Lbr	2005	15,487	20,615	168	25	20	ucc	1,578 teu: ex Independent Pursuit-10, Heide E-06
9670822	Cap Corrientes	Lbr	2013	42,690	51,759	228	37	22	ucc	3,820 teu: l/a Vil Dardanelles
9407885	Choapa Trader	Pmd	2009	52,726	65,549	294	32	24	ucc	5,303 teu: ex CSAV Rio de Janeiro-14, l/a Medondra-09
9273959	Christmas Island *	Mhl	2003	25,709	33,891	208	30	21	ucc	2,524 teu: ex Cap Melville-14
9232761	Colette *	Mhl	2002	32,284	39,216	211	32	22	ucc	2,732 teu: ex CMA CGM Montreal-15, Antje Wulff-14, Ibn Abdoun-10, CMA CGM Seagull-05, P&O Nedlloyd Dammam-03, Antje-Helen Wulff-02
9219355	CS Discovery	Lbr	2001	35,645	42,089	220	32	22	ucc	3,104 teu: ex Norasia Balkans-10, Norasia Taurus-05, APL Mexico-04, l/a Katjana, l/dn Celine
9298648	Daphne	Lbr	2006	35,881	41,748	220	32	22	ucc	3,104 teu: ex Emirates Yangtze-12, CCNI Arica-11, l/dn Daphne
9298636	Demeter	Lbr	2005	35,645	41,850	220	32	22	ucc	3,104 teu: ex NileDutch Lion-14, Demeter-12, CCNI Antillanca-11, Demeter-06
9273947	Easter Island *	Mhl	2003	25,709	33,891	208	30	21	ucc	2,524 teu: ex Cap Palmas-14, NYK Fantasia-05, c/a Cap Palmas
9589621	Edgar *	Lbr	2011	65,976	118,936	260	43	14	bbu	
9306287	Emirates Dana	Lbr	2007	73,934	81,243	304	40	25	ucc	6,539 teu: ex Puelche-15
9306184	Emirates Sana	Lbr	2006	73,934	81,236	304	40	25	ucc	6,539 teu: ex Petrohue-15

Hanjin Sooho : Peter Döhle Schiffahrts-KG: *Chris Brooks*

IMO	name	flag	year	gt	dwt	loa	bm	kts	type	comments
9306160	Emirates Wafa	Lbr	2006	73,934	81,236	304	40	25	ucc	6,539 teu: ex Pangal-15, l/dn Alda
9502910	Hanjin Africa	Iom	2012	141,754	140,973	366	48	24	ucc	13,092 teu: c/a Rio Lilly
9502946	Hanjin America	Iom	2012	141,754	140,973	366	48	24	ucc	13,092 teu: c/a Rio Lucy
9502867	Hanjin Asia	Iom	2012	141,754	140,974	366	48	24	ucc	13,092 teu: l/a Rio Eliza
9502972	Hanjin Blue Ocean	Iom	2013	141,754	140,900	366	48	24	ucc	13,092 teu: c/a Rio Ragna
9502908	Hanjin Europe	Iom	2012	141,754	140,973	366	48	24	ucc	13,092 teu: c/a Rio Lara
9502960	Hanjin Gold	Iom	2013	141,754	140,700	366	48	24	ucc	13,092 teu: c/a Rio Nadia
9503732	Hanjin Green Earth	Iom	2013	141,754	140,700	366	48	24	ucc	13,092 teu: l/a Rio Theresa
9502958	Hanjin Harmony	Iom	2013	141,754	141,005	366	48	24	ucc	13,092 teu: c/a Rio Marie
9501239	Hanjin Sooho	Iom	2012	141,754	140,973	366	48	24	ucc	13,092 teu: l/a Rio Elena
9334375	Hebe	Lbr	2008	35,824	42,213	220	32	22	ucc	3,104 teu: ex CSAV Itajai-13, l/dn Hebe
9306237	Independent Accord	Lbr	2007	15,345	20,955	168	25	20	ucc	1,578 teu
9306213	Independent Concept	Lbr	2007	15,345	20,994	168	25	20	ucc	1,578 teu
9619385	Jadrana	Pmd	2014	48,338	58,037	255	37	22	ucc	4,957 teu
9477359	Jamila	Lbr	2010	16,137	17,152	161	25	20	ucc	1,388 teu
9477335	Jan	Lbr	2009	16,137	17,121	161	25	19	ucc	1,388 teu
9308417	Jeju Island *	Mhl	2006	27,786	37,854	222	30	22	ucc	2,742 teu: ex Cape Mondego -14, DAL Reunion-09, YM Mondego-07, Cape Mondego-06
9619402	Jogela	Pmd	2014	48,338	58,032	255	37	22	ucc	4,957 teu
9477347	Jost	Lbr	2010	16,137	17,157	161	25	20	ucc	1,388 teu
9477294	Juliana	Lbr	2009	16,137	17,197	161	25	20	ucc	1,388 teu
9377559	Laila	Pmd	2008	28,048	37,950	215	30	21	ucc	2,700 teu: ex Donau Trader-15, TS Xingang-09, Donau Trader-08
9589633	Laura D *	Lbr	2012	65,976	118,817	260	43	14	bbu	
9311880	Leto	Lbr	2006	35,881	42,200	220	32	22	ucc	3,104 teu: ex CCNI Antofagasta-15, Leto-13, CCNI Antofagasta-12, c/a Leto
9395525	Malleco	Pmd	2009	75,572	81,002	306	40	25	ucc	6,589 teu
9400095	Mataquito	Pmd	2010	75,572	81,002	306	40	25	ucc	6,589 teu
9400071	Maullin	Lbr	2010	75,572	81,002	306	40	25	ucc	6,589 teu
9246712	Minna	Pmd	2005	35,881	41,800	220	32	22	ucc	3,104 teu: ex Emirates Liberty-09, Minna-06, Zeus-05
9535151	MOL Garland	Pmd	2011	59,307	71,409	275	40	24	ucc	5,605 teu
9535137	MOL Gateway	Pmd	2011	59,307	71,429	275	40	24	ucc	5,605 teu
9535216	MOL Generosity	Lbr	2012	59,307	71,416	275	40	24	ucc	5,605 teu
9535199	MOL Genesis	Pmd	2012	59,307	71,416	275	40	24	ucc	5,605 teu
9535175	MOL Guardian	Lbr	2011	59,307	71,416	275	40	24	ucc	5,605 teu
9447847	MSC Fabiola	Pmd	2010	140,259	146,093	366	48	25	ucc	12,552 teu
9447885	MSC Faustina	Pmd	2011	140,259	146,148	366	48	25	ucc	12,552 teu
9447902	MSC Fillippa	Lbr	2011	140,259	146,073	366	48	25	ucc	12,552 teu
9447861	MSC Filomena	Pmd	2010	140,259	146,161	366	48	25	ucc	12,552 teu
9339583	Pomerenia Sky *	Lbr	2007	25,320	34,191	209	30	22	ucc	2,504 teu: ex Hammonia Pomerenia-15, CCNI Busan-09
9693290	Rana	Pmd	2015	25,546	38,569	180	32	14	bbu	
9693329	Ricarda	Pmd	2015	25,546	38,569	180	32	14	bbu	
9437048	Sonche Trader	Pmd	2009	52,726	65,700	294	32	24	ucc	5,303 teu: ex CSAV Suape-14, l/a Medbaffin-09
9294812	Tabea	Pmd	2006	66,280	68,228	276	40	25	ucc	5,527 teu: ex MSC Turchia-10, Cholguan-06
9290787	Talassa	Pmd	2005	66,280	68,228	276	40	25	ucc	5,527 teu: ex MSC Malta-10, Choapa-06
9290945	Tamina	Pmd	2004	66,280	68,228	276	40	25	ucc	5,527 teu: ex MSC France-10, Copiapo-06, Amazonia-04
9290799	Tessa	Lbr	2005	66,280	68,228	276	40	25	ucc	5,527 teu: ex MSC Egypt-10, Chillan-05, l/dn Arizona
9348493	TS Hongkong	Pan	2006	15,487	20,599	168	25	20	ucc	1,579 teu: l/a Hammonia Xenia
9333395	Valdivia	Mhl	2006	17,360	22,229	179	28	21	ucc	1,875 teu
9344722	Valentina	Mhl	2007	17,360	22,263	179	28	21	ucc	1,875 teu
9437062	Vargas Trader	Pmd	2010	52,726	65,710	294	32	24	ucc	5,303 teu: ex CSAV Brasilia-15, Vargas Trader-10, l/a Med Superior
9290177	Vera D.	Pmd	2004	17,188	22,513	179	28	21	ucc	1,719 teu: ex Maersk Vera Cruz-09, l/a Pyxis
9290165	Victoria	Pmd	2004	17,188	22,506	179	28	21	ucc	1,719 teu: ex Maersk Victoria-09, l/a Palomar
9404443	Vil Atlantic	Lbr	2010	24,165	37,852	190	28	13	bbu	l/a Salta
9492402	Vil Baltic	Lbr	2010	33,044	57,021	189	32	14	bbu	ex Wuhan-11
9344710	Violetta	Mhl	2007	17,360	22,267	179	28	21	ucc	1,875 teu: ex DAL Madagascar-10, Violetta-09, CMA CGM Providencia-08, MOL Drakensberg-07, l/a Violetta

IMO	name	flag	year	gt	dwt	loa	bm	kts	type	comments
9333369	Viona	Pmd	2006	17,189	22,300	179	28	21	ucc	1,719 teu: ex Emirates Dar es Salaam-13, Viona-12, Safmarine Mbashe-09, Viona-06
9236535	YM Portland	Lbr	2003	51,364	58,255	286	32	25	ucc	4,444 teu: ex Norasia Enterprise-07, Amaranta-03
newbuildings:										
9693331	Riva	Pmd	2016	25,546	38,569	180	32	14	bbu	Jiangsu Hantong HT38-135
9696826	Rosalia		2016	25,546	38,569	180	32	14	bbu	Jiangsu Hantong HT38-167
9696838	R		2016	24,270	38,569	180	32	14	bbu	Jiangsu Hantong HT38-168
9725512	Rubina		2016	24,270	38,569	180	32	14	bbu	Jiangsu Hantong HT38-211
9725524	R		2016	24,270	38,569	180	32	14	bbu	Jiangsu Hantong HT38-212
			2016		63,800	200	32	14	bbu	Yangzijiang
			2016		63,800	200	32	14	bbu	Yangzijiang
			2016		63,800	200	32	14	bbu	Yangzijiang
			2016		63,800	200	32	14	bbu	Yangzijiang
			2017		37,000		35	18	ucc	2,708 teu Jiangsu Yangzijiang
			2017		37,000		35	18	ucc	2,708 teu

also 8 x 1,000 teu ucc [Yangzijiang SY] , 4 x 4,750 teu ucc (Jiangsu 4800)
2 x 3,800teu containerships [Jiangsu New Jiangzi SY. (2018)] for Hamburg-Süd 7-year charter [reported 11.2015] originally HS option
also owns/manages a large number of smaller vessels and has a 13% minority interest in Navieros Group controlled Compania Chilena de Navegacion Interoceanica SA, Chile (CCNI)
* managed by Midocean (IOM) Ltd, part of Döhle IOM Ltd, UK (formed 1994 as Midocean Maritime Ltd to 2001 – www.doehle-iom.com)

Hammonia Reederei GmbH & Co. KG, Germany
funnel: black with black 'PD' on white diamond on broad red band bordered by narrow white bands or charterer's colours. *hull:* various with red boot-topping. *history:* founded 2003 jointly by Peter Döhle and HCI Hanseatische Capital AG.
web: www.hammonia-reederei.de

IMO	name	flag	year	gt	dwt	loa	bm	kts	type	comments
9316323	Apulia	Lbr	2005	30,047	35,741	208	32	22	ucc	2,763 teu: ex CCNI Punta Arenas-11, l/d Amasia
9149304	Belgica	Lbr	1997	25,608	34,015	208	30	21	ucc	2,468 teu: ex Emirates Rafiki-11, Belgica-10, Cap Egmont-08, Cap Norte-06, Santos Express-03, Sea Ocelot-02, Transroll Argentina-00, Cap Norte-99, Impala-98, Brasil Star-98, Impala-97
9399753	CMA CGM Pointe Marin	Lbr	2008	32,901	35,534	225	31	21	ucc	2,872 teu: ex Hammonia Antofagasta-16, Maersk Jennings-13, Antofagasta-08
9280665	CMA CGM Wagner	Pmd	2004	65,247	73,235	277	40	24	ucc	5,770 teu
9622019	Hammonia America	Lbr	2014	47,873	56,619	250	37	21	ucc	4,896 teu: l/a Box King, l/d Seavelvet
9376012	Hammonia Bavaria	Lbr	2009	26,435	34,000	209	30	22	ucc	2,504 teu
9336177	Hammonia Berolina	Lbr	2007	26,435	34,236	209	30	22	ucc	2,546 teu
9477309	Hammonia Calabria	Lbr	2010	40,541	50,488	260	32	24	ucc	4,253 teu: ex CSAV La Ligua-14, c/a Hammonia Calabria
9326823	Hammonia Emden	Lbr	2006	26,836	34,248	210	30	21	ucc	2,556 teu: ex Emirates Nile-14, Libra Ipanema-11, l/a Hammonia Emden
9400186	Hammonia Galicia	Lbr	2010	42,609	52,788	268	32	24	ucc	4,178 teu
9122394	Hammonia Gallicum †Lbr		1996	29,383	34,671	196	32	22	ucc	2,959 teu: ex Mare Gallicum-12, YM Hiroshima-10, Mare Gallicum-06, Ipex Emperor-02, OOCL Haven-01, Mare Gallicum-00, Acapulco-98, TMM Acapulco-97, Mare Gallicum-96
9477311	Hammonia Grenada	Pmd	2010	40,541	50,488	260	32	24	ucc	4,253 teu: ex CSAV Laraquete-15, c/a Hammonia Grenada
9326835	Hammonia Husum	Lbr	2006	26,836	34,253	210	30	21	ucc	2,546 teu: ex Libra Copacabana-11, l/a Hammonia Husum
9175975	Hammonia Internum	Lbr	1997	29,383	34,705	196	32	22	ucc	2,959 teu: ex Mare Internum-12, Maersk Pittsburg-07, Mare Internum-04
9143518	Hammonia Ionium †	Lbr	1997	29,750	34,800	196	32	21	ucc	2,959 teu: ex Mare Ionium-12, Tiger Star-11, Mare Ionium-10, Maersk Peterhead-09, OOCL Harmony-04, Mare Ionium-00
9477323	Hammonia Istra	Lbr	2013	48,338	57,988	255	37	22	ucc	4,760 teu: ex Emirates Pearl-14, l/a Hammonia Istria
9358436	Hammonia Jutlandia	Lbr	2006	35,564	44,174	223	32	22	ucc	3,398 teu; ex AS Jutlandia-13, Johannesburg-10, MOL Will-08, Johannesburg-06
9515759	Hammonia Korsika	Lbr	2010	32,987	56,722	205	32	14	bbu	
9515747	Hammonia Malta	Lbr	2010	32,987	56,700	205	32	14	bbu	

IMO	name	flag	year	gt	dwt	loa	bm	kts	type	comments
9383261	Hammonia Massilia	Lbr	2008	26,435	34,000	209	30	22	ucc	2,546 teu: ex TS India-10, Hammonia Massilia-08
9336165	Hammonia Palatium	Lbr	2006	26,435	34,305	209	30	22	ucc	2,546 teu: ex Emirates Zambesi-15, Hammonia Palatium-11, MOL Stability-09, CCNI Ningbo-09, l/dn Hammonia Palatium
9401051	Hammonia Pescara	Lbr	2009	39,900	50,849	260	32	24	ucc	4,526 teu: UASC Shuwaikh-14, l/a Benjamin Schulte-09
9383259	Hammonia Roma	Lbr	2009	25,320	33,800	209	30	22	ucc	2,546 teu: ex TS Malaysia-10, l/a Hammonia Roma
9622007	Hammonia Sapphire	Lbr	2014	47,873	56,592	250	37	24	ucc	ex Sapphire-15, l/a Seaviolet
9151527	Hammonia Thracium	Lbr	1997	29,383	34,705	196	32	22	ucc	2,959 teu: ex Mare Thracium-12, Maersk Petersburg-07, Mare Thracium-04, MSC Oregon-01, Mare Thracium-00
9383247	Hammonia Teutonica	Lbr	2008	26,435	34,376	209	30	22	ucc	2,546 teu: ex MOL Serenity-10, Hammonia Teutonica-08
9477385	Hammonia Toscana	Lbr	2013	48,338	58,170	255	37	22	ucc	4,770 teu: ex CCNI Busan-14, c/a Hammonia Toscana
9400203	Hammonia Venetia	Lbr	2010	42,609	52,788	268	32	24	ucc	4,178 teu: ex Valparaiso Express-12, c/a Hammonia Venetia
9623843	Hammonia Virginia	Lbr	2014	47,911	56,300	250	37	24	ucc	c/a Marina L
9273806	HR Constellation	Lbr	2006	10,899	12,476	157	22	17	ghl	cr: 2(240): ex Beluga Constellation-11, l/a Beluga Constitution
9273791	HR Constitution	Atg	2006	10,899	12,479	157	22	17	ghl	cr: 2(240); ex Beluga Constitution-11, l/a Beluga Constellation
9214563	HR indication	Lbr	2000	11,434	13,289	162	20	17	ghl	cr: 2(350), 1(150): ex Beluga Indication-11, Nirint Iberia-07, Beluga Indication-06, CEC Apollon-04 (len-07)
9214551	HR Intonation	Lbr	2000	11,434	13,426	162	20	17	ghl	cr: 2(350), 1(150): ex Beluga Intonation-11, Nirint Atlas-07, Beluga Intonation-05, Nirint Atlas-04, TMC Atlas-03, Atlas-02, Industrial Atlas-02, CEC Atlas-01 (len-07)
9187033	HR Margaretha	Lbr	1999	11,894	17,539	143	22	16	ggc	ex SE Verdant-12, Margaretha Green-10, Newpac Cumulus-05, Margaretha Green-04, Nirint Voyager-02, Coral Green-01, Margaretha Green-00
9164017	HR Maria	Lbr	1998	11,894	17,539	143	22	16	ggc	ex SE Viridian-12, Maria Green-10, BBC India-08, Maria Green-04
9164029	HR Marion	Lbr	1999	11,894	17,539	143	22	16	ggc	ex SE Verdigris-12, Marion Green-10, BBC Malaysia-08, Marion Green-06
9336189	Independent Pursuit	Lbr	2007	26,435	34,282	209	30	22	ucc	2,546 teu: ex Hammonia Fortuna-11
9336191	Independent Spirit	Lbr	2007	26,435	34,242	209	30	22	ucc	2,546 teu: ex Hammonia Pacificum-15
9481532	Independent Voyager	Lbr	2011	28,561	39,164	225	30	22	ucc	2,790 teu: l/a Hammonia Baltica, l/d Positano
9246683	Letavia	Lbr	2005	35,881	42,157	220	32	22	ucc	3,104 teu: ex Emirates Freedom-09, Letavia-06, Norasia Atlas-05, l/a Cosima
9246695	Lutetia	Lbr	2005	35,881	41,802	220	32	22	ucc	3,104 teu: ex Emirates Marina-11, CSAV Rio Trancura-06, Coletta-05
9085534	Maersk Kotka	Pmd	1996	81,488	84,900	318	43	25	ucc	7,908 teu: ex Knud Maersk-08
9301495	MSC Bilbao	Pmd	2006	89,941	102,759	334	43	25	ucc	8,204 teu: l/dn Hammonia Bremen
9085558	MSC Karlskrona	Pmd	1996	81,488	82,135	318	43	25	ucc	7,908 teu: ex Maersk Karlskrona-16, Karen Maersk-08
9085546	MSC Kleven	Pmd	1996	81,488	84,900	318	43	25	ucc	7,908 teu: ex Maersk Kleven-16, Kate Maersk-08
9301483	MSC Paris	Pmd	2006	89,941	102,761	334	43	25	ucc	8,204 teu: ex CSAV Paris-12, MSC Paris-11, c/a Hammonia Hamburg
9301471	MSC Valencia	Pmd	2006	89,941	102,756	335	43	25	ucc	8,204 teu: ex CSAV Valencia-12, MSC Valencia-12, c/a Hammonia Jork
9219379	Polonia	Lbr	2003	35,645	41,850	221	32	22	ucc	3,104 teu: ex Libra Rio-12, l/a Katharina, l/dn Albona
9219393	Saxonia	Pmd	2003	35,645	42,062	220	32	22	ucc	3,104 teu: ex X-Press Godavari-13, Saxonia-13, Emirates Ganges-13, TS Dubai-12, Azalea-06, APL Shanghai-07, Azalea-03, l/d Clarissa
9219408	Westphalia	Lbr	2003	35,645	41,850	220	32	22	ucc	3,104 teu: ex Emirates Kabir-13, APL Jakarta-06, Julia-03, Alessa-03, l/d Carmen

IMO	name	flag	year	gt	dwt	loa	bm	kts	type	comments
9383235	Westwood Robson	Lbr	2008	26,435	34,330	209	30	21	ucc	2,546 teu: ex Hammonia Holsatia-15, TS Qingdao-13, APL Qingdao-10, Hyundai Qingdao-09, l/a Hammonia Holsatia
9398424	Zim Chicago	Lbr	2010	91,158	108,574	334	43	25	ucc	8,242 teu
9398436	Zim Djibouti	Lbr	2009	114,044	116,440	349	46	25	ucc	10,070 teu
9398395	Zim Los Angeles	Lbr	2009	91,158	108,574	349	46	25	ucc	8,242 teu

† managed by Hansa Mare Reederei

Dole Food Co. U.S.A.

funnel: *dark blue with red 'Dole' symbol on white band between two narrow red bands.* **hull:** *white or cream with red 'Dole' symbol above blue line, red boot-topping.* **history:** *founded 1851 and 1975 merged with Castle & Cook Inc. 1991.* **web:** *www.dole.com*

IMO	name	flag	year	gt	dwt	loa	bm	kts	type	comments
9046328	Dole Africa	Bhs	1994	10,584	10,288	150	23	21	grf	
9046502	Dole America	Bhs	1994	10,584	10,288	150	23	21	grf	
9046526	Dole Asia	Bhs	1994	10,584	10,288	150	23	21	grf	
9703069	Dole Atlantic	Bhs	2016	25,669	27,513	190	30	20	ucc	1,540 teu
8513467	Dole California	Bhs	1989	16,488	11,800	179	27	20	ucc	890 teu
9185281	Dole Chile	Bhs	1999	31,779	30,145	205	32	21	ucc	2,046 teu
9185293	Dole Colombia	Bhs	1999	31,779	30,145	205	32	21	ucc	2,046 teu
8900335	Dole Costa Rica	Bhs	1991	16,488	11,800	179	27	20	ucc	890 teu
8513479	Dole Ecuador	Bhs	1989	16,488	11,800	179	27	20	ucc	890 teu
9046514	Dole Europa	Bhs	1994	10,584	10,288	150	23	21	grf	
8900323	Dole Honduras	Bhs	1991	16,488	11,800	179	27	20	ucc	910 teu
9703057	Dole Pacific	Bhs	2015	25,669	27,513	190	30	20	ucc	1,540 teu
8408882	Tropical Sky	Bhs	1986	9,749	11,998	149	22	20	grf	
8408894	Tropical Star	Bhs	1986	9,749	11,998	149	22	20	grf	

newbuilding:
IMO	name	flag	year	gt	dwt	loa	bm	kts	type	comments
9703071	Dole Caribbean	Bhs	2016	25,600	27,500	190	30	20	ucc	1,540 teu Hyundai Mipo 4087

vessels operated by Dole Ocean Cargo Express and managed by subsidiary Reefership Marine Services Ltd, Costa Rica (formed 1976 as Intercontinental Transportation Services Ltd to 1991 and Dole Fresh Fruit International Ltd to 2000)

Dorian LPG Management Corp. Greece

funnel: *white with broad red band over broad blue band, black top.* **hull:** *light blue with LPG in white, red boot topping* **history:** *Dorian (Hellas) founded 1973 entered LPG market in 2002, expanded in 2006 and in 2014 purchased vessels orifinally ordered by Scorpio.* **web:** *www.dorianlpg.com*

IMO	name	flag	year	gt	dwt	loa	bm	kts	type	comments
9347504	Captain John NP	Bhs	2007	47,173	58,585	225	37	19	lpg	82,000 m³
9315680	Captain Markos NL	Bhs	2006	47,173	58,691	225	37	19	lpg	82,000 m³
9351919	Captain Nicholas ML	Bhs	2008	47,173	58,690	225	37	19	lpg	82,000 m³
9722807	Caravelle	Bhs	2016	47,379	54,490	225	37	19	lpg	84,000 m³
9722792	Challenger	Bhs	2015	47,379	54,509	225	37	19	lpg	84,000 m³
9714393	Chaparral	Bhs	2015	47,379	54,584	225	37	19	lpg	84,000 m³
9706504	Cheyenne	Bhs	2015	47,379	54,555	225	37	19	lpg	84,000 m³
9706487	Clermont	Bhs	2015	47,379	54,543	225	37	19	lpg	84,000 m³
9702015	Cobra	Bhs	2015	48,060	54,501	225	37	19	lpg	84,000 m³
9689914	Comet	Bhs	2014	48,060	54,335	225	37	19	lpg	84,000 m³
9734692	Commander	Bhs	2015	48,060	54,410	225	37	19	lpg	84,000 m³
9702027	Commodore	Bhs	2015	47,379	54,561	225	37	19	lpg	84,000 m³
9734678	Concorde	Bhs	2015	48,060	54,336	225	37	19	lpg	84,000 m³
9734680	Constellation	Bhs	2015	48,060	54,336	225	37	19	lpg	84,000 m³
9706499	Constitution	Bhs	2015	47,379	54,533	225	37	19	lpg	84,000 m³
9714381	Continental	Bhs	2015	47,379	54,490	225	37	19	lpg	84,000 m³
9706516	Copernicus	Bhs	2015	48,000	51,550	225	37	19	lpg	84,000 m³: l/a STI Tokyo
9689926	Corsair	Bhs	2014	48,060	54,336	225	37	19	lpg	84,000 m³
9703837	Corvette	Bhs	2015	48,050	54,336	225	37	19	lpg	84,000 m³
9702003	Cougar	Bhs	2015	47,379	54,450	225	37	19	lpg	84,000 m³
9702041	Cratis	Bhs	2015	48,963	54,656	225	37	19	lpg	84,000 m³: l/a STI Geneva
9702039	Cresques	Bhs	2015	48,963	54,646	225	37	19	lpg	84,000 m³: l/a STI Dubai

DT-Bereederungs GmbH & Co. KG Germany

funnel: *yellow or charterers colours.* **hull:** *black, green, blue and grey with red boot-topping.* **history:** *controlled by Danz (shipowners since 1870) and Tietjens (since 1824) families formed as Danz und Tietjens Schiffahrts KG in 1982, being renamed in 2003.* **web:** *www.danz-tietjens.de*

IMO	name	flag	year	gt	dwt	loa	bm	kts	type	comments
9113446	Bavaria *	Atg	1996	14,473	18,355	159	24	19	ucc	1,205 teu: ex CSAV Cedar-09, Bavaria-08, ANL Yanderra-08, Bavaria-07, TS Kelang-06, ACX Primrose-04, Doris Wulff-03, Sakura-01, Norasia Montreal-00, Direct Jabiru-99, OOCL Amity-98, Doris Wulff-97, Nuova Ionia-96, Doris Wulff-96, Nuova Ionia-*96*, I/a Doris Wulff
9497323	Burgia	Atg	2010	43,717	79,403	229	32	15	bbu	
9230787	Gloria *	Atg	2001	16,803	22,967	185	25	20	ucc	1,728 teu: ex Vento di Meltemi-15, Gloria-15, P&O Nedlloyd Pessoa-04, P&O Nedlloyd Lagos-02, I/a Gloria
9277400	Öland	Mlt	2003	7,519	8,621	137	21	19	ucc	822 teu: I/a Frisia
9497335	Selandia	Atg	2011	43,717	79,508	229	32	14	bbu	

* owned or managed by associated BBC-Burger Bereederungs Kontor GmbH & Co KG, Germany

Dynacom Tankers Management

Greece

funnel: *black with broad white band.* **hull:** *black with red boot-topping.* **history:** *founded 1991* **web:** *www.dynacomtm.com*

IMO	name	flag	year	gt	dwt	loa	bm	kts	type	comments
9597018	Agistri	Lbr	2012	81,476	149,999	274	48	15	tcr	
9476654	Amazon	Lbr	2011	85,496	149,999	274	50	15	tcr	
9114608	Apollo	Lbr	1996	79,832	148,435	269	46	15	tcr	ex Hellespont Trader-12
9389564	Athina	Lbr	2008	42,331	74,999	228	32	14	tco	
9595216	Boston	Lbr	2012	166,093	299,996	333	60	15	tcr	
9280354	Commander	Lbr	2004	38,833	71,056	229	32	15	tcr	ex Sanko Commander-10
9280366	Confidence	Lbr	2004	38,833	71,024	229	32	15	tcr	ex Sanko Confidence-10
9406910	Constantinos	Lbr	2009	42,010	73,307	228	33	15	tco	
9595228	Dalian	Lbr	2013	166,093	299,981	330	60	15	tcr	
9432048	Demetrios	Lbr	2011	85,496	149,999	274	50	15	tcr	
9432062	Eleni	Lbr	2011	85,496	149,999	274	50	15	tcr	
9387578	Eliza	Lbr	2008	160,836	299,999	333	60	15	tcr	
9296389	Equator	Lbr	2006	78,845	149,997	274	48	15	tcr	
9575943	Evgenia I	Mlt	2011	156,651	296,793	333	60	15	tcr	
9297436	Felicity	Lbr	2005	38,832	71,029	228	32	14	tco	

Amazon : Dynacom Tankers Mgmt : *Chris Brooks*

IMO	name	flag	year	gt	dwt	loa	bm	kts	type	comments
9597006	Fleves	Lbr	2012	81,476	149,999	274	48	15	tcr	
9389033	Georgios	Lbr	2009	160,598	299,999	333	60	15	tcr	
9432050	Giannis	Lbr	2011	85,496	149,999	275	50	15	tcr	
9378834	Gladiator	Lbr	2008	78,845	149,944	274	48	15	tcr	
9596947	Houston	Mlt	2012	160,534	318,701	333	60	15	tcr	
9301732	Ice Energy	Ven	2006	38,832	70,377	228	32	14	tco	
9333656	Ice Fighter	Lbr	2006	38,832	70,374	228	32	14	tco	
9296406	Ice Transporter	Lbr	2006	77,636	146,270	274	48	14	tcr	
9301744	Ice Victory	Ven	2006	38,832	70,372	228	32	14	tco	
9387566	Ioanna	Lbr	2008	160,836	318,325	333	60	15	tcr	
9526461	Ithaki	Mlt	2011	160,487	317,916	333	60	15	tcr	
9508859	Kalliopi	Mlt	2010	156,651	296,659	333	60	15	tcr	
9410208	Karolos	Lbr	2009	85,362	149,991	276	50	15	tco	
9390927	Kerala	Lbr	2009	42,331	74,999	228	32	14	tco	
9403542	Leader	Lbr	2009	42,331	74,999	228	32	14	tco	
9407847	Maistros	Lbr	2009	42,010	73,307	228	32	14	tco	
9426594	Margarita	Lbr	2008	42,331	74,998	228	32	14	tco	
9389021	Marina	Lbr	2009	160,598	299,999	333	60	15	tcr	
9407823	Meltemi	Lbr	2009	42,010	73,307	228	32	14	tco	
9110183	Morning Glory	Lbr	1996	57,145	98,743	245	41	15	tco	ex Morning Glory III-10
9509011	Mount Fuji	Lbr	2010	85,362	149,998	276	48	14	tcr	
9296377	Navigator	Lbr	2006	78,845	149,996	275	48	14	tcr	
9633446	Novo	Mlt	2012	85,436	149,999	274	50	15	tcr	
9633458	Odessa	Mlt	2013	85,436	149,999	274	50	15	tcr	
9509023	Pissiotis	Lbr	2010	85,362	149,998	276	50	15	tcr	
9493767	Pola	Lbr	2011	83,562	149,996	275	48	15	tcr	
9575955	Polymnia I	Mlt	2011	156,651	296,812	333	60	15	tcr	l/a Polymnia
9378876	Samurai	Lbr	2009	78,845	149,993	274	48	15	tcr	
9407835	Scirocco	Lbr	2009	42,010	73,382	228	32	15	tco	
9403554	Serengeti	Lbr	2009	42,331	74,998	228	32	14	tco	
9118458	Shanghai	Lbr	1996	80,639	148,018	274	48	15	tcr	ex Hellespont Trinity-12
9493779	Smyrni	Lbr	2011	83,562	149,998	274	48	15	tcr	
9286657	South Sea	Lbr	2005	78,845	149,993	274	48	15	tcr	
9390939	Sovereign	Lbr	2009	42,331	74,998	228	32	14	tco	
9133848	Tajimare	Mlt	2006	148,330	265,539	333	60	15	tcr	ex Tajima-11
9410210	Tataki	Lbr	2010	85,362	149,992	276	50	15	tco	
9623685	Texas	Mlt	2012	160,534	318,563	333	60	15	tcr	
9432036	Tony	Lbr	2010	85,496	149,995	274	50	15	tco	
9414931	Yiangos	Mlt	2010	156,651	296,800	333	60	15	tcr	
9410222	Zouzou N.	Lbr	2010	85,362	149,997	276	50	15	tco	

Eastern Pacific Shipping Pte. Ltd.   Singapore

funnel: light blue with broad yellow band. **hull:** black, grey, red or white with red boot-topping. **history:** formed 2013 by Idal Ofer, following split of Zodiac Maritime Agencies **web:** www.epshipping.com.sgp

IMO	name	flag	year	gt	dwt	loa	bm	kts	type	comments
9317717	Andaman Sea	Sgp	2005	59,158	115,567	244	42	14	tcr	ex Forward Fortune-13
9161314	Aral Sea	Sgp	1999	58,129	104,884	244	42	14	tcr	ex Bali Sea-04
9337406	Banda Sea	Lbr	2007	56,172	105,576	238	42	14	tcr	ex BM Mimosa-12
9192258	Barents Sea	Sgp	2000	57,680	105,588	248	43	15	tcr	
9238753	Bavaria	Lbr	2003	39,941	50,811	260	32	24	ucc	4,253 teu: ex NileDutch Giraffe-15, Bavaria-14, Bavaria Express-12, CP Indigo-06, Contship Indigo-05, APL Panama-04
9232096	Bella	Lbr	2002	50,242	58,814	282	32	24	ucc	4,367 teu: ex MSC Bellatrix-15, Norasia Bellatrix-13, Hanjin Pennsylvania - 04
9367827	Blackpool Tower	Sgp	2009	26,638	34,252	213	29	22	ucc	2,578 teu
9192260	Blue Sun	Lbr	2000	57,680	105,856	244	43	15	tcr	ex Arafura Sea-14
9162497	Botswana	Lbr	1998	75,637	81,819	300	40	24	ucc	6,214 teu: ex MSC Botswana-12, NYK Andromeda-10
9538945	Bridgegate	Lbr	2010	29,977	53,477	190	32	23	bbu	
9588146	Brightway	Sgp	2012	83,824	160,396	274	48	14	tcr	
9324734	Cambridge	Lbr	2006	23,003	26,427	174	28	16	lpg	ex Camberley-14
9629380	Cap Arnauti	Lbr	2013	69,809	80,578	271	43	23	ucc	6,622 teu
9577044	Catalan Sea	Lbr	2011	64,089	116,719	250	44	15	tcr	ex Sharp Lady-14
9259599	Celtic Sea	Lbr	2003	56,204	105,611	229	42	14	tcr	ex Sea Lady -14
9242156	Ceylon	Sgp	2002	28,099	46,001	180	32	15	tco	ex Akebono-04
9253313	Coral Sea	Sgp	2003	57,680	105,666	248	43	14	tcr	
9493200	Crystalgate	Lbr	2010	17,025	28,183	169	27	14	bbu	
9325178	CSAV Rio Aysen *	Lbr	2007	46,800	12,322	183	32	20	mve	4,902 ceu
9494905	CSAV Rio Grey	Lbr	2009	60,387	17,245	200	32	20	mve	6,295 ceu
9627916	CSAV Trancura	Lbr	2013	96,628	115,997	300	48	21	ucc	8,600 teu

Brightway : Eastern Pacific Shipping : *Hans Kraijenbosch*

Catalan Sea : Eastern Pacific Shipping : *Hans Kraijenbosch*

IMO	name	flag	year	gt	dwt	loa	bm	kts	type	comments
8807650	Cumbria	Lbr	1990	13,455	13,453	146	23	14	lpg	17,957 m³ ex Victoire-04, Kelvin-96
9293155	Davis Sea	Lbr	2005	57,164	106,062	244	42	14	tco	ex Asian Jade-15, l/a KWK Jade
9689184	Devongate	Lbr	2014	34,570	61,517	200	32	14	bbu	
9363857	Ebony Ray	Sgp	2008	11,590	19,998	146	24	14	tco	ex Millennium Park-14
9594896	Emerald Summit	Sgp	2013	42,392	74,986	228	32	14	tco	
9590319	Fairway	Sgp	2013	83,824	160,025	274	48	14	tcr	
9640102	Golden Ray	Lbr	2012	11,733	19,802	146	24	14	tco	ex Beihai Park-14
9276262	Green Ray *	Gbr	2003	11,590	19,940	146	24	14	tco	ex Green Park-14
9631113	Hanjin New Jersey	Lbr	2013	40,855	52,040	228	37	21	ucc	3,614 teu
9332884	Hyundai Long Beach *	Gbr	2009	71,786	72,982	293	40	26	ucc	6,350 teu
9393319	Hyundai Loyalty	Sgp	2009	94,511	95,810	340	46	27	ucc	8,562 teu
9393307	Hyundai Mercury *	Lbr	2009	94,511	95,810	340	46	27	ucc	8,562 teu
9385025	Hyundai New York	Sgp	2009	71,786	72,982	293	40	26	ucc	6,350 teu
9385001	Hyundai Tacoma *	Lbr	2009	71,786	72,982	293	40	26	ucc	6,350 teu
9521394	Indian Friendship	Lbr	2014	95,009	181,125	292	45	14	bbu	
9626651	Indian Harmony	Lbr	2013	42,576	75,385	225	32	14	bbu	
9626663	Indian Solidarity	Lbr	2014	42,576	75,398	225	32	14	bbu	
9727364	Irongate	Lbr	2015	17,027	28,316	169	27	14	bbu	
9505986	Ivory Ray	Lbr	2011	11,987	19,991	146	24	14	tco	ex Highbury Park-14, Sanko Noble-12
9367815	Jakarta Tower	Lbr	2008	26,638	34,325	213	29	22	ucc	2,578 teu: ex Thirsk-08
9402328	Kara Sea	Sgp	2010	59,180	115,191	244	42	14	tcr	
9343118	Kent	Lbr	2007	22,914	26,438	174	28	15	lpg	35,205 m³
9395379	Koro Sea	Lbr	2008	56,355	105,905	241	41	14	tco	ex Asian Jasper-15, Blue Jasper-11
9713882	Lake Geneva	Lbr	2015	59,516	18,770	200	32	19	mve	6,203 ceu
9308792	Lake Kivu *	Lbr	2006	46,800	12,322	183	32	20	mve	4,902 ceu: CSAV Rio Imperial-13
9162485	Lesotho	Lbr	1997	75,637	81,819	300	40	24	ucc	6,214 teu: ex MSC Lesotho-12, NYK Antares-10
9577032	Ligurian Sea	Lbr	2011	64,089	116,715	250	44	14	tcr	ex Smart Lady-14
9463059	Maersk Effingham	Sgp	2011	141,649	140,700	366	48	25	ucc	13,092 teu: ex CMA CGM Effingham-14, Maersk Effingham-12
9463047	Maersk Enfield	Sgp	2011	141,649	141,406	366	48	25	ucc	13,092 teu: ex CMA CGM Enfield-14, Maersk Enfield-12
9463035	Maersk Eubank	Sgp	2011	141.649	141.398	366	48	25	ucc	13,092 teu
9184392	Maritime Jewel	Lbr	2000	157,833	299,364	332	58	15	tcr	ex Limburg-03
9446116	Marmara Sea	Lbr	2009	56,355	105,860	241	41	14	tco	ex Asian Sapphire-15, Blue Sapphire-11
9289908	Morning Miracle *+	Lbr	2006	46,800	12,600	183	32	20	mve	4,902 ceu
9493755	Mount Apo	Lbr	2012	91,792	175,800	292	45	14	bbu	ex Cape Seagull-15
9409118	Mount Austin	Lbr	2010	92,248	178,623	292	45	14	bbu	ex First Emu-15
9738832	Mount Bolivar	Lbr	2016	92,992	181,070	292	45	14	bbu	l/a Aquacargo
9446635	Mount Dampier	Lbr	2011	92,752	181,469	292	45	14	bbu	ex Cape Raptor-15, Frontier Oasis-14
9345609	Mount Faber	Lbr	2008	89,603	176,943	289	45	14	bbu	ex Cape Pelican-15, Ocean Comet-14
9512939	Mount Hedland	Lbr	2010	93,369	181,196	292	45	14	bbu	ex Cape Peregrine-15, Sanko Power-14
9737840	Mount Hermon	Lbr	2016	93,297	182,503	292	45	14	bbu	c/a Megalodon
9337107	Mount Kinabalu	Lbr	2007	101,933	203,185	300	50	14	bbu	ex Cape Albatross-15
9300594	Mount Nevis	Pan	2005	89,651	177,005	289	45	14	bbu	ex Cape Harrier-15
9296212	Mount Ophir	Lbr	2004	90,091	180,181	290	45	14	bbu	ex Cape Gannet-15, Cape Condor-13
9446635	Mount Rainier	Lbr	2011	92,752	181,469	292	45	14	bbu	ex Cape Raptor-15, Frontier Oasis-14
9311440	Mount Sinai	Lbr	2006	88,490	177,656	290	45	15	bbu	ex Shagang First-15
9675638	Mount Uluru	Lbr	2014	92,722	181,513	292	45	15	bbu	ex Atlantic Maru-15
9152296	Mozambique	Lbr	1998	76,847	82,275	299	40	24	ucc	6,208 teu: ex MSC Mozambique-12, NYK Canopus-10
9618264	MSC Abidjan	Pan	2013	95,390	110,875	300	48	22	ucc	8,827 teu: l/d MSC Edna
8803410	MSC Claudia	Pan	1989	50,538	59,285	291	32	23	ucc	4,038 teu: ex Montreal-11, Maersk Montreal-10, Oriental Bay-06
9110391	MSC Dymphna	Pan	1996	64,054	51,120	275	40	25	ucc	5,711 teu: ex Hyundai Discovery-13, MSC Discovery-11, Hyundai Discovery-09
9606326	MSC Istanbul	Pan	2015	176,490	186,650	399	54	23	ucc	15,908 teu
9074042	MSC Messina	Lbr	1995	60,117	63,014	300	37	23	ucc	4,963 teu: ex Sandra Blanca-07, NYK Vega-01
9110377	MSC Samantha	Pan	1996	64,054	68,537	275	40	25	ucc	5,711 teu: ex Hyundai Independence-13, MSC Independence -11
9647473	MSC Venice	Lbr	2015	176,490	186,650	399	54	23	ucc	15,908 teu
9364215	Nectar Sea	Lbr	2008	55,894	105,370	229	42	14	tcr	ex Sky Lady-14
9411082	Nobleway	Sgp	2010	86,266	164,028	275	48	14	tcr	ex Knock Clune-14
9232096	Norasia Bellatrix	Lbr	2002	50,242	58,814	282	32	24	ucc	4,369 teu: ex Hanjin Pennsylvania-04
9432919	Osaka Car	Sgp	2009	46,800	12,321	183	32	19	mve	4,902 ceu

108

IMO	name	flag	year	gt	dwt	loa	bm	kts	type	comments
9238777	Osaka Tower	Gbr	2003	39,941	50,759	260	32	24	ucc	4,253 teu: ex Hammonia Express-11, CP Aguascalientes-06, TMM Aguascalientes-05
9402782	Pacific Beryl	Sgp	2010	26,916	47,377	180	32	14	tco	ex Sanko Lynx-11
9573660	Pacific Diamond	Lbr	2010	28,778	47,917	180	32	14	tco	
9539597	Pacific Onyx	Lbr	2013	28,426	50,006	183	32	14	tco	
9573696	Pacific Quartz	Lbr	2011	28,778	47,941	180	32	14	tco	
9539573	Pacific Zircon	Lbr	2013	28,426	50,015	183	32	14	tco	
9280861	Pusan	Lbr	2004	53,453	62,740	294	32	24	ucc	4,992 teu: ex Zim Pusan -14
9457593	Ross Sea	Sgp	2011	59,180	114,542	244	42	14	tcr	
9442017	Serene Sea	Lbr	2009	55,894	105,244	229	42	14	tcr	ex Moon Lady-14
9493133	Silver Ray	Lbr	2013	11,600	19,801	141	24	14	tco	ex Kenton Park-14
9493212	Stargate	Gbr	2011	17,025	28,221	169	27	14	bbu	
9311521	Sulu Sea	Lbr	2005	56,204	105,522	229	42	14	tcr	ex Star Lady-14
9238765	Thuringia *	Gbr	2003	39,941	50,785	260	32	24	ucc	4,253 teu: ex Thuringia Express-12, CP Tamarind-06, Contship Tamarind-05, APL Honduras-04, Lykes Adventurer-03
9432892	Triumph	Gbr	2008	46,800	12,300	183	32	20	mve	4,902 ceu
9493224	Westgate	Gbr	2011	17,025	28,202	169	27	14	bbu	
9276250	Yellow Ray *	Gbr	2003	11,590	19,937	146	24	14	tco	ex Belsize Park-14
9332872	Zim Hamburg *	Lbr	2009	71,786	72,982	293	40	25	ucc	6,350 teu: ex APL Toyko-14
9322358	Zim India *	Lbr	2007	39.912	50,607	261	32	24	ucc	4,253 teu
newbuildings:										
9725859	Scarlet Ray	Sgp	2016	12,200	19,951	145	24	14	tch	Kitanihon 612
9742895	Diamondway	Lbr	2016	81,300	158,000	277	48	14	tcr	Samsung 2041
9742900	Goldway	Lbr	2016	81,300	158,000	277	48	14	tcr	Samsung 2042
9742912	Silverway	Lbr	2016	81,300	158,000	277	48	14	tcr	Samsung 2043
9760495	North Sea	Lbr	2016	55,000	106,000	229	42	14	tcr	
9760500	Solomon Sea	Lbr	2016	55,000	106,000	229	42	14	tcr	
	Manitoba	Lbr	2016		28,026				lpg	37,240 m³ Hyundai Mipo
	Nova Scotia	Lbr	2016		28,026				lpg	37,240 m³ Hyundai Mipo
	Ontario	Lbr	2016		28,026				lpg	37,240 m³ Hyundai Mipo
	Quebec	Lbr	2017		28,026				lpg	37,240 m³ Hyundai Mipo
	Dragongate	Lbr	2016		63,000	200	32	14	bbu	
		Lbr	2019	29,000	49,700	183	32	14	tco	

Pusan : Eastern Pacific Shipping : *Chris Brooks*

IMO	name	flag	year	gt	dwt	loa	bm	kts	type	comments
		Lbr	2019	29,000	49,700	183	32	14	tco	

* owned by Lombard Corporate December 3   + chartered to Glovis

Ecuadorian Line Inc.   U.S.A.

funnel: *dark blue with yellow 'EL' on red disc.* **hull:** *orange with red boot-topping.* **history:** *founded 1988.*
web: *www.ecuadorianline.com*

IMO	name	flag	year	gt	dwt	loa	bm	kts	type	comments
9059602	Albemarle Island	Bhs	1993	14,061	14,160	179	25	21	grf	
9059614	Barrington Island	Bhs	1993	14,061	14,140	179	25	21	grf	
9059616	Charles Island	Bhs	1993	14,061	14,140	179	25	21	grf	
9059638	Duncan Island	Bhs	1993	14,061	14,140	179	25	21	grf	
9059640	Hood Island	Bhs	1994	14,601	14,140	179	25	21	grf	

managed by Trireme Vessel Management n.v., Belgium

Eletson Corp.   Greece

funnel: *buff base with red-edged blue five-pointed star on broad white band edged with narrow blue bands, black top.* **hull:** *black with red boot-topping.* **history:** *formed 1966 as Eletson Maritime Services Inc to 1982.* **web:** *www.eletson.com*

IMO	name	flag	year	gt	dwt	loa	bm	kts	type	comments
9232448	Agathonissos	Grc	2002	57,062	106,149	244	42	15	tco	
9250531	Alonissos	Grc	2004	57,062	106,149	244	42	15	tco	
9176773	Angistri	Grc	2000	39,283	76,019	213	37	15	tc0	
9281853	Antikeros	Grc	2004	40,038	69,714	228	32	14	tco	ex LMZ Artemis-07
9282998	Antimilos	Grc	2004	41,526	72,514	228	32	14	tco	ex Senatore-14, Ariadne Jacob-05
9306562	Dhonoussa	Grc	2005	40,038	69,180	228	32	15	tco	ex LMZ Afroditi -07
9254850	Erikoussa	Grc	2003	41,679	70,142	228	32	15	tco	
9405564	Fourni	Grc	2010	29,663	51,611	183	32	15	tco	
9405552	Kastos	Grc	2010	29,663	51,589	183	32	15	tco	
9277735	Keros	Grc	2004	42,432	74,999	225	32	14	tco	ex Anna Victoria-14, Torm Anna-10
9405540	Kimolos	Grc	2010	29,663	51,522	183	32	15	tco	
9405538	Kinaros	Grc	2009	29,663	51,601	183	32	15	tco	
9232450	Makronissos	Grc	2002	57,062	106,149	244	42	15	tco	
9250543	Megalonissos	Grc	2004	57,062	106,290	244	42	15	tco	
9286023	Meganisi	Grc	2004	41,526	72,515	228	32	14	tco	ex Noemi-14, Colin Jacob-05
9176761	Pelagos	Grc	1999	39,283	76,020	213	37	15	tco	
9306574	Polyaigos	Grc	2005	40,038	69,509	228	32	15	tco	ex LMZ Nefeli-07
9254862	Skopelos	Grc	2003	41,679	70,146	228	32	15	tco	
9074585	Stavronisi	Grc	1996	38,667	68,232	243	32	14	tco	
9319545	Strofades	Grc	2006	40,038	69,431	228	32	15	tco	ex LMZ Nafsika-07
9031961	Velopoula	Grc	1993	39,265	66,895	228	32	14	tco	

Eletson Gas

history: *formed 10:2013 as j/v between Eletson Corp. and Blackstone Technical Opportunities as lpg transport company*

IMO	name	flag	year	gt	dwt	loa	bm	kts	type	comments
9411733	Anafi	Grc	2009	22,971	26,577	173	28	16	lpg	35,000 m³
9711509	Astipalea	Grc	2015	13,794	15,034	147	24	16	lpg	12,000 m³
9711535	Dilos	Grc	2016	13,794	15,050	147	24	16	lpg	12,000 m³
9711523	Kithnos	Grc	2016	13,794	15,003	147	24	16	lpg	12,000 m³
9262948	Mathraki	Grc	2003	16,769	19,621	156	25	16	lpg	20,500 m³ : ex Mado-13
9412062	Nisyros	Grc	2009	22,971	26,540	173	28	16	lpg	35,000 m³
9406269	Symi	Grc	2012	22,971	26,597	173	28	16	lpg	35,000 m³
9412086	Telendos	Grc	2010	22,971	26,634	173	28	16	lpg	35,000 m³
9412074	Tilos	Grc	2009	22,971	26,587	173	28	16	lpg	35,000 m³
9711494	Othoni	Grc	2015	13,794	15,028	147	24	16	lpg	12,000 m³
9711511	Paros	Grc	2015	13,794	15,009	147	24	16	lpg	12,000 m³

newbuildings:

IMO	name	flag	year	gt	dwt	loa	bm	kts	type	comments
9714630	*Psara*	Grc	2016	18,000	24,000	160	25	15	lpg	22,000 m³ Nantong Sinopacific 1021 Q1 16
9714642	*Halki*	Grc	2016	18,000	24,000	160	25	15	lpg	22,000 m³ Nantong Sinopacific 1022 Q1 16
9714654	*Antiparos*	Grc	2016	18,000	24,000	160	25	15	lpg	22,000 m³ Nantong Sinopacific 1023 Q2 16
9742742		Grc	2016	18,000	24,000	160	25	15	lpg	22,000 m³ Nantong Sinopacific 1024 Q4 16
9742754		Grc	2017	18,000	24,000	160	25	15	lpg	22,000 m³ Nantong Sinopacific 1025 Q1 17

Enesel S.A.   Greece

funnel: *blue with white logo* **hull:** *grey with red boot topping* **history:** *ship management derivative of the Lemos Shipping dynasty. Enesel formed 2003 by merger of Avra Shipmanagement & Sealuck Shg. Corp.* **web:** *eneselsa.com*

IMO	name	flag	year	gt	dwt	loa	bm	kts	type	comments
9285823	Irene SL	Grc	2004	161,175	319,247	333	60	14	tcr	

IMO	name	flag	year	gt	dwt	loa	bm	kts	type	comments
9274616	Pantelis	Cyp	2004	62,877	114,500	250	44	14	tcr	
9274800	Sparto	Cyp	2004	62,877	114,549	250	44	14	tcr	
9315367	Spyros	Grc	2007	161,175	319,247	333	60	14	tcr	
9665633	Thalassa Avra +	Sgp	2014	148,667	152,344	368	51	17	ucc	13,808 teu
9667186	Thalassa Axia +	Sgp	2014	148,667	152,344	368	51	17	ucc	13,808 teu
9667174	Thalassa Doxa +	Sgp	2014	148,667	152,344	368	51	17	ucc	13,808 teu
9665621	Thalassa Elpida +	Sgp	2014	148,667	152,344	368	51	17	ucc	13,808 teu
9665592	Thalassa Hellas +	Sgp	2013	148,667	152,344	368	51	17	ucc	13,808 teu
9667150	Thalassa Mana +	Sgp	2014	148,667	152,343	368	51	17	ucc	13,808 teu
9665645	Thalassa Niki +	Sgp	2014	148,667	152,344	368	51	17	ucc	13,808 teu
9665607	Thalassa Patris +	Sgp	2013	148,667	152,344	368	51	17	ucc	13,808 teu
9665619	Thalassa Pistis +	Sgp	2014	148,667	152,343	368	51	17	ucc	13,808 teu
9667162	Thalassa Tyhi +	Sgp	2014	148,667	152,343	368	51	17	ucc	13,808 teu
9633939	Cap San Artemissio *	Sgp	2014	118,938	124,426	333	48	21	ucc	9,814 teu
9633941	Cap San Maleas *	Sgp	2014	118,938	124,426	333	48	21	ucc	9,814 teu
9633953	Cap San Sounio *	Sgp	2014	118,938	124,426	333	48	21	ucc	9,814 teu
9633965	Cap San Tainaro *	Sgp	2014	118,938	124,426	333	48	21	ucc	9,814 teu

* chartered to Hamburg-Süd . + managed by Enesel Singapore Pte. Ltd., operated by Evergreen Containers Line

Enterprises Shipping & Trading S.A.   Greece

funnel: *light grey with black top or * black with gold anchor on broad white band below narrow green band and black top or ** grey with narrow white band on broad blue band.* **hull:** *black or red with red boot-topping, * black with with yellow 'GOLDEN ENERGY' or ** brown with white 'SafOre'.* **history:** *formed 1973 and part of Restis Group, who acquired bulk shipping interest of Safmarine (founded 1948) in 1999.* **web:** *www.estsa.gr*

IMO	name	flag	year	gt	dwt	loa	bm	kts	type	comments
9398682	Braverus	Iom	2009	88,479	170,015	287	45	15	bbu	
9398694	Citius	Iom	2009	88,479	170,024	287	45	14	bbu	
9398709	Colossus	Iom	2010	88,479	170,060	287	45	14	bbu	
9438054	Delphi Ranger	Bhs	2009	31,091	53,800	190	32	14	bbu	
9398711	Divinus	Iom	2010	88,479	170,022	287	45	15	bbu	
9493652	Dynamic Striker	Bhs	2010	33,044	56,736	190	32	14	bbu	
9387281	Energy Centaur *	Iom	2008	42,296	74,995	228	32	14	tco	
9387970	Energy Centurion *	Iom	2008	42,998	74,471	228	32	14	tco	
9259329	Energy Century *	Iom	2003	41,397	70,470	228	32	14	tco	
9288265	Energy Challenger *	Iom	2005	42,172	70,681	228	32	14	tco	
9288356	Energy Champion *	Iom	2005	42,172	70,681	228	32	14	tco	
9292606	Energy Chancellor *	Iom	2005	42,172	70,558	228	32	14	tco	
9275658	Energy Commander *	Iom	2004	42,172	70,691	228	32	14	tco	
9275660	Energy Conqueror *	Iom	2004	42,172	70,616	228	32	14	tco	
9388015	Energy Panther *	Iom	2008	29,494	46,846	183	32	14	tco	
9388003	Energy Patriot *	Iom	2008	29,494	46,606	183	32	14	tco	
9281920	Energy Pioneer *	Iom	2004	30,008	51,224	183	32	14	tco	
9281932	Energy Power *	Iom	2004	30,008	51,383	183	32	14	tco	
9278052	Energy Pride *	Iom	2004	30,008	51,318	183	32	14	tco	
9387279	Energy Progress *	Iom	2008	29,494	46,606	183	32	14	tco	
9278064	Energy Protector *	Iom	2004	30,008	51,314	183	32	14	tco	

Thalassa Patris : Enesel S.A. : *Nico Kemps*

Energy Centurion : Enterprises Shg. & Trading - Golden Energy Mgmt. : *Nico Kemps*

Energy Pride : Enterprises Shg. & Trading - Golden Energy Mgmt. : *Hans Kraijenbosch*

Paramount Hanover : Enterprises Shg. & Trading - AET Ltd. : *Chris Brooks*

IMO	name	flag	year	gt	dwt	loa	bm	kts	type	comments
9388027	Energy Puma *	Iom	2008	29,494	49,549	183	32	14	tco	
9117325	Energy Ranger *	Iom	1996	26,330	45,950	190	32	14	bbu	ex Energy Saver-02, Cape Infanta-02
9117313	Force Ranger	Iom	1996	26,330	45,950	189	32	14	bbu	ex Cape Agulhas-02
9398735	Furious	Iom	2010	88,479	170,037	287	45	15	bbu	
9398747	Generous	Iom	2010	88,479	170,024	287	45	15	bbu	
9398759	Genius	Iom	2010	88,479	170,057	287	45	15	bbu	
9605853	Gladiator	Bhs	2012	33,044	57,000	190	32	14	bbu	
9304241	Good Hope Max	Iom	2005	40,039	76,739	225	32	14	bbu	ex Georgios F-06, Ocean Lady-05
9588603	Helvetia One	Lbr	2012	51,195	92,737	229	38	14	bbu	ex Trans Beijing-12
9493676	Heroic Striker	Bhs	2010	33,044	56,820	190	32	14	bbu	
9403504	Imperius	Iom	2011	93,196	179,062	292	45	15	bbu	
9169249	Iron Baron	Iom	1999	88,385	169,981	289	45	14	bbu	ex Philippe L.D.-04
9589140	Jaguar Max	Bhs	2012	44,326	81,309	229	32	14	bbu	
9493664	Magic Striker	Bhs	2010	33,044	56,803	190	32	14	bbu	
9266956	Olympius	Iom	2004	87,720	171,314	289	45	14	bbu	
9593402	Panther Max	Bhs	2012	44,326	81,283	229	32	14	bbu	
9453987	Paramount Halifax +	Iom	2009	62,851	114.062	250	44	14	tcr	
9426207	Paramount Hamilton +	Iom	2010	62,851	114,022	250	44	14	tcr	
9498723	Paramount Hanover +	Iom	2010	62,851	114,014	250	44	14	tcr	
9453975	Paramount Hatteras +	Iom	2010	62,851	114,028	250	44	14	tcr	
9453963	Paramount Helsinki +	Iom	2010	62,851	114,165	250	44	14	tcr	
9453999	Paramount Hydra +	Iom	2011	62,851	113,968	250	44	14	tcr	
9123740	Power Ranger	Iom	1996	26,330	45,946	189	32	14	bbu	ex Cape Recife-02
9589152	Puma Max	Bhs	2012	44,326	81,339	229	32	14	bbu	
9221205	SA Altius	Bhs	2001	87,542	171,480	289	45	14	bbu	
9221217	SA Fortius	Bhs	2001	87,542	171,509	289	45	14	bbu	
9303528	Spartacus	Iom	2011	93,196	179,156	292	45	15	bbu	
9403530	Taurus	Iom	2011	93,169	179,067	292	45	15	bbu	
9273375	Victorius	Iom	2004	87,720	171,314	289	45	14	bbu	
9493690	Virtuous Striker	Bhs	2010	33,044	56,822	190	32	14	bbu	
9605865	Warrior	Bhs	2012	33,044	56,800	190	32	14	bbu	

* operated by subsidiaries Golden Energy Management SA, Greece (formed 2003), + owned by AET Inc. Ltd., Bermuda
also operates chartered bulk carriers as SwissMarine.

John T. Essberger GmbH & Co. KG   Germany

funnel: buff, narrow red band on black-edged broad white band and black top or buff with broad green band. **hull:** black with red boot-topping or light grey with blue 'DEUTSCHE AFRIKA-LINIEN'. **history:** formed 1924 and now managed by third generation of Essberger/von Rantzau family. Acquired Deutsche Afrika Linien in 1941. **web:** www.rantzau.de

IMO	name	flag	year	gt	dwt	loa	bm	kts	type	comments
9294408	Maersk Launceston	Pmd	2005	50,736	62,994	266	37	24	ucc	5,057 teu: ex DAL Kalahari-14
9607459	Selinda	Pmd	2013	24,366	34,236	180	30	14	bbu	
9607447	Swakop	Pmd	2013	24,341	34,274	180	30	14	bbu	
9124392	UAFL Zanzibar	Lbr	1996	16,264	22,386	178	25	19	ucc	1,684 teu: ex R Sea-12, Nordsea-11, CSAV Maya-08, Nordsea-07, Nordseas-06, MOL Sprinter-04, Malacca Star-03, Nordsea-01, Nordseas-01, Pacific Voyager-01, Nordsea-00, Panaustral-98, Nordsea-97
9690078	Ubena	Pmd	2016	25,175	27,366	185	30	19	ucc	2,268 teu
9612246	Zambezi	Pmd	2013	24,341	34,205	180	30	14	bbu	

newbuildings:

IMO	name	flag	year	gt	dwt	loa	bm	kts	type	comments
9690080	Ulanga	Pmd	2016	25,175	27,366	185	30	19	ucc	2,268 teu: Yangfan CV22H JT02

also operates a fleet of small tankers

Eurobulk Ltd.   Greece

funnel : black with black 'E' inside five-pointed star on broad white band **hull:** black with red boot topping **history:** established May 2005, but initial Pittas family origins date back to 1873, Eurobulk formed 1994 **web:** www.euroseas.gr

IMO	name	flag	year	gt	dwt	loa	bm	kts	type	comments
9146302	Aggeliki P *	Lbr	1998	23,809	30,360	188	30	21	ucc	2,078 teu: ex Oder Trader-10, Maruba Cathay-07, Oder Trader-05, Zim Lisbon I-03, Oder Trader-02, Cielo d'America-02, Maersk Rio Grande-99, c/a Oder Trader
9224532	Akinada Bridge **	Pan	2001	68,687	71,366	285	40	25	ucc	5,610 teu
9223485	Aspasia Luck	Lbr	2000	37,722	72,270	225	32	14	bbu	ex Konmax-13, Coral Eagle-03
9294501	Blessed Luck	Lbr	2004	40,052	76,704	225	32	14	bbu	ex Oinoussian Lady-15

IMO	name	flag	year	gt	dwt	loa	bm	kts	type	comments
9301988	Candido Rondon **	Bra	2007	32,903	37,125	206	32	22	ucc	2,785 teu: ex Alianca St. Martin-15, EM Psara-14, CMA CGM Telopea-12, Artus-10, MSC Cameroun-10, Cala Pancaldo-09
8919001	Captain Costas *	Mhl	1992	21,053	30,007	182	29	19	ucc	1,742 teu: ex Oel Transworld-09, Clan Gladiator-08, Alberta-05, Fesco Enterprise-00, Nedlloyd Singapore-99, Santa Victoria-96, MSC Victoria-95, Muscat Bay-94, l/a Santa Victoria
9146314	Diamantis P.	Lbr	1998	23,809	30,340	188	30	21	ucc	2,078 teu: Arkona Trader-10, CMA CGM Tucano-08, Arkona Trader-03
9284879	Eirini P. *	Lbr	2004	39,974	76,466	225	32	15	bbu	ex Million Trader II-14
9128025	Eleni P. *	Lbr	1997	37,707	72,119	224	32	14	bbu	ex Glorious Wind-00
9259379	EM Andros **	Lbr	2003	27,227	33,216	200	32	22	ucc	2,495 teu: ex Torge S-12, Maersk Nassau-08, Torge S-04, l/a Superior Container
9243617	EM Astoria **	Lbr	2004	30,024	35,600	208	32	22	ucc	2,672 teu: ex Mate-11, Kota Perkasa-07, Mate-04
9203538	EM Athens **	Mhl	2000	25,294	32,350	207	30	22	ucc	2,506 teu: ex Santa Adriana-10, P&O Nedlloyd Algoa-05, MOL Parana-02, P&O Nedlloyd Algoa-01, l/a Santa Adriana
9203514	EM Chios **	Mhl	2000	25,294	32,321	207	30	22	ucc	2,506 teu; ex Santa Arabella-10, P&O Nedlloyd Accra-06, MOL Salvador-02, P&O Nedlloyd Accra-01, Santa Arabella-00
9231494	EM Corfu **	Cyp	2001	26,582	34,649	210	30	22	ucc	2,556 teu: ex Maersk Nairobi-14, Donata Schulte-06
9338937	EM Hydra **	Lbr	2005	18,334	23,679	176	27	20	ucc	1,740 teu: ex Lambert Schulte-10, Cap Agulhas-08, l/a Lambert Schulte
9178537	EM Ithaki **	Lbr	1999	25,497	28,917	194	32	20	ucc	2,135 teu: ex MOL Volta-12, Santos Challenger-01
9334351	EM Kea **	Lbr	2007	35,824	41,850	221	32	22	ucc	3,104 teu: ex Cap Egmont-15, Cap Norte-12
9403413	EM Spetses **	Cyp	2007	18,321	23,579	175	27	20	ucc	1,740 teu: ex Leopold Schulte-10, Cap Andreas-09,
9207443	Ergina Luck	Lbr	1999	38,530	73,976	224	32	14	bbu	ex Excalibur-13, Euro Ace-07, Euro Trader-03
9231482	Evridiki G. *	Lbr	2001	26,582	34,717	210	30	22	ucc	2,556 teu: ex Maersk Noumea-14, Elisabeth Schulte-06
9055448	Kuo Hsiung *	Pan	1993	15,183	18,154	167	27	17	ucc	1,169 teu
9101493	Manolis P. *	Mhl	1995	14,962	20,346	167	25	18	ucc	1,388 teu: ex Birthe Richter-07, Cala Piedad-02, Kaduna-00, TNX Express-98, Zim Argentina II-98, CCNI Anakena-96, c/a Birte Richter
9179218	Monica P. *	Lbr	1998	27,011	46,667	190	31	14	bbu	ex Solar Europe-09, Solar Bay-02
8909082	Ninos *	Pan	1990	15,122	18,253	167	27	16	ucc	998 teu: ex YM Qingdao I-07, Kuo Jane-04
9207730	Pantelis *	Lbr	2000	38,380	74,010	225	32	14	bbu	ex Four Coal-09
9287170	Santa Cruz	Lbr	2005	39,969	76,440	225	32	14	bbu	ex Michele d'Amato-14
9204477	Vento di Grecale *	Lbr	1999	16,802	22,878	184	25	19	ucc	1,730 teu: ex Johanna-15, Wehr Flottbek-13, CCNI Fortuna-09, Wehr Flottbek-08, Alianca Bahia-01, Wehr Flottbek-00
9711133	Xenia	Mhl	2016	44,190	82,019	229	32	14	bbu	

newbuildings:

IMO	name	flag	year	gt	dwt	loa	bm	kts	type	comments
9723045	Alexandros P. *		2016	36,000	63,500				bbu	Yangzhou Dayang 160 04.2016
9723057			2016	36,000	63,500				bbu	Yangzhou Dayang 161 07.2016
			2018	44,000	82,500	229	32	14	bbu	Jiangsu Yangzijiang 1153

* vessels operated by Euroseas Ltd.
** operated by Euromar LLC a j/v between Euroseas [14.28% holding] and 2 private equity firms, Eton Park & Rhone Capital formed 2010

Evergas Management AS   Denmark

funnel: green with Evergas logo, **hull:** dark blue with 'Ineos' and 'Shale gas slogans in white, red boot topping **history:** Evergas founded 2001 as Eitzen Gas A/S, name changed to Evergas 2011. Ineos founded 2005 when BP divested its Grangemouth petrochemical facility. Ethane is a major feedstock and a fleet of specifically designed dual-fuel tankers built to transport shale gas ethane from USA to Europe has been chartered from Evergas. **web:** www.ineos.com, www.evergas.net

IMO	name	flag	year	gt	dwt	loa	bm	kts	type	comments
9685437	JS Ineos Ingenuity	Dis	2015	22,887	20,897	180	27	19	lpg	27,500 m³
9685425	JS Ineos Insight	Dis	2015	22,887	20,918	180	27	19	lpg	27,500 m³
9685451	JS Ineos Inspiration	Mlt	2016	22.887	20,918	180	27	19	lpg	27,500 m³

EM Athens : Eurobulk Ltd. : *Chris Brooks*

Monica P : Eurobulk Ltd. : *ARO*

IMO	name	flag	year	gt	dwt	loa	bm	kts	type	comments
9685449	JS Ineos Intrepid	Dis	2015	22,887	20,917	180	27	19	lpg	27,500 m³

newbuildings : 4 further LPG tankers (Nantong Sinopacific Offshore & Engineering)
vessels managed by Evergas Management AS, whoc also operate a fleet of smaller lpg tankers

Evergreen Marine Corp. (Taiwan) Ltd.   Taiwan

funnel: black with green eight-pointed star above 'EVERGREEN' within brown globe outline on broad white band. **hull:** dark green with white 'EVERGREEN', red or green boot-topping. **history:** founded 1968. Formerly part-owned Uniglory Marine Corp merged 2002. **web:** www.evergreen-marine.com

9595448	Ever Laden	Pan	2012	98,882	104,409	335	46	24	ucc	8,452 teu
9595436	Ever Lambent	Gbr	2012	98,882	104,409	335	46	24	ucc	8,452 teu
9595450	Ever Lasting	Gbr	2012	98,882	104,409	335	46	24	ucc	8,452 teu
9595474	Ever Laurel	Sgp	2012	98,882	104,409	335	46	24	ucc	8,452 teu
9595498	Ever Lawful	Sgp	2012	98,882	104,409	335	46	24	ucc	8,452 teu
9595503	Ever Leader	Sgp	2013	98,882	104,504	335	46	24	ucc	8,452 teu
9595462	Ever Leading	Gbr	2012	98,882	104,409	335	46	24	ucc	8,452 teu
9604108	Ever Learned	Gbr	2013	98,882	104,409	335	46	24	ucc	8,452 teu
9595515	Ever Legacy	Sgp	2013	98.882	104,409	335	46	24	ucc	8,452 teu
9604093	Ever Legend	Sgp	2013	98,892	104,409	335	46	24	ucc	8,452 teu
9604110	Ever Legion	Sgp	2013	98,882	104,409	335	46	24	ucc	8,452 teu
9604146	Ever Lenient	Gbr	2014	98,882	104,409	335	46	24	ucc	8,452 teu
9604160	Ever Liberal	Gbr	2014	98,882	104,409	335	46	24	ucc	8,452 teu
9595486	Ever Libra	Twn	2012	98,882	104,409	335	46	24	ucc	8,452 teu
9629122	Ever Lifting	Gbr	2015	98,882	104,409	335	46	24	ucc	8,508 teu
9629043	Ever Linking	Gbr	2013	99,998	104,701	335	46	24	ucc	8,508 teu
9629079	Ever Lissome	Gbr	2014	98,998	104,409	335	46	24	ucc	8,508 teu
9604134	Ever Lively	Sgp	2014	98,882	104,409	335	46	24	ucc	8,452 teu
9595527	Ever Liven	Twn	2013	98,882	104,409	335	46	24	ucc	8,452 teu
9629031	Ever Living	Sgp	2013	99,998	104,652	335	46	24	ucc	8,508 teu
9629081	Ever Loading	Gbr	2014	98,882	104,409	335	46	24	ucc	8,508 teu
9604081	Ever Logic	Twn	2013	98,882	104,366	335	46	24	ucc	8,452 teu
9604122	Ever Lotus	Pan	2013	98,882	104,262	335	46	24	ucc	8,452 teu
9629110	Ever Lovely	Sgp	2015	98,882	104,357	335	46	24	ucc	8,508 teu
9604158	Ever Loyal	Twn	2014	98,882	104,409	335	46	24	ucc	8,452 teu
9629067	Ever Lucent	Sgp	2014	98,998	104,606	335	46	24	ucc	8,508 teu
9629055	Ever Lucid	Twn	2014	99,998	104,555	335	46	24	ucc	8,508 teu
9604172	Ever Lucky	Pan	2014	98,882	104,205	335	46	24	ucc	8,452 teu
9629093	Ever Lunar	Twn	2015	98,882	104,409	335	46	24	ucc	8,508 teu
9629108	Ever Lyric	Twn	2015	98,882	104,409	335	46	24	ucc	8,508 teu
9300465	Ever Safety	Pan	2007	75,246	78,618	300	43	25	ucc	7,024 teu
9300477	Ever Salute	Pan	2008	75,246	78,733	300	43	25	ucc	7,024 teu
9300386	Ever Shine *	Gbr	2005	75,246	78,693	300	43	25	ucc	7,024 teu: ex Hatsu Shine-08
9300398	Ever Sigma *	Gbr	2005	75,246	78,693	300	43	25	ucc	7,024 teu: ex Hatsu Sigma-08
9300403	Ever Smart *	Gbr	2006	75,246	78,693	300	43	25	ucc	7,024 teu: ex Hatsu Smart-08
9300415	Ever Smile *	Gbr	2006	75,246	78,796	300	43	25	ucc	7,024 teu: ex Hatsu Smile-09
9300439	Ever Steady	Pan	2006	75,246	78,664	300	43	25	ucc	7,024 teu
9300441	Ever Strong	Pan	2007	75,246	78,715	300	43	25	ucc	7,024 teu

Ever Lovely : Evergreen Marine Corp : *Hans Kraijenbosch*

IMO	name	flag	year	gt	dwt	loa	bm	kts	type	comments
9300453	Ever Summit	Pan	2007	75,246	78,612	300	43	25	ucc	7,024 teu
9300427	Ever Superb	Pan	2006	75,246	78,661	300	43	25	ucc	7,024 teu: l/a Ever Spring
9168831	Ever Uberty **	Sgp	1999	69,246	63,216	285	40	25	ucc	5,652 teu
9116577	Ever Ultra	Pan	1996	69,218	63,388	285	40	24	ucc	5,364 teu
9196955	Ever Ulysses **	Sgp	2000	69,200	62,700	285	40	25	ucc	5,652 teu: ex LT Ulysses-05, l/a Ever Ulysses
9196967	Ever Unicorn **	Sgp	2000	69,246	63,400	285	40	25	ucc	5,652 teu: ex LT Unicorn-05, l/a Ever Unicorn
9168843	Ever Unific **	Sgp	1999	69,246	63,216	285	40	25	ucc	5,652 teu
9116618	Ever Union	Pan	1997	69,218	63,388	285	40	24	ucc	5,364 teu
9116606	Ever Unique **	Sgp	1997	69,218	63,388	285	40	24	ucc	5,364 teu
9116591	Ever Unison **	Sgp	1996	69,218	63,388	285	40	24	ucc	5,364 teu
9116589	Ever United **	Sgp	1996	69,218	62,386	285	40	24	ucc	5,364 teu: ex LT United-03, Ever United-00
9169158	Ever Unity	Pan	1999	69,246	62,700	285	40	25	ucc	5,652 teu: ex LT Unity-04, Ever Unity-00
9168855	Ever Uranus	Pan	1999	69,246	63,216	285	40	24	ucc	5,652 teu
9169160	Ever Urban	Pan	2000	69,246	63,216	285	40	24	ucc	5,652 teu
9168867	Ever Ursula	Pan	1999	69,246	62,700	285	40	25	ucc	5,652 teu: ex LT Ursula-04, Ever Ursula-00
9168879	Ever Useful	Pan	1999	69,246	62,700	285	40	24	ucc	5,652 teu
9188154	Ever Utile	Pan	2000	69,246	63,216	285	40	25	ucc	5,652 teu: ex LT Utile-05, Ever Utile-00

newbuildings:
also 10 x 14,000 teu ucc (Hyundai) 2016/7 and 7 x 14,000 teu containerships for 10 year charter from Sumitomo Corp (2016/7)
5 x 14,000teu from Shoei Kisen Kaisha (2015/6)
the company also operates largea number of smaller container ships under 5,000teu (Ever-A, Ever-P., Uni-A and Uni-P classes) mainly in Far East services.

Italia Marittima SpA, Italy
funnel: *cream with blue 'LT' below narrow blue band, blue top.* **hull:** *blue with white 'ITALIA' or 'L TRIESTINO', red boot-topping.*
history: *founded in 1836 as Linee Triestine per l'Oriente SA di Nav. Oriens, then Lloyd Austriaco to 1918 and formed as Lloyd Triestino di Navigazione SpA in 1937. Acquired from Italian state-owned Finmare in 1998 and renamed 2006, joined Evergreen Group. 05:2007*
web: *www.italiamarittima.it*

IMO	name	flag	year	gt	dwt	loa	bm	kts	type	comments
9330501	Ital Fulgida	Ita	2007	36,483	42,930	239	32	23	ucc	3,451 teu
9315953	Ital Massima *	Pan	2007	42,020	53,728	264	32	23	ucc	4,363 teu: l/a E.R. Napier
9315915	Ital Mattina	Ita	2007	42,020	53,644	264	32	23	ucc	4,363 teu: l/a E.R. Nelson
9315965	Ital Melodia *	Pan	2007	42,020	53,697	264	32	23	ucc	4,363 teu: ex E.R. Tauranga
9349617	Ital Milione	Ita	2008	42,020	53,641	264	32	24	ucc	4,363 teu: l/a E.R. Cook
9349629	Ital Moderna	Ita	2009	42,020	53,685	264	32	24	ucc	4,353 teu: l/a E.R. Bounty
9196981	Ital Unica	Ita	2001	68,888	63,216	285	40	25	ucc	5,652 teu: ex LT Unica-08
9196993	Ital Universo	Ita	2001	68,888	63,216	285	40	25	ucc	5,652 teu: ex LT Universo-06
9196979	Ital Usodimare	Ita	2000	68,888	63,216	285	40	25	ucc	5,652 teu: ex LT Usodimare-08

* formerly owned now on charter from Wisdom Marine Lines, Taiwan

Excellence : Exmar n.v. : *Chris Brooks*

Exmar N.V.   Belgium

funnel: blue with dark and light blue stylized 'E' on broad white band. **hull:** red with dark red boot-topping. **history:** *formed 1991 following demerger from CMB Group.* **web:** *www.exmar.be*

IMO	name	flag	year	gt	dwt	loa	bm	kts	type	comments
9318321	Antwerpen *	Hkg	2005	22,901	26,361	174	28	16	lpg	35,223 m³
9237747	Bastogne	Bel	2002	22,902	26,616	174	28	16	lpg	35,229 m³ ex BW Hugin-11, Berge Hugin-07, Lancashire-05
9265548	Berlian Ekuator	Pan	2004	22,209	26,776	170	29	16	lpg	35,437 m³
9132789	Brugge Venture *	Hkg	1997	22,352	26,777	170	27	16	lpg	35,418 m³
9142150	Brussels	Bel	1997	22,323	26,943	170	27	16	lpg	35,454 m³ ex Oxfordshire-05
8818843	Chaconia	Bel	1990	19,643	29,271	166	27	16	lpg	28,070 m³
8804725	Courcheville	Bel	1989	19,719	29,171	166	27	16	lpg	28,006 m³
9102203	Elversele	Bel	1996	23,519	28,993	179	27	18	lpg	37,511 m³
9177806	Eupen	Bel	1999	23,952	29,121	180	27	18	lpg	38,961 m³
9230050	Excalibur (st)	Bel	2002	93,786	77,822	268	43	19	lng	138,034 m³
9246621	Excel (st)	Bel	2003	93,786	77,774	277	43	19	lng	138,107 m³ l/a Peace River
9322255	Excelerate (st)	Bel	2006	93,786	77,822	277	43	19	lng	138,074 m³
9252539	Excellence (st)	Bel	2005	93,937	77,348	277	43	19	lng	138,120 m³
9239616	Excelsior (st)	Bel	2005	93,719	76,500	277	43	19	lng	138,060 m³
9389643	Expedient (st)	Bel	2010	100,361	83,166	291	43	19	lng	151,015 m³
9444649	Exemplar (st)	Bel	2010	100,361	83,125	291	43	19	lng	151,072 m³
9638525	Experience	Mhl	2014	116,486	95,105	295	46	19	lng	173,660 m³
9361445	Express (st)	Bel	2009	114,987	83,200	277	43	19	lng	151,116 m³
9361079	Explorer (st)	Bel	2008	100,325	82,500	291	43	19	lng	150,981 m³
9381134	Exquisite (st)	Bel	2009	114,987	77,822	277	43	19	lng	151,017 m³
9687485	Kaprijk	Bel	2015	25,952	29,639	180	30	19	lpg	38,405 m³
9687497	Knokke	Bel	2016	26,261	29,425	180	30	19	lpg	38,405 m³
9292761	Libramont	Bel	2006	25,994	29,328	180	29	16	lpg	38,466 m³
7357452	Methania (st)	Bel	1978	81,792	67,879	280	42	19	lng	131,235 m³ † laid up 10.2015
9292113	Sombeke (st)	Bel	2006	25,994	29,213	180	29	19	lpg	38,447 m³ ex BW Sombeke-11, Berge Sombeke-06
9045807	Temse	Bel	1995	10,018	13,289	143	21	16	lpg	12,030 m³ ex Kemira Gas-14
9134165	Touraine	Hkg	1996	25,337	30,309	196	29	19	lpg	39,270 m³ ex Antwerpen Venture-97
9659103	Waasmunster	Bel	2014	25,143	28,518	174	30	19	lpg	38,115 m³
9659127	Waregem	Bel	2015	25,143	28,576	174	30	19	lpg	38,115 m³
9659115	Warinsart	Bel	2014	25,143	28,521	174	30	19	lpg	38,115 m³
9659139	Warisoulx	Bel	2015	25,143	28,590	174	30	19	lpg	38,115 m³
newbuildings:										
9687502	Kontich	Bel	2016	26,000	29,000	180	30	19	lpg	38,405 m³ Hanjin Subic P0102
9687514	Kortrijk	Bel	2016	26,000	29,000	180	30	19	lpg	38,405 m³ Hanjin Subic P0103
9719276									lpg	38,405 m³ Hanjin Subic P0126
9719288									lpg	38,405 m³ Hanjin Subic P0127
9719290									lpg	38,405 m³ Hanjin Subic P0135
9719305			2018						lpg	38,405 m³ Hanjin Subic P0136

vessels managed by subsidiary Exmar LPG, a 50:50 JV between Exmar N.V. and Teekay LPG,
* chartered from Hong Kong owners
also operates LNG tankers in joint venture with Golar and Lpg tankers in Pool with Møller and Bergesen.

ExxonMobil Corp.   U.S.A.

history: *Formed by 1999 amalgamation of Exxon Corp (formerly Standard Oil Co. of New Jersey to 1892 and Standard Oil Co until 1972) with Mobil Oil Corp (founded 1888 as Socony-Vacuum Oil to 1955 and Socony Mobil Oil Co until 1966)* **web:** *www.exxon.mobil.com*

SeaRiver Maritime Inc., U.S.A.

funnel: blue with white band separated from upper broad red band by further white band, narrow black top. **hull:** black with red or blue boot-topping. **history:** *founded 1920 as Humble Oil & Refining Co to 1973, later Exxon Shipping Co to 1993 and Exxon Co.*

IMO	name	flag	year	gt	dwt	loa	bm	kts	type	comments
9642083	Liberty Bay	Usa	2014	62,318	114,820	251	44	15	tcr	
9642095	Eagle Bay	Usa	2015	62,318	114,762	251	44	15	tcr	
9118628	S/R American Progress	Usa	1997	26,092	45,435	183	32	14	tcr	ex Despotico-97

Fednav Ltd.   Canada

funnel: white, red design incorporating part of maple leaf with interlinked 'F' and 'C', broad black top. **hull:** red or dark blue with red boot-topping. **history:** *founded 1946 as Federal Commerce & Navigation Ltd to 1984.* **web:** *www.fednav.com*

IMO	name	flag	year	gt	dwt	loa	bm	kts	type	comments
7517507	Arctic	Can	1978	20,236	28,418	221	23	15	cbo	
9200419	Federal Asahi	Hkg	1999	20,659	36,500	200	24	14	bbu	
9304095	Federal Baffin ‡	Pan	2007	30,721	55,309	190	32	14	bbu	.
9697806	Federal Baltic	Mhl	2015	20,789	34,564	200	24	14	bbu	
9697820	Federal Barents	Mhl	2015	20,789	34,564	200	24	14	bbu	
9697818	Federal Beaufort	Mhl	2015	20,789	34,564	200	24	14	bbu	

IMO	name	flag	year	gt	dwt	loa	bm	kts	type	comments
9697832	Federal Bering	Mhl	2015	20,789	34,564	200	24	14	bbu	
9697856	Federal Biscay	Mhl	2015	20,789	34,564	200	24	14	bbu	
9697844	Federal Bristol	Mhl	2015	20,789	34,564	200	24	14	bbu	
9732163	Federal Cardinal	Pan	2015	32,750	57,955	190	32	14	bbu	
9671096	Federal Caribou	Mhl	2016	20,789	34,564	200	24	14	bbu	
9671101	Federal Cedar	Mhl	2016	20,789	34,564	200	24	14	bbu	
9671058	Federal Champlain	Hkg	2016	20,789	34,564	200	28	14	bbu	
9732151	Federal Crimson	Sgp	2015	32,750	57,981	190	32	14	bbu	
9271511	Federal Danube ††	Mhl	2004	22,654	37,116	200	24	14	bbu	
9230000	Federal Elbe ††	Mhl	2003	22,654	37,038	200	24	14	bbu	
9229984	Federal Ems ††	Mhl	2002	22,654	37,058	200	24	14	bbu	
9317547	Federal Franklin	Pan	2008	30,721	55,303	190	32	14	bbu	
9205902	Federal Hudson *	Hkg	2000	20,659	36,563	200	24	14	bbu	
9205938	Federal Hunter *	Hkg	2001	20,659	36,563	200	24	14	bbu	
9293923	Federal Katsura	Pan	2005	19,165	32,594	190	24	14	bbu	
9606053	Federal Kibune ‡	Pan	2012	22,866	36,824	178	29	14	bbu	
9205885	Federal Kivalina *	Hkg	2000	20,659	36,563	200	24	14	bbu	
9244257	Federal Kumano ‡	Hkg	2003	20,661	36,489	200	24	14	bbu	
9284702	Federal Kushiro ‡	Mhl	2004	19,200	32,762	190	24	14	bbu	
9229996	Federal Leda ††	Mhl	2003	22,665	37,180	200	24	14	bbu	
9668063	Federal Lyra	Pan	2014	31,779	55,725	190	32	14	bbu	
9118135	Federal Maas	Brb	1997	20,837	34,372	200	24	14	bbu	
9299460	Federal Mackinac	Mhl	2004	18,825	27,638	185	24	14	bbu	
9299472	Federal Margaree **	Mhl	2005	18,825	27,787	185	24	14	bbu	
9315537	Federal Mattawa **	Lbr	2005	18,825	27,782	185	24	14	bbu	
9529578	Federal Mayumi	Mhl	2012	20,465	35,885	200	24	14	bbu	
9278791	Federal Nakagawa **	Hkg	2005	20,661	36,489	200	24	14	bbu	
9200330	Federal Oshima *	Hkg	1999	20,659	36,563	200	24	14	bbu	
9110925	Federal Rhine	Brb	1997	20,837	34,372	200	23	14	bbu	
9200445	Federal Rideau *	Hkg	2000	20,659	36,563	200	24	14	bbu	
9595888	Federal Sable	Mhl	2012	24,196	37,169	190	28	14	bbu	
9110913	Federal Saguenay	Brb	1996	20,837	34,167	200	23	14	bbu	
9288291	Federal Sakura	Pan	2005	19,165	32,594	190	24	14	bbu	
9515101	Federal Satsuki	Mhl	2012	20,465	35,885	200	24	14	bbu	
9118147	Federal Schelde	Brb	1997	20,837	34,372	200	23	14	bbu	
9267209	Federal Seto ‡	Hkg	2004	20,861	36,300	200	23	14	bbu	
9606821	Federal Severn	Hkg	2012	24,196	37,200	190	28	14	bbu	
9218404	Federal Shimanto ‡	Pan	2001	19,125	32,787	190	24	14	bbu	
9595890	Federal Skeena	Mhl	2012	24,196	37,168	190	28	14	bbu	
9606833	Federal Skye	Hkg	2012	24,196	37,169	190	28	14	bbu	
9610456	Federal Spey	Mhl	2012	24,196	37,141	190	28	14	bbu	
9610468	Federal Spruce	Mhl	2012	24,196	37,141	190	28	14	bbu	
9110896	Federal St. Laurent	Brb	1996	20,837	34,372	200	23	14	bbu	
9595917	Federal Sutton	Mhl	2012	24,196	37,168	190	28	14	bbu	
9595905	Federal Swift	Hkg	2012	24,196	37,140	190	28	14	bbu	
9644495	Federal Tambo	Mhl	2013	31,590	55,160	190	32	14	bbu	
9644483	Federal Tiber	Mhl	2013	31,590	55,160	190	32	14	bbu	

Federal Tambo : Fednav : *Hans Kraijenbosch*

IMO	name	flag	year	gt	dwt	loa	bm	kts	type	comments
9725445	Federal Tokoro ‡	Pan	2015	31,887	55,543	190	32	14	bbu	
9658977	Federal Trident	Mhl	2016	31,584	55,178	190	32	14	bbu	
9658898	Federal Tweed	Mhl	2013	31,590	55,317	190	32	14	bbu	
9658903	Federal Tyne	Mhl	2014	31,590	55,160	190	32	14	bbu	
9205916	Federal Welland *	Hkg	2000	20,659	35,750	200	24	14	bbu	
9229972	Federal Weser ††	Cyp	2002	22,654	37,372	200	24	14	bbu	
9218416	Federal Yoshino ‡	Mhl	2001	19,125	32,845	190	24	14	bbu	
9476977	Federal Yukina	Hkg	2010	20,465	35,868	200	24	14	bbu	
9205897	Federal Yukon *	Hkg	2000	20,659	36,563	200	24	14	bbu	
9308247	Neptune Pioneer ‡	Pan	2007	31,236	55,921	190	32	14	bbu	
9673850	Nunavik	Mhl	2014	22,622	24,997	189	27	14	bbi	
9324150	Triton Seagull ‡	Pan	2007	31,247	56,058	190	32	14	bbu	
9334715	Umiak I	Can	2006	22,462	31,992	189	27	14	bbi	
9339959	Windsor Adventure ‡	Pan	2008	31,247	55,975	190	32	14	bbu	
newbuildings:										
9671060		Hkg	2016			200	28	14	bbu	Oshima 10738
9671072		Hkg	2016			200	28	14	bbu	Oshima 10744
9671084		Hkg	2016			200	28	14	bbu	Oshima 10745

further 4 x 34,500dwt bbu [Oshima Shipbuilding Co. (2018)]

Fischer Gp. (Citrosuco) — Brasil

funnel: *green with broad white band with 'Fischer' in green.* **hull:** *white over green wave, red boot topping.* **history:** *Fischer Gp. founded 1932, Citrosuco founded 1963 merged with Citrovita 2012 to form largest orange juice produce.* **web:** *citrosuco.com.br*

IMO	name	flag	year	gt	dwt	loa	bm	kts	type	comments
9230995	Carlos Fischer	Lbr	2002	33,005	43,067	204	32	20	tfj	
9018646	Ouro do Brasil	Lbr	1993	15,218	19,519	173	26	20	tfj	
9242089	Premium do Brasil *	Lbr	2003	33,005	43,002	205	32	20	tfj	
9018658	Sol do Brasil	Lbr	1994	15,218	19,563	173	26	20	tfj	

* owned by Rudolf A. Oetker : all vessels managed by Citrosuco Europe n.v., Belgium

Foreland Shipping Ltd. — U.K.

funnel: *yellow with 4-coloured 'propeller' on green band, black top.* **hull:** *green with red boot-topping.* **history:** *founded 2001 as equal partnership between Andrew Weir, Bibby Line, Hadley Shipping and James Fisher plc* **web:** *www.foreland-shipping.co.uk*

IMO	name	flag	year	gt	dwt	loa	bm	kts	type	comments
9248540	Anvil Point *	Gbr	2003	23,235	13,274	193	26	17	urr	
9234070	Eddystone *	Gbr	2002	23,235	13,274	193	26	17	urr	
9248538	Hartland Point *	Gbr	2002	23,235	13,274	193	26	17	urr	
9234068	Hurst Point *	Gbr	2002	23,235	13,274	193	26	17	urr	

* vessels managed by AW Ship Management Ltd.(www.awshipmanagement.com) and on charter to UK Government

Fratelli d'Amico Armatori SpA — Italy

funnel: *yellow with blue Maltese cross with black top over narrow red band.* **hull:** *black with red boot-topping.* **history:** *founded early 1930s.* **web:** *www.damicofratelli.it*

IMO	name	flag	year	gt	dwt	loa	bm	kts	type	comments
9446374	Mare Doricum	Ita	2009	81,499	158,253	274	48	14	tcr	
9346885	Mare Nostrum	Ita	2009	59,611	110,295	245	42	14	tcr	
9346873	Mare Oriens	Ita	2008	59,611	110,295	245	42	14	tcr	
9449405	Mare Picenum	Ita	2009	81,499	158,253	274	48	14	tcr	
9457892	Mare Siculum	Ita	2011	81,499	158,466	274	48	14	tcr	
9260823	Mare Tirrenum	Ita	2004	59,574	110,673	245	42	14	tcr	

Frontline Management AS — Norway

funnel: *white with light blue 'f' symbol on dark blue vertical rectangle above 'FRONTLINE'.* **hull:** *black, brown or light blue with red or dark blue boot-topping.* **history:** *originally founded 1986 as Uddevalla Shipping AB by Swedish government, privatised 1989, controlling interest acquired in 1996 by John Fredriksen through Hemen Holdings and 1998 amalgamated with London & Overseas Freighters Ltd (founded 1949).Company restructured 2012 with some assets transferred to Frontline 2012 Ltd., reabsorbed 2015 and merged with Knightsbridge Tankers* **web:** *www.frontline.bm*

IMO	name	flag	year	gt	dwt	loa	bm	kts	type	comments
9408217	Everbright *	Mhl	2010	83,805	156,719	274	48	15	tcr	
9150834	Front Ardenne *	Mhl	1998	79,633	153,152	258	46	15	tcr	ex Ardenne-00
9196606	Front Ariake *	Iom	2001	158,397	298,530	333	60	15	tcr	ex Oliva-12, Ariake-06, Berge Ariake-01
9654555	Front Arrow	Mhl	2013	29,993	49,452	183	32	14	tco	
9654567	Front Avon	Mhl	2013	29,993	49,466	183	32	14	tco	
9408695	Front Balder *	Mhl	2009	83,562	156,436	274	48	14	tcr	ex Roxen Star-15, I/a Seasalvia
9155808	Front Brabant *	Nis	1998	79,633	152,550	269	46	15	tcr	ex Brabant-00
9418614	Front Brage	Mhl	2011	83,850	156,480	275	48	14	tcr	ex Chapter Genta-15, Orient Progesss-11
9400681	Front Cecilie	Hkg	2010	156,988	296,995	330	60	15	tcr	
9166675	Front Century *	Mhl	1998	157,976	311,189	334	58	15	tcr	
9686637	Front Cheetah	Mhl	2016	64,018	109,900	250	44	14	tco	

IMO	name	flag	year	gt	dwt	loa	bm	kts	type	comments
9166742	Front Circassia *	Mhl	1999	163,346	306,009	333	58	15	tcr	ex Omala-06, New Circassia-04, l/a Golden Circassia
9654579	Front Clyde	Mhl	2014	29,993	49,478	183	32	14	tco	
9654581	Front Dee	Mhl	2014	29,993	49,494	183	32	14	tco	
9353802	Front Eminence *	Mhl	2009	162,198	321,300	333	60	15	tcr	
9353797	Front Endurance	Mhl	2009	162,198	321,300	333	60	15	tcr	
9192228	Front Energy *	Cyp	2004	164,300	305,318	330	60	15	tcr	ex Sea Energy-05, l/a Mt. Pertamina 2
9654775	Front Esk	Mhl	2014	29,993	49,452	183	32	14	tco	
9238856	Front Falcon *	Bhs	2002	160,904	308,875	333	58	-	tcr	l/a Mosfalcon
9292163	Front Force *	Mhl	2004	156,873	305,442	330	60	15	tcr	ex Onobo-12, Front Force-09, Sea Force-05, l/a Mt. Pertamina 1
9196644	Front Hakata *	Bhs	2002	159,383	298,465	333	60	15	tcr	
9600944	Front Idun	Mhl	2015	81,670	156,880	275	48	14	tcr	l/a Seasprite
9384590	Front Kathrine	Mhl	2009	156,651	297,974	330	60	15	tcr	
9664770	Front Lion	Mhl	2014	65,358	115,162	250	44	15	tco	
9406013	Front Loki	Mhl	2010	83,805	156,720	274	48	15	tco	
9726592	Front Lynx	Mhl	2016	62,700	109,900	250	44	14	tco	
9654787	Front Mersey	Mhl	2014	29,993	49,452	183	32	14	tco	
9408205	Front Njord	Hkg	2010	83,805	156,760	274	48	15	tcr	
9726580	Front Ocelot	Mhl	2016	62,700	109,900	250	44	14	tco	
9406001	Front Odin	Hkg	2010	83,805	156,840	274	48	15	tcr	
9248497	Front Page *	Lbr	2002	156,916	299,164	330	60	15	tcr	l/a Front Saga
9664782	Front Panther	Mhl	2015	65,364	115,239	250	44	15	tco	
9664794	Front Puma	Mhl	2015	65,358	115,054	250	44	15	tco	
9384605	Front Queen	Mhl	2009	156,651	297,936	330	60	15	tcr	
9172856	Front Scilla *	Mhl	2000	160,805	302,561	333	60	16	tcr	ex Oscilla-05
9248473	Front Serenade *	Lbr	2002	156,916	299,152	333	60	16	tcr	
9410997	Front Signe	Hkg	2010	156,991	297,007	330	60	15	tcr	l/a Front Monarch
9248485	Front Stratus *	Lbr	2002	156,916	299,517	330	60	16	tcr	
9399480	Front Thor	Mhl	2010	83,805	156,719	274	48	15	tcr	ex Northia-14
9664809	Front Tiger	Mhl	2015	65,364	115,024	250	44	15	tco	
9172868	Front Tina	Lbr	2000	159,463	298,824	333	60	15	tcr	
9600932	Front Ull	Mlt	2014	81,670	156,848	275	48	14	tcr	l/a Seagrace
9153513	Front Vanguard *	Mhl	1998	159,423	300,058	333	60	14	tcr	ex New Vanguard-04
9408190	Glorycrown *	Mhl	2009	83,805	156,654	274	48	14	tcr	

Front Queen : Frontline Mgmt. : *Chris Brooks*

IMO	name	flag	year	gt	dwt	loa	bm	kts	type	comments
9722417	Sea Behike	Mhl	2016	94,091	180,491	292	45	14	bbu	ex SBI Behike-16
9722429	Sea Monterrey	Mhl	2016	94,091	180,513	292	45	14	bbu	ex SBI Monterrey-16

newbuildings:
also reported: 4 x 160,000dwt tcr [New Times SB, CHN (2016)] + 4 options, 2 x 111,000dwt [New Times SB (2016)]+ 2 options taken up for 2017
* owned by Ship Finance International Also see other chartered ships with 'Front' prefix in index.

Golar LNG Ltd., Bermuda

funnel: blue with white swallowtail flag having blue 5-point star inside blue ring or * black with three narrow white bands. **hull:** black with white 'LNG', red boot-topping. **history:** founded 1940 as T Gotaas & Co, renamed Gotaas-Larsen Shipping Corp in 1946. Golar Management (formed 1969) acquired by Singapore-based Osprey Maritime Ltd in 1997, then purchased by World Shipholding (indirectly controlled by John Fredriksen) in 2001. **web:** www.golar.com

IMO	name	flag	year	gt	dwt	loa	bm	kts	type	comments
7361934	Gandria (st)	Mhl	1977	96,011	66,999	288	43	19	lng	125,000 m³ ex Höegh Gandria-08
7382732	Gimi (st)	Mhl	1976	96,235	72,703	293	42	19	lng	125,000 m³
9253105	Golar Arctic	Mhl	2003	94,934	80,800	280	43	19	lng	138,500 m³ ex Granatina-09
9626039	Golar Bear	Mhl	2014	102,100	82,017	281	43	19	lng	160,000 m³
9626027	Golar Celsius	Mhl	2013	102,100	82,029	281	43	19	lng	160,000 m³
9624926	Golar Crystal	Mhl	2014	102,100	82,058	281	43	19	lng	160,000 m³
9655042	Golar Frost	Mhl	2014	102,100	82,005	281	43	19	lng	160,000 m³
9654696	Golar Glacier	Mhl	2014	105,832	79,602	289	46	19	lng	162,000 m³
9303560	Golar Grand	Mhl	2006	97,491	84,894	277	43	19	lng	145,700 m³ ex Grandis-10, l/a Golar Asia
9637325	Golar Ice	Mhl	2015	102,200	81,534	281	43	19	lng	160,000 m³
9654701	Golar Kelvin	Mhl	2015	105,832	90,607	289	46	19	lng	162,000 m³
9320374	Golar Maria	Mhl	2006	97,491	84,823	277	43	19	lng	145,700 m³ ex Granosa-09
9165011	Golar Mazo (st)	Lbr	2000	111,835	76,210	290	47	19	lng	135,000 m³
9624938	Golar Penguin	Mhl	2014	102,100	82,200	281	43	19	lng	160,000 m³
9624914	Golar Seal (tf)	Mhl	2013	100,008	82,048	281	43	19	lng	160,000 m³
9635315	Golar Snow	Mhl	2015	102,200	82,200	281	43	19	lng	160,000 m³
9655808	Golar Tundra	Mhl	2015	106,806	87,159	294	44	19	lng	160,000 m³
9253715	Methane Princess (st)	Mhl	2003	93,899	77,707	277	43	19	lng	138,000 m³

conversion: Golar Eskimo converted to FSRU floating, storage and regassification units
vessels managed by Golar Wilhelmsen Management. Also operates LNG vessels in joint venture with Exmar q.v.

Golden Ocean Group Ltd., Norway/Bermuda

funnel: dark blue with company logo of winged overlapping GO motif in gold. **hull:** dark blue with red boot topping. **history:** incorporated in 1996. During 2014 formed share swap deal with Frontline 2012 to set up major Cape size bulker businesss as Knightsbridge Shipping, 2014 merged with Golden Ocean and 2015 name changed to present **web:** www.goldenocean.no

IMO	name	flag	year	gt	dwt	loa	bm	kts	type	comments
9457402	Battersea	Mhl	2009	89,510	169,361	291	45	14	bbu	
9443592	Belgravia`	Mhl	2009	89,510	169,173	291	45	14	bbu	
9699270	Golden Aries	Hkg	2015	36,332	63,605	200	32	14	bbu	l/a Golden Libra
9701334	Golden Aso	Hkg	2015	93,237	182,472	292	45	14	bbu	
9721487	Golden Barnet	Hkg	2016	94,145	180,355	292	45	14	bbu	l/a KTL Barnet
9439412	Golden Beijing	Hkg	2010	91,971	175,820	292	45	14	bbu	
9721499	Golden Bexley	Mhl	2016	94,145	180,228	292	45	14	bbu	l/a KTL Bexley
9438638	Golden Brilliant	Hkg	2013	41,586	74,232	225	32	14	bbu	l/a Ice Trail-13
9438626	Golden Bull	Hkg	2012	41,586	74,500	225	32	14	bbu	
9692674	Golden Cathrine	Hkg	2015	34,311	60,263	200	32	14	bbu	
9692662	Golden Cecilie	Hkg	2015	34,311	60,263	200	32	14	bbu	
9590759	Golden Daisy	Mhl	2012	44,485	81,507	229	45	14	bbu	
9470387	Golden Diamond	Hkg	2013	41,718	74,138	225	32	14	bbu	
9481465	Golden Endurer	Hkg	2011	43,498	79,457	229	32	14	bbu	
9481439	Golden Eminence	Hkg	2010	43,498	79,444	229	32	14	bbu	
9481441	Golden Empress	Hkg	2010	43,498	79,471	229	32	14	bbu	
9481453	Golden Endeavour	Hkg	2010	43,498	79,454	229	32	14	bbu	
9435648	Golden Feng	Mhl	2009	89,510	169,232	290	45	14	bbu	
9701346	Golden Finsbury	Hkg	2015	93,237	182,481	292	45	14	bbu	
9443607	Golden Future	Hkg	2010	91,971	175,861	292	45	14	bbu	
9699282	Golden Gemini	Hkg	2015	36,332	63,655	200	32	14	bbu	
9745598	Golden Hawk *	Pan	2015	32,714	58,068	190	32	14	bbu	
9401362	Golden Ice	Hkg	2009	41,655	75,750	225	32	14	bbu	
9701322	Golden Kathrine	Hkg	2015	93,237	182,486	292	45	14	bbu	
9494230	Golden Magnum	Hkg	2009	93,526	179,788	292	45	14	bbu	
9389813	Golden Opportunity	Hkg	2008	41,655	75,750	225	32	14	bbu	
9486726	Golden Opus	Hkg	2010	95,047	180,716	292	45	14	bbu	
9470375	Golden Pearl	Hkg	2013	41,718	74,300	225	32	14	bbu	
9590747	Golden Rose	Mhl	2012	44,485	81,516	229	32	14	bbu	
9383857	Golden Saguenay	Hkg	2008	41,655	75,750	225	32	14	bbu	
9702479	Golden Scape	Hkg	2016	109,716	211,122	300	49	14	bbu	
9437696	Golden Shui	Mhl	2009	89,510	169,332	289	45	14	bbu	
9413420	Golden Strength	Hkg	2009	41,655	75,744	115	32	14	bbu	
9438614	Golden Suek	Hkg	2011	28,395	74,500	225	32	14	bbu	

Golar Seal : Frontline Mgmt - Golar LNG : *Chris Brooks*

Golden Brilliant : Frontline Mgmt. - Golden Ocean Gp. : *Hans Kraijenbosch*

Golden Ice : Frontline Mgmt. - Golden Ocean Gp. : *ARO*

IMO	name	flag	year	gt	dwt	loa	bm	kts	type	comments
9699294	Golden Taurus	Hkg	2015	36,332	63,548	200	32	14	bbu	
9443619	Golden Zhejiang	Hkg	2010	91,971	175,837	292	45	14	bbu	
9448554	Golden Zhoushan	Hkg	2011	91,971	175,834	292	45	14	bbu	
9483138	KSL China	Mhl	2013	94,523	179,109	292	45	14	bbu	
9719941	KSL Sakura	Hkg	2015	94,528	181,062	292	45	14	bbu	
9683271	KSL Salvador	Hkg	2014	94,528	180,958	292	45	14	bbu	
9719927	KSL Santiago	Hkg	2014	93,366	180,020	292	45	14	bbu	
9719939	KSL Santos	Hkg	2014	94,528	181,055	292	45	14	bbu	
9719915	KSL San Francisco	Hkg	2014	93,366	180,066	292	45	14	bbu	
9683257	KSL Sapporo	Hkg	2014	94,528	180,960	292	45	14	bbu	
9683245	KSL Seattle	Hkg	2014	94,528	181,015	292	45	14	bbu	
9723502	KSL Seoul	Hkg	2015	94,528	181,010	292	45	14	bbu	
9723540	KSL Seville	Hkg	2015	93,366	181,003	292	45	14	bbu	
9719903	KSL Singapore	Hkg	2014	94,528	181,062	292	45	14	bbu	
9723514	KSL Stockholm	Hkg	2015	94,528	181,043	292	45	14	bbu	
9683269	KSL Sydney	Hkg	2014	94,528	181,009	292	45	14	bbu	
9439539	Sea Bay	Hkg	2009	60,193	108,760	243	42	14	tcr	
9439541	Sea Hope	Hkg	2009	60,193	108,701	243	42	14	tcr	
newbuildings:										
9721982	Golden Leo	Hkg	2016	35,900	63,800	200	32	14	bbu	
9721994	Golden Virgo	Hkg	2016	35,900	63,800	200	32	14	bbu	
9723526	Golden Surabaya	Hkg	2016	93,366	180,000	292	45	14	bbu	
9723538	KSL Savannah	Hkg	2016	93,366	180,000	292	45	14	bbu	

* time chartered from Mi-Das Line
also on order: Capesize bulkers, 2 x SWS (2016), 3 x DSCI (2015/6), 1 x JMU (2016), + 2 Bohai (2016)
8 x Capesize bulkers [New Times SB (2016/7)] two changed to tcr orders and sold to Frontline
3 x 64,000dwt [Chengxi (2016)]

GasLog Logistics Ltd. Monaco

funnel: *black with blue company logo on broad white band, or, BG owned vessels, black with three narrow white bands.* **hull:** *dark blue with pink boot topping or BG vessels, black with white 'LNG' and red boot-topping.* **history:** **web:** *www.gaslogltd.com*

IMO	name	flag	year	gt	dwt	loa	bm	kts	type	comments
9390185	GasLog Chelsea (df)	Sgp	2010	100,374	86,778	289	44	19	lng	153,600 m³ ex STX Frontier-13
9687019	GasLog Greece (tf)	Bmu	2016	112,764	87,975	291	45	20	lng	174,000 m³
9638915	GasLog Salem	Bmu	2015	98,075	82,023	285	43	19	lng	154,800 m³
9600530	GasLog Santiago (tf)	Bmu	2013	98,075	82,178	285	43	19	lng	154,800 m³
9638903	GasLog Saratoga	Bmu	2014	98,075	81,855	285	43	19	lng	154,800 m³
9352860	GasLog Savannah	Bmu	2010	97,818	82,339	285	43	19	lng	154,800 m³
9634086	GasLog Seattle	Bmu	2013	98,075	81,982	285	43	19	lng	154,800 m³
9355604	GasLog Singapore	Bmu	2010	97,818	82,339	285	43	19	lng	154,800 m³
9600528	GasLog Shanghai	Bmu	2013	98,075	82,104	285	43	19	lng	154,800 m³
9626285	GasLog Skagen (tf)	Bmu	2013	97,818	74,600	285	43	19	lng	154,800 m³
9626273	GasLog Sydney (tf)	Bmu	2013	97,818	74,600	285	43	19	lng	154,800 m³
9321768	Methane Alison Victoria *	Bmu	2007	95,753	79,058	283	43	20	lng	145,000 m³
9516129	Methane Becki Anne (tf)	Bmu	2010	109,004	86,269	290	45	20	lng	170,000 m³
9321744	Methane Heather Sally (st) *	Bmu	2007	95,753	79,085	283	43	20	lng	145,000 m³
9307190	Methane Jane Elizabeth (st) *	Bmu	2006	95,753	78,984	283	43	20	lng	145,000 m³
9412880	Methane Julia Louise (tf)	Bmu	2010	109,004	86,125	290	45	19	lpg	170,000 m³
9256793	Methane Kari Elin (st) *	Bmu	2004	93,410	73,989	279	43	19	lng	138,000 m³
9307205	Methane Lydon Volney (st) *	Bmu	2006	95,753	78,957	283	43	20	lng	145,000 m³
9520376	Methane Mickie Harper (tf) *	Bmu	2010	109,004	86,170	290	45	19	lng	170,000 m³
9321770	Methane Nile Eagle (st) *	Bmu	2007	95,753	79,006	283	43	20	lng	145,000 m³
9425277	Methane Patricia Camila (tf) *	Bmu	2010	109,004	86,272	290	45	19	lng	170,000 m³
9307188	Methane Rita Andrea (st) *	Bmu	2006	95,753	79,046	283	43	20	lng	145,000 m³
9321756	Methane Shirley Elisabeth (st) *	Bmu	2007	95,753	78,997	283	43	20	lng	145,000 m³
9634098	Solaris + (tf)	Bmu	2014	98,075	81,853	285	43	20	lng	155,000 m³
newbuildings:										
9687021	GasLog Glasgow		2016	111,000	85,000					174,000 m³ Samsung 2073
9797508			2016	111,000	85,000					174,000 m³ Samsung 2102
9797510			2016	111,000	85,000					174,000 m³ Samsung 2103

* managed by GasLog LNG Services for BG Group (UK) www.bg-group.com, + chartered to Shell Tankers (Singapore)
newbuildings: 6 x 174,000 m³ lng tankers [Samsung (2017)] : 2 x 174,000 m³ lng tf tankers [Hyundai HI (2017)]

Genco Shipping & Trading U.S.A.

funnel: *dark blue with white 'G' in white diamond on broad light blue band between two narrow white bands, black top* **hull:** *black with red boot-topping.* **history:** *US based company founded 2004* **web:** *www.gencoshipping.com*

IMO	name	flag	year	gt	dwt	loa	bm	kts	type	comments
9176711	Genco Acheron	Hkg	1999	37,695	72,495	225	32	14	bbu	ex Anita-06, Monviken-04, Far Eastern Jennifer-00
9490624	Genco Aquitaine	Mhl	2009	32,837	57,970	190	32	14	bbu	ex Major-10
9490636	Genco Ardennes	Mhl	2009	32,837	57,970	190	32	14	bbu	ex Tabor-10
9361249	Genco Augustus	Hkg	2007	90,106	180,151	288	45	14	bbu	l/a Ferro Goa
9557123	Genco Auvegne	Mhl	2009	32,837	58,020	190	32	14	bbu	ex Molitor-10
9450753	Genco Avra	Lbr	2011	23,456	34,391	180	32	14	bbu	
9450715	Genco Bay	Lbr	2010	23,456	34,296	180	30	14	bbu	l/a Handy Bay
9200380	Genco Beauty	Hkg	1999	38,646	73,941	225	32	14	bbu	ex Top Beauty-06
9490662	Genco Bourgogne	Mhl	2010	32,837	58,020	190	32	14	bbu	l/a Sefor
9490698	Genco Brittany	Mhl	2010	32,837	58,020	190	32	14	bbu	l/a Matador
9149392	Genco Carrier	Hkg	1998	26,098	47,180	186	31	14	bbu	ex Top Carrier-04
9345818	Genco Cavalier	Mhl	2007	31,261	53,617	190	32	14	bbu	ex CMB Yangtze-08, Nikomarine-07
9287429	Genco Challenger	Hkg	2003	16,978	28,428	169	27	14	bbu	ex Orchid Bay-08
9350094	Genco Champion	Hkg	2006	16,960	28,445	169	27	14	bbu	ex Stentor-08
9324710	Genco Charger	Hkg	2005	16,960	28,398	169	27	14	bbu	ex Captain Adams-08
9444819	Genco Claudius	Mhl	2010	88,397	169,025	288	45	14	bbu	
9422079	Genco Commodus	Mhl	2009	88,397	167,025	288	45	14	bbu	
9361251	Genco Constantine	Hkg	2008	90,106	180,200	288	45	14	bbu	
9199842	Genco Explorer *	Hkg	1999	18,036	29,952	170	27	14	bbu	ex Top Explorer-04
9422067	Genco Hadrian	Mhl	2008	88,397	169,694	288	45	14	bbu	
9368871	Genco Hunter	Mhl	2007	32,379	57,982	190	32	14	bbu	ex Tomahawk-08
9200378	Genco Knight	Hkg	1999	38,646	73,941	225	32	14	bbu	ex Top Knight-05
9490686	Genco Languedoc	Mhl	2010	32,837	58,020	190	32	14	bbu	l/d Tenor
9200366	Genco Leader	Hkg	1999	38,646	73,941	225	32	14	bbu	ex Top Leadrr-05
9511820	Genco Loire	Mhl	2009	31,117	53,100	190	32	14	bbu	ex Fructidor-10
9430038	Genco London	Hkg	2007	91,373	177,852	292	45	14	bbu	
9474785	Genco Lorraine	Mhl	2009	31,117	53,146	190	32	14	bbu	ex Nantor-10
9450765	Genco Mare	Lbr	2011	23,456	34,428	180	30	14	bbu	l/a Handy Mare
9125906	Genco Marine	Hkg	1996	26,040	45,222	188	31	14	bbu	ex Lucky Marine-05
9422081	Genco Maximus	Mhl	2009	88,397	167,025	288	45	14	bbu	
9234214	Genco Muse	Hkg	2001	28,097	48,913	190	32	14	bbu	ex Western Muse-05, l/a Muse Venture

Baltic Breeze : Genco Shg. & Trading - Baltic Trading Ltd. : *ARO*

IMO	name	flag	year	gt	dwt	loa	bm	kts	type	comments
9347877	Genco Normandy	Mhl	2007	31,107	53,500	190	32	14	bbu	ex Thermidor-10
9450739	Genco Ocean	Lbr	2010	23,456	34,402	180	30	14	bbu	l/a Handy Ocean
9301720	Genco Picardy	Mhl	2005	31,264	55,257	190	32	14	bbu	ex Dalior-10
9197935	Genco Pioneer	Hkg	1998	18,036	29,952	170	27	14	bbu	ex Top Pioneer-05
9316165	Genco Predator	Mhl	2005	31,069	55,407	190	32	14	bbu	ex Predator-07
9199830	Genco Progress *	Hkg	1998	18,036	29,952	170	27	14	bbu	ex Top Progress-05
9121742	Genco Prosperity	Hkg	1997	26,094	47,180	186	31	14	bbu	ex Top Prosperity-05
9316220	Genco Provence	Mhl	2004	31,264	55,317	190	32	14	bbu	ex Messidor-10
9511832	Genco Pyrenees	Mhl	2010	32,837	58,018	190	32	14	bbu	c/a Chun He 56, l/d Pearlor
9330812	Genco Raptor	Mhl	2007	41,115	76,499	225	32	14	bbu	ex CMB Laetitia
9200407	Genco Reliance *	Hkg	1999	18,036	29,952	170	27	14	bbu	ex Top Reliance-05
9490832	Genco Rhone	Mhl	2011	32,839	57,970	190	32	14	bbu	
9450777	Genco Spirit	Lbr	2011	23,456	34,393	180	30	14	bbu	
9121730	Genco Success	Hkg	1997	26,094	47,186	186	31	14	bbu	ex Top Success-05
9191034	Genco Sugar	Hkg	1998	18,036	29,952	170	27	14	bbu	ex Top Sugar-05
9184914	Genco Surprise	Hkg	1998	37,695	72,495	225	32	14	bbu	ex Koby-06, Norviken-04, Far Eastern Wendy-00
9331555	Genco Tiberius	Hkg	2007	88,675	175,874	292	45	14	bbu	l/a Ferro Fos
9593452	Genco Tiger	Mhl	2011	93,290	179,185	292	45	14	bbu	ex Baltic Tiger-15, l/d K. Happiness
9410959	Genco Titus	Hkg	2007	91,373	177,729	292	45	14	bbu	
9332212	Genco Thunder	Mhl	2007	41,115	76,499	225	32	14	bbu	ex CMB Aurelie-08
9200392	Genco Vigour	Hkg	1999	38,646	73,941	225	32	14	bbu	ex Top Vigour-04
9316153	Genco Warrior	Mhl	2005	31,069	55,435	190	32	14	bbu	ex Innovator-07
9149380	Genco Wisdom	Hkg	1997	26,094	47,000	186	31	14	bbu	ex Top Wisdom-05

* operated by Lauritzen Bulkers, most vessels chartered out

Baltic Trading Ltd., Marshall Islands

funnel: *dark blue with white 'B' on broad light blue band between two narrow white bands.* **hull:** *black with red boot-topping.*
history: *formed as subsidiary of Genco in 2010.* **web:** *www.baltictrading.com*

IMO	name	flag	year	gt	dwt	loa	bm	kts	type	comments
9469259	Baltic Bear	Mhl	2010	91,373	177,700	292	45	14	bbu	ex Inna-10
9450741	Baltic Breeze	Lbr	2010	23,456	34,386	180	30	14	bbu	ex Handy Breeze-10
9387358	Baltic Cougar	Mhl	2009	31,117	53,100	190	32	14	bbu	ex Spice-10
9450727	Baltic Cove	Lbr	2009	23,456	34,403	180	30	14	bbu	ex Handy Cove-10
9397248	Baltic Fox	Mhl	2010	19,831	31,883	176	29	14	bbu	ex Clipper Hope-13
9397236	Baltic Hare	Mhl	2009	19,831	31,887	176	29	14	bbu	ex Clipper Harmony-13
9721932	Baltic Hornet	Mhl	2014	36,353	63,574	200	32	14	bbu	
9387360	Baltic Jaguar	Mhl	2009	31,117	53,100	190	32	14	bbu	ex Inta-10
9387334	Baltic Leopard	Mhl	2009	31,117	53,100	190	32	14	bbu	ex Borak-10
9593464	Baltic Lion	Mhl	2012	93,290	179,185	292	45	14	bbu	l/d K Global Pride
9729489	Baltic Mantis	Mhl	2015	36,353	63,470	200	32	14	bbu	
9387346	Baltic Panther	Mhl	2009	31,117	53,100	190	32	14	bbu	ex Sinova-10
9729477	Baltic Scorpion	Mhl	2015	36,353	63,462	190	32	14	bbu	
9722015	Baltic Wasp	Mhl	2015	36,353	63,389	190	32	14	bbu	
9450703	Baltic Wind	Lbr	2009	23,456	34,408	180	30	14	bbu	ex Handy Wind-10
9492335	Baltic Wolf	Mhl	2010	91,373	177,752	292	45	14	bbu	ex Smyrna-10

Gener8 George T : Gener8 Maritime Corp : *Hans Kraijenbosch*

IMO	name	flag	year	gt	dwt	loa	bm	kts	type	comments

Gener8 Maritime Corp.   U.S.A.

funnel: *black with yellow 'G' inside yellow edged green diamond on yellow edged broad dark blue band or charterers colours.* **hull:** *black with red boot-topping.* **history:** *formed 1997. Acquired Soponata SA in 2004 and merged with Arlington Tankers (27%) in 2008. Filed for Chapter 11 bankruptcy in 2011, but refinanced by Oaktree Capital Management in April 2012 and merged with Navig8 Crude Tankers Inc. in May 2015.* **web:** *www.gener8maritime.com*

IMO	name	flag	year	gt	dwt	loa	bm	kts	type	comments
9272204	Concord	Bmu	2005	27,357	47,171	183	32	14	tco	ex Stena Concept-14
9258600	Concord *	Mhl	2004	27,357	47,171	183	32	14	tco	ex GenMar Concord-13, Stena Concord-09
9723083	Gener8 Apollo	Mhl	2016	157,092	299,995	333	60	15	tcr	l/d STI Perth
9723095	Gener8 Ares	Mhl	2016	157,092	299,999	333	60	15	tcr	l/d STI Dundee
9185530	Gener8 Argus	Mhl	2000	81,151	159,901	274	48	15	tcr	ex GenMar Argus-15, Crude Tria-03
9723071	Gener8 Athena	Mhl	2015	157,092	299,999	333	60	15	tcr	l/d STI Edinburgh
9322281	Gener8 Atlas	Mhl	2007	157,844	306,506	332	58	15	tcr	ex GenMar Atlas-15, Crudesky-10
9223318	Gener8 Daphne	Mhl	2002	57,683	106,548	241	42	15	tcr	ex Genmar Daphne-15, Fidelity-08
9247974	Gener8 Defiance	Lbr	2002	56,225	105,538	239	42	14	tcr	ex GenMar Defiance-15, Peneda-04
9233313	Gener8 Elektra *	Mhl	2002	57,683	106,560	241	42	14	tcr	ex Genmar Elektra-15, Fantasy-08
9336971	Gener8 George T.	Mhl	2007	79,235	149,847	274	48	15	tcr	ex GenMar George T.-15
9302982	Gener8 Harriet G.	Lbr	2006	79,325	150,205	274	48	15	tcr	ex GenMar Harriet G-15
9723100	Gener8 Hera	Mhl	2016	157,092	300,000	333	60	15	tcr	
9322279	Gener8 Hercules	Mhl	2007	157,844	306,506	332	58	15	tcr	ex GenMar Hercules-15, Crudesun-10
9173757	Gener8 Horn	Mhl	1999	81,526	159,474	274	48	15	tcr	ex Crude Horn-03, Nord Horn-00
9302994	Gener8 Kara G.	Lbr	2007	79,235	150,296	274	48	15	tcr	ex GenMar Kara G-15, GenMar Horn-15
9461764	Gener8 Maniate	Mhl	2010	84,735	164,716	274	50	15	tcr	ex GenMar Maniate-15 Crude Zita-10
9723069	Gener8 Neptune	Mhl	2015	157,092	299,999	333	60	15	tcr	l/d STI Glasgow
9224271	Gener8 Orion	Mhl	2002	81,381	159,992	274	48	15	tcr	ex GenMar Orion-15, Crude Okto-03, Antares-02
9247986	Gener8 Pericles	Lbr	2003	56,225	105,674	239	42	15	tcr	ex GenMar Strength-15 Portel-04
9182746	Gener8 Phoenix	Mhl	1999	80,058	153,015	269	46	15	tcr	ex GenMar Phoenix-15, Crude Ena-03
9236250	Gener8 Poseidon	Mhl	2002	154,348	305,796	332	58	15	tcr	ex GenMar Poseidon-15, Crude Progress-10, Poros-04
9461776	Gener8 Spartiate	Mhl	2011	84,735	164,714	274	50	15	tcr	ex GenMar Spartiate-15, l/a Crude Ita
9185528	Gener8 Spyridon	Mhl	2000	81,151	159,959	274	48	15	tcr	ex GenMar Spyridon-15, Crude Dio-03
9336983	Gener8 St. Nikolas	Mhl	2008	79,235	149,876	274	48	15	tcr	ex GenMar St. Nikolas-15
9734642	Gener8 Strength	Mhl	2015	160,449	300,960	333	60	15	tcr	
9727003	Gener8 Success	Mhl	2016	160,449	300,932	333	60	15	tcr	
9734654	Gener8 Supreme	Mhl	2016	159,957	300,960	333	60	15	tcr	
9254082	Gener8 Ulysses	Mhl	2003	160,889	318,692	333	60	15	tcr	ex GenMar Ulysses-15, Crudestar-10
9255933	Gener8 Companion *	Bmu	2004	41,589	72,637	229	32	15	tco	ex GenMar Companion-15, Stena Companion-09
9255945	GenMar Compatriot *	Bmu	2004	41,589	72,000	229	32	15	tco	ex Stena Compatriot-09
9205093	GenMar Victory	Bmu	2001	163,761	312,638	335	70	16	tcr	ex Stena Victory-09
9205081	GenMar Vision	Bmu	2001	163,761	312,679	335	70	16	tcr	ex Stena Vision-09
9411032	GenMar Zeus	Mhl	2010	160,502	318,325	333	60	15	tcr	ex Crudemed-10

Seychelles Pioneer : German Tanker Shipping - Seychelles Petroleum : *F. de Vries*

IMO	name	flag	year	gt	dwt	loa	bm	kts	type	comments
newbuildings:										
9728693	Gener8 Nautilus			171,500	300,000				tcr	Hyundai Samho 768
9728708				171,500	300,000				tcr	Hyundai Samho 769
9728710				171,500	300,000				tcr	Hyundai Samho 770
9728722				171,500	300,000				tcr	Hyundai Samho 771
9739501				171,500	300,000				tcr	Hyundai Gunsan 2794
9739513				171,500	300,000				tcr	Hyundai Gunsan 2795
9727015				171,500	319,000				tcr	SWS 1556
9727027				171,500	319,000				tcr	SWS 1558
9727039				171,500	319,000				tcr	SWS 1558

also Hanjin HI 137, 138,

German Tanker Shipping GmbH & Co. KG   Germany

funnel: *yellow with red 'GT' on white segments of white/blue diagonally quartered flag, narrow black top.* **hull:** *black with red boot-topping.* **history:** *company founded 1998 in Bremen.* **web:** *www.german-tanker.de*

IMO	name	flag	year	gt	dwt	loa	bm	kts	type
9251640	Seabass	Lbr	2001	21,353	32,480	178	28	14	tco
9352315	Seacod	Deu	2006	26,548	40,558	188	32	16	tco
9352298	Seaconger	Deu	2005	21,329	32,200	178	28	16	tco
9255488	Seahake	Deu	2003	21,329	32,480	178	28	16	tco
9251652	Sealing	Deu	2003	21,356	32,480	178	28	16	tco
9380489	Seamarlin	Deu	2007	26,548	40,550	188	32	15	tco
9204776	Seamullet	Deu	2001	21,353	32,230	178	28	15	tco
9423449	Seapike	Lbr	2009	28,449	43,550	188	32	16	tco
9255490	Searay	Deu	2004	21,353	32,310	178	28	16	tco
9298193	Seashark	Deu	2004	21,329	32,310	178	28	16	tco
9380477	Seasprat	Deu	2007	26,548	40,597	188	32	16	tco
9352303	Seatrout	Deu	2006	26,548	40,600	188	32	15	tco
9204764	Seaturbot	Deu	2000	21,353	32,230	178	28	14	tco
9365635	Seychelles Patriot *	Sey	2008	27,007	45,680	189	32	14	tco
9255517	Seychelles Pioneer *	Sey	2005	22,346	37,500	185	28	14	tco
9365623	Seychelles Prelude *	Sey	2007	27,007	45,680	189	32	14	tco
9251664	Seychelles Pride *	Sey	2002	21,353	32,580	178	28	14	tco
9298181	Seychelles Progress *	Sey	2005	22,346	37,557	185	28	14	tco

* managed for Seychelles Petroleum Co., founded 1985 www.seypet.com

Goldenport Holdings Inc.   Greece

funnel: *white with gold 'G' above the right of two blue waves, black top.* **hull:** *black with red boot-topping.* **history:** *founded 1975 by Dragnis family as Goldenport Cia. Nav. (Cyprus) until 1992* **web:** *www.goldenport.biz*

IMO	name	flag	year	gt	dwt	loa	bm	kts	type	comments
9460136	Alpine Amalia *	Lbr	2010	57,237	105,304	244	42	14	tco	
9469687	Alpine Aquilina *	Lbr	2011	57,237	105,304	244	42	14	tco	
9379301	Alpine Penelope *	Lbr	2008	41,696	74,471	228	32	14	tco	
9379961	Alpine Persephone *	Lbr	2008	41,696	74,268	228	32	14	tco	
9210050	Carlotta Star	Lbr	2000	37,113	40,018	243	32	23	ucc	3,430 teu: ex Santa Carlotta-11, P&O Nedlloyd Olinda-05, l/a Santa Carlotta
9210062	Carolina Star	Lbr	2000	37,113	40,125	243	32	22	ucc	3,430 teu: ex Santa Carolina-11, P&O Nedlloyd Surat-05, Santa Carolina-01

Alpine Penelope : Goldenport Holdings : *Chris Brooks*

IMO	name	flag	year	gt	dwt	loa	bm	kts	type	comments
9210086	Celina Star	Lbr	2001	37,113	40,018	243	32	23	ucc	3,430 teu: ex Santa Celina-11, P&O Nedlloyd Chusan-05, Santa Celina-
8800511	Champion *	Lbr	1990	22,572	39,468	176	32	14	tco	ex Champion Pioneer-13, Scottish Wizard-06, Stride-02, Osco Stripe-95
9210098	Cristina Star	Lbr	2001	37,113	39,978	243	32	23	ucc	3,430 teu: ex Santa Cristina-11, P&O Nedlloyd Bantam-05, l/a Santa Cristina
9587453	D. Skalkeas	Lbr	2011	51,225	93,281	229	38	14	bbu	
9577410	Eleni D.	Lbr	2010	34,374	58,429	196	32	14	bbu	
9472103	Erato	Lbr	2011	26,374	34,162	209	30	22	ucc	2,546 teu
9438016	Ermis	Lbr	2009	30,669	53,800	190	32	14	bbu	ex Marie-Paule-14
9112272	Fortunate	Pan	1996	64,054	68,363	275	40	25	ucc	5,551 teu: ex MSC Fortunate-15, Fortune-09, Hyundai Fortune-06
9634969	Ioanna D.	Lbr	2012	22,434	35,000	180	28	24	bbu	
9577422	Maria	Lbr	2011	34,335	58,407	186	32	14	bbu	
9472098	Milos	Lbr	2010	32,983	56,988	190	32	14	bbu	
9108398	Paris JR	Mlt	1996	14,241	18,400	159	24	18	ucc	1,129 teu: ex HC Maria-11, Delmas Anemone-09, Saturn-06, TMM Leon-01, CMB Endurance-97, Saturn-96
9456367	Pisti	Lbr	2011	32,983	56,898	190	32	14	bbu	
8309567	Sentinel I	Lbr	1985	28,195	51,546	180	32	14	tco	ex Ocean Pearl-14, Synergy-08
9456379	Sifnos	Lbr	2010	32,983	57,050	190	32	14	bbu	
9472086	Sofia	Lbr	2011	32,983	56,899	190	32	14	bbu	
9642019	Stenaweco Spirit *	Lbr	2012	30,017	49,995	183	32	16	tco	
9660657	Stenaweco Venture *	Lbr	2013	29,623	49,995	183	32	16	tco	
9194878	TG Aphrodite	Lbr	1999	25,630	33,855	207	30	21	ucc	2,474 teu: ex E.R. Copenhagen-14, Maersk Valencia-09, E.R. Copenhagen-99
9239886	TG Athena	Lbr	2002	27,332	33,800	212	30	22	ucc	2,496 teu: ex E.R. Bremerhaven -15, Safmarine Cunene-12, E.R. Bremerhaven-02
9301457	TG Nike	Lbr	2005	26,836	34,263	210	30	21	ucc	2,556 teu: ex E.R. Cannes-15, CMA CGM La Boussole-10, E.R. Cannes-05 sold 04:2015
9194866	TG Poseidon	Deu	1999	25,630	33,855	207	30	21	ucc	2,474 teu: ex E.R. Stralsund-14, Maersk Napier-09, E.R. Stralsund-05, Indamex Tuticorin-04, E.R. Stralsund-03, Maersk Mendoza-02, l/a E.R. Stralsund
9166651	Thasos	Lbr	1998	25,499	34,116	200	30	21	ucc	2,452 teu: ex Gallia-13, Alianca Shanghai-09, P&O Nedlloyd Eagle-03, Columbus Texas-01, Gallia-98
9134490	Thira	Lbr	1997	24,053	28,370	205	27	20	ucc	2,109 teu: ex Conti Seattle-13, Delmas Libreville-12, Tiger Bay-07, APL Melbourne-06, Vancouver-04, Ivory Star 1-03, Conti Seattle-02, CCNI Antartico-02, Sea Lynx-00, Conti Seattle-97
9762883	Tramno Baumann	Lbr	2016	25,611	38,635	180	32	14	bbu	
9762895	Tramno Independent	Lbr	2016	25,594	38,629	180	32	14	bbu	
9762912	Tramno Laoura	Lbr	2016	25,500	38,600	180	32	14	bbu	
9762871	Tramno Stanton	Lbr	2015	25,594	38,629	180	32	14	bbu	

*vessels operated by Goldenport Shipmanagement Ltd, Greece   * managed by associated Oceangold Tankers Inc.*

Green Management Sp.z.o.o. Poland

funnel: *dark green with green 'G' on white square.* **hull:** *dark green with white 'GREEN REEFERS', red boot-topping.* **history:** *founded 1989 as Nomadic Shipping ASA to 2003. Green Reefers ASA sold to parent company Caiano Gp., May 2012, renamed Transit Invest ASA, merged with Reach Subsea AS, November 2012.* **web:** *www.greenreefers.no*

IMO	name	flag	year	gt	dwt	loa	bm	kts	type	comments
8819299	Green Austevoll	Bhs	1991	5,084	6,116	109	18	19	grf	ex Nordice-01, Wisida Nordic-00, Erikson Nordic-96
8804555	Green Bodo	Bhs	1990	5,085	6,129	109	18	19	grf	ex Frost-01, Wisida Frost-00, Erikson Frost-96
9045792	Green Brazil *	Bhs	1994	7,743	7,721	131	20	19	grf	ex Pittsburg-05, Pioneer-96, Crystal Pioneer-96
8912156	Green Chile *	Bhs	1992	7,743	7,726	131	20	19	grf	ex Privilege-06, Crystal Privilege-03
9011038	Green Concordia	Bhs	1991	5,617	7,072	120	19	17	grf	ex Hachinohe Bay-05, Sashima-00
8804543	Green Cooler	Bhs	1990	5,084	6,123	109	18	19	grf	ex Erikson Cooler-96
8912120	Green Costa Rica *	Bhs	1991	7,743	7,726	131	20	19	grf	ex Prince-06, Crystal Prince-04
8920995	Green Crystal	Bhs	1992	5,084	6,116	109	18	19	grf	ex Carmencita-98
8804567	Green Egersund	Bhs	1990	5,084	6,120	109	18	19	grf	ex Snow-01, Wisida Snow, 00, Erikson Snow-96
8819304	Green Freezer	Bhs	1993	5,084	6,120	109	18	19	grf	ex Erikson Freezer-96

Green Crystal : Green Reefers : *Chris Brooks :*

Star Lindesnes : Grieg Star Shipping : *Chris Brooks*

IMO	name	flag	year	gt	dwt	loa	bm	kts	type	comments
9004401	Green Glacier	Bhs	1991	5,136	6,488	115	18	19	grf	ex Glacier-06, Green Glacier-00, Platina Reefer-96, Capewind-94
8912144	Green Guatemala *	Bhs	1992	7,743	7,726	131	20	19	grf	ex Primadonna-05, Crystal Primadonna-04
8912132	Green Honduras *	Bhs	1992	7,743	7,721	131	20	19	grf	ex Pride-06, Crystal Pride-03
9045780	Green Italia *	Bhs	1994	7,743	7,721	131	20	19	grf	ex Pilgrim-06, Crystal Pilgrim-96
8804531	Green Karmoy	Bhs	1989	5,084	6,120	109	18	19	grf	ex Ice-01, Green Kormoy-01, Wisida Arctic-00, Belinda-96, Erikson Arctic-94
8822583	Green Magic	Bhs	1989	5,103	6,116	136	16	20	grf	ex Magic-06
9011492	Green Magnific	Bhs	1992	5,103	6,116	136	16	20	grf	ex Magnific-06
8804579	Green Maloy	Bhs	1990	5,084	6,120	109	18	19	grf	ex Wintertide-01, Wisida Winter-00, Erikson Winter-96
9043055	Green Maveric	Bhs	1993	5,103	6,105	136	16	20	grf	ex Maveric-06
8822595	Green Music	Bhs	1990	5,103	6,116	136	16	20	grf	ex Music-07
8804529	Green Selje	Bhs	1989	5,084	6,120	109	18	19	grf	ex Erikson Crystal-02
9015785	Green Toledo	Bhs	1991	5,617	7,075	120	19	17	grf	ex Japan Star-05, Kamishima-05

vessels owned by Transit Invest ASA, (Caiano Group),Norway, formerly Green Reefers ASA until May 2012: also operates smaller vessels
* chartered to SeaTrade b.v.

Grieg Star Shipping   Norway

funnel: *yellow with two blue stars on white panel with blue top and bottom edges.* **hull:** *blue, red or grey with red or blue boot-topping.*
history: *formed 1961 as Star Shipping, restructured 1984 as Grieg Shipping Group until June 2012.* **web:** *www.griegstar.com*

IMO	name	flag	year	gt	dwt	loa	bm	kts	type	comments
9738208	Star Artemis	Nis	2015	35,873	63,205	200	32	14	bbu	
9497880	Star Athena	Nis	2012	32,839	57,809	190	32	14	bbu	
9228144	Star Canopus ‡	Grc	2002	25,388	45,635	180	31	14	bbu	ex Star Mizuho-07
9228071	Star Capella ‡	Grc	2001	25,388	45,601	180	31	14	bbu	
9738210	Star Eos	Nis	2015	35,812	63,200	200	32	14	bbu	
9499450	Star Eracle	Nis	2012	32,839	58,018	190	32	14	bbu	c/a Chun He 125
8309830	Star Fuji	Nis	1985	25,345	40,850	187	29	15	goh	
8420799	Star Gran	Nis	1986	27,192	43,759	198	29	16	goh	ex Triton-86
8420787	Star Grip	Nis	1986	27,192	43,712	198	29	16	goh	
9103128	Star Hansa	Nis	1996	32,749	46,580	198	31	16	goh	
9103130	Star Harmonia	Nis	1998	32,749	46,604	198	31	16	goh	
9071557	Star Herdla	Nis	1994	32,744	47,942	198	31	16	goh	
9071569	Star Hidra	Nis	1994	32,749	46,547	198	31	16	goh	
9182978	Star Isfjord	Nis	2000	29,898	41,749	185	31	16	goh	
9182966	Star Ismene	Nis	1999	28,898	41,777	185	31	16	goh	
9182954	Star Istind	Nis	1999	29,898	41,749	185	31	16	goh	
9254654	Star Japan	Nis	2004	32,844	46,387	198	31	16	goh	
9310513	Star Java	Nis	2006	32,879	46,387	198	31	16	goh	
9254642	Star Juventus	Nis	2004	32,844	44,837	198	31	16	goh	
9316139	Star Kilimanjaro	Nis	2009	37,158	49,862	208	32	16	goh	
9396141	Star Kinn	Nis	2010	37,158	49,850	209	32	16	goh	
9316927	Star Kirkenes	Nis	2009	37,158	49,924	208	32	16	goh	
9396153	Star Kvarven	Nis	2010	37,158	49,924	209	32	16	goh	

Grande Abidjan : Grimaldi Group : *Mike Rhodes*

IMO	name	flag	year	gt	dwt	loa	bm	kts	type	comments
9593854	Star Laguna	Nis	2012	37,447	50,827	204	32	15	goh	
9593866	Star Lima	Nis	2012	37,447	50,761	204	32	15	goh	
9593878	Star Lindesnes	Nis	2013	37,447	50,748	204	32	15	goh	
9593907	Star Livorno	Nis	2013	37,447	50,700	204	32	15	goh	
9603790	Star Loen	Nis	2013	37,447	50,792	204	32	15	goh	
9593892	Star Lofoten	Nis	2013	37,447	50,728	204	32	15	goh	
9593880	Star Louisiana	Nis	2013	37,447	50,748	204	32	15	goh	
9603805	Star Luster	Nis	2013	37,447	50,740	204	32	15	goh	
9616838	Star Lygra	Nis	2013	37,447	50,741	204	32	15	goh	
9616840	Star Lysefjord	Nis	2014	37,447	50,700	204	32	15	goh	
9355513	Star Minerva *	Jpn	2008	30,360	50,757	190	32	14	goh	ex Sanko Mineral-14

Grimaldi Group   Italy

funnel: blue with either white 'G', 'I' or 'A' symbol or white 'S' within white ring. *hull:* yellow with black 'GRIMALDI LINES' on white upperworks, red boot-topping. *history:* founded 1941 as Fratelli Grimaldi Armatori to 1993. *web:* www.grimaldi.napoli.it

IMO	name	flag	year	gt	dwt	loa	bm	kts	type	comments
9030852	Fides +	Mlt	1993	33,825	16,802	178	27	17	urc	400 teu, 1,500 ceu
9143702	Gran Bretagna *	Ita	1999	51,714	18,461	181	32	20	urc	716 teu, 4,650 ceu
9117900	Grand Benelux *	Ita	2001	37,712	12,594	176	31	20	mve	4,600 ceu
9680712	Grande Abidjan	Ita	2015	71,543	30,801	236	36	20	urc	1,800 teu, 5,700 lm
9246607	Grande Amburgo †	Ita	2003	56,642	26,170	214	32	19	urc	1,321 teu, 3,515 ceu
9130937	Grande America †	Ita	1997	56,642	26,169	214	32	18	urc	1,321 teu, 3,515 ceu
9343156	Grande Angola †	Ita	2008	47,115	26,881	211	32	21	urc	800teu, 2,500 ceu
9287417	Grande Anversa *	Ita	2004	38,651	12,353	177	31	20	mve	4,600 ceu
9130951	Grande Atlantico	Ita	1999	56,640	26,170	214	32	18	urc	1,321 teu, 3,515 ceu
9343170	Grande Benin †	Ita	2009	47,218	26,097	211	32	21	urc	1,360 teu, 3,890 ceu
9253210	Grande Buenos Aires	Ita	2004	56,642	26,169	214	32	19	urc	1,321 teu, 3,515 ceu
9377482	Grande Cameroon †	Ita	2010	47,218	26,652	211	32	20	urc	1,360 teu, 3,890 ceu
9318527	Grande Colonia †	Ita	2007	38,651	12,292	177	31	20	mve	4,300 ceu
9437921	Grande Congo †	Ita	2010	47,658	25,682	211	32	21	urc	1,360 teu, 3,890 ceu
9465382	Grande Costa d'Avorio	Ita	2011	47,218	24,800	211	32	21	urc	1,360 teu, 3,890 ceu
9672105	Grande Cotonou	Ita	2015	71,543	31,340	236	36	20	urc	1,800 teu, 5,700 lm
9680724	Grande Dakar	Ita	2015	71,543	30,796	236	36	20	urc	1,800 teu, 5,700 lm
9293272	Grande Detroit	Ita	2005	38,651	12,420	177	31	20	mve	4,300 ceu
9220627	Grande Ellade *	Ita	2001	52,485	18,440	181	32	19	urc	400 teu, 2,550 ceu
9138381	Grande Europa *	Ita	1998	51,714	18,461	181	32	19	urc	400 teu, 2,500 ceu
9246592	Grande Francia †	Ita	2002	56,642	26,170	214	32	19	urc	1,321 teu, 3,515 ceu
9437933	Grande Gabon †	Ita	2011	47,658	24,400	211	32	21	urc	1,360 teu, 3,890 ceu
9343168	Grande Ghana †	Ita	2009	47,115	25,000	211	32	21	urc	1,360 teu, 3,890 ceu
9437919	Grande Guinea †	Ita	2010	47,658	25,799	211	32	21	urc	1,360 teu, 3,890 ceu
9227912	Grande Italia *	Ita	2001	37,712	12,594	176	31	20	mve	4,300 ceu
9672088	Grande Lagos †	Ita	2014	71,543	30,990	236	36	20	urc	1,800 teu, 5,700 lm
9724738	Grande Luanda	Ita	2015	71,543	31,340	236	36	20	urc	1,800 teu, 5,700 lm
9437907	Grande Marocco †	Ita	2010	47,635	24,400	211	32	20	urc	1,360 teu: 3,890 ceu
9138393	Grande Mediterraneo *	Ita	1998	51,714	18,427	181	32	20	urc	716 teu, 4,650 ceu
9247924	Grande Napoli *	Ita	2003	44,408	14,565	197	31	20	mve	5,300 ceu
9246580	Grande Nigeria †	Ita	2002	56,642	26,170	214	32	19	urc	1,321 teu, 3,515 ceu
9245598	Grande Portogallo *	Ita	2002	37,712	12,594	176	31	20	mve	4,300 ceu
9247936	Grande Roma *	Ita	2003	42,600	14,900	201	31	20	mve	5,300 ceu
9253208	Grande San Paolo	Ita	2003	56,642	26,170	214	32	18	urc	1,321 teu, 3,515 ceu
9220615	Grande Scandinavia *	Ita	2001	52,487	18,440	181	32	20	urc	716 teu, 4,650 ceu
9377470	Grande Senegal †	Ita	2010	47,218	26,653	211	32	21	urc	1,360 teu, 3,890 ceu
9437945	Grande Sierra Leone †	Ita	2011	47,658	24,400	211	32	21	urc	1,360 teu, 3,890 ceu
9312092	Grande Sicilia	Ita	2006	38,651	12,353	177	31	20	mve	4,300 ceu
9227924	Grande Spagna *	Ita	2002	37,712	12,594	176	31	20	mve	4,300 ceu
9672090	Grande Tema	Ita	2014	71,543	31,340	236	36	20	urc	1,800 teu, 5,760 lm
9465370	Grande Togo	Ita	2011	47,218	26,650	211	32	21	urc	1,360 teu, 3,890 ceu
9138410	Repubblica Argentina †	Ita	1998	51,925	23,882	206	30	19	urc	800 teu,1,200 ceu
9138422	Repubblica del Brasile †	Ita	1998	51,925	23,800	206	30	19	urc	800 teu: 1,200 ceu
9030864	Spes *	Ita	1993	33.823	16,806	178	27	19	mve	400 teu: 1,500 ceu

newbuildings :

*ships owned by related Italian companies Grimaldi Compagnia di Navigazione SpA, * by Atlantica SpA di Navigazione or † by Industria Armamento Meridionale SpA (INARME,) or + Malta Motorways of the Sea Ltd.*

IMO	name	flag	year	gt	dwt	loa	bm	kts	type	comments

ACL Shipmanagement AB, Sweden

funnel: blue with white 'G'. **hull:** Atlantic * vessels : blue with blue 'ACL' and wave symbol on white upperworks. Grande X vessels, yellow with black 'GRIMALDI LINES' on white upperworks, red boot-topping **history:** originally formed 1965 as Atlantic Container Line by Wallenius, Swedish-America, Transatlantic, Holland-America, Cunard-Brocklebank and CGT added 1967. Consortium dissolved 1990 and ACL acquired by Transatlantic (Bilspedition subsidiary). Grimaldi acquired 44% share in 2000 and balance in 2001.
web: www.aclcargo.com

IMO	name	flag	year	gt	dwt	loa	bm	kts	type	comments
8215481	Atlantic Cartier	Swe	1985	58,358	51,648	292	32	17	urc	2,908 teu: (len-87)
8214176	Atlantic Compass	Swe	1984	57,255	51,648	292	32	17	urc	2,908 teu: (len-87)
8214164	Atlantic Concert	Swe	1984	57,255	51,648	292	32	17	urc	2,908 teu: ex Concert Express-94, Atlantic Concert-87 (len-87)
9670585	Atlantic Sail	Gbr	2016	100,430	55,631	296	38	18	urc	3,800 teu, 1,307 ceu
9670573	Atlantic Star	Gbr	2015	100,430	55,649	296	38	18	urc	3,800 teu, 1,307 ceu
9130949	Grande Africa *	Gib	1998	56,642	26,195	214	32	18	urc	1,321 teu, 3,515 ceu
9198135	Grande Argentina *	Gib	2001	56,642	26,170	214	32	18	urc	1,321 teu, 3,515 ceu
9198123	Grande Brasile *	Gib	2000	56,642	26,170	214	32	18	urc	1,321 teu, 3,515 ceu
9293272	Grande Detroit *	Ita	2005	38,651	12,353	176	31	20	mve	4,300 ceu
9312092	Grande Sicilia *	Ita	2006	38,651	12,353	176	31	20	mve	4,300 ceu
newbuildings:										
9670597	Atlantic Sea	Gbr	2016	100,430	56,700	296	38	18	urc	3,800 teu, 1,307 ceu Zhonghua 1697A
9670602	Atlantic Sky	Gbr	2016	100,430	56,700	296	38	18	urc	3,800 teu, 1,307 ceu Zhonghua 1698A
9670614	Atlantic Sun	Gbr	2016	100,430	56,700	296	38	18	urc	3,800 teu, 1,307 ceu Zhonghua 1699A

* owned by ACL Invest, managed and operated by Grimaldi

Gulf Energy Maritime   Dubai

funnel: white with company logo and GEM in blue under narrow dark blue band **hull:** green with red boot topping **history:** formed 2004 as j/v company between Emirates National Oil Co.(35%), Abu Dhabi International Petroleum Investments Co. (30%), Oman Oil Co. (30%) and Thales, France **web:** gemships.com

IMO	name	flag	year	gt	dwt	loa	bm	kts	type	comments
9381562	Gulf Baynunah	Bhs	2008	29,518	46,522	183	32	14	tco	
9389837	Gulf Castle	Bhs	2009	42,446	74,999	228	32	14	tco	
9389849	Gulf Cobalt	Bhs	2009	42,446	74,999	228	32	14	tco	
9389851	Gulf Coral	Bhs	2009	42,446	74,999	228	32	14	tco	
9298674	Gulf Coast	Bhs	2005	42,446	74,999	228	32	14	tco	
9389863	Gulf Crystal	Bhs	2009	42,446	74,999	228	32	14	tco	
9335109	Gulf Elan	Bhs	2007	29,490	46,894	183	32	14	tco	
9335094	Gulf Esprit	Bhs	2006	29,490	46,891	183	32	14	tco	
9297412	Gulf Horizon	Bhs	2005	42,443	74,999	228	32	14	tco	
9381823	Gulf Jumeirah	Bhs	2008	29,508	46,488	183	32	14	tco	
9335135	Gulf Mews	Bhs	2007	23,656	37,448	184	27	14	tco	
9335147	Gulf Mist	Bhs	2007	23,656	37,434	184	27	14	tco	
9335123	Gulf Moon	Bhs	2007	23,656	37,488	184	27	14	tco	
9381835	Gulf Muttrah	Bhs	2009	29,508	46,556	183	32	14	tco	
9281425	Gulf Pearl	Bhs	2005	42,443	74,999	228	32	14	tco	
9381847	Gulf Rastaq	Bhs	2009	29,508	46,554	183	32	14	tco	
9298662	Gulf Stream	Bhs	2005	42,443	74,999	228	32	14	tco	
9505821	Gulf Valour	Bhs	2013	61,338	114,900	249	48	14	tco	
9505819	Gulf Vision	Bhs	2012	61,338	114,900	249	48	14	tco	

Hafnia Tankers   Denmark

funnel: white with stylised 'HT' on blue circle, black top **hull:** red or black with black or red boot-topping. **history:** founded 2010, acquired Lauritzen Tankers vessels during 2014. Also manages two tanker pools, MR/Handy tankers pool with Gotland Class Shipping AB, Kirk Kapital and Donnelly Tankers, and Straits Tankers a 50/50 j/v with Mitsui OSK Lines, a product Pool for LR1 tankers with Marinvest, MOL, Reederei Nord, and UACC **web:** www.hafniatankers.com

IMO	name	flag	year	gt	dwt	loa	bm	kts	type	comments
9540819	Andes †	Cyp	2011	29,429	49,995	183	32	15	tco	
9419723	Anja Kirk *	Gbr	2009	29,955	51,332	183	32	15	tco	ex Blue Emerald-11
9414292	Christina Kirk *	Gbr	2010	31,510	53,540	186	32	14	tco	ex Freja Scandia-10
9302657	Edith Kirk *	Gbr	2004	23,244	37,255	183	28	14	tco	ex Kerlaz-10
9367683	Freja Baltic	Pan	2008	26,897	47,538	183	32	14	tco	
9375604	Gotland Aliya	Bhs	2008	29,283	53,121	183	32	14	tco	
9328132	Gotland Carolina	Bhs	2006	29,283	53,160	183	32	14	tco	
9375575	Gotland Marieann	Bhs	2008	29,283	53,143	183	32	14	tco	
9328144	Gotland Sofia	Bhs	2007	29,283	53,187	183	32	14	tco	
9476812	Gunhild Kirk *	Gbr	2009	30,241	50,436	183	32	14	tco	ex Stealth Argentina-10
9263203	Hafnia Adamello *	Sgp	2004	22,521	40,002	182	27	14	tco	ex Mount Adamello-14
9461661	Hafnia Andromeda	Gbr	2011	30,241	50,386	183	32	14	tco	ex Freja Andromeda-14
9709776	Hafnia Ane	Dnk	2015	29,715	49,999	183	32	15	tco	
9278519	Hafnia Atlantic	Dis	2004	30,004	45,967	183	32	14	tco	ex Freja Atlantic -14, Crozon-04
9725603	Hafnia Bering	Sgp	2015	24,100	39,067	183	24	15	tco	
9461697	Hafnia Crux	Dis	2012	30,241	52,550	183	32	14	tco	ex Freja Crux-14
9360441	Hafnia Green *	Sgp	2007	22,521	40,003	182	27	14	tco	ex Mount Green-14
9360415	Hafnia Hope *	Sgp	2007	22,521	40,009	182	27	14	tco	ex Mount Hope-14

IMO	name	flag	year	gt	dwt	loa	bm	kts	type	comments
9360427	Hafnia Karava *	Sgp	2007	22,521	40,020	182	27	14	tco	ex Mount Karava-14
9726619	Hafnia Lene	Mlt	2015	29,715	49,999	183	32	15	tco	
9476824	Hafnia Leo	Dis	2013	30,241	52,300	183	32	14	tco	ex Freja Leo-14
9617959	Hafnia Libra	Dis	2013	30,312	52,385	183	32	14	tco	ex Freja Libra-14
9461685	Hafnia Lupus	Dis	2012	30,241	52,550	183	32	14	tco	ex Freja Lupus-14
9725615	Hafnia Magellan	Mlt	2015	24,120	39,067	182	27	14	tco	
9725627	Hafnia Malacca	Sgp	2015	24,120	39,067	182	27	14	tco	
9426283	Hafnia Nordica	Pan	2010	31,510	53,520	186	32	14	tco	ex Freja Nordica-14
9461659	Hafnia Pegasus	Gbr	2010	30,241	50,391	183	32	14	tco	ex Freja Pegasus-14
9461702	Hafnia Phoenix	Dnk	2013	30,312	52,340	183	32	14	tco	ex Freja Phoenix-14
9263186	Hafnia Rainier *	Cyp	2004	22,518	40,012	182	27	14	tco	ex Mount Rainier-14
9263198	Hafnia Robson *	Sgp	2004	22,518	40,014	182	27	14	tco	ex Mount Robson-14
9729271	Hafnia Soya	Sgp	2015	24,120	38,667	183	28	14	tco	
9725639	Hafnia Sunda	Sgp	2015	24,120	39,067	183	28	14	tco	
9461673	Hafnia Taurus	Gbr	2011	30,241	50,385	183	32	14	tco	ex Freja Taurus-14
9360439	Hafnia Victoria *	Sgp	2007	22,521	40,055	182	27	14	tco	ex Mount Victoria-14
9540807	Himalaya †	Cyp	2011	29,429	49,996	183	32	15	tco	
9276004	Mare Caribbean	Mhl	2004	29,327	46,718	183	32	15	tco	ex Cape Bauld-07, Rudy-05, Mashuk-04
9419735	Marianne Kirk *	Gbr	2009	29,955	51,291	183	32	14	tco	ex Blue Jade-11
9302669	Marie Kirk	Gbr	2004	23,244	37,217	186	27	14	tco	ex Freja Polaris-14, Kermaria-07
9462897	Seameridian	Hkg	2011	30,241	50,309	183	32	14	tco	

Hafnia Crux : Hafnia Tankers, Hafnia MR Pool : *F. de Vries*

Iris Victoria : Hafnia Tankers, Straits Tankers LR1 Pool : *ARO*

IMO	name	flag	year	gt	dwt	loa	bm	kts	type	comments
newbuildings:										
9729283	Hafnia Torres		2016	24,000	38,700	183	24	14	tco	Hyundai Mipo 2574
9709788	*Hafnia Daisy*		2016	30,000	49,999	183	32	14	tco	Guangzhou 13130042
9726607	*Hanfia Henriette*		2016	30,000	49,999	183	32	14	tco	Guangzhou 13130043
9726621	*Hafnia Lise*		2016	30,000	49,999	183	32	14	tco	Guangzhou 13130064
9732682	*Hafnia Kirsten*		2016	30,000	49,999	183	32	14	tco	Guangzhou 13130045
9732694	*Hafnia Lotte*		2016	30,000	49,999	183	32	14	tco	Guangzhou 13130065
9732709	Hafnia Mikala		2016	30,000	49,999	183	32	14	tco	Guangzhou 13130066

† *owned by Donnelly Tanker Management operates in Hafnia Handy Pool* * *managed by Donnelly Tanker Mgmt MAI*

Straits Tankers LR1 pool

IMO	name	flag	year	gt	dwt	loa	bm	kts	type	comments
9321160	Advance Victoria	Bhs	2006	40,964	74,995	228	32	14	tco	
9595632	Bow Pioneer	Sgp	2013	45,452	81,305	228	37	14	tco	
9321172	Breezy Victoria	Bhs	2007	40,974	74,998	228	32	14	tco	
9336517	Classy Victoria	Hkg	2007	40,934	74,993	228	32	14	tco	
9321196	Fortune Victoria	Pan	2007	40,953	74,998	228	32	14	tco	
9321201	Grace Victoria	Pan	2007	40,953	74,998	228	32	14	tco	
9467811	Hafnia Africa	Sgp	2010	42,392	74,540	228	32	15	tco	ex Kihada-15
9336505	Hafnia America	Sgp	2006	41,021	74,996	229	32	14	tco	ex Summit America-14
9332640	Hafnia Arctic	Sgp	2010	42,889	74,910	228	32	15	tco	ex Arctic Char-15, l/a W-O Skol
9467809	Hafnia Asia	Sgp	2010	42,392	73,719	228	32	15	tco	ex Maguro-15
9467794	Hafnia Australia	Sgp	2010	42,392	74,540	228	32	15	tco	ex Karel-15
9336490	Hafnia Europe *	Sgp	2006	41,021	74,997	229	32	14	tco	ex Summit Europe-14
9564671	Iris Victoria	Mhl	2010	40,975	74,905	228	32	15	tco	
9571038	Justice Victoria	Pan	2010	40,975	74,902	228	32	14	tco	
9684102	Kamome Victoria	Pan	2011	40,976	74,908	228	32	14	tco	
9589815	Lilac Victoria	Mhl	2011	40,976	74,913	228	32	14	tco	
9608867	Magic Victoria	Mhl	2012	40,976	74,902	228	32	14	tco	
9326885	Mari Ugland	Nis	2008	42,835	74,997	228	32	14	tco	ex Marietta-08
9326897	Mariann	Nis	2008	42,996	74,999	228	32	14	tco	
9326873	Maribel	Nis	2007	42,835	74,999	228	32	14	tco	
9332614	Marika	Nis	2006	42,893	74,996	228	32	14	tco	
9326861	Marilee	Nis	2006	42,835	74,898	228	32	14	tco	
9332626	Marinor	Nis	2008	42,893	74,997	229	32	14	tco	
9310848	Maritina	Nis	2006	40,803	74,993	228	32	14	tco	ex Eternal Pride-10
9610389	Nexus Victoria	Iom	2015	40,976	74,910	228	32	15	tco	
9485631	UACC									
	Ibn Al Haitham	Mlt	2009	42,010	73,338	229	32	14	tco	
9550694	UACC Eagle	Mhl	2009	42,010	73,410	229	32	14	tco	ex Summit Asia-11
9550682	UACC Falcon	Mhl	2009	42,010	73,427	229	32	14	tco	ex Summit Australia-11
9485629	UACC Ibn Sina	Mlt	2008	42,010	73,338	229	32	14	tco	

Reederei Hamburger Lloyd GmbH & Co. KG   Germany

funnel: *black with broad white band and red top or charterers colours.* **hull:** *dark blue, red or black with black or red boot-topping.*
history: *founded 2007 and financially linked to Hansa Hamburg Shg. International GmbH & Co KG.* **web:** *www.hamburger-lloyd.com*

IMO	name	flag	year	gt	dwt	loa	bm	kts	type	comments
9313228	Barmbek	Lbr	2005	16,324	15,955	169	27	21	ucc	1,600 teu
9313199	Eilbek	Lbr	2005	16,324	15,952	169	27	21	ucc	1,600 teu ex Cast Prosperity-06, Eilbek-05
9313216	Flottbek	Lbr	2005	16,324	15,952	169	27	21	ucc	1,600 teu
9313204	Reinbek	Lbr	2005	16,324	15,952	169	27	21	ucc	1,600 teu: ex Cast Prestige-06, Reinbek-05
9357846	RHL Audacia	Lbr	2007	18,480	23,745	177	27	20	ucc	1,732 teu: ex Mell Sentosa-14,974 CSAV Venezuela-11, G. W. Lessing-07
9373486	RHL Agilitas	Lbr	2007	18,480	23,664	177	27	20	ucc	1,732 teu: ex Wilhelm Busch-07
9373498	RHL Aqua	Lbr	2007	18,480	23,732	177	27	20	ucc	1,732 teu: ex Theodor Fontane-07
9334844	RHL Astrum	Lbr	2006	18,480	23,640	177	27	20	ucc	1,732 teu: ex Heinrich Heine-11
9334832	RHL Aurora	Lbr	2006	18,480	23,685	177	27	20	ucc	1,721 teu: ex Mell Semangat-15, RHL Aurora-12,Matthias Claudias-11
9495777	RHL Calliditas	Lbr	2013	48,799	58,014	260	37	23	ucc	4,620 teu
9539688	RHL Concordia	Lbr	2012	48,799	58,189	260	37	23	ucc	4,620 teu: CCNI Andes-13, l/a RHL Concordia
9539664	RHL Conscientia	Lbr	2012	48,799	58,197	260	37	23	ucc	4,620 teu: ex CCNI Aysen-13, RHL Conscientia-12
9495765	RHL Constantia	Lbr	2013	48,799	58,027	260	37	23	ucc	4,620 teu
9497426	RHL Novare	Lbr	2011	19,994	31,754	177	28	14	bbu	ex Vega Venus-15

Hanjin Shipping Co. Ltd.   South Korea

funnel: *orange with white 'H' inside white ring.* **hull:** *black with white 'HANJIN', red boot-topping.* **history:** *formed 1988. Senator Lines GmbH (formed 1987 as Senator Linie, a subsidiary of Bremer Vulkan shipyard), later merged with former East German company Deutsche Seerederei Rostock and became 80% owned affiliate in 1997, before closing in early 2009.* **web:** *www.hanjin.com*

IMO	name	flag	year	gt	dwt	loa	bm	kts	type	comments
9632480	Hanjin Aqua ††	Pan	2013	51,032	62,448	250	37	21	ucc:	4,532 teu
9632765	Hanjin Argentina	Pan	2013	37,199	45,349	221	35	21	ucc	3,560 teu
9389394	Hanjin Atlanta	Pan	2009	40,487	51,733	261	32	24	ucc	4,275 teu
9312779	Hanjin Bremerhaven	Pan	2006	74,962	80,855	304	40	26	ucc	6,655 teu
9312937	Hanjin Budapest	Pan	2006	74,962	80,866	304	40	26	ucc	6,655 teu
9408865	Hanjin China	Pan	2011	113,412	118,835	350	46	25	ucc	9,954 teu
9347449	Hanjin Chongqing	Pan	2008	74,962	80,855	304	40	26	ucc	6,622 teu
9375513	Hanjin Durban	Pan	2008	40,487	51,750	261	32	24	ucc	4,275 teu
9389409	Hanjin Gdynia	Pan	2009	40,487	51,733	261	32	24	ucc	4,275 teu
9461491	Hanjin Hamburg	Pan	2011	91,621	102,455	336	43	24	ucc	8,580 teu
9624275	Hanjin Indigo	Pan	2013	45,169	58,200	255	38	22	ucc	4,600 teu
9389382	Hanjin Kingston	Pan	2008	40,487	51,733	261	32	24	ucc	4,275 teu
9408853	Hanjin Korea	Pan	2010	113,412	118,800	350	46	25	ucc	9,954 teu
9461465	Hanjin Long Beach	Pan	2010	91,621	102,518	336	43	25	ucc	8,580 teu: ex CSAV Tortel-13, Hanjin Long Beach-13
9128130	Hanjin Los Angeles	Kor	1997	51,754	62,799	290	32	24	ucc	4,024 teu
9632507	Hanjin Mar ††	Pan	2013	51,032	61,740	250	37	22	ucc	4,532 teu
9632492	Hanjin Marine ††	Pan	2013	51,032	61,740	250	37	22	ucc	4,532 teu
9389411	Hanjin Monaco	Pan	2009	40,487	51,733	261	32	24	ucc	4,275 teu
9347425	Hanjin Mumbai	Pan	2007	74,962	85,250	304	40	26	ucc	6,622 teu
9408841	Hanjin Netherlands	Pan	2011	113,515	118,712	350	46	25	ucc	9,954 teu
9461505	Hanjin New York	Pan	2011	91,621	102,518	336	43	25	ucc	8,580 teu
9404194	Hanjin Newport	Mhl	2009	40,542	50,574	261	32	24	ucc	4,250 teu
9375496	Hanjin Norfolk	Pan	2008	40,487	51,752	261	32	24	ucc	4,275 teu
9375501	Hanjin Piraeus	Pan	2008	40,487	50,542	261	32	24	ucc	4,275 teu
9312949	Hanjin Port Kelang	Pan	2006	75,061	80,811	304	40	26	ucc	6,655 teu
9375305	Hanjin Rio de Janiero	Pan	2008	40,487	51,648	261	32	24	ucc	4,275 teu
9461489	Hanjin Rotterdam	Pan	2011	91,621	102,539	336	43	25	ucc	8,588 teu
9624287	Hanjin Scarlet	Pan	2013	45,169	58,200	255	38	14	ucc	4,600 teu
9461477	Hanjin Seattle	Pan	2011	91,621	102,529	336	43	25	ucc	8,580 teu
9347437	Hanjin Shenzhen	Pan	2008	74,962	80,855	304	40	26	ucc	6,622 teu
9408877	Hanjin Spain	Pan	2011	113,412	118,814	350	46	25	ucc	9,954 teu
9312767	Hanjin Tianjin	Pan	2007	74,962	80,855	304	40	25	ucc	6,655 teu
9406738	Hanjin United Kingdom	Pan	2011	113,412	118,888	350	46	25	ucc	9,954 teu
9624299	Hanjin White	Pan	2014	45,169	58,200	255	38	22	ucc	4,600 teu
9312755	Hanjin Xiamen	Pan	2007	74,962	80,855	304	40	26	ucc	6,655 teu

Hansa Heavy Lift   # Germany

funnel: *white* **hull:** *red with white 'Hansa Heavy Lift', red boot-topping.* **history:** *founded 2011 with acquired various interests from former Beluga Shipping GmbH founded 1995.* **web:** *www.hansaheavylift.com*

IMO	name	flag	year	gt	dwt	loa	bm	kts	type	comments
9466996	HHL Amazon	Lbr	2009	9,611	12,662	138	21	17	ghl	cr: 2(180): ex Beluga Fairy-11
9435753	HHL Amur	Atg	2009	9,611	12,678	138	21	15	ghl	cr: 2(180): ex Beluga Fidelity-11
9467005	HHL Congo	Atg	2011	9,616	12,546	138	21	15	ghl	cr: 2(180): ex Beluga Fealty-11
9433262	HHL Elbe	Lbr	2008	9,627	12,709	138	21	15	ghl	cr: 2(150): ex Elbe-14, BBC Alaska-13
9448360	HHL Fremantle	Atg	2011	17,644	19,382	169	25	17	ghl	cr: 2(700) 1(180): I/a Beluga Protection

HHL Fremantle : Hansa Heavy Lift : *Hans Kraijenbosch*

IMO	name	flag	year	gt	dwt	loa	bm	kts	type	comments
9419008	HHL Hamburg	Atg	2009	15,377	16,577	166	23	17	ghl	cr: 2(400) 1(120): ex Beluga Cape Town-11, Beluga Profession-10
9448384	HHL Kobe	Atg	2012	17,644	19,864	169	25	17	ghl	cr: 2(700) 1(180)
9448358	HHL Lagos	Atg	2011	17,644	19,379	169	25	17	ghl	cr: 2(700) 1(180): ex Beluga Progression-11
9448372	HHL New York	Atg	2011	17,644	19,866	169	25	17	ghl	cr: 2(700) 1(180): l/a Beluga Publication
9443669	HHL Nile	Gib	2009	9,611	12,744	138	21	15	ghl	cr: 2(180): ex Beluga Faculty-11
9435765	HHL Mississippi	Atg	2009	9,611	12,669	138	21	15	ghl	cr: 2(180): ex OXL Fantasy-11, Beluga Fantasy-11
9467017	HHL Rhine	Lbr	2009	9,616	12,951	138	21	15	ghl	cr: 2(180): ex Beluga Feasibility-11
9448308	HHL Richards Bay	Atg	2010	17,644	19,329	169	25	17	ghl	cr: 2(700) 1(180): ex Beluga London-11, l/a Beluga Passion
9424546	HHL Rio di Janiero	Lbr	2009	17,628	20,171	169	25	17	ghl	cr: 2(700) 1(180)ex Beluga Houston-11, Beluga H-10, Beluga Houston-10, l/d Beluga Presentation
9448346	HHL Tokyo	Atg	2011	17,644	19,496	169	25	17	ghl	cr: 2(700) 1(180): ex Beluga Toyko-11, Beluga Procession-11
9433274	HHL Tyne	Lbr	2009	9,627	12,771	138	21	15	ghl	cr: 2(150): ex Tyne-14, BBC Montana-13
9424558	HHL Valparaiso	Lbr	2010	17,634	19,413	169	25	17	ghl	cr: 2(700) 1(180)ex Beluga Bremen-11, l/a Beluga Perfection
9418987	HHL Venice	Atg	2010	15,377	18,373	166	23	17	ghl	cr :2(400) 1(120): ex Beluga Mumbai-11, l/a Beluga Promotion
9381392	HHL Volga	Lbr	2007	9,611	12,782	138	21	15	ghl	cr: 2(150): ex Volga-11, Beluga Family-11

Hansa Treuhand GmbH & Co. KG　　　　　　　　Germany

funnel: white with blue houseflag or charterers colours. **hull:** dark blue, red or black with black or red boot-topping. **history:** founded 1997 as ship management arm within Hansa Treuhand Group (founded 1983). **web:** www. hansashipping.de

IMO	name	flag	year	gt	dwt	loa	bm	kts	type	comments
9368742	Alianca Santa Fé	Lbr	2008	16,162	17,350	161	24	20	ucc	1,347 teu: HS Liszt-15
9315355	ANL Bindaree	Lbr	2007	38,320	46,313	247	32	23	ucc	3,500 teu: ex HS Bizet-14
9228526	Bella	Atg	2001	30,024	35,980	208	32	22	ucc	2,672 teu: ex CSCL Jakarta-09, l/a Bella
9228514	Bonny	Atg	2001	30,024	36,019	208	32	22	ucc	2,672 teu: ex CSCL Barcelona-09, l/a Bonny
9222091	Bravo	Atg	2001	30,026	36,189	208	32	22	ucc	2,672 teu: ex CSCL Genoa-09, l/a Bravo
9228538	Chief	Atg	2001	30,024	36,003	208	32	22	ucc	2,672 teu: ex CSCL Kelang-08, l/a Chief
9124378	Glory	Atg	1996	23,897	30,447	188	30	20	ucc	2,080 teu: ex Clan Amazonas-09, Glory-05, Cap Vincent-01, Glory-00, Crowley Americas-99, Glory-99, Pacifico-98
9124524	Hansa Constitution	Deu	1997	31,730	34,954	193	32	22	ucc	2,507 teu: ex Norasia Alps-10, Hansa Constitution-05, MSC Florida-03, Hansa Constitution-98, Ibn Al Akfani-98, Hansa Constitution-97
9217034	Hansa Liberty	Deu	2000	25,369	33,912	207	30	21	ucc	2,470 teu: ex CSCL Yantian-07, Hansa Liberty-00
9217022	Hansa Victory	Deu	2000	25,369	33,899	207	30	21	ucc	2,470 teu: ex Alianca Gavea-09, Cala Palos-08, CSCL Xiamen-07, Hansa Victory-00
9221970	HS Alcina	Lbr	2001	83,723	160,183	274	48	14	tcr	ex Somjin-06
9323015	HS Bach	Lbr	2007	38,320	44,985	247	32	23	ucc	3,500 teu
9477804	HS Baffin	Mlt	2013	48,338	58,027	255	32	24	ucc	4,750 teu
9252266	HS Beethoven	Lbr	2002	50,243	58,213	282	32	24	ucc	4,350 teu: ex APL Italy-09, MSC Arizona-05, HS Voyager-03, l/a Hansa Voyager
9315343	HS Berlioz	Lbr	2007	38,320	46,288	247	32	23	ucc	3,500 teu
9392559	HS Bruckner	Lbr	2009	35,981	42,004	231	32	22	ucc	3,534 teu
9248095	HS Caribe	Lbr	2002	50,242	58,512	282	32	24	ucc	4,367 teu: ex Maersk Drammen-13, CMA CGM Mercure-06, l/a HS Caribe
9242120	HS Carmen	Lbr	2003	62,254	113,033	250	44	14	tcr	ex Avor-06
9243605	HS Challenger	Lbr	2004	30,024	35,924	207	32	22	ucc	2,672 teu: ex Hansa Challenger-04
9323027	HS Chopin	Lbr	2007	38,320	46,345	247	32	23	ucc	3,500 teu
9248083	HS Colon	Lbr	2002	50,242	58,399	282	32	24	ucc	4,367 teu: ex Maersk Dampier-13, CMA CGM Neptune-06, l/a HS Colon-02, l/dn Hansa Colon

IMO	name	flag	year	gt	dwt	loa	bm	kts	type	comments
9225079	HS Columbia	Lbr	2001	65,131	67,955	275	40	26	ucc	5,447 teu: ex MSC Brindisi-12, CSCL Seattle-09, l/a HS Columbia, l/dn Hansa Columbia
9436484	HS Debussy	Lbr	2009	36,007	41,973	231	32	23	ucc	3,534 teu: ex SCI New Delhi-12, HS Debussy-09
9243590	HS Discoverer	Deu	2003	30,123	35,600	207	32	22	ucc	2,672 teu: ex Zim Charleston-07, HS Discoverer-06, Hansa Discoverer-04
9618587	HS Everest	Mlt	2014	48,338	58,059	255	32	24	ucc	4,750 teu
9392561	HS Haydn	Lbr	2010	35,981	41,989	231	32	23	ucc	3,534 teu
9618599	HS Marco Polo	Lbr	2014	48,338	58,087	255	32	24	ucc	4,750 teu
9134608	HS Master	Deu	1997	23,897	30,416	188	30	21	ucc	2,080 teu: ex Master-14, Maruba Imperator-09, Master I-08, P&O Nedlloyd Brunel-06, Master I-03, Master-02, CMA CGM Paris-02, Lykes Kestrel-01, MOL Europe-00, Maersk Miami-99, l/a Master
9242118	HS Medea	Lbr	2003	62,254	113,033	250	44	14	tcr	ex Sinova-06
9252254	HS Mozart	Lbr	2002	50,243	58,486	282	32	24	ucc	4,350 teu: ex APL Australia-09, MSC Lausanne-04, HS Explorer-02, l/a Hansa Explorer
9300984	HS Oceano	Lbr	2006	32,968	38,686	214	32	23	ucc	2,800 teu: ex Ital Oceano-14, HS Cook-06
9300972	HS Onore	Lbr	2006	32,968	38,609	214	32	23	ucc	2,800 teu: ex Ital Onore-14, HS Amundsen-06
9526502	HS Paris	Lbr	2012	75,015	84,155	300	40	25	ucc	6,588 teu
9538658	HS Rome	Lbr	2014	75,015	84,154	300	40	25	ucc	6,588 teu
9565338	HS Rossini	Lbr	2012	39,753	46,020	228	32	22	ucc	3,421 teu: ex Niledutch Leopard-14, l/a HS Rossini
9477799	HS Shackleton	Mlt	2013	48,338	58,070	255	32	24	ucc	4,750 teu
9312652	HS Smetana	Lbr	2006	18,327	23,377	176	27	20	ucc	1,740 teu: ex Viking Merlin-09
9288851	HS Tosca	Lbr	2004	62,796	115,635	250	44	15	tcr	
9436472	HS Wagner	Lbr	2008	36,007	42,100	231	32	23	ucc	3,534 teu: ex Maruba America-10, HS Wagner-08
9124380	Primus	Atg	1997	23,897	30,502	188	30	20	ucc	2,080 teu: ex Hanjin Palermo-11, Genoa Senator-09, Safmarine Letaba-05, Primus-02, CSAV Guayas-99, Primus-99, Sea Parana-99, Primus-97
9368730	Tiger Goman	Lbr	2007	16,162	17,350	161	25	20	ucc	1,347 teu: ex HS Puccini-14, Mell Stamford-13, HS Puccini-12

vessels managed by Hansa Shipping GmbH & Co. KG
see also Norddeutsche Reederei H Schuldt GmbH, KG Projex-Schiffahrts GmbH & Co, F A Vinnen & Co and Oskar Wehr KG.

Hanseatic Lloyd AG   Switzerland

funnel: black with red dot over blue wave on broad white band or charterers colours. **hull:** blue or light grey with red boot-topping.
history: formed 2003. **web:** www.hanseatic-lloyd.com

9345960	APL Denver	Gib	2008	43,071	55,612	267	32	25	ucc	4,730 teu: l/a HLL Pacific
9332250	APL Oakland	Gib	2008	43,071	55,476	267	32	25	ucc	4,730 teu: l/a HLL Arafura
9345972	MSC Atlanta	Gib	2008	43,071	55,482	267	32	25	ucc	4,730 teu: ex APL Atlanta-14, l/a HLL Adriatic
9345958	MSC Los Angeles	Gib	2008	43,071	55,387	267	32	25	ucc	4,730 teu: ex APL Los Angeles-14, l/a HLL Java
9316232	Sharon Sea +	Lbr	2006	42,167	73,870	229	32	15	tco	

newbuildings,
owned by subsidiaries of Hanseatic Lloyd Schiffahrt GmbH & Co KG, Germany.   + managed by Harren & Partner

Hansa Mare Reederei GmbH & Co. KG, Germany

funnel: black with red dot over blue wave on broad white band or charterers colours. **hull:** blue or light grey with red boot-topping.
history: formed 1991 and jointly owned by Hanseatic Lloyd Reederei and Schlüssel Reederei KG (founded 1950).
web: www.hansamare.de

9213284	Mare Arcticum *	Gib	2000	40,306	52,250	261	32	22	ucc	4,038 teu: ex APL Chile-12, Mare Arcticum-04, YM New York-04, Trade Tesia-03, Mare Arcticum-01
9213272	Mare Atlanticum *	Atg	2000	40,306	52,250	261	32	24	ucc	4,038 teu: ex MSC Scandinavia-11, Donau Bridge-04, Mare Atlanticum-01
9235074	Mare Britannicum *	Gib	2000	40,306	52,250	261	32	22	ucc	4,038 teu: ex APL Kaohsiung-12, Kaohsiung-09, APL Kaohsiung-08, APL Panama-06, APL Britannicum-04, YM Wilmington-04, Trade Freda-03, l/a Mare Britannicum

IMO	name	flag	year	gt	dwt	loa	bm	kts	type	comments
9235086	Mare Caribicum *	Gib	2000	40,306	52,250	261	32	22	ucc	4,038 teu: ex APL Argentina-12, YM Savannah-04, Trade Hallie-03, Mare Caribicum-01
9193238	Mare Lycium *	Atg	1999	40,306	47,660	261	32	24	ucc	4,038 teu: ex Libra Mexico-11, Mumbai Express-07, Mare Lycium-06, P&O Nedlloyd Cobra-05, Mare Lycium-03, Mosel Bridge-02, l/a Mare Lycium
9193226	Mare Phoenicium *	Gib	1999	40,306	52,330	261	32	24	ucc	4,038 teu: ex Ems Bridge-01, l/a Mare Phoenicium
9169134	Mare Siculum *	Atg	1998	40,306	52,357	261	32	25	ucc	3,987 teu: ex Alvsborg Bridge-14, Maersk Dulles-09, Maersk Tangier-06, P&O Nedlloyd Tiger-05, Weser Bridge-04, l/a Mare Siculum

* managed by Schlüssel Reederei

Hapag-Lloyd AG   Germany

funnel: *orange with blue 'HL' symbol.* **hull:** *black with white 'Hapag-Lloyd' and red boot-topping.* **history:** *formed in 1970 by amalgamation of Hamburg-Amerika Linie (founded 1847) and Norddeutscher Lloyd (founded 1857). Rickmers Linie became wholly owned subsidiary in 1987 (part-owned since 1974), later being resold to Rickmers family. Control of Hapag acquired by Preussag AG in 1997 and Hapag acquired control of TUI Group in 1998, Preussag (now TUI) acquiring remaining shares in 2002 and in 2005 TUI acquired CP Ships (originally founded 1883 as Canadian Pacific Railway Co, first ship chartered 1886, later Canadian Pacific Steamships (founded 1922) and Canadian Pacific Ltd from 1981. Canada Maritime founded 1987, jointly with CMB (43%) whose share was acquired 1993. Acquired Cast (1983) Ltd in 1995, Lykes Bros Steamship Co (founded 1900) and Contship in 1997, Ivaran Lines and ANZDL in 1998, TMM and CCAL in 2000 and Italia Line in 2002). Merged with C.S.A.V December 2014* **web:** *www.hapag-lloyd.com*

IMO	name	flag	year	gt	dwt	loa	bm	kts	type	comments
9612789	Antofagasta Express	Chl	2015	38,654	48,039	224	35	21	ucc	3,508 teu: ex NileDutch Rotterdam-16
9612997	Antwerpen Express	Deu	2013	142,295	142,020	366	48	24	ucc	13,196 teu
9501344	Basle Express	Deu	2012	142,295	142,051	366	48	24	ucc	13,092 teu
9229855	Berlin Express	Deu	2003	88,493	100,019	320	43	26	ucc	7,179 teu
9343728	Bremen Express	Deu	2008	93,750	103,567	336	43	25	ucc	8,749 teu
9450430	Budapest Express	Deu	2010	93,750	103,662	336	43	25	ucc	8,749 teu
9243162	Charleston Express *	Usa	2002	40,146	36,644	243	32	20	ucc	3,237 teu: ex CP Everglades-07, Lykes Ranger-05
9295268	Chicago Express	Deu	2006	93,811	103,691	336	43	25	ucc	8,749 teu
9295244	Colombo Express	Deu	2005	93,750	103,800	335	43	25	ucc	8,749 teu
9229829	Dalian Express	Deu	2001	88,493	100,006	320	43	26	ucc	7,506 teu: ex Hamburg Express-11
9193288	Dallas Express	Deu	2000	54,437	67,145	294	32	24	ucc	4,864 teu: ex Antwerpen Express-12, Tokyo Express-99
9232577	Dublin Express	Deu	2002	46,009	54,157	281	32	25	ucc	4,121 teu: ex Maersk Dale-08, CP Australis-06, Contship Australis-05
9143556	Düsseldorf Express	Deu	1998	53,523	66,525	294	32	23	ucc	4,639 teu
9501370	Essen Express	Deu	2013	142,295	142,022	366	48	24	ucc	13,196 teu: l/a Ludwigshafen Express
9450442	Frankfurt Express	Deu	2010	93,750	103,994	335	43	25	ucc	8,749 teu
9232589	Glasgow Express	Deu	2002	46,009	54,221	281	32	25	ucc	4,121 teu: ex Maersk Dayton-08, CP Borealis-06, Contship Borealis-05
9461051	Hamburg Express	Deu	2012	142,295	142,092	366	48	23	ucc	13,169 teu
9343716	Hanover Express	Deu	2007	93,750	103,760	336	43	25	ucc	8,749 teu
9501356	Hong Kong Express	Deu	2013	142,295	142,018	366	48	24	ucc	13,092 teu
9143544	Kobe Express	Deu	1998	53,523	67,537	294	32	23	ucc	4,612 teu: ex Shanghai Express-02
9343730	Kuala Lumpur Express	Deu	2008	93,811	103,538	336	43	25	ucc	8,749 teu
9295256	Kyoto Express	Deu	2005	93,750	103,890	335	43	25	ucc	8,749 teu
9613006	Leverkusen Express	Deu	2013	142,295	142,007	366	48	24	ucc	13,092 teu: l/a Beijing Express
9290816	Limari	Deu	2005	42,382	51,870	268	32	25	ucc	4,043 teu
9108128	Lisbon Express	Bmu	1995	33,735	34,330	216	32	20	ucc	2,298 teu: ex CP Prospect-06, Cast Prospect-05, CanMar Fortune-03
9232565	Liverpool Express	Deu	2002	46,009	54,156	281	32	25	ucc	4,121 teu: ex Maersk Dexter-07, CP Aurora-06, Contship Aurora-05
9143568	London Express	Deu	1998	53,523	66,577	294	32	23	ucc	4,621 teu
9613018	Ludwigshafen Express	Deu	2014	142,295	142,035	366	48	24	ucc	13,092 teu: l/d Essen Express
9112296	Milan Express	Bmu	1996	33,663	33,659	216	32	20	ucc	2,486 teu: ex CP Los Angeles-06, Cielo di Los Angeles-05, Cast Premier-05, OOCL Canada-03
9165358	Mississauga Express	Bmu	1998	39,174	40,881	245	32	21	ucc	2,808 teu: ex CP Pride-06, CanMar Pride-05
9253741	Montreal Express	Gbr	2003	55,994	62,300	294	32	22	ucc	4,402 teu: ex CP Spiri-06, CanMar Spirit-05
9450428	Nagoya Express	Deu	2010	93,750	103,646	335	43	25	ucc	8,749 teu: ex Basle Express-12
9501332	New York Express	Deu	2012	142,295	142,028	367	48	24	ucc	13,169 teu

IMO	name	flag	year	gt	dwt	loa	bm	kts	type	comments
9229843	Ningbo Express	Deu	2002	88,493	100,016	320	43	26	ucc	7,179 teu: ex Hong Kong Express-12, Berlin Express-02
9320697	Osaka Express	Deu	2007	93,750	103,662	336	43	25	ucc	8,749 teu
9165360	Ottawa Express	Bmu	1998	39,174	40,120	245	32	21	ucc	2,808 teu: ex CP Honour-06, CanMar Honour-05
9243203	Philadelphia Express *	Usa	2003	40,146	40,478	243	32	22	ucc	3,237 teu: ex CP Yosemite-06, TMM Yucatan-05
9450399	Prague Express	Deu	2010	93,750	104,014	336	43	25	ucc	8,749 teu
9294836	Quebec Express	Deu	2006	42,382	51,870	268	32	25	ucc	4,043 teu: ex Longavi-15
9193317	Rotterdam Express	Deu	2000	54,465	66,975	294	32	24	ucc	4,843 teu
9612777	San Antonio Express	Chl	2015	39,106	46,000	224	35	21	ucc	3,510 teu: ex NileDutch Dordrecht-16
9193305	Seoul Express	Deu	2000	54,465	66,971	294	32	24	ucc	4,890 teu: ex Bremen Express-07
9501368	Shanghai Express	Deu	2013	142,295	142,023	366	48	24	ucc	13,092 teu
9450404	Sofia Express	Deu	2010	93,750	104,007	336	43	25	ucc	8,749 teu
9243186	St. Louis Express †	Usa	2002	40,146	40,478	244	32	22	ucc	3,237 teu: ex CP Yellowstone-06, TMM Guanajuato-05
9193290	Tokyo Express	Deu	2000	54,465	67,145	294	32	24	ucc	4,843 teu
9253727	Toronto Express	Gbr	2003	55,994	47,840	294	32	22	ucc	4,402 teu: ex CP Venture-06, CanMar Venture-05
9320702	Tsingtao Express	Deu	2007	93,750	103,631	336	43	25	ucc	8,749 teu
9613020	Ulsan Express	Deu	2014	142,295	141,666	366	48	23	ucc	13,092 teu: l/a Leverkusen Express
9108130	Valencia Express	Bmu	1996	33,735	34,330	216	32	20	ucc	2,298 teu: ex CP Performer-06, Lykes Performance-05, Cast Prominence-05, CanMar Courage-03
9450416	Vienna Express	Deu	2010	93,750	103,648	335	43	25	ucc	8,749 teu
9243198	Washington Express†	Usa	2003	40,146	40,478	243	32	22	ucc	3,237 teu: ex CP Denali-06, Lykes Flyer-05
9229831	Yantian Express	Deu	2002	88,493	100,003	320	43	26	ucc	7,179 teu: ex Shanghai Express-12, l/a Berlin Express
9243174	Yorktown Express *	Usa	2002	40,146	40,478	243	32	21	ucc	3,237 teu: ex CP Shenandoah-07, TMM Colima-05, Contship Tenacity-02

newbuildings:

IMO	name	flag	year	gt	dwt	loa	bm	kts	type	comments
9777589				116,000	120,000	333	48		ucc	11,000 teu Hyundai S832 10.2016
9777606				116,000	120,000				ucc	11,000 teu Hyundai S833 12:2016
9777618				116,000	120,000				ucc	11,000 teu Hyundai S834 01:2017
9777620				116,000	120,000				ucc	11,000 teu Hyundai S835 02:2017
9777632				116,000	120,000				ucc	11,000 teu Hyundai S836 04:2017

owned by Hapag-Lloyd USA LLC and managed by Marine Transport Management, † owned by Wilmington Trust Co.
see other chartered ships with 'Express' suffix under various non-operating owners

Compania Sud-Americana de Vapores S.A., Chile

funnel: *red with deep black top.* **hull:** *grey or white with red or green boot-topping.* **history:** *founded 1872, acquired Norasia Services SA, Switzerland in 2008 and has a minority 27% interest in Navieros Group controlled Compania Chilena de Navegacion Interoceanica SA, Chile (CCNI). Container business merged with Hapag-Lloyd 2014.* **web:** *www.csav.com*

IMO	name	flag	year	gt	dwt	loa	bm	kts	type	comments
9687552	Cauquenes	Lbr	2015	93,685	104,449	300	48	22	ucc	9,324 teu: c/a Corcovado
9687538	Cautin	Lbr	2014	93,685	104,450	300	48	22	ucc	9,324 teu
9295957	Chacabuco	Lbr	2006	66,280	68,228	276	40	25	ucc	5,527 teu
9687576	Cisnes	Lbr	2015	93,685	104,416	300	48	22	ucc	9,324 teu
9687540	Cochrane	Lbr	2015	93,685	104,695	300	48	22	ucc	9,324 teu
9687526	Copiapo	Lbr	2014	93,685	104,544	300	48	22	ucc	9,324 teu
9687564	Corcovado	Lbr	2015	93,685	104,633	300	48	22	ucc	9,324 teu
9687588	Coyhaique	Lbr	2015	93,685	104,589	300	48	22	ucc	9,324 teu
9400083	Maipo	Lbr	2010	75,752	81,002	306	40	25	ucc	6,589 teu
9197351	Mapocho	Chl	1999	16,986	21,182	168	27	20	ucc	1,587 teu: ex Kribi-02, ANL Okapi-02, Fesco Endeavor-01, Kribi-00
9400100	Mehuin	Lbr	2011	75,752	81,002	306	40	25	ucc	6,589 teu
9306196	Palena	Lbr	2006	73,934	81,248	304	40	25	ucc	6,541 teu
9447897	Tempanos	Lbr	2011	88,586	94,649	300	46	23	ucc	8,005 teu
9612882	Tirua	Lbr	2012	88,586	94,375	300	46	23	ucc	8,005 teu
9612870	Tolten	Lbr	2012	88,586	94,600	300	46	23	ucc	8,005 teu
9447914	Torrente	Lbr	2011	88,586	94,661	300	46	23	ucc	8,005 teu
9447873	Tubul	Lbr	2011	88,586	94,666	300	46	23	ucc	8,005 teu
9569970	Tucapel	Lbr	2012	88,586	94,650	300	46	23	ucc	8,005 teu

vessels managed by Southern Shipmanagement (Chile) Ltd (www.ssm.cl)

Torrente : Hapag-Lloyd - C.S.A.V. : *Chris Brooks*

Combi Dock I : Harren & Partner : *Hans Kraijenbosch*

IMO	name	flag	year	gt	dwt	loa	bm	kts	type	comments

Harren & Partner Schiffahrts GmbH   Germany

funnel: cream with two dark sails above three waves. **hull:** *light grey, black, green or blue ** with red boot-topping.*
history: *formed 1989.* **web:** *www.harren-partner.de*

IMO	name	flag	year	gt	dwt	loa	bm	kts	type	comments
9505510	Amoenitas	Atg	2010	11,473	9,973	134	23	16	urh	ex Palanpur-14, Hyundai Phoenix-12, I/a Palanpur
9400485	Blue Giant (2)	Atg	2008	18,169	10,480	169	25	16	urh	cr: 1(200, 2(350) ex OIG Giant-11, Blue Giant-11, Combi Dock II-08
9512381	Calypso	Atg	2011	11,473	9,917	134	23	16	urh	
9400473	Combi Dock I (2)	Atg	2008	17,341	10,480	169	25	15	urh	cr: 1(200), 2(350)
9432828	Combi Dock III (2)	Atg	2008	18,169	10,480	169	25	15	urh	cr: 1(200), 2(350)
9538892	EIT Palmina *	Atg	2009	12,679	9,391	142	23	15	urh	cr: 2(350) ex Hyundai Britania-11, Scan Britania-09
9538907	EIT Paloma *	Atg	2010	12,679	9,503	142	23	15	urh	cr: 2(350): Scan Espana-11
9614842	Pabal	Atg	2012	41,213	75,377	225	32	15	bbu	
9614854	Pabur	Atg	2012	41,213	75,426	225	32	15	bbu	
9324174	Pacao	Pmd	2005	14,308	16,403	155	25	18	ucc	1,221 teu: ex Cape Fraser-15, USL Kea-08, Cape Fraser-06
9275103	Pacita	Pmd	2004	14,308	16,439	155	25	18	ucc	1,221 teu: ex Anita L.-15, Cape Fresco-11, CNC Hongkong-08, Cape Fresco-04
9275115	Pacon	Pmd	2005	14,308	16,397	156	25	18	ucc	1,221 teu: ex Cape Falster-15, Vento di Tramontana-12, Cape Falster-
9501863	Palmerton	Atg	2009	11,473	10,124	134	23	16	urh	
9312080	Patagonia **	Cyp	2005	11,935	16,772	144	23	14	tco	ex Maersk Nairn-10, I/a Patagonia
9305180	Patalya **	Mlt	2005	11,935	16,664	144	23	14	tco	ex Maersk Newport-13, Patalya-05
9373644	Patani **	Mlt	2008	11,935	16,611	144	23	14	tco	ex Marida Patani-11, Patani-09
9344423	Patara	Mlt	2007	12,164	16,979	144	23	14	tco	ex Gan-Ocean-10
9373622	Patea **	Mlt	2005	11,935	16,651	144	23	14	tco	ex Marida Patea-11
9365477	Paterna **	Cyp	2006	11,935	16,748	149	22	15	tco	ex Marida Paterna-11
9365489	Patnos **	Cyp	2006	11,935	16,714	149	22	14	tco	ex Marida Patnos-10
9348297	Patras **	Mlt	2007	12,137	16,744	144	23	14	tco	ex Gan-Sword-10
9312078	Patricia **	Cyp	2005	11,935	16,642	144	23	14	tco	ex Maersk Naantali-10, Patricia-05
9305178	Patrona I **	Mlt	2005	11,935	16,716	144	23	14	tco	ex Maersk Nordenham-14, Patrona-05
9262522	Puffin	Jam	2003	22,654	37,641	199	24	14	bbu	

vessels owned or managed by Harren & Partners Ship Management GmbH & Co KG..
*† managed for H&H Schiffahrts GmbH or * managed for EIT European Investment & Trading or ** managed by Brostrom AB*

Hartmann Schiffahrts GmbH & Co. KG   Germany

funnel: blue with blue 'h' symbol in white circle or charterers colours. **hull:** *blue or red, with white 'UCC' (Frisia vessels) or UBC (UBC vessels) or (GasChem)or Italia (Ital vessels), red boot-topping.* **history:** *formed 1981.* **web:** *www.hartmann-reederei.de*

IMO	name	flag	year	gt	dwt	loa	bm	kts	type	comments
9337262	Frisia Amsterdam	Lbr	2007	27,779	39,332	222	30	23	ucc	2,824 teu: ex Ital Ottima-15, c/a Frisia Amsterdam-15
9470961	Frisia Bonn	Lbr	2010	21,842	28,632	190	28	21	ucc	1,970 teu: ex CCNI Columbia-12, Frisia Bonn-11
9337250	Frisia Goteborg	Lbr	2006	27,779	38,345	222	30	23	ucc	2,824 teu: ex Ital Ordine-14
9320013	Frisia Hannover	Lbr	2006	25,406	33,743	207	30	22	ucc	2,478 teu: ex Itajai Express-13, I/a Frisia Hannover
9299044	Frisia Helsinki	Lbr	2005	25,406	33,750	207	30	21	ucc	2,478 teu: ex Libra Santa Catarina-11, Santos Star-09, Frisia Helsinki-05
9302437	Frisia Kiel	Lbr	2004	25,406	33,847	207	30	21	ucc	2,478 teu: ex Cap Doukato-09, I/a Frisia Kiel
9299020	Frisia Lissabon	Lbr	2004	25,406	33,829	207	30	22	ucc	2,478 teu: ex CSAV Santos-11, Frisia Lissabon-09, Cap Flinders-08, Cabo Prior-06, I/a Frisia Lissabon
9320001	Frisia Loga	Lbr	2005	25,406	33,900	207	30	22	ucc	2,478 teu: ex Paranagua Express-11, Frisia Loga-06
9302449	Frisia Lübeck	Lbr	2004	25,406	33,781	207	30	22	ucc	2,478 teu: ex CSAV Rio Lontue-11, Frisia Lübeck-09, Libra Santa Catarina-09, Frisia Lübeck-04
9470973	Frisia Nürnberg	Lbr	2010	21.842	28,520	190	28	21	ucc	1,970 teu
9311842	Frisia Rostock	Lbr	2004	25,406	33,900	207	30	21	ucc	2,478 teu: ex CSAV Santos-09, I/a Frisia Rostock
9299032	Frisia Rotterdam	Deu	2004	25,406	33,784	207	30	21	ucc	2,478 teu: ex Cap Saray-09, I/a Frisia Rotterdam
9311830	Frisia Wismar	Lbr	2004	25,406	27,400	207	30	21	ucc	2,478 teu: ex CSAV Rio Lontue-09, I/a Frisia Wismar
9402586	Gaschem Adriatic	Lbr	2010	13,879	18,775	156	23	17	lpg	17,000 m³
9402598	Gaschem Antarctic	Lbr	2010	13,879	18,110	156	23	17	lpg	17,134 m³
9471032	Gaschem Bremen	Lbr	2010	22,977	26,645	173	28	16	lpg	35,232 m³
9471018	Gaschem Hamburg	Lbr	2010	22,977	26,599	173	28	16	lpg	35,193 m³

Frisia Lübeck : Hartmann Schiffahrts : *Chris Brooks*

UBC Ottawa : Hartmann Schiffahrts : *Chris Brooks*

IMO	name	flag	year	gt	dwt	loa	bm	kts	type	comments
9402562	Gaschem Nordsee	Lbr	2009	13,878	18,844	155	23	17	lpg	17,133 m³
9402574	Gaschem Pacific	Lbr	2009	13,879	18,844	155	23	17	lpg	17,131 m³
9471123	Gaschem Stade	Lbr	2010	22,977	26,618	173	28	16	lpg	35,193 m³
9338058	Ital Oriente	Lbr	2007	27,779	39,269	222	30	23	ucc	2,824 teu
9395238	Laguna	Lbr	2009	31,094	53,477	190	32	14	bbu	ex UBC Laguna-15, l/a Dessau
9395226	Lemessos	Mlt	2008	31,094	53,571	190	32	14	bbu	ex UBC Lemessos-15, Daewoo Challenge-09, l/a Cuxhaven
9395252	Limas	Mlt	2009	31,094	53,406	190	32	14	bbu	ex UBC Limas -15, l/a Gerolstein
9395264	Livorno	Mlt	2009	31,094	53,428	190	32	14	bbu	ex UBC Livorno-15, l/a Husum
9395214	Longkou	Mlt	2008	31,094	53,408	190	32	14	bbu	ex ex UBC Longkou-15, Dawoo Brave-09, l/a Handorf
9395240	Luzon	Lbr	2009	31,094	53,507	190	32	14	bbu	ex UBC Luzon-15, l/a Flensburg
9463671	UBC Odessa	Lbr	2011	65,976	118,585	260	43	14	bbu	
9462366	UBC Ohio	Lbr	2011	65,976	118,532	260	43	14	bbu	
9463669	UBC Olimbus	Lbr	2011	65,976	118,472	260	43	14	bbu	
9463645	UBC Onsan	Lbr	2011	65,976	118,590	260	43	14	bbu	
9463657	UBC Oristano	Lbr	2011	65,976	118,467	260	43	14	bbu	
9463633	UBC Ottawa	Lbr	2011	65,976	118,626	260	43	14	bbu	

dry cargo and containerships managed by Hartmann Dry Cargo Germany
'Frisia' vessels operate in United Container Carrier (UCC) pool formed in 2004. The company also operates smaller container ships in the Mini-Container Pool (MCP). Also see United Product Tanker (UPT) pool under Schöller Holdings Ltd. Formed United Ethane Carriers in 2014, a j/v with Jaccar Holdings, based in Singapore, to operate 5 x 85,000 m³ ethane carriers to be built at Sinopacific Offshore
UBC vessels operated by United Bulk Carriers, USA

Intership Navigation Co. Ltd., Cyprus

funnel: *blue with blue 'h' symbol in white circle or charterers colours* **hull:** *red with white UBC (UBC vessels), red boot-topping.*
history: *management company formed 1988* **web:** *www.intership-cyprus.com*

IMO	name	flag	year	gt	dwt	loa	bm	kts	type	comments
9223904	Atlantic Patriot	Cyp	2003	12,993	17,531	143	23	15	ggc	ex HAL Patriot-13, Federal Patriot-10, BBC Russia-08, c/a Atlantic Progress
9190107	Atlantic Progress	Cyp	2000	12,993	17,451	143	23	15	ggc	ex HAL Pride-13, Federal Pride-10, Seaboard Chile II-07, Atlantic Pride-05, Seaboard Rover-02, Atlantic Pride-01
9190080	Onego Pioneer	Cyp	1999	12,993	17,451	143	23	15	ggc	ex Atlantic Pioneer-15, CCNI Tumbes-13, Federal Pioneer-11, Seaboard Pioneer-07, Atlantic Pioneer-01
9190119	Onego Power	Cyp	2000	12,993	17,451	143	23	15	ggc	ex Atlantic Power-15, Federal Power-13, Seaboard Power-07, Atlantic Power-01
9255050	Santiago	Cyp	2002	19,746	31,759	172	27	14	bbu	ex UBC Singapore-15
9393589	Seaboard America	Cyp	2010	19,128	25,747	160	28	16	ggc	
9393553	Seaboard Pacific	Cyp	2010	19,128	25,733	160	28	16	ggc	l/a Pacific Alliance
9393577	Seaboard Peru	Cyp	2010	19,128	25,774	160	28	16	ggc	
9393539	Seaboard Valparaiso	Cyp	2009	19,128	25,820	160	28	16	ggc	ex AAL Galveston-16, Pacific Adventure-15, HAL Ambassadore-13, Pacific Adventure-12, Opal Amber-09

UBC Baton Rouge : Hartmann Schiffahrts - Intership Navigation : *Chris Brooks*

IMO	name	flag	year	gt	dwt	loa	bm	kts	type	comments
9152466	UBC Balboa	Cyp	1997	14,661	23,484	154	26	14	bbu	ex Bahia-14, UBC Bilboa-13, Brooknes-01, Ocean Giant-98
9177973	UBC Baton Rouge	Cyp	1998	14,706	24,035	154	26	14	bbu	ex Baynes-01
9152478	UBC Boston	Cyp	1997	14,661	23,544	154	26	14	bbu	ex Bahia-13, Brimnes-01
9177961	UBC Bremen	Cyp	1998	14,706	24,073	154	26	14	bbu	ex Birknes-01
9236080	UBC Sacramento	Cyp	2001	19,746	31,773	172	27	14	bbu	ex Stemnes-01
9426867	UBC Sagunto	Cyp	2010	21,018	33,313	182	28	14	bbu	
9255062	UBC Saiki	Cyp	2002	19,746	31,770	172	27	14	bbu	
9426881	UBC Salaverry	Cyp	2010	21,018	33,305	182	28	14	bbu	
9380805	UBC Santa Marta	Cyp	2008	19,748	31,582	172	27	14	bbu	
9376000	UBC Santos	Cyp	2008	19,748	31,568	172	27	14	bbu	
9220976	UBC Savannah	Cyp	2001	19,743	31,923	172	27	14	bbu	ex Sandnes-01
9220988	UBC Seattle	Cyp	2000	19,743	31,923	172	27	14	bbu	ex Seattle-15, UBC Seattle-04, Stornes-01
9287340	UBC Stavanger	Cyp	2004	19,748	31,751	172	27	14	bbu	
9236078	UBC Sydney	Cyp	2001	19,746	31,759	172	27	14	bbu	ex Spraynes-01
9416707	UBC Tampa	Cyp	2009	24,140	37,724	182	29	14	bbu	
9285354	UBC Tampico	Cyp	2004	24,140	37,821	182	29	14	bbu	
9416719	UBC Tarragona	Cyp	2009	24,140	37,706	182	29	14	bbu	
9416721	UBC Tilbury	Cyp	2010	24,140	37,702	182	29	14	bbu	
9300752	UBC Tokyo	Cyp	2005	24,140	37,865	182	29	14	bbu	
9300764	UBC Toronto	Cyp	2005	24,140	37,832	182	29	14	bbu	

Hellespont Group   Greece
funnel: blue with broad above narrow blue bands, interrupted by blue 'ΦΒΠ' within blue ring on white disc. **hull:** white with red boot-topping. **history:** originally founded in Canada by Phrixos B.Papachristidis in late 1946, to Papachristidis (UK) Ltd to 1988. **web:** www.hellespont.com

IMO	name	flag	year	gt	dwt	loa	bm	kts	type	comments
9351414	Hellespont Pride	Mhl	2006	42,010	73,727	229	32	14	tco	
9351426	Hellespont Progress	Mhl	2006	42,010	73,727	229	32	14	tco	
9351438	Hellespont Promise	Lbr	2006	42,010	73,669	229	32	14	tco	
9351452	Hellespont Protector	Lbr	2006	42,010	73,821	229	32	14	tco	

vessels managed by Hellespont Ship Management GmbH & Co KG, Germany

Holy House Shipping AB   Sweden
funnel: blue with yellow cockerel, black top or operators colours **hull:** white with blue boot topping or various **history:** established 1970's in Stockholm, specialises in reefer ship management **web:** www.holyhouse.se

IMO	name	flag	year	gt	dwt	loa	bm	kts	type	comments
9128037	Crown Emma *	Brb	1996	10,519	10,351	152	23	18	grf	ex Crown Emerald-14
9055709	Fegulus *	Brb	1993	10,374	10,545	150	23	20	grf	ex Rugulus-09, Regent Star-05, Naura-00, Hornsound-95, Chiquita Nauru-94
8802088	Hansa Bremen *	Brb	1989	10,842	12,942	157	23	21	grf	
8909068	Hansa Lübeck *	Brb	1990	10,842	12,942	157	23	21	grf	
8917534	Lapponian Reefer	Brb	1992	7,944	11,095	141	20	21	grf	

* operated by SeaTrade Groningen

Horizon Tankers Ltd. S.A.   Greece
funnel: blue with black 'HT' on broad white band between two yellow bands and blue top **hull:** black with red boot topping, **history:** established 2007 in Piraeus, Greece **web:** www.horizontankers.gr

IMO	name	flag	year	gt	dwt	loa	bm	kts	type	comments
9407366	Horizon Aphrodite	Lbr	2008	29,828	50,236	183	32	14	tco	
9407354	Horizon Armonia	Lbr	2008	29,828	50,326	183	32	14	tco	
9404223	Horizon Ekavi	Mhl	2008	29,734	51,099	183	32	14	tco	ex Super Star-15, Emirates Star-14
9418119	Horizon Elektra	Mhl	2008	29,734	51,069	183	32	14	bbu	ex Harbour Star-15, Abu Dhabi Star-14
9407392	Horizon Theano	Lbr	2009	29,828	50,268	183	32	14	tco	
9407407	Horizon Theoni **	Ven	2009	29,828	50,221	183	32	14	tco	
9407380	Horizon Thetis	Lbr	2009	29,828	50,326	183	32	14	tco	
9589748	Rio Apure	Mhl	2011	81,354	158,658	274	48	14	tcr	ex Melita-13
9589750	Rio Arauca *	Mhl	2011	81,384	158,671	274	48	14	tcr	ex Melodia-13
9586722	Rio Caroni	Mhl	2011	81,354	158,777	274	48	14	tcr	ex Amarylis-13
9586734	Rio Orinoco	Mhl	2011	81,354	158,589	274	48	14	tcr	ex Anemone-13

* managed by Bernard Schulte Cyprus,   ** operated by Hanseatic Consultorio Naval, Venezuela

Horn-Linie (GmbH & Co.)   Germany
funnel: grey with white 'H' on blue above red bands. **hull:** white with red boot-topping. **history:** founded 1864 and shipping company formed 1951 as Heinrich C Horn. **web:** www.hornlinie.com

IMO	name	flag	year	gt	dwt	loa	bm	kts	type	comments
8802002	Hornbay	Lbr	1990	12,887	9,069	154	23	20	urr	
8802014	Horncap	Lbr	1991	12,887	9,069	154	23	20	urr	
9012041	Horncliff	Lbr	1992	12,877	9,184	154	23	20	urr	

managed by Norbulk Shipping UK Ltd (www.norbulkshipping.com).

Leif Höegh & Co. Ltd.Norway

funnel: White with blue/grey top and houseflag interrupting white band or ** dark blue/grey 'A' on broad white band between blue/grey bands above white base. **hull:** Dark grey with dark blue 'HÖEGH AUTOLINERS' on white superstructure, red boot-topping. **history:** founded 1927 as Leif Höegh & Co. to 1938, Leif Höegh & Co ASA to 2003 and Leif Höegh & Co AS to 2006. Formed Höegh-Ugland Auto Liners (HUAL) in 1968 jointly with Ugland International, but took complete control in 2000 and renamed as Höegh Autoliners in 2005. Tanker and OBO vessels demerged into Bona Shipping AS in 1992. Acquired Cool Carriers in 1994, renamed Unicool in 1997 as joint venture with Safmarine, who withdrew in 1999, Cool Carriers subsequently sold to Lauritzen in 2001. Open-hatch activities transferred to Saga Forest Carriers and liner business sold in 2001. Moller-Maersk acquired 37.5% share in Höegh Autoliners in 2008. **web:** www.Höeghautoliners.com

Höegh Autoliners Shipping AS, Norway

IMO	name	flag	year	gt	dwt	loa	bm	kts	type	comments
8507664	City of Mumbai	Sgp	1987	27,887	7,894	158	27	19	mve	2,300 ceu: ex Höegh Mumbai-08, Maersk Sun-08
9191876	Höegh Asia	Bhs	2000	68,060	27,000	229	32	19	mve	7,859 ceu: ex Hual Asia-06 (len-08)
9318474	Höegh Bangkok	Nis	2007	55,775	16,632	200	32	20	mve	6,500 ceu
9431836	Höegh Beijing +	Nis	2010	47,232	12,250	183	32	19	mve	4,300 ceu
9368895	Höegh Brasilia *	Pan	2007	51,731	17,252	180	32	19	mve	5,400 ceu
8507652	Höegh Chennai	Sgp	1987	27,887	7,902	158	27	19	mve	3,000 ceu: ex Maersk Sea-08
9420057	Höegh Copenhagen	Nis	2010	68,392	27,351	229	32	19	mve	7,850 ceu
9312470	Höegh Detroit	Nis	2006	68,871	27,100	229	32	20	mve	7,850 ceu: (len-08)
9088249	Höegh Inchon	Sgp	1997	44,219	12,490	179	32	19	mve	4,300 ceu: ex Maersk Tide -08
9673379	Höegh Jacksonville +	Nis	2014	58,531	20,578	200	32	19	mve	6,500 ceu
9673381	Höegh Jeddah +	Nis	2014	58,531	20,130	200	32	19	mve	6,500 ceu
9330616	Höegh Kobe	Sgp	2006	52,691	21,500	199	32	19	mve	5,400 ceu: ex Maersk Wizard-08
9088237	Höegh Kunsan	Sgp	1996	44,219	13,778	179	32	19	mve	4,300 ceu: ex Maersk Taiyo-08
9342205	Höegh London	Nis	2008	68,871	21,500	229	32	20	mve	7,850 ceu: ex Alliance Charleston-13, Höegh London-10 (len-08)
9368912	Höegh Manila	Nis	2007	51,964	17,252	180	32	19	mve	5,400 ceu
9431850	Höegh Maputo	Nis	2011	47,266	12,250	183	32	19	mve	4,300 ceu: I/a Höegh Singapore
9166704	Höegh Masan	Sgp	1998	44,219	12,490	179	32	19	mve	4,300 ceu: ex CSAV Rio Salado-12, Höegh Masan-11, Maersk Teal-08
9295830	Höegh New York	Nis	2005	57,280	15,990	200	32	20	mve	6,500 ceu: ex Prestige New York-14, Alliance New York-10, Höegh New York-05, Hual New York-05
9185463	Höegh Osaka	Sgp	2000	51,770	16,886	180	32	20	mve	5,400 ceu: ex Maersk Wind-11
9382396	Höegh Oslo	Nis	2008	51,964	17,252	180	32	19	mve	5,400 ceu
9153783	Höegh Pusan	Sgp	1998	44,219	13,695	179	32	19	mve	4,300 ceu: ex CSAV Rio Serrano-13, Höegh Pusan-11, Maersk Taiki-08
9285495	Höegh Seoul	Nis	2004	68,871	27,178	228	32	20	mve	7,600 ceu: ex Hual Seoul-09, len-09
9312482	Höegh Shanghai	Nis	2007	68,871	27,178	229	32	20	mve	7,850 ceu: (len-09)
9420045	Höegh St. Petersburg	Nis	2009	68,392	27,352	229	32	19	mve	7,850 ceu
9431862	Höegh Singapore	Nis	2011	47,266	12,250	183	32	19	mve	4,300 ceu: I/a Höegh Maputo
9368900	Höegh Sydney *	Jpn	2007	51.731	17,311	180	32	19	mve	5,400 ceu
9684976	Höegh Target	Nis	2015	76,420	22,068	200	36	19	mve	8,500 ceu
9285483	Höegh Tokyo	Nis	2004	68,871	21,500	229	32	20	mve	7,850 ceu: ex Alliance Beaumont-13, Höegh Tokyo-10, Hual Tokyo-07 (len-08)
9684990	Höegh Tracer ++	Nis	2016	75,717	20,766	200	36	19	mve	8,500 ceu
9171280	Höegh Trader	Bhs	1998	68,060	27,100	229	32	20	mve	7,850 ceu: ex Hual Trader-06 (len-09)
9176395	Höegh Transporter	Nis	1999	57,757	21,300	200	32	20	mve	6,600 ceu: ex Hual Transporter-07
9075709	Höegh Trident	Bhs	1995	56,164	21,423	200	32	20	mve	6,500 ceu: ex Hual Trident–06
9684988	Höegh Trigger	Nis	2015	76,420	22,088	200	36	19	mve	8,500 ceu
8608080	Höegh Triton	Nis	1988	52,422	23,052	200	32	18	mve	6,000 ceu: ex Morning Meridian-10, Hual Triton-04, Auto Diana-00, I/a Auto Daewoo
9075711	Höegh Trooper	Bhs	1995	56,164	21,414	200	32	20	mve	6,500 ceu; ex Hual Trooper-05
9186302	Höegh Trove	Bhs	2000	58,684	21,200	200	32	19	mve	6,500 ceu: ex Hual Trove-05, Hual Maritita-00
9431848	Höegh Xiamen +	Nis	2010	47,232	12,250	183	32	19	mve	4,300 ceu
9185451	Höegh Yokohama	Sgp	2000	51,770	16,919	180	32	20	mve	5,400 ceu: ex Maersk Wave-14
8608078	Morning Mercator †	Nis	1988	52,422	23,096	200	32	18	mve	6,000 ceu: ex Hual Tricorn-04, Hual Champ-00, Auto Champ-00

newbuildings:

IMO	name	flag	year	gt	dwt	loa	bm	kts	type	comments
9706918	Höegh Trapper	Nis	2016	75,717	20,766	200	36	19	mve	8,500 ceu Xiamen XS1462D
9710737	Höegh Traveller ++		2016	75,717	20,576	200	36	19	mve	8,500 ceu Xiamen XS1462E
9710749	Höegh Trotter ++		2016	75,717	20,576	200	36	19	mve	8,500 ceu Xiamen XS1462F

managed by Höegh Fleet Services AS, Norway (formed 1995), + owned by Aker ASA, Oslo ++ bareboat chartered from Ocean Yield for 12 years * owned by subsidiary of Tsuneishi Holdings Corp, . † chartered to Hyundai Glovis See also Cido Shipping, Gram Car Carriers

Höegh LNG AS, Norway

funnel: white with houseflag interrupting white band on broad blue band, red top or owners colours **hull:** red, black or blue with red boot-topping **web:** www.hoehglng.com

Höegh Trove : Höegh Autoliners : *ARO*

Hyundai Dream : Hyundai Merchant Marine : *Hans Kraijenbosch*

IMO	name	flag	year	gt	dwt	loa	bm	kts	type	comments
9284192	Arctic Lady (st)	Nis	2006	121,597	84,878	288	49	19	lng	147,835 m³
9271248	Arctic Princess (st)	Nis	2006	121,597	84,878	288	49	19	lng	147,835 m³
9390680	GDF Suez									
	Cape Ann (df)	Nis	2010	96,153	80,780	283	43	19	lng	145,130 m³
9385673	GDF Suez									
	Neptune (df)	Nis	2009	96,153	80,986	283	43	19	lng	145,130 m³
7413232	LNG Libra (st) *	Mhl	1979	95,084	72,650	274	44	19	lng	126,400 m³
7391214	Matthew (st)	Nis	1979	88,919	64,991	289	41	19	lng	126,538 m³ ex Suez Matthew-09, Matthew, Gamma-88, El Paso Howard Boyd

* laid up, Singapore

Hyundai Merchant Marine Co. Ltd.   South Korea

funnel: *white with yellow edged green triangle.* **hull:** *blue with white 'HYUNDAI', red or pink boot-topping.* **history:** *founded 1976 as subsidiary of Hyundai Corporation.* **web:** *www.hmm21.com or www.hyundaicorp.com*

IMO	name	flag	year	gt	dwt	loa	bm	kts	type	comments
9323510	Hyundai Bangkok	Pan	2007	74,651	80,108	304	40	26	ucc	6,800 teu
9346304	Hyundai Brave **	Pan	2008	94,511	99,123	340	46	27	ucc	8,652 teu
9323508	Hyundai Colombo	Pan	2007	74,651	80,108	340	40	26	ucc	6,800 teu
9347542	Hyundai Courage	Pan	2008	94,511	99,052	340	46	27	ucc	8,562 teu: ex CMA CGM Courage-09, Hyundai Courage-08
9637222	Hyundai Dream	Mhl	2014	141,868	146,046	366	48	22	ucc	13,154 teu
9637246	Hyundai Drive	Mhl	2014	141,868	145,979	366	48	22	ucc	13,154 teu
9347554	Hyundai Faith **	Pan	2008	94,511	98,967	340	46	27	ucc	8,750 teu
9347566	Hyundai Force	Pan	2008	94,511	99,043	340	46	27	ucc	8,750 teu: ex CMA CGM Force-09, Hyundai Force-08
9637234	Hyundai Hope	Mhl	2014	141,868	145,683	366	48	22	ucc	13,154 teu
9323522	Hyundai Jakarta	Pan	2007	74,651	80.108	304	40	26	ucc	6,800 teu
9637260	Hyundai Pride	Mhl	2014	141,868	145,683	366	48	22	ucc	13,154 teu
9637258	Hyundai Victory	Pan	2014	141,868	145,966	366	48	22	ucc	13,154 teu

only larger container ships trading to Western Europe are listed, also operates smaller container ships and fleets of bulk carriers and lng tankers operating in the Far East

Glovis Co. Ltd.

funnel: *white with blue 'Glovis'.or owners colours* **hull:** *blue with blue 'Glovis' on cream upperworks,, red boot-topping.* **history:** *founded 2001 as subsidiary of Hyundai/Kia Motor Group.* **web:** *www.glovis.net*

IMO	name	flag	year	gt	dwt	loa	bm	kts	type	comments
9441867	Dong-A Glaucos +*	Mhl	2011	72,408	26,985	232	32	20	mve	7,568 ceu: ex A Ladybug-14
9419747	Dong-A Metis +*	Mhl	2010	60,396	22,582	199	32	20	mve	6,700 ceu: ex STX Changxing Rose-13, STX Condor-10
9707015	Glovis Captain	Mhl	2015	59,760	19,956	200	32	19	mve	6,000 ceu
9419759	Glovis Cardinal	Mhl	2012	60,404	22,342	199	32	20	mve	6,000 ceu: ex STX Eagle-13
9590589	Glovis Century *	Pan	2012	58,288	20,895	200	32	20	mve	6,000 ceu
9590591	Glovis Challenge *	Pan	2012	58,288	20,895	200	32	19	mve	6,000 ceu
9651113	Glovis Champion *	Mhl	2013	59,060	20,661	200	32	19	mve	6,000 ceu
9158604	Glovis Chorus *	Pan	1997	55,729	21,505	200	32	19	mve	6,000 ceu: ex Asian Chorus-15
9122942	Glovis Comet *	Pan	1996	55,680	21,421	200	32	19	mve	6,000 ceu: ex Asian Legend -14
9293583	Glovis Composer [F]	Hkg	2005	58,631	18,881	200	32	19	mve	5,213 ceu: ex Excellent Ace-12
9414876	Glovis Condor	Mhl	2011	60,396	22,351	199	32	19	mve	6,000 ceu: ex STX Dove-13
9293909	Glovis Conductor [F]	Pan	2006	60,118	17,709	200	32	19	mve	5,231 ceu; ex Favorite Ace-12
9122930	Glovis Corona *	Pan	1996	55,680	21,421	200	32	19	mve	6,000 ceu: ex Asian Grace-14
9707027	Glovis Cosmos	Mhl	2015	59,760	20,072	200	32	19	mve	6,000 ceu
9451898	Glovis Cougar *	Pan	2012	60,404	22,532	199	32	20	mve	6,000 ceu: ex STX Flamingo-13
9476721	Glovis Countess +	Mhl	2010	60,213	18,701	200	32	19	mve	6,340 ceu: ex CSAV Rio
9651101	Glovis Courage *	Mhl	2013	59,060	20,880	200	32	19	mve	6,000 ceu
9706994	Glovis Crown	Mhl	2014	59,760	20,019	200	32	19	mve	6,000 ceu
9707003	Glovis Crystal	Mhl	2015	59,760	20,019	200	32	19	mve	6,000 ceu
9043691	Glovis Pacific	Pan	1993	47,367	12,271	180	32	19	mve	4,215 ceu: ex Jade Arrow-13
9114165	Glovis Phoenix *	Pan	1995	44,891	13,292	184	32	18	mve	4,200 ceu: ex Asian Sun-15
9114177	Glovis Prime *	Pan	1995	44,891	13,241	184	32	18	mve	4,200 ceu: ex Asian Venture-13
9749582	Glovis Sirius *	Mhl	2016	64,697	19,638	199	35	19	mve	7,300 ceu
9445409	Glovis Solomon *	Mhl	2011	72,635	27,200	232	32	20	mve	7,568 ceu: ex C Ladybug-14
9674165	Glovis Spirit *	Mhl	2013	64,650	20,138	199	35	19	mve	7,300 ceu
9702431	Glovis Splendor *	Mhl	2014	64,546	20,056	199	35	19	mve	7,300 ceu
9749570	Glovis Stella	Mhl	2016	64,697	19,638	199	35	19	mve	7,300 ceu
9702417	Glovis Summit *	Mhl	2014	64,546	20,056	199	35	19	mve	7,300 ceu
9749568	Glovis Sun	Mhl	2015	64,697	19,410	199	35	19	mve	7,300 ceu
9702405	Glovis Sunrise *	Mhl	2014	64,546	20,056	199	35	19	mve	7,300 ceu
9674177	Glovis Supreme *	Mhl	2013	64,650	20,138	199	35	19	mve	7,300 ceu
9674189	Glovis Superior *	Mhl	2013	64,650	20,138	199	35	19	mve	7,300 ceu
9702429	Glovis Symphony	Mhl	2014	64,546	20,056	200	32	19	mve	7,300 ceu

Glovis Cougar : Glovis Co Ltd : *Mike Rhodes*

Maersk Langkloof : International Maritime Enterprises : *ARO*

IMO	name	flag	year	gt	dwt	loa	bm	kts	type	comments

newbuildings:

IMO	name	flag	year	gt	dwt	loa	bm	kts	type	comments
9749594		Mhl	2016	64,546	20,100	199	35	19	mve	7,300 ceu Hyundai Samho S808

* owned or managed by subsidiary Haeyoung Maritime Services Co. Ltd., South Korea
+ owned by Dong-A Tanker Corp., Korea, [F] owned by Ship Finance International
see also, Cido Shipping, Leif Höegh & Co., Ray Car Carriers, Rickmers Reederei, Zodiac Maritime Agencies
also operates a fleet of owned and chartered bulkers trading in the Far East

International Maritime Enterprises SAM   Monaco

funnel: *yellow with black top over broad blue band, or charterers colours* **hull:** *grey with red boot topping* **history:** *part of Embiricos Enterprises* **web:** *none found*

IMO	name	flag	year	gt	dwt	loa	bm	kts	type	comments
9221839	Agios Minas	Lbr	2001	73,059	79,465	300	40	25	ucc	6,628 teu: ex CMA CGM Ravel-14
9635688	DAL Karoo	Lbr	2013	71,112	80,115	270	43	22	ucc	6,881 teu: ex Skiathos
9222302	Diaporos	Lbr	2001	73,157	80,238	300	40	25	ucc	6,628 teu: ex CMA CGM Bizet-14
9247560	Folegandros	Lbr	2001	66,332	67,170	279	40	25	ucc	5,576 teu: ex CCNI Ancud-14, Folegandros-14, APL Xiamen-11, Folegandros-10, Rotterdam Bridge-10, YM Rotterdam-06, Rotterdam Bridge-04
9679555	Paxi	Lbr	2014	70,262	80,087	271	43	22	ucc	6,700 teu: ex CCNI Iquique-15, l/a Paxi
9261449	Ikaria	Lbr	2002	66,332	67,164	279	40	25	ucc	5,576 teu: ex CCNI Antartico-12, Ikaria-10, long Beach Bridge-10
9677026	Kea	Lbr	2013	71,112	80,229	270	43	22	ucc	6,881 teu: ex Maersk Ceres-15, Kea-14
9635640	Maersk Elgin	Lbr	2013	71,112	80,163	270	43	22	ucc	6,881 teu: ex Amoliani-14
9635652	Maersk Langkloof	Lbr	2013	71,112	80,228	270	43	22	ucc	6,881 teu: ex Rhodos-14
9695028	UASC Jilfar	Lbr	2014	94,930	112,160	300	48	22	ucc	8,762 teu: l/d Symi
9695016	UASC Tabuk	Lbr	2014	94,930	112,171	300	48	22	ucc	8,762 teu: ex Skyros-14
9261451	Zante	Lbr	2002	66,332	67,164	279	40	25	ucc	5,576 teu: ex Kota Singa-12, Zante-10, Shanghai Bridge-10

newbuilding:

IMO	name	flag	year	gt	dwt	loa	bm	kts	type	comments
9679567				69,600	80,000	270	43	22	ucc	6,881 teu: Hanjin Subic 096

vessels managed by Aeolos Management

Orient Accord : Interorient Navigation Co. : *ARO*

International Shipholding Corporation U.S.A.

Central Gulf Lines Inc., U.S.A.
funnel: *white with blue symbol within blue ring, narrow black top or buff with 8-pointed white star on white edged broad red band or green with two broad white bands.* **hull:** *black with red boot-topping.* **history:** *founded 1947 as Central Gulf SS Corp to 1974.*
web: *www.intship.com* or *www.waterman-steamship.com*

IMO	name	flag	year	gt	dwt	loa	bm	kts	type	comments
8106068	Bali Sea (2) ++	Sgp	1982	24,201	22,268	175	36	13	urr	ex Super Servant 5-95, Dan Lifter-85 (len-95)
8106056	Banda Sea (2) ++	Sgp	1982	24,201	13,282	175	36	13	urr	ex Super Servant 6-95, Dan Mover-85 (len-95)
9426245	Bulk Colombia +	Lbr	2011	32,309	57,937	190	32	14	bbu	
9500675	Bulk Honduras +	Lbr	2012	32,309	57,959	190	32	14	bbu	
8026799	Energy Enterprise (st)	Usa	1983	28,250	33,373	203	29	15	bsd	ex Energy Independence-96
9339818	Green Bay	Usa	2007	59,217	18,090	200	32	19	mve	6,402 ceu: l/a Grand Winner
9181560	Green Cove	Usa	1999	57,566	22,747	200	32	19	mve	5,053 ceu: ex Pegasus Leader-12
9181376	Green Dale	Usa	1999	50,087	15,894	179	32	19	mve	4,148 ceu: ex Altair Leader-99
9158288	Green Lake	Usa	1998	57,623	22,799	200	32	19	mve	5,055 ceu: ex Cygnus Leader-01
9177428	Green Ridge	Usa	1998	57,449	21,523	200	32	19	mve	6,000 ceu: ex Hercules Leader-05
9190092	Oslo Wave *	Usa	2000	12,993	17,451	143	23	15	ggc	ex Green Wave-13, Federal Patroller-

11, African Patroller-06, Atlantic Patroller-05, Forest Patroller-03, Atlantic Patroller-01
*owned by * LCI Shipholdings Inc., + Dry Bulk Americas Ltd. ++ Gulf South Shg. Pte., Singapore*

Interorient Navigation Co. Ltd. Cyprus
funnel: *buff with blue 'IN' symbol inside blue ring.* **hull:** *black or light grey with red boot-topping.* **history:** *founded 1977.*
web: *www.interorient.com*

IMO	name	flag	year	gt	dwt	loa	bm	kts	type	comments
9410002	Avenca	Lbr	2008	30,010	51,238	183	32	14	tco	ex Agamemnon II-13
9233777	Bacaliaros	Mhl	2003	81,310	159,988	274	48	15	tcr	ex Cape Bowen-15
9410882	Kalahari	Cyp	2009	62,775	112,827	250	44	14	tco	ex Northern Spirit-13
9467627	Orient Accord	Mlt	2010	23,426	33,755	180	30	14	bbu	
9496329	Orient Adventure	Cyp	2011	23,426	33,755	180	30	14	bbu	
9496331	Orient Alliance	Mlt	2012	23,426	33,755	180	30	14	bbu	
9436460	Orient Cavalier	Cyp	2009	63,993	114,751	255	43	14	bbu	
9464572	Orient Centaur	Cyp	2010	63,993	114,841	255	43	14	bbu	
9464584	Orient Champion	Cyp	2010	63,993	115,000	255	43	14	bbu	
9464596	Orient Crusader	Cyp	2010	63,993	114,861	255	43	14	bbu	
9522881	Orient Defender	Cyp	2011	22,683	36,892	186	28	14	bbu	
9522893	Orient Delivery	Cyp	2012	22,683	36,746	186	28	14	bbu	
9522908	Orient Dispatch	Cyp	2013	22,683	36,892	186	28	14	bbu	
9464663	Orient Strength	Cyp	2012	63,993	114,840	255	43	14	bbu	
9464675	Orient Sun	Cyp	2013	63,993	114,775	255	43	14	bbu	
9467548	Orient Target	Cyp	2009	23,426	33,755	180	30	14	bbu	
9467550	Orient Tide	Cyp	2010	23,426	33,755	180	30	14	bbu	
9467562	Orient Tiger	Mlt	2011	23,426	33,500	180	30	14	bbu	
9467574	Orient Trader	Cyp	2009	23,426	33,757	180	30	14	bbu	
9467586	Orient Trail	Mlt	2011	23,426	33,762	180	30	14	bbu	

Till Jacob : Jacob Ernst GmbH: *Nico Kemps*

IMO	name	flag	year	gt	dwt	loa	bm	kts	type	comments
9467598	Orient Transit	Cyp	2010	23,426	33,755	180	30	14	bbu	
9467603	Orient Tribune	Cyp	2011	23,426	33,500	180	30	14	bbu	
9410894	Southern Spirit	Mlt	2009	62,775	113,043	250	44	15	tco	
9228655	Tonos *	Mhl	2003	81,310	160,289	274	48	15	tcr	ex Cape Bata-15, Sea Eagle-03

*managed by Interorient Marine Services Ltd, Cyprus, except * owned or managed by subsidiary Interorient Navigation (Germany) GmbH & Co KG, Germany (formed 1995 as Interorient Navigation Hamburg GmbH to 2000 and INC Interorient Navigation Hamburg GmbH & Co KG to 2007). also operate vessels in Norient Product Pool ApS which see: See also König & Cie GmbH & Co KG.,*

Islamic Republic of Iran Shipping Lines (I.R.I.S.L.)   Iran

funnel: *to be confirmed,* **hull:** *black with red boot-topping formerly grey with IRISL in black, green boot topping.* **history:** *founded 1967 as Arya National Shipping Lines to 1980, then Iran National Shipping Lines to 1981. UN and EU sanctions applied in 2007 caused their vessels to be 'hidden' under various shell companies and given frequent name and flag changes to try to evade detention. Sanctions lifted early 2016 and first liner service to Northern Europe recommenced March 2016. New livery and funnel colours not yet known* **web:** *www.irisl.net*

IMO	name	flag	year	gt	dwt	loa	bm	kts	type	comments
9283021	Artenos	Irn	2004	25,391	33,850	207	30	21	ucc	2,742 teu: ex Salis-12, Sewak-11, Iran Fars-09
9270684	Azad	Irn	2012	23,289	29,870	187	30	21	ucc	2,230 teu: ex Shah e Kord-15
9283019	Azargoun	Irn	2003	25,391	33,850	207	30	21	ucc	2,742 teu:ex Armis-13, Visea-11, Iran Zanjan-09
9346546	Basht	Irn	2008	54,851	66,441	294	32	22	ucc	5,125 teu: ex Agata-12, Tuchal-08
9346558	Behnavaz	Irn	2010	54,851	66,460	294	32	22	ucc	5,125 teu: ex Benita-12, Palmary-11, c/a Zagros, l/a Iran Zagros
9349590	Behta	Irn	2009	74,175	85,878	299	40	23	ucc	6,572 teu: ex Oriana-12, Third Ocean-11
9283033	Golbon	Irn	2004	27,681	37,894	207	30	21	ucc	2,742 teu; ex Hadis-12, Sepitam-11, Iran Ilam-08
9270696	Iran Kashan	Irn	2016	23,200	29,870	187	30	21	ucc	2,230 teu
9209324	Pendar	Irn	2000	36,014	41,962	240	32	22	ucc	3,280 teu: ex Teresa-12, Daffodil-12, Eleventh Ocean-09, Iran Hormozgan-07
9209336	Sana	Irn	2000	36,014	41,937	240	32	22	ucc	3,280 teu: ex Gabriela-12, Rosemary-11, Dandelion-11, New State-08, Iran Tehran-08
9346524	Shabgoun	Irn	2008	54,851	66,488	294	32	22	ucc	5,125 teu: ex Alva-12, Sabalan-11, Iran Sabalan-09
9349576	Shahraz	Irn	2008	74,175	85,896	299	40	23	ucc	6,572 teu: ex Marisol-12, First Ocean-11
9270658	Shamim	Irn	2004	23,285	30,145	187	30	21	ucc	2,230 teu: ex Silver Zone-12, Iran Busher-08
9270646	Shiba	Irn	2010	23,289	30,239	187	30	21	ucc	2,230 teu: ex Valili-12, Iran Arak-10
9328900	Touska	Irn	2008	54,851	66,432	294	32	22	ucc	5,125 teu: ex Adalia-12, Sahand-12, Iran Sahand-08

company also operates a fleet of general cargo vessels and tankers.

Ernst Jacob GmbH & Co. KG   Germany

funnel: *black, white diagonal cross on broad blue band with blue 'J' on white centre diamond or charterers colours.* **hull:** *grey or red with red boot-topping or white with blue boot-topping.* **history:** *founded 1955.* **web:** *www.ernstjacob.de*

IMO	name	flag	year	gt	dwt	loa	bm	kts	type	comments
9482873	Cordula Jacob	Lbr	2012	43,904	75,619	229	32	15	tco	
9482859	Georg Jacob	Lbr	2011	43,904	75,618	229	32	15	tco	
9164201	Jacques Jacob *	Gib	2000	40,705	71,345	229	32	15	tco	ex Chaleur Bay-09
9257498	Jill Jacob *	Lbr	2003	40,037	72,909	229	32	15	tco	ex Four Clipper-04
9189134	Johann Jacob *	Lbr	2000	40,037	73,001	229	32	15	tco	ex Four Brig-04
9482847	Konstantin Jacob	Lbr	2011	43,904	76,547	229	32	15	tco	
9188788	Max Jacob *	Deu	2000	81,565	157,449	274	48	14	tcr	ex Soyang-01
9233741	Nell Jacob *	Lbr	2003	81,236	160,292	274	48	14	tcr	ex Four Sun-08
9257503	Tanya Jacob *	Lbr	2003	40,037	73,004	229	32	15	tco	ex Four Ketch-07
9482861	Till Jacob	Lbr	2012	43,904	75,564	229	32	15	tco	
9179622	Yves Jacob *	Lbr	2000	40,705	61,130	229	32	15	tco	ex Los Roques-09

* managed for Hansa Hamburg Shipping International GmbH & Co KG

Kristian Gerhard Jebsen Skipsrederi AS   Norway

Gearbulk Holding Ltd., Bermuda

funnel: *black with large white 'G'.* **hull:** *black with white 'GEARBULK', red boot-topping.* **history:** *associated company founded 1968 as Gearbulk Ltd. to 1991 and 49% owned by Mitsui OSK. Acquired Borgestad Shipping AS in 2006.* **web:** *www.gearbulk.com*

IMO	name	flag	year	gt	dwt	loa	bm	kts	type	comments
9720043	Acer Arrow +	Sgp	2014	35,503	61,066	200	32	14	bbu	
9008706	Aracari Arrow *	Bhs	1992	29,369	46,956	199	31	15	goh	ex Bridge Arrow-08, Westwood Bridge-05, Saga River-03, Sea River-92
9448255	Avocet Arrow	Bhs	2015	37,128	62,823	200	32	14	goh	

IMO	name	flag	year	gt	dwt	loa	bm	kts	type	comments
9720055	Betula Arrow +	Pan	2014	35,503	61,007	200	32	14	bbu	
9687095	Biwa Arrow +	Pan	2014	31,864	55,978	190	32	14	bbu	
9635377	Bluebird Arrow	Bhs	2013	15,607	19,336	157	24	14	tas	
9725574	Bulk Aquila +	Pan	2014	37,227	66,613	200	36	14	bbu	
9725586	Bulk Castor +	Pan	2015	38,227	66,624	200	36	14	bbu	
9430844	Bulk Neptune +	Pan	2009	31,259	55,657	190	32	14	bbu	
9500039	Bulk Orion +	Mhl	2011	31,760	56,155	190	32	14	bbu	
9403205	Bulk Pegasus +	Pan	2009	32,379	58,736	190	32	14	bbu	
9425758	Bulk Titan +	Pan	2009	32,354	58,090	190	32	14	bbu	
9107318	Canelo Arrow	Bhs	1997	32,520	48,077	187	31	14	goh	
9232802	Cedar Arrow	Bhs	2001	32,458	47,818	190	31	14	goh	
7342469	CHL Innovator †	Sgp	1976	19,426	26,931	175	26	15	brs	ex Rodney-86, Cape Rodney-85
8130681	CHL Progressor †	Sgp	1985	32,333	48,251	189	32	14	brs	ex Therassia-89
9552886	Condor Arrow +	Pan	2012	37,046	61,860	200	32	14	ggc	
9385477	Corella Arrow	Bhs	2009	44,684	72,863	225	32	14	goh	
8512982	Cotinga Arrow	Bhs	1987	28,805	45,252	200	31	15	goh	ex Westwood Anette-07
9720067	Cypress Arrow +	Pan	2015	35,503	61,022	200	32	14	bbu	
9529592	Eagle Arrow +	Pan	2011	37,046	61,860	200	32	15	ggc	
9144392	Emu Arrow	Bhs	1997	36,008	51,419	200	32	14	goh	
8512956	Falcon Arrow	Bhs	1986	28,805	45,295	200	31	15	goh	ex Norsul Europa-04, Westwood Belinda-03
9574860	Finch Arrow +	Bhs	2013	46,295	72,914	210	36	14	goh	
9720079	Gingko Arrow +	Pan	2015	35,503	61,026	200	32	14	bbu	
9077070	Grebe Arrow	Bhs	1997	35,998	51,633	200	32	16	goh	
8918215	Grouse Arrow	Bhs	1991	44,398	42,276	185	30	15	goh	
8308159	Harefield	Bhs	1985	27,818	41,651	188	29	13	goh	
8313685	Hawk Arrow	Bhs	1985	28,092	40,269	188	29	14	goh	
8313702	Ibis Arrow	Bhs	1986	28,239	42,497	188	29	14	goh	ex Singapore Express-91, Ibis Arrow-91
9007532	Jacamar Arrow *	Bhs	1992	29,369	46,998	199	31	15	goh	ex Borg Arrow-06, Westwood Borg-04, Spero-98, Saga Ocean-95
9215347	Jaeger Arrow	Bhs	2001	29,103	24,101	171	25	18	ggc	
9529530	Japin Arrow	Bhs	2013	44,865	73,296	210	36	14	goh	
9635389	Kingbird Arrow	Bhs	2013	15,607	19,308	157	24	14	tas	
9077082	Kite Arrow	Bhs	1997	36,008	51,800	200	32	16	goh	
9385491	Kashi Arrow +	Pan	2009	30,983	54,204	190	32	15	bbu	
9282730	Kuljak Arrow	Bhs	2003	30,054	52,408	190	32	14	bbu	ex Bulk Saturn-12
8316704	Kumul Arrow	Bhs	1985	27,818	41,619	188	29	13	goh	ex Westfield-13
9687162	Lawin Arrow	Bhs	2014	37,150	62,841	200	32	14	goh	
9566617	Macaw Arrow	Bhs	2014	44,866	72,400	210	36	14	goh	
9443918	Macuru Arrow	Bhs	2010	44,684	71,460	225	32	14	goh	
9515228	Maitaca Arrow	Bhs	2013	44,865	73,296	225	32	14	goh	
9105035	Mandarin Arrow	Bhs	1996	35,998	51,733	200	32	16	goh	
9687083	Matsu Arrow +	Pan	2014	31,864	55,975	190	32	15	bbu	
9155303	Merlin Arrow *	Bhs	1999	36,008	51,459	200	32	15	goh	ex Tolten-04
9448243	Misago Arrow	Bhs	2015	37,128	62,843	200	32	14	goh	
9385506	Momi Arrow +	Pan	2009	30,983	54,204	190	32	15	goh	

BTG Rainier : K. G. Jebsens - Bulk Trading Group : *Nico Kemps*

IMO	name	flag	year	gt	dwt	loa	bm	kts	type	comments
8918227	Mozu Arrow	Bhs	1992	44,398	42,276	185	30	15	goh	
9529280	Nandu Arrow +	Pan	2011	37,046	61,860	200	32	14	ggc	
9687174	Osprey Arrow	Bhs	2015	37,150	62,924	200	32	14	goh	
9151814	Penguin Arrow	Bhs	1997	36,008	51,738	200	32	16	goh	
9607083	Petrel Arrow	Bhs	2013	46,112	72,924	210	36	14	goh	
9107306	Pine Arrow	Bhs	1996	32,520	48,041	190	31	14	goh	
9552898	Pipit Arrow +	Pan	2012	37,046	61,860	200	32	14	ggc	
9144407	Plover Arrow	Bhs	1997	36,008	51,880	200	32	14	goh	
9235141	Poplar Arrow	Bhs	2005	35,250	47,818	190	31	14	goh	
9566605	Puffin Arrow +	Pan	2011	36,925	62,967	200	32	14	ggc	
9007544	Quetzal Arrow	Nis	1992	29,369	46,908	199	31	15	goh	ex Breeze Arrow-08, Westwood Breeze-03, Saga Breeze-98
9108037	Rakiura Maru	Pan	1996	17,940	23,872	180	30	14	goh	
9574858	Raven Arrow +	Pan	2012	46,295	72,871	210	36	14	goh	
9607095	Siskin Arrow +	Mhl	2014	46,295	72,927	210	36	14	goh	
9232814	Spruce Arrow	Bhs	2002	32,458	47,818	190	31	14	goh	
9323821	Sunbird Arrow	Bhs	2005	12,959	15,002	144	24	14	tas	
8918239	Swift Arrow	Bhs	1992	44,398	42,276	185	30	15	goh	
9567740	Tanchou Arrow	Bhs	2014	44,866	73,296	210	36	15	goh	
9401879	Tawa Arrow +	Pan	2008	30,983	53,560	190	32	15	ggc	
9385489	Tenca Arrow	Bhs	2009	44,684	72,863	225	32	14	goh	
9434539	Toki Arrow +	Pan	2010	36,925	62,942	200	32	14	ggc	
9105023	Toucan Arrow	Bhs	1996	35,998	51,880	200	32	16	goh	
9443920	Tuju Arrow	Bhs	2010	44,684	72,863	225	32	14	goh	
9151826	Weaver Arrow	Bhs	1997	36,008	51,364	200	32	14	goh	

newbuildings: 3 options declared for 81,000dwt bbu [JMU (2016)]
*vessels owned by Gearbulk Shipowning Ltd, Norway or * by Gearbulk Shipping AS, Norway*
† refined sugar carrier managed for CHL Shipping BV, Netherlands (subsidiary of TNT Shipping & Development Ltd., Australia)
+ chartered vessels

Bulk Trading Group Ltd.,
funnel: *grey with BTG in white on black band, narrow black top.* **hull:** *blue with grey boot topping.* **history:** *originally founded 1981 but ceased trading 2006, reactivated 2012 as 50:50 j/v with J.P.Morgan Investment Gp.* **web:** *www.btg.no*

IMO	name	flag	year	gt	dwt	loa	bm	kts	type	comments
9687851	BTG Denali	Bhs	2015	43,229	81,084	229	32	14	bbu	
9731834	BTG Eiger	Bhs	2016	43,229	81,031	229	32	14	bbu	
9687837	BTG Everest	Bhs	2015	43,229	81,014	229	32	14	bbu	
9687849	BTG Kailash	Bhs	2015	43,229	81,084	229	32	14	bbu	
9731822	BTG Matterhorn	Bhs	2016	43,229	81,060	229	32	14	bbu	
9710139	BTG Rainier	Bhs	2015	43,229	81,070	229	32	14	bbu	
9710141	BTG Olympos	Bhs	2015	43,229	81,086	229	32	14	bbu	

newbuilding:

IMO	name	flag	year	gt	dwt	loa	bm	kts	type	comments
9731846	BTG Fuji	Bhs	2016	43,229	81,000	229	32	14	bbu	JMU Maizuru 5067

vessels managed by KGJ Bulk Fleet Management AS., Norway

SKS OBO & Tankers AS., Norway
funnel: *pale green with white 'SKS' on broad red band, narrow black top.* **hull:** *red with green boot-topping.* **history:** *founded 1996 jointly with Nordship AS subsidiary of CSAV to 2004.* **web:** *www.sksobo.com*

IMO	name	flag	year	gt	dwt	loa	bm	kts	type	comments
9461843	SKS Darent	Bhs	2011	65,830	119,456	250	45	15	tco	
9428994	SKS Dee	Nis	2010	65,830	119,456	250	45	15	tco	
9426312	SKS Delta	Nis	2010	65,380	119,456	250	45	15	tco	
9531636	SKS Demini	Nis	2012	65,830	119,456	250	45	15	tco	
9531648	SKS Doda	Nis	2012	65,380	119,456	250	45	15	tco	
9461831	SKS Dokka	Pan	2010	65,830	119,456	250	45	15	tco	
9461855	SKS Donggang	Bhs	2011	65,830	119,456	250	45	15	tco	
9428982	SKS Douro	Nis	2010	65,830	119,456	250	45	15	tco	
9429003	SKS Doyles	Nis	2010	65,830	119,456	250	45	15	tco	
9428970	SKS Driva	Nis	2010	65,830	119,456	250	45	15	tco	
9240445	SKS Mersey	Nis	2003	70,933	120,499	250	44	15	cbo	
9240433	SKS Mosel	Nis	2003	70,933	120,670	250	44	15	cbo	
9248813	SKS Saluda	Nis	2003	81,270	159,438	274	50	15	tco	
9301524	SKS Satilla	Nis	2006	81,380	158,842	274	48	15	tco	
9326718	SKS Segura	Nis	2007	81,380	158,784	274	48	15	tco	
9232931	SKS Sinni	Nis	2003	81,270	159,385	274	48	15	tco	
9301536	SKS Skeena	Nis	2006	81,380	158,943	274	48	15	tco	
9326720	SKS Spey	Nis	2007	81,380	158,842	274	48	15	tco	
9133458	SKS Tagus *	Nis	1997	63,515	109,933	244	42	15	cbo	
9172662	SKS Tanaro	Nis	1999	63,515	109,787	244	42	14	cbo	
9172650	SKS Tiete	Nis	1999	63,515	109,773	244	42	14	cbo	
9161273	SKS Torrens	Nis	1999	63,515	109,846	244	42	14	cbo	

IMO	name	flag	year	gt	dwt	loa	bm	kts	type	comments
9133446	SKS Trent *	Nis	1997	63,515	109,832	244	42	15	cbo	
9161285	SKS Trinity	Nis	1999	63,515	109,798	244	42	14	cbo	
9133460	SKS Tugela *	Nis	1997	63,515	109,913	244	42	15	cbo	
9122928	SKS Tweed *	Nis	1996	63,515	109,832	244	42	15	cbo	
9116955	SKS Tyne *	Nis	1996	63,515	109,891	244	42	14	cbo	

* vessels managed by KGJ Bulk Fleet Management AS., Norway

Jüngerhans Maritime Services GmbH & Co. KG Germany

funnel: white with pale blue 'J' inside pale blue diamond outline between two narrow pale blue bands or charterers colours.
hull: black or grey with red boot-topping. **history:** founded 1983 as Reederei Heinrich Jüngerhans to 1995, then Jüngerhans & Co Reedereiverwaltung OHG to 2003. **web:** www.juengerhans.de

IMO	name	flag	year	gt	dwt	loa	bm	kts	type	comments
9238686	Corona J	Atg	2002	16,129	16,794	161	25	19	ucc	1,209 teu: ex Maersk Rio Grande-08, Corona J-02
9506734	Eris J	Atg	2010	12,810	14,288	153	23	17	ggc	ex HHL Everest-14, Industrial Fighter-13, l/a Eris J
9506758	Industrial Faith	Atg	2011	12,810	14,288	153	23	17	ggc	l/a Senda J
9506746	Industrial Force	Atg	2011	12,810	14,359	153	23	17	ggc	l/a Ran J
9457000	Merkur Planet	Lbr	2012	50,885	61,962	249	37	24	ucc	4,334 teu: ex Polaris J-13
9456977	Zim Colombo *	Lbr	2009	41,331	51,535	262	32	24	ucc	4,300 teu: l/a Atlas J

also owns a fleet of smaller vessels, mostly container feeder ships   * managed by F.A. Vinnen

Kahn Scheepvaart B.V. Netherlands

funnel: white with red elephant and red/blue eight-pointed star between narrow green bands. **hull:** Dark blue with white web address, red boot-topping. **history:** founded 1956 and subsidiary Jumbo Shipping Co formed 1969. **web:** www.jumboshipping.nl

IMO	name	flag	year	gt	dwt	loa	bm	kts	type	comments
9650585	Fairmaster	Nld	2015	18,099	12,989	153	27	17	uhl	cr: 2(1,500)
9243849	Fairpartner	Nld	2004	15,022	11,350	143	27	17	uhl	cr: 2(800)
9371579	Fairplayer	Nld	2008	15,027	13,278	145	27	17	uhl	cr: 2(900)
9243837	Jumbo Javelin	Nld	2004	15,022	12,870	143	27	17	uhl	cr: 2(800)
9371581	Jumbo Jubilee	Nld	2008	15,022	12,870	145	27	17	uhl	cr: 2(900)
9634165	Jumbo Kinetic	Nld	2014	18,099	13,000	153	27	17	uhl	cr: 2(1,500)

also owns smaller heavy-lift vessels.

Kawasaki Kisen K.K. ('K' Line) Japan

funnel: bright red with white 'K', above grey base. **hull:** grey with red boot-topping. **history:** formed 1919 as Kawasaki Kisen Kaisha and merged 1964 with Iino Kisen Kaisha (formed 1918). Taiyo Nippon Kisen subsidiary formed 2000 by merger of Taiyo Kaiun KK with Kobe Nippon KK (founded 1917). **web:** www.kline.co.jp

IMO	name	flag	year	gt	dwt	loa	bm	kts	type	comments
9442885	Adriatic Highway **	Pan	2008	58,990	18,869	200	32	20	mve	6,237 ceu
9464388	Aegean Highway **	Jpn	2008	60,320	18,867	200	32	20	mve	6,237 ceu
9409039	Alexandria Bridge	Pan	2009	40,839	51,314	261	32	24	ucc	4,228 teu
9409027	Ambassador Bridge	Phl	2009	40,839	51,314	261	32	24	ucc	4,228 teu
9205976	American Highway	Pan	2000	49,212	16,750	179	32	20	mve	5,052 ceu
9078842	Arcadia Highway	Pan	1994	49,012	15,507	180	32	20	mve	5,008 ceu
9451484	Arica Bridge	Pan	2010	27,213	32,997	200	32	22	ucc	2,450 teu
9409041	Astoria Bridge	Pan	2009	40,839	51,314	261	32	24	ucc	4,228 teu
9409053	Athens Bridge	Pan	2009	40,839	51,314	261	32	24	ucc	4,228 teu

Hawaiian Highway : Kawasaki Kisen K. K. : *Mike Rhodes*

IMO	name	flag	year	gt	dwt	loa	bm	kts	type	comments
9443073	Athens Highway **	Pan	2008	59,440	18,809	200	32	20	mve	6,237 ceu
9250232	Atlantic Highway	Pan	2002	55,493	17,232	200	32	20	mve	6,015 ceu
8612251	Atlas Highway	Lbr	1987	45,742	14,487	180	32	20	mve	4,857 ceu
9463346	Bai Chay Bridge	Pan	2011	44,234	52,452	267	35	24	ucc	4,432 teu
9243461	Baltic Highway	Pan	2001	42,238	17,828	179	32	20	mve	4,004 ceu
9463281	Baltimore Bridge	Pan	2010	44,234	52,184	267	35	24	ucc	4,432 teu
9506710	Bangkok Highway **	Pan	2009	48,927	15,306	180	32	20	mve	5,036 ceu
9463267	Bay Bridge	Pan	2010	44,234	52,118	267	35	24	ucc	4,432 teu
9463293	Bear Mountain Bridge	Pan	2011	44,234	52,118	267	35	24	ucc	4,432 teu
9409340	Bishu Highway **	Pan	2009	56,978	17,649	200	32	20	mve	6,135 ceu
9510151	Blue Ridge Highway **	Pan	2009	48,927	15,290	180	32	20	mve	5,036 ceu
9519107	Bosporus Highway	Pan	2009	59,440	18,792	200	32	20	mve	6,237 ceu
9519119	Brasilia Highway	Pan	2009	59,440	18,793	200	32	20	mve	6,327 ceu
9458999	Brooklyn Bridge	Pan	2010	44,459	52,055	267	35	24	ucc	4,432 teu
9463310	Brussels Bridge	Pan	2011	44,234	52,452	267	35	24	ucc	4,432 teu
9574078	California Highway **	Pan	2010	59,447	18,644	200	32	18	mve	6,215 ceu
9574066	Canadian Highway **	Pan	2010	59,447	18,581	200	32	18	mve	6,215 ceu
9565558	Cape Town Highway **	Pan	2011	58,535	21,676	200	32	19	mve	6,249 ceu
9243473	Caribbean Highway	Pan	2002	42,238	17,866	179	32	20	mve	4,004 ceu
8319718	Century Highway No. 2	Pan	1985	44,616	15,509	186	32	18	mve	5,401 ceu
9565546	Chesapeake Highway **	Pan	2010	58,535	21,643	200	32	19	mve	6,249 ceu
9224544	Chiswick Bridge	Pan	2001	68,687	68,280	285	40	25	ucc	5,610 teu
9323780	Colorado Highway **	Pan	2005	44,382	12,806	183	30	20	mve	4,318 ceu
9238519	Continental Highway	Pan	2001	55,493	17,201	200	32	20	mve	6,249 ceu
9565560	Dalian Highway **	Pan	2011	58,535	21,616	200	32	20	mve	6,249 ceu
9536959	Delhi Highway **	Pan	2011	58,997	18,891	200	32	20	mve	6,120 ceu
9293636	Diamond Highway **	Pan	2004	60,175	19,086	200	32	20	mve	6,354 ceu: ex Utopia Ace-13
9574107	Dover Highway **	Jpn	2011	59,030	18,720	200	32	21	mve	6,215 ceu
9728069	Drive Green Highway	Pan	2016	76,387	20,034	200	38	19	mve	7,500 ceu
9536961	Durban Highway **	Pan	2011	58,997	18,906	200	32	20	mve	6,120 ceu
9325764	Eastern Highway **	Pan	2006	39,422	12,991	188	28	20	mve	3,893 ceu
8602828	Emden	Pan	1987	38,062	13,898	178	29	17	mve	3,788 ceu
9604938	Euphrates Highway **	Pan	2012	59,447	18,709	200	32	21	mve	6,215 ceu
9604938	Eurasian Highway **	Jpn	2012	59,029	18,709	200	32	21	mve	6,215 ceu
9206011	European Highway	Pan	1999	48,039	15,057	180	32	20	mve	5,064 ceu
9670016	Galaxy River	Pan	2014	46,885	54,081	230	37	19	lpg	82,391 m³
9675573	Galveston Highway +	Pan	2014	59,525	18,549	200	32	20	mve	6,215 ceu
9302073	George Washington Bridge	Pan	2006	68,687	71,309	285	40	25	ucc	5,642 teu
9339820	Georgia Highway **	Jpn	2007	56,973	17,685	200	32	20	mve	6,135 ceu
9302097	Glen Canyon Bridge	Pan	2006	68,687	71,291	285	40	25	ucc	5,642 teu
9726695	Global Highway	Pan	2016	75,036	20,686	200	38	19	mve	7,500 ceu
9302085	Greenwich Bridge	Pan	2006	68,687	71,270	285	40	25	ucc	5,642 teu
9302102	Guang Dong Bridge	Pan	2006	68,687	71,283	285	40	25	ucc	5,642 teu
9294367	Guangzhou Highway **	Pan	2006	48,927	15,301	180	32	20	mve	5,036 ceu
9351159	Hamburg Bridge	Pan	2009	98,747	98,849	336	46	25	ucc	9,040 teu
9712644	Hamburg Highway	Pan	2015	75,126	20,606	200	38	19	mve	7,500 ceu
9395147	Hammersmith Bridge	Pan	2009	98,747	98,849	336	46	25	ucc	9,040 teu
9566394	Hangzhou Bay Bridge	Pan	2013	96,790	96,980	335	46	25	ucc	9,040 teu
9302138	Hannover Bridge	Pan	2006	98,747	99,214	336	46	25	ucc	9,040 teu
9588093	Hanoi Bridge	Pan	2012	96,790	96,980	335	46	25	ucc	8,930 teu
9302152	Harbour Bridge	Pan	2007	98,747	98,849	336	46	25	ucc	9,040 teu
9712632	Hawaiian Highway	Pan	2015	75,126	20,606	200	38	19	mve	7,500 ceu
9588081	Helsinki Bridge	Pan	2012	96,801	96,980	335	46	24	ucc	8,930 teu
9302176	Henry Hudson Bridge	Pan	2008	98,747	99,214	336	46	24	ucc	9,040 teu
8612316	Hercules Highway	Jpn	1987	46,875	14,977	180	32	18	mve	4,925 ceu
9395161	Hong Kong Bridge	Sgp	2009	98,747	98,849	336	46	25	ucc	8,212 teu
9588079	Honolulu Bridge	Pan	2012	96,790	96,980	335	46	24	ucc	8,930 teu
9566382	Houston Bridge	Pan	2012	96,801	96,980	335	46	24	ucc	8,930 teu
9302140	Humber Bridge	Pan	2006	98,747	98,849	336	46	24	ucc	8,212 teu
9302164	Humen Bridge	Pan	2007	98,747	98,849	336	46	24	ucc	8,212 teu
9272888	Indiana Highway **	Jpn	2003	55,457	17,442	200	32	20	mve	6,043 ceu
9362267	London Highway	Pan	2006	55,600	17,765	200	32	20	mve	6,057 ceu
9689603	Mackinac Bridge	Jpn	2015	152,297	147,404	366	51	23	ucc	13,870 teu
9689615	Manhattan Bridge	Jpn	2015	152,297	147,420	366	51	23	ucc	13,870 teu

IMO	name	flag	year	gt	dwt	loa	bm	kts	type	comments
9250220	Mediterranean Highway **	Pan	2002	55,493	17,228	200	32	20	mve	6,015 ceu
9339832	Michigan Highway **	Jpn	2008	56,951	17,673	200	32	20	mve	6,135 ceu
9330745	Neva River (st)	Pan	2007	117,895	77,163	290	50	19	lng	147,804 m³: ex Celestine River-10
9205964	Nippon Highway	Pan	1999	49,212	16,827	179	32	20	mve	5,052 ceu
9205988	Ocean Highway	Pan	2000	49,212	16,733	179	32	20	mve	5,052 ceu
9381665	Oregon Highway **	Pan	2007	57,147	17,699	200	32	20	mve	6,135 ceu
9728071	Orion Highway	Pan	2016	76,299	20,500	200	38	19	mve	7,500 ceu
9206023	Pacific Highway	Pan	2000	48,039	15,127	180	32	20	mve	5,064 ceu
9078830	Pegasus Highway	Pan	1994	49,012	15,553	180	32	18	mve	5,008 ceu
9560364	San Francisco Bridge	Pan	2010	71,787	72,890	293	40	25	ucc	6,350 teu
9560352	Seattle Bridge	Pan	2010	71,787	72,890	293	40	25	ucc	6,350 teu
9238521	Seven Seas Highway **	Pan	2001	55,493	17,232	200	32	22	mve	6,015 ceu
9294343	Shanghai Highway **	Pan	2005	48,927	15,413	180	32	22	mve	5,036 ceu
9043689	Shenandoah Highway	Pan	1992	47,368	12,308	180	32	18	mve	4,211 ceu
9325439	Sierra Nevada Highway **	Pan	2007	44,364	12,851	183	30	20	mve	4,318 ceu
9338632	Southern Highway **	Pan	2008	39,422	12,892	188	28	20	mve	3,893 ceu
9272890	Texas Highway **	Jpn	2003	55,458	17,481	200	32	20	mve	6,043 ceu
9319404	Trinity Arrow (st)	Pan	2008	101,080	79,556	278	44	19	lng	154,982 m³
9350927	Trinity Glory (st)	Pan	2009	101,126	79,605	278	44	19	lng	154,200 m³
8612263	Triton Highway	Jpn	1987	45,783	14,484	180	32	18	mve	4,857 ceu
9230309	Tsing Ma Bridge	Pan	2002	68,687	71,310	285	40	25	ucc	5,610 teu
9293454	Vecchio Bridge	Pan	2005	54,519	64,983	294	32	23	ucc	4,738 teu
9293442	Venice Bridge	Pan	2005	54,519	64,989	294	32	23	ucc	4,738 teu
9325776	Western Highway **	Pan	2007	39,422	12,980	188	28	19	mve	3,893 ceu
newbuildings:										
9689627			2018	152,297	150,000				ucc	13,870 teu Imabari Hiroshima 2537
9689639			2018	152,297	150,000				ucc	13,870 teu
9689641			2018	152,297	150,000				ucc	13,870 teu
			2018						ucc	13,870 teu
			2018						ucc	13,870 teu
9726700		Pan	2016	75,036	20,500	200	38	19	mve	7,500 ceu Shin Kurushima 5876
9728083		Pan	2016	76,300	20,000	200	38	19	mve	7,500 ceu JMU Ariake 5068
9728095		Pan	2016	76,300	20,000	200	38	19	mve	7,500 ceu JMU Ariake 5069

further 13,870 teu 366 x 51 [Imabari (2018)] – ordered 09:2014   2 further x 7,500ceu mve, 200 x 38 (Shin Kurushima (2017))
*managed by 'K' Line Ship Management Co Ltd, Japan or by subsidiaries * Stargate Shipmanagement GmbH, Germany or ** Taiyo Nippon Kisen (founded 1944 as Kobe Nippon KK and merged 2000 with Taiyo Kaiun KK – www.nipponkisen.co.jp) † owned by Shoei Kisen Kaisha, Japan.*
+ chartered in from other owners
The company and its many subsidiaries own or manage over 200 vessels, only the larger container ship and vehicle carriers being listed. The owned and managed fleet also includes a large number of bulk carriers used in the Australia to Japan trade, wood-chip carriers, product and Lpg tankers, 23 Lng tankers and several smaller vehicle carriers.
Also see Cido Shipping and various chartered ships with 'Bridge' and 'Highway' suffixes in index.

Klaveness Maritime Logistics AS   Norway

funnel: *yellow with house flag,narrow black top* **hull:** *grey or orange with red boot-topping.* **history:** *founded 1946 as Gorrissen & Klaveness A/S to 1958 and as Torvald Klaveness & Co AS to 2005.* **web:** *www.tk-group.com or www.klaveness.com*

IMO	name	flag	year	gt	dwt	loa	bm	kts	type	comments
9308728	Bakkedal	Mhl	2007	38,883	72,450	225	32	14	bbu	
9603594	Balao	Mhl	2013	26,412	34,145	209	30	18	ucc	2,504 teu
9506394	Baleares	Mhl	2014	26,374	34,021	209	30	22	ucc	2,546 teu: l/a Rio Angelina
9603609	Ballenita	Mhl	2013	26,412	34,123	209	30	18	ucc	2,504 teu
9603611	Balsa	Mhl	2013	26,412	34,171	209	30	18	ucc	2,504 teu
9504607	Banak	Mhl	2014	26,374	34,067	261	32	24	ucc	2,546 teu: l/d Julius Schulte
9214135	Banasol	Mhl	2001	38,889	72,562	225	32	14	bbu	
9228045	Banastar	Mhl	2001	38,889	72,562	225	32	16	bbu	
9228057	Bangor	Nis	2002	38,889	72,562	225	32	14	bbu	ex Al Mansour-12
9214147	Barcarena	Nis	2001	38,889	72,562	225	32	14	bbu	ex Baniyas-15
9304067	Bantry	Mhl	2005	38,883	72,562	225	32	14	bbu	
9504592	Bardu	Mhl	2014	26,374	34,086	261	32	24	ucc:	2,546 teu: l/a Jacob Schulte
9289051	Baro *	Sgp	2004	18,334	23,679	175	27	20	ucc	1,740 teu: ex Amundsen-14, Oceanlady-10, Ocean Progress I-09, Cap Arnauti-09, c/a Philipp Schulte
9237503	Barry *	Sgp	2004	35,881	41,800	220	32	22	ucc	3,091 teu: ex Anke Ritscher-10, CSAV Sao Paulo-09, Norasia Andes-06, Anke Ritscher-04
9711145	Bavang	Mhl	2016	44,190	82,028	229	32	14	bbu	

Iberica Knutsen : Knutsen OAS Shipping : *Hans Kraijenbosch*

Ingrid Knutsen : Knutsen NYK Offshore Tankers : *Hans Kraijenbosch*

IMO	name	flag	year	gt	dwt	loa	bm	kts	type	comments
newbuildings:										
9729764		Mhl	2016	44,000	82,000	229	32	14	bbu	Jiangsu New Yangzi 2013-1151 02.2016
9729738		Mhl	2016		80,500				bbu	Zhejiang Ouhua 677
9729740		Mhl	2016		80,500				bbu	Zhejiang Ouhua 678
		Mhl	2017		80,500				bbu	Zhejiang Ouhua

also Jiangsu New Yangzi SB Co., 2 further options declared 04:2014 (in conjunction with Tufton Oceanic), two converted to 2,700teu ucc, 2013-1152 cancelled but new order placed for 3 x 82,500dwt combo vessels, delivery 2018
* managed by Klaveness Asia Pte. Ltd. Also operates time-chartered vessels in Bulkhandling and Baumarine Pools

Knutsen OAS Shipping AS   Norway

funnel: *black with two red bands.* **hull**: *orange (larger vessels with white 'KNUTSEN OAS'), red boot-topping.* **history**: *founded 1896 as Knut Knutsen OAS until 1982.* **web**: *www.knutsenoas.com*

IMO	name	flag	year	gt	dwt	loa	bm	kts	type	comments
9401295	Barcelona Knutsen	Cni	2010	110,920	97,730	290	46	19	lng	173,400 m³
9483516	Birgit Knutsen	Nis	2010	11,889	16,536	144	23	13	tco	
9236432	Bilbao Knutsen (st)	Cni	2004	90,835	68,530	284	43	19	lng	135,049 m³
9246578	Cadiz Knutsen (st)	Cni	2003	90,835	68,411	284	43	19	lng	135,240 m³
9409261	Eli Knutsen	Gbr	2009	11,889	16,544	144	23	13	tco	
9326603	Iberica Knutsen (st)	Nis	2006	93,915	77,541	277	43	19	lng	135,230 m³
9141405	Kristin Knutsen	Nis	1998	12,184	19,152	148	23	15	tco	
9409273	Liv Knutsen	Gbr	2009	11,899	16,585	144	23	13	tco	
9442249	Louise Knutsen	Gbr	2010	11,889	16,512	144	23	13	tco	
9477593	Ribera del Duero Knutsen (df)	Nis	2010	111,109	96,740	290	46	19	lng	173,400 m³
9338797	Sestao Knutsen (st)	Cni	2007	90,583	68,530	284	43	19	lng	135,357 m³
9414632	Sevilla Knutsen (df)	Cni	2010	110,920	97,730	290	46	19	lng	166,600 m³
9343266	Valencia Knutsen (df)	Cni	2010	110,920	97,730	290	46	19	lng	173,400 m³
newbuildings:										
9721724	La Mancha Knutsen	Nis	2016	114,000	81,605			19	lng	Hyundai Ulsan 2733
9721736	Rioja Knutsen	Nis	2016	114,000	81,605			19	lng	Hyundai Ulsan 2734

Knutsen NYK Offshore Tankers, Norway

funnel: *back with two red bands or * yellow with white 'BR' on green square, black top.* **hull**: *orange with white 'KNOT' or * black with red boot-topping* **history**: *founded 2010, j/v between Knutsen OAS (50%) and NYK (50%)*

IMO	name	flag	year	gt	dwt	loa	bm	kts	type	comments
9176929	Anneleen Knutsen	Nis	2002	24,242	35,140	183	27	15	tcs	(conv. tco-11)
9172870	Betty Knutsen	Nis	1999	24,185	35,309	183	27	14	tcs	(conv. tco-04)
9472529	Bodil Knutsen	Iom	2011	93,147	157,644	285	50	14	tcs	
9623635	Carmen Knutsen	Mlt	2013	82,803	156,296	281	48	14	tcs	
8714994	Catherine Knutsen †	Nis	1992	77,352	141,200	277	43	14	tcs	ex Tanana-99, Wilomi Tanana-98, Tanana-98, Wilomi Tanana-97
9513440	Dan Cisne **	Dis	2012	36,303	59,335	207	32	14	tcs	
9183609	Dan Eagle	Dis	1999	28,448	46,185	183	32	14	tcs	ex Freja Pacific-08, Soundless-06, Hellas Serenity-05
9513438	Dan Sabia **	Dis	2012	36,303	59,317	207	32	14	tcs	
9131357	Elisabeth Knutsen (me2)	Nor	1997	71,880	124,788	265	43	14	tcs	
9499876	Fortaleza Knutsen *	Bhs	2011	63,560	106,316	247	42	14	tcs	
9041057	Gerd Knutsen	Iom	1996	79,244	134,510	277	44	14	tcs	ex Knock An-03
9313527	Gijon Knutsen	Gbr	2006	24,242	35,309	187	27	15	tcs	(conv. tco-06)
9248447	Grena Knutsen	Bhs	2013	81,141	148,553	278	46	14	tcs	ex Grena-14
9273064	Heather Knutsen †	Can	2005	80,918	148,644	277	46	14	tcs	l/a Rose Knutsen
9628300	Hilda Knutsen	Nis	2013	80,850	123,166	276	46	14	tcs	
9649225	Ingrid Knutsen	Iom	2013	66,038	111,634	258	44	15	tcs	
9273557	Jasmine Knutsen †	Nis	2005	80,918	148,706	277	46	14	tcs	
9169615	Karen Knutsen (2)	Iom	1999	87,827	154,390	276	50	14	tcs	ex Knock Whillan-03
9160619	Loch Rannoch + (2)	Gbr	1998	75,526	130,031	270	46	14	tcs	
9685396	Raquel Knutsen	Mlt	2015	83,936	152,208	276	46	14	tcs	
9499888	Recife Knutsen *	Bhs	2011	63,560	105,928	247	42	14	tcs	
9169627	Sallie Knutsen (2)	Iom	1999	87,827	154,390	276	50	14	tcs	ex Knock Sallie-03
9247168	Siri Knutsen #	Gbr	2004	24,916	35,309	187	27	15	ows	(conv. tcs-14, conv. tco-05)
9630030	Torill Knutsen	Nis	2013	80,850	123,166	276	46	14	tcs	
8715546	Tove Knutsen ††	Nis	1989	60,719	112,508	246	43	14	tcs	
9316115	Windsor Knutsen *	Nis	2007	87,146	162,258	281	50	14	tcs	(conv tcr-11)

newbuildings: 1 x 152,200dwt tcs [COSCO Zhoushan (2017) 2 tcs + 1 option taken up 06:2015 [HHI (2017)]
* operated by Petrobras Transportes S.A., Brazil, † by Canship Ugland Ltd (formed jointly by A/S Ugland Rederi and Canship Ltd), Canada (www.canship.com) or + BP Shipping Ltd. ** bareboat chartered to Transpetro until 2023/4 †† laid up 04:2012
 # also fitted for use as a well stimulation vessel

König & Cie. GmbH & Co. KG   Germany

funnel: *blue with black top or operators/charterers colours.* **hull:** *red with red boot topping.* **history:** *Investment organisation founded 1999 by Thomas König and 40% owned by Schöller Holdings Ltd. Refinanced during 2014 with investment from US based Delos Gp. & Tennenbaum Capital.* **web:** *www.koenig-cie.de*

IMO	name	flag	year	gt	dwt	loa	bm	kts	type	comments
9293117	Cape Bari *	Mhl	2005	81,076	159,186	274	48	15	tcr	
9293129	Cape Bastia *	Mhl	2005	81,076	159,156	274	48	15	tcr	
9248825	Cape Baxley	Mhl	2003	81,270	159,385	274	48	15	tco	ex SKS Senne-13
9232929	Cape Bellavista	Mhl	2002	81,270	159,453	274	48	15	tco	ex SKS Sira-13
9293131	Cape Bonny *	Mhl	2005	81,085	159,152	274	48	15	tcr	
9293143	Cape Brindisi *	Mhl	2006	81,076	159,195	274	48	15	tcr	
9308390	Cape Melville	Mhl	2005	27,786	37,883	222	30	22	ucc	2,742 teu: ex Cosco Melbourne-10, l/a Cape Melville
9308405	Cape Moreton	Mhl	2005	27,786	38,882	222	30	22	ucc	2,742 teu: ex Cosco Dammam-10
8902541	HH Joanna	Deu	1991	53,783	67,680	294	32	23	ucc	4,639 teu: ex Portland Express-15, Leverkusen Express-12
8902565	Kalliopi R.C.	Deu	1991	53,833	67,680	294	32	23	ucc	4,639 teu: ex Hoechst Express-15
9421843	King Robert *	Mhl	2008	89,510	169,676	291	45	14	bbu	ex Golden Sentosa-08
9149316	RT Aegir	Mhl	1997	25,608	34,015	208	30	21	ucc	2,468 teu: ex Austria-14, CSAV Chicago-10, Maersk Freeport-99, Liberta-99, Montebello-99, l/a Liberta
9176682	RT Dagr	Pmd	1998	16,811	20,976	168	27	21	ucc	1,651 teu: ex Hispania-14, Alianca Andes-09, Cap Reinga-06, Columbus Coromandel-03, l/a Hispania
9221061	RT Odin	Lbr	2001	15,988	20,461	170	25	20	ucc	1,552 teu: ex Hansa Aalesund-15, Al Yamamah-08, Hansa Aalesund-04, MSC New Plymouth-04, l/a Hansa Aalesund
9333058	Stadt Köln **	Atg	2007	35,375	44,234	223	32	22	ucc	3,400 teu: ex Emirates Indus-11, Stadt Köln-11
9320037	Stadt Rostock **	Atg	2006	27,971	37,929	222	30	21	ucc	2,700 teu: ex SCI Jyoti-09, l/dn Stadt Rostock
9490454	Voge Challenger +	Lbr	2010	43,692	79,648	229	32	15	bbu	l/a King Harvey

* managed by Columbia Shipmanagement (Deutschland) ** managed by Ahrenkiel Steamship + managed by TSC The Shipmanagement Co.

Mercator Navigation GmbH, Germany

funnel: *blue with black top or operators/ charterers colours.* **hull:** *red, some with Scorship in white, red boot topping.* **history:** *established 2005 as j/v between König and Scorpio Shipping. Traded as Scorship Navigation from 2007, but in 2014 changed to present name.* **web:** *www.mercator-navigation.de*

IMO	name	flag	year	gt	dwt	loa	bm	kts	type	comments
9407287	King Daniel	Mhl	2008	42,010	73,720	229	32	14	tco	
9407251	King Darius **	Mhl	2007	42,010	73,634	229	32	14	tco	
9347856	King Darwin **	Mhl	2007	42,010	73,604	229	32	14	tco	
9374844	King Dorian **	Mhl	2007	42,010	73,611	229	32	14	tco	ex King David-08
9407275	King Douglas	Mhl	2008	42,010	73,666	229	32	14	tco	
9407263	King Duncan **	Mhl	2008	42,010	73,720	229	32	14	tco	
9290490	King Edward *	Mhl	2004	23,246	37,384	183	27	14	tco	ex Ruby-06, Baltic Admiral-04
9267027	King Emerald *	Mhl	2004	25,507	38,875	183	27	14	tco	ex Meriom Breeze-08
9305532	King Ernest *	Mhl	2004	23,246	37,106	183	28	14	tco	ex Ganges-07
9228837	King Everest *	Mhl	2001	23,217	37,230	183	27	14	tco	ex Marne-06, l/a Ruby Star
9490442	King Hadley	Mhl	2011	43,507	79,642	229	32	14	bbu	
9421843	King Robert	Mhl	2008	89,510	169,676	291	45	14	bbu	l/a Golden Sentosa
9567439	Mare Tracer +	Mhl	2011	33,032	57,000	190	32	14	bbu	
9567415	Mare Trader +	Mhl	2010	33,032	56,745	190	32	14	bbu	
9567403	Mare Transporter +	Mhl	2011	33,033	56,745	190	32	14	bbu	
9567427	Mare Traveller +	Mhl	2011	33,032	56,745	190	32	14	bbu	

vessels managed by Columbia Shipmanagement (Deutschland) GmbH)
* operates in the Scorpio Handymax Product Pool, ** operates in the Scorpio Panamax Pool
+ managed for Marenave Schiffahrts A.G.

Marenave Schiffahrts A.G., Germany

funnel: *white with dark blue M on broad yellow band between two narrow dark blue bands.* **hull:** *black with red boot topping.* **history:** *associated with Investment organisation König, established 2006* **web:** *www.marenave.com*

IMO	name	flag	year	gt	dwt	loa	bm	kts	type	comments
9295842	Höegh Berlin	Bhs	2005	68,871	27,176	229	32	19	mve	7,850 ceu (len-08)
9295335	Mare Action	Mhl	2005	23,240	37,467	183	27	14	tco	ex Baltic Action-07
9190505	Mare Ambassador	Mhl	2005	23,240	37,371	183	27	14	tco	ex Baltic Ambassador-07
9216559	Mare Atlantic	Mlt	2001	39,085	68,467	229	32	14	tco	ex Latgale-07, Inca-01
9384095	Mare Baltic	Mhl	2008	24,112	38,402	183	27	14	tco	l/a Meriom Ruby
9276004	Mare Caribbean	Mhl	2004	29,327	46,718	183	32	14	tco	ex Cape Bauld-07
9248942	Mare Fox	Mhl	2003	14,308	16,435	155	25	18	ucc	1,221 teu: ex St. John Glory-13, Tiger RMB-10, Cape Fox-08, YM Da Nang-08, TS Yokohama-04, Cape Fox-03

King Duncan : Konig & Cie - Mercator Nav. : *Chris Brooks :*

Al Yarmouk : Kuwait Oil Tanker Co. : *Chris Brooks*

IMO	name	flag	year	gt	dwt	loa	bm	kts	type	comments
9248930	Mare Frio	Mhl	2003	14,308	16,442	155	25	18	ucc	1,221 teu: ex Cape Frio-13, TS Taichung-10, Cape Frio-05
9216547	Mare Pacific *	Mlt	2001	39,085	68,467	229	32	14	tco	ex Zemgale-07, Maya-01

* managed by Columbia Shipmanagement (Deutschland)
see other vessels managed by Columbia Shipmanagement (Deutschland) GmbH. Also see United Product Tanker (UPT) pool under Schoeller Holdings Ltd

Kuwait Oil Tanker Co. S.A.K.   Kuwait

funnel: *red with gold Arabic characters on green oval disc on broad white band beneath black top.* **hull:** *black with white 'KOTC', red or grey boot-topping.* **history:** *founded 1957 as subsidiary of Kuwait Petroleum Corp.* **web:** *www.kotc.com.kw*

9653446	Al Dasma	Kwt	2014	63,066	109,719	250	42	15	tco	
9653410	Al Derwazah	Kwt	2014	165,168	316,884	333	60	15	tcr	
9653408	Al Funtas	Kwt	2014	165,168	316,648	333	60	15	tcr	
9329708	Al Jabriyah II	Kwt	2007	161,113	317,250	333	60	14	tcr	
9653434	Al Kout	Kwt	2014	165,178	317,019	333	60	15	tcr	
9534808	Al Riqqa	Kwt	2011	162,625	319,704	332	60	15	tcr	
9328168	Al Salam II	Kwt	2007	42,798	69,790	228	32	15	tco	
9162875	Al Salheia	Kwt	1998	158,503	310,453	334	58	15	tcr	
9534793	Al Salmi	Kwt	2011	162,625	319,634	332	60	15	tcr	
9162887	Al Shegaya	Kwt	1998	158,503	310,433	334	58	15	tcr	
9329784	Al Soor II	Kwt	2007	42,798	69,835	228	32	15	tco	
9653422	Al Yarmouk	Kwt	2014	165,178	317,033	333	60	15	tcr	
8619479	Arabiyah	Kwt	1988	75,029	121,109	250	43	13	tco	
9595008	Bahra	Kwt	2012	62,925	110,751	250	42	15	tco	
9595010	Bneider	Kwt	2012	62,925	110,587	250	42	15	tco	
9656034	Bubyan	Kwt	2014	31,445	47,760	186	32	14	tch	
9656022	Burgan	Kwt	2014	31,445	46,330	186	32	14	tch	
9534779	Dar Salwa	Kwt	2011	162,625	319,761	332	60	15	tcr	
9005065	Gas Al-Gurain	Kwt	1993	44,868	49,874	230	37	16	lpg	76,893 m³
9329710	Gas Al Kuwait II	Kwt	2007	48,104	57,738	225	37	16	lpg	80,607 m³
9005053	Gas Al Mutlaa	Kwt	1993	44,868	49,874	230	37	16	lpg	76,905 m³
9329722	Gas Al-Negeh	Kwt	2007	48,104	57,748	225	37	16	lpg	80,681 m³
8619467	Hadiyah	Kwt	1988	75,029	121,109	250	43	16	tco	
9656046	Kaifan	Kwt	2014	31,445	46,327	186	32	14	tch	
9329693	Kazimah II	Kwt	2006	161,113	317,250	333	60	15	tcr	
9656058	Mutriba	Kwt	2014	31,445	46,327	186	32	14	tch	
9534781	Umm Al Aish	Kwt	2011	162,625	319,634	332	60	15	tcr	
9328170	Wafrah	Kwt	2007	63,440	113,849	250	44	15	tco	

Reederei F. Laeisz GmbH & Co. KG   Germany

funnel: *yellow or charterers colours.* **hull:** *black with red boot-topping or white with blue boot-topping.* **history:** *founded 1824 as F. Laeisz until 1982 and F Laeisz Schiffahrts GmbH to 1993. Fleet merged in 1993 with privatised East German state fleet of Deutsche Seereederei Rostock as joint venture with Hamburg business associate until 1999, when fully taken-over.* **web:** *www.laeisz.de*

9141273	Hanjin Haiphong	Deu	1997	53,324	63,527	294	32	23	ucc	4,545 teu: ex Peking Senator-09, Cho Yang Ark-00
9139490	Hanjin Mundra	Deu	1997	53,324	63,533	294	32	23	ucc	4,545 teu: ex Penang Senator-09, Cho Yang Atlas-01
9141302	Hanjin San Diego	Deu	1997	53,324	63,645	294	32	23	ucc	4,545 teu: ex Portland Senator-09, Cho Yang Alpha-01
9320025	Ilva	Lbr	2006	27,971	37,786	222	30	21	ucc	2,700 teu: ex Stadt Wismar-13
9330549	Kaya	Lbr	2007	28,616	39,338	222	30	21	ucc	2,824 teu: ex Valentina Schulte-13, Cap Capricorn-12, Valentina Schulte-07
9427926	Paganella	Gib	2009	47,020	11,453	183	32	21	mve	5,000 ceu: CSAV Rio Illapel-14, l/a Paganella
9422328	Paganini	Pmd	2008	40,170	75,118	225	32	14	bbu	ex Utopie-14, Umberto d'Amato-08
9427938	Paganino	Lbr	2009	47,020	11,372	183	32	20	mve	5,000 ceu: ex CSAV Rio Itata-15, l/a Paganino
9427940	Paglia	Gib	2010	47,057	11,368	183	32	20	mve	5,000 ceu: ex CSAV Rio Blanco-12, l/a Paglia
9427952	Pagna	Gib	2010	47,057	11,314	183	32	20	mve	5,000 ceu: ex CSAV Rio Bueno-12, l/a Pagna
9149794	Paradise N *	Deu	1997	155,051	322,398	332	58	13	bor	ex Peene Ore-02
9427964	Parana	Gib	2012	47,053	12,868	183	32	20	mve	5,000 ceu
9491874	Passama	Gib	2012	47,053	12,806	183	32	20	mve	5,000 ceu
9491886	Passero	Gib	2012	47,053	12,755	183	32	20	mve	5,000 ceu
9491898	Patara	Gib	2012	47,053	12,755	183	32	20	mve	5,000 ceu
9293430	Pazific	Gib	2005	25,852	42,937	205	32	16	lpg	60,000 m³ ex Pacific-12, BW Hesiod-11, Pacific Viking-06

IMO	name	flag	year	gt	dwt	loa	bm	kts	type	comments
9232084	Phoenix I †	Lbr	2002	50,242	58,423	282	32	24	ucc	4,389 teu: ex Hanjin Phoenix-14, I/a Phoenix
9289063	Pinara	Lbr	2004	18,334	23,579	175	27	20	ucc	1,740 teu: ex Laura Schulte-13, Maersk Varna-08, Laura Schulte-04, I/a Maximilian Schulte, I/dn Konrad Schulte
9292216	Polar	Gib	2004	35,853	42,854	205	32	16	lpg	60,000 m³ ex BW Herdis-11, Polar Viking-06
9349875	Pona	Lbr	2007	27,968	37,570	222	30	22	ucc	2,741 teu: ex CMA CGM Copernic-09, Pona-07
9334519	Pontremoli †	Lbr	2006	28,270	32,900	213	32	22	ucc	2,646 teu: ex ANL Benalla-15, Pontremoli-11, Gulf Bridge-10, I/a Pontremoli
9334521	Pontresina	Lbr	2008	28,270	32,949	213	32	22	ucc	2,646 teu: ex Kota Permas-12, Pontresina-08
9481520	Porto	Lbr	2010	28,561	39,267	225	30	22	ucc	2,790 teu
9349887	Posen †	Lbr	2007	27,968	37,570	222	30	22	ucc	2,790 teu: ex OOCL Bremen-09, Posen-07
9232113	Pretoria	Lbr	2002	50,242	58,768	282	32	24	ucc	4,389 teu: ex Hanjin Pretoria-13
9272967	Pugnani	Gib	2004	39,727	76,602	225	32	14	bbu	ex Euro Carrier-14

Paganella : Reederei F. Laeisz GmbH : *Mike Rhodes*

Kristjanis Valdemars : Latvian Shipping Co. : *Nico Kemps*

IMO	name	flag	year	gt	dwt	loa	bm	kts	type	comments

newbuildings: 2 x mve [COSCO Dalian (2016)]
owned or managed by Reederei F. Laeisz GmbH or † by associated company Hamburgische Seehandlung GmbH, * managed for Gebab Konzepitons-und Emissions
also see managed vessels under BW Gas and NSB Niederelbe Schiffahrt GmbH.

Latvian Shipping Company   Latvia

funnel: red with red 'Lat' symbol on broad white band **hull:** black or red with red boot-topping. **history:** formed 1940 and formerly government controlled; privatised 1996 and since 2002 j/s company with JSC Ventspils Nafta holding 49.94% stake.
web: www.lk.lv or www.lscsm.lv

IMO	name	flag	year	gt	dwt	loa	bm	kts	type	comments
9323405	Ainazi	Mhl	2008	30,641	52,606	195	32	14	tco	
9323314	Ance	Mhl	2006	30,641	52,622	195	32	14	tco	
9509449	Elandra Oak **	Mhl	2016	29,767	49,990	183	32	14	tco	
9746267	Elandra Palm **	Mhl	2016	29,767	49,990	183	32	14	tco	
9746243	Elandra Spruce **	Mhl	2016	29,767	49,990	183	32	14	tco	l/a Lady Chik
9323326	Jurkalne	Mhl	2006	30,641	52,622	195	32	14	tco	
9314856	Kandava	Mhl	2007	23,315	37,258	183	27	14	tco	
9314868	Kazdanga	Mhl	2007	23,315	37,312	183	27	14	tco	
9314844	Kraslava	Mhl	2007	23,315	37,258	183	27	14	tco	
9314870	Krisjanis Valdemars	Mhl	2007	23,315	37,266	183	27	14	tco	
9482550	Latgale	Mhl	2011	29,694	51,408	183	32	14	tco	
9635755	Leopard Moon *	Sgp	2013	29,939	49,999	183	32	14	tco	
9635779	Leopard Sea *	Sgp	2013	29,939	49,999	183	32	14	tco	
9635767	Leopard Star *	Sgp	2013	29,939	49,999	183	32	14	tco	
9635781	Leopard Sun *	Sgp	2013	29,939	49,999	183	32	14	tco	
9323376	Piltene	Mhl	2007	30,641	52,648	195	32	14	tco	
9323338	Puze	Mhl	2006	30,641	52,622	195	32	14	tco	
9323390	Salacgriva	Mhl	2008	30,641	52,620	195	32	14	tco	
9323340	Targale	Mhl	2007	30,641	52,622	195	32	14	tco	
9323352	Ugale	Mhl	2007	30,641	52,642	195	32	14	tco	
9323364	Usma	Mhl	2007	30,641	52,684	195	32	14	tco	
9323388	Uzava	Mhl	2008	30,541	52,650	195	32	14	tco	
9482562	Zemgale	Mhl	2011	29,694	51,406	183	32	14	tco	

vessels managed by LSC Shipmanagement Sia, Latvia (formed 1999)
* managed for Mansel Ltd. London, ** managed for Elandra Tankers Sgp. Pte.

J. Lauritzen A/S   Denmark

Lauritzen Bulkers A/S

funnel: red upper part with white 'LB', white lower part with red over blue 'ivs' logo or black with red over blue 'ivs' logo on white square.
hull: red (owned vessels), black or grey with white 'Lauritzen Bulkers',or black with white 'IVS', red boot-topping. **history:** subsidiary formed in 1997 to re-enter the bulk carrier trade. Operates mainly chartered vessels, including a 'Handysize' joint venture with South African-based Island View Shipping (acquired by Grindrod Group in 1999). **web:** www.lauritzenbulkers.com

IMO	name	flag	year	gt	dwt	loa	bm	kts	type	comments
9470820	Admiral Bulker **	Pan	2008	17,023	28,320	170	27	14	bbu	
9736418	African Bulker **	Pan	2015	22,426	36,228	180	30	14	bbu	
9336763	Alpha Bulker **	Pan	2006	19,885	32,741	177	28	14	bbu	ex Crystal Ocean-11
9736420	American Bulker **	Pan	2016	22,426	36,228	180	30	14	bbu	
9310599	Amine Bulker **	Mlt	2007	17,663	28,700	177	26	14	bbu	
9544152	Anne Mette Bulker	Iom	2012	23,950	38,191	185	31	14	bbu	
9459151	Apollo Bulker **	Hkg	2011	21,483	33,124	177	29	14	goh	
9527180	Asahi Bulker **	Pan	2012	21,483	33,179	177	29	14	goh	
9674799	Atlantic Bulker **	Pan	2014	21,718	36,309	177	29	14	bbu	
9527192	Azure Bulker **	Pan	2012	21,483	33,179	177	29	14	goh	
9270919	Aurora Bulker **	Pan	2004	19,891	32,723	177	28	14	bbu	
9707833	Bunun Fortune **	Hkg	2015	23,281	37,790	180	30	14	bbu	
9744752	Captain D **	Mhl	2016	22,457	34,958	177	30	14	bbu	
9667322	Chise Bulker **	Pan	2014	21,174	33,355	177	27	14	bbu	
9713820	Daiwan Fortune **	Hkg	2015	22,314	35,531	177	30	14	bbu	
9424132	Elvira Bulker	Dis	2011	19,812	31,858	176	29	14	bbu	
9497177	Emilie Bulker	Iom	2010	20,809	32,691	180	28	14	bbu	
9242091	Emma Bulker	Dis	2010	19,812	31,887	176	29	14	bbu	
9713959	Erietta **	Lbr	2015	34,821	61,166	200	32	14	bbu	
9544164	Eva Bulker	Iom	2012	23,950	38,191	180	30	14	bbu	
9423255	Ever Alliance **	Pan	2011	32,309	57,991	190	32	14	bbu	ex Tess Bulker-14
9602174	Graig Cardiff **	Gbr	2012	23,444	34,827	180	30	14	bbu	
9602186	Graig Rotterdam **	Gbr	2012	23,444	35,898	180	30	14	bbu	
9424120	Hedvig Bulker	Dis	2011	19,812	31,872	176	29	14	bbu	
9580015	Hokkaido Bulker	Pan	2013	19,812	31,848	176	29	14	bbu	
9668910	Kaya Manx **	Iom	2014	32,360	57,964	190	32	14	bbu	
9385087	Karine Bulker **	Pan	2008	20,236	32,271	177	28	14	goh	
9695004	Kmarin Jasmine **	Pan	2014	23,247	37,430	180	30	14	bbu	

IMO	name	flag	year	gt	dwt	loa	bm	kts	type	comments
9694995	Kmarin									
	Mugunghwa **	Pan	2014	23,247	37,423	180	30	14	bbu	
9471678	Long Cheer **	Lbr	2013	24,150	37,393	190	29	14	bbu	I/a African Sirio
9424089	Louise Bulker	Dis	2009	19,812	31,881	176	29	14	bbu	
9544138	Milau Bulker **	Sgp	2012	38,191	47,233	185	31	14	bbu	
9544140	Nicoline Bulker	Iom	2012	38,191	47,233	185	31	14	bbu	
9379674	Nona Bulker **	Pan	2009	19,825	31,922	176	29	14	bbu	
9610638	Ocean Satoko **	Pan	2011	22,662	37,215	186	28	14	bbu	
9528017	Orchard Bulker *	Sgp	2010	20,928	32,535	180	28	14	bbu	
9674787	Pacific Bulker **	Pan	2015	21,718	36,309	177	29	14	bbu	
9599755	Queen Sapphire **	Pan	2011	34,795	61,388	200	32	14	bbu	
9527996	Sentosa Bulker *	Sgp	2010	20,809	32,755	180	28	14	bbu	
9497165	Signe Bulker *	Sgp	2010	20,809	32,755	180	28	14	bbu	
9668908	Teal Bulker **	Pan	2014	32,370	57,903	190	32	14	bbu	
9676101	Tern Bulker **	Pan	2014	32,370	57,896	190	32	14	bbu	
9605023	Tokyo Bulker **	Pan	2012	34,795	61,439	200	32	14	bbu	
9731808	Uni Bulker **	Hkg	2016	23,269	37,800	180	30	14	bbu	
9579391	Unison Star **	Hkg	2011	24,735	38,190	189	30	14	bbu	

newbuildings:

	Asian Bulker				34,700					Shin Kurushima
	Australian Bulker				34,700					Shin Kurushima

also on order : Imabari 1 x 63,000dwt (2016), 2 x 63,000dwt (2018), 3 x 37,600dwt (2017)
Dalian Cosco Kawasaki 2 x 81,000dwt (2016), Hakodate 2 x 34,000dwt (2017), Namura 2 x 34,358dwt (2017)
* vessels owned by J. Lauritzen Singapore Pte.Ltd. ** chartered in from various Japanese, Hong Kong, Singapore, Greek etc. owners

C. M. Lemos & Co. Ltd. U.K.

funnel: *yellow with blue 'L' on white houseflag, black top.* **hull:** *black or grey with red boot-topping.* **history:** *parent founded 1950 and subsidiary formed 1967.* **web:** *none found for either Lemos or Nereus Shipping*

IMO	name	flag	year	gt	dwt	loa	bm	kts	type
9541813	Asiatic	Grc	2012	34,456	58,451	196	32	14	bbu
9290933	Authentic	Grc	2004	78,922	150,249	274	48	15	tcr
9194983	Cosmic	Grc	2000	78,918	150,284	274	48	15	tcr
9541837	Doric	Grc	2013	34,456	58,514	196	32	14	bbu
9510187	Epic	Grc	2010	93,360	182,060	292	45	14	bbu
9326067	Gloric	Grc	2006	156,933	298,495	330	60	15	tcr
9510199	Heroic	Grc	2010	93,360	182,060	292	45	14	bbu
9541849	Ionic	Grc	2013	34,456	58,468	196	32	14	bbu
9541825	Laconic	Grc	2012	34,375	58,474	196	32	14	bbu
9194995	Majestic	Grc	2000	78,918	150,284	274	48	15	tcr
9239848	Poetic	Grc	2003	78,922	150,103	274	48	15	tcr
9303247	Romantic	Grc	2004	78,922	150,247	274	48	15	tcr
9326055	Symphonic	Grc	2006	156,933	298,522	330	60	15	tcr

vessels operated by subsidiary Nereus Shipping SA, Greece.
newbuildings : 2 + 2 options 116,000dwt tcr [Hyundai (2016)]

Leonhardt & Blumberg Schiffahrts GmbH & Co. KG   Germany

funnel: *black with red 'x' and black '+' combined on broad white band, * black with blue single wave on white rectangle with white 'Maltese Cross' on dark blue square in top corner or charterers colours.* **hull:** *dark grey, blue or black with red boot-topping or white with blue boot-topping.* **history:** *original company founded 1903 by Adolf Leonhardt and Arthur Blumberg to succeed Leonhardt & Heeckt (formed 1899). Present company formed in 1987 as joint venture with Hansa Treuhand (25%).*
web: *www.leonhardt-blumberg.com*

IMO	name	flag	year	gt	dwt	loa	bm	kts	type	comments
9155391	ANL Echuca	Lbr	2003	18,335	23,606	175	27	18	ucc	1,740 teu: ex Hansa Augustenburg-15, Maersk Vilnius-07, Hansa Augustenburg-03
9334820	ANL Elanora	Lbr	2007	18,327	23,452	176	27	18	ucc	1,740 teu: ex Hansa Coburg-15, NileDutch Asia-10, Hansa Coburg-07
9516739	Hansa Altenburg	Lbr	2011	18,358	23,370	175	27	18	ucc	1,740 teu
9459424	Hansa America	Lbr	2014	38,388	47,069	240	32	23	ucc	3,646 teu
9221059	Hansa Arendal †	Lbr	2001	15,988	20,700	170	25	16	ucc	1,262 teu: ex TMM Chiapas-05, Hansa Arendal-02
9459400	Hansa Asia	Deu	2013	38,388	47,116	240	32	23	ucc	3,646 teu: c/a Asia
9373474	Hansa Augsburg	Lbr	2008	18,327	23,388	176	27	18	ucc	1,740 teu: ex NileDutch Tianjin-09, Hansa Augsburg-08
9459436	Hansa Australia	Pmd	2014	38,388	48,200	240	32	23	ucc	3,646 teu: I/a Australia
9153612	Hansa Calypso †	Lbr	1998	16,915	21,480	168	27	19	ucc	1,601 teu: ex Maersk Pireaus-07, Hansa Calypso-00, CMA Hakata-00, Hansa Calypso-99
9152595	Hansa Castella †	Lbr	1998	16,915	21,480	168	27	19	ucc	1,601 teu: ex Damaskus-06, CMA Mersin-00, Hansa Castella-99

IMO	name	flag	year	gt	dwt	loa	bm	kts	type	comments
9152600	Hansa Centurion †	Lbr	1998	16,915	21,473	168	27	19	ucc	1,601 teu: ex Maersk Athens-07, Hansa Centurion-00, CMA Kobe-00, Hansa Centurion-99
9357860	Hansa Cloppenburg	Lbr	2007	18,327	23,396	176	27	18	ucc	1,740 teu: ex NileDutch Singapore-10, l/a Hansa Cloppenburg
9535096	Hansa Duburg	Pmd	2012	18,296	18,001	175	27	18	ucc	1,740 teu
9459412	Hansa Europe	Deu	2012	38,388	47,267	240	32	23	ucc	3,646 teu: ex Europe-12
9155365	Hansa Flensburg	Lbr	2000	18,335	23,579	175	27	18	ucc	1,740 teu: ex Melbourne Express-06, CP Condor-06, Direct Condor-05, Hansa Flensburg-00
9535101	Hansa Fresenburg	Lbr	2013	18,296	18,001	175	27	19	ucc	1,740 teu
9256389	Hansa Freyburg	Lux	2003	18,334	23,508	175	27	19	ucc	1,740 teu: ex Maersk Volos-08, l/a H.Freyburg, l/dn Hansa Freyburg
9256418	Hansa Fyn *	Lux	2003	16,145	20,367	170	25	19	ucc	1,581 teu: ex H Fyn-14, Maersk Vaasa-07, l/a H. Fyn
9436082	Hansa Homburg *	Lux	2009	18,252	23,579	175	27	20	ucc	1,740teu: ex STX Qingdao-14
9241449	Hansa Kirkenes	Lux	2002	15,988	20,463	175	27	18	ucc	1,550 teu: ex Zim Itajai-11, H Kirkenes-08, l/a Hansa Kirkenes
9256406	Hansa Langeland *	Lux	2003	16,145	20,170	170	25	19	ucc	1,581 teu: ex MOL Accord-10, H. Langeland-06, CSAV Ilha Bela-05, Cap Pilar-04, H. Langeland-03
9323481	Hansa Limburg	Lbr	2008	18,327	23,447	175	27	18	ucc	1,740 teu
9516741	Hansa Ludwigsburg	Lbr	2011	18,358	23,305	175	27	18	ucc	1,740 teu
9256377	Hansa Magdeburg	Lbr	2003	18,334	23,454	175	27	18	ucc	1,740 teu: ex Maersk Voshod-09, Cap Aguilar-05, Hansa Augustenburg-03
9334818	Hansa Marburg	Lux	2007	18,327	23,419	175	27	18	ucc	1,740 teu
9373462	Hansa Meersburg	Lbr	2007	18,327	23,419	176	27	18	ucc	1,740 teu: ex NileDutch Hong Kong-10, Hansa Meersburg-07
9151864	Hansa Narvik †	Lbr	1998	15,988	20,630	170	25	20	ucc	1,270 teu: ex Kota Serikat-03, Hansa Narvik-02, Direct Eagle-00, Hansa Narvik-99
9430870	Hansa Neuberg	Lbr	2010	18,327	23,295	175	27	19	ucc	1,740 teu: ex Corvette-15
9236212	Hansa Nordburg †	Lbr	2002	18,334	23,493	175	27	18	ucc	1,740 teu: ex Cap Azul-09, P&O Nedlloyd Nelson-04, l/a Hansa Nordburg
9516765	Hansa Offenburg	Lux	2011	18,358	23,314	175	27	18	ucc	1,740 teu
9236224	Hansa Oldenburg †	Lux	2002	18,334	23,493	175	27	18	ucc	1,740 teu: ex ex Delmas Kerguelen-09, l/a Hansa Oldenburg
9357858	Hansa Papenburg	Lbr	2007	18,327	23,579	176	27	18	ucc	1,740 teu: ex Niledutch Shenzhen-10, Maruba Aldebaran-09, l/a Hansa Papenburg
9435246	Hansa Ravensburg	Lbr	2008	18,327	23,415	176	27	18	ucc	1,740 teu
9435258	Hansa Reggensburg	Lbr	2008	18,327	23,357	175	27	18	ucc	1,740 teu
9155377	Hansa Rendsburg	Lbr	2000	18,335	23,992	175	27	18	ucc	1,740 teu: ex CP Jabiru-06, Direct Jabiru-05, Hansa Rendsburg-01
9256391	Hansa Ronneburg *	Lbr	2004	18,334	23,508	175	27	19	ucc	1,740 teu: ex Maruba Parana-10, Maersk Ventspils-07, l/a H. Ronneburg
9401673	Hansa Rotenburg	Lbr	2009	18,326	23,332	175	27	19	ucc	1,740 teu: ex Mell Selarang-14, Thorstar-12, Cape North-12
9516753	Hansa Salzburg	Lbr	2011	18,358	23,301	175	27	18	ucc	1,740 teu
9401661	Hansa Siegburg	Lbr	2008	18,326	23,324	175	27	20	ucc	1,740 teu: ex Thorsriver-14, Cape Nelson-12
9436094	Hansa Steinburg	Lbr	2010	18,321	23,579	175	27	20	ucc	1,740 teu: ex STX Dalian-14

*managed for * Hansa HamburgShipping   † Hansa Treuhand GmbH & Co. KG*

Livanos Group   Greece

funnel: *black with red 'Λ' between 'Greek key' borders on broad white band.* **hull:** *black or grey with red boot-topping.* **history:** *formed 1920.* **web:** *www.sunenterprises.gr*

Alios Bulkers, Greece

IMO	name	flag	year	gt	dwt	loa	bm	kts	type	comments
9228069	Atlantic Hawk	Bhs	2002	38,727	74,204	225	32	14	bbu	ex Jin Kang-04
9291119	Atlantic Hero	Bhs	2005	38,871	75,804	225	32	14	bbu	ex Lotus Blossom-08
9303106	Atlantic Horizon	Bhs	2006	38,877	75,709	225	32	14	bbu	
9286956	Bellamys	Lbr	2005	39,964	76,286	225	32	14	bbu	ex Kanishka-15, Mineral Star-12
9247285	Ioannis Zafirakis	Bhs	2004	39,037	73,305	225	32	14	bbu	
9346160	Tubarao	Bhs	2007	32,474	53,350	190	32	14	bbu	ex City-09

Sun Enterprises, Greece

IMO	name	flag	year	gt	dwt	loa	bm	kts	type	comments
9458494	Achilleas	Grc	2010	81,278	158,370	274	48	15	tcr	
9305051	Aliakmon	Grc	2006	30,020	46,792	183	32	14	tco	
9275969	Amazon Beauty	Grc	2003	43,075	72,909	228	40	15	tco	

IMO	name	flag	year	gt	dwt	loa	bm	kts	type	comments
9294678	Amazon Brilliance	Grc	2005	43,075	72,910	228	40	15	tco	
9231511	Amazon Explorer	Grc	2002	43,075	72,910	228	40	15	tco	
9222132	Amazon Gladiator	Grc	2001	43,075	72,910	228	40	15	tco	
9197739	Amazon Guardian	Grc	1999	43,075	72,910	228	40	15	tco	
9660358	Amazon Victory	Grc	2014	44,776	72,412	228	40	14	tco	
9660360	Amazon Virtue	Grc	2014	44,776	72,412	228	40	14	tco	
9294666	Axios	Grc	2006	30,020	46,792	183	32	14	tco	
9290921	Evros	Grc	2005	30,020	47,120	183	32	14	tco	
9197909	Meandros	Grc	2000	157,883	309,498	335	58	15	tcr	
9290919	Strymon	Grc	2005	30,020	47,120	183	32	14	tco	
newbuildings:										
9772113	Chios	Grc	2016	81,000	159,000	274	48	14	tcr	Hyundai HI H-2834
9772125	Christina	Grc	2016	81,000	159,000	274	48	14	tcr	Hyundai HI H-2835
9779587			2016	44,776	72,400	229	40	14	tco	Hyundai HI H-2852

vessels operated by subsidiary Sun Enterprises Ltd, Greece, established 1968

Lomar Shipping Ltd.   U.K.

funnel: *dark blue with two narrow white bands, upper interrupted by pointed peak or charterers colours.* **hull:** *black, dark blue or light grey with red boot-topping.* **history:** *founded 1976 by Logothetis family to own and operate reefers. Subsidiary of Greek Libra Group since 2003. In 2009 acquired Allocean Ltd, formed 1993 as Allco UK, subsidiary of Allco Finance Group (established 1979 in Australia), the ship-owning vehicle for Andreas Ugland & Sons, being renamed Allocean when UB Shipping acquired in 2002.* **web:** *www.lomarshipping.com*

IMO	name	flag	year	gt	dwt	loa	bm	kts	type	comments
9111474	Acapulco ‡	Gbr	1996	10,730	14,148	163	22	17	ucc	1,162 teu: ex MSC Acapulco-10, MOL Faithful-08, Sophie Schulte-05, Marfret Guyane-03, Sophie Schulte-03, CMA CGM Oyapock-02, X-press Annapurna-01, Sophie Schulte-00
9701372	Alexia	Sgp	2015	36,353	63,731	200	32	14	bbu	
9700122	Arabella	Sgp	2015	36,353	63,616	200	32	14	bbu	
9304746	Antwerp Trader	Mlt	2005	27,059	34,444	212	30	22	ucc	2,492 teu: ex Rio Eider-14,Maersk Narvik-10, l/a Rio Eider
9658446	Barry Trader	Sgp	2014	24,720	25,294	185	30	19	ucc	2,190 teu
9419668	Busan Trader	Pan	2009	27,051	34,567	210	30	23	ucc	2,664 teu: ex NYK Veronica-14
9226413	Calais Trader	Deu	2001	25,705	33,795	208	30	22	ucc	2,524 teu: ex Ulf Ritscher-15, NYK Espirito-09, Sea Tiger-04, l/a Ulf Ritscher Purchased 02:15
9571301	Cape Madrid	Mlt	2011	35,708	41,636	212	32	22	ucc	2,758 teu
9261815	Cardiff Trader	Mlt	2003	25,703	33,673	208	30	21	ucc	2,524 teu: ex Rio Valiente-13, Cap Valiente-09, Cabo Creus-07, l/a Rio Valiente
9436422	Cartagena Trader	Lbr	2008	35,991	42,057	231	32	23	ucc	3,554 teu: ex Georg Schulte-14, Cap Mondego-13, Georg Schulte-08
9235701	Crawford	Mhl	2003	25,382	40,081	176	32	15	tco	ex Ocean Spirit-15, STI Matador-12, l/a Felix G
9230775	Gdynia Trader	Atg	2001	16,803	22,900	185	25	20	ucc	1,728 teu: ex Marie Schulte-15
9357107	Georgia Trader	Lbr	2007	22,801	30,608	204	28	22	ucc	2,130 teu: ex Conti Ariadne-15, NileDutch Kudu-14, Conti Ariadne-12, CMA CGM Esperanza-12, c/a Conti Ariadne
9701293	Kalamata Trader	Sgp	2016	25,145	25,000	185	30	19	ucc	2,192 teu
9701360	Kambos	Sgp	2015	36,353	63,696	200	32	14	bbu	
9261827	Kiel Trader	Mlt	2003	25,703	33,741	208	29	21	ucc	2,524 teu: ex Rio Verde-13, Cap Verde-09, Alianca Sao Paulo-07, Rio Verde-03
9700196	Komi	Mlt	2015	36,353	63,628	200	32	14	bbu	
9658458	Kimolos Trader	Sgp	2014	25,145	25,331	185	30	19	ucc	2,190 teu
9327798	Los Angeles Trader	Mlt	2007	66,199	67,797	276	40	26	ucc	6,039 teu: ex Wan Hai 602-15
9327803	Long Beach Trader	Mlt	2007	66,199	67,797	276	40	26	ucc	6,039 teu: ex Wan Hai 603-15
9357121	Louisiana Trader	Lbr	2007	22,801	30,580	204	28	21	ucc	2,127 teu: ex Conti Daphne-15, Maruba Asia-11, l/a Conti Daphne
9292151	Maine Trader	Mlt	2004	54,271	66,672	294	32	23	ucc	4,367 teu: ex HS Humboldt-14, Maersk Dortmund-09, HS Humboldt-04
9251846	Miami Trader	Mlt	2002	25,587	33,940	201	30	21	ucc	2,462 teu: ex Luna-13, ANL Binburra-08, Cap Spencer-07, Alianca Bahia-02, l/a Kassandra
9239733	Milan Trader	Sgp	2002	25,580	34,019	201	30	20	ucc	2,462 teu: ex R.R. America-14, NileDutch Ningbo-12, R.R. America-10, c./a Cielo d'America
9571296	New Hampshire Trader	Mlt	2011	35,708	41,411	212	32	22	ucc	2,758 teu: ex Cape Maas-15

IMO	name	flag	year	gt	dwt	loa	bm	kts	type	comments
9241827	Ocean Gladiator	Mhl	2003	25,382	40,083	176	31	15	tco	ex Ocean Force-15, STI Gladiator-12, l/a Carlos G
9249257	Ocean Prefect	Gbr	2003	29,323	53,035	189	32	14	bbu	ex Scandinavian Express-06, Anni Selmer-04
9254458	Ocean Prelate	Gbr	2002	30,011	52,433	190	32	15	bbu	ex John Oldendorff-05
9108233	Ocean Probe	Hkg	1995	15,095	18,585	169	27	17	ucc	1,471 teu; ex TS Colombo-09, Andalusian Express-08, Young Chance-02, Choyang Challenger-01
9108221	Ocean Prologue	Hkg	1995	15,095	18,294	169	27	17	ucc	1,471 teu: ex Algerian Express-09, Syms Express I-08, Algerian Express-07, Young Liberty-05, Choyang Leader-01, Kuo Fah-95
9215892	Ocean Promise	Gbr	2001	26,718	33,871	210	30	22	ucc	2,556 teu: ex Henrika Schulte-07, P&O Nedlloyd Atacama-05, l/a Henrika Schulte
9344564	Oregon Trader	Lbr	2006	27,322	34,200	212	30	22	ucc	2,492 teu: ex CMA CGM Auckland-15, Rio Ardeche-06
9137521	Osaka Trader	Sgp	1996	18,602	24,376	193	28	20	ucc	1,613 teu: ex Iga-14
9656096	Porto Leone	Sgp	2014	36,353	63,756	200	32	14	bbu	
9656084	Puerto Rosario	Sgp	2014	36,353	64,698	200	32	14	bbu	
9700134	Queen Cuki	Sgp	2015	36,353	63,707	200	32	14	bbu	
9419644	Seoul Trader	Mlt	2009	27,051	34,528	210	30	23	ucc	2,664 teu; ex NYK Rosa-14
9290414	Shanghai Trader	Deu	2005	54,809	67,255	294	32	25	ucc	4,839 teu: ex SCI Nhava Sheva-15, Santa Patricia-12, Cap Scott-12, Maersk Dolores-10, P&O Nedlloyd Delft-05, l/dn Santa Patricia
9070163	Sima Singapore *	Mlt	1995	29,195	35,551	196	32	20	ucc	2,227 teu: ex Ocean Promoter-11, MSC Greece-09, Trade Maple-02, MSC Hamburg-02, Trade Maple-01
9297474	Sydney Trader *	Lbr	2005	54,771	67,222	294	32	25	ucc	5,043 teu: ex Santa Priscilla-15, UACC Dammam-12, Maersk Donegal-10, P&O Nedlloyd Dublin-05, l/dn Santa Paula
9295165	Texas Trader	Lbr	2005	54,271	66,762	294	32	23	ucc	4,992 teu: ex Charles Dickens-15, Maersk Danbury-13, c/a Charles Dickens
9292149	Vermont Trader	Mlt	2004	54,271	68,187	294	32	23	ucc	4,367 teu: ex HS Livingstone-14, Maersk Darmstadt-09, HS Livingstone-04, l/dn Maersk Dunkirk
9344552	Virginia Trader	Lbr	2006	27,322	34,200	212	30	22	ucc	2,492 teu: ex Rio Adour-14, CMA CGM Iguacu-14, Rio Adour-06

newbuildings:

IMO	name	flag	year	gt	dwt	loa	bm	kts	type	comments
9701279	Queen Esther	Sgp	2016	24,720	25,000	185	30	19	ucc	2,192 teu Guangzhou Wenchong #428
9701281	Kea Trader	Sgp	2016	24,720	25,000	185	30	19	ucc	2,192 teu Guangzhou Wenchong #429
	Kalamoti Trader	Sgp	2017	24,720	25,000	185	30	19	ucc	2,192 teu

Vermont Trader : Lomar Shipping : *Chris Brooks*

IMO	name	flag	year	gt	dwt	loa	bm	kts	type	comments
	Queen Raquel	Sgp	2017	36,353	64,000	200	32	14	bbu	Cosco Zhoushan
9723203		Sgp	2017	36,353	64,000	200	32	14	bbu	Cosco Zhoushan N599
9723215		Sgp	2017	36,353	64,000	200	32	14	bbu	Cosco Zhoushen N600
9771652	Carolina Trader		2017	25,000	37,000	186	35	18	ucc	2,700 teu Jiangsu YZJ2014-1164
9771664	California Trader		2017	25,000	37,000	186	35	18	ucc	2,700 teu Jiangsu YZJ2014-1165
	Delaware Trader		2017	25,000	37,000	186	35	18	ucc	2,700 teu Guangzhou Wenchong
	Washington Trader		2018	25,000	37,000	186	35	18	ucc	2,700 teu Guangzhou Wenchong
	Connecticut Trader		2018	25,000	37,000	186	35	18	ucc	2,700 teu Guangzhou Wenchong
	NevadaTrader		2018	25,000	37,000	186	35	18	ucc	2,700 teu Guangzhou Wenchong
acquisitions										
9149902			1999	16,177	23,021	184	26	19	ucc	1,730 teu: ex Wehr Blankenese-16, CSAV Montreal-07, Norasia Montreal-01, Illapel-00, I/a Wehr Blankenese

also operates smaller container ships, tankers and LPG tankers
* managed by subsidiary Lomar Deutschland GmbH, ‡ managed by Bernhard Schulte Shipmanagement companies.

Louis Dreyfus Armateurs SAS   France
funnel: black with blue 'LD & C' on white band between two narrow red bands. **hull:** *black with red boot topping.* **history:** *founded 1851 as Louis-Dreyfus et Cie to 1972 taking the current company name in 1995.* **web:** *www.lda.fr*

LD Bulk, France
IMO	name	flag	year	gt	dwt	loa	bm	kts	type	comments
9311593	Jean LD	Mlt	2005	89,076	171,908	289	45	14	bbu	
9618006	La Briantais *	Mlt	2013	24,725	40,481	180	30	14	bbu	
9733260	La Chambordais	Mlt	2015	24,725	40,481	180	30	14	bbu	
9691034	La Chesnais	Mlt	2015	24,604	40,600	180	30	14	bbu	ex Moon Star-15
9618018	La Guimorais *	Mlt	2014	24,725	40,481	180	30	14	bbu	
9646895	La Landriais *	Mlt	2014	24,725	40,481	180	30	14	bbu	
9691046	La Partenais	Mlt	2015	24,604	40,652	180	30	14	bbu	ex Crescent Star-15
9646900	La Richardais *	Mlt	2014	24,725	40,481	180	30	14	bbu	
9733272	La Sauternais	Mlt	2015	24,725	40,481	180	30	14	bbu	
9733284	La Sillonais	Mlt	2015	24,275	40,481	180	30	14	bbu	
9733258	La Solognais	Mlt	2015	24,275	40,481	180	30	14	bbu	
9311608	Pierre LD	Mlt	2006	89,070	171,877	289	45	14	bbu	
9617519	Leopold LD	Mlt	2014	93,801	179,816	292	45	14	bbu	
9617521	Simon LD	Mlt	2014	91,801	179,816	292	45	14	bbu	

* owned by LDA Roullier, a j/v between Dreyfus and Roullier Gp. Company also operates a number of ro-ro ferries and cable layers

Joint Stock Co. LUKoil   Russia

Murmansk Shipping Co., Russia
funnel: blue with white polar bear, (or white with polar bear on broad blue band) and black top. **hull**: *grey, black or red with red boot-topping.* **history**: *established in 1939 and controlled since 1998 by LUKoil (founded 1997 and controlled by Russian government).* **web**: *www.msco.ru*

IMO	name	flag	year	gt	dwt	loa	bm	kts	type	comments
7721237	Aleksandr Suvorov	Rus	1979	16,257	23,169	181	23	14	bbu	(len-06)

Estrella : Lundqvist Rederierna AB : *Chris Brooks*

IMO	name	flag	year	gt	dwt	loa	bm	kts	type	comments
9385879	Grumant	Rus	1978	15,868	22,945	181	23	14	bbu	ex Co-operation-06, Emelyan Pugachev-06 (len/rbt-06) [ex IMO 7721287]
8837928	Ivan Papanin	Rus	1990	14,184	10,105	166	23	17	urc	
8406729	Kapitan Danilkin	Rus	1987	18,574	19,763	174	25	17	urc	
8218706	Kapitan Sviridov	Rus	1982	16,253	23,357	181	23	14	bbu	(len-06)
8610887	Khatanga	Rus	1987	14,937	23,050	158	26	15	tco	ex Bauska-04, Nord Skagerrak-87
7721263	Kuzma Minin	Rus	1980	16,257	23,169	181	23	14	bbu	(len-06)
7721249	Mikhail Kutuzov	Rus	1979	16,257	23,169	181	23	14	bbu	(len-06)
8915794	Nataly	Rus	1993	77,537	143,386	274	43	14	tcr	ex Velez-Blanco-05
9549281	Novaya Zemlya	Rus	1977	15,868	23,645	181	23	14	bbu	ex North Way-08, Fourth-08, Aleksandr Nevskiy-08 (len/rbt-09) [ex IMO 7721213]
8131893	Pavel Vavilov	Rus	1981	16,253	23,357	181	23	15	bbu	(len-06)
9428499	Pomorye	Rus	1977	15,868	23,645	181	23	14	bbu	ex Goodwill-07, Yuriy Dolgorukiy-06 (len/rbt-07) [ex IMO 7721299]
7721225	Pyotr Velikiy	Rus	1978	16,257	23,169	181	23	14	bbu	(len-06)
9551923	Severnaya Zemlya	Rus	1977	15,868	23,645	181	23	15	bbu	ex Victory-09, Fifth-08, Dimitriy Donskoy-07 (len/rbt-09) [ex IMO 7721196]
7500401	Varzuga	Rus	1977	11,290	15,954	164	22	14	tco	ex Uikku-03
8131934	Viktor Tkachyov	Rus	1981	14,141	19,240	162	23	15	bbu	
8406705	Yuriy Arshenevskiy	Rus	1986	18,574	19,724	177	25	17	urc	
9524205	Zapolyarye	Rus	1977	15,868	23,645	181	23	14	bbu	ex Perseverence-08, Third-08, Ivan Bogun-08 (len/rbt-08) [ex IMO 7721304]

Lundqvist Rederierna AB   Finland

funnel: *white with yellow diamond interrupting thin blue band on blue edged broader yellow band.* **hull:** *brown or black with red boot-topping.* **history:** *Lundqvist Rederierna is the common name for Ångfartygs Aktiebolaget Alfa (established in 1927) and Rederiaktiebolaget Hildegaard (established in 1935).* **web:** *www.lundqvist.aland.fi*

IMO	name	flag	year	gt	dwt	loa	bm	kts	type	comments
9696773	Alfa Baltica	Bhs	2015	57,200	106,373	228	48	14	tcr	
9154232	Alfa Britannia	Bhs	1998	56,115	99,222	248	43	14	tcr	
9158551	Alfa Germania	Bhs	1998	56,115	99,193	248	43	14	tcr	
9255880	Alfa Italia	Bhs	2002	59,719	105,588	249	43	15	tcr	
9696761	Estrella	Bhs	2014	57,312	106,282	229	44	14	tcr	
9194139	Hildegaard	Bhs	1999	56,115	99,122	248	43	14	tcr	
9325908	Penelop	Bhs	2006	62,448	115,091	254	44	15	tcr	
9238052	Sarpen	Bhs	2002	59,719	105,655	248	43	15	tcr	
9226970	Thornbury	Bhs	2001	56,115	99,220	248	43	15	tcr	

MACS – Maritime Carrier AG   Switzerland

funnel: *blue with white 'macs'.* **hull:** *black with white rhinoceros symbol and 'macs', some with white band above red boot-topping.* **history:** *formed 1987.* **web:** *www.macship.com*

IMO	name	flag	year	gt	dwt	loa	bm	kts	type	comments
9138123	Amber Lagoon	Mhl	1997	23,401	31,916	187	27	17	gpc	1,486 teu
9465411	Blue Master II	Mhl	2013	30,469	37,444	200	30	14	gpc	2,000 teu
9231119	Bright Horizon	Mhl	2002	23,132	30,396	193	28	19	gpc	cr : 2(100) ex Cape Denison-13, Bright Horizon-11, Pacific Destiny-10, Tasman Explorer-08, Cape Denison-06, CCNI Hong Kong-06, Cape Denison- 04
9465435	Bright Sky	Mhl	2013	30,469	37,450	200	30	14	gpc	2,000 teu
9465423	Golden Karoo	Mhl	2013	30,469	37,472	200	30	14	gpc	2,000 teu
9502312	Green Mountain	Mhl	2013	30,469	37,511	200	30	14	gpc	2,000 teu
9151905	Grey Fox	Mhl	1998	23,401	33,684	192	27	16	gpc	1,486 teu
9138135	Purple Beach #	Mhl	1998	23,401	31,916	187	27	17	gpc	1,486 teu
9231092	Red Cedar	Mhl	2001	23,132	30,537	193	28	19	gpc	cr: 2(100): 1,680 teu: ex Cape Darby-13, Red Cedar-12, Rickmers Houston-09, Golden Isle-08, Cape Darby-07, Golden Isle-06, Cape Darby-04

newbuildings : 2 further 37,000dwt gpc [Qingshan Wuhu]
 # had serious fire May 2015, may be broken up.

Maestro Group   Cyprus

funnel: *white with green stylised 'M'.* **hull:** *reefers: white with green 'MAESTRO REEFERS', green boot-topping. bulkers: red with white 'MAESTRO' green band above red boo ttopping.* **history:** *formed 2005.* **web:** *www.maestroshipping.com*

IMO	name	flag	year	gt	dwt	loa	bm	kts	type	comments
8706789	Ice Glacier	Mhl	1988	12,348	14,933	144	24	18	grf	ex Amazonas-12, Argentinean Reefer-03

Bright Sky : MACS - Maritime Carrier AG : *Hans Kraijenbosch*

Ice Glacier : Maestro Gp. : *Mike Lennon*

Maestro Lion : Maestro Gp. : *Hans Kraijenbosch*

Marfret Marajo : Cie. Maritime Marfret : *Hans Kraijenbosch*

Columbia : Marlow Ship Mgmt. : *Hans Kraijenbosch*

Warnow Mars : Marlow Ship Mgmt. : *ARO*

IMO	name	flag	year	gt	dwt	loa	bm	kts	type	comments
8706777	Ice Grace	Mhl	1988	12,348	14,932	144	24	18	grf	ex Parana-12, Anglian Reefer-03
8311132	Ice Ranger	Mhl	1985	12,411	14,572	144	23	18	grf	ex African Reefer-00
8311118	Ice River	Mhl	1985	12,401	14,519	144	23	18	grf	ex American Reefer-96
8311106	Ice Rose	Mhl	1985	12,401	14,567	144	24	18	grf	ex Reefer Jambu-96
8311120	Ice Runner	Mhl	1984	12,411	14,499	144	24	18	grf	ex Rauma Reefer-06
9711705	Maestro Diamond	Mhl	2015	22,872	36,920	179	29	14	bbu	
9189665	Maestro Lion	Mhl	1999	19,743	31,757	172	27	14	bbu	ex UBC Salvador-10
9711717	Maestro Pearl	Mhl	2015	22,872	37,115	179	29	14	bbu	
9189677	Maestro Tiger	Mhl	1999	19,743	31,828	172	27	14	bbu	ex UBC Svea-10

also operates 4 ro-ro vessels and 2 small reefers, managed by Maesto Ship Management

Marconsult Schiffahrt (GmbH & Co.) KG   Germany

funnel: white with red MC in white diamond on broad dark blue top **hull:** black or grey with red boot-topping. **history:** formed 2003 following end of merger between Marconsult Gesellschaft fur Reedereiberatung (formed 1991) and Johs Thode GmbH (founded 1890). **web:** www.mc-schiffahrt.de

IMO	name	flag	year	gt	dwt	loa	bm	kts	type	comments
9415155	Marbacan	Pmd	2010	20,491	29,618	190	24	14	bbu	ex Fritz-15
9415167	Marbioko	Pmd	2010	20,491	29,720	190	24	14	bbu	ex Lübbert-14
9489986	MarCarolina	Atg	2010	23,548	33,741	185	30	14	bbu	
9202053	MarChicora *	Atg	2000	13,066	20,140	153	24	17	ggc	ex NileDutch Kuito-09, MSC Toulouse-07, Trina Oldendorff-04, Cielo del Caribe-03, Trina Oldendorff-01
9489974	MarColorado	Atg	2010	23,548	33,712	185	30	14	bbu	ex Colorado-12, l/a MarColorado

* managed for subsidiary of HCI Capital AG   also operates a fleet of smaller vessels under 10,000gt

Compagnie Maritime Marfret   France

funnel: blue with red 'MF', black top. **hull:** black or light grey with red or pink boot-topping. **history:** formed 1957 as Armement Marseille-Fret SA until 1989. **web:** www.marfret.fr

IMO	name	flag	year	gt	dwt	loa	bm	kts	type	comments
9256365	Durande	Rif	2003	18,334	23,579	175	27	18	ucc	1,740 teu: ex BG Freight Iberia-13, Marfret Durande-12, Delmas Forbin-06, Durande-03, l/a Hansa Sonderburg
9362334	Marfret Guyane *	Fra	2007	17,594	18,860	170	27	19	ucc	1,691 teu
9431360	Marfret Marajo *	Rif	2008	17,594	21,260	170	27	19	ucc	1,691 teu

* owned by subsidiary Marseilles Fret S.A.

Marlow Ship Management Deutschland GmbH   Germany

funnel: white with house-flag, **hull:** black with red boot topping, **history:** company formed 2004, associated with Marlow Navigation, Cyprus founded 1982 **web:** marlow-shipmanagement.de

IMO	name	flag	year	gt	dwt	loa	bm	kts	type	comments
9395123	Arsos	Cyp	2007	15,375	18.480	166	25	19	ucc	1,284 teu
9314947	Camellia *	Hkg	2006	28,927	39,200	222	30	23	ucc	2,824 teu: ex CMA CGM Camellia-08
9314935	CMA CGM Pointe du Diamante *	Hkg	2006	28,927	39,262	222	30	23	ucc	2,824 teu: ex Violet-16, CMA CGM Violet-12
9252242	Columbia *	Hkg	2002	41,834	53,511	266	32	24	ucc	4,200 teu: ex APL Columbia-13, Maerk Dammam-07, HLL Pacific-03
9314959	Dahlia *	Hkg	2006	29,927	39,159	222	30	23	ucc	2,824 teu: ex CMA CGM Dahlia-08
9395082	Fouma	Cyp	2007	15,375	18,480	166	25	19	ucc	1,284 teu: ex Maersk Recife-10
9484522	Lana	Lbr	2010	42,112	54,345	247	32	24	ucc	4,400 teu: ex Lania-11
9314923	Lilac *	Hkg	2005	28,927	39,295	222	30	23	ucc	2,824 teu: ex ANL Kardinia-15, Lilac-14, CMA CGM Lilac-13, l/a E.R. Miami
9594494	Paris Trader	Atg	2011	22,863	33,217	179	28	15	ggc	
9484534	Rosa	Lbr	2010	42,112	54,339	247	32	24	ucc	4,400 teu: ex Agros-11
9395044	Varamo *	Cyp	2007	15,375	18,480	166	25	19	ucc	1,284 teu
9437127	Warnow Beluga	Atg	2008	15,334	18,444	166	25	19	ucc	1,284 teu: ex Vento di Maestrale-13, Warnow Beluga-11
9509803	Warnow Boatswain	Cyp	2012	17,068	21,281	180	25	18	ucc	1,496 teu
9449857	Warnow Chief	Cyp	2009	17,068	21,191	180	25	18	ucc	1,496 teu
9395070	Warnow Dolphin	Cyp	2007	15,375	18,276	166	25	19	ucc	1,284 teu: ex TS Kaohsiung-08
9594482	Warnow Jupiter	Lbr	2011	22,863	33,403	179	28	15	ggc	
9509712	Warnow Mars	Lbr	2011	22,863	33,200	179	28	15	ggc	
9449833	Warnow Master	Lbr	2009	17,068	21,146	180	25	18	ucc	1,496 teu
9509786	Warnow Mate	Lbr	2010	17,068	21,200	180	25	18	ucc	1,496 teu
9509695	Warnow Merkur	Lbr	2010	22,863	33,192	179	28	15	ggc	
9437141	Warnow Porpoise	Atg	2008	15,334	18,464	166	25	19	ucc	1,284 teu
9509619	Warnow Star	Lbr	2010	22,863	33,271	179	28	15	ggc	
9509633	Warnow Sun	Lbr	2010	22,863	33,227	179	28	15	ggc	
9594509	Warnow Venus	Lbr	2012	22,863	33,217	179	28	15	ggc	
9395032	Warnow Whale	Cyp	2007	15,375	18,318	166	25	19	ucc	1,284 teu: ex CMA CGM Corfu-09, Warnow Whale-07

* managed by Marlow Navigation Co.Ltd., Cyprus : also operates a number of small container feeder ships

IMO	name	flag	year	gt	dwt	loa	bm	kts	type	comments

Martime-Gesellschaft für Maritime Diens GmbH — Germany

funnel: *large blue 'M' or charterers colours.* **hull:** *grey with red boot-topping.* **history:** *formed 1996, associated with Schöller Holdings.* **web:** *www.martime.de*

IMO	name	flag	year	gt	dwt	loa	bm	kts	type	comments
9313242	Conti Emden *	Mlt	2006	27,915	38,122	215	30	21	ucc	2,702 teu: ex Medusa-06, Zim Norfolk-07, Conti Emden-06
9187863	Isodora **	Lbr	1999	25,535	33,917	200	30	21	ucc	2,452 teu: ex Cap Bonavista-09, P&O Nedlloyd La Spezia-02, l/a Cap Bonavista
9187875	Isolde **	Lbr	2000	25,535	34,026	200	30	21	ucc	2,452 teu: ex Cap Delgado-09, P&O Nedlloyd Salerno-02, Cap Delgado-00
9236652	Katharina **	Lbr	2001	25,535	35,976	200	30	21	ucc	2,452 teu: ex MOL Symphony-13, CSCL Lianyungang-08, Katharina-01
9312432	Larentia	Lbr	2005	27,915	38,121	215	30	21	ucc	2,702 teu: ex Cosco Brisbane-10
9320142	Minerva	Lbr	2005	27,915	38,117	215	30	21	ucc	2,702 teu: Cosco Panama-11
9326706	Najade	Lbr	2007	27,915	38,131	215	30	21	ucc	2,702 teu: ex Europa Bridge-09, Najade-07
9374571	Olivia	Lbr	2007	28,050	38,096	215	30	21	ucc	2,702 teu: ex Cap Campbell-12, Americas Bridge-09, l/a Olivia
9374583	Olympia	Lbr	2007	28,050	38,013	215	30	21	ucc	2,702 teu: ex APL Chennai-11, Olympia-10, Cap Campbell-09, Olympia-07
9374595	Pandora	Lbr	2008	28,097	37,763	215	30	21	ucc	2,702 teu: ex Cap Castillo-13, l/a Pandora
9372860	Primavera	Lbr	2008	36,087	42,594	229	32	23	ucc	3,428 teu: ex CSAV Rungue-13, Primavera-08
9372872	Quadriga	Lbr	2008	36,087	42,566	229	32	23	ucc	3,428 teu: ex CSAV Romeral-13, Quadriga-08

* managed for Conti Holdings GmbH & Co KG, ** for Gebab Conzeptions-und Emissions GmbH,

MC-Seamax Shipping LLC — U.S.A.

funnel: *operators colours* **hull:** *operators colours* **history:** *non-operating owner. Mitsubishi backed U.S. investment fund founded 2012* **web:** *www.mcseamax.com*

IMO	name	flag	year	gt	dwt	loa	bm	kts	type	comments
9732589	Aisopos	Mhl	2015	93,702	117,293	300	48	22	ucc	9,443 teu
9732606	Andronikos	Mhl	2016	93,702	117,366	300	48	22	ucc	9,443 teu
9286267	CMA CGM Vivaldi	Mhl	2004	90,745	101,661	334	43	24	ucc	8,238 teu
9243409	OOCL Long Beach *	Hkg	2003	89,097	99,508	323	43	25	ucc	8,063 teu
9243394	OOCL Shenzhen *	Hkg	2003	89,097	99,518	323	43	25	ucc	8,063 teu
9302645	YM Ultimate	Lbr	2007	90,389	101,411	336	43	25	ucc	8,200 teu
9302633	YM Unison	Mhl	2006	90,389	101,030	336	43	25	ucc	8,200 teu
9623855	Seamax Stamford	Lbr	2015	47,911	55,937	248	37	21	ucc	4,896 teu: l/a Penelope L

* owned by associated Outbound Ltd.

Mediterranean Shipping Co. S.A. — Switzerland

funnel: *cream with cream 'MSC' on black disc, narrow black band below black top.* **hull:** *black with cream 'MSC', red boot-topping.* **history:** *formed 1970.* **web:** *www.mscgva.ch*

IMO	name	flag	year	gt	dwt	loa	bm	kts	type	comments
9625970	Anastasia	Pan	2012	51,168	92,216	230	38	14	bbu	ex MSC Anastasia-12
9618290	MSC Adelaide	Pan	2013	95,390	110,617	300	48	22	ucc	8,827 teu: l/d MSC Denisse
8512906	MSC Adele	Pan	1986	21,633	31,205	187	28	17	ucc	1,742 teu: ex Norasia Sharjah-94
9169055	MSC Adriana	Pan	1998	25,219	18,779	216	27	25	ucc	1,388 teu: ex MSC Malaysia-04, Warwick-03, ADCL Sheba-02, Norasia Sheba-00
9123166	MSC Alabama	Pan	1996	37,518	42,966	243	32	23	ucc	3,424 teu: ex APL Italy-01, Chetumal-00, TMM Chetumal-97
9129873	MSC Alexa	Pan	1996	42,307	51,111	244	32	22	ucc	3,301 teu
9461374	MSC Alexandra	Pan	2010	153,115	165,908	366	51	24	ucc	14,000 teu: l/d CPO Trieste
8714190	MSC Alice	Pan	1988	35,598	43,184	242	32	21	ucc	3,032 teu: ex MSC Maya-15, Maersk Levant-04, MSC Jamie-02, Hanjin Seattle-98
9235050	MSC Alyssa	Pan	2001	43,575	61,487	274	32	23	ucc	4,340 teu
9008603	MSC America *	Pan	1993	34,231	45,668	216	32	19	ucc	2,680 teu: ex American Senator-04, DSR-America-00
9351593	MSC Angela	Pan	2008	41,225	50,568	265	32	24	ucc	4,254 teu
9203942	MSC Aniello	Pan	2000	40,631	56,916	260	32	23	ucc	4,056 teu
9227297	MSC Anisha R [F]	Lbr	2002	45,803	53,328	281	32	25	ucc	4,112 teu: ex Santa Rafaela-15, Southampton Express-09, Maersk Denia-07, P&O Nedlloyd Remuera-06, l/a Santa Rafaela
8521402	MSC Annamaria	Pan	1987	21,633	31,205	187	28	17	ucc	1,742 teu: ex Norasia Al-Mansoorah-94
9282261	MSC Ans	Pan	2004	54,304	68,588	294	32	24	ucc	4,900 teu

IMO	name	flag	year	gt	dwt	loa	bm	kts	type	comments
9702273	MSC Antonella [C]	Pmd	2016	95,497	110,800	300	48	22	ucc	8,800 teu
8408832	MSC Antonia	Pan	1985	22,667	33,864	188	28	18	ucc	1,802 teu: ex Mixteco-94, Birthe Oldendorff-93, Ville de Castor-92, DSR Oakland-92, London Senator-91, ScanDutch Hispania-89, Commander-87, Astoria-86, World Champion-85
9710426	MSC Anzu [C]	Pan	2015	95,403	109,619	300	48	22	ucc	8,814 teu
9484443	MSC Ariane	Pan	2012	143,521	154,503	366	48	25	ucc	13,050 teu
9244881	MSC Arushi R. [F]	Lbr	2002	45,803	53,115	281	32	25	ucc	4,112 teu: ex Santa Rufina-14, Maersk Denton-10, MSC Marbella-09, Maersk Denton-08, P&O Nedlloyd Mairangi-06, Santa Rufina-02
9162631	MSC Asli	Mlt	2000	24,836	14,150	217	27	25	ucc	1,388 teu: ex Lincoln-04, ADCL Salwa-02, Norasia Salwa-00
9263344	MSC Astrid *	Pan	2004	35,954	42,186	231	32	22	ucc	3,400 teu: ex MSC Delhi-07, Northern Distinction-04
9339296	MSC Asya	Pan	2008	107,849	112,063	337	46	26	ucc	9,200 teu
8913447	MSC Atlantic	Pan	1991	37,071	46,975	237	32	21	ucc	2,668 teu: ex Rostock Senator-02, DSR-Rostock-00
8512891	MSC Augusta	Pan	1986	21,648	31,205	187	28	17	ucc	1,879 teu: ex Norasia Pearl-94
9484481	MSC Aurora	Pan	2012	143,521	154,494	366	48	25	ucc	13,050 teu
9263332	MSC Banu *	Pan	2004	35,954	42,186	231	32	22	ucc	3,400 teu: ex MSC Queensland-07, l/a Northern Devotion
9226932	MSC Barbara	Pan	2002	73,819	85,250	304	40	25	ucc	6,730 teu
9399014	MSC Beatrice	Pan	2009	151,559	156,085	366	51	25	ucc	13,300 teu
9203904	MSC Belle	Mlt	1998	12,004	14,174	149	23	19	ucc	1,116 teu: ex Libra J-13, Tausala Samoa-05, l/a Libra J
9399038	MSC Bettina	Pan	2010	151,559	156,131	366	51	25	ucc	13,300 teu
9103685	MSC Brianna	Pan	1996	51,931	60,348	294	32	23	ucc	4,507 teu: ex MSC Colombia-12, Maersk Doha-07, P&O Nedlloyd Caribbean-03, Germany-02, APL Germany-02, OOCL Germany-98
9702106	MSC Brunella [C]	Pan	2015	95,894	109,832	300	48	22	ucc	8,814 teu
9169043	MSC Caitlin	Pan	1998	25,219	18,779	216	27	25	ucc	1,388 teu: ex Oxford-05, ADCL Shamsaa-01, Norasia Shamsaa-00, Norasia Salome-99

MSC Clara : Mediterranean Shipping Co. : *ARO*

IMO	name	flag	year	gt	dwt	loa	bm	kts	type	comments
9404651	MSC Camille	Pan	2009	153,092	165,844	366	51	25	ucc	13,300 teu
9102722	MSC Canberra	Pan	1995	29,181	41,583	203	31	19	ucc	2,604 teu: ex Joseph-01, TMM Puebla-01, Joseph-00, Zim Venezia I-98, Med Fos-97, Joseph Lykes-96
9339284	MSC Candice	Pan	2007	107,849	111,749	337	46	26	ucc	9,200 teu
9465289	MSC Capella	Pan	2012	141,635	141,103	366	48	24	ucc	13,102 teu
9349813	MSC Carmen	Pan	2008	50,963	63,359	275	32	23	ucc	4,860 teu
9295397	MSC Carolina	Pan	2005	65,483	72,037	275	40	26	ucc	5,599 teu
9705005	MSC Caterina [C]	Pan	2015	95,403	109,581	300	48	22	ucc	8,819 teu
9316361	MSC Celine	Pan	2007	32,060	39,000	211	32	21	ucc	2,732 teu: ex Westerdiek-15, MSC Mendosa-09, Westerdiek-07
9710438	MSC Channe [C]	Pan	2015	95,403	109,495	300	48	22	ucc	8,800 teu
8420892	MSC Chiara	Pan	1988	31,430	41,815	199	32	18	ucc	2,078 teu: ex TMM Morelos-01, Morelos-00 (conv bbu-02)
9708693	MSC Clara [M]	Pan	2015	192,237	199,273	396	59	24	ucc	19,224 teu: l/a Ocean Triumph
9484429	MSC Clorinda	Pan	2012	153,115	165,960	366	51	25	ucc	13,050 teu
9307267	MSC Corinna	Pan	2006	27,100	34,495	210	30	22	ucc	2,582 teu: JPO Sagittarius-14
9453298	MSC Cristiana *	Pan	2011	59,835	21,500	200	32	19	mve	5,500 ceu
9250983	MSC Damla	Pan	2002	71,902	74,453	293	40	25	ucc	6,402 teu: ex MOL Progress-14
9399002	MSC Daniela	Pan	2008	151,559	156,301	366	51	25	ucc	13,798 teu
9404649	MSC Danit	Pan	2009	153,092	165,517	366	46	25	ucc	13,798 teu
9461415	MSC Deila	Pan	2012	153,115	166,093	366	51	24	ucc	14,000 teu
8509375	MSC Denisse	Pan	1988	31,430	41,771	199	32	18	ucc	2,072 teu: ex MSC Alexandra-10, MSC Orinoco-99, Toluca-99, MSC Nicole-99, Toluca-98
8517891	MSC Didem *	Pan	1987	35,598	43,108	241	32	21	ucc	3,032 teu: ex Savannah-05, SCI Asha-03, Savannah-02, Hanjin Savannah-01
9202649	MSC Diego	Pan	1999	40,631	56,889	260	32	23	ucc	4,056 teu
9720201	MSC Domitille [X]	Pan	2015	94,469	110,699	300	48	22	ucc	9,400 teu
9102746	MSC Don Giovanni *	Pan	1996	29,181	41,583	203	31	19	ucc	2,604 teu: ex Jean-96, l/a Jean Lykes
9237151	MSC Donata *	Lbr	2002	40,108	52,806	258	32	24	ucc	4,132 teu
9169029	MSC Edith	Mlt	1998	25,219	18,779	216	27	25	ucc	1,384 teu: ex Lykes Crusader-05, Ayrshire-04, Safmarine Prime-04, Ayrshire-03, ADCL Samantha-01, Norasia Samantha-00
9282259	MSC Ela	Pan	2004	54,304	68,307	294	32	24	ucc	5,048 teu
9278143	MSC Eleni	Pan	2004	54,881	68,254	294	32	24	ucc	5,048 teu
9064750	MSC Eleonora *	Pan	1994	28,892	41,667	203	31	20	ucc	2,604 teu: ex MSC Beijing-03, Trade Cosmos-02, Sea Excellence-96, Trade Cosmos-95
9704972	MSC Elodie [C]	Pan	2015	95,403	109,576	300	48	22	ucc	8,819 teu
8917778	MSC Eloise *	Pan	1991	37,902	44,541	241	32	18	ucc	2,440 teu: ex Maersk Niigata-07, Arafura-06
9399052	MSC Emanuela	Pan	2010	151,559	156,078	366	51	25	ucc	13,978 teu
9043756	MSC Erminia *	Pan	1993	48,220	47,384	277	32	25	ucc	3,720 teu: ex Newport Bridge-11
9304411	MSC Esthi	Lbr	2006	107,849	110,838	337	46	26	ucc	9,178 teu
9000493	MSC Eugenia	Pan	1992	53,521	65,535	275	37	24	ucc	4,469 teu: ex Bunga Pelangi-07
9401130	MSC Eva	Pan	2010	151,559	156,097	366	51	25	ucc	13,798 teu
8201648	MSC Eyra *	Pan	1982	21,586	21,370	203	25	20	ucc	1,254 teu: ex Pelineo-04, Miden Agan-02, Maersk Toronto-00, Miden Agan-97, CMA Le Cap-95, Kapitan Kozlovskiy-95 (len-89)
9279965	MSC Fabienne	Pan	2004	54,774	66,825	294	32	24	ucc	5,050 teu
8715869	MSC Federica	Pan	1990	52,181	60,189	294	32	25	ucc	4,814 teu: ex Marie Maersk-11
9369758	MSC Fiammetta	Pan	2008	66,399	73,355	277	40	24	ucc	5,762 teu
9467433	MSC Flavia	Pan	2012	140,096	139,467	366	48	22	ucc	12,400 teu
9251705	MSC Florentina	Pan	2003	75,590	85,832	304	40	25	ucc	6,750 teu
8521397	MSC Floriana	Pan	1986	21,648	31,205	187	28	17	ucc	1,879 teu: ex Princess-95, Norasia Princess-94
9401116	MSC Francesca	Pan	2008	131,771	131,356	366	46	25	ucc	11,660 teu
8413875	MSC Gabriella	Pan	1985	21,887	31,290	189	28	17	ucc	1,893 teu: ex Safmarine Europe-11, CMBT Europe-00, Norasia Susan-94, Norasia Helga-85 (len-89)
9401141	MSC Gaia	Pan	2010	151,559	156,084	366	51	25	ucc	13,798 teu
9202663	MSC Gina	Pan	1999	40,631	56,889	260	32	23	ucc	4,056 teu
8408818	MSC Giorgia	Pan	1985	22,667	33,823	188	28	18	ucc	1,923 teu: ex Maya-94, DSR Yokohama-93, Tokyo Senator-91, ScanDutch Massilia-88, Azuma-87, Pacific Pride-86

176

IMO	name	flag	year	gt	dwt	loa	bm	kts	type	comments
8505836	MSC Giovanna	Pan	1987	27,103	25,904	178	32	18	ucc	1,762 teu: ex MSC Provence-99, Dubrovnik Express-99, Koper Express-96
9720196	MSC Giselle [X]	Pan	2015	94,469	110,412	300	48	22	ucc	9,400 teu
8918057	MSC Grace *	Pan	1991	13,258	24,330	155	23	16	ucc	ex Putney Bridge-02, Melanesian Chief-00, Putney Bridge-99, Mikhail Tsarev-97, Zim Rio-96, Mikhail Tsarev-94, Contship Columbus-93, Mikhail Tsarev-93
9316347	MSC Hannah	Pan	2006	32,060	38,700	211	32	21	ucc	2,732 teu: ex Westertal-15, CMA CGM Melbourne-08, Westertal-06
9309473	MSC Heidi	Pan	2006	94,489	107,895	332	43	25	ucc	8,402 teu
9127540	MSC Himanshi	Lbr	1997	23,896	30,600	188	30	21	ucc	2,064 teu: ex Westerems-14, Maersk Novazzano-10, P&O Nedlloyd Horizon-05, Westerems-05, ANL Addax-03, Westerems-02, Lykes Voyager-01, Westerems-98, Maersk Cordoba-98, Westerems-97
9305714	MSC Ines	Lbr	2006	107,551	108,461	337	46	25	ucc	9,115 teu
9181651	MSC Ingrid *	Pan	1999	53,208	67,678	294	32	25	ucc	4,396 teu: ex Saudi Jeddah-02
9399040	MSC Irene	Pan	2010	151,559	156,082	366	51	25	ucc	13,798 teu
8201624	MSC Iris *	Pan	1982	21,586	21,370	203	25	20	ucc	1,254 teu: ex Pelat-04, MSC Eyra-04, Pelat-04, Lisboa-02, P&O Nedlloyd Ottawa-00, Sea-Land Canada-99, Lisboa-97, Kapitan Gavrilov-95 (len-89)
9154206	MSC Ishyka +	Lbr	1997	25,713	34,083	205	27	20	ucc	2,468 teu: ex Conti Cartagena-14, MOL Splendor-09, Cap Pilar-07, Conti Cartagena-05, CMA CGM Eagle-04, Conti Cartagena-03, MSC Provence-01, Sea-Land Argentina -00, l/a Conti Cartagena
9398371	MSC Ivana	Pan	2009	131,771	131,489	364	46	25	ucc	11,660 teu
9110975	MSC Japan	Grc	1996	37,518	42,938	243	32	23	ucc	3,424 teu: ex APL Panama-01, Manzanillo-00, TMM Manzanillo-97, Manzanillo-96, Carmen-96
8420907	MSC Jasmine	Pan	1988	31,430	41,771	199	32	18	ucc	2,078 teu: ex TMM Oaxaca-00, Contship Houston-97, Oaxaca-96
9051478	MSC Jemima	Pan	1994	30,971	36,887	202	32	20	ucc	2,394 teu: ex Nuevo Leon-05, TMM Nuevo Leon-03, Nuevo Leon-00
8502717	MSC Jilhan *	Pan	1986	14,068	19,560	162	25	18	ucc	1,317 teu: ex Kapitan Kurov-04, Contship Italy-93, Red Sea Europa-91, CGM Roussillon-90, Sandra K-88, Sea Merchant-88, JSS Scandinavia-88, l/a Sandra K
9304435	MSC Joanna	Lbr	2006	107,849	110,800	337	46	25	ucc	9,178 teu
8918980	MSC Jordan	Lbr	1993	37,071	47,120	237	32	21	ucc	3,005 teu: ex Sovcomflot Senator-03
9039250	MSC Joy	Mlt	1992	30,567	31,160	203	31	19	ucc	1,939 teu: ex Northern Joy-10, Canada Senator-08, Northern Joy-01, CMA Xingang-01, Contship Mexico-99, Northern Joy-98, Sea Vigor-97, Hyundai Tacoma-96, Sea Hawk-94, Northern Joy-93
9299549	MSC Judith	Pan	2006	89,954	105,083	325	43	25	ucc	8,089 teu
9227338	MSC Julia R. [F]	Lbr	2002	45,803	53,081	281	32	25	ucc	4,112 teu: ex Santa Romana-14, Maersk Damascus-11, P&O Nedlloyd Palliser-06, l/a Santa Romana
9704996	MSC Julie [C]	Pan	2015	95,403	109,587	300	48	22	ucc	8,819 teu
9399026	MSC Kalina	Pan	2009	151,559	156,086	366	52	25	ucc	13,798 teu
9467457	MSC Katie	Pan	2012	140,096	139,287	366	48	22	ucc	13,000 teu
9467445	MSC Katrina	Pan	2012	140,096	139,439	366	48	22	ucc	13,000 teu
9227302	MSC Katya R. [F]	Deu	2002	45,803	53,410	281	32	25	ucc	4,112 teu: ex Santa Rebecca-15, Maersk Decartur-11, P&O Nedlloyd Encounter-06, l/a Santa Rebecca
9062960	MSC Kerry	Pan	1995	37,323	45,530	240	32	22	ucc	3,501 teu: ex Ville de Norma-98
9351581	MSC Kim	Pan	2008	41,225	50,547	265	32	24	ucc	4,254 teu
9123154	MSC Korea	Grc	1996	37,518	42,938	243	32	23	ucc	3,424 teu: ex APL Spain-01, Sinaloa-00, TMM Sinaloa-97, Sinaloa-96
9051507	MSC Krittika	Pan	1994	30,971	36,999	202	32	21	ucc	2,394 teu: ex Lykes Commander-05, TMM Mexico-01, Sea Guardian-96, Mexico-94
9372470	MSC Krystal	Pan	2008	66,399	72,900	277	40	24	ucc	5,762 teu

IMO	name	flag	year	gt	dwt	loa	bm	kts	type	comments
9064748	MSC Lara *	Pan	1994	28,892	38,270	203	31	20	ucc	2,604 teu: ex MSC Bruxelles-04, Trade Apollo-02, Jadroplov Trader-95, Chesapeake Bay-95, Sea Excellence-94, Trade Sol-94
9225665	MSC Laura	Pan	2002	75,590	85,928	300	40	24	ucc	6,750 teu
9467407	MSC Lauren	Pan	2011	140,096	139,324	366	48	23	ucc	13,029 teu
9467419	MSC Laurence	Pan	2011	140,096	139,408	366	48	23	ucc	13,029 teu
9162643	MSC Lea	Mlt	2000	24,836	14,150	217	27	25	ucc	1,350 teu: ex Shropshire-04, ADCL Sabrina-01, l/a Norasia Sabrina
9320439	MSC Leigh	Pan	2006	50,963	63,411	275	32	23	ucc	4,884 teu
9106479	MSC Leila	Mlt	1995	10,917	13,700	151	24	18	ucc	1,158 teu: ex Cape Sable-13, Deja Bhum-09, Cape Sable-05
9702065	MSC Letizia [C]	Pan	2015	95,497	110,800	300	48	22	ucc	8,829 teu
8608200	MSC Levina *	Pan	1989	36,420	43,140	241	32	21	ucc	2,670 teu: ex Hanjin Le Havre-98
8201674	MSC Lieselotte *	Pan	1983	21,586	21,370	203	25	20	ucc	1,438 teu: ex Aveiro-03, Tiger Sea-02, Aveiro-02, Nikolay Tikhonov-95 (len-89)
9704960	MSC Lily [C]	Pan	2015	95,403	109,542	300	48	22	ucc	8,819 teu
9281279	MSC Lisa	Pan	2004	54,304	68,577	294	32	24	ucc	5,048 teu
9320403	MSC Lorena	Pan	2006	50,963	59,587	261	32	24	ucc	4,860 teu
9230490	MSC Loretta	Pan	2002	73,819	85,801	304	40	25	ucc	6,750 teu
8413887	MSC Lucia	Pan	1985	21,887	31,290	189	28	17	ucc	1,893 teu: ex Safmarine Asia-11, CMBT Asia-00, Norasia Samantha-84 (len-89)
9398383	MSC Luciana	Pan	2009	131,771	131,463	364	46	24	ucc	11,660 teu
9289104	MSC Lucy	Pan	2005	89,954	104,954	325	43	25	ucc	8,034 teu
9251690	MSC Ludovica *	Pan	2003	75,590	85,882	304	40	25	ucc	6,750 teu
9225677	MSC Luisa	Pan	2002	75,590	84,920	304	40	25	ucc	6,750 teu
9305702	MSC Madeleine	Lbr	2006	107,551	108,637	337	46	25	ucc	9,100 teu: l/a Ambika
9289128	MSC Maeva	Pan	2005	89,954	105,007	325	43	25	ucc	8,034 teu
9625932	MSC Magali	Pan	2013	62,704	104,229	253	43	14	bbu	
8201636	MSC Malin *	Pan	1982	21,586	21,370	203	25	20	ucc	1,438 teu: ex Pelado-04, Tavira-03, Maersk Montreal-00, Tavira-97, Kapitan Kanlevskiy -95 (len-89)
8918966	MSC Mandy	Pan	1993	37,071	47,120	237	32	21	ucc	2,668 teu: ex SCI Vaibhav-04, Bremen Senator-03
9238741	MSC Margarita [F]	Lbr	2002	65,289	67,644	277	40	24	ucc	5,762 teu: ex Santa Virginia-14, Cap Verde-13, Santa Virginia-10, OOCL Thailand-09, l/a Santa Virginia
9304423	MSC Maria Elena	Pan	2006	107,849	108,200	337	46	25	ucc	9,178 teu: ex MSC Fiorenza-06
8616520	MSC Maria Laura	Pan	1988	36,389	42,513	229	32	20	ucc	2,631 teu: ex Sea Cheetah-00, Cap Verde-00, CGM La Perouse-98, Ville de la Fontaine-93, La Fontaine-92, CGM La Perouse-91
9155107	MSC Maria Pia	Pan	1997	29,115	40,117	196	32	22	ucc	2,808 teu: ex MSC Bremen-04, Lykes Innovator-03, Safmarine Erebus-02, CMBT Erebus-01, Northern Vision-97

MSC Oliver : Mediterranean Shipping Co. : *Hans Kraijenbosch*

IMO	name	flag	year	gt	dwt	loa	bm	kts	type	comments
9467421	MSC Maria Saveria	Pan	2011	140,096	139,295	366	48	23	ucc	13,029 teu
9226920	MSC Marianna	Pan	2002	73,819	85,250	304	40	25	ucc	6,750 teu: I/a MSC Loraine
9275971	MSC Marina	Pan	2003	73,819	85,806	304	40	24	ucc	6,750 teu
9295385	MSC Marta	Pan	2005	65,483	72,044	275	40	26	ucc	5,599 teu
9060637	MSC Martina	Pan	1993	37,398	43,436	243	32	22	ucc	3,398 teu: ex Maersk Hong Kong-97, Hansa America-93
9169031	MSC Marylena	Mlt	1998	25,219	23,487	216	27	25	ucc	1,388 teu: ex Cheshire-05, ADCL Savannah-01, Norasia Savannah-00
9181663	MSC Matilde *	Pan	1999	53,208	67,615	294	32	25	ucc	4,400 teu: ex Saudi Jubail-02
9251717	MSC Maureen	Pan	2003	75,590	85,832	304	40	25	ucc	6,750 teu
9720287	MSC Maxine [XT]	Pan	2015	94,469	110,629	300	48	22	ucc	9,400 teu
9708679	MSC Maya [S]	Pan	2015	192,237	199,272	396	59	24	ucc	19,224 teu: I/a Ocean Genius
9102710	MSC Mediterranean	Pan	1995	29,181	41,583	203	31	19	ucc	2,604 teu: ex Nautic II-04, CMA CGM Monet-02, James-00, James Lykes-96
9404675	MSC Melatilde	Pan	2010	153,092	165,478	366	51	24	ucc	14,000 teu
9702077	MSC Meline [C]	Pan	2015	95,497	110,029	300	48	22	ucc	8,814 teu
9226918	MSC Melissa	Pan	2002	73,819	85,250	304	40	25	ucc	6,750 teu
9256755	MSC Methoni	Pan	2003	73,819	85,250	304	40	25	ucc	6,750 teu: ex MSC Viviana-11
9169067	MSC Mia Summer	Pan	1999	25,219	18,779	216	27	25	ucc	1,388 teu: ex Buckinghamshire-05, ADCL Scarlet-01, Norasia Scarlet-00
9230488	MSC Michaela	Pan	2002	73,819	85,797	304	40	25	ucc	6,750 teu
8709640	MSC Mirella	Pan	1989	27,103	25,904	178	32	18	ucc	1,762 teu: ex Zagreb Express-99,
9060649	MSC Monica	Pan	1993	37,398	43,378	243	32	22	ucc	3,424 teu: ex Ville d'Aquila-97, Hansa Asia-93
9704984	MSC Naomi [C]	Pan	2015	95,403	109,510	300	48	22	ucc	8,819 teu
8918954	MSC Nederland	Pan	1992	37,071	47,120	237	32	21	ucc	2,668 teu: ex Vladivostok Mariner-03, Vladivostok Senator-02
9278155	MSC Nerissa	Pan	2004	54,881	68,178	294	32	24	ucc	5,048 teu
8509387	MSC Nicole	Pan	1989	31,430	41,787	199	32	18	ucc	2,073 teu: ex Contship America-00, Monterrey-00, MSC Lima-98, Nedlloyd Montevideo-98, Monterrey-97
9051492	MSC Nilgun	Pan	1994	30,971	36,887	202	32	20	ucc	2,394 teu: ex P&O Nedlloyd Pinta-05, Contship Inspiration-02, TMM Yucatan-01, Yucatan-00
9084607	MSC Nita +	Mhl	1996	15,859	20,100	167	27	19	ucc:	1,512 teu: ex Sawasdee Busan-12, San Fernando-12, P&O Nedlloyd Tema-04, San Fernando-02, Lykes Condor-01, Ivaran Condor-99, San Fernando-98
8419702	MSC Noa *	Pan	1986	35,953	43,270	241	32	20	ucc	3,044 teu: ex Hanjin Newyork-02
9349825	MSC Nuria	Pan	2008	50,963	63,377	275	32	23	ucc	4,884 teu
9703306	MSC Oliver [S]	Pan	2015	192,237	199,273	396	59	24	ucc	19,224 teu
9372482	MSC Oriane	Pan	2008	66,399	72,900	277	40	24	ucc	5,762 teu
9281267	MSC Ornella	Pan	2004	54,304	68,372	294	32	24	ucc	5,048 teu
9703291	MSC Oscar [S]	Pan	2014	192,237	199,272	396	59	24	ucc	19,224 teu
9441001	MSC Paloma	Pan	2010	153,092	165,564	366	51	24	ucc	14,000 teu
9290531	MSC Pamela	Pan	2005	107,849	110,592	337	46	26	ucc	9,178 teu
9161297	MSC Paola *	Cyp	1998	37,579	56,902	243	32	23	ucc	3,398 teu: ex MSC Christina-11, P&O Nedlloyd Chicago-04
8209729	MSC Perle *	Pan	1983	17,414	25,329	166	29	18	ucc	1,429 teu: ex Corona-03, Nautic I-02, City of Dublin-00, City of Antwerp-98, City of London-97, Pacific Span-93, Incotrans Pacific-90, ScanDutch Arcadia-90, Korean Senator-88, Corona-87, Atlantic Corona-85, Corona-84, ScanDutch Corona-84, Corona-83
8715871	MSC Pilar	Pan	1990	52,181	60,350	294	32	23	ucc	4,814 teu: ex Magelby Maersk-11, Magelby-10, Magelby Maersk-10
9339272	MSC Pina	Pan	2007	107,849	112,053	337	46	25	ucc	9,580 teu
9279977	MSC Poh Lin	Pan	2004	54,774	66,786	294	32	24	ucc	5,050 teu
9154191	MSC Positano	Mlt	1997	25,713	34,083	206	30	22	ucc	2,468 teu: ex Conti Bilbao-14, Tiger Speed-11, Kota Pertama-07, CMA CGM Albatross-04, Conti Bilbao-03, Brasilia-02, Sea-Land Brasil-99, I/a Conti Bilbao
9290282	MSC Rachele	Pan	2005	90,745	101,874	335	43	25	ucc	8,238 teu
9129885	MSC Rafaela	Pan	1996	42,307	51,210	243	32	22	ucc	3,301 teu
9309447	MSC Rania	Pan	2006	94,489	107,898	332	43	25	ucc	8,402 teu
9139505	MSC Rebecca *	Pan	1997	37,579	42,954	243	32	22	ucc	3,200 teu: ex Grand Concord-97
9202651	MSC Regina	Pan	1999	40,631	56,890	260	32	23	ucc	4,056 teu
9465291	MSC Regulus †	Pan	2012	141,635	140,951	366	48	24	ucc	13,102 teu: I/a E.R. Regulus

IMO	name	flag	year	gt	dwt	loa	bm	kts	type	comments
9224051	MSC Rhiannon +	Lbr	2001	23,652	29,894	188	30	21	ucc	2,078 teu: ex Wellington Express-15, CP Tabasco-06, TMM Tabasco-05, Silvia-01
9289116	MSC Rita	Pan	2005	89,954	104,850	325	43	25	ucc	8,089 teu
9141297	MSC Rochelle	Lbr	1997	53,334	62,200	294	32	23	ucc	4,545 teu: ex Pugwash-14, MSC Curitiba-14, Pugwash-13, CSAV Appennini-12, Pugwash Senator-07
8905878	MSC Ronit *	Pan	1990	18,000	26,282	177	28	18	ucc	1,743 teu: ex Conti Arabian-08, YM Cairo I-04, Conti Arabian-04, Delmas Mascareignes-03, Kaedi-02, Conti Arabian-00, Maruba Challenger-00, Conti Arabian-97, Arabian Senator-97
9461398	MSC Rosa M	Pan	2010	153,115	165,991	366	51	24	ucc	14,036 teu
9320453	MSC Rosaria	Pan	2007	50,963	63,427	275	32	23	ucc	4,884 teu
9065443	MSC Rossella	Pan	1993	37,398	43,604	243	32	22	ucc	3,424 teu: ex Ville de Carina-97, Hansa Europe-93
8714205	MSC Sabrina	Pan	1989	35,598	43,078	243	32	21	ucc	3,032 teu: ex Hanjin Oakland-98
9203965	MSC Sandra	Pan	2001	43,575	61,468	274	32	23	ucc	4,340 teu
8913411	MSC Santhya	Pan	1991	37,071	46,600	237	32	21	ucc	2,668 teu: ex Baykal Senator-04, DSR Senator-00, Vladivostok-91
9147071	MSC Sao Paulo	Lbr	1998	53,334	63,537	294	32	23	ucc	4,545 teu: ex Pohang-13, CSAV Pyrenees-13, Pohang Senator-08
9181675	MSC Sarah *	Pan	1999	53,208	67,795	294	32	24	ucc	4,400 teu: ex Saudi Yanbu-02
9702261	MSC Sara Elena [C]	Pan	2015	95,497	110,800	300	48	22	ucc	8,814 teu
8715857	MSC Sariska	Pan	1990	52,181	60,639	294	32	23	ucc	4,814 teu: ex Majestic-11, Majestic Maersk-10
8913423	MSC Shannon	Pan	1991	37,071	47,120	237	32	21	ucc	2,668 teu; ex Berlin Senator-04
9180968	MSC Sheila	Pan	1999	12,396	16,211	150	23	14	ggc	ex Atlantik Trader-05
9224049	MSC Shirley +	Lbr	2000	23,652	29,841	188	30	20	ucc	2,078 teu: ex Canberra Express-15, CP Eagle-06, Lykes Eagle-05, Clivia-00
9309459	MSC Silvana	Pan	2006	94,489	107,964	332	43	25	ucc	8,402 teu
9720457	MSC Silvia [H]	Pan	2015	94,469	110,697	300	48	22	ucc	9,400 teu
9336048	MSC Sindy	Pan	2007	107,849	111,894	337	46	26	ucc	9,580 teu
9702091	MSC Sofia Celeste [C]	Pan	2015	95,497	110,039	300	48	22	ucc	8,814 teu
9401104	MSC Sola	Pan	2008	131,771	131,346	366	46	25	ucc	11,660 teu
9404663	MSC Sonia	Pan	2010	153,092	165,691	366	51	24	ucc	14,000 teu
9073062	MSC Sophie	Pan	1993	37,398	43,294	243	32	22	ucc	3,424 teu: ex Maersk Colombo-97, Hansa Australia-93
9372494	MSC Soraya	Pan	2008	66,399	73,262	277	40	24	ucc	5,762 teu
9279989	MSC Stella	Pan	2004	73,819	85,680	304	40	24	ucc	6,724 teu
8918978	MSC Suez	Pan	1993	37,071	47,120	237	32	21	ucc	3,005 teu: ex Hamburg Senator-02
9290543	MSC Susanna	Pan	2005	107,849	110,623	337	46	25	ucc	9,178 teu
9708681	MSC Sveva [S]	Pan	2015	192,237	199,272	396	59	24	ucc	19,224 teu: I/a Ocean Honor
9008574	MSC Tasmania *	Pan	1993	34,231	45,696	216	32	19	ucc	2,700 teu: ex Japan Senator-04, Choyang Elite-98, DSR-Asia-96
9469560	MSC Teresa	Pan	2011	153,115	166,101	366	51	24	ucc	14,000 teu
9309461	MSC Tomoko	Pan	2006	94,489	107,915	332	43	25	ucc	8,402 teu
9227340	MSC Vaishnavi R. [F]	Lbr	2002	45,803	52,800	281	32	25	ucc	4,112 teu: ex Santa Rosanna-14, Maersk Duffield-10, Columbus New Zealand-06, P&O Nedlloyd Resolution-02, I/a Santa Rosanna
9461439	MSC Valeria	Pan	2012	153,115	165,967	366	51	24	ucc	14,000 teu
9484467	MSC Vandya	Pan	2012	143,521	154,185	366	48	24	ucc	13,050 teu
9251688	MSC Vanessa *	Pan	2003	75,590	85,844	300	40	25	ucc	6,570 teu
9238739	MSC Vidhi [F]	Lbr	2001	66,500	67,796	277	40	24	ucc	5,762 teu: ex Santa Victoria-14, CCNI Angamos-13, Cap Valiente-12, Santa Victoria-10, OOCL Korea-09, I/a Santa Victoria
9227326	MSC Vidisha R. [F]	Lbr	2002	45,803	53,462	281	32	25	ucc	4,112 teu: ex Santa Roberta-15, Cap Roberta-13, Maersk Dominica-10, Sydney Express-06, P&O Nedlloyd Pegasus-03, I/a Santa Roberta
9702089	MSC Vita [C]	Pan	2015	95,497	110,800	300	48	22	ucc	8,800 teu
9299551	MSC Vittoria	Pan	2006	89,954	105,101	325	43	25	ucc	8,089 teu
9227314	MSC Zlata R. [F]	Deu	2002	45,803	53,452	281	32	25	ucc	4,112 teu: ex Santa Ricarda-15, Cap Ricarda-13, Maersk Dunafare-10, P&O Nedlloyd Botany-05, I/a Santa Ricarda
9703318	MSC Zoe [X]	Pan	2015	192,237	199,272	396	59	24	ucc	19,224 teu

180

IMO	name	flag	year	gt	dwt	loa	bm	kts	type	comments
newbuildings:										
9720471	MSC Jeongmin [H]	Pan	2016	94,469	110,000	300	48	22	ucc	9,411 teu Jiangnan Changxin H3003
9720483	MSC Chloe [H]	Pan	2016	91,883	110,000	300	48	22	ucc	9,411 teu Jiangnan Changxin H3004
9720495	MSC Branka [H]	Pan	2016	91,883	110,000	300	48	22	ucc	9,411 teu Jiangnan Changxin H3005
9720500	MSC Sasha [H]	Pan	2016	91,883	110,000	300	48	22	ucc	9,411 teu Jiangnan Changxin H3006
9720512	MSC [H]	Pan		91,883	110,000	300	48	22	ucc	9,411 teu Jiangnan Changxin H3007
9720524	MSC [H]	Pan		91,883	110,000	300	48	22	ucc	9,411 teu Jiangnan Changxin H3008
9762326	MSC Jade [M]	Pan	2016	193,000	199,000	399	59	22	ucc	19,437 teu Daewoo 4296
9762338	MSC Mirja [M]	Pan	2016	193,000	199,000	399	59	22	ucc	19,437 teu Daewoo,4299
9762340	MSC [M]	Pan	2017	193,000	199,000	399	59	22	ucc	19,437 teu Daewoo 4301
9754953	MSC [S]	Pan	2016	193,000	199,000	399	59	22	ucc	19,437 teu Daewoo 4297
9754965	MSC [S]	Pan	2016	193,000	199,000	399	59	22	ucc	19,437 teu Daewoo 4298
9755191	MSC [S]	Pan	2016	193,000	199,000	399	59	22	ucc	19,437 teu Daewoo 4300
	†		2016						ucc	11,500 teu Jinhai 234
	†		2016						ucc	11,500 teu Jinhai 235
	†		2016						ucc	11,500 teu Jinhai 236
	†		2016						ucc	11,500 teu Jinhai 237
	†		2016						ucc	11,500 teu Jinhai 238
	†		2017						ucc	11,500 teu Jinhai 262
	†		2017						ucc	11,500 teu Jinhai 263
	†		2017						ucc	11,500 teu Jinhai 264
	†		2017						ucc	11,500 teu Jinhai 265
	†		2017						ucc	11,500 teu Jinhai 266

* managed by MSC Ship Management (Hong Kong) Ltd., Hong Kong   + chartered vessels   † owned by SinOceanic ASA ,
[F] owned by Ship Finance International
[H] owned by Bank of Communications, Hanyuan
[C] owned by China International Marine Containers Gp.[CIMC] chartered for 17 years then purchase option
[S] owned by Bank of Communications Shanghai
[M] owned by Minsheng Financial
[X] owned by Xingxing International Ship Finance
[XT] owned by Xingtai International Ship Finance

Mibau Holding GmbH   Germany

funnel: white with yellow 'H' over yellow wave on blue square, narrow black top. *hull:* blue with yellow 'mibau+stema', red boot-topping. *history:* formed 2003. *web:* www.mibau.de

IMO	name	flag	year	gt	dwt	loa	bm	kts	type	comments
9432206	Beltnes	Atg	2009	20,234	33,173	176	26	14	bsd	
9384370	Bulknes	Atg	2009	20,234	33,171	176	26	14	bsd	
9490105	Fitnes	Atg	2010	20,234	33,169	176	26	14	bsd	
9306029	Sandnes	Atg	2005	17,357	28,000	167	25	15	bsd	
9101730	Splittnes (2)	Atg	1994	9,855	16,073	148	21	14	bsd	ex Kari Arnhild-02
9226396	Stones	Atg	2001	17,357	28,115	166	25	14	bsd	

Jointly owned by Heidelberg Zement GmbH and Hans-Jurgen Hartmann, operated by Mibau & Stema and managed by HJH Shipmanagement

Minerva Marine Inc.   Greece

funnel: white with light blue over dark blue trianges. *hull:* black or dark grey with blue 'MINERVA' or red with red boot-topping.
history: formed 1996 and associated with Thenamaris (Ships Management) Inc. *web:* wwwminervatank.gr

IMO	name	flag	year	gt	dwt	loa	bm	kts	type	comments
9619555	Afales	Mlt	2012	91,407	177,935	292	45	15	bbu	
9298650	Amalthea	Grc	2006	60,007	107,115	248	43	14	tcr	
9455973	Amphitrite	Grc	2010	162,203	320,137	333	60	15	tcr	
9352561	Andromeda	Grc	2008	162,198	321,300	333	60	15	tcr	I/a Mars Glory
9419474	Apolytares	Grc	2009	160,619	316,679	336	60	15	tcr	
9282792	Atalandi	Grc	2004	59,781	105,306	244	42	14	tcr	ex Valpiave-04
9198094	Minerva Alexandra	Grc	2000	58,125	104,643	244	42	14	tcr	
9309435	Minerva Alice	Grc	2006	63,619	114,850	253	44	14	tcr	ex Urals Star-11
9298507	Minerva Anna	Grc	2005	30,053	50,939	183	32	14	tco	
9322827	Minerva Antarctica *	Cym	2006	61,371	114,849	250	44	15	tcr	ex Stena Antarctica-14, I/a Four Antarctica
9380398	Minerva Antonia	Grc	2008	29,295	46,923	183	32	14	tco	
9412177	Minerva Aries	Mlt	2008	57,135	105,484	244	42	15	tcr	ex Libyan Galaxy-12
9230098	Minerva Astra	Mlt	2001	59,693	105,830	248	43	15	tcr	I/a Stromness
9322839	Minerva Atlantica *	Cym	2006	61,371	114,896	250	44	15	tcr	ex Stena Atlantica-15, I/a Four Atlantica
9297333	Minerva Clara	Grc	2006	58,156	104,500	244	42	14	tcr	
9271406	Minerva Concert	Grc	2003	56,477	105,817	241	42	15	tcr	
9304617	Minerva Doxa	Grc	2007	83,722	159,438	277	50	15	tcr	
9276573	Minerva Eleonora	Grc	2004	58,156	104,875	244	42	14	tcr	
9297321	Minerva Ellie	Grc	2005	58,156	103,194	244	42	14	tcr	
9440526	Minerva Elpida	Mlt	2010	62,571	112,793	250	44	14	tco	ex Gan-Destiny-13
9380063	Minerva Emily	Mlt	2009	26,900	47,408	183	32	14	tco	ex Sabrina Express–12

IMO	name	flag	year	gt	dwt	loa	bm	kts	type	comments
9296195	Minerva Emma	Grc	2003	58,118	107,597	247	42	14	tcr	ex Domua Aurea-11
9332157	Minerva Georgia	Grc	2008	84,914	163,417	274	50	14	tcr	
9382750	Minerva Gloria	Grc	2009	61,341	115,873	249	44	14	tcr	
9305855	Minerva Grace	Grc	2005	30,053	50,922	183	32	14	tcr	
9276561	Minerva Helen	Grc	2004	58,156	104,875	244	42	14	tcr	
9323986	Minerva Indiana	Mlt	2007	56,285	105,547	239	42	14	tcr	ex River Pride-15
9285861	Minerva Iris	Grc	2004	58,156	103,124	244	42	14	tcr	
9280386	Minerva Joanna	Grc	2008	29,295	46,968	183	32	14	tco	
9363479	Minerva Joy	Mlt	2008	28,056	45,990	180	32	14	tco	ex Hallinden-13, Torm Hellerup-13
9380831	Minerva Julie	Grc	2008	28,960	50,922	183	32	14	tcr	
9723289	Minerva Leo	Grc	2015	24,090	38,725	184	27	14	tco	
9317951	Minerva Libra	Grc	1999	58,156	105,344	244	42	15	tcr	l/a Al Bizzia
9276597	Minerva Lisa	Grc	2004	58,156	103,622	244	42	14	tcr	
9262900	Minerva Lydia	Mlt	2004	28,799	47,999	180	32	14	tco	ex Sunny Express-12
9411939	Minerva Marina	Grc	2009	81,467	157,954	274	48	14	tcr	
9233234	Minerva Maya	Grc	2002	57,508	105,709	244	42	14	tcr	
9367671	Minerva Mediterranea	Mlt	2008	26,897	47,522	183	32	14	tco	ex Nor Obtainer-15
9255696	Minerva Nike	Grc	2004	57,301	105,330	244	42	14	tcr	
9309423	Minerva Nounou	Grc	2006	63,619	114,850	253	44	14	tcr	ex Urals Princess-11
9380075	Minerva Oceania	Mlt	2009	26,900	47,402	183	32	14	tco	ex Sapphire Express -15
9325831	Minerva Pacifica	Mlt	2006	28,059	45,822	180	32	14	tco	ex Challenge Plus-15
9410179	Minerva Pisces	Mlt	2008	57,135	105,475	244	42	14	tcr	ex Arctic Galaxy-12
9305867	Minerva Rita	Mlt	2005	30,050	50,922	183	32	14	tco	
9276585	Minerva Roxanne	Grc	2004	58,156	103,622	244	42	14	tcr	
9382762	Minerva Sophia	Grc	2009	61,341	115,873	249	44	14	tcr	
9304605	Minerva Symphony	Grc	2006	83,722	159,450	277	50	15	tcr	
9723291	Minerva Tychi	Grc	2016	24,090	38,725	183	27	14	tco	
9018008	Minerva Vaso	Grc	2006	28,960	50,921	183	32	14	tco	
9411941	Minerva Vera	Grc	2009	81,478	158,016	274	48	14	tcr	
9307827	Minerva Virgo	Grc	2006	28,960	50,921	183	32	14	tco	
9318010	Minerva Xanthe	Grc	2006	28,960	50,921	183	32	14	tco	
9410909	Minerva Zen	Grc	2009	29,442	52.941	183	32	14	tco	ex Torm Lana-09
9236248	Minerva Zenia	Grc	2002	59,693	105,946	248	43	15	tcr	ex Torness-02, l/a Wrabness
9255684	Minerva Zoe	Grc	2004	57,301	105,330	244	42	14	tcr	
9455686	Monemvasia	Grc	2009	91,373	177,933	292	45	15	bbu	
9469869	Parapola	Grc	2008	91,373	177,736	292	45	15	bbu	

Minerva Indiana : Minerva Marine Inc. : *Chris Brooks*

IMO	name	flag	year	gt	dwt	loa	bm	kts	type	comments
9469871	Sapienza	Grc	2008	91,373	177,730	292	45	15	bbu	
9662409	Schinousa	Mlt	2014	91,374	176,000	292	45	15	bbu	
9276016	Surfer Rosa	Mlt	2004	29,327	46,719	183	32	14	tco	ex Kazbek-04
9679593	Zourva	Mlt	2014	164,169	318,513	333	60	15	tcr	

bareboat chartered from MSEA Tankers

MISC Berhad   Malaysia

funnel: *blue, broad red band divided by white band with 14-pointed yellow star.* **hull:** *black or red with white 'MISC' or 'MISC MALAYSIA', red or grey boot-topping.* **history:** *founded 1968 as Malaysian International Shipping Corporation Berhad to 1995, then Malaysia International Shipping Corp Berhad to 2005. Government's majority share sold in 1997 to national oil company Petronas Group (Petroleum Nasional Berhad) founded 1974.* **web:** *www.misc.com.my*

AET Inc. Ltd., Bermuda

funnel: *white with grey eagle-head symbol on grey edged blue disc.* **hull:** *orange with red boot-topping.* **history:** *subsidiary of MISC founded 1994 as American Eagle Tankers by Neptune Orient Lines and acquired in 2003.* **web:** *www.aetweb.com*

IMO	name	flag	year	gt	dwt	loa	bm	kts	type	comments
9273337	Bunga Kasturi *	Mys	2003	156,967	299,999	330	60	15	tcr	
9292632	Bunga Kasturi Dua *	Mys	2005	157,008	300,542	330	60	15	tcr	
9337133	Bunga Kasturi Empat *	Mys	2007	156,967	300,325	330	60	17	tcr	
9327554	Bunga Kasturi Enam *	Mys	2008	157,209	299,319	330	60	15	tcr	
9327114	Bunga Kasturi Lima *	Mys	2007	157,209	300,246	330	60	17	tcr	
9302968	Bunga Kasturi Tiga *	Mys	2006	156,967	300,398	330	60	17	tcr	
9131125	Bunga Kelana Dua *	Mys	1997	57,017	105,575	244	42	14	tcr	
9178331	Bunga Kelana 3 *	Mys	1998	57,017	105,784	244	42	14	tcr	
9178343	Bunga Kelana 4 *	Mys	1999	57,017	105,815	244	42	14	tcr	
9169706	Bunga Kelana 5 *	Mys	1999	57,017	105,811	244	42	14	tcr	
9169718	Bunga Kelana 6 *	Mys	1999	57,017	105,400	244	42	14	tcr	
9284582	Bunga Kelana 7 *	Mys	2004	58,194	105,193	244	42	14	tcr	
9284594	Bunga Kelana 8 *	Mys	2004	58,194	105,193	244	42	14	tcr	
9292979	Bunga Kelana 9 *	Mys	2004	58,194	105,200	244	42	14	tcr	
9189122	Bunga Kenanga *	Mys	2000	40,037	73,083	229	32	15	tcr	ex Four Cutter-00
9182942	Eagle Anaheim	Sgp	1999	57,929	107,160	247	42	14	tcr	
9182930	Eagle Atlanta *	Sgp	1999	57,929	107,160	247	42	14	tcr	
9176034	Eagle Augusta	Sgp	1999	58,156	105,345	244	42	14	tcr	
9176022	Eagle Austin	Sgp	1998	58,156	105,000	244	42	14	tcr	
9111632	Eagle Baltimore	Sgp	1996	57,456	99,405	253	44	14	tcr	
9676125	Eagle Barents	Bhs	2015	88,099	119,690	276	46	14	tcs	
9111644	Eagle Beaumont	Sgp	1996	57,456	99,448	253	44	14	tcr	
9676137	Eagle Bergen	Bhs	2015	82,789	120,567	276	46	14	tcs	
9123192	Eagle Birmingham	Sgp	1997	57,456	99,343	253	44	14	tcr	
9111620	Eagle Boston	Sgp	1996	57,456	99,328	253	44	14	tcr	
9136046	Eagle Columbus	Sgp	1997	57,949	107,166	247	42	14	tcr	
9417024	Eagle Kangar	Sgp	2010	60,379	107,481	244	42	14	tcr	
9422196	Eagle Kinabalu	Sgp	2011	60,379	107,481	244	42	14	tcr	
9422201	Eagle Kinarut	Sgp	2011	60,379	107,481	244	42	14	tcr	
9417892	Eagle Klang	Sgp	2010	60,379	107,481	244	42	14	tcr	
9417012	Eagle Kuantan	Sgp	2010	60,379	107,481	244	42	14	tcr	
9417000	Eagle Kuching	Sgp	2009	60,379	107,481	244	42	14	tcr	
9518892	Eagle Louisiana	Sgp	2011	60,379	107,481	244	42	14	tcr	
9598256	Eagle Paraiba	Mys	2012	62,912	105,153	248	42	14	tcs	
9598268	Eagle Parana	Mys	2012	62,912	105,048	248	42	14	tcs	
9161259	Eagle Phoenix	Sgp	1998	56,346	106,127	241	42	14	tcr	ex Paola I-01
9594822	Eagle San Antonio	Sgp	2012	80,783	157,661	274	49	14	tcr	
9594834	Eagle San Diego	Sgp	2012	80,783	157,900	274	49	14	tcr	
9594846	Eagle San Juan	Sgp	2012	80,872	157,850	274	49	14	tcr	
9594858	Eagle San Pedro	Sgp	2012	80,782	157,850	274	49	14	tcr	
9198082	Eagle Seville	Sgp	1999	58,156	105,365	244	42	14	tcr	ex Minerva Emma-08
9412995	Eagle Stavanger	Pan	2009	55,898	105,355	229	42	14	tcr	
9235000	Eagle Stealth	Mhl	2001	56,346	105,322	239	42	14	tcr	ex Nord Stealth-07
9413004	Eagle Sydney	Pan	2009	55,898	105,419	229	42	14	tcr	
9257042	Eagle Tacoma	Sgp	2002	57,950	107,123	247	42	14	tcr	
9253076	Eagle Tampa	Sgp	2003	58,166	107,123	247	42	14	tcr	
9518907	Eagle Texas	Mhl	2011	60,379	107,481	244	42	14	tcr	
9250892	Eagle Toledo	Sgp	2002	58,166	107,092	247	42	14	tcr	
9360453	Eagle Torrance	Sgp	2007	58,168	107,123	247	42	14	tcr	
9250907	Eagle Trenton	Sgp	2003	58,166	107,123	247	42	14	tcr	
9253064	Eagle Tucson	Sgp	2003	58,166	107,123	247	42	14	tcr	
9360465	Eagle Turin	Sgp	2008	58,168	107,123	247	42	14	tcr	
9597240	Eagle Vancouver	Sgp	2013	161,974	320,299	333	60	15	tcr	
9597252	Eagle Varna	Sgp	2013	161,974	320,299	333	60	15	tcr	
9234654	Eagle Vermont	Sgp	2002	161,233	318,338	333	60	16	tcr	

IMO	name	flag	year	gt	dwt	loa	bm	kts	type	comments
9230878	Eagle Virginia	Sgp	2002	161,233	318,338	333	60	16	tcr	
9412036	Stealth Skyros †	Mhl	2011	62,884	116,337	250	44	15	tcr	

newbuildings:
* owned by AET Petroleum Tanker, Malaysia: vessels managed by AET Shipmanagemen Pte. Ltd. Singapore
managed for : † Stealth Maritime Corp SA (Brave Maritime Corp Inc), Greece.

Mitsui OSK Lines   Japan

funnel: *bright red.* **hull:** *light blue with white 'MOL' or grey with green waterline and red boot-topping.* **history:** *formed 1884 as Osaka Shosen Kaisha, merged in 1964 with Mitsui Senpaku KK to form Mitsui OSK. Merged 1999 with Navix Line which had been formed by 1989 merger of Japan Line (founded 1930 and 1964 merger of Nitto Shosen KK with Daido Kaiun KK) and Yamashita-Shinnihon Steamship Co (founded 1903 and 1964 merger of Yamashita Kisen KK with Shinnihon Kisen KK).* **web:** *www.mol.co.jp*

IMO	name	flag	year	gt	dwt	loa	bm	kts	type	comments
9321251	MOL Celebration †	Bhs	2008	86,692	90,649	316	46	25	ucc	8,110 teu
9321249	MOL Charisma	Bhs	2008	86,692	90,649	316	46	25	ucc	8,110 teu: ex APL France -10, MOL Charisma-07
9629902	MOL Commitment	Mhl	2013	86,695	90,120	316	46	25	ucc	8,540 teu
9339662	MOL Competence †	Pan	2008	86,692	90,613	316	46	25	ucc	8,110 teu
9629914	MOL Contribution	Mhl	2014	86,695	90,120	316	46	25	ucc	8,540 teu
9321263	MOL Courage	Bhs	2008	86,692	90,634	316	46	25	ucc	8,110 teu: ex APL Poland-12, l/a MOL Comfort
9321237	MOL Creation †	Bhs	2007	86,692	90,678	316	46	25	ucc	8,110 teu
9333840	MOL Earnest	Pan	2007	54,098	56,100	294	32	24	ucc	4,803 teu: ex APL Earnest-10, MOL Earnest- 08
9333852	MOL Endowment †	Pan	2007	54,098	62,949	294	32	24	ucc	4,803 teu
9333838	MOL Experience	Pan	2007	54,098	62,953	294	32	23	ucc	4,803 teu: ex APL Experience-10, MOL Experience-08
9333826	MOL Explorer	Pan	2007	53,822	62,958	294	32	24	ucc	4,803 teu
9415727	MOL Maestro †	Mhl	2010	78,316	79,423	302	43	24	ucc	6,724 teu
9424900	MOL Magnificence	Mhl	2010	78,316	79,417	302	43	24	ucc	6,724 teu
9424912	MOL Majesty †	Mhl	2010	78,316	79,443	302	43	24	ucc	6,724 teu
9475648	MOL Maneuver †	Mhl	2011	78,316	79,423	302	43	24	ucc	6,724 teu
9574612	MOL Marvel †	Mhl	2010	78,316	79,460	302	43	24	ucc	6,724 teu
9424924	MOL Matrix †	Mhl	2010	78,316	79,312	302	43	24	ucc	6,724 teu
9424936	MOL Maxim	Mhl	2010	78,316	79,373	302	43	24	ucc	6,724 teu
9475650	MOL Mission †	Mhl	2011	78,316	79,491	302	43	24	ucc	6,724 teu
9475636	MOL Modern	Mhl	2011	78,316	79,283	302	43	24	ucc	6,724 teu
9475624	MOL Motivator	Mhl	2011	78,316	79,278	302	43	24	ucc	6,724 teu
9307059	MOL Paramount	Pan	2005	71,892	72,968	293	40	25	ucc	6,350 teu
9444261	MOL Premium	Pan	2008	71,776	72,912	293	40	25	ucc	6,350 teu
9245029	MOL Solution	Pan	2001	71,902	72,300	293	40	25	ucc	5,220 teu
newbuildings:										
9769271		Pan		199,000	197,500	400	58		ucc	21,100 teu Samsung 2167 04.2017
9769283		Pan		199,000	197,500	400	58		ucc	21,100 teu Samsung 2168 06.2017
9769295		Pan		199,000	197,500	400	58		ucc	21,100 teu Samsung 2169 07.2017
9769300		Pan		199,000	197,500	400	58		ucc	21,100 teu Samsung 2170 08.2017

+ 2 x 20,000teu (Imabari (2017)) chartered from Shoei Kisen Kaisha).
* owned or managed by MOL Ship Management Co. Ltd., Japan, † by New Asian Shipping Co., Hong Kong or ** by Thome Ship Management, Singapore.   One of the world's largest shipping groups with many subsidiaries owning or managing over 500 vessels. Only the largest container vessels are listed, and their large fleet of tankers and bulkers trade largely between Japan and Middle East/Australia

MOL Auto Carrier Express (MOL ACE)

funnel: *bright red.* **hull:** *light blue with white 'MOL' or grey with green waterline and red boot-topping.* **history:** *formed July 1 2015 as dedicated auto carrier division*

IMO	name	flag	year	gt	dwt	loa	bm	kts	type	comments
9397999	Amethyst Ace	Cym	2008	60,143	18,700	200	32	20	mve	6,334 ceu
9297987	Aquamarine Ace	Cym	2008	60,143	18,772	200	32	20	mve	6,334 ceu
9150339	Aquarius Ace	Pan	1998	36,615	14,353	175	29	15	mve	3,027 ceu
9182368	Astral Ace	Pan	2000	36,615	14,280	175	29	18	mve	3,027 ceu
9542283	Azalea Ace	Lbr	2011	43,810	15,154	180	30	18	mve	3,930 ceu
9403281	Bergamot Ace	Cym	2010	42,401	14,996	186	28	19	mve	4,216 ceu
9207120	Bravery Ace	Pan	2000	52,276	17,686	189	32	20	mve	4,518 ceu
9598012	Brilliant Ace	Cym	2011	59,022	18,448	200	32	17	mve	6,172 ceu
9103180	Camellia Ace	Pan	1994	55,336	18,938	200	32	18	mve	5,500 ceu
9544920	Carnation Ace	Cym	2011	60,975	16,416	200	32	21	mve	6,282 ceu
9544918	Cattleya Ace	Cym	2011	60,975	16,384	200	32	21	mve	6,282 ceu
9363950	Clover Ace	Bhs	2008	60,065	17,280	200	32	20	mve	6,287 ceu
9182356	Comet Ace	Pan	2000	36,615	14,283	175	29	18	mve	3,027 ceu
9153563	Cosmos Ace	Pan	1998	46,346	15,439	182	31	19	mve	4,095 ceu
9051375	Cougar Ace	Sgp	1993	55,328	18,922	200	32	19	mve	5,542 ceu
9252204	Courageous Ace	Pan	2003	56,439	19,927	198	32	20	mve	5,281 ceu
9539224	Crystal Ace	Mhl	2011	60,131	18,381	161	27	16	mve	6,312 ceu
9610432	Divine Ace	Pan	2013	59,022	18,134	200	32	19	mve	5,048 ceu
9561265	Elegant Ace	Cym	2010	58,939	18,833	200	32	19	mve	6,233 ceu

IMO	name	flag	year	gt	dwt	loa	bm	kts	type	comments
9539236	Emerald Ace	Mhl	2012	60,154	18,334	200	32	19	mve	6,312 ceu
9293571	Eminent Ace	Pan	2005	58,616	18,947	200	32	20	mve	5,213 ceu
9606479	Eternal Ace	Pan	2011	59,022	18,418	200	32	19	mve	6,163 ceu
9293595	Euphony Ace	Pan	2005	58,631	18,944	200	32	20	mve	5,214 ceu
9293911	Felicity Ace	Pan	2006	60,118	17,738	200	32	20	mve	5,232 ceu
9293894	Firmament Ace	Pan	2006	60,118	17,713	200	32	20	mve	5,232 ceu
9293662	Freedom Ace	Pan	2005	60,175	19,093	200	32	20	mve	6,354 ceu
9209271	Frontier Ace	Pan	2000	52,126	17,693	189	32	20	mve	4,518 ceu
9624237	Galaxy Ace	Lbr	2012	59,583	22,250	200	32	19	mve	6,233 ceu
9610418	Genuine Ace	Lbr	2012	59,022	18,900	200	32	19	mve	6,163 ceu
9561277	Glorious Ace	Cym	2010	58,939	18,836	200	32	19	mve	6,233 ceu
9047996	Harmony Ace	Pan	1992	47,519	14,256	180	32	19	mve	4,774 ceu
9252216	Heroic Ace	Pan	2002	56,439	19,879	198	32	20	mve	5,281 ceu
9515474	Iris Ace	Cym	2011	43,709	14,349	188	28	19	mve	4,064 ceu
9363948	Lavender Ace	Bhs	2008	60,065	17,262	200	32	20	mve	6,287 ceu
9293650	Liberty Ace	Pan	2004	60,175	19,106	200	32	20	mve	6,354 ceu
9110107	Luminous Ace	Phl	1995	45,796	15,181	188	31	18	mve	4,095 ceu
9014808	Maple Ace II	Lbr	1992	38,349	15,361	188	28	18	mve	3,241 ceu
8610526	Marina Ace	Pan	1987	54,332	17,319	200	32	19	mve	5,272 ceu
9426386	Marguerite Ace	Cym	2009	60,067	17,237	200	32	19	mve	5,214 ceu
9293519	Marvelous Ace	Pan	2006	59,422	18,900	200	32	20	mve	6,141 ceu
9209518	Meridian Ace	Pan	2000	55,878	20,144	200	32	19	mve	5,059 ceu
9561289	Mermaid Ace	Pan	2010	58,939	18,828	200	32	19	mve	6,233 ceu
9293521	Miraculous Ace	Cym	2006	59,422	19,381	200	32	20	mve	6,141 ceu
9177052	Mosel Ace	Pan	2000	37,237	12,761	177	31	19	mve	3,919 ceu
9584059	Neptune Ace	BHs	2012	59,006	18,436	200	32	19	mve	6,172 ceu
9539212	Onyx Ace	Cym	2012	60,131	18,529	200	32	19	mve	6,312 ceu
9539183	Opal Ace	Cym	2011	60,131	18,507	200	32	19	mve	6,312 ceu
9381677	Orchid Ace	Jpn	2008	59,262	17,289	200	32	20	mve	6,287 ceu
9293648	Paradise Ace	Pan	2004	60,175	19,080	200	32	20	mve	6,354 ceu
9051818	Pearl Ace	Pan	1994	45,796	15,194	188	31	18	mve	4,095 ceu
9150341	Pegasus Ace	Pan	1998	36,615	14,348	175	29	19	mve	3,027 ceu
9014810	Planet Ace	Pan	1992	38,349	15,327	188	28	18	mve	3,241 ceu
9153549	Polaris Ace	Pan	1997	46,346	15,522	182	31	19	mve	4,095 ceu
9554200	Precious Ace	Cym	2014	59,402	19,045	200	32	19	mve	6,124 ceu
9610444	Prime Ace	Pan	2014	59,007	18,304	200	32	19	mve	5,048 ceu
9355185	Primrose Ace	Cym	2007	59,952	17,339	200	32	20	mve	5,213 ceu
9267687	Progress Ace	Pan	2003	57,789	19,512	200	32	20	mve	5,342 ceu
9267699	Prominent Ace	Pan	2004	57,789	19,550	200	32	20	mve	5,342 ceu
8712324	Queen Ace	Pan	1988	55,423	18,777	200	32	19	mve	5,542 ceu
9476757	Ruby Ace	Cym	2010	60,148	18,724	200	32	19	mve	6,334 ceu
9338876	Salvia Ace	Cym	2008	42,401	15,013	186	28	19	mve	4,216 ceu
9409481	Sanderling Ace	Cym	2007	58,684	18,865	200	32	19	mve	5,222 teu
9051806	Sapphire Ace	Pan	1993	45,796	15,204	188	31	18	mve	4,055 ceu
9252228	Splendid Ace	Pan	2003	56,439	19,893	198	32	19	mve	5,281 ceu
9338864	Sunlight Ace	Bhs	2009	58,911	18,855	200	32	19	mve	5,220 ceu
9338840	Sunrise Ace	Bhs	2009	58,685	18,864	200	32	19	mve	5,220 ceu
9338852	Sunshine Ace	Bhs	2009	58,917	18,858	200	32	19	mve	5,220 ceu
9610391	Supreme Ace	Pan	2011	59,022	18,384	200	32	19	mve	6,163 ceu
9338620	Swallow Ace	Bhs	2007	58,685	18,864	200	32	20	mve	6,237 ceu
9338826	Swan Ace	Bhs	2008	58,685	18,867	200	32	20	mve	6,237 ceu
9338838	Swift Ace	Bhs	2008	58,685	18,865	200	32	20	mve	6,237 ceu
9561253	Tranquil Ace	Cym	2009	58,939	18,840	200	32	19	mve	6,233 ceu
9519121	Triton Ace	Pan	2009	60,876	22,723	200	32	19	mve	6,502 ceu
9209506	Triumph Ace	Pan	2000	55,880	20,131	194	32	20	mve	5,059 ceu
9610420	Valiant Ace	Mhl	2012	59,022	18,143	200	32	20	mve	6,163 ceu
9610406	Victorious Ace	Pan	2011	59,022	18,396	200	32	20	mve	6,163 ceu
9355197	Wisteria Ace	Cym	2007	59,952	17,325	200	32	20	mve	6,287 ceu

newbuildings:
4 x mve (Minaminippon (2017/8)

MOL LNG Transport (Europe) Ltd., U.K.

IMO	name	flag	year	gt	dwt	loa	bm	kts	type	comments
9338266	Al Aamriya	Mhl	2008	136,685	121,935	315	50	19	lng	210,168 m³
9307176	Al Deebel (st)	Bhs	2005	95,824	78,594	283	43	20	lng	145,000 m³
9613159	Beidou Star †	Hkg	2015	114,500	96,355	290	47	19	lng	172,000 m³
9265500	Dukhan *	Lbr	2004	111,162	72,533	298	46	19	lng	137,661 m³
9360817	Fraiha	Mhl	2008	136,685	121,914	315	50	19	lng	210,175 m³
9256200	Fuwairit	Bhs	2004	93,227	74,067	279	43	19	lng	138,200 m³
9375721	GDF Suez Point Fortin +	Pan	2010	101,129	79,592	289	45	20	lng	154,200 m³

Supreme Ace : Mitsui OSK Lines - MOL Auto Express : *ARO*

LNG Pioneer : Mitsui OSK Lines - MOL LNG Transport Europe : *Chris Brooks*

IMO	name	flag	year	gt	dwt	loa	bm	kts	type	comments
9360922	Gigira Laitebo	Bhs	2010	114,277	91,305	299	46	19	lng	177,410 m³: ex Abdelkader-14
7390181	LNG Aquarius (st)	Idn	1977	95,087	72,622	285	44	19	lng	126,400 m³
7390208	LNG Capricorn (st)	Mhl	1978	95,084	72,555	285	44	19	lng	126,400 m³
9256602	LNG Pioneer (st)	Bhs	2005	93,786	77,712	283	43	19	lng	138,122 m³ l/a Pioneer
9360805	Murwab	Mhl	2008	136,685	121,843	315	50	19	lng	210,075 m³
9613135	Papua	Hkg	2015	114,166	96,318	290	47	19	lng	172,000 m³
9613147	Southern Cross	Hkg	2015	114,166	96,319	290	47	19	lng	172,000 m³
9361639	Spirit of Hela	Bhs	2009	114,277	87,130	298	46	19	lng	177,410 m³ ex Ben Badis-14
9645736	LNG Venus (st)	Jpn	2014	136,710	86,241	288	49	19	lng	155,873 m³
9645748	LNG Mars (st)	Jpn	2015	136,700	86,300	288	49	19	lng	155,873 m³
newbuilding:										
9613161	Kumul	Hkg	2016	114,500	96,500	290	27	19	lng	172,000 m³ Hudong Zhonghua 1673A

owned by: * Qatar LNG Transport + Los Halillos Shg./Shoei Kisen Kaisha,

A. P. Møller

Denmark

A. P. Møller-Maersk A/S, Denmark

funnel: *black with white seven-pointed star on broad light blue band.* **hull:** *light blue with black 'Maersk Line', red boot-topping.*
history: *formed 2003 by merger of A/S Dampskibs Svendborg (founded 1904) and Dampskibs af 1912 A/S (founded 1912). Acquired liner services of Chargeurs Reunis and CMB (both 1987), also Torm (2002) and the container lines of Sea-Land and Safmarine (both 1999) and P&O Nedlloyd (2005). Acquired Brostrom AB in 2009.* **web:** *www.maersk.com or www.maerskline.com*

IMO	name	flag	year	gt	dwt	loa	bm	kts	type	comments
9214898	A. P. Møller	Dis	2000	92,198	110,381	347	43	25	ucc	9,600 teu
9260457	Adrian Maersk	Dis	2004	93,496	109,000	353	43	25	ucc	8,272 teu
9260469	Albert Maersk	Dis	2004	93,496	109,000	352	43	25	ucc	8,272 teu
9164237	Alexander Maersk	Dis	1998	14,120	17,375	155	25	18	ucc	1,092 teu: ex Adrian Maersk-04
9260421	Anna Maersk	Dis	2003	93,496	109,000	352	43	25	ucc	8,272 teu
9260433	Arnold Maersk	Dis	2003	93,496	109,000	352	43	25	ucc	8,272 teu
9260445	Arthur Maersk	Dis	2003	93,496	109,000	352	43	25	ucc	8,272 teu
9260419	Axel Maersk	Dis	2003	93,496	109,000	352	43	25	ucc	8,272 teu
9214903	Caroline Maersk	Dis	2000	92,198	110,381	347	43	25	ucc	9,600 teu
9219795	Carsten Maersk	Dis	2000	92,198	110,381	347	43	25	ucc	9,600 teu
9064401	Cecilie Maersk	Dis	1994	20,842	28,550	190	28	18	ucc	1,827 teu
9245744	Charlotte Maersk	Dis	2002	92,198	109,657	347	43	25	ucc	9,600 teu
9219800	Chastine Maersk	Dis	2001	92,198	110,387	347	43	25	ucc	9,600 teu
9064396	Claes Maersk	Dis	1994	20,842	28,550	190	28	18	ucc	1,827 teu
8820016	Clara Maersk	Dis	1992	18,979	25,275	176	28	18	ucc	1,658 teu
9245770	Clementine Maersk	Dis	2002	91,921	110,000	347	43	25	ucc	9,600 teu
9198575	Clifford Maersk	Dis	1999	92,198	110,387	347	43	25	ucc	9,600 teu
9245768	Columbine Maersk	Dis	2002	91,921	110,000	347	43	25	ucc	9.600 teu
9245756	Cornelia Maersk	Dis	2002	91,921	104,750	347	43	25	ucc	9,600 teu
9198587	Cornelius Maersk	Dis	2000	92,198	110,387	347	43	25	ucc	9,600 teu
9321524	Ebba Maersk	Dis	2007	170,794	156,900	398	56	25	ucc	15.508 teu
9321548	Edith Maersk	Dis	2007	170,794	156,900	398	56	25	ucc	15.508 teu
9321500	Eleonora Maersk	Dis	2007	170,794	156,900	398	56	25	ucc	15,508 teu
9321536	Elly Maersk	Dis	2007	170,794	156,907	398	56	25	ucc	15,508 teu
9321483	Emma Maersk	Dis	2006	170,794	156,907	398	56	25	ucc	15,508 teu
9321495	Estelle Maersk	Dis	2006	170,794	156,907	398	56	25	ucc	15,508 teu
9321550	Eugen Maersk	Dis	2008	170,794	156,907	398	56	25	ucc	15,508 teu
9321512	Evelyn Maersk	Dis	2007	170,794	156,907	398	56	25	ucc	15,508 teu
9320257	Georg Maersk	Dis	2006	98,648	115,700	367	43	25	ucc	10,888 teu
9320245	Gerd Maersk	Dis	2006	98,648	115,700	367	43	25	ucc	10,888 teu
9359052	Gerda Maersk	Dis	2009	98,268	116,100	367	43	25	ucc	10,150 teu: ex Mathilde Maersk-14
9359002	Gerner Maersk	Dis	2008	98,268	115,993	367	43	25	ucc	10,150 teu: ex Margrethe Maersk-14
9320233	Gjertrud Maersk	Dis	2005	98,648	115,700	367	43	25	ucc	10,888 teu
9302889	Grete Maersk	Dis	2005	98,648	115,700	367	43	25	ucc	10,888 teu
9302877	Gudrun Maersk	Bhs	2005	98,648	115,700	367	43	25	ucc	10,888 teu
9359014	Gunde Maersk	Dis	2008	98,268	115,993	367	43	25	ucc	10,150 teu: ex Marchen Maersk-14
9359026	Gunhilde Maersk	Dis	2009	98,268	115,993	367	43	25	ucc	10,150 teu: ex Maren Maersk-14
9302891	Gunvor Maersk	Dis	2005	98,648	115,700	367	43	25	ucc	10,888 teu
9359038	Gustav Maersk	Dis	2009	98,268	115,993	367	43	25	ucc	10,150 teu: ex Mette Maersk-14
9359040	Guthorm Maersk	Bhs	2009	98,268	115,993	367	43	25	ucc	10,150 teu: ex Marit Maersk-14
9215177	Jens Maersk	Dis	2001	30,166	27,300	216	32	23	ucc	2,833 teu
9215165	Jepperson Maersk	Dis	2001	30,166	35,097	216	32	22	ucc	2,833 teu
9215189	Johannes Maersk	Dis	2001	30,166	27,300	216	32	23	ucc	2,833 teu
9215191	Josephine Maersk	Dis	2002	30,166	27,300	216	32	23	ucc	2,833 teu
9294379	Lars Maersk	Dis	2004	50,657	62,994	266	37	24	ucc	4,248 teu
9190731	Laura Maersk	Dis	2001	50,721	63,200	266	37	24	ucc	4,258 teu
9190743	Laust Maersk	Dis	2001	50,721	63,000	266	37	24	ucc	4,258 teu
9190755	Leda Maersk	Dis	2001	50,721	63,200	266	37	24	ucc	4,258 teu
9190767	Lexa Maersk	Dis	2001	50,721	63,400	266	37	24	ucc	4,258 teu
9190779	Lica Maersk	Dis	2001	50,721	63,400	266	37	24	ucc	4,258 teu

IMO	name	flag	year	gt	dwt	loa	bm	kts	type	comments
9190781	Luna Maersk	Dis	2002	50,721	63,395	266	37	25	ucc	4,259 teu: ex DAL Stellenbosch-14, Luna Maersk-13
9619945	Madison Maersk (2)	Dis	2014	194,849	194,394	399	59	22	ucc	18,270 teu
9164225	Maersk Ahram *	Egy	1998	14,063	17,728	155	25	18	ucc	1,092 teu
9313929	Maersk Bentonville	Dis	2006	48,853	53,201	294	32	29	ucc	4,196 teu: ex Bentonville-13, Maersk Bentonville-10
9313931	Maersk Brooklyn	Dis	2007	48,853	53,201	294	32	29	ucc	4,196 teu: ex Brooklyn-12, Maersk Brooklyn-10
9525493	Maersk Cabinda	Sgp	2012	50,869	61,570	249	37	21	ucc	4,500 teu
9525479	Maersk Cairo	Hkg	2012	50,869	61,561	249	37	21	ucc	4,500 teu
9235567	Maersk Gairloch	Dis	2002	50,698	62,242	292	32	24	ucc	4,318 teu

Maersk Savannah : A. P. Møller-Maersk A/S : *Chris Brooks*

Magleby Maersk : A. P. Møller-Maersk A/S : *Nico Kemps*

IMO	name	flag	year	gt	dwt	loa	bm	kts	type	comments
9235579	Maersk Garonne	Dis	2003	50,698	61,636	282	32	24	ucc	4,318 teu: ex DAL Karoo-13, Maersk Garonne-12
9235543	Maersk Gateshead	Dis	2002	50,686	62,242	292	32	24	ucc	4,318 teu
9235555	Maersk Gironde	Dis	2002	50,757	61,636	292	32	24	ucc	4,318 teu
9162227	Maersk Kimi †	Nld	1998	80,942	88,669	300	43	24	ucc	6,930 teu: ex P&O Nedlloyd Kowloon-06
9526899	Maersk La Paz	Hkg	2011	89,097	106,043	300	46	22	ucc	8,850 teu
9526875	Maersk Lima	Hkg	2011	89,097	106,043	300	46	22	ucc	8,850 teu
9526887	Maersk Lirquen	Hkg	2011	89,097	106,043	300	46	22	ucc	8,850 teu
9619907	Maersk Mc-Kinney Møller (2)	Dnk	2013	194,849	194,153	399	59	22	ucc	18,340 teu
9356127	Maersk Newport	Dis	2008	25,888	35,483	210	30	22	ucc	2,474 teu
9356139	Maersk Norfolk	Dis	2008	25,888	35,205	207	30	22	ucc	2,474 teu
9352016	Maersk Salalah	Dis	2008	92,293	107,978	334	46	25	ucc	9,662 teu
9352030	Maersk Salina	Hkg	2008	92,293	107,978	334	43	25	ucc	9,662 teu
9732591	Maersk Sarat [F]	Lbr	2015	92,628	111,614	300	48	22	ucc	9,443 teu: l/d Aristoklis
9352028	Maersk Savannah	Dis	2008	92,293	107,978	334	46	25	ucc	9,662 teu
9728253	Maersk Shivling [F]		2016	93,000	111,000	300	48	21	ucc	9,162 teu: l/d Aristomenis D Mangalia 4098
9740457	Maersk Skarstind [F]	Lbr	2016	93,702	111,614	300	48	22	ucc	9,472 teu: l/d Asklipos
9352004	Maersk Stepnica	Dis	2008	92,293	107,978	334	46	25	ucc	9,662 teu
9352042	Maersk Stockholm	Hkg	2008	92,293	107,978	334	43	25	ucc	9,662 teu
9619957	Magelby Maersk (2)	Dis	2014	194,849	194,496	399	59	22	ucc	18,340 teu
9619919	Majestic Maersk (2)	Dis	2013	194,849	194,431	399	59	22	ucc	18,340 teu
9632143	Marchen Maersk (2)	Dis	2015	194,849	194,897	399	59	22	ucc	18,340 teu
9632129	Maren Maersk (2)	Dis	2014	194,849	195,118	399	59	22	ucc	18,340 teu
9632064	Marete Maersk (2)	Dis	2014	194,849	194,915	399	59	22	ucc	18,340 teu
9632131	Margrethe Maersk (2)	Dis	2015	194,849	195,071	399	59	22	ucc	18,340 teu
9619969	Maribo Maersk (2)	Dis	2014	194,849	194,433	399	59	22	ucc	18,340 teu
9619933	Marie Maersk (2)	Dis	2013	194,849	194,327	399	59	22	ucc	18,340 teu
9632167	Marit Maersk (2)	Dis	2015	194,849	194,500	399	59	22	ucc	18,340 teu
9619971	Marstal Maersk (2)	Dis	2014	194,849	194,692	399	59	22	ucc	18,340 teu
9619921	Mary Maersk (2)	Dis	2013	194,849	194,252	399	59	22	ucc	18,340 teu
9632179	Mathilde Maersk (2)	Dis	2015	194,849	194,500	399	59	22	ucc	18,340 teu
9619983	Matz Maersk (2)	Dis	2014	194,849	194,283	399	59	22	ucc	18,340 teu
9619995	Mayview Maersk (2)	Dis	2014	194,849	194,533	399	59	22	ucc	18,340 teu
8819990	MCC Mergui	Dis	1992	16,982	21,825	162	28	18	ucc	1,446 teu: ex Thies Maersk-16, Cornelia Maersk-01
9632155	Mette Maersk (2)	Dis	2015	194,849	194,829	399	59	22	ucc	18,340 teu
9632090	Mogens Maersk (2)	Dis	2014	194,849	194,679	399	59	22	ucc	18,340 teu
9632105	Morten Maersk (2)	Dis	2014	194,849	194,790	399	59	22	ucc	18,340 teu
9632117	Munkebo Maersk (2)	Dis	2015	194,849	194,690	399	59	22	ucc	18,340 teu
9192442	Nele Maersk	Dis	2000	27,733	30,194	199	30	21	ucc	2,240 teu
9220885	Nexø Maersk	Dis	2001	27,733	30,420	199	30	21	ucc	2,240 teu
9192454	Nicolai Maersk	Dis	2000	27,733	30,420	199	30	21	ucc	2,240 teu
9192466	Nicoline Maersk	Dis	2000	27,733	30,191	199	30	21	ucc	2,240 teu
9192478	Nora Maersk	Dis	2000	27,733	30,194	199	30	21	ucc	2,240 teu
9220897	Nysted Maersk	Dis	2001	27,733	30,194	197	30	21	ucc	2,240 teu
9251614	Olga Maersk	Dis	2003	34,202	41,028	237	32	24	ucc	3,028 teu
9251638	Olivia Maersk	Dis	2003	34,202	41,097	237	32	24	ucc	3,028 teu
9251626	Oluf Maersk	Dis	2003	34,202	41,028	237	32	24	ucc	3,028 teu
9120865	Sally Maersk	Dis	1998	92,198	110,387	347	43	25	ucc	9,200 teu
9146455	Sine Maersk	Dis	1998	92,198	110,381	347	43	25	ucc	9,200 teu
9166792	Skagen Maersk	Dis	1999	92,198	110,387	347	43	25	ucc	9,200 teu
9146479	Sofie Maersk	Dis	1999	92,198	110,381	347	43	25	ucc	9,200 teu
9166780	Sorø Maersk	Dis	1999	92,198	110,387	347	43	25	ucc	9,200 teu
9120841	Sovereign Maersk	Dis	1997	92,198	110,381	347	43	25	ucc	9,200 teu
9120853	Susan Maersk	Dis	1997	92,198	110,387	347	43	25	ucc	9,200 teu
9166778	Svend Maersk	Dis	1999	92,198	110,381	347	43	25	ucc	9,200 teu
9146467	Svendborg Maersk	Dis	1998	92,198	110,387	347	43	25	ucc	9,200 teu
9064684	Tåsinge Maersk	Dis	1994	20,842	28,550	190	28	18	ucc	1,827 teu: ex Maersk California-02, Caroline Maersk-97
9064267	Thomas Maersk	Dis	1994	18,859	25,368	176	28	18	ucc	1,446 teu: ex Maersk Tennesse-02, Thomas Maersk-97
8819976	Thurø Maersk	Dis	1991	16,982	21,825	162	28	18	ucc	1,446 teu: ex Chastine Maersk-01
9064279	Tinglev Maersk	Dis	1994	18,859	25,431	176	28	18	ucc	1,325 teu: ex Maersk Texas-02, Tinglev Maersk-97
8819988	Tove Maersk	Dis	1992	16,982	21,825	162	28	18	ucc	1,446 teu: ex Charlotte Maersk-01
8820004	Troense Maersk	Dis	1992	16,982	21,825	162	28	18	ucc	1,446 teu: ex Maersk Colorado-03, Clifford Maersk-97

newbuildings:

IMO	name	flag	year	gt	dwt	loa	bm	kts	type	comments
9778791		Dnk	2017	196,000	200.000	400	59		ucc	19,630 teu Daewoo 4302

IMO	name	flag	year	gt	dwt	loa	bm	kts	type	comments
9778806			2017	196,000	200,000	400	59		ucc	19,630 teu Daewoo 4303
9778818			2017	196,000	200,000	400	59			19,630 teu Daewoo 4304
9778820			2017	196,000	200,000	400	59			19,630 teu Daewoo 4305
9778832			2017	196,000	200,000	400	59			19,630 teu Daewoo 4306
9778844			2017	196,000	200,000	400	59			19,630 teu Daewoo 4307
9780445			2017	196,000	200,000	400	59			19,630 teu Daewoo 4308
9780457			2018	196,000	200,000	400	59			19,630 teu Daewoo 4309
9780469			2018	196,000	200,000	400	59			19,630 teu Daewoo 4310
9780471			2018	196,000	200,000	400	59			19,630 teu Daewoo 4311
9780283			2018	196,000	200,000	400	59			19,630 teu Daewoo 4312
										14,000 teu Hyundai 2871 01.2017
										14,000 teu Hyundai 2872 02.2017
										14,000 teu Hyundai 2873 03.2017
										14,000 teu Hyundai 2874 04.2017
										14,000 teu Hyundai 2875 05.2017
										14,000 teu Hyundai 2876 06.2017
										14,000 teu Hyundai 2877 07.2017
										14,000 teu Hyundai 2878 08.2017
										14,000 teu Hyundai 2879 09.2017

newbuildings: 7 x 3,600teu ucc 200 x 35.2 [COSCO SY Gp. Zhoushan (April 2017/8)] for Seago
11 x 19,630 teu ucc 400 x 59m [DSME (2017)] in list
9 (+ 8 options) x 14,000teu ucc (Hyundai HI (2017)) for Maersk Singapore options may not be taken up, Nov. 2015 report
*vessels are owned or managed by subsidiaries * by Maersk Egypt SAE, Egypt*
[F] by Ship Finance International
† by various finance houses
≠ owned/managed by Eastwind Group or ‡‡ by MC Shipping. See also MPC Munchmeyer Petersen & Co.

Maersk Shipping Hong Kong Ltd.
hull *and* **funnel:** *as above.* **history:** *founded 1975.* **web:** *www.maerskline.com*

IMO	name	flag	year	gt	dwt	loa	bm	kts	type	comments
9175781	Antwerp	Hkg	1999	14,063	17,720	155	25	18	ucc	1,092 teu: ex Maersk Antwerp-13
9175793	Maersk Aberdeen	Hkg	1999	14,130	17,720	155	25	18	ucc	1,092 teu
9164249	Maersk Arizona	Hkg	1998	14,120	17,375	155	25	18	ucc	1,092 teu: ex Agnete Maersk-08
9164245	Maersk Arun	Hkg	1999	14,063	14,175	155	25	18	ucc	1,092 teu
9175808	Maersk Atlantic	Hkg	1999	14,063	17,720	155	25	18	ucc	1,092 teu: ex Swan River Bridge-00, Maersk Atlantic-99
9164275	Maersk Avon	Hkg	1999	14,063	17,728	155	25	18	ucc	1,092 teu
9525455	Maersk Cabo Verde	Hkg	2012	50,869	61,643	249	37	21	ucc	4,500 teu
9525479	Maersk Cairo	Hkg	2012	50,869	61,561	249	37	21	ucc	4,500 teu
9525467	Maersk Casablanca	Hkg	2012	50,869	61,588	249	37	21	ucc	4,500 teu
9525481	Maersk Cubango	Hkg	2012	50,869	61,608	249	37	21	ucc	4,500 teu
9155119	Maersk Georgia	Hkg	1997	50,698	62,242	292	32	24	ucc	4,306 teu: ex Gudrun Maersk-02
9162215	Maersk Karachi	Hkg	1998	80,942	88,669	300	43	24	ucc	6,674 teu: ex P&O Nedlloyd Kobe-06
9153850	Maersk Kiel	Hkg	1998	80,942	88,669	300	43	24	ucc	6,674 teu: ex P&O Nedlloyd Southampton-06
9211482	Maersk Klaipeda	Hkg	2001	80,654	87,343	300	43	24	ucc	6,802 teu: ex Maersk Kingston-07, P&O Nedlloyd Stuyvesant-06
9211494	Maersk Kyrenia	Hkg	2001	80,654	87,343	300	43	24	ucc	6,802 teu: ex P&O Nedlloyd Shackleton
9526978	Maersk Laberinto	Hkg	2012	89,505	99,863	300	45	24	ucc	8,850 teu
9527063	Maersk Labrea	Hkg	2013	89,505	99,798	300	45	24	ucc	8,850 teu
9527051	Maersk Lamanai	Hkg	2013	89,505	99,865	300	45	24	ucc	8,850 teu
9527049	Maersk Lanco	Hkg	2013	89,505	99,792	300	45	24	ucc	8,850 teu
9526928	Maersk Lavras	Hkg	2011	89,097	106,043	300	45	24	ucc	8,850 teu
9526930	Maersk Lebu	Hkg	2011	89,097	106,043	300	45	22	ucc	8,850 teu
9526916	Maersk Leticia	Hkg	2011	89,097	106,043	300	45	22	ucc	8,850 teu
9527025	Maersk Lins	Hkg	2012	89,505	100,062	300	45	24	ucc	8,850 teu
9527037	Maersk Londrina	Hkg	2012	89,505	99,778	300	45	24	ucc	8,850 teu
9526904	Maersk Luz	Hkg	2011	89,097	106,043	300	46	22	ucc	8,850 teu
9105932	Maersk Wyoming	Hkg	1996	50,698	61,927	292	32	24	ucc	3,614 teu: ex Dirch Maersk-09
9355355	Safmarine Bayete	Hkg	2009	35,835	43,197	223	32	22	ucc	2,787 teu
9355367	Safmarine Benguela	Hkg	2009	35,835	43,197	223	32	22	ucc	2,787 teu
9525388	Safmarine Chachai	Hkg	2012	50,869	61,614	249	37	21	ucc	4,500 teu
9525376	Safmarine Chambal	Hkg	2012	50,869	62,557	249	37	21	ucc	4,500 teu
9525364	Safmarine Chilka	Hkg	2012	50,869	61,614	249	37	21	ucc	4,500 teu
9314210	Safmarine Mafadi	Hkg	2007	50,698	61,433	292	32	25	ucc	4,154 teu
9318319	Safmarine Makutu	Hkg	2007	50,698	61,407	292	32	25	ucc	4,154 teu
9311696	Safmarine Meru	Hkg	2006	50,686	61,392	292	32	25	ucc	4,154 teu
9311701	Safmarine Mulanje	Hkg	2007	50,686	61,447	292	32	25	ucc	4,154 teu
9356103	Safmarine Nakuru	Hkg	2008	25,904	35,137	211	30	21	ucc	2,478 teu
9356098	Safmarine Nile	Hkg	2008	25,904	35,181	211	30	21	ucc	2,478 teu
9294381	Safmarine Nomazwe	Hkg	2004	50,657	62,994	266	37	25	ucc	4,045 teu

IMO	name	flag	year	gt	dwt	loa	bm	kts	type	comments
9356115	Safmarine Nuba	Hkg	2008	25,904	35,144	211	30	21	ucc	2,478 teu
9356086	Safmarine Nyassa	Hkg	2008	25,904	35,292	211	30	21	ucc	2,478 teu
9106170	Sea Land Champion	Hkg	1995	49,985	59,840	292	32	24	ucc	4,082 teu
9143013	Sea-Land Eagle	Hkg	1997	49,985	59,840	292	32	24	ucc	4,082 teu
9106194	Sea-Land Mercury	Hkg	1995	49,985	59,961	292	32	24	ucc	4,082 teu: ex CSX Mercury-03, Sea-Land Mercury-00
9106209	Sea-Land Meteor	Hkg	1996	49,985	59,938	292	32	24	ucc	4,082 teu
9116890	Sea-Land Racer	Hkg	1996	49,985	59,964	292	32	24	ucc	4,082 teu: ex MSC Everest-09, Sea-Land Racer-07

vessels managed by Moller-Maersk A/S

A. P. Moller Singapore Pte. Ltd., Singapore

hull *and* **funnel:** *as above.* **history:** *formed 1978 as Maersk Co. (Singapore) Pte Ltd to 1989.* **web:** *www.apmsingapore.com.sg*

IMO	name	flag	year	gt	dwt	loa	bm	kts	type	comments
9193276	Grasmere Maersk	Sgp	2000	50,698	62,007	292	32	24	ucc	4,338 teu
9342516	Maersk Alfirk	Sgp	2008	108,393	110,401	338	46	25	ucc	9,580 teu
9342528	Maersk Algol	Sgp	2008	108,393	110,228	338	46	25	ucc	9,580 teu
9342499	Maersk Altair	Sgp	2007	108,393	110,295	338	46	25	ucc	9,580 teu
9342504	Maersk Antares	Sgp	2007	108,393	110,271	338	46	25	ucc	9,580 teu
9394870	Maersk Bali	Sgp	2008	35,835	43,206	224	32	22	ucc	3,194 teu
9355331	Maersk Batam	Sgp	2008	35,835	43,133	224	32	22	ucc	3,194 teu
9402029	Maersk Batur	Sgp	2009	35,835	43,273	224	32	22	ucc	3,194 teu
9355288	Maersk Bintan	Sgp	2008	35,835	43,097	224	32	22	ucc	3,194 teu
9394882	Maersk Bogor	Sgp	2009	35,835	43,177	223	32	22	ucc	3,194 teu
9409352	Maersk Brani	Sgp	2010	35,835	43,239	223	32	22	ucc	3,194 teu
9394894	Maersk Bratan	Sgp	2009	35,835	43,114	223	32	22	ucc	3,194 teu
9355343	Maersk Balam	Sgp	2008	35,836	43,177	224	32	22	ucc	3,194 teu
9392925	Maersk Buton	Sgp	2008	35,835	43,123	224	32	22	ucc	3,194 teu
9525302	Maersk Calabar	Sgp	2011	50,869	61,614	249	37	21	ucc	4,500 teu
9525326	Maersk Cameroun	Sgp	2011	50,869	61,614	249	37	21	ucc	4,500 teu
9525314	Maersk Cape Coast	Sgp	2011	50,869	61,614	249	37	21	ucc	4,500 teu
9525352	Maersk Cape Town	Sgp	2011	50,869	61,614	249	37	21	ucc	4,500 teu
9525338	Maersk Chennai	Sgp	2011	50,869	61,614	249	37	21	ucc	4,500 teu
9525390	Maersk Colombo	Sgp	2012	50,869	61,614	249	37	21	ucc	4,500 teu
9525285	Maersk Conokry	Sgp	2011	50,869	61,614	249	37	21	ucc	4,500 teu
9525340	Maersk Congo	Sgp	2011	50,869	61,614	249	37	21	ucc	4,500 teu
9525405	Maersk Copenhagen	Sgp	2012	50,869	61,120	249	37	21	ucc	4,500 teu
9525297	Maersk Cotonou	Sgp	2011	50,869	61,614	249	37	21	ucc	4,500 teu
9561497	Maersk Cuanza	Sgp	2012	50,869	61,614	249	37	21	ucc	4,500 teu
9561485	Maersk Cunene	Sgp	2011	50,869	61,614	249	37	21	ucc	4,500 teu
9694579	Maersk Danube	Sgp	2014	51,872	62,292	255	37	20	ucc	5,466 teu: ex Maersk Nile-15, l/a Wide Foxtrot
9694581	Maersk Ganges	Sgp	2014	51,872	65,223	255	37	20	ucc	5,466 teu: ex Maersk Tigris-15, l/a Wide Golf
9348170	Maersk Innoshima	Sgp	2008	35,491	41,337	232	32	22	ucc	3,364 teu
9348156	Maersk Inverness	Sgp	2008	35,491	41,350	232	32	22	ucc	3,364 teu
9348168	Maersk Izmir	Sgp	2008	35,491	41,238	232	32	22	ucc	3,364 teu
9294161	Maersk Jalan	Sgp	2005	28,592	39,384	221	30	23	ucc	2,824 teu: ex Maersk Juan-15, Jaun-05

Maersk Lota : Moller-Maersk - AP Moller Singapore : *Hans Kraijenbosch*

IMO	name	flag	year	gt	dwt	loa	bm	kts	type	comments
9526942	Maersk Laguna	Sgp	2012	89,096	106,043	300	46	22	ucc	8,850 teu
9526966	Maersk Leon	Sgp	2012	89,505	98,858	300	45	22	ucc	8,850 teu
9526954	Maersk Lota	Sgp	2012	89,505	100,072	300	45	22	ucc	8,850 teu
9231470	Maersk Newbury	Sgp	2001	26,582	34,662	210	30	21	ucc	2,556 teu: ex Caroline Schulte-15, Cap Bisti-11, Libra Houston-06, Caroline Schulte-02, Thekla Schulte-01
9215878	Maersk Newcastle	Sgp	2001	26,626	34,717	210	30	22	ucc	2,556 teu: ex Anna Schulte-15, P&O Nedlloyd Andes-05, P&O Nedlloyd Rose-01, l/a Anna Schulte
9215880	Maersk Newhaven	Sgp	2001	26,626	34,717	210	30	22	ucc	2,556 teu; ex Susanne Schulte-15, P&O Nedlloyd Aconcagua-05, l/a Susanne Schulte
9215919	Maersk Northampton	Sgp	2001	26,718	34,677	210	30	22	ucc	2,556 teu; ex Thekla Schulte-15, P&O Nedlloyd Antisana-05, Thekla Schulte-01, l/a Caroline Schulte
9222118	Maersk Northwood	Sgp	2001	26,582	33,871	210	30	22	ucc	2,556 teu: ex Cape Bianco-16, Esther Schulte-15, P&O Nedlloyd Altiplano-05, Esther Schulte-02, l/a Marianne Schulte
9168207	Maersk Palermo	Nld	1998	31,333	38,250	210	32	22	ucc	2,890 teu: ex P&O Nedlloyd Auckland-06
9168221	Maersk Patras	Sgp	1998	31,333	37,845	210	32	22	ucc	2,890 teu: ex P&O Nedlloyd Marseille-06
9168180	Maersk Pembroke	Nld	1998	31,333	38,400	210	32	22	ucc	2,890 teu: ex P&O Nedlloyd Sydney-06
9168192	Maersk Penang	Nld	1998	31,333	38,170	210	32	22	ucc	2,890 teu: ex P&O Nedlloyd Jakarta-06
9168219	Maersk Phuket	Sgp	1998	31,333	37,845	210	32	22	ucc	2,890 teu: ex P&O Nedlloyd Genoa-06
9315238	Maersk Sebarok	Sgp	2007	79,702	87,534	318	40	25	ucc	5,648 teu
9315197	Maersk Seletar	Sgp	2007	79,702	87,545	318	40	25	ucc	5,648 teu
9315252	Maersk Semakau	Sgp	2007	79,702	87,621	318	40	25	ucc	5,648 teu
9315226	Maersk Sembawang	Sgp	2007	79,702	87,534	318	40	25	ucc	5,648 teu
9315240	Maersk Senang	Sgp	2007	79,702	87,608	318	40	25	ucc	5,648 teu
9315202	Maersk Sentosa	Sgp	2007	79,702	87,618	318	40	25	ucc	5,648 teu
9315214	Maersk Serangoon	Sgp	2007	79,702	87,624	318	40	25	ucc	5,648 teu
9334662	Maersk Taikung	Sgp	2007	94,193	107,329	332	43	24	ucc	8,112 teu
9332511	Maersk Tanjong	Sgp	2007	94,193	107,500	332	43	24	ucc	8,112 teu
9334674	Maersk Taurus	Sgp	2008	94,193	107,266	332	43	24	ucc	8,112 teu
9334686	Maersk Tukang	Sgp	2008	94,193	107,404	332	43	24	ucc	8,112 teu
9411381	Maersk Vallvik	Sgp	2011	20,927	25,500	180	28	20	ucc	1,800 teu
9411379	Maersk Varna	Sgp	2011	20,927	25,500	180	28	20	ucc	1,800 teu
9408956	Maersk Vilnius	Sgp	2010	20,927	26,036	180	28	20	ucc	1,800 teu
9411367	Maersk Visby	Sgp	2010	20,927	26,036	180	28	20	ucc	1,800 teu
9292137	Maersk Volta	Sgp	2005	18,334	23,351	176	28	19	ucc	1,696 teu: ex Maximilian Schulte-13, CSAV Rotterdam-11, l/a Maximilian Schulte, l/dn Laura Schulte
9215907	Marianne	Sgp	2001	26,718	34,643	210	30	21	ucc	2,556 teu: ex Marianne Schulte-15, P&O Nedlloyd Acapulco-05, l/a Marianne Schulte

Marianne : Moller-Maersk - AP Moller Singapore : *Hans Kraijenbosch*

IMO	name	flag	year	gt	dwt	loa	bm	kts	type	comments
9289180	Safmarine Cameroun +	Sgp	2004	24,488	28,936	196	32	20	ucc	2,096 teu
9289207	Safmarine Kuramo +	Sgp	2004	24,488	28,844	196	32	20	ucc	2,096 teu
9289192	Safmarine Nimba +	Sgp	2004	24,488	28,897	196	32	20	ucc	2,096 teu
9106182	Sea-Land Comet	Sgp	1995	49,985	59,840	292	32	24	ucc	4,082 teu
9143001	Sea-Land Charger	Sgp	1997	49,985	59,961	292	32	24	ucc	4,082 teu
9143025	Sea-Land Intrepid	Sgp	1997	49,985	59,840	292	32	24	ucc	4,082 teu
9143037	Sea-Land Lightning	Sgp	1996	49,985	59,938	292	32	24	ucc	4,082 teu
9356165	Mercosul Manaus **	Bra	2009	25,888	35,220	207	30	22	ucc	2,474 teu
9356153	Mercosul Santos ***	Bra	2009	25,888	35,239	207	30	22	ucc	2,487 teu
9356141	Mercosul Suape ***	Bra	2008	25,888	35,221	207	30	22	ucc	2,474 teu

* owned by Maersk b.v. and managed by The Maersk Co.U.K. Ltd.
** owned by Maersk b.v. and operated by Mercosul Line Navegacao, Brasil
***owned by Mercosul Line Navegacao, Brasil and managed by A.P. Møller Singapore AP Pte. Ltd.

The Maersk Co. Ltd., U.K.
hull and **funnel:** As above. **history:** formed 1972. **web:** www.maersk.co.uk

IMO	name	flag	year	gt	dwt	loa	bm	kts	type	comments
9153862	Maersk Kalmar *	Nld	1998	80,942	88,669	300	43	24	ucc	6,674 teu: ex P&O Nedlloyd Rotterdam-06
9215311	Maersk Kampala *	Nld	2001	80,654	88,967	300	43	24	ucc	6,674 teu: ex P&O Nedlloyd Houtman-06
9215323	Maersk Kithira	Hkg	2001	80,654	88,700	300	43	24	ucc	5,618 teu: ex P&O Nedlloyd Cook-06
9167150	Maersk Rapier	Iom	2000	22,181	34,985	171	27	15	tco	ex Robert Maersk-00

* vessels owned by Maersk b.v., managed by Maersk Co, UK Ltd.

Maersk Line Ltd., U.S.A.
hull and **funnel:** As above. **history:** formed 1947. **web:** www.maersklinelimited.com

IMO	name	flag	year	gt	dwt	loa	bm	kts	type	comments
9303546	Alliance Fairfax *	Usa	2005	52,691	21,500	199	32	19	mve	5,400 ceu: ex Höegh Kyoto-13, Maersk Willow-08
9303558	Alliance Richmond *	Usa	2006	52,691	21,500	199	32	19	mve	5,400 ceu: ex Höegh Chiba-12, Maersk Welkin-08
9332547	Alliance Norfolk *	Usa	2007	57,280	15,880	200	32	20	mve	6,000 ceu: ex Höegh Madrid-07
9285500	Alliance St. Louis *	Usa	2006	57,280	15,972	200	32	20	mve	6,000 ceu: ex Höegh Paris-08, Hual Paris-06
9457218	Cragside	Usa	2011	29,429	11,325	193	26	20	urr	
9164251	Maersk Arkansas	Usa	1998	14,120	17,375	155	25	18	ucc	1,092 teu: ex Angelica Maersk-04, Albert Maersk-04
9348649	Maersk Atlanta	Usa	2006	74,642	84,676	299	40	25	ucc	6,477 teu: ex Maersk Kowloon-13
8820195	Maersk California	Usa	1992	18,979	25,375	176	28	18	ucc	1,394 teu: ex Christian Maersk-08
9155133	Maersk Carolina	Usa	1998	50,698	62,229	292	32	24	ucc	4,306 teu: ex Grete Maersk-02
9332975	Maersk Chicago	Usa	2007	74,642	84,775	299	40	25	ucc	6,477 teu: ex Maersk Kuantan-13
9332987	Maersk Columbus	Usa	2007	74,642	84,704	299	40	25	ucc	6,477 teu: ex Maersk Kushiro-13
9332999	Maersk Denver	Usa	2007	74,642	84,771	300	43	24	ucc	6,188 teu: ex Maersk Kendal-13
9333034	Maersk Detroit	Usa	2008	74,642	84,626	299	40	25	ucc	6,188 teu: ex Safmarine Kariba-13
9333008	Maersk Hartford	Usa	2007	74,642	84,783	300	43	24	ucc	6,188 teu: ex Maersk Kelso-13
9193264	Maersk Idaho	Usa	2000	50,698	61,986	292	32	24	ucc	4,338 teu: ex Gosport Maersk-09
9298686	Maersk Iowa	Usa	2006	50,686	61,454	292	32	24	ucc	4,154 teu: ex Maersk Greenock-07
9333010	Maersk Kensington	Usa	2007	74,642	84,897	300	43	24	ucc	6,188 teu
9193240	Maersk Kentucky	Usa	1999	50,698	61,986	292	32	24	ucc	4,338 teu: ex Glasgow Maersk-09
9333022	Maersk Kinloss	Usa	2008	74,642	84,835	299	40	24	ucc	6,188 teu
9348651	Maersk Memphis	Usa	2007	74,642	84,676	299	40	25	ucc	6,477 teu: Maersk Kwangyang-13
9255244	Maersk Michigan	Usa	2003	28,517	47,047	183	32	14	tco	ex Marco-08, St. Marco-08
9155121	Maersk Missouri	Usa	1998	50,698	62,226	292	32	24	ucc	4,306 teu: ex Gerd Maersk-02
9305312	Maersk Montana	Usa	2006	50,686	61.499	292	32	24	ucc	4,154 teu: ex Maersk Guernsey-07
9298698	Maersk Ohio	Usa	2006	50,686	61,454	292	32	24	ucc	4,154 teu: ex Maersk Gosforth-07
9278492	Maersk Peary	Usa	2004	25,487	38,177	183	32	14	tco	ex Jutul-11
9342176	Maersk Pittsburg	Usa	2008	74,642	84,688	299	40	25	ucc	6,188 teu: ex Safmarine Komati-13
9305300	Maersk Utah	Usa	2006	50,686	62,000	292	32	25	ucc	4,154 teu: ex Maersk Gloucester-09
9235531	Maersk Virginia	Usa	2002	50,686	62,009	292	32	24	ucc	4,318 teu: ex Maersk Geelong-03
9193252	Maersk Wisconsin	Usa	2000	50,698	62,441	292	32	24	ucc	4,338 teu: ex Greenwich Maersk-09
9356074	Safmarine Ngami	Usa	2008	25,904	35,119	211	30	21	ucc	2,478 teu
9430222	Safmarine Shaba **	Hkg	2012	14,859	18,010	162	25	17	ggc	

* owned by Wilmington Trust Co., USA and operated by Farrell Lines; also owns twelve other vessels long-term chartered to US military fleet
** owned by Safmarine MPV Ltd., vessels managed by Enzian Ship Mgmt

Safmarine Container Lines, Belgium
funnel: blue with 'Safmarine' houseflag (white with orange cross) on large white disc. **hull:** white with blue 'Safmarine',or blue with white 'Safmarine', red or green boot-topping. **history:** container subsidiary founded 1996 as Safmarine & CMBT Lines NV to 1998 and acquired 1999. **web:** www.safmarine.com

IMO	name	flag	year	gt	dwt	loa	bm	kts	type	comments
9294393	Safmarine Nokwanda	Hkg	2005	50,657	62,994	266	37	24	ucc	4,045 teu

vessel managed by A.P. Møller-Maersk AS, also see other chartered vessels with 'Safmarine' prefix in index.

Seago Lines, Denmark

funnel: *white with double arrow head device* **hull :** *blue with 'Seago' in white* **history :** *founded 2011 as Maersk's intra-European and Mediterranean carrier* **web:** *www.seagoline.com*

IMO	name	flag	year	gt	dwt	loa	bm	kts	type	comments
9313905	Seago Antwerp *	Dis	2006	48,808	53,701	294	32	29	ucc	4,196 teu: ex Maersk Boston-12, Boston-12, Maersk Boston
9313967	Seago Bremerhaven **	Dis	2007	48,853	53,890	294	32	29	ucc	4,196 teu: ex Maersk Beaumont-12, Beaumont-12, Maersk Beaumont-10
9313917	Seago Felixstowe *	Dis	2006	48,853	53,634	294	32	29	ucc	4,196 teu: ex Baltimore-12, Maersk Baltimore-10
9313943	Seago Istanbul **	Dis	2007	48,853	53,701	294	32	29	ucc	4,196 teu: ex Maersk Buffalo-12, Buffalo-12, Maersk Buffalo-11
9313955	Seago Piraeus **	Dis	2007	48,853	53,807	294	32	29	ucc	4,196 teu: ex Maersk Brownsville-13, Brownsville-12, Maersk Brownsville-11

*managed by *Maersk Line A/S   ** The Maersk Co. UK Ltd.*
newbuildings : *7 [2] x 3,600teu [COSCO (04-11:2017)]*

Maersk Tankers A/S

hull *and* **funnel:** *as above.* **history:** *.* **web:** *www.maersktankers.com*

IMO	name	flag	year	gt	dwt	loa	bm	kts	type	comments
9340582	Brigit Maersk	Dis	2006	19,758	29,017	175	29	14	tco	
9341433	Britta Maersk	Dis	2007	19,758	29,017	175	29	14	tco	
9171503	Carla Maersk +	Dis	1999	29,289	44,999	183	32	15	tco	ex Maersk Carla-11, Bro Promotion-10, Iver Example-06
9219276	Freja Maersk +	Dis	2001	21,517	31,632	177	28	14	tco	ex Bro Provider-10, Iver Prosperity-06
9219264	Frida Maersk +	Dis	2001	21,517	31,687	177	28	14	tco	ex Bro Priority-10, Iver Progress-05
9423712	Karen Maersk	Dis	2010	24,412	39,708	183	28	15	tco	
9299458	Maersk Barry	Dis	2006	19,758	29,040	176	29	14	tco	
9299434	Maersk Bristol	Dis	2006	19,758	29,050	176	29	14	tco	
9274630	Maersk Edgar +	Dis	2004	26,634	37,188	186	31	15	tco	ex Bro Edgar -10, Geestestern-06
9274654	Maersk Edward	Dis	2005	26,659	37,300	184	30	14	tco	ex Bro Edward-10

Ras Maersk : Moller-Maersk - Maersk Tankers A/S : *ARO*

IMO	name	flag	year	gt	dwt	loa	bm	kts	type	comments
9210907	Maersk Ellen	Dis	2002	24,099	36,962	184	30	15	tco	ex Bro Ellen-10
9274678	Maersk Elliot	Dis	2005	26,659	36,809	184	30	14	tco	ex Bro Elliot-10
9274628	Maersk Erin +	Dis	2004	26,634	37,178	186	31	15	tco	ex Bro Erin -10, Huntestern-07
9274642	Maersk Etienne	Dis	2004	26,659	36,941	184	30	14	tco	ex Bro Etienne-10
9367750	Maersk Maya ++	Pan	2009	26,900	47,401	183	32	14	tco	
9252292	Maersk Riesa ++	Bhs	2003	22,184	34,558	171	27	14	tco	
9252307	Maersk Remlin ++	Bhs	2003	22,184	34,530	171	27	14	tco	
9236987	Maersk Rosyth	Dis	2003	22,184	34,811	171	27	14	tco	
9236999	Ras Maersk	Dis	2003	22,181	34,999	171	27	14	tco	
9265407	Ribe Maersk	Dis	2004	22,181	34,806	171	27	14	tco	

Maersk Arctic : Maersk Tankers Singapore Pte : *Hans Kraijenbosch*

Maersk Adriatic : Maersk Tankers Singapore Pte : *Nico Kemps*

IMO	name	flag	year	gt	dwt	loa	bm	kts	type	comments
9214757	Richard Maersk	Dis	2001	22,184	34,909	171	27	14	tco	
9298820	Rita Maersk	Dis	2004	22,184	35,199	171	27	14	tco	
9237008	Robert Maersk	Dis	2003	22,181	34,801	171	27	14	tco	
9251406	Romø Maersk	Dis	2003	22,161	34,808	171	27	14	tco	
9306940	Rosa Maersk	Dis	2005	22,184	35,192	171	27	14	tco	
9306938	Roy Maersk	Dis	2005	22,184	35,190	171	27	14	tco	

acquisitions:

IMO	name	flag	year	gt	dwt	loa	bm	kts	type	comments
9460136			2011	57,237	105,304	229	42	14	tco	ex Alpine Amalia-16
9469687			2011	57,237	105,304	229	42	14	tco	ex Alpine Aqualina-16
9655975			2014	29,705	49,999	183	32	14	tco	ex Alpine Maria-16
9655987			2014	29,705	49,999	183	32	14	tco	ex Alpine Mary-16

newbuildings : 8 x MR tco [Sungdong (2016)] : 9 x MR tco 49,940 dwt [Samsung Ningbo (2017/18)]
+ managed by Handytankers K/S, ++ chartered vessels managed by Handytankers K/S

Broström AB, Denmark

funnel: *blue with houseflag (blue 'AB' on white disc over red/blue horizontal bands) overlapping green rectangle on broad white band.*
hull: *Blue or grey with red boot-topping.* **history:** *Brostrôm AB formed 1934, Nordic subsidiary founded 1965 as A/B Tirfing to 1978, renamed Bröstrom van Ommeren Shipping after merger in 1998. Bröstrom Tankers SAS formed 1934 as Phs van Ommeren (France) SA (founded 1839), merged 1987 with Société d'Armement Fluvial et Maritime (SOFLUMAR) as Soflumar van Ommeren France SA to 1992, then van Ommeren Tankers SA to 2000. Bröstrom AB taken over by Maersk Tankers in 2009 and manages vessels under 25,000dwt.* **web:** *www.brostrom.com*

IMO	name	flag	year	gt	dwt	loa	bm	kts	type	comments
9255268	Baltico ‡	Fin	2003	15,980	25,000	170	24	14	tco	ex Purha-15
9255270	Bonito ‡	Fin	2004	15,980	25,049	169	24	14	tco	ex Jurmo-15
9313096	Bro Deliverer +	Dis	2006	11,344	14,766	147	22	13	tco	
9313101	Bro Designer +	Dis	2006	11,344	14,846	147	22	13	tco	
9313125	Bro Developer +	Dis	2006	11,344	14,737	147	22	13	tco	
9313113	Bro Distributor +	Dis	2007	11,344	14,907	147	22	13	tco	
9323584	Bro Nakskov +	Dis	2007	12,105	16,427	144	23	14	tco	ex Nakskov Maersk-12
9322700	Bro Nibe +	Dis	2007	12,105	16,534	144	23	14	tco	ex Nibe Maersk-10
9340623	Bro Nissum +	Dis	2008	12,105	16,654	144	23	14	tco	ex Nissum Maersk-13
9322712	Bro Nordby +	Dis	2007	12,105	16,511	144	23	14	tco	ex Nordby Maersk-12
9323819	Bro Nuuk +	Dis	2008	12,105	16,631	144	23	14	tco	ex Nuuk Maersk-12
9322695	Bro Nyborg +	Dis	2007	12,105	16,564	144	23	14	tco	ex Nakskov Maersk-12
9308546	Evinco (me) ‡	Swe	2005	13,769	19,999	156	24	14	tco	
9308558	Excello ‡	Swe	2008	13,798	19,925	155	24	14	tco	
9212589	Prospero (me) ‡	Swe	2000	11.793	18,119	146	22	14	tco	

+ managed by Brostrom AB   ‡ owned by Rederi AB Donsotank, Sweden (founded 1952 – www.donsotank.se).

Maersk Tankers Singapore Pte., Singapore

hull and **funnel:** *as above.* **history:.** **web:** *www.maersktankers.com*

IMO	name	flag	year	gt	dwt	loa	bm	kts	type	comments
9348302	Bro Agnes	Sgp	2008	12,162	16,791	144	23	14	tco	
9356610	Bro Alma	Sgp	2008	12,162	17,069	144	23	14	tco	
9344435	Bro Anna	Sgp	2008	12,164	16,979	144	23	14	tco	
9636632	Maersk Adriatic	Sgp	2012	23,297	37,538	183	27	15	tco	ex Alga-15
9636644	Maersk Aegean	Sgp	2013	23,297	37,538	183	27	15	tco	ex Sea Auva-15
9311751	Maersk Arctic	Sgp	2006	23,246	36,993	183	27	15	tco	ex Elbtank Italy-15, Ravi Spirit-08, Rhine-07
9340594	Maersk Beaufort	Sgp	2006	19,758	29,015	175	29	14	tco	
9299446	Maersk Belfast	Sgp	2005	19,758	29,031	175	29	14	tco	
9299422	Maersk Bering	Sgp	2005	19,758	29,057	176	29	14	tco	
9341445	Maersk Borneo	Sgp	2007	19,758	29,013	176	29	14	tco	
9316608	Maersk Erik *	Sgp	2008	25,382	40,083	176	31	14	tco	ex Nord Fast-14, F.D. Nord Fast-10, Nord Fast-08
9524982	Maersk Jamnagar	Sgp	2011	56,326	104,588	228	42	14	tco	ex Rich Duke II-15
9524994	Maersk Jeddah	Sgp	2011	56,326	104,623	228	42	14	tco	ex Rich Duchess II-15
9374428	Maersk Kara	Sgp	2008	24,112	38,936	183	27	14	tco	ex Saffo-15
9431276	Maersk Kate	Sgp	2010	24,412	39,756	183	28	15	tco	ex Kate Maersk-12
9256298	Maersk Kalea	Sgp	2004	25,507	38,850	168	29	14	tco	ex Meriom Pride-08
9431317	Maersk Katalin	Sgp	2012	24,412	39,724	183	27	14	tco	
9431290	Maersk Katarina	Sgp	2011	24,412	39,724	183	27	14	tco	
9431288	Maersk Kaya	Sgp	2011	24,412	39,729	183	27	14	tco	
9431305	Maersk Kiera **	Sgp	2011	24,412	39,724	183	27	14	tco	
9447732	Maersk Magellan	Sgp	2010	29,669	51,551	183	32	14	tco	ex Gan-Trophy-13
9447768	Maersk Malaga	Sgp	2012	29,669	51,551	183	32	14	tco	ex Flagship Iris-15
9315056	Maersk Marmara	Sgp	2006	30,029	51,182	183	32	14	tco	ex Gan-Sure-11
9314911	Maersk Mediterranean	Sgp	2007	29,348	46,616	183	32	14	tco	ex Gan-Voyager-12
9544592	Maersk Messina	Sgp	2009	28,777	48,056	180	32	14	tco	ex Eastern Force-14
9555319	Maersk Mississippi	Sgp	2010	28,777	47,990	180	32	14	tco	ex Future Prosperity-15
9315446	Maersk Pearl	Sgp	2005	61,764	109,570	245	42	15	tco	
9319686	Maersk Pelican	Sgp	2007	61,724	109,647	245	42	14	tco	

IMO	name	flag	year	gt	dwt	loa	bm	kts	type	comments
9319674	Maersk Penguin	Sgp	2007	61,724	109,647	245	42	15	tco	
9306639	Maersk Petrel	Sgp	2007	61,724	109,672	245	42	15	tco	ex Torm Mette-11
9283291	Maersk Phoenix	Sgp	2005	61,764	109,571	245	42	15	tco	
9319703	Maersk Piper	Sgp	2008	61,724	109,672	245	42	15	tco	ex Torm Marianne-11
9308948	Maersk Princess	Sgp	2005	61,724	109,637	245	42	15	tco	
9263643	Maersk Privilege	Sgp	2003	56,285	105,483	248	43	15	tco	ex Unique Privilege-07
9308950	Maersk Producer	Sgp	2006	61,724	109,647	248	43	15	tco	
9283289	Maersk Progress	Sgp	2005	61,764	109,181	248	43	15	tco	
9315458	Maersk Promise	Sgp	2006	61,724	109,647	248	43	15	tco	
9215050	Maersk Prosper	Sgp	2001	61,784	109,326	245	42	15	tco	ex Donax-10, Maersk Prosper-04
9236975	Maersk Rhode Island	Sgp	2002	22,161	34,801	171	27	14	tco	l/a Maersk Ramsey
9708617	Maersk Tacoma	Sgp	2015	29,445	49,828	183	32	15	tco	
9708629	Maersk Tampa	Sgp	2015	29,445	49,834	183	32	15	tco	
9726451	Maersk Tangier	Sgp	2016	29,445	49,835	183	32	15	tco	
newbuildings:										
9726463	Maersk Teesport	Sgp	2016	29,445	50,000	183	32	15	tco	Sungdong 3086 ex Horizon Tkrs
9718064	Maersk Tianjin	Sgp	2016	30,000	51,800	183	32		tco	Sungdong 3095
9718076	Maersk Tokyo	Sgp	2016	30,000	51,800				tco	Sungdong 3096
9718088	Maersk Torshavn			30,000	51,800				tco	Sungdong 3097
9718090				30,000	51,800				tco	Sungdong 3098
9732929				30,000	51,800				tco	Sungdong 3099
9732931				30,000	51,800				tco	Sungdong 3100

A/S J. Ludwig Mowinckels Rederi   Norway

funnel: *cream with narrow blue band on white band on broad red band beneath black top.* **hull:** *black, grey or brown with red boot-topping.* **history:** *originally founded 1898 and split into separate family operating subsidiaries Viken and Vista in 2002.* **web:** *www.jlmr.no*

9389825	Goya	Nis	2008	41,655	75,750	225	32	14	bbu	
9310410	Heina	Nis	2005	39,736	76,598	225	32	14	bbu	
9413418	Ogna	Nis	2009	40,500	75,750	225	32	14	bbu	
9587207	Vinga *	Nis	2012	81,453	158,982	274	48	15	tcr	

* owned by Mowinckel Suezmax Tankers AS

MPC Münchmeyer Petersen Group   Germany

Ahrenkiel Steamship GmbH & Co., Germany

funnel: *buff or buff with houseflag on blue band, or charterers colours.* **hull:** *black, dark blue, green or grey with red boot-topping.* **history:** *formed 2014 by MPC Münchmeyer Group after acquiring C. F. Ahrenkiel, and Thien & Heyringa, founded 1977. Christian F. Ahrenkiel founded 1950 having previously being on the board of Hapag and his father having owned ships since 1910. Tankreederei Ahrenkiel founded in 1971, now United Chemical Transport (UCT) joint venture. Ahrenkiel Liner Services (ALS) formed 1982. In September 2012 entered into a joint marketing agreement with MPC for containership operations* **web:** *www.ahrenkiel.net*

9225794	AS Amalia	Lbr	2003	26,061	30,453	196	30	22	ucc	2,226 teu: ex Sag Westfalen-15, CMA CGM Esmeraldas-11, Kaedi-06, Irma Delmas-03
9309409	AS Carelia	Lbr	2006	28,592	39,374	222	30	22	ucc	2,824 teu: ex CMA CGM Tulip-11

AS Mariella : MPC Münchmeyer Peterson - Ahrenkiel Steamship : *Hans Kraijenbosch*

IMO	name	flag	year	gt	dwt	loa	bm	kts	type	comments
9241205	AS Carinthia	Lbr	2003	28.596	39,421	222	30	22	ucc	2,824 teu: ex CMA CGM Galilee-09, Norasia Rigel-07, Carinthia-04
9315812	AS Cypria	Lbr	2006	28,592	39,426	222	30	22	ucc	2,824 teu: ex CMA CGM Orchid-11
9485887	AS Elbia	Lbr	2011	23,443	34,394	180	30	14	bbu	
9485899	AS Elenia	Lbr	2011	23,443	34,421	180	30	14	bbu	ex Confiance-12, AS Elenia-11
9395109	AS Fabiana	Atg	2007	15,375	18,278	166	25	19	ucc	1,284 teu: ex Vliet Trader-15, Medpacific-08
9437191	AS Fatima	Atg	2008	15,334	18,343	166	25	19	ucc	1,284 teu: ex Warnow Vaquita-15
9395068	AS Federica	Nld	2007	15,375	18,350	166	25	19	ucc	1,284 teu: ex Vecht Trader-15, Medatlantic-08
9395020	AS Felicia	Atg	2006	15,375	18,291	166	25	19	ucc	1,284 teu: ex Medocean-15, APL Managua-14, EWL Caribbean-07, l/a Medocean
9395111	AS Fiorella	Lbr	2007	15,375	18,270	166	25	19	ucc	1,284 teu: ex Warnow Orca-15, APL Colima-12
9450935	AS Magnolia	Lbr	2009	42,112	54,383	260	32	24	ucc	4,380 teu: ex Moranto-15
9450947	AS Mariana	Lbr	2010	42,112	54,369	260	32	24	ucc	4,380 teu: ex Makita-15
9484510	AS Mariella	Lbr	2010	42,112	54,374	260	32	24	ucc	4,380 teu: ex Mereda-15
9456953	AS Morgana	Lbr	2010	41,331	51,693	262	32	24	ucc	4,334 teu: ex Rio Cardiff-15
9340489	AS Olivia +	Phl	2007	11,570	19,881	145	24	16	tco	ex Bow Omaria-11
9363819	AS Omaria +	Phl	2007	11,570	19,974	145	24	16	tco	ex Bow Omaria-11
9340439	AS Ophelia +	Phl	2006	11,561	19,991	145	24	16	tco	ex Bow Ophelia-11
9363821	AS Orelia +	Phl	2008	11,570	19,971	145	24	16	tco	ex Bow Orelia-11
9294513	AS Palatia	Lbr	2006	27,100	34,496	210	30	22	ucc	2,600 teu: ex Niledutch Durban-15, AS Palatia-11, CMA CGM Oceano-08, Palatia-08, MOL Supremacy-08, Palatia-06
9294525	AS Patria	Lbr	2006	27,100	34,495	210	30	22	ucc	2,600 teu: ex Niledutch Guangzhou-14, Patria I-10, MOL Sunrise-08, Patria-06
9509774	AS Ragna	Atg	2009	17,068	21,120	180	25	18	ucc	1,496 teu: ex Medfrisia-15
9449869	AS Riccarda	Nld	2012	17,068	21,800	180	25	18	ucc	1,496 teu: ex Spaarne Trader-15, l/a Medmonte
9449821	AS Romina	Atg	2009	17,068	21,281	180	25	18	ucc	1,496 teu: ex Medpearl-15
9449845	AS Rosalia	Atg	2009	17,068	21,206	180	25	18	ucc	1,496 teu: ex Medcoral-15
9216729	AS Savonia	Mlt	2000	17,167	21,614	169	27	20	ucc	ex Bahamian Express-08
9453250	AS Valdivia	Lbr	2011	32,929	56,779	190	32	14	bbu	
9453212	AS Valentia	Lbr	2009	32,929	56,785	190	32	14	bbu	
9453262	AS Varesia	Lbr	2011	32,929	56,738	190	32	14	bbu	
9225433	AS Vega	Lbr	2000	23,722	29,240	194	28	21	ucc	1,804 teu: ex Vega-15, Maersk Valparaiso-08, Maersk Wellington-01, Maersk Itajai-01, Vega-00
9442641	AS Victoria	Lbr	2009	32,929	56,785	190	32	14	bbu	
9453236	AS Vincentia	Lbr	2010	32,929	56,785	190	32	14	bbu	
9453224	AS Virginia	Lbr	2009	32,929	56,799	190	32	14	bbu	
9253026	Cardonia	Lbr	2003	27,779	39,383	222	30	22	ucc	2,826 teu: ex CMA CGM Ukraine-06, Cardonia-03
9253038	Carpathia	Lbr	2003	27,779	39,443	222	30	22	ucc	2,826 teu: ex CMA CGM Greece-06, Carpathia-04

Rio Thelon : MPC Münchmeyer Peterson - Ahrenkiel Steamship : *Hans Kraijenbosch*

IMO	name	flag	year	gt	dwt	loa	bm	kts	type	comments
9241190	Cimbria	Lbr	2002	27,779	39,358	222	30	22	ucc	2,826 teu
9253014	Cordelia	Lbr	2003	27,779	40,878	222	30	22	ucc	2,826 teu:
9258466	Danubia	Lbr	2004	38,975	68,524	229	32	15	tco	ex Ocean Principal-05, Tavropos-04
9437115	Medontario	Pmd	2008	15,334	18,445	166	25	19	ucc	1,284 teu
9216999	Rio Barrow	Lbr	2001	65,059	68,122	275	40	26	ucc	5,551 teu: ex Navegantes Express-15, Rio Barrow-11, MSC Hong Kong-10, CSCL Hong Kong-08
9216987	Rio Blackwater	Lbr	2000	65,059	68,122	275	40	26	ucc	5,551 teu: ex Buenos Aires Express-15, Rio Blackwater-10, MSC Shanghai-10, CSCL Shanghai-08
9360764	Rio Cadiz	Lbr	2008	40,807	55,301	261	32	24	ucc	4,334 teu: ex CSAV Lonquen-12
9362449	Rio Charleston	Lbr	2008	40,807	55,313	261	32	24	ucc	4,334 teu: ex CSAV Lonquimay, c/a Rio Charleston
9286774	Rio Taku	Lbr	2004	26,833	34,287	210	30	22	ucc	2,556 teu: ex Maersk Nolanville-12, P&O Nedlloyd Susana-05, l/a Rio Taku
9283693	Rio Teslin	Lbr	2004	26,833	34,567	210	30	22	ucc	2,556 teu: ex Nedlloyd Teslin-12, P&O Nedlloyd Teslin-05, l/dn Rio Teslin
9283708	Rio Thelon	Lbr	2004	26,833	34,567	210	30	22	ucc	2,556 teu: ex Nedlloyd Maxima-12, P&O Nedlloyd Maxima-05, l/a RioThelon
9286786	Rio Thompson	Lbr	2004	26,833	34,567	210	30	22	ucc	2,556 teu: ex Nedlloyd Evita-12, P&O Nedlloyd Evita-06
9362712	Sevillia	Lbr	2008	21,019	25,884	180	28	20	ucc	1,795 teu: l/dn Manchester Strait
9430935	Sicilia	Lbr	2008	21,018	25,927	180	28	20	ucc	1,795 teu: l/dn Montreal Strait
9333060	Stadt Aachen	Atg	2007	35,573	44,146	223	32	22	ucc	3,400 teu
9445904	Stadt Cadiz	Atg	2010	35,878	41,234	197	32	22	ucc	2,758 teu
9450923	Stadt Coburg	Atg	2009	42,112	54,327	260	32	24	ucc	4,380 teu
9320049	Stadt Dresden	Atg	2006	27,971	37,938	222	30	21	ucc	2,700 teu: ex SCI Kiran-09, l/dn Stadt Dresden
9459278	Stadt Freiburg	Atg	2010	42,112	54,325	260	32	24	ucc	4,380 teu
9395094	Stadt Gera	Cyp	2007	15,375	18,236	166	25	19	ucc	1,284 teu: ex Maersk Rades-09
9395135	Stadt Gotha	Atg	2008	15,375	18,299	166	25	19	ucc	1,284 teu: l/dn Stadt Dresden
9395056	Stadt Jena	Atg	2007	15,375	18,279	166	25	19	ucc	1,284 teu: ex TS Xiamen-08, Stadt Jena-07
9450911	Stadt Marburg	Pan	2009	42,112	54,405	260	32	24	ucc	4,380 teu: ex Amsterdam Bridge-13 c/a Stadt Marburg
9440306	Stadt Sevilla	Atg	2010	35,878	41,253	197	32	22	ucc	2,758 teu
9135913	Yangtze River	Lbr	1998	25,791	44,114	199	30	15	bbu	ex Alianca River-15, Yangtze River-11 Gerdt Oldendorff-05

newbuildings :

IMO	name	flag	year	gt	dwt	loa	bm	kts	type	comments
9719434			2016	30,000	50,300	183	32	14	tco	SPP Sacheon S1173
9719446				30,000	50,300	183	32	14	tco	SPP Sacheon S1174
9719458				30,000	50,300	183	32	14	tco	SPP Sacheon S1175
9719460				30,000	50,300	183	32	14	tco	SPP Sacheon S1176

+ owned by Safemarine Corp., Japan

Navalmar (U.K.) Ltd.   U.K.

funnel: black. hull: black or grey with white 'NAVALMAR', red boot-topping. history: founded 1990. web: www.navalmar.co.uk

IMO	name	flag	year	gt	dwt	loa	bm	kts	type	comments
9102485	Arundel Castle	Pan	1997	30,928	48,139	200	31	14	ggc	ex Meghna Pride-12, Syrena-10, Seaboard Syrena-00, Syrena-98
9189926	Bedford Castle	Pan	1998	29,688	50,655	195	32	15	goh	ex Sanko Sincere-14

managed by B Navi Shipmanagement Srl. Italy (www.bnavi.it)

Navig8 Group   Singapore

funnel: dark blue with dark/light blue '8' on white panel. hull: dark blue or red with red boot-topping. history: founded 2003 as FR8 Shipmanagement Pte. Ltd. changed to current name 2007. Owns and manages vessels operating in several product pools. Group includes Navig8 Chemical Tankers, founded 2013 and Navig8 Product Tankers. Navig8 Crude Tankers was sold to General Maritime in share swap deal in 2015. web: www.navig8group.com : www.navig8chemicaltankers.com : www.navi8producttankers.com

IMO	name	flag	year	gt	dwt	loa	bm	kts	type	comments
9727584	Navig8 Achroite	Mhl	2016	23,676	37,596	184	27	14	tco	
9727546	Navig8 Adamite	Mhl	2015	23,676	37,596	184	27	14	tco	
9727572	Navig8 Alabaster	Mhl	2015	23,676	37,568	184	27	14	tco	
9714068	Navig8 Almandine	Mhl	2015	23,676	37,596	184	27	14	tco	
9719769	Navig8 Amazonite	Mhl	2015	23,676	37,596	184	27	14	tco	
9714056	Navig8 Amber	Mhl	2015	23,676	37,596	184	27	14	tco	
9719745	Navig8 Amessi *	Mhl	2015	23,676	37,596	184	27	14	tco	
9714501	Navig8 Amethyst	Mhl	2015	23,676	37,596	184	27	14	tco	
9714513	Navig8 Ametrine	Mhl	2015	23,676	37,596	184	27	14	tco	
9727534	Navig8 Ammolite	Mhl	2015	23,676	37,632	184	27	14	tco	
9711559	Navig8 Andesine	Mhl	2015	23,676	37,596	184	27	14	tco	

IMO	name	flag	year	gt	dwt	loa	bm	kts	type	comments
9711573	Navig8 Aquamarine *	Mhl	2015	23,676	37,596	184	27	14	tco	
9727558	Navig8 Aragonite	Mhl	2015	23,676	37,596	184	27	14	tco	
9711561	Navig8 Aronaldo *	Mhl	2015	23,676	37,596	184	27	14	tco	
9711547	Navig8 Aventurine	Mhl	2015	23,676	37,568	184	27	14	tco	
9719771	Navig8 Axinite	Mhl	2015	23,676	36,608	184	27	14	tco	
9719757	Navig8 Azotic *	Mhl	2015	23,676	37,589	184	27	14	tco	
9727560	Navig8 Azurite	Mhl	2015	23,676	37,596	184	27	14	tco	
9735608	Navig8 Exceed	Sgp	2016	42,750	74,600	219	38	14	tco	
9735579	Navig8 Excel	Mhl	2015	42,750	74,547	219	38	14	tco	
9735581	Navig8 Excelsior	Mhl	2016	42,750	74,665	219	38	14	tco	
9735593	Navig8 Expedite	Mhl	2016	42,750	74,634	219	38	14	tco	
9735610	Navig8 Experience	Mhl	2016	42,750	74,669	219	38	14	tco	
9379155	Navig8 Faith	Mhl	2008	29,597	46,745	183	32	14	tco	
9556181	Navig8 Honor	Mhl	2011	42,295	74,996	219	38	14	tco	
9719707	Navig8 Sanctity	Mhl	2016	63,915	109,999	250	44	14	tco	
9708588	Navig8 Solace	Mhl	2016	63,915	109,999	250	44	14	tco	
9708576	Navig8 Solidarity	Mhl	2015	63,915	109,999	250	44	14	tco	
9337327	Navig8 Spirit	Mhl	2006	30,105	50,600	183	32	14	tco	ex Fr8 Spirit-07
9712840	Navig8 Stability	Mhl	2016	63,915	109,999	250	44	14	tco	
9252072	Navig8 Stealth	Mhl	2002	27,335	47,355	183	32	14	tco	ex Jasmine-07
9396725	Navig8 Stealth S.V.	Mhl	2008	30,040	50,760	183	32	14	tco	ex Tandara Spirit-15, Mexico-11, l/a Helcion
9418145	Navig8 Strength	Mhl	2009	30,075	50,497	183	32	14	tco	
9418133	Navig8 Success	Mhl	2009	30,075	50,571	183	32	14	tco	
9719692	Navig8 Symphony	Mhl	2016	63,915	109,999	250	44	14	tco	
9753674	Navig8 Turquoise *	Mhl	2016	29,492	49,516	183	32	14	tco	
9690614	Navig8 Victoria	Hkg	2015	29,531	49,126	183	32	14	tco	
9690626	Navig8 Violette	Hkg	2015	29,531	49,126	183	32	14	tco	
newbuildings:										
9735622	Navig8 Executive		2016	42,250	74,000	219	38	14	tco	STX Jinhae 1656 04.2016
9735634	Navig8 Express		2016	42,250	74,000	219	38	14	tco	STX Jinhae 1657 05.2016
9735646	Navig8 Excellence		2016	42,250	74,000	219	38	14	tco	STX Jinhae 1658 05.2016
9737747	Navig8 Pride		2016		74,000				tco	SPP S1181 07.2016
9737759	Navig8 Providence		2016		74,000				tco	SPP S1182 09.2016
9760213	Navig8 Precision		2016		74,000				tco	SPP S1185 10.2016
9760225	Navig8 Prestige		2016		74,000				tco	SPP S1186 12:2016
9712864	Navig8 Grace		2016		113,000				tco	CSCC Offshore Guangzhou H057
9712876	Navig8 Gallantry		2016		113,000				tco	CSCC Offshore Guangzhou H058
9717101	Navig8 Guard		2016		113,000				tco	CSCC Offshore Guangzhou H059
9717113	Navig8 Guide		2016		113,000				tco	CSCC Offshore Guangzhou H060
9717125	Navig8 Goal		2016		113,000				tco	CSCC Offshore Guangzhou H061
9717137	Navig8 Gauntlet		2016		113,000				tco	CSCC Offshore Guangzhou H062
9722170	Navig8 Gladiator		2016		113,000				tco	CSCC Offshore Guangzhou H067
9722182	Navig8 Gratitude		2016		113,000				tco	CSCC Offshore Guangzhou H068
9719719	Navig8 Steadfast		2016		109,999				tco	Sungdong 3084 Q2 2016
9719721	Navig8 Supreme		2016		109,999				tco	Sungdong 3085 Q3 2016
	Navig8 Sirius				25,000				tch	Kitanihon
	Navig8 Sky				25,000				tch	Kitanihon
	Navig8 Spark				25,000				tch	Kitanihon
	Navig8 Stellar				25,000				tch	Kitanihon
	Navig8 Saiph				25,000				tch	Kitanihon
	Navig8 Spectrum				25,000				tch	Kitanihon
	Navig8 Spica				25,000				tch	Fukuoka
	Navig8 Sol				25,000				tch	Fukuoka
9753686	Navig8 Topaz *	Mhl	2016	30,000	49,500	183	32	14	tco	STX Jinhae 1722
9753698	Navig8 Tanzanite *	Mhl	2016	30,000	49,500	183	32	14	tco	STX Jinhae 1723
9753703	Navig8 Tourmaline *	Mhl	2016	30,000	49,500	183	32	14	tco	STX Jinhae 1724
9723306										Hyundai Mipo 2525

* owned by Aker ASA, Oslo

Navigation Maritime Bulgare   Bulgaria

funnel: *yellow with yellow 'B' on broad red band, narrow black top.* **hull:** *black with red boot-topping.* **history:** *founded 1892 and Government controlled, but with 43% owned since 2000 by British Orient Holdings.* **web:** *www.navbul.com*

IMO	name	flag	year	gt	dwt	loa	bm	kts	type	comments
9158159	Balgarka	Mlt	2004	25,065	41,425	186	30	14	bbu	ex Dolly-03
9498262	Belasitsa	Mlt	2011	19,906	30,685	186	24	14	bbu	
9576014	Belmeken	Mlt	2010	18,873	30,000	178	26	14	bbu	ex Fu An Hai-15
9132492	Bogdan	Mlt	1997	10,220	13,960	142	22	13	bbu	
9404431	Bulgaria	Mlt	2010	24,165	37,852	189	28	14	bbu	ex Cordoba-10
9354791	Hemus	Mlt	2008	25,327	42,704	186	30	14	bbu	
9575527	Kamenitza	Mlt	2010	20,887	32,588	180	28	14	bbu	ex Regina-15
9132480	Kom	Mlt	1997	10,220	13,971	142	22	13	bbu	

IMO	name	flag	year	gt	dwt	loa	bm	kts	type	comments
9575436	Koznitza	Mlt	2010	20,939	32,631	180	28	124	bbu	ex Tesoro-15
9498248	Lyulin	Mlt	2011	19,906	30,685	186	24	14	bbu	
9015656	Midjur	Mlt	1992	13,834	21,537	168	25	13	bbu	
9188908	Murgash	Mlt	2006	25,312	41,675	186	30	14	bbu	ex Wanderlust-14, Furtransbulk-06, l/a Talon II
9498250	Osogovo	Mlt	2011	19,906	30,692	186	24	14	bbu	
9132507	Perelik	Mlt	1998	10,220	13,902	142	22	13	bbu	
9578995	Persenk	Mlt	2010	18,873	30,361	178	26	14	bbu	ex Hui An Hai-15
9381861	Pirin	Mlt	2007	13,965	21,211	169	25	14	bbu	
9004176	Plana	Mlt	1991	13,834	19,985	169	25	13	bbu	
9404429	Rodina	Mlt	2009	24,165	37,852	190	28	14	bbu	
9498274	Rodopi	Mlt	2012	19,857	30,685	186	24	14	bbu	
9104811	Sakar	Mlt	1995	13,957	21,591	168	25	13	bbu	
9381873	Stara Planina	Mlt	2007	25,327	42,704	186	30	14	bbu	
9565140	Strandja	Mlt	2010	19,865	30,682	186	24	14	bbu	ex Federal Yangtze-10, l/a Eastwind York
9145231	Trapezitsa	Mlt	2003	13,967	21,250	169	25	14	bbu	
9145229	Tzarevetz	Mlt	1998	13,965	21,470	169	25	14	bbu	
9136931	Verila	Mlt	1996	14,431	23,723	151	26	14	bbu	
9564138	Vitosha	Mlt	2010	19,865	30,692	186	24	14	bbu	ex Federal Pearl-10, l/a Eastwind Yates
9044700	Vola 1	Mlt	1992	13,834	20,620	168	25	13	bbu	ex Vola-03
newbuildings:										
9754903	Ruen	Mlt	2016	25,000	42,300	185	31	14	bbu	Nantong Hongqiang HQ135
9754915		Mlt	2016	25,000	42,300	185	31	14	bbu	Nantong Hongqiang HQ136
9754927		Mlt		25,000	42,300	185	31	14	bbu	Nantong Hongqiang HQ137
9754939		Mlt		25,000	42,300	185	31	14	bbu	Nantong Hongqiang HQ138

newbuildings: + 2 options (declared 03:2015) [Nantong Hongqiang SY] Bluetech 42 design 185 x 31, 14kn

Navigator Gas LLC   U.K.

funnel: light blue with blue 'N' over gold anchor on broad white band **hull:** red with maroon boot-topping **history:** company restructured after emerging from Chapter 11 bankruptcy in 2006. **web:** www.navigatorgas.com

IMO	name	flag	year	gt	dwt	loa	bm	kts	type	comments
9403762	Navigator Aries	Idn	2008	18,311	23,333	160	26	16	lpg	20,750 m³
9661558	Navigator Atlas	Lbr	2014	17,208	16,988	160	26	16	lpg	21,000 m³
9661807	Navigator Europa	Lbr	2014	17,208	17,004	160	26	16	lpg	21,000 m³
9403774	Navigator Capricorn	Lbr	2009	18,311	23,333	159	26	16	lpg	20,657 m³ ex Maersk Harmony-13
9704506	Navigator Centauri	Lbr	2015	17,208	16,679	160	25	16	lpg	22,000 m³
9704518	Navigator Ceres	Lbr	2015	17,208	16,672	160	25	16	lpg	22,000 m³

Valrossa : Navigazione Montenari SpA : *Chris Brooks*

IMO	name	flag	year	gt	dwt	loa	bm	kts	type	comments
9536363	Navigator Galaxy	Lbr	2011	16,823	16,686	154	26	16	lpg	22,500 m³ ex Maersk Galaxy-13
9404780	Navigator Gemini	Lbr	2009	18,311	23,358	160	26	16	lpg	20,750 m³
9531519	Navigator Genesis	Lbr	2011	16,823	16,687	154	26	16	lpg	22,500 m³ ex Maersk Genesis-13
9536375	Navigator Global	Lbr	2011	16,823	16,819	154	26	16	lpg	22,500 m³ ex Maersk Global -13
9531466	Navigator Glory	Lbr	2010	16,823	16,819	154	26	16	lpg	22,500 m³ ex Maersk Glory-13
9531478	Navigator Grace	Lbr	2010	16,823	16,687	154	26	16	lpg	22,500 m³ ex Maersk Grace-13
9531507	Navigator Gusto	Lbr	2011	16,823	16,686	154	26	16	lpg	22,500 m³ ex Maersk Gusto-13
9482574	Navigator Leo	Lbr	2011	18,321	22,844	160	26	16	lpg	20,600 m³
9482586	Navigator Libra	Lbr	2012	18,321	22,911	160	26	16	lpg	20,600 m³
9157478	Navigator Magellan	Lbr	1998	17,980	20,815	159	26	18	lpg	20,928 m³ ex Maersk Humber-13, Burgos-05, Maersk Humber-00
9177545	Navigator Mars	Lbr	2000	17,840	23,495	170	24	16	lpg	22,085 m³
9177583	Navigator Neptune	Lbr	2000	17,840	23,495	170	24	16	lpg	22,085 m³
9671216	Navigator Oberon	Lbr	2014	17,208	23,600	160	26	16	lpg	21,000 m³
9407328	Navigator Pegasus	Lbr	2009	17,840	23,640	170	24	16	lpg	22,200 m³ ex Desert Orchid-12
9407330	Navigator Phoenix	Lbr	2009	17,807	23,618	170	24	16	lpg	22,200 m³ ex Dancing Brave-12
9177571	Navigator Pluto	Idn	2000	17,849	23,484	170	24	16	lpg	22,085 m³
9177569	Navigator Saturn	Lbr	2000	17,840	23,495	170	24	16	lpg	22,085 m³
9404792	Navigator Scorpio	Lbr	2009	18,311	23,333	159	26	16	lpg	20,657 m³ ex Maersk Heritage-13
9404807	Navigator Taurus	Lbr	2009	18,311	23,316	160	26	16	lpg	20,750 m³
9671228	Navigator Triton	Lbr	2015	17,208	23,600	160	26	16	lpg	21,000 m³
9704491	Navigator Umbrio	Lbr	2015	17,208	23,600	160	26	16	lpg	21,000 m³
9177557	Navigator Venus	Lbr	2000	17,849	23,503	170	24	16	lpg	22,085 m³
9404819	Navigator Virgo	Lbr	2009	18,311	23,273	159	26	16	lpg	20,657 m³ ex Maersk Honour -13
newbuildings:										
9704520	Navigator Copernico	Lbr	2016	17,800	23,600	159	26	16	lpg	22,000 m³
9704532	Navigator Ceto	Lbr	2016	17,800	23,600	159	26	16	lpg	22,000 m³

also 2 further 22,000 m³ lpg [Hyundai Mipo (Q1:2017)]

Navigazione Montanari SpA   Italy

funnel: white with house flag, black top **hull:** greyor red with red boot-topping **history:** origins date back to a family company established 1889, present company founded 1999 as Nav. Alta Italy SpA but changed to current name following financial injection from G. & A. Montanari **web:** www.navmont.com

IMO	name	flag	year	gt	dwt	loa	bm	kts	type
9384112	Valcadore	Ita	2008	23,335	37,481	184	27	14	tco
9231705	Valdaosta	Ita	2002	19,408	25,527	177	27	14	tco
9417309	Valfoglia	Ita	2009	50,185	109,060	243	42	14	tcr
9384124	Valgardena	Ita	2008	23,335	37,481	184	27	14	tco
9391488	Valle Azzurra	Ita	2007	29,987	50,697	183	32	14	tco
9387580	Valle Bianca	Ita	2007	29,987	50,633	183	32	14	tco
9220940	Valle di Andalusia	Ita	2001	25,063	40,218	176	31	14	tco
9220914	Valle di Aragona	Ita	2001	25,063	40,218	176	31	14	tco
9220926	Valle di Castiglia	Ita	2001	25,063	40,218	176	31	14	tco
9295311	Valle di Cordoba	Ita	2005	25,063	40,200	176	31	14	tco
9292278	Valle di Granada	Ita	2005	25,063	40,218	176	31	14	tco
9251547	Valle di Navarra	Ita	2002	25,063	40,218	176	31	14	tco
9288942	Valle di Nervion	Ita	2004	25,063	40,218	176	31	14	tco

Harmony N : Navios Maritime Partners : *Chris Brooks*

IMO	name	flag	year	gt	dwt	loa	bm	kts	type	comments
9220938	Valle di Siviglia	Ita	2001	25,063	42,721	176	31	14	tco	
9251559	Vallermosa	Ita	2003	25,063	40,218	176	31	14	tco	
9417311	Vallesina	Ita	2009	60,185	109,060	243	42	14	tcr	
9391505	Valrossa	Ita	2008	29,987	50,344	183	32	14	tco	
9385178	Valsesia	Ita	2008	23,335	37,481	184	27	14	tco	
9292840	Valtamed	Ita	2004	83,669	158,609	274	48	14	tcr	
9384136	Valtellina	Ira	2008	23,335	37,481	184	27	14	tco	
9391490	Valverde	Ita	2008	29,987	50,344	183	32	14	tco	

Navios Maritime Holdings Greece

funnel: *blue with white 'N' on red circle over two narrow white bands* **hull:** *dark red with 'Navios' in white, red or green boot-topping*
history: *company founded 1954, comprises Navios Maritime Partners, Navios Maritime Acquisition Corp, Navios Tankers Management and others* **web:** *www.navios.com*

IMO	name	flag	year	gt	dwt	loa	bm	kts	type	comments
9433066	Acrux N	Cyp	2010	18,326	23,338	175	27	20	ucc	ex ANL Euroa-15, Noble Acrux-15, OS Samsun-12
9433054	ANL Elinga	Cyp	2010	18,326	23,359	175	27	20	ucc	ex Vita N-15, Noble Antares-15, OS Marmaris-13, l/a Cape Nemo
9346445	Aurora N	Cyp	2008	38,899	63,495	228	32	14	tco	ex Ice Beam-13
9311816	Beaufiks **	Pan	2004	90,085	180,310	289	45	14	bbu	
9581693	Bourgainville	Mhl	2013	29,880	50,626	183	32	14	tco	
9334349	Castor N	Cyp	2007	35,824	41,850	220	32	22	ucc	3,091 teu: ex Fesco Amalthea-15, Amalthea-11, Cap Prior-10, l/a Almathea
9531454	Copernicus N	Lbr	2010	51,239	93,062	229	38	14	bbu	ex Benfica-16, Daniela Schulte-13
9583005	Dream Canary **	Pan	2015	92,379	180,528	292	45	14	bbu	
9747948	Dream Coral **	Pan	2015	92,722	181,249	292	45	14	bbu	
9339868	Esperanza N	Cyp	2008	23,633	27,155	191	28	20	ucc	ex CMA CGM Comoe-13, Rio Sao Francisco-08
9509126	Ete N	Cyp	2012	35,887	41,139	212	31	22	ucc	3,421 teu: ex Noble Regor-15, l/a OS Izmir,
9509138	Fleur N	Cyp	2012	35,887	41,129	212	31	22	ucc	3,421 teu: ex Noble Rigel-15, l/a OS Antalya
9374208	Golden Heiwa **	Pan	2007	39,737	76,662	225	32	14	bbu	
9309411	Harmony N	Lbr	2006	28.592	39,418	222	30	22	ucc	2,824 teu: ex AS Caria-13, Maersk Jakarta-11, Caria-06
9305659	Hyundai Busan	Cyp	2006	74,651	80,102	304	40	26	ucc	6,763 teu
9305661	Hyundai Hongkong	Cyp	2006	74,651	80,102	304	40	26	ucc	6,763 teu
9305647	Hyundai Shanghai	Cyp	2006	74,651	80,262	304	40	26	ucc	6,763 teu
9305685	Hyundai Singapore	Cyp	2006	74,651	85,250	304	40	26	ucc	6,763 teu
9305673	Hyundai Tokyo	Cyp	2006	74,651	80,059	304	30	26	ucc	6,763 teu
9384100	Hector N	Mhl	2008	24,112	38,402	183	27	14	tco	ex King Edgar-14, l/a Meriom Gem
9567441	Joie N	Mhl	2011	33,032	57,000	190	32	14	bbu	ex King Felipe-15
9537915	Jupiter N	Lbr	2010	51,239	93,099	229	38	14	bbu	ex Barcelona-16, Dorian Schulte-14
9490612	King Ore **	Pan	2010	89,605	176,944	289	45	14	bbu	
9746255	Largo Sun	Lbr	2016	29,767	49,990	183	32	14	tco	l/a Lady Mei
9346457	Lumen N	Cyp	2008	38,899	63,599	228	32	15	tco	ex Ice Blade-13

Nave Synergy : Navios Maritime Partners : *Hans Kraijenbosch*

IMO	name	flag	year	gt	dwt	loa	bm	kts	type	comments
9509176	Matar N	Cyp	2013	39,824	46,998	212	31	22	ucc	3,421 teu: ex Noble Matar-15, OS Marmara-14
9465241	MSC Cristina	Lbr	2011	141,635	141,184	366	48	24	ucc	13,100 teu: l/a E.R. Cristina, l/d E.R. Sartori
9364277	N Amalthia **	Pan	2006	39,643	75,318	225	32	14	bbu	ex Nord Orion-13
9342815	N Bonanza **	Pan	2006	39,738	76,596	225	32	14	bbu	ex Double Rejoice-13
9487483	Nave Alderamin	Pan	2013	30,052	49,998	183	32	14	tco	
9580405	Nave Andromeda	Lbr	2011	42,338	74,999	228	32	14	tco	
9459072	Nave Aquila	Pan	2012	30,052	49,991	183	32	14	tco	
9301964	Nave Ariadne	Cyl	2007	42,514	74,875	228	32	14	tco	ex Ariadne Jacob-11
9459060	Nave Atria	Pan	2012	30,052	49,992	183	32	14	tco	
9638563	Nave Atropos	Mhl	2013	42,341	74,695	228	32	14	tco	
9459084	Nave Bellatrix +	Pan	2013	30,052	49,999	183	32	14	tco	
9514561	Nave Buena Suerte	Hkg	2011	152,727	297,491	330	60	15	tcr	ex Peace China-14
9487471	Nave Capella	Pan	2013	30,052	49,995	183	32	14	tco	
9589932	Nave Cassiopeia	Lbr	2012	42,341	74,711	228	32	14	tco	
9589944	Nave Cetus	Lbr	2012	42,341	74,581	228	32	14	tco	
9301976	Nave Cielo	Cym	2007	42,514	74,896	228	32	14	tco	ex Colin Jacob-11
9489118	Nave Constellation	Mhl	2013	29,279	45,281	183	32	14	tco	l/a UACC Muharraq
9457024	Nave Cosmos	Mlt	2010	17,846	25,130	170	26	14	tco	
9325336	Nave Dorado **	Pan	2005	28,799	47,999	180	32	14	tco	Kuroshio Express-13
9244867	Nave Electron	Hkg	2002	159,016	305,178	332	58	15	tcr	ex Charles Eddie-14
9399923	Nave Equator	Mlt	2009	30,083	49,999	183	32	14	tco`	ex Bull-14
9351634	Nave Equinox	Mhl	2007	30,119	50,922	183	32	14	tco	ex Indigo Point-13
9580417	Nave Estella	Lbr	2012	42,338	74,999	228	32	14	tco	
9384617	Nave Galactic	Hkg	2009	156,651	297,168	333	60	15	tcr	ex Great China-14, c/a Front President
9657038	Nave Jupiter	Mhl	2014	29,724	49,999	183	32	14	tco	
9245794	Nave Neutrino	Hkg	2003	159,456	298,330	333	60	15	tcr	ex Venture Spirit -14
9399935	Nave Orbit	Mlt	2009	30,083	49,999	183	32	14	tco	ex Buddy-14
9459096	Nave Orion +	Pan	2013	30,052	49,999	183	32	14	tco	
9371608	Nave Photon	Hkg	2008	156,702	297,556	333	60	15	tcr	ex New Founder-15, Yangtze Pearl-14
9457749	Nave Polaris	Mhl	2011	17,846	25,145	170	26	14	tco	
9379313	Nave Pulsar	Mhl	2007	30,119	50,922	183	32	14	tco	ex Ivory Point-13
9697430	Nave Pyxis	Pan	2014	30,310	49,998	183	32	14	tco	
9514559	Nave Quasar	Hkg	2010	152,727	297,376	330	60	15	tcr	ex Grand China-13, Hebei King-10
9638551	Nave Rigel	Mhl	2013	42,341	74,673	228	32	14	tco	
9697442	Nave Sextans	Pan	2015	30,310	51,200	183	32	15	tco	
9376751	Nave Spherical	Hkg	2009	156,702	297,572	333	60	15	tcr	ex New Talent-15, Yangtze Rhyme-14
9513763	Nave Synergy	Hkg	2010	160,102	299,973	333	60	15	tcr	ex Synergy Queen-14, Sanko Queen-12
9487469	Nave Titan +	Pan	2013	30,052	49,996	183	32	14	tco	
9489106	Nave Universe	Mhl	2013	29,279	45,313	183	32	15	tco	l/a UACC Marwan
9657052	Nave Velocity	Mhl	2014	29,724	49,999	183	32	15	tco	
9221114	Navios Achilles	Grc	2001	29,499	52,055	189	32	14	bbu	ex Agios Haralambos-03
9442859	Navios Aldebaran **	Pan	2008	39,737	76,529	225	32	14	bbu	
9284893	Navios Alegria	Pan	2004	39,974	76,466	225	32	14	bbu	ex Alegria-06, l/a Million Trader III
9310288	Navios Altair **	Pan	2006	42,887	83,001	229	32	14	bbu	

Navios Venus : Navios Maritime Partners : *ARO*

IMO	name	flag	year	gt	dwt	loa	bm	kts	type	comments
9589827	Navios Altamira	Pan	2011	92,668	179,165	292	45	14	bbu	
9736341	Navios Amber **	Pan	2015	43,291	80,994	226	32	14	bbu	
9328572	Navios Amitié *	Mlt	2005	39,643	75,395	225	32	14	bbu	ex Pacific Star-13
9481257	Navios Antares	Pan	2010	88,421	169,053	288	45	14	bbu	
9211145	Navios Apollon **	Pan	2000	29,499	52,073	189	32	14	bbu	ex Despina-03
9267431	Navios Arc	Pan	2003	30,002	53,514	190	32	14	bbu	
9407495	Navios Armonia **	Pan	2008	30,816	55,522	190	32	14	bbu	
9304253	Navios Asteriks *	Mlt	2005	40,014	76,801	225	32	14	bbu	ex Asteriks-07
9364796	Navios Astra	Pan	2006	30,002	53,468	190	32	14	bbu	
9481245	Navios Aurora II	Pan	2009	88,421	169,031	288	45	14	bbu	
9590084	Navios Avior	Pan	2012	44,282	81,355	229	32	14	bbu	
9589839	Navios Azimuth	Pan	2011	92,715	179,165	292	45	14	bbu	
9446996	Navios Bonavis	Pan	2009	94,232	180,033	292	45	14	bbu	
9481348	Navios Bonheur	Pan	2010	92,715	179,204	292	45	14	bbu	
9481233	Navios Buena Ventura	Pan	2010	92,715	179,109	292	45	14	bbu	
9496226	Navios Celestial	Pan	2009	32,343	58,063	190	32	14	bbu	
9590072	Navios Centaurus	Pan	2012	44,282	81,472	229	32	14	bbu	
9481312	Navios Etoile	Pan	2010	92,715	179,234	292	45	14	bbu	
9325013	Navios Fantastiks	Pan	2005	90,085	180,265	289	45	14	bbu	ex Fantastiks-08
9161675	Navios Felicity	Pan	1997	38,364	73,867	225	32	14	bbu	ex Felicity-05, Andhika Lourdes-04, Caya-02
9500986	Navios Fulvia	Pan	2010	92,668	179,263	292	45	14	bbu	
9244221	Navios Galaxy I	Pan	2001	38,846	74,195	225	32	14	bbu	ex Navios Galaxy-06
9326536	Navios Galileo *	Mlt	2006	39,738	76,596	225	32	14	bbu	ex Double Joy-13
9682942	Navios Gem	Pan	2014	92,722	181,336	292	45	14	bbu	
9072173	Navios Gemini S	Pan	1994	36,074	68,636	224	32	14	bbu	ex Gemini S-05, Energy Prosperity-02
9447005	Navios Happiness *	Mlt	2009	94,232	180,022	292	45	14	bbu	
9301055	Navios Harmony *	Pan	2006	42,887	82,790	229	32	14	bbu	ex Micaela Della Gatta-13
9330317	Navios Helios	Pan	2005	40,698	77,075	225	32	14	bbu	ex Oceanic Breeze-12
9213143	Navios Herakles *	Grc	2001	29,499	52,061	189	32	14	bbu	ex Agios Anastasios-03
9254733	Navios Hios *	Grc	2003	31,169	55,180	190	32	14	bbu	ex Nissos Hios-04
9328558	Navios Hope	Pan	2005	39,643	75,397	225	32	14	bbu	ex Navios Aurora I-09, Navios Aurora-08
9223564	Navios Horizon	Pan	2001	27,980	50,346	190	32	14	bbu	
9260627	Navios Hyperion	Pan	2004	38,871	75,707	225	32	14	bbu	
9211133	Navios Ionian *	Grc	2000	29,499	52,067	189	32	14	bbu	ex Agios Georgios-04
9664873	Navios Joy *	Pan	2013	92,722	180,600	292	45	14	bbu	
9598127	Navios Koyo **	Pan	2011	92,752	181,415	292	45	14	bbu	
9254721	Navios Kypros *	Grc	2003	31,169	55,000	190	32	14	bbu	ex Nissos Kypros-03
9678329	Navios La Paix	Pan	2014	34,797	61,485	200	32	14	bbu	
9100085	Navios Libra II **	Pan	1995	37,550	70,136	224	32	14	bbu	ex Libra II-06, K Fortune-03
9500637	Navios Lumen	Pan	2009	94,817	180,661	292	45	14	bbu	
9481295	Navios Luz	Pan	2010	92,715	179,144	292	45	14	bbu	
9498626	Navios Lyra **	Pan	2012	23,448	34,707	180	30	14	bbu	
9214068	Navios Magellan	Pan	2000	39,052	74,333	225	32	14	bbu	
9454280	Navios Marco Polo **	Pan	2011	42,711	80,647	225	32	14	bbu	
9747950	Navios Mars	Pan	2016	92,740	181,259	292	45	14	bbu	
9451276	Navios Melodia	Pan	2010	92,715	179,132	292	45	14	bbu	
9267405	Navios Mercator	Pan	2002	29,988	53,553	190	32	14	bbu	
9659919	Navios Mercury **	Sgp	2013	34,815	61,393	200	32	14	bbu	
9237137	Navios Meridian	Pan	2002	27,986	50,316	190	32	14	bbu	
9328560	Navios Northern Star *	Mlt	2005	39,643	75,395	225	32	14	bbu	ex Sunrise Star-13
9614880	Navios Obeliks **	Pan	2012	92,732	181,415	292	45	14	bbu	
9286865	Navios Orbiter	Pan	2004	39,727	76,602	225	32	14	bbu	
9614969	Navios Oriana **	Pan	2012	34,795	61,442	200	32	14	bbu	
9552276	Navios Phoenix	Pan	2009	90,423	180,242	289	45	14	bbu	
9460033	Navios Pollux	Pan	2009	94,917	180,727	292	45	14	bbu	
9325350	Navios Primavera **	Pan	2007	30,001	53,464	190	32	14	bbu	
9392420	Navios Prosperity **	Pan	2007	43,158	82,535	229	32	14	bbu	
9456692	Navios Ray *	Pan	2012	93,667	179,515	292	45	14	bbu	ex Berge McClintock-14, Bulk Canada-13
9316866	Navios Sagittarius	Pan	2006	38,849	75,756	225	32	14	bbu	
9398432	Navios Serenity	Lbr	2011	23,448	34,690	180	30	14	bbu	
9724180	Navios Sky **	Pan	2015	43,439	81,700	229	32	14	bbu	
9558892	Navios Soleil	Pan	2009	33,218	57,334	190	32	14	bbu	ex Prisco Akaban-12
9518115	Navios Southern Star **	Sgp	2013	43,013	82,224	229	32	14	bbu	
9738818	Navios Sphera *	Pan	2016	45,223	84,872	228	35	14	bbu	
9243502	Navios Star	Pan	2002	39,727	76,662	225	32	14	bbu	
9498781	Navios Stellar	Pan	2009	88,420	169,001	288	45	14	bbu	

IMO	name	flag	year	gt	dwt	loa	bm	kts	type	comments
9342865	Navios Sun	Pan	2005	39,738	76,619	225	32	14	bbu	ex Maritime Suzana-14
9302762	Navios Taurus *	Mlt	2005	39,738	76,596	225	32	14	bbu	ex IVS Pinotage-13
9317494	Navios Ulysses	Mlt	2007	30,681	55,728	190	32	14	bbu	ex Ikan Sembak-08
9241358	Navios Vector	Pan	2002	27,986	50,296	190	32	14	bbu	
9403102	Navios Vega *	Mlt	2009	32,379	58,792	190	32	14	bbu	
9713492	Navios Venus **	Pan	2015	34,777	61,339	200	32	14	bbu	
9360257	Protostar N	Cyp	2007	28,007	37,905	222	30	22	ucc	2,742 teu: ex Cape Manuel-13
9488803	Rainbow N	Mhl	2011	43,507	79,642	229	32	14	bbu	ex King Harold-15
9346172	Rubena N **	Sgp	2006	101,933	203,233	300	50	14	bbu	ex Splendiks-06
9567453	Serenitas N	Mhl	2011	33,032	57,000	190	32	14	bbu	ex King Fraser-15
9515931	Shinyo Kieran	Hkg	2011	157,036	297,066	330	60	14	tcr	
9303754	Solar N	Cyp	2006	35,581	44,053	231	32	23	ucc	3,398 teu: ex Mark Twain-13, Emirates Eminence-09, CMA CGM Respect-09, I/a Mark Twain
9303778	Solstice N	Lbr	2007	35,581	44,022	231	32	23	ucc	3,400 teu: ex William Shakespeare-15, Emirates Kanako-12, William Shakespeare-07
9429314	Spectrum N	Lbr	2009	26,435	34,333	209	30	22	ucc	2,500teu: ex Ada S-15
9411135	Star N	Pan	2009	23,312	37,836	184	25	14	tco	ex Mekong Star-13
9490466	Unity N	Mhl	2011	43,506	79,642	229	32	14	bbu	ex King Hakan-15
9302619	YM Unity	Lbr	2006	90,389	101,411	336	43	25	ucc	8,204 teu
9302621	YM Utmost	Lbr	2006	90,389	101,597	336	43	25	ucc	8,204 teu
newbuildings :										
9756743	Navios Felix **		2016	92,740	180,000	292	45	14	bbu	03.2016
	Navios Coral **		2016		84,000				bbu	11.2016
9703198					30,000	51,200				tco	Dae Sun
9703203					30,000	51,200				tco	Dae Sun

* owned by Kleimar n.v., Belgium, ** chartered tonnage, + operates in Hafnia Tankers Pool

Neptune Orient Lines Ltd.   Singapore

funnel: blue with horizontal blue and diagonal green triple wave design on broad white band, narrow black top or blue with white 'eagle' symbol on red band (APL). **hull:** light grey with blue 'NOL' or black with white 'APL' with red or dark grey boot-topping. **history:** Singapore government controlled and founded 1969. American President Lines (founded 1896 and 1973 amalgamation with American Mail Lines) acquired 1997. Controlling interest purchased by CMA CGM to be ratified mid-2016 **web:** www.nol.com.sg or www.apl.com

IMO	name	flag	year	gt	dwt	loa	bm	kts	type	comments
9139713	APL Agate *	Usa	1997	65,475	63,693	272	40	24	ucc	5,020 teu: ex MOL Freedom-09, APL Agate-08, NOL Agate-00
9532795	APL Antwerp **	Pan	2013	87,865	90,647	336	46	24	ucc	8,110 teu
9462043	APL Barcelona	Sgp	2012	128,929	131,196	348	46	25	ucc	10,700 teu
9218686	APL Belgium	Sgp	2002	65,792	67,500	277	40	24	ucc	5,514 teu
9597496	APL Boston	Sgp	2013	109,712	108,550	328	45	24	ucc	9,200 teu
9234109	APL Cairo	Sgp	2001	25,305	34,133	207	30	21	ucc	2,506 teu
9631981	APL Changi	Sgp	2013	151,963	150,951	367	51	23	ucc	13,900 teu: ex MOL Quality-15, I/d APL Advance
9597551	APL Charleston	Sgp	2013	109,712	108,566	328	45	24	ucc	9,200 teu
9074389	APL China *	Usa	1995	64,502	67,432	276	40	24	ucc	4,832 teu
9461867	APL Chongxing	Sgp	2011	113,735	122,200	349	46	25	ucc	10,106 teu
9597525	APL Columbus	Sgp	2014	109,712	108,557	328	45	24	ucc	9,200 teu: I/d APL Detroit
9139749	APL Coral *	Sgp	1998	65,475	64,145	275	40	24	ucc	5,020 teu: ex NOL Coral-01
9139725	APL Cyprine	Sgp	1997	65,475	64,156	275	40	24	ucc	5,020 teu: ex NOL Cyprine-00
9234135	APL Dalian	Sgp	2002	25,305	34,133	207	30	21	ucc	2,506 teu: ex Indamex Dalian-04, APL Dalian-03
9632208	APL Detroit	Sgp	2014	109,712	108,559	328	45	25	ucc	9,200 teu
9601314	APL Dublin	Sgp	2012	128,929	131,203	349	46	24	ucc	10,100 teu
9218650	APL England	Sgp	2001	65,792	67,967	277	40	24	ucc	5,514 teu
9350032	APL Florida	Lbr	2008	71,787	72,300	293	40	25	ucc	6,350 teu
9461879	APL Gwangyang	Sgp	2011	113,735	123,159	349	46	25	ucc	10,106 teu
9218674	APL Holland	Sgp	2001	65,792	67,500	277	40	24	ucc	5,514 teu
9597537	APL Houston	Sgp	2014	109,712	108,635	328	45	24	ucc	9,200 teu
9144756	APL Iolite	Sgp	1997	63,900	62,693	272	40	26	ucc	4,918 teu: ex MSC Hudson-04, APL Iolite-03, NOL Iolite-00
9144768	APL Iris	Sgp	1998	63,900	62,693	272	40	24	ucc	4,918 teu; ex NOL Iris-01
9074391	APL Japan *	Sgp	1995	64,502	66,520	276	40	24	ucc	4,832 teu; ex Hyundai Japan-09, APL Japan-07
9234111	APL Jeddah	Sgp	2001	25,305	34,122	207	30	21	ucc	2,506 teu: ex Indamex Malabar-04, APL Jeddah-03
9074535	APL Korea *	Usa	1995	64,502	66,370	276	40	24	ucc	4,832 teu
9461881	APL Le Havre	Sgp	2012	113,735	123,127	349	46	25	ucc	10,100 teu
9632014	APL Merlion	Sgp	2014	151,015	150,166	367	51	23	ucc	13,900 teu: I/a APL Ambassador
9632210	APL Mexico City	Sgp	2014	109,712	108,564	328	45	25	ucc	9,200 teu
9597549	APL Miami	Sgp	2014	109,712	108,577	328	45	24	ucc	9,200 teu

IMO	name	flag	year	gt	dwt	loa	bm	kts	type	comments
9597484	APL New York	Sgp	2013	109,712	108,550	328	45	25	ucc	9,200 teu
9495040	APL Ningbo **	Pan	2010	86,679	90,488	316	46	26	ucc	8,540 teu
9532783	APL Oregon **	Pan	2010	71,787	72,912	293	40	26	ucc	6,350 teu
9139737	APL Pearl *	Sgp	1998	65,475	64,050	275	40	24	ucc	5,020 teu: ex NOL Pearl-99
9077276	APL Philippines *	Usa	1996	64,502	66,370	276	40	24	ucc	4,832 teu
9597501	APL Phoenix	Sgp	2013	109,712	108,615	328	45	24	ucc	9,200 teu
9234123	APL Pusan	Sgp	2002	25,305	34,122	207	30	21	ucc	2,506 teu: ex Indamex Chesapeake-04, APL Pusan-02
9461893	APL Qingdao	Sgp	2012	113,735	123,137	349	46	25	ucc	10,100 teu
9631979	APL Raffles	Sgp	2013	151,963	150,951	367	51	23	ucc	13,900 teu: l/d APL Accolade
9462029	APL Salalah	Spg	2012	128,929	131,477	347	45	25	ucc	10,700 teu
9597563	APL Santiago	Sgp	2014	109,712	108,500	328	45	25	ucc	9,200 teu
9597513	APL Savannah	Sgp	2013	109,712	108.567	328	45	24	ucc	9,200 teu
9218662	APL Scotland	Sgp	2001	65,792	67,500	277	40	24	ucc	5,514 teu
9632040	APL Sentosa	Sgp	2014	151,015	150,936	367	51	23	ucc	13,900 teu: l/d APL Aspire
9074547	APL Singapore *	Usa	1995	64,502	66,370	276	40	24	ucc	4,832 teu
9462017	APL Southampton	Sgp	2012	128,929	131,358	347	45	25	ucc	10,700 teu
9288409	APL Spain **	Lbr	2004	66,300	66,100	281	40	25	ucc	5,888 teu
9631955	APL Temasek	Sgp	2013	151,963	150,936	367	51	23	ucc	13,900 teu: l/d APL Absolute
9077123	APL Thailand *	Usa	1995	64,502	66,370	276	40	24	ucc	4,832 teu
9082336	APL Tourmaline	Sgp	1995	52,086	60,323	294	32	24	ucc	4,369 teu: ex MOL Innovation-10, APL Tourmaline-04, MOL Innovation-04, MOL Tourmaline-03, APL Tourmaline-02, NOL Tourmaline-98
9082348	APL Turquoise *	Sgp	1996	52,086	60,323	294	32	24	ucc	4,369 teu: ex NOL Turquoise-98
9597472	APL Vancouver	Sgp	2013	109,712	108,600	328	45	25	ucc	9,200 teu
9631993	APL Vanda	Sgp	2013	151,963	150,951	367	51	23	ucc	13,900 teu: l/d APL Adviser
9462031	APL Yangshan	Sgp	2012	128,929	131,229	347	45	25	ucc	10,700 teu
9632002	MOL Quartz +	Sgp	2013	151,963	150,951	367	51	23	ucc	13,900 teu: l/d APL Agile
9632026	MOL Quasar +	Sgp	2014	151,015	150,951	367	51	23	ucc	13,900 teu: l/d APL Ambition
9631967	MOL Quest +	Sgp	2013	151,963	150,951	367	51	23	ucc	13,900 teu: l/d APL Achieve
9632038	MOL Quintet +	Sgp	2014	151,015	150,961	367	51	23	ucc	13,900 teu: l/d APL Ascend

+ chartered to MOL for 3 years

managed by Neptune Shipmanagement Services (Pte) Ltd, Singapore, except * owned by subsidiary APL Maritime Ltd, USA (founded 1984 as American Automar Inc to 2005) and managed by American Ship Management LLC, USA ** chartered from Japanese owners or banks.

APL Raffles : Neptune Orient Lines : *Chris Brooks*

IMO	name	flag	year	gt	dwt	loa	bm	kts	type	comments

Neste Oil Corporation

Finland

funnel: *black with diamond divided green over blue.* **hull:** *black or dark blue, some with pale green or white 'NESTESHIP', red or pink boot-topping.* **history:** *subsidiary of Fortum Oy, founded 1948 as government controlled Neste Oil to 1999, then Fortum Oil Oy until 2005. Ceased shipowning during 2014.* **web:** *www.nesteoil.com*

IMO	name	flag	year	gt	dwt	loa	bm	kts	type
9255282	Futura †	Fin	2004	15,980	25,084	170	24	14	tco
9235892	Mastera (me2) †	Fin	2003	64,259	106,208	252	44	14	tci
9255294	Neste †	Fin	2004	15,980	25,117	170	24	14	tco
9235880	Tempera (me2) †	Fin	2002	64,259	106,034	252	44	14	tci

† vessels owned by OSM Group AS, Norway and chartered to Neste

APL Sentosa : Neptune Orient Lines : *Chris Brooks*

MSC Carina : Niki Shipping : *Hans Kraijenbosch*

IMO	name	flag	year	gt	dwt	loa	bm	kts	type	comments

Niki Shipping Co. Inc. Greece

funnel: *charterer's colours.* **hull:** *charterer's colours.* **history:** *founded 2001.* **web:** *none found*

IMO	name	flag	year	gt	dwt	loa	bm	kts	type	comments
9322463	Ital Laguna	Ita	2006	54,152	68,038	294	32	24	ucc	5,090 teu
9322475	Ital Libera	Ita	2007	54,152	67,986	294	32	24	ucc	5,090 teu
9322487	Ital Lirica	Ita	2007	54,152	68,138	294	32	24	ucc	5,090 teu
9322499	Ital Lunare	Ita	2007	54,152	68,009	294	32	24	ucc	5,090 teu
9297864	MSC Anya	Lbr	2005	54,771	66,821	294	32	25	ucc	5,042 teu: ex Santa Pelagia-14, Cap Serrat-12, Santa Pelagia-10, Maersk Detroit-10, l/a Santa Pelagia
9467392	MSC Beryl	Pan	2010	140,096	139,419	366	48	23	ucc	12,400 teu
9297876	MSC Bhavya	Deu	2005	54,771	66,799	294	32	25	ucc	5,043 teu: ex Santa Petrissa-14, UASC Sharjah-12, Maersk Douglas-10, l/a Santa Petrissa
9625944	MSC Carina	Pan	2013	62,704	106,600	253	43	14	bbu	
9463205	MSC Immacolata	Pan	2012	59,835	22,196	299	22	19	mve	6,700 ceu

NileDutch Africa Line b.v. Netherlands

funnel: *blue base below broad white band with orange flash above blue 'NileDutch', deep orange top or charterers colours.* **hull:** *black or blue with red or black boot-topping.* **history:** *founded 1988.* **web:** *www.niledutch.com*

IMO	name	flag	year	gt	dwt	loa	bm	kts	type	comments
9612791	Arica Express +	Nld	2015	38,654	48,044	224	35	21	ucc	3,508 teu: ex NileDutch Antwerpen-16
9334387	NileDutch Luanda *	Mlt	2011	34,642	41,850	221	32	22	ucc	3,104 teu: ex Port Gdynia-11, l/a Albert
9612765	San Vicente									
	Express +	Nld	2014	39,106	48,044	224	35	21	ucc	3,508 teu: ex NileDutch Breda-16

*managed/owned by * POL-Levant Shipping Lines, see other chartered vessels in index with NileDutch prefixes.*
+ chartered to Hapag-Lloyd

Nippon Yusen Kaisha (NYK) Japan

funnel: *black with two narrow red bands on broad white band.* **hull:** *black or dark blue (vehicle carriers) with white/grey/pale blue diagonal stripes and white 'NYK LINE' with red boot-topping.* **history:** *founded 1870 as Tsukumo Shokai being renamed Mitsukawa Shokai in 1872, Mitsubishi Shokai in 1873, Mitsubishi Kisen then Mitsubishi Mail Steamship Co in 1875. Merged in 1885 with Kyodo Unyu Kaisha to form NYK. Became joint-stock corporation in 1893 and name changed to Nippon Yusen Kabushiki Kaisha. Acquired Dai-ni Tokyo Kisen Kaisha in 1926 and Kinkai Yusen Kaisha in 1939. Merged with Mitsubishi Shipping in 1964 and Showa Line in 1998.* **web:** *www.nykline.com*

IMO	name	flag	year	gt	dwt	loa	bm	kts	type	comments
9054119	Aegean Leader	Pan	1993	47,171	13,157	180	32	18	mve	4,736 ceu: ex Ocean Beluga-99, Mercury Diamond-96
9539171	Altair Leader *	Jpn	2011	60,295	18,688	200	32	19	mve	6,341 ceu
9273909	Andromeda Leader *	Pan	2004	62,195	21,443	200	32	20	mve	5,427 ceu
9539169	Antares Leader *	Jpn	2011	60,294	18,646	200	32	19	mve	6,341 ceu
9335953	Aphrodite Leader *	Pan	2007	62,571	21,443	200	32	19	mve	6,333 ceu
9402706	Apollon Leader *	Pan	2008	60,213	18,573	200	32	20	mve	6,341 ceu
9158276	Aquarius Leader *	Pan	1998	57,623	22,815	200	32	19	mve	5,055 ceu
9676864	Aries Leader	Pan	2014	69,931	18,808	200	36	19	mve	7,000 ceu
9355202	Artemis Leader	Pan	2009	62,571	21,424	200	32	20	mve	6,333 ceu
9531741	Asteria Leader	Jpn	2010	63,084	21,349	200	32	19	mve	6,341 ceu
9531739	Atlas Leader	Jpn	2010	63,085	21,323	200	32	19	mve	6,341 ceu
9402718	Auriga Leader *	Sgp	2008	60,213	18,686	200	32	19	mve	6,341 ceu
9367607	Canopus Leader †	Sgp	2009	51,917	17,382	180	32	19	mve	5,195 ceu
9283863	Capricornus Leader †	Sgp	2004	61,854	20,120	200	32	20	mve	5,415 ceu
9182073	Cassiopeia Leader	Pan	1999	57,455	21,547	200	32	19	mve	5,066 ceu
9713894	Castor Leader	Pan	2015	70,048	21,186	200	35	19	mve	7,124 ceu
9284740	Centaurus Leader †	Pan	2004	62,195	21,471	200	32	20	mve	5,415 ceu
8502468	Century Leader No.3	Jpn	1986	44,830	14,154	179	32	18	mve	4,726 ceu
9308883	Cepheus Leader *	Pan	2006	62,571	21,402	200	32	20	mve	6,333 ceu
9291133	Cetus Leader	Pan	2005	62,195	21,466	200	32	20	mve	5,427 ceu
9345623	Champion Pleasure	Pan	2008	56,362	105,852	241	42	15	tco	
9318486	Coral Leader †	Bhs	2006	40,986	12,164	176	31	20	mve	4,750 ceu
9464455	Cronus Leader	Pan	2008	61,804	20,096	200	32	19	mve	6,501 ceu
9491812	Cubal	Bhs	2012	110,723	82,834	285	43	19	lng	160,400 m³
9426362	Daedalus Leader	Jpn	2009	62,993	21,423	200	32	19	mve	6,332 ceu
9174282	Delphinus Leader	Pan	1998	57,391	21,514	200	32	19	mve	5,066 ceu
9477921	Demeter Leader	Pan	2009	61,804	20,019	200	32	19	mve	5,415 ceu
9738777	Deneb Leader	Pan	2015	70,048	21,155	200	36	19	mve:	7,124 ceu
9561954	Dione Leader	Pan	2013	62,838	21,111	200	32	19	mve	6,332 ceu
9426350	Dionysus Leader	Jpn	2009	62,993	21,438	200	32	19	mve	6,332 ceu
9308895	Dorado Leader *	Pan	2006	62,571	21,410	200	32	29	mve	6,333 ceu
9361811	Emerald Leader †	Bhs	2008	40,986	10,819	176	31	20	mve	4,750 ceu
9342906	Equuleus Leader *	Pan	2005	61,804	20,141	200	32	19	mve	6,501 ceu
9498602	Eridanus Leader *	Pan	2010	59,637	18,056	200	32	19	mve	6,400 ceu
9536818	Gaia Leader	Sgp	2011	62,838	21,286	200	32	20	mve	6,331 ceu

IMO	name	flag	year	gt	dwt	loa	bm	kts	type	comments
9194969	Gas Diana	Lbr	2000	46,021	49,999	230	37	16	lpg	78,888 m³
9225342	Gas Taurus	Lbr	2001	46,021	48,500	230	37	16	lpg	78,921 m³
9056296	Gemini Leader	Pan	1994	51,819	14,930	180	32	19	mve	5,120 ceu: ex Green Point-15, Triton Diamond-98
9403217	Glorious Express	Shp	2008	51,917	17,212	180	32	19	mve	5,195 ceu
9566629	Daio Southern Cross	Pan	2012	49,098	60,434	210	37	15	bwc	
9315707	Grace Acacia +	Bhs	2007	100,341	85,214	288	44	20	lng	150,000 m³
9315719	Grace Barleria	Bhs	2007	100,450	84,812	288	44	20	lng	149,700 m³
9323675	Grace Cosmos +	Bhs	2008	100,481	85,224	288	44	20	lng	150,000 m³
9540716	Grace Dahlia [st]	Jpn	2013	141,671	86,512	300	52	19	lng	177,000 m³
9338955	Grand Aniva (st) ++	Cyp	2008	122,239	74,044	288	49	19	lng	145,000 m³
9332054	Grand Elena (st) ++	Cyp	2007	122,239	74,127	288	49	20	lng	145,000 m³
9621077	Pacific Arcadia [st]	Bhs	2014	123,005	78,311	288	49	19	lng	145,400 m³
8905426	Heijin *	Pan	1989	47,521	14,366	180	32	18	mve	4,264 teu
9476745	Helios Leader *	Jpn	2009	60,212	18.692	200	32	19	mve	6,341 ceu
9531753	Hercules Leader *	Jpn	2011	63,083	21,385	300	32	19	mve	6,331 ceu
9355226	Hestia Leader *	Jpn	2008	63,007	21,419	200	32	19	mve	6,324 ceu
8916267	Hojin *	Vut	1990	57,871	18,273	200	32	19	mve	4,681 ceu
8607749	Hudson Leader	Pan	1987	47,707	14,104	180	32	18	mve	4,264 ceu: ex Green Lake-01
9403279	Hyperion Leader	Pan	2010	41,886	14,381	190	28	19	mve	3,921 ceu
9021423	Jingu *	Jpn	1992	42,164	17,216	196	32	18	mve	4,508 ceu: ex Jingu Maru-10
8913514	Jinsei Maru	Jpn	1990	55,489	17,914	199	32	19	mve	4,985 ceu
9402756	Jupiter Leader	Sgp	2008	44,412	12,889	183	31	19	mve	4,318 ceu
9053505	Kaijin *	Pan	1994	41,931	17,183	196	29	18	mve	4,513 ceu
9181558	Leo Leader	Pan	1999	57,566	22,733	200	32	19	mve	5,055 ceu
9174490	Libra Leader †	Pan	1998	57,674	22,734	200	32	19	mve	5,980 ceu
9206396	Linden Pride *	Pan	2001	46,021	49,999	230	37	16	lpg	78,911 m³
9367578	Lord Vishnu	Sgp	2008	51,917	17,341	180	32	19	mve	5,195 ceu
9284752	Lyra Leader *	Pan	2005	62,510	21,453	200	32	20	mve	5,427 ceu
9490959	Malanje	Bhs	2011	100,723	82,728	285	43	19	lng	160,400 m³
9392353	Mercury Leader *	Pan	2010	42,487	15,045	186	28	20	mve	4,115 ceu
9021332	New Nada *	Pan	1992	47,519	14,180	180	32	19	mve	4,760 ceu
9468293	NYK Adonis	Pan	2010	105,644	89,692	332	45	24	ucc	9,592 teu
9468308	NYK Altair	Pan	2010	105,644	89,692	332	45	24	ucc	9,592 teu
9162497	NYK Andromeda *	Pan	1998	75,637	81,819	300	40	23	ucc	6,492 teu
9162485	NYK Antares *	Pan	1997	75,637	81,819	300	40	23	ucc	6,492 teu
9247754	NYK Aphrodite *	Pan	2003	75,484	81,171	300	40	25	ucc	6,492 teu
9247730	NYK Apollo *	Pan	2002	75,484	81,171	300	40	25	ucc	6,492 teu
9262704	NYK Aquarius *	Pan	2003	75,484	81,171	300	40	25	ucc	6,492 teu
9262716	NYK Argus *	Pan	2004	75,484	81,171	300	40	25	ucc	6,492 teu
9247742	NYK Artemis *	Pan	2003	75,484	81,171	300	40	25	ucc	6,492 teu
9247786	NYK Athena	Pan	2003	75,484	81,171	300	40	25	ucc	6,492 teu
9262728	NYK Atlas *	Pan	2004	75,519	81,171	300	40	25	ucc	6,492 teu
9741372	NYK Blue Jay	Pan	2016	144,285	139,335	364	51	21	ucc	14,000 teu
9152296	NYK Canopus	Pan	1998	76,847	82,275	300	40	23	ucc	6,208 teu
9152284	NYK Castor *	Pan	1998	76,847	82,275	300	40	23	ucc	6,208 teu
9337626	NYK Constellation *	Mhl	2007	55,534	65,919	294	32	25	ucc	4,888 teu

Yu Heng Xian Feng : Nippon Yusen Kaisha - NYK-Cos : *Mike Rhodes*

IMO	name	flag	year	gt	dwt	loa	bm	kts	type	comments
9337614	NYK Daedalus *	Pan	2007	55,534	65,867	294	32	25	ucc	4,882 teu
9337652	NYK Delphinus *	Pan	2007	55,534	65,950	294	32	25	ucc	4,888 teu
9337664	NYK Demeter	Pan	2008	55,534	65,965	294	32	25	ucc	4,888 teu
9337676	NYK Deneb *	Pan	2008	55,534	65,953	294	32	25	ucc	4,882 teu
9337688	NYK Diana *	Pan	2008	55,534	65,976	294	32	25	ucc	4,888 teu
9229348	NYK Libra	Pan	2002	75,201	77,900	300	40	26	ucc	6,178 teu
9229324	NYK Lynx	Pan	2002	75,201	77,950	300	40	26	ucc	6,178 teu
9229336	NYK Lyra *	Pan	2002	75,201	77,950	300	40	26	ucc	6,178 teu
9337638	NYK Meteor [c]	Pan	2007	55,534	65,935	294	42	23	ucc	4,888 teu
9337640	NYK Nebula [c]	Pan	2007	55,534	65,600	294	42	23	ucc	4,888 teu
9312975	NYK Oceanus *	Pan	2007	98,799	99,563	336	46	25	ucc	8,628 teu
9312987	NYK Olympus	Pan	2008	98,799	99,563	336	40	25	ucc	8,628 teu
9312999	NYK Orion *	Pan	2008	98,799	99,563	336	40	25	ucc	9,050 teu
9313008	NYK Orpheus *	Jpn	2008	99,543	99,563	336	40	25	ucc	9,050 teu
9416965	NYK Remus *	Pan	2009	55,534	65,981	294	32	23	ucc	4,888 teu
9416977	NYK Rigel *	Pan	2009	55,534	66,051	294	32	23	ucc	4,888 teu
9416989	NYK Romulus	Sgp	2009	55,534	65,883	294	32	23	ucc	4,888 teu
9416991	NYK Rumina	Sgp	2010	55,534	66,171	294	32	23	ucc	4,999 teu
9354167	NYK Terra *	Pan	2008	76,928	80,282	300	40	25	ucc	6,661 teu
9356696	NYK Themis *	Pan	2008	76,928	80,282	300	40	25	ucc	6,661 teu
9356701	NYK Theseus *	Pan	2008	79,280	79,030	300	40	25	ucc	6,661 teu
9356713	NYK Triton	Pan	2008	76,614	79,280	300	40	25	ucc	6,661 teu
9312781	NYK Vega *	Pan	2006	97,825	103,310	338	46	25	ucc	9,012 teu
9312793	NYK Venus *	Pan	2007	97,825	100,900	338	46	25	ucc	9,012 teu
9312808	NYK Vesta	Pan	2007	97,825	103,260	338	46	26	ucc	9,012 teu
9312810	NYK Virgo *	Pan	2007	97,825	103,284	338	46	25	ucc	8,100 teu
9165516	Ocean Ceres	Sgp	1999	88,385	171,850	289	45	14	bbu	ex Charles LD-04
9300582	Ocean Cygnus	Pan	2006	89,603	178,996	289	45	15	bbu	
9553488	Oceanus Leader	Pan	2013	62,838	21,351	200	32	19	mve	5,374 ceu
9318498	Opal Leader	Bhs	2007	40,986	12,200	176	31	20	mve	4,750 ceu
9182289	Orion Leader	Pan	1999	57,513	21,526	200	32	19	mve	5,066 ceu
9283875	Phoenix Leader *	Pan	2004	61,804	20,146	200	32	20	mve	5,415 ceu
9676876	Pisces Leader	Pan	2014	69,931	18,781	200	36	20	mve	7,000 ceu
9426374	Pleiades Leader *	Jon	2009	62,994	21,462	200	32	21	mve	6,332 ceu
9335965	Poseidon Leader *	Jpn	2007	63,001	21,449	200	32	20	mve	6,324 ceu
9207754	Procyon Leader	Pan	2000	51,259	17,361	180	32	19	mve	4,666 ceu
9338888	Prometheus Leader	Sgp	2008	41,886	14,382	190	28	20	mve	3,305 ceu
9284738	Pyxis Leader	Pan	2004	62,195	21,466	200	32	20	mve`	5,427 ceu
8712324	Queen Ace	Pan	1988	55,423	18,777	200	32	19	mve	5,542 ceu
9355214	Rhea Leader *	Jpn	2008	63,004	21,428	200	32	19	mve	5,371 ceu
9604940	Rigel Leader *	Pan	2012	59,692	18,884	200	32	21	mve	6,153 ceu
9055486	Ryujin	Pan	1993	47,737	14,080	180	32	19	mve	4,759 ceu
9283887	Sagittaurus Leader	Pan	2005	61,804	20,098	200	32	20	mve	6,501 ceu
9498597	Selene Leader	Pan	2010	59,637	18,082	200	32	20	mve	6,400 ceu
9073701	Shohjin	Pan	1994	50,308	16,178	179	32	19	mve	4,148 ceu: ex Green Cove-12, Shohjin-00
9213806	Sirius Leader	Pan	2000	51,496	16,451	180	32	19	mve	4,323 ceu
9536909	Spica Leader	Sgp	2012	41,886	14,378	190	28	20	mve	3,921 ceu
9700550	Taurus Leader †	Sgp	2015	69,931	19,278	200	36	20	mve	7,000 ceu
9553115	Themis Leader	Pan	2010	61,804	20,037	200	32	19	mve	5,415 ceu
9553103	Triton Leader	Pan	2010	60,876	22,657	200	32	19	mve	6,502 ceu
9213818	Vega Leader	Pan	2000	51,496	16,396	180	32	19	mve	4,323 ceu
9392341	Venus Leader *	Pan	2010	42,487	15,031	186	28	20	mve	4,115 ceu
9273894	Virgo Leader *	Pan	2004	61,854	20,111	200	32	20	mve	5,415 ceu
9166895	Yu Heng									
	Xian Feng ††	Chn	1998	51,790	14,909	180	32	19	mve	4,305 ceu: ex Alioth Leader-13
9476733	Zeus Leader *	Jpn	2009	60,212	18,697	200	32	20	mve	6,341 ceu
newbuildings:										
9676840					59,000		200	36	mve	7,000 ceu Imabari Marugami
9676852					59,000		200	36	mve	7,000 ceu Imabari Marugami
9741384	NYK Ibis	Pan	2016	144,285	139,335	364	51	21	ucc	14,000 teu JMU 5062 06.2016
9741396	NYK Eagle	Pan	2016	144,285	139,300	364	51	21	ucc	14,000 teu JMU 5063 09.2016
9741401	NYK Crane	Pan	2017	144,285	139,300	364	51	21	ucc	14,000 teu JMU 5064 01.2017
9741413	NYK Falcon	Pan	2017	144,285	139,300	364	51	21	ucc	14,000 teu JMU 5075 04.2017
9741425	NYK Wren	Pan	2017	144,285	139,300	364	51	21	ucc	14,000 teu JMU 5076 08.2017
9741437	NYK Robin	Pan	2017	155,285	139,300	364	51	21	ucc	14,000 teu JMU 5077 11.2017
9741449	NYK Hawk	Pan	2018	144,285	139,300	364	51	21	ucc	14,000 teu JMU 5078 03.2018
		Pan	2018	144,285	139,300	364	51	21	ucc	14,000 teu JMU 5111 06.2018
		Pan	2018	144,285	139,300	364	51	21	ucc	14,000 teu JMU 5112 09.2018

* managed by NYK Ship Management Co. Ltd, Singapore (formed 2001) or ** NYK Ship Management, Hong Kong (formed 1989).
† chartered vessels   †† operated by NYKCos Car Carrier Co. (j/v with COSCO (51%) established 2003),
+ operated by Gazocean, Marseilles   ++ jointly owned with Sovcomflot

The company and its numerous subsidiaries own or manage over 410 vessels with many others on charter. Only the largest container ships and vehicle carriers are listed. The company also owns, manages or operates 22 large LNG tankers, 46 wood-chip carriers, many other bulk carriers, crude oil tankers and smaller container ships. See also Ray Shipping, Stolt-Nielsen, Torm.

Nissan Motor Car Carriers   Japan

funnel: *white with red 'NISSAN' above grey pane topped by red line, narrow black top'.* **hull:** *grey with white upperworks separated by red line, red boot-topping.* **history:** *company founded 1965, originally for export of Nissan cars to US market. Owned 10% by Nissan Motor Car Co., 90% by Mitsui OSK Lines who purchased Höegh's 20% holding during 2015.* **web:** *nissancarrier.co.jp*

IMO	name	flag	year	gt	dwt	loa	bm	kts	type	comments
9372327	Andromeda Spirit	Pan	2007	43,810	15,261	180	30	19	mve	3,505 ceu
9153551	Euro Spirit	Lbr	1988	46,346	15,483	188	31	20	mve	5,100 ceu
9509401	Jupiter Spirit	Lbr	2011	45,961	13,954	183	30	19	mve	5,000 ceu
9620295	Leo Spirit	Pan	2012	60,825	16,758	200	32	20	mve	6,400 ceu
9372315	Luna Spirit	Pan	2007	43,810	15,261	180	30	19	mve	3,505 ceu
9409326	Pleiades Spirit	Pan	2008	60,330	17,424	200	32	19	mve	6,400 ceu
9185047	United Spirit	Lbr	2000	37,949	14,067	175	29	20	mve	3.200 ceu
9505900	Venus Spirit	Lbr	2011	45,959	13,951	183	30	20	mve	5,000 ceu
9175925	World Spirit	Lbr	2000	37,949	14,101	175	29	19	mve	3,200 ceu

also operates two smaller units, City of Amsterdam and City of Barcelona

Norddeutsche Vermögen Holding GmbH & Co. KG   Germany

Norddeutsche Reederei H. Schuldt GmbH & Co. KG, Germany

funnel: *white with red 'S' on white triangle on blue square or charterers colours.* **hull:** *black or red with red boot-topping.* **history:** *parent founded 1984 and subsidiary 2002 following merger of 'NRG' Norddeutsche Reederei Beteiligungs GmbH with H Schuldt OHG (founded 1868) and Engineering Consulting & Management GmbH which had merged in 1989. Reederei K. Schlüter joined Norddeutsche Vermögen Gp. group in 2007 and merged fleet with Norddeutsche Reederei H. Schulte during 2011.* **web:** *www.norddeutsche-reederei.de*

IMO	name	flag	year	gt	dwt	loa	bm	kts	type	comments
9196905	APL Egypt	Lbr	2000	54,415	66,922	294	32	24	ucc	4,843 teu: ex MOL Virtue-03, APL Egypt-02, l/a Northen Glory
9295177	Ernest Hemingway	Lbr	2005	54,271	66,762	294	32	23	ucc	4,992 teu: ex Maersk Davenport-13, Ernest Hemingway-05
9357872	Fritz Reuter	Lbr	2006	18,480	23,700	177	27	20	ucc	1,732 teu: ex Maruba Zonda-08, l/a Fritz Reuter
9323493	Hermann Hesse	Lbr	2007	18,480	23,716	177	27	20	ucc	1,732 teu
9294991	Houston Express	Deu	2005	94,483	108,106	332	43	25	ucc	8,411 teu: l/dn Northern Jade
9431812	Jack London	Lbr	2010	40,541	50,278	261	32	24	ucc	4,250 teu: ex APL Melbourne-15, l/a Jack London
9431824	Jonathan Swift	Lbr	2010	40,541	50,201	261	32	24	ucc	4,250 teu: ex APL Shanghai-15, l/a Jonathan Swift
9216365	Judith Borchard	Pmd	2001	14,278	15,273	159	26	21	ucc	1,216 teu: ex Kybo-13, Jock Rickmers-13, Vento di Scirroco-12, Jock Rickmers-11, OOCL Advance-09, Jock Rickmers-04, APL Magnolia-01, l/a Jock Rickmers
9404209	Jules Verne	Lbr	2010	40,541	50,367	261	32	24	ucc	4,250 teu: ex CSAV Lluta-14, l/a Jules Verne
9253301	MSC Prague	Lbr	2003	41,078	48,874	260	32	23	ucc	3,963 teu: ex Barcelona Bridge-06, l/a Northern Delicacy
9253296	MSC Vienna	Lbr	2003	41,078	48,923	260	32	23	ucc	3,963 teu: ex Potomac Bridge-06, l/a Northern Decency
9353228	Northern Debonair	Lbr	2007	35,975	42,183	231	32	23	ucc	3,400 teu: ex NYK Lyttelton-12, Northern Debonair-11 CSAV Rahue-07
9346017	Northern Decision	Lbr	2008	36,007	42,011	231	32	23	ucc	3,534 teu: ex CSAV Rupanco-14, l/a Northern Decision
9329631	Northern Dedication	Lbr	2007	35,975	42,131	231	32	23	ucc	3,554 teu: ex Kota Sabas-12. c/a Northern Dedication
9329643	Northern Defender	Lbr	2007	35,975	42,121	231	32	23	ucc	3,400 teu: ex CSAV Renaico-13, l/a Northern Defender
9346005	Northern Delegation	Lbr	2008	36,007	42,002	231	32	23	ucc	3,534 teu: ex CCNI Valparaiso-15, Northern Delegation-14, NYK Lyttelton-13, CSAV Ranquil-12, l/a Northern Delegation
9391787	Northern Democrat	Lbr	2009	36,007	41,986	231	32	22	ucc	3,534 teu
9345984	Northern Dependant	Lbr	2008	36,007	42,019	231	32	23	ucc	3,400 teu: ex APL Dallas-13, MOL Wave-08, APL Dallas-07, l/a Northern Dependant

212

IMO	name	flag	year	gt	dwt	loa	bm	kts	type	comments
9345996	Northern Dexterity	Lbr	2008	36,007	41,964	231	32	23	ucc	3,534 teu: ex APL Minneapolis-13, MOL Wind -12, APL Minneapolis-11, MOL Wind-08, APL Minneapolis-08, I/a Northern Dexterity
9405033	Northern Diamond	Lbr	2010	40,541	42,054	231	32	23	ucc	3,534 teu: ex X-Press Makalu-13, CSAV Ranco-12, I/a Northern Diamond
9353230	Northern Diplomat	Lbr	2009	36,007	42,106	231	32	23	ucc	3,534 teu
9391799	Northern Discovery	Lbr	2008	36,007	41,977	231	32	23	ucc	3,534 teu: ex CSAV Rauten-14, I/a Northern Discovery
9230074	Northern Endeavour	Lbr	2001	25,713	33,900	208	30	21	ucc	2,456 teu: ex Cap Frio-08, Northern Endeavour-03, Andhika Loreto-01
9230086	Northern Endurance	Lbr	2001	25,713	33,838	208	30	21	ucc	2,456 teu: ex Cap Matapan-08, Alianca Singapore-07, Cap Matapan-04, Northern Endurance-03, Andhika Fatima-01
9344708	Northern General	Lbr	2008	41,835	53,870	264	32	24	ucc	4,319 teu: ex Cap Gabriel -13, c/a Northern General
9348431	Northern Genius	Lbr	2008	41,835	53,874	264	32	24	ucc	4,319 teu: ex Cap George-13, c/a Northern Genius
9348443	Northern Gleam	Lbr	2008	41,835	53,874	264	32	24	ucc	4,319 teu: ex Cap Gilbert -13, c/a Northern Gleam
9196890	Northern Grace	Lbr	2000	54,415	66,895	294	32	24	ucc	4,843 teu: ex APL Arabia-15, MOL Vigilance-03, Vantage-03, MOL Vantage-02, APL Arabia-02, I/a Northern Grace
9348455	Northern Guard	Lbr	2008	41,835	53,870	264	32	24	ucc	4,319 teu: ex Cap Graham-13, c/a Northern Guard
9348467	Northern Guild	Lbr	2008	41,835	53,870	264	32	24	ucc	4,319 teu: ex Cap Gregory-14, I/dn Northern Guild
9466972	Northern Jaguar	Lbr	2009	94,407	108,731	334	43	25	ucc	8,400 teu: ex APL Dhaka -12, Northern Jaguar-12
9450363	Northern Jamboree	Lbr	2010	94,419	108,827	333	43	25	ucc	8,400 teu
9466960	Northern Jasper	Lbr	2009	94,407	108,804	334	43	25	ucc	8,400 teu: ex APL Portugal-12, Northern Jasper-12
9465095	Northern Javelin	Lbr	2009	94,407	108,677	334	43	25	ucc	8,400 teu ex APL Italy-12, Northern Javelin-11
9450337	Northern Jubilee	Lbr	2009	94,419	108,770	333	43	25	ucc	8,400 teu
9294989	Northern Julie	Deu	2005	94,483	101,500	332	43	25	ucc	8,411 teu: ex Savannah Express-14, I/dn Northern Julie
9466984	Northern Jupiter	Lbr	2010	94,407	108,622	334	43	24	ucc	8,400 teu: ex Alianca Urca-13, Northern Jupiter-12
9450351	Northern Justice	Lbr	2010	94,419	108,836	333	43	24	ucc	8,400 teu: ex Alianca Charrua-13, Northern Justice-12
9450349	Northern Juvenile	Lbr	2009	94,419	108,828	333	43	25	ucc	8,400 teu: ex CSAV Taltal-13, APL Manila-12, Northern Juvenile-12
9252553	Northern Magnitude	Deu	2003	75,590	85,810	300	40	25	ucc	6,732 teu: ex Bangkok Express-15, ex Northern Magnitude-04
9252541	Northern Magnum	Lbr	2003	75,590	85,810	300	40	25	ucc	6,732 teu: ex Los Angeles Express-15, I/a Northern Magnum
9252565	Northern Majestic	Deu	2004	75,590	85,400	300	40	25	ucc	6,732 teu: ex San Francisco Express-15, I/a Northern Majestic
9252577	Northern Monument	Deu	2004	75,590	85,810	300	40	25	ucc	6,732 teu: ex Busan Express-15, I/a Northern Monument
9467055	Northern Power	Lbr	2010	47,855	59,346	264	32	24	ucc	4,600 teu
9450301	Northern Practise	Lbr	2009	47,855	59,352	264	32	24	ucc	4,600 teu: ex APLXingang-11, Ankara Bridge-10
9450296	Northern Precision	Lbr	2009	47,855	59,431	264	32	24	ucc	4,319 teu: ex CCNI Patagonia-12, Northern Precision-10, Adriatic Bridge-10
9450325	Northern Prelude	Lbr	2009	47,855	59,404	264	32	24	ucc	4,600 teu
9450313	Northern Priority	Lbr	2009	47,855	59,368	264	32	24	ucc	4,319 teu: ex Cap Irene-14, Northern Priority-11, Bunga Raya Sebelas-10, I/a Northern Priority
9467043	Northern Promotion	Lbr	2010	47,855	59,483	264	32	24	ucc	4,600 teu
9304693	Northern Valence	Lbr	2005	27,437	37,921	222	30	22	ucc	2,742 teu: ex-Sinotrans Shanghai-11, I/a Northern Valence
9304708	Northern Vigour	Lbr	2005	27,437	37,901	222	30	22	ucc	2,742 teu: ex CMA CGM Qingdao-12, Sinotrans Qingdao-09
9304966	Northern Vivacity	Lbr	2005	27,437	37,856	222	30	22	ucc	2,742 teu: ex Sinotrans Tianjin-12, I/a Northern Vivacity

IMO	name	flag	year	gt	dwt	loa	bm	kts	type	comments
9304978	Northern Volition	Lbr	2006	27,437	37,813	222	30	22	ucc	2,742 teu: ex Sinotrans Dalian-12, APL Yokohama-09, Northern Volition-06, Sinotrans Dalian-06, I/a Northern Volition
9452854	Tasman Castle	Mlt	2011	32,987	56,868	190	32	14	bbu	
9248667	Thomas Mann	Mlt	2003	28,270	33,282	213	32	23	ucc	2,586 teu: ex TS Tokyo-12, Thomas Mann-10

Dampskibsselskabet 'Norden' A/S   Denmark

funnel: *black with narrow red band on broad white band.* **hull:** *black or dark blue with red boot-topping.* **history:** *formed 1871 and now 32% owned by A/S Dampskibsselskabet Torm.* **web:** *www.ds-norden.com*

IMO	name	flag	year	gt	dwt	loa	bm	kts	type	comments
9595254	Nord Aarhus *	Sgp	2012	21,934	33,221	179	29	14	bbu	
9544750	Nord Auckland *	Sgp	2011	22,683	36,782	186	28	14	bbu	
9544748	Nord Barcelona *	Sgp	2011	22,683	35,746	186	28	14	bbu	
9727065	Nord Beluga	Sgp	2015	43,729	81,841	229	32	14	bbu	
9623752	Nord Capella +	Sgp	2015	42,995	81,944	229	32	14	bbu	
9448023	Nord Delphinus *	Sgp	2010	63,864	114,167	250	43	14	bbu	
9448035	Nord Dorado *	Sgp	2010	63,864	114,167	250	43	14	bbu	
9713911	Nord Draco +	Mhl	2014	45,229	84,694	229	35	14	bbu	
9403114	Nord Express *	Sgp	2007	32,379	58,785	190	32	14	bbu	
9479046	Nord Fuji	Sgp	2011	31,250	55,628	190	32	14	bbu	
9334789	Nord Highlander	Mhl	2007	23,304	37,145	183	28	14	tco	ex STI Highlander-15, Panna-10, Jag Panna-09
9599004	Nord Hong Kong *	Sgp	2011	20,969	32,289	180	28	14	bbu	
9543251	Nord Houston *	Sgp	2011	20,924	32,389	180	28	14	bbu	
9710787	Nord Hydra +	Sgp	2014	40,937	77,134	225	32	14	bbu	
9710799	Nord Libra +	Sgp	2014	40,937	77,134	225	32	14	bbu	
9599016	Nord London *	Sgp	2011	20,969	32,312	180	28	14	bbu	
9425875	Nord Manatee *	Sgp	2010	32,296	57,982	190	32	14	bbu	ex CMB Maxime-16
9284491	Nord Maru *	Sgp	2006	30,684	55,745	190	32	14	bbu	
9577898	Nord Melbourne *	Bhs	2011	20,924	32,417	180	28	14	bbu	
9725457	Nord Mississippi +	Pan	2015	34,558	60,456	200	32	14	bbu	
9725469	Nord Missouri +	Pan	2015	34,558	60,463	200	32	14	bbu	
9612284	Nord Montreal *	Sgp	2012	22,850	36,570	180	28	14	bbu	
9612313	Nord Mumbai *	Sgp	2012	22,746	36,612	187	28	14	bbu	
9310537	Nord Neptune	Dis	2006	38,892	75,726	225	32	14	bbu	
9566564	Nord Peak *	Sgp	2011	33,990	61,649	200	32	14	bbu	
9687186	Nord Penguin	Sgp	2015	43,729	81,500	229	32	14	bbu	
9448059	Nord Pisces *	Sgp	2010	63,864	114,167	250	43	14	bbu	
9623740	Nord Pluto +	Pan	2014	42,995	81,944	229	32	14	bbu	
9728174	Nord Pollux +	Pan	2016	43,042	81,839	229	32	24	bbu	
9448047	Nord Pyxis *	Sgp	2010	63,864	114,167	250	43	14	bbu	
9612296	Nord Quebec *	Sgp	2013	22,850	36,546	180	26	14	bbu	
9544762	Nord Rotterdam *	Sgp	2011	22,683	36,599	186	28	14	bbu	
9544736	Nord Seoul *	Sgp	2010	22,683	36,781	186	29	14	bbu	
9612325	Nord Shanghai *	Sgp	2012	22,746	36,746	187	28	14	bbu	
9529504	Nord Summit *	Sgp	2012	33,990	61,649	200	32	14	bbu	
9577886	Nord Sydney *	Sgp	2011	20,924	32,688	180	28	14	bbu	
9566459	Nord Treasure +	Pan	2014	31,882	55,888	190	32	14	bbu	
9598995	Nord Vancouver *	Sgp	2011	20,969	32,353	180	28	14	bbu	
9711937	Nord Virgo +	Pan	2014	43,291	81,001	229	32	14	bbu	
9253181	Nordkap	Dis	2002	40,066	77,229	225	32	14	bbu	
9253193	Nordpol	Dis	2002	40,066	77,195	225	32	14	bbu	
newbuildings:										
9658965	Nord Everest		2016	32,300	55,450	190	32	14	bbu	Oshima 10727

* owned by subsidiary Norden Shipping (Singapore) Pte Ltd. + chartered tonnage
the company currently operates vessels within the Norient Product Pool (formed 2010 with Interorient Navigation Co Ltd)

Norient Product Pool ApS, Denmark

funnel: *owners colours* **hull:** *red or blue with white logo and 'NORIENT', red boot topping* **history:** *limited company founded in Denmark as 50/50 joint venture between Interorient Navigation Co. and Dampskibsselskabet Norden A/S. Diamond S were admitted to the pool with 8 vessels in 2015. Also manages vessels for third party owners.* **web:** *norientpool.com*

IMO	name	flag	year	gt	dwt	loa	bm	kts	type	comments
9380518	Alpine Madeleine	Hkg	2008	29,266	47,128	183	32	15	tco	
9380526	Alpine Mathilde	Hkg	2008	29,266	47,128	183	32	15	tco	
9391426	Alpine Mia †	Hkg	2008	29,266	47,128	183	32	15	tco	
9318034	Arctic Bay +	Mlt	2006	30,053	50,921	183	32	14	tco	ex West Point-06
9350862	Arctic Blizzard +	Mlt	2006	30,053	50,922	183	32	14	tco	ex Baltic Point-06
9350850	Arctic Breeze +	Mlt	2006	30,053	50,922	183	32	14	tco	ex Ice Point-06
9307815	Arctic Bridge +	Mlt	2005	30,053	50,930	183	32	14	tco	ex Ice Point-06
9332303	Atlantic Frontier †	Hkg	2007	29,266	47,128	183	32	15	tco	

Nord Beluga : Dampskibsselskabet 'Norden' : *Nico Kemps*

Baltic Mariner I : Dampskibsselskabet 'Norden', Norient Product Pool : *ARO*

IMO	name	flag	year	gt	dwt	loa	bm	kts	type	comments
9332315	Atlantic Gemini	Hkg	2008	29,266	47,128	183	32	15	tco	
9383962	Atlantic Jupiter	Hkg	2009	23,342	36,677	184	27	14	tco	
9354894	Atlantic Lily †	Hkg	2008	29,266	47,128	183	32	15	tco	
9392781	Atlantic Pisces	Hkg	2009	29,266	47,128	183	32	15	tco	
9360324	Atlantic Titan †	Hkg	2008	29,266	47,128	183	32	15	tco	
9425552	Axel	Pan	2010	28,465	50,090	183	32	15	tco	
9299862	Baltic Advance +	Cyp	2006	23,240	37,332	183	27	14	tco	
9260029	Baltic Champion +	Mlt	2003	23,240	37,333	183	27	14	tco	ex British Experience-07, Baltic Champion-05
9208112	Baltic Commander I +	Cyp	2000	23,235	37,418	183	27	14	tco	ex Baltic Commander-02, l/a Antifon
9260017	Baltic Commodore +	Mlt	2003	23,240	37,343	183	27	14	tco	ex British Engineer-07, Baltic Commodore-05
9327372	Baltic Favour +	Cyp	2006	23,337	37,106	183	27	14	tco	
9327396	Baltic Freedom +	Cyp	2006	23,337	37,048	183	27	14	tco	
9327401	Baltic Frost +	Cyp	2006	23,337	37,340	183	27	14	tco	ex Baltic Front-11
9314820	Baltic Mariner I	Cyp	2006	23,240	37,304	183	27	14	tco	ex Baltic Mariner-14
9314818	Baltic Monarch +	Cyp	2006	23,240	37,273	183	27	14	tco	
9443425	Baltic Sapphire +	Cyp	2009	23,339	37,250	184	27	14	tco	
9228801	Baltic Sky I +	Mlt	2001	23,235	37,272	183	27	14	tco	ex Flores-06, Flores I-01
9228813	Baltic Soul +	Mlt	2001	23,235	37,244	183	27	14	tco	ex Sicilia-06
9286059	Baltic Sun II +	Mlt	2005	23,235	37,305	183	27	15	tco	ex Baltic Sun-05
9464376	Baltic Swift +	Cyp	2010	23,339	37,565	184	27	14	tco	
9259991	Baltic Wave +	Mlt	2003	23,235	37,300	183	27	15	tco	ex Prostar-05, Ice Point-03
9261401	Baltic Wind +	Mlt	2003	23,235	37,296	183	27	15	tco	ex Prosky-05
9215115	Blue Marlin	Lbr	2001	23,682	35,970	183	25	15	tco	ex Blu Star-12, Blue Star-08, British Energy-06
9561370	Bright Fortune	Pan	2010	28,777	48,009	180	32	14	tco	
9251286	Dukhan	Qat	2003	25,408	37,284	176	31	14	tco	
9544607	FS Sincerity	Pan	2009	28,797	48,045	180	32	14	tco	ex Siva Sincerity-14, JBU Sincerity-12
9286047	Giannutri +	Mlt	2004	23,235	37,272	183	27	14	tco	
9366275	High Mars	Hkg	2008	29,733	51,542	183	32	14	tco	
9366263	High Saturn †	Hkg	2008	29,733	51,527	183	32	14	tco	
9283784	Hugli Spirit †	Bhs	2005	29,242	46,889	183	32	14	tco	ex Brazos-07, l/a Athenian Splendour
9629691	James Cook	Sgp	2013	29,983	49,995	183	32	15	tco	ex Nord Strength-14
9241695	Kerel +	Mlt	2002	23,235	37,272	183	27	14	tco	

Nord Geranium : Dampskibsselskabet 'Norden', Norient Product Pool : *Nico Kemps*

IMO	name	flag	year	gt	dwt	loa	bm	kts	type	comments
9541306	Miss Benedetta	Mlt	2012	29,814	50,895	183	32	15	tco	
9561382	New Breeze	Pan	2010	28,777	48,064	180	32	15	tco	
9309980	Nord Bell	Dis	2007	24,048	38,461	183	27	14	tco	
9448310	Nord Butterfly	Dis	2008	24,048	38,431	183	27	14	tco	
9293947	Nord Farer *	Sgp	2005	25,382	40,083	176	31	14	tco	ex F.D. Nord Farer-10, Nord Farer-08
9448724	Nord Gainer	Dis	2011	30,241	50,281	183	32	14	tco	
9670949	Nord Gardenia	Dis	2014	25,028	39,895	183	31	14	tco	
9670937	Nord Geranium	Dis	2014	25,028	39,826	183	31	14	tco	
9448712	Nord Guardian	Dis	2011	30,241	50,420	183	32	14	tco	
9352195	Nord Hummock	Dis	2007	23,204	37,159	183	27	14	tco	ex Payal-11, Jag Payal-09
9547506	Nord Imagination	Pan	2009	28,777	48,006	180	32	15	tco	
9568043	Nord Independence	Pan	2010	28,777	48,005	180	32	15	tco	
9555292	Nord Innovation	Pan	2010	28,777	47,981	180	32	15	tco	
9441855	Nord Inspiration	Pan	2010	28,798	47,987	180	32	15	tco	
9568031	Nord Integrity	Pan	2010	28,777	48,026	180	32	15	tco	
9561368	Nord Intelligence	Sgp	2010	28,813	47,975	180	32	15	tco	
9303730	Nord Mermaid	Dis	2007	24,048	38,461	183	27	14	tco	
9376816	Nord Nightingale *	Dis	2008	24,048	38,461	183	27	14	tco	
9338814	Nord Observer	Lbr	2007	26,900	47,344	183	32	14	tco	
9367748	Nord Organiser	Pan	2008	26,900	47,399	183	32	14	tco	
9303728	Nord Princess	Dis	2007	24,048	38,500	183	27	14	tco	
9536820	Nord Sakura	Mhl	2012	28,736	45,953	182	32	16	tco	
9376828	Nord Snow Queen *	Dis	2008	24,066	38,500	183	27	14	tco	
9629706	Nord Steady *	Sgp	2013	29,983	49,994	183	32	14	tco	
9692129	Nord Superior *	Dis	2015	30,108	50,800	182	32	15	tco	
9692131	Nord Supreme *	Dis	2015	30,108	50,800	183	32	15	tco	
9692143	Nord Sustainable *	Sgp	2015	30,108	49,578	183	32	14	tco	
9448322	Nord Swan *	Dis	2009	24,066	38,431	183	27	14	tco	
9692155	Nord Swift *	Sgp	2015	30,108	49,585	183	32	14	tco	
9309978	Nord Thumbelina	Dis	2006	24,048	38,461	183	27	14	tco	
9394040	Norient Saturn +	Cyp	2007	25,864	40,435	180	32	15	tco	l/a Nordic Saturn
9436678	Norient Scorpius +	Mlt	2009	25,814	40,400	180	32	15	tco	
9396373	Norient Solar +	Mlt	2008	25,864	40,429	180	32	15	tco	
9396385	Norient Star +	Mlt	2008	25,814	40,400	180	32	15	tco	
9459230	Orient Star	Pan	2010	28,725	45,994	182	32	14	tco	
9399868	Oriental Diamond	Pan	2008	30,110	50,323	183	32	14	tco	
9425497	Perseus N	Lbr	2009	23,332	36,264	184	27	14	tco	ex Elbtank France-13
9257022	Ridgebury Alice M	Mhl	2003	56,172	105,745	239	42	14	tco	ex ACS Bright-14, Sanko Bright-12
9439785	Ridgebury Alexandra Z	Mhl	2009	29,905	50,251	183	32	14	tco	ex Yasa Seyhan-13
9439773	Ridgebury Cindy A	Mhl	2009	29,905	50,162	183	32	14	tco	ex Yasa Ceyhan-13
9349631	Ridgebury John B	Mhl	2007	28,062	45,975	180	32	15	tco	ex Challenge Pioneer-14
9333187	Ridgebury Julia M	Mhl	2007	28,063	45,980	180	32	15	tco	ex Challenge-Paradise-14
9439797	Ridgebury Katherine Z	Mhl	2009	29,905	50,215	183	32	14	tco	ex Yasa Marmaris-13
9439802	Ridgebury Rosemary E	Mhl	2009	29,905	50,261	183	32	14	tco	ex Yasa Bodrum-14
9257010	Ridgebury Sally B	Mhl	2003	56,172	105,672	239	42	14	tco	ex ACS Brave-14, Sanko Brave-12
9414278	Rita M	Pan	2009	28,054	45,997	180	32	14	tco	ex Nord Star-15, Torm Helsingor-13
9377664	Single	Mlt	2007	23,248	37,824	183	27	14	tco	ex Rova-13
9380350	Sky	Mlt	2007	23,248	37,879	183	27	14	tco	ex Cotton-13
9321938	Star Eagle	Pan	2007	30,068	51,214	183	32	14	tco	ex Nord Strait -12, Gan-Spirit-10
9325611	Star Falcon	Pan	2007	31,433	53,815	186	32	14	tco	ex Freja Selandia-12
9321940	Star Kestrel	Pan	2008	30,068	51,228	183	32	14	tco	ex Nord Sound-13, Gan-Sabre-10
9325609	Star Merlin	Pan	2007	31,500	53,755	186	32	14	tco	ex Freja Dania-13
9315068	Star Osprey	Pan	2007	30,068	51,213	183	32	14	tco	ex Nord Sea -13, Gan-Shield-10
9283722	Teesta Spirit	Bhs	2004	29,242	46,921	183	32	14	tco	ex Jeanette-07, l/a Athenian Harmony
9402809	Unique Developer	Hkg	2010	26,914	47,366	183	32	15	tco	
9540821	Unique Guardian	Hkg	2012	29,411	50,475	183	32	15	tco	
9540833	Unique Infinity	Hkg	2013	29,479	50,378	183	32	15	tco	
newbuildings:										
9697909			2016	30,000	49,973			14	tco	Hyundai Vinashin S-417

2 x 50,000dwt tco [Onomichi(2016/17)], 2 x 50,000dwt tco (JMU (2018))
vessels owned by: + Interorient Navigation, * Dampskibsselskabet Norden A/S   † Diamond S Shipping

Nordic American Tankers Ltd.   Bermuda

funnel: white with blue and red coloured/striped rectangle, black top. **hull:** Black or red with red or green boot-topping. **history:** formed 1995 as Navion ASA to 2003, when it was acquired from Statoil ASA. **web:** www.nat.bm

IMO	name	flag	year	gt	dwt	loa	bm	kts	type	comments
9248423	Nordic Apollo	Mhl	2003	81,310	159,988	274	48	14	tcr	ex Glyfada Spirit-06, Euro Spirit-03
9159672	Nordic Aurora *	Lbr	1999	80,668	147,262	274	48	14	tcr	ex Hellespont Trust-11

Nordic Olympic : Nordic Bulk Carriers AS : *Hans Kraijenbosch*

Nordic Buxtehude : Nordic Hamburg Gp. : *F. de Vries*

Nordic Anne : Nordic Shipholding A/S : *F. de Vries*

IMO	name	flag	year	gt	dwt	loa	bm	kts	type	comments
9588445	Nordic Breeze	Lbr	2011	86,266	158,597	274	48	14	tcr	ex Calm Sea-06, Euro Sea-03
9233765	Nordic Cosmos	Mhl	2003	81,310	159,999	274	48	14	tcr	ex Yasa Southern Cross-15
9438418	Nordic Cross	Mhl	2010	81,493	158,525	274	48	15	tcr	ex Front Hunter-05
9157727	Nordic Discovery	Nis	1998	79,669	153,328	269	46	14	tcr	ex Front Hunter-05
9157715	Nordic Fighter	Nis	1998	79,669	153,328	269	46	14	tcr	ex Front Fighter-05
9288887	Nordic Freedom	Bhs	2005	83,594	159,331	274	48	14	tcr	ex Santiago Spirit-05
9230892	Nordic Grace *	Cym	2002	84,598	149,921	274	50	14	tcr	ex Seagrace-09
9131137	Nordic Harrier	Mhl	1997	80,187	151,459	274	46	14	tcr	ex Gulf Scandic-10, British Harrier-04
9131149	Nordic Hawk	Bhs	1997	80,187	151,475	274	46	14	tcr	ex British Hawk-04
9131151	Nordic Hunter	Bhs	1997	80,100	151,401	274	46	14	tcr	ex British Hunter-04
9160205	Nordic Jupiter	Mhl	1998	81,565	157,411	274	48	14	tcr	ex Sacramento-06
9436446	Nordic Light	Mhl	2010	81,493	158,555	274	48	15	tcr	ex Yasa Scorpion-15
9233210	Nordic Mistral	Mhl	2002	84,586	164,236	274	50	15	tcr	ex Pentathlon-09, Cape Balboa-08, Pentathlon-03
9224283	Nordic Moon	Mhl	2002	81,310	160,200	274	48	14	tcr	ex Summer Sky-06, Euro Sky-03
9229386	Nordic Passat	Mhl	2002	84,586	164,487	274	50	15	tcr	ex Decathlon-10, Cape Baker-08, Decathlon-03
9167198	Nordic Saturn	Mhl	1998	81,565	157,331	274	48	14	tcr	ex Sabine-05
9297515	Nordic Skier *	Cym	2005	81,345	159,089	274	48	15	tcr	ex Energy Skier-14
9297503	Nordic Sprinter **	Cym	2005	81,345	159,089	274	48	15	tcr	ex Energy Sprinter-14
9159684	Nordic Sprite	Nis	1999	80,668	147,188	274	48	14	tcr	ex Seasprite-09
9412581	Nordic Vega	Bhs	2010	86,266	163,940	275	48	14	tcr	
9102930	Nordic Voyager *	Cym	1996	79,494	149,775	270	45	15	tcr	ex Wilma Yangtze-07
9588469	Nordic Zenith	Lbr	2011	81,509	158,645	274	48	14	tcr	
newbuildings:										
9748679	Nordic Star	Lbr	2016	84,000	158,000	277	48	14	tcr	Sungdong 2048
9748681	Nordic Space	Lbr	2017	84,000	158,000	277	48	14	tcr	Sungdong 2049

*vessels managed by Orion Tankers Ltd, UK except: * Hellespont Ship Management, ** V-Ships Norway AS*

Nordic Bulk Carriers AS

funnel: *white with large blue 8-pointed star, narrow black top* **hull:** *red with 'sharks teeth' around bow, red boot topping*
history: *founded, specialises in Arctic transportation* **web:** *www.nordicbulkcarriers.com*

IMO	name	flag	year	gt	dwt	loa	bm	kts	type	comments
9079169	Nordic Barents	Pan	1995	27,078	43,732	190	31	14	bbu	ex Cedar 4-09, Izara Princess-09, Ice Power II-08, Baffin-08
9079157	Nordic Bothnia	Pan	1995	27,078	43,706	190	31	14	bbu	ex ID Bothnia-09, Cedar 5-09, Moon Dancer-09, Ice Trader II-08, Frankin-08
9727120	Nordic Oasis	Pan	2016	41,071	76,180	225	32	14	bbu	
9687239	Nordic Odin	Pan	2015	41,071	76,180	225	32	14	bbu	
9529451	Nordic Odyssey	Pan	2010	40,142	75,603	225	32	14	bbu	ex Sanko Odyssey-12
9727118	Nordic Olympic	Pan	2015	41,071	76,180	225	32	14	bbu	
9529463	Nordic Orion	Pan	2011	40,142	75,603	225	32	14	bbu	ex Sanko Orion-12
9687227	Nordic Oshima	Pan	2014	41,071	76,180	225	32	14	bbu	

Nordic Hamburg Group GmbH   Germany

funnel: *blue with with light blue 'N' on anchor logo on white panel.* **hull:** *light blue with red boot-topping.* **history:** *group founded 2006, Nordic Hamburg Shipmanagement founded 2008* **web:** *nordic-hamburg.de*

IMO	name	flag	year	gt	dwt	loa	bm	kts	type	comments
9647289	Amelie *	Iom	2013	24,187	35,000	180	30	14	bbu	l/a Nordic Wuhan
9667576	Andalucia *	Iom	2013	24,212	37,500	180	30	14	bbu	l/a Nordic Shanghai
9689562	Nordic Alianca	Imo	2014	24,212	37,500	180	32	14	bbu	l/a Nordic Yangzhou-14
9509140	Nordic Beijing	Lbr	2013	39,905	46,150	228	32	22	ucc	3,421 teu: ex NileDutch Cheetah-14, c/a RBD Fiona
9483695	Nordic Bremen	Cyp	2011	10,318	13,200	152	24	18	ucc	1,036 teu
9497414	Nordic Buxtehude	Lbr	2010	32,929	56,755	190	32	14	bbu	ex AS Venetia-15
9667588	Nordic Dalian	Iom	2013	24,212	37,500	180	30	14	bbu	
9761889	Nordic Darwin	Mhl	2016	24,337	27,300	180	30	14	bbu	
9514755	Nordic Hamburg	Cyp	2010	10,585	13,000	152	24	18	ucc	1,036 teu
9585338	Nordic Harbin	Iom	2011	33,044	57,000	190	32	14	bbu	ex Corbita-15, Ultra Corbita-14, U-Sea Corbita-12
9509152	Nordic Hong Kong	Lbr	2013	39,905	46,580	228	32	22	ucc	2,758 teu
9483683	Nordic Luebeck	Cyp	2011	10,318	13,200	152	24	18	ucc	1,036 teu: ex AS Florentia-11
9509164	Nordic Macau	Lbr	2014	39,905	45,749	228	32	22	ucc	3,405 teu
9602679	Nordic Malmoe	Iom	2012	24,212	35,038	180	30	13	bbu	
9647291	Nordic Nanjing	Iom	2013	24,187	35,000	180	30	13	bbu	
9737888	Nordic Perth	Iom	2016	24,198	37,300	180	30	14	bbu	
9483669	Nordic Philip	Cyp	2010	10,318	13,031	152	24	18	ucc	1,036 teu: ex AS Franconia-11
9563407	Nordic Riga	Iom	2010	22,409	35,000	180	30	14	bbu	
9453248	Nordic Stade	Lbr	2011	32,929	56,808	190	32	14	bbu	ex AS Valeria-14
9483671	Nordic Stani	Cyp	2010	10,318	13,200	152	24	18	ucc	1,036 teu: ex AS Frisia-11
9563392	Nordic Stockholm	Iom	2010	22,409	35,033	180	30	14	bbu	
9565340	Nordic Stralsund	Mhl	2014	39,753	46,000	228	32	22	ucc	3,405 teu

NOCC Atlantic : Norwegian Car Carriers : *Hans Kraijenbosch*

Pago : NSC Holdings : *Chris Brooks*

Tana Sea : NSC Holdings : *F. de Vries*

IMO	name	flag	year	gt	dwt	loa	bm	kts	type	comments
9238325	Nordic Suzhou	Lbr	2002	22,072	34,676	180	28	14	bbu	ex Victory-15, Leopold Oldendorf-f06, IVS Victory-03
9632789	Nordic Tianjin	Iom	2012	33,032	57,000	190	32	13	bbu	
9563380	Nordic Visby	Iom	2010	22,409	35,052	180	30	14	bbu	
9539482	Nordic Wismar	Lbr	2011	39,753	46,131	228	32	22	ucc	3,405 teu: ex NileDutch Beijing-14
9689574	Nordic Yarra	Iom	2014	24,212	37,500	180	32	14	bbu	l/a Nordic Guangzhou

* managed by A. Bolten, other vessels managed by Nordic Hamburg Shipmanagement GmbH

Nordic Shipholding A/S   Denmark

funnel: *white with blue logo, black top.* **hull:** *blue or black, red boot-topping.* **history:** *original company established 1984.* **web:** *www.nordicshipholding.com*

IMO	name	flag	year	gt	dwt	loa	bm	kts	type	comments
9422639	Nordic Agnetha	Sgp	2009	23,224	37,791	184	27	15	tco	
9488413	Nordic Anne	Sgp	2009	42,143	73,774	229	32	15	tco	
9422641	Nordic Amy	Sgp	2009	23,224	37,759	184	27	15	tco	ex Amy-14
9340128	Nordic Hanne	Sgp	2007	24,112	38,396	183	27	15	tco	ex Amy-08
9340104	Nordic Pia	Sgp	2006	24,112	38,396	183	27	15	tco	l/a Grazia
9208473	Nordic Ruth	Sgp	2000	23,842	35,820	183	27	15	tco	ex Hanne-06

Norwegian Car Carriers ASA   Norway

funnel: *white with large blue square divided by white diagonal and narrow black top.* **hull:** *dark blue, white superstructure with logo and 'NOCC' in dark blue towards stern, red boot-topping.* **history:** *founded 1930 by Ditlev-Simonsen & Co as A/S Eidsiva, becoming Eidsiva Rederi ASA in 1996. Renamed 2010 after acquisition of Dyvi Holdings AS, formed 1955 as Jan-Erik Dyvi to 2003 and now 32% shareholders.* **web:** *www.nocc.no or www.eidsiva.nor*

IMO	name	flag	year	gt	dwt	loa	bm	kts	type	comments
9176632	Asian Emperor +	Pan	1999	55,729	21,479	200	32	20	mve	6,402 ceu
9203291	Asian King +	Pan	1998	55,729	21,511	200	32	19	mve	6,402 ceu
9460899	Glovis Companion +	Mhl	2010	60,213	18,671	200	32	20	mve	6,340 ceu: ex Ocean Challenger-13
9430519	NOCC Atlantic *	Nis	2009	60,868	22,500	200	32	19	mve	6,754 ceu: ex Dyvi Atlantic-11
9279812	NOCC Kattegat +	Mhl	2004	44,408	14,650	197	30	19	mve	5,253 ceu: ex Grande Lagos-10
9624029	NOCC Oceanic *	Nis	2012	57,600	15,770	200	32	19	mve	6,540 ceu
9177038	NOCC Pamplona †	Nis	1999	37,237	12,778	180	31	19	mve	4,287 ceu; ex Dyvi Pamplona-10
9177026	NOCC Puebla †	Nis	1999	37,237	12,780	180	31	19	mve	4,287 ceu: ex Dyvi Puebla-11

vessels chartered out to * Höegh, ** Eukor, † K Line, + Hyundai Glovis :

NSC Holding GmbH & Cie. KG   Germany

funnel: *lower half dark blue and top half light blue with white star, separated with white band and white with white 'NSC' on dark blue/grey houseflag or charterers colours.* **hull:** *blue or red (bbu) with red boot-topping.* **history:** *formed 2003.* **web:** *www.nsc-ship.com*

IMO	name	flag	year	gt	dwt	loa	bm	kts	type	comments
9399789	Algarrobo	Lbr	2009	32,901	34,700	224	31	21	ucc	2,797 teu
9399739	Andes	Lbr	2007	32,901	34,345	225	31	21	ucc	2,872 teu: ex Fesco Korea-15, Andes-12, Maersk Jena-12, Andes-07
9399765	Andino	Lbr	2008	32,901	35,391	225	31	21	ucc	2,872 teu: ex Maersk Jefferson-13, Andino-08
9399791	Angeles	Lbr	2010	32,901	35,377	224	31	21	ucc	2,797 teu: ex ANL Kurango-16, Angeles-14
9399806	Angol	Lbr	2010	32,901	35,446	224	31	21	ucc	2,797 teu: ex Alianca Corrientes-16, Angol-15
9419797	ANL Barwon	Lbr	2010	35,998	42,011	231	32	23	ucc	3,554 teu: ex Pescara-14
9629718	Antofagasta †	Chl	2013	29,893	49,996	183	32	14	tco	ex Nord Strong-15
9399741	Arica *	Lbr	2007	32,901	34,700	225	31	21	ucc	2,872 teu: ex Maersk Jakobstad-12, Arica-07
9629495	Arica †	Chl	2013	29,983	49,998	183	32	14	tco	ex Nord Stability-15
9399777	Austral	Lbr	2008	32,901	35,556	224	31	21	ucc	2,872 teu: ex Maersk Jambi-13, Austral-08
9395941	Bahamas	Lbr	2010	40,741	51,400	260	32	24	ucc	4,308 teu: ex APL Doha-15, c/a Bahamas
9395939	Barbados	Lbr	2010	40,741	52,326	260	32	24	ucc	4,308 teu: ex APL Riyadh-15, l/a Barbados
9395927	Bermuda	Lbr	2010	40,741	52,383	260	32	24	ucc	4,308 teu: ex APL Bahrain-15, l/a Bermuda
9395953	Bonaire	Lbr	2010	40,741	52,360	260	32	24	ucc	4,308 teu: ex APL Seoul-15, l/a Bonaire
9419230	Catamarca	Lbr	2009	35,240	53,021	196	32	15	ggc	ex Alcmene-12, Andromeda-09, l/a Bodega Sea
9718935	CCNI Andes	Lbr	2015	95,138	113,072	300	48	22	ucc	9,300 teu: l/a San Ambrosio
9683867	CCNI Angol	Lbr	2015	95,138	113,212	300	48	22	ucc	9,030 teu
9683843	CCNI Arauco	Lbr	2015	95,138	113,174	300	48	22	ucc	9,030 teu
9419254	Corrientes	Lbr	2010	35,240	53,035	196	32	15	ggc	ex Athena-12, Artemis-10, l/a Beagle Sea
9235359	Fernando **	Lbr	2003	23,132	30,345	193	28	19	ghl	cr: 2(100): ex Cape Delgardo-12

IMO	name	flag	year	gt	dwt	loa	bm	kts	type	comments
9358888	Gral. Manuel Belgrano	Lbr	2008	40,628	12,303	176	31	20	mve	4,870 ceu: ex STX Bluebird-13, Andino-11
9348687	Maersk Danang	Lbr	2008	54,675	68,411	294	32	24	ucc	5,085 teu: l/a Chicago
9348663	Maersk Denpasar	Lbr	2008	54,675	68,463	294	32	24	ucc	5,085 teu: l/a Miami
9348675	Memphis	Lbr	2008	54,675	68,463	294	32	24	ucc	5,085 teu: ex Maersk Damietta-16, l/a Memphis
9348699	MSC Dhahran	Lbr	2008	54,675	67,410	294	32	24	ucc	5,085 teu: ex Maersk Dhahran-16, l/a Las Vegas
9382097	Montreal	Lbr	2009	40,619	12,245	176	31	20	mve	4,870 ceu: ex STX Oriole-13, c/a Montreal
9333072	Natal	Lbr	2007	35,573	44,234	223	32	22	ucc	3,388 teu: ex APL Chicago-15, c/a Natal
9333046	Nelson	Lbr	2007	35,573	44,239	223	32	22	ucc	3,388 teu: ex APL Seattle-15, Seattle-07, l/a Cape Rexton, l/d Nelson
9322504	Newark **	Lbr	2006	35,573	44,133	223	32	22	ucc	3,388 teu: ex APL Brisbane-15, c/a Newark
9322516	Noro	Lbr	2007	35,573	44,165	223	32	22	ucc	3,398 teu: ex APL Guangzhou-15, Guangzhou-07, c/a Noro
9418640	Pago	Lbr	2009	35,998	41,982	231	32	23	ucc	3,554 teu
9419785	Partici	Lbr	2010	35,998	41,974	231	32	23	ucc	3,554 teu
9419773	Praia	Lbr	2009	35,998	41,996	231	32	23	ucc	3,554 teu
9419242	Salta	Lbr	2009	35,240	52,998	196	32	15	ggc	ex Aphrodite-11, l/a Botany Sea
9231133	San Rafael **	Lbr	2003	23,132	30,490	193	28	19	ghl	cr: 2(100) ex Cape Donington-12, Golden Isle-04, Cape Donington-03
9423566	Santa Fe	Lbr	2010	35,240	52,928	196	32	15	ggc	ex Asteria-12, l/a Biscay Bay
9498846	Tana Sea	Lbr	2011	50,729	93,246	229	38	14	bbu	
9484704	Tango Sea	Lbr	2011	51,253	93,028	229	38	14	bbu	
9498810	Thira Sea	Lbr	2010	50,697	92,500	229	38	14	bbu	
9398462	Tianjin	Lbr	2010	114,044	116,440	349	46	25	ucc	10,070 teu: ex Zim Tianjin-11
9498834	Tonda Sea	Lbr	2011	50,729	92,500	229	38	14	bbu	
9622916	Tonic Sea	Lbr	2012	51,253	93,005	229	38	14	bbu	
9231121	Vicente **	Lbr	2002	23,132	30,490	193	28	19	ghl	cr: 2(100): ex Hyundai Rhino-11, CCNI Antartico-08, CSAV Genova-04, Cape Dorchester-03
9401776	Zim Moskva	Lbr	2009	40,741	52,316	259	32	24	ucc	4,300 teu
9403396	Zim Ukrayina	Lbr	2009	40,741	52,316	259	32	24	ucc	4,300 teu
newbuildings:										
9718947	*CCNI Atacama*	Lbr	2016	95,138	113,174	300	48	22	ucc	9,030 teu	HHIC Phil.
9718959	CCNI tbc	Lbr		95,138	113,174	300	48	22	ucc	9,030 teu

** managed for United Reefer Services S.A., Switzerland or ** Ocean Multipurpose Schiffahrts . † owned by CCNI*

Oceanbulk Containers   Greece

funnel: *broad white band with company logo in green and blue, dividing blue base and green top.* **hull:** *dark blue, red boot-topping.*
history: *j/v established January 2013 between Oceanbulk Maritime S.A. and Oaktree Capital.* **web:** *www.oceanbulkcontainers*

IMO	name	flag	year	gt	dwt	loa	bm	kts	type	comments
9697416	Cezanne	Mhl	2015	94,730	111,044	300	48	22	ucc	9,962 teu
9718105	CMA CGM Mekong	Mhl	2015	94,730	111,044	300	48	22	ucc	9,962 teu
9718117	CMA CGM Ganges	Mhl	2015	94,730	111,044	300	48	22	ucc	9,962 teu
9697428	Dali	Mhl	2015	94,730	111,032	300	48	22	ucc	9,962 teu
9725706	Maersk Saltoro	Mhl	2015	94,730	117,176	300	48	22	ucc	9,962 teu: l/a Jenny Box
9726669	Maersk Shams	Mhl	2015	94,730	117,176	300	48	22	ucc	9,962 teu: l/a Matisse
9725718	Maersk Sirac	Mhl	2015	94,730	117,175	300	48	22	ucc	9,962 teu: l/a Modigliani
9726671	Maersk Stadelhorn	Mhl	2015	94.730	117,172	300	48	22	ucc	9,962 teu: l/a El Greco
newbuildings:										
9742168			2016	112,300	126,368	330	48	22	ucc	11.010 teu Hanjin Subic 0117 09.2016
9742170			2016	112,300	126,368	330	48	22	ucc	11.010 teu Hanjin Subic 0141 10.2016
			2017						ucc	10,920 teu SWS H-1388 05.2017
			2017						ucc	10,920 teu SWS H-1389 07.2017
			2017						ucc	10,920 teu SWS H-1390 09.2017

parent company Oceanbulk Maritime merged with Star Bulk 2014 and operate a large number of bulkers

Odfjell SE   Norway

funnel: *white with blue diagonal chain link symbol, black top.* **hull:** *orange with blue 'ODFJELL SEACHEM', red or black boot-topping.*
history: *formed 1914 as Storli ASA to 1998; Seachem merged 1989 and Ceres Hellenic merged 2000. Acquired 50% of Flumar Brazil in 1999 and remainder in 2008 from Kristian Gerhard Jebsen Skips.* **web:** *www.odfjell.com*

IMO	name	flag	year	gt	dwt	loa	bm	kts	type	comments
9319480	Bow Architect ‡	Pan	2005	18,405	30,058	170	26	14	tco	
9102928	Bow Atlantic	Sgp	1995	10,369	17,480	142	23	14	tco	ex Brage Atlantic-07
9114244	Bow Cardinal	Nis	1997	23,196	37,479	183	32	16	tco	
9143219	Bow Cecil **	Nis	1998	23,206	37,545	183	32	16	tco	

Dali : Oceanbulk Containers : *ARO*

Bow Heron : Odfjell ASA : *Nico Kemps*

IMO	name	flag	year	gt	dwt	loa	bm	kts	type	comments
9087013	Bow Cedar	Nis	1996	23,196	37,455	183	32	16	tco	
9214317	Bow Chain	Nis	2002	23,190	37,518	183	32	16	tco	
9047518	Bow Clipper	Nis	1995	23,197	37,221	183	32	16	tco	
8112914	Bow Eagle	Nis	1985	15,829	24,728	172	28	14	tco	ex Northern Eagle-89, Mangueira-88
9388302	Bow Elm	Sgp	2011	26,327	46,098	183	32	14	tco	ex Gulf Mishref -11
9317860	Bow Engineer	Nis	2006	18,405	30,086	170	26	14	tco	
9047764	Bow Fagus	Nis	1995	23,197	37,221	183	32	16	tco	
9114232	Bow Faith	Nis	1997	23,196	37,479	183	32	16	tco	
9250751	Bow Firda	Nis	2003	23,190	37,427	183	32	16	tco	
9143207	Bow Flora	Nis	1998	23,206	37,369	183	32	16	tco	
9047491	Bow Flower	Nis	1994	23,197	37,221	183	32	16	tco	
9168635	Bow Fortune	Nis	1999	23,206	37,395	183	32	16	tco	
9379909	Bow Harmony	Pan	2008	19,420	33,619	170	27	14	tco	
9363493	Bow Hector †	Phl	2009	20,145	33,694	174	28	15	tco	
9363481	Bow Heron †	Phl	2008	20,145	33,707	174	28	15	tco	
9379894	Bow Kiso	Pan	2008	19,420	33,641	170	27	14	tco	
9388314	Bow Lind	Sgp	2011	26,327	46,047	183	32	14	tco	ex Stolt Gulf Mizhar-11, I/a Gulf Mizhar
9143321	Bow Oceanic	Sgp	1997	10,369	16,094	142	23	14	tco	ex Brage Pacific-07
9595632	Bow Pioneer	Sgp	2013	45,452	81,305	228	37	15	tco	
9215309	Bow Saga **	Nis	2007	29,965	40,085	183	32	15	tco	
9379911	Bow Sagami	Pan	2008	19,420	33,614	170	27	14	tco	
9303651	Bow Santos *	Pan	2004	11,986	19,997	148	24	14	tco	
9215282	Bow Sea	Sgp	2006	29,965	40,036	183	32	15	tco	
9215295	Bow Sirius	Nis	2006	29,965	40,048	183	32	15	tco	
9215268	Bow Sky	Sgp	2005	29,965	40,005	183	32	15	tco	
9215256	Bow Spring	Nis	2004	29,965	39,942	183	32	15	tco	
9197296	Bow Star	Nis	2004	29,971	39,832	183	32	15	tco	
9215270	Bow Summer	Sgp	2005	29,965	40,036	183	32	15	tco	
9197284	Bow Sun	Sgp	2003	29,965	39,942	183	32	15	tco	I/a George L., I/d Multicarrier
9669873	Bow Trajectory	Nis	2014	30,521	49,622	183	32	15	tco	
9669884	Bow Tribute	Nis	2014	30,521	49,622	183	32	15	tco	
9669897	Bow Trident	Nis	2014	30,521	49,622	183	32	15	tco	
9669902	Bow Triumph	Nis	2015	30,521	49,622	183	32	15	tco	

owned * by Odfjell Asia II Pte Ltd, Singapore (formed 2000) or ** Odfjell (UK) Ltd (formed 2002,
 † owned by Safemarine Corp. and managed by Victoria Ship Management Inc, Philippines or ‡ chartered from other owners.
Also see chartered vessels under The National Shipping Company of Saudi Arabia.

Odfjell Gas Carriers ASA, Norway
newbuildings :

			year	gt	dwt				type	comments
9712553			2016	14,000	18,000				lpg	17,000 m³ Nantong Sinopacific S1026
9712565			2016	14,000	18,000				lpg	17,000 m³ Nantong Sinopacific S1027
9712577			2016	14,000	18,000				lpg	17,000 m³ Nantong Sinopacific S1028
9712589			2016	14,000	18,000				lpg	17,000 m³ Nantong Sinopacific S1029

also on order 4 x 22,000 m³

J. O. Odfjell A/S   Norway

JO Tankers A/S, Norway
funnel: blue with white interlinked 'JO' symbol. hull: orange some with blue 'JO TANKERS', red boot-topping or black with red boot-topping history: parent founded 1977, Dutch subsidiary JO Tankers BV in 1981 as Winterport Tankers to 1990 and JO Management b.v. to 1996, Norwegian subsidiary JO Tankers AS in 1989 as JO Management A/S to 1996. web: www.jotankers.com

IMO	name	flag	year	gt	dwt	loa	bm	kts	type	comments
8919049	Cedar +	Nis	1994	22,415	36,733	182	32	15	tco	ex Jo Cedar-10
9272668	Jo Acer *	Nis	2004	18,703	29,709	170	26	15	tco	
9266267	Jo Betula *	Nis	2003	15,992	25,032	159	25	15	tco	
9505936	Jo Ilex	Nis	2010	11,668	19,735	144	24	14	tco	ex Golden Topstar-11
9266243	Jo Kashi	Pan	2003	15,895	25,148	159	26	15	tco	
9266231	Jo Kiri	Pan	2003	11,769	19,508	145	24	15	tco	
9617650	Jo Larix	Nis	2015	22,424	30,297	183	28	14	tch	
9617648	Jo Lotus	Nis	2014	22,424	30,345	183	28	14	tch	
9592680	Jo Pinari	Nis	2012	42,420	74,455	228	32	14	tco	
9592692	Jo Provel	Nis	2013	42,392	74,450	228	32	14	tco	
9602722	Jo Redwood	Nis	2013	42,894	73,847	229	36	14	tch	
9602710	Jo Rowan	Nis	2013	43,053	73,811	229	36	14	tch	
8919051	Selje +	Nld	1993	22,380	36,800	182	32	15	tco	ex Jo Selje-10
9235062	Sequoia * +	Nis	2003	23,129	37,622	183	32	15	tco	ex Jo Sequoia-14, Sequoia-13, Jo Sequoia-10
8919037	Spruce +	Nis	1993	22,415	36,778	182	32	15	tco	ex Jo Spruce-14, Spruce-13, Jo Spruce-10
9198563	Sycamore * +	Nis	2000	23,200	37,500	183	32	15	tco	ex Jo Sycamore-10
9150315	Sypress +	Nld	1998	22,415	36,752	182	32	15	tco	ex Jo Sypress-10

IMO	name	flag	year	gt	dwt	loa	bm	kts	type	comments
newbuildings:										
9719238	Jo Alm	Nis	2016	21,000	33,000	185	25	15	tch	New Times SB 0303301
9719240			2016	21,000	33,000			15	tch	New Times SB 0303302
9719252			2016	21,000	33,000			15	tch	New Times SB 0303303
9719264			2016	21,000	33,000			15	tch	New Times SB 0303304
9744893			2017	21,000	33,000			15	tch	New Times SB 0303305
9744908			2017	21,000	33,000			15	tch	New Times SB 0303306
9764491			2017	21,000	33,000			15	tch	New Times SB 0303307
9764506			2017	21,000	33,000			15	tch	New Times SB 0303308
9737515			2016		74,500				tco	New Times SB 0307371
9737527			2016		74,500				tco	New Times SB 0307372

* managed by JO Tankers UK Ltd (formed 2003)   Also see A/S Borgestad ASA and Knutsen O.A.S. Shipping A/S, both Norway.
+ time chartered to Stolt-Nielsen Joint Service

Rudolf A. Oetker   Germany

Hamburg-Südamerikanische Dampfschiffahrts-ges (HSDG)

funnel: white with red top or yellow 'CCL' on blue/red diagonally divided with black top. **hull:** red with white 'HAMBURG SÜD' red boot-topping. **history:** HSDG founded 1871. Dr. August Oetker acquired an interest in 1934 and Rudolf A Oetker (founded 1951) took control in 1952, amalgamating the companies in 1973. Acquired 50% of Ybarra Cia Sudamericana in 1989, Furness-Withy (Shipping) Ltd from CY Tung (OOCL) in 1990, Laser Lines from Nordstjernan (Johnson Line) in 1991, Alianca in 1998, Transroll in 1999, Ellerman in 2003, the balance of Ybarra in 2005, Costa Container Lines (formed 1947) in 2007 and the container liner services of CCNI in March 2015. **web:** www.hamburgsud.com

IMO	name	flag	year	gt	dwt	loa	bm	kts	type	comments
9311775	Cap Blanche *	Atg	2006	28,371	37,883	222	30	22	ucc	2,742 teu: ex Fesco Baykal-06, l/a Cape Martin
9484560	Cap Jackson	Lbr	2010	47,877	59,336	264	32	22	ucc	4,600 teu
9484572	Cap Jervis	Lbr	2010	47,877	59,266	264	32	22	ucc	4,600 teu
9311799	Cap Pasado *	Atg	2006	27,786	37,883	222	30	22	ucc	2,742 teu: ex Fesco Bratsk-06
9622241	Cap San Antonio	Deu	2014	118,938	124,436	333	48	21	ucc	9,669 teu
9622239	Cap San Augustin	Deu	2013	118,938	124,470	333	48	21	ucc	9,669 teu
9717204	Cap San Juan	Deu	2015	118,615	123,101	331	48	22	ucc	10,600 teu
9717216	Cap San Lazaro	Deu	2015	118,615	123,205	331	48	22	ucc	10,600 teu
9622227	Cap San Lorenzo	Deu	2013	118,938	124,429	333	48	21	ucc	9,669 teu
9622215	Cap San Marco	Deu	2013	118,938	124,453	333	48	21	ucc	9,669 teu

Cap San Marco : Hamburg-Südamerikanische Dampfschiffahrts-ges : *Hans Kraijenbosch*

IMO	name	flag	year	gt	dwt	loa	bm	kts	type	comments
9622203	Cap San Nicolas	Deu	2013	118,938	124,458	333	48	21	ucc	9,669 teu
9622253	Cap San Raphael	Deu	2014	118,938	124,460	333	48	21	ucc	9,669 teu
9717228	Cap San Vincent	Deu	2015	118,615	123,383	331	48	22	ucc	10,600 teu
9348077	Monte Aconcagua	Deu	2009	69,132	64,847	272	40	23	ucc	5,568 teu
9348065	Monte Alegre	Deu	2008	69,132	71,273	272	40	23	ucc	5,560 teu
9348053	Monte Azul	Deu	2008	69,132	71,256	272	40	23	ucc	5,568 teu
9283186	Monte Cervantes	Deu	2004	69,132	64,963	272	40	23	ucc	5,560 teu: ex P&O Nedlloyd Salsa-06, Monte Cervantes-05
9283198	Monte Olivia	Deu	2004	69,132	64,730	272	40	23	ucc	5,560 teu
9283203	Monte Pascoal	Deu	2004	69,132	65,066	272	40	23	ucc	5,560 teu: ex P&O Nedlloyd Lambada-06, Monte Pascoal-05
9283215	Monte Rosa	Deu	2004	69,132	64,888	272	40	23	ucc	5,560 teu
9283227	Monte Sarmiento	Deu	2004	69,132	65,028	272	40	23	ucc	5,560 teu
9357949	Monte Tamaro	Deu	2007	69,132	71,588	272	40	23	ucc	5,560 teu
9283239	Monte Verde	Deu	2005	69,132	65,005	272	40	23	ucc	5,560 teu: ex Alianca Maua-11, Monte Verde-05
9348089	Rio Blanco	Lbr	2009	73,899	80,115	287	40	23	ucc	5,905 teu
9348091	Rio Bravo	Lbr	2009	73,899	80,226	287	40	23	ucc	5,905 teu
9357963	Rio de Janeiro	Deu	2008	73,899	80,398	287	40	23	ucc	5,905 teu
9357951	Rio de la Plata	Deu	2008	73,899	80,455	287	40	23	ucc	5,905 teu
9348106	Rio Madeira	Deu	2009	73,899	80,294	287	40	23	ucc	5,905 teu
9357975	Rio Negro	Deu	2008	73,899	80,410	287	40	23	ucc	5,905 teu
9699191	San Christobal	Lbr	2014	94,930	112,231	300	48	22	ucc	9,034 teu
9699189	San Clemente	Lbr	2014	94,930	112,231	300	48	22	ucc	9,034 teu
9698628	San Felipe †	Mhl	2014	96,386	115,356	300	48	22	ucc	8,700 teu: l/a SFL Loire
9698630	San Felix †	Mhl	2014	96,386	115,181	300	48	22	ucc	8,700 teu: l/a SFL Seine
9698642	San Fernando †	Mhl	2015	96,386	115,489	300	48	22	ucc	8,714 teu: l/d SFL Somme
9698654	San Francisca †	Mhl	2015	96,386	115,414	300	48	22	ucc	8,714 teu: l/d SFL Taurion
9699206	San Vicente	Lbr	2014	94,930	112,224	300	48	22	ucc	9,034 teu
9430399	Santa Barbara	Deu	2012	86,601	93,430	300	43	22	ucc	7,090 teu
9444730	Santa Catarina	Lbr	2011	85,676	93,592	300	43	22	ucc	7,090 teu
9444716	Santa Clara	Deu	2010	85,676	93,552	300	43	22	ucc	7,090 teu
9444742	Santa Cruz	Lux	2011	85,676	93,424	300	43	22	ucc	7,090 teu
9444845	Santa Ines	Lbr	2012	86,601	92,910	300	43	22	ucc	7,090 teu
9444728	Santa Isabel	Deu	2010	85,676	93,603	300	43	22	ucc	7,090 teu: ex Paranagua Express-14, Leblon-12, Santa Isabel-11
9425382	Santa Rita	Deu	2011	85,676	93,404	300	43	22	ucc	7,090 teu
9430363	Santa Rosa	Lbr	2011	85,676	93,398	300	43	22	ucc	7,090 teu
9430375	Santa Teresa	Lbr	2011	85,676	93,591	300	43	22	ucc	7,090 teu
9430387	Santa Ursula	Deu	2012	86,601	93,430	300	43	22	ucc	7,090 teu
9731705	Ultra Daniela	Lbr	2015	34,748	61,288	200	32	14	bbu	
9311787	Vilano *	Atg	2006	27,786	37,883	222	30	22	ucc	2,742 teu: ex Cap Vilano-13, Fesco Barguzin-06

newbuildings: 4 x 3,800teu Jiangsu New YZJ
managed by Columbus Shipmanagement GmbH (formed 1998)
* chartered by HSDG from Premium Capital Emissionshaus GmbH & Co KG (founded 2004) and managed by Reederei Alnwick Harmstorf & Co GmbH & Co KG, Germany (formed 1950 as A F Harmstorf & Co GmbH to 2000 – www.harmstorf-co.com) since Oct 2012 subsidiary of Schlüssel Reederei.
† chartered from Ship Finance Management, Oslo, managed by Schulte Singapore

Aliança Navegação e Logística Ltda., Brazil

funnel: yellow with broad white over red bands beneath black top, black triangular 'A' on white band or HSDG colours. **hull:** blue with white 'ALIANCA', red boot-topping. **history:** founded 1950 as Alianca Transportes Maritimos SA to 2000. **web:** www.alianca.com.br

IMO	name	flag	year	gt	dwt	loa	bm	kts	type	comments
9273961	Alianca Manaus	Bra	2004	25,709	33,925	208	30	21	ucc	2,524 teu: ex Cap Nelson-08, Santos Express-05, l/a Cap Nelson
9273923	Alianca Santos	Bra	2003	25,709	33,890	208	30	21	ucc	2,524 teu: ex Cap Carmel-09
9603233	Américo Vespúcio	Bra	2013	42,564	52,039	228	37	20	ucc	3,820 teu
9625384	Bartolomeu Dias	Bra	2014	47,799	57,818	228	37	20	ucc	3,820 teu: l/a Cap Salinas
9603221	Fernao de Magalhaes	Bra	2013	42,564	52,072	234	37	20	ucc	3,820 teu
9603219	Pedro Álvares Cabral	Bra	2013	42,789	52,065	228	37	20	ucc	3,820 teu
9602875	Sebastiao Caboto	Bra	2013	42,564	52,065	228	37	20	ucc	3,820 teu
9625396	Vicente Pinzón	Bra	2014	47,799	57,882	255	37	20	ucc	4,500 teu: c/a Cap Saray

Reederei Claus-Peter Offen GmbH & Co.   Germany

funnel: white with white Maltese Cross between narrow white bands on broad blue band, black top, or charterers colours. *hull:* light grey, black, blue or red with red boot-topping. *history:* founded in Hamburg, 1971. *web:* www.offenship.de

CPO Containerschiffreederei, Germany

IMO	name	flag	year	gt	dwt	loa	bm	kts	type	comments
9326794	ANL Waratah *	Lbr	2005	54,809	67,310	294	32	25	ucc	4,839 teu: ex Santa Placida-14, Maersk Dieppe-13, P&O Nedlloyd Doha-05, l/a Santa Placida
9440796	Cap Harrisson	Lbr	2009	41,358	51,699	262	32	24	ucc	4,255 teu: l/a CPO Baltimore
9440825	Cap Hatteras	Lbr	2009	41,358	51,671	262	32	24	ucc	4,255 teu: ex CPO Charleston-15, UASC Ramadi -15, l/a CPO Charleston
9440837	Cap Hudson	Lbr	2009	41,358	51,701	262	32	24	ucc	4,255 teu: ex CPO Savannah-15, UASC Shuaiba-15, l/a CPO Savannah
9344643	Cap Palmerston *	Lbr	2007	22,914	28,203	186	28	21	ucc	1,819 teu: l/a San Alberto
9344667	Cap Patton *	Lbr	2007	22,914	28,179	186	28	21	ucc	1,819 teu: ex Tasman Crusader-09, San Alfonso-07
9469572	CMA CGM Alaska	Lbr	2011	140,259	146,112	366	48	25	ucc	12,562 teu: l/a CPO Marseille
9365790	CMA CGM Butterfly	Lbr	2008	111,249	120,934	350	43	25	ucc	9,661 teu: ex Butterfly-14, CMA CGM Butterfly-12, l/a Santa Lorena
9365805	CMA CGM Ivanhoe	Lbr	2009	111,249	120,944	350	43	25	ucc	9,661 teu: l/a Santa Luciana
9471408	CMA CGM Nevada	Mlt	2011	140,259	146,182	366	48	26	ucc	12,562 teu; l/a CPO Toulon
9364992	CMA CGM Orfeo	Mlt	2008	111,249	120,892	350	43	25	ucc	9,661 teu: l/a Santa Laetitia
9365788	CMA CGM Pelleas	Mlt	2008	111,249	120,853	350	43	25	ucc	9,661 teu: ex Pelleas-14, CMA CGM Pelleas-12, l/a Santa Liana
9445588	CPO Miami	Lbr	2009	41,358	51,738	262	32	24	ucc	4,255 teu: ex UASC Khor Fakkan-15, l/a CPO Miami
9440813	CPO Norfolk	Lbr	2009	41,358	51,727	262	32	24	ucc	4,255 teu: ex Cap Henri-15, l/a CPO Norfolk
9440772	CPO New York	Lbr	2009	41,358	51,808	262	32	24	ucc	4,255 teu: ex Cap Harald-14, l/a CPO New York
9330070	Maersk Semarang *	Lux	2007	94,322	108,448	332	43	25	ucc	8,400 teu: l/a Santa Livia
9480174	MSC Alicante	Lbr	2011	61,870	74,477	270	40	23	ucc	5,568 teu: l/a CPO Alicante
9480186	MSC Barcelona	Lbr	2011	61,870	74,456	270	40	23	ucc	5,568 teu: l/a CPO Barcelona
9461441	MSC Bari	Lbr	2011	153,115	154,906	366	51	24	ucc	14,000 teu: l/a CPO Napoli
9289099	MSC Beijing	Mlt	2005	89,954	105,034	325	43	25	ucc	8,034 teu: l/a Santa Laurentia
9290567	MSC Bruxelles *	Deu	2005	107,849	110,860	337	46	25	ucc	9,178 teu: l/a Santa Loretta
9289087	MSC Busan	Mlt	2005	89,954	104,904	325	43	25	ucc	8,034 teu: l/a Santa Larissa
9480203	MSC Cadiz	Lbr	2011	61,870	74,526	270	40	23	ucc	5,568 teu: l/a CPO Cadiz
9299537	MSC Charleston *	Deu	2006	89,954	105,014	325	43	25	ucc	8,034 teu: l/a Santa Leopalda
9290555	MSC Chicago *	Deu	2005	107,849	110,852	337	46	25	ucc	9,178 teu: l/a Santa Linea
9480215	MSC Coruna	Lbr	2011	62,870	74,506	270	40	23	ucc	5,568 teu: l/a CPO Valencia
9461386	MSC Genova	Lbr	2010	153,115	166,041	366	51	24	ucc	14,036 teu: l/a CPO Genova
9461403	MSC La Spezia	Deu	2010	153,115	165,978	366	51	24	ucc	14,036 teu: l/a CPO La Spezia
9304459	MSC Lisbon	Lbr	2007	107,849	110,697	337	46	25	ucc	9,178 teu: l/a Santa Lucilla
9461427	MSC Livorno	Deu	2010	153,115	165,918	366	51	24	ucc	14,036 teu: l/a CPO Livorno
9480198	MSC Madrid	Lbr	2011	61,870	74,376	270	40	23	ucc	5,568 teu: l/a CPO Bilbao
9484455	MSC Rapallo	Lbr	2011	143,521	154,539	366	48	24	ucc	13,050 teu
9484431	MSC Ravenna	Lbr	2011	153,115	165,963	366	51	24	ucc	14,036 teu: l/a CPO Ancona
9304447	MSC Roma	Lbr	2006	107,849	110,634	337	46	25	ucc	9,178 teu: l/a Santa Louisa
9460356	MSC Savona	Lbr	2010	153,115	165,887	366	51	24	ucc	14,036 teu: l/a CPO Savona
9295373	MSC Shanghai	Lbr	2005	65,483	72,064	275	40	26	ucc	5,606 teu: l/a Santa Viola
9475258	MSC Taranto	Lbr	2011	153,115	166,085	366	51	24	ucc	14,036 teu: l/a CPO Palermo
9469560	MSC Teresa	Pan	2011	153,115	166,101	366	51	24	ucc	14,036 teu
9295361	MSC Tokyo	Lbr	2005	65,483	71,949	275	40	26	ucc	5,606 teu: l/a Santa Vanessa
9299525	MSC Toronto *	Deu	2006	89,954	105,084	325	43	25	ucc	8,034 teu: l/a Santa Leonarda
9484479	MSC Trieste	Mlt	2011	143,521	154,664	366	48	24	ucc	13,050 teu: l/a CPO Trieste
9480227	MSC Vigo	Lbr	2012	61,870	73,840	270	40	23	ucc	5,600 teu: l/a CPO Vigo
9306483	Rossini	Mlt	2005	25,406	33,900	207	30	22	ucc	2,478 teu: ex Julia Schulte-14, Maersk Nanhai-09, P&O Nedlloyd Savannah-05, l/a Julia Schulte
9344681	San Alvaro *	Lbr	2007	22,914	28,123	186	28	21	ucc	1,819 teu: ex Rio Tamanaco-14, Cap Preston-12, l/a San Alvaro
9344693	San Amerigo *	Lbr	2008	22,914	28,186	186	28	21	ucc	1,819 teu Borealis Maritime 08:2014 ??
9347267	San Antonio *	Lbr	2008	22,914	28,197	186	28	21	ucc	1,819 teu; ex Ibn Rushd-09, l/a San Antonio
9338084	Santa Bettina	Mlt	2007	28,616	39,277	222	30	23	ucc	2,824 teu: ex Cap Byron-11, l/a Santa Bettina

IMO	name	flag	year	gt	dwt	loa	bm	kts	type	comments
9162253	Santa Fiorenza	Lbr	1998	21,583	30,007	183	30	20	ucc	2,048 teu: ex Westwood Discovery-15, Santa Fiorenzo-11, CMA CGM Niger-09, Santa Fiorenzo-07, P&O Nedlloyd Arica-02, l/a Santa Fiorenzo
9188219	Santa Francesca	Deu	1998	21,583	30,029	183	30	20	ucc	2,169 teu: ex CMA CGM Volta-09, Santa Francesca-07, P&O Nedlloyd Sao Paulo-02, l/a Santa Francesca
9141780	Santa Giannina *	Lbr	1997	21,531	30,173	182	30	20	ucc	2,061 teu: ex Cala Palamos-08, P&O Nedlloyd Salsa-05, Santa Giannina-02, P&O Nedlloyd Kingston-02, l/a Santa Giannina
9347281	San Aurelio	Lbr	2008	22,914	28,170	186	28	21	ucc	1,819 teu
9126481	Santa Giuliana	Lbr	1996	21,531	30,201	182	30	19	ucc	2,061 teu: ex Delmas Bouake-09, Clan Tangun-08, Santa Giuliana-05, P&O Nedlloyd Orinoco-01, Nedlloyd Orinoco-99, Santa Giuliana-96
9141778	Santa Giulietta	Deu	1997	21,531	30,252	182	30	20	ucc	2,061 teu: ex Delmas Abuja-09, Santa Giulietta-07, P&O Nedlloyd Parana-02, l/a Santa Giulietta
9330068	Santa Laura	Lbr	2006	94,322	108,351	332	43	25	ucc	8,400 teu: ex Maersk Surabaya-14, l/a Santa Laura
9330513	Satie	Mlt	2006	28,616	39,360	222	30	23	ucc	2,824 teu: ex Santa Balbina-15, Maersk Jackson-11, l/a Santa Balbina
9450375	Seattle Express	Mlt	2009	91,203	103,845	334	43	25	ucc	8,580 teu: l/a CPO Hamburg
9445576	UASC Jeddah	Lbr	2009	41,358	51,687	262	32	24	ucc	4,255 teu: l/a CPO Jacksonville
9450387	Vancouver Express	Mlt	2009	91,203	103,773	334	43	25	ucc	8,598 teu: l/a CPO Bremen
9162265	Westwood Pacific	Deu	1998	21,583	29,700	182	30	20	ucc	2,048 teu: ex Santa Federica-11, P&O Nedlloyd Santiago-02, l/a Santa Frederica

*managed for: * MPC Group   + for Gebab Konzeptions-und Emissions GmbH*

Claus-Peter Offen Bulkschiffreederei (Offen Bulkers), Germany

funnel: *as above,* **hull:** *black with red boot topping*

IMO	name	flag	year	gt	dwt	loa	bm	kts	type	comments
9522647	CPO America	Lbr	2011	94,250	179,570	292	45	15	bbu	
9522635	CPO Asia	Lbr	2011	94,250	179,558	292	45	15	bbu	
9522087	CPO Europe	Lbr	2010	94,250	179,448	292	45	15	bbu	
9522099	CPO Oceana	Lbr	2010	94,250	179,701	292	45	15	bbu	

Claus-Peter Offen Tankschiffreederei (Offen Tankers), Germany

funnel: *as above* **hull:** *red or blue with red boot topping*

IMO	name	flag	year	gt	dwt	loa	bm	kts	type	comments
9443140	CPO Australia	Gbr	2011	29,636	51,763	183	32	15	tco	
9434204	CPO China	Gbr	2010	29,636	51,672	183	32	15	tco	
9353149	CPO England	Gbr	2008	23,353	37,313	184	28	15	tco	
9353101	CPO Finland	Gbr	2008	23,353	37,293	184	28	15	tco	
9347308	CPO France	Gbr	2008	23,353	37,304	184	28	15	tco	
9353096	CPO Germany	Gbr	2008	23,270	37,297	184	28	15	tco	
9434228	CPO India	Gbr	2010	29,636	51,703	183	32	15	tco	
9353137	CPO Italy	Gbr	2008	23,270	37,282	184	28	15	tco	
9434216	CPO Japan	Gbr	2010	29,636	51,747	183	32	15	tco	
9433901	CPO Korea	Gbr	2009	29,636	51,747	183	32	15	tco	
9443164	CPO Malaysia	Gbr	2011	29,637	51,762	183	32	15	tco	
9443152	CPO New Zealand	Gbr	2011	29,636	51,717	183	32	15	tco	
9353113	CPO Norway	Gbr	2008	23,270	37,321	184	28	15	tco	
9353125	CPO Russia	Gbr	2008	23,353	37,296	184	28	15	tco	
9434230	CPO Singapore	Gbr	2011	29,636	51,737	183	32	15	tco	
9353084	CPO Sweden	Gbr	2008	23,353	37,280	184	28	15	tco	

Egon Oldendorff OHG   Germany

funnel: *grey with white 'EO' on broad blue band, or charterers colours.* **hull:** *grey, black or red with 'oldendorff' in white, red boot-topping.* **history:** *founded 1921 as Nordische Dampfer Reederei (Lillenfeld & Oldendorff) GmbH to 1936. Oldendorff Express Lines (formerly CEC) 60% owned from 2006 other 40% Flamar, Belgium.* **web:** *www.oldendorff.com*

IMO	name	flag	year	gt	dwt	loa	bm	kts	type	comments
9696905	Alfred Oldendorff	Lbr	2015	53,723	93,682	235	38	14	bsd	
9183776	Alice Oldendorff *	Lbr	2000	28,747	48,000	190	32	14	bsd	
9692698	Alwine Oldendorff	Pmd	2014	34,349	60,915	198	32	14	bbu	
9240809	Anna Oldendorff *	Mlt	2002	29,369	52.466	190	32	14	bbu	ex Vega Pioneer-12
9696917	Antonie Oldendorff	Lbr	2015	53,723	93,770	235	38	14	bsd	
9692686	August Oldendorff	Pmd	2015	34,349	60,915	198	32	14	bbu	
8602476	Bold Challenger	Lbr	1988	112,895	227,183	325	52	14	bor	ex Beate Oldendorff-15, Kazusa-10, Kazusa Maru-95

CPO France : Claus-Peter Offen Tankschiffreederei : *ARO*

Gisela Oldendorff : Egon Oldendorff : *Nico Kemps*

IMO	name	flag	year	gt	dwt	loa	bm	kts	type	comments
8900529	Bernhard Oldendorff	Lbr	1991	43,332	77,548	245	32	14	bsd	ex Yeoman Burn-94
8900517	Caroline Oldendorff	Lbr	1991	43,332	77,548	245	32	14	bsd	ex Yeoman Brook-11
9244219	Diamond	Lbr	2001	38,846	74,274	225	32	14	bbu	ex Diamond Seas-15, Sundance-07, Panaxia-07, Lake Harmony-05
9489211	Dora Oldendorff	Lbr	2010	19,992	33,108	177	28	14	bbu	ex Peace Success-14
9475715	Dorothea Oldendorff	Lbr	2009	19.992	32,929	177	28	14	bbu	ex Peace Traffic-14
8007808	E. Oldendorff *	Lbr	1982	45,777	78,488	243	32	14	bsd	ex Nobel Fountain-07, Fountain Spirit-04, Teekay Fountain-03, Bona Fountain-99, Höegh Fountain-92 (conv cbo-05)
9676591	Eckert Oldendorff	Mlt	2014	25,431	38,330	180	30	14	goh	
9702613	Edward Oldendorff	Mlt	2015	25,431	38,330	180	30	14	goh	
9717668	Edwine Oldendorff	Lux	2016	25,431	38,300	180	30	14	goh	
9676618	Eibe Oldendorff	Mlt	2015	25,431	38,330	180	30	14	goh	
9717656	Elisabeth Oldendorff	Lux	2015	24,184	38,330	180	30	14	goh	
9702625	Elsa Oldendorff	Mlt	2015	25,431	38,330	180	30	14	goh	
9676606	Emma Oldendorff	Mlt	2014	25,431	38,300	180	30	14	goh	
9702637	Ernst Oldendorff	Mlt	2015	24,184	38,300	180	30	14	goh	
9358838	Friedrich Oldendorff	Mhl	2006	40,485	74,483	225	32	14	bbu	ex Pearl Seas-16, Cap Bona-07, F.D. Mariano-07
9727596	Gebe Oldendorff	Pmd	2015	44,218	80,446	229	32	14	bbu	
9702596	Georg Oldendorff	Pmd	2015	44,218	80,866	229	32	14	bbu	
9727601	Gertrude Oldendorff	Pmd	2016	44,218	81,400	229	32	14	bbu	
9702601	Gisela Oldendorff	Pmd	2015	44,218	80,839	229	32	14	bbu	
9681950	Gerdt Oldendorff	Pmd	2014	44,218	80,444	229	32	14	bbu	
9681962	Gretke Oldendorff	Pmd	2015	44,218	80,444	229	32	14	bbu	
9120334	Harmen Oldendorff *	Pmd	2005	39,568	69,700	225	32	14	bsd	
9713040	Helga Oldendorff	Pmd	2016	107,666	209,172	300	50	14	bbu	
9731573	Hille Oldendorff	Pmd	2016	107,735	199,985	300	50	14	bbu	
9722338	Indra Oldendorff	Pmd	2016	36,294	63,490	200	32	14	bbu	
9725744	Iris Oldendorff	Pmd	2015	36,426	63,452	200	32	14	bbu	ex Yangze 9-15
9710892	Jobst Oldendorff	Mlt	2014	34,612	61,112	200	32	14	bbu	
9684471	Johann Oldendorff	Mlt	2014	34,612	61,112	200	32	14	bbu	
9057446	Johanna Oldendorff *	Lbr	1998	37,978	67,508	225	32	14	bsd	ex Sofia III-06, Aifos-03, Ever Victory-02
9684469	Julia Oldendorff	Mlt	2014	34,612	61,097	200	32	14	bbu	
9691931	Lavinia Oldendorff +	Lbr	2014	107,413	207,562	300	50	14	bbu	
9691943	Leopold Oldendorff	Pmd	2015	107,413	207,562	300	50	14	bbu	
9691929	Linda Oldendorff	Pmd	2014	107,413	207,562	300	50	14	bbu	
9587166	Lucy Oldendorff *	Lbr	2011	20,867	32,491	180	28	14	bbu	
9691955	Ludolf Oldendorff *	Pmd	2015	107,413	207,562	300	50	14	bbu	
9714240	Luise Oldendorff	Pmd	2015	107,413	207,562	300	50	14	bbu	
9699634	Lydia Oldendorff +*	Lbr	2015	107,413	207,562	300	50	14	bbu	
9638044	Magdalena Oldendorff *	Lbr	2013	106,884	206,010	300	50	14	bbu	
9648893	Magnus Oldendorff	Lbr	2014	106,884	206,030	300	50	14	bbu	
9648908	Margret Oldendorff	Lbr	2014	108,051	208,086	300	50	14	bbu	
9678824	Marlene Oldendorff *	Lbr	2014	108,051	208,003	300	50	14	bbu	
9678812	Martha Oldendorff *	Lbr	2014	106,884	206,048	300	50	14	bbu	
9678800	Mathilde Oldendorff	Lbr	2013	106,847	206,000	300	50	14	bbu	
9600425	Max Oldendorff ++	Lbr	2014	107,158	205,361	300	50	14	bbu	
9638056	May Oldendorff *	Lbr	2013	106,884	206,108	300	50	14	bbu	
9678795	Mina Oldendorff *	Lbr	2013	106,847	206,118	300	50	14	bbu	
9639517	Moritz Oldendorff ++	Hkg	2013	107,162	205,170	300	50	14	bbu	
9138109	Sophie Oldendorff *	Lbr	2000	41,428	70,037	225	32	14	bsd	
9291406	Theodor Oldendorff	Mlt	2008	40,097	77,171	225	32	14	bbu	ex Nord Mercury-13
9642370	Trina Oldendorff *	Lbr	2013	41,091	75,200	225	32	14	bbu	
9700316	Vanessa Oldendorff	Pmd	2015	23,856	38,165	183	31	14	bbu	I/a AEC Ability

newbuildings:

IMO	name	flag	year	gt	dwt	loa	bm	kts	type	comments
9717670	Erna Oldendorff	Lux	2016	24,184	38,300	180	30	14	goh	Jinling JLZ 9120425
9731602	Hubertus Oldendorff	Lbr	2016	106,909	208,000	300	50	14	bbu	Jiangsu Hantong HT 208 195
9731614	Hanna Oldendorff	Lbr	2016	110,000	208,000	300	50	14	bbu	Jiangsu Hantong HT 208 196
9750402	Hannes Oldendorff	Lbr	2016	110,000	208,000	300	50	14	bbu	Jiangsu Hantong HT 208 197
9750414	Hauke Oldendorff	Lbr	2016	110,000	208,000	300	50	14	bbu	Jiangsu Hantong HT 208 198
9718351	Helena Oldendorff +	Lbr	2016	110,000	208,000	300	50	14	bbu	Taizhou Catic 401 sold BB back
9718363	Hera Oldendorff +	Lbr	2016	110,000	208,000	300	50	14	bbu	Taizhou Catic 402 sold TC back
9718375	Hermine Oldendorff	Lbr	2016	110,000	208,000	300	50	14	bbu	Taizhou Catic 403
9718387	Heinrich Oldendorff	Lbr	2017	110,000	208,000	300	50	14	bbu	Taizhou Catic 404
	Hedwig Oldendorff	Lbr	2017	110,000	208,000	300	50	14	bbu	Taizhou Catic 405
	Hendrik Oldendorff	Lbr	2017	110,000	208,000	300	50	14	bbu	Taizhou Catic 406
9731585	Hermann Oldendorff	Lbr	2016	110,000	208,000	300	50	14	bbu	Taizhou Catic 408
9713052	Henriette Oldendorff	Lbr	2016	110,000	208,000	300	50	14	bbu	Jiangsu NYZ JZJ2013 1125

IMO	name	flag	year	gt	dwt	loa	bm	kts	type	comments
9713064	*Hinrich Oldendorff*	Lbr	2016	110,000	208,000	300	50	14	bbu	Jiangsu NYZ JZJ2013 1126
9713076	*Hugo Oldendorff* +	Lbr	2016	110,000	208,000	300	50	14	bbu	Jiangsu NYZ JZJ2013 1127
9731597	*Hans Oldendorff*	Lbr	2017	110,000	208,000	300	50	14	bbu	Jiangsu NYZ JZJ2013 1128
9740366	*Henry Oldendorff*	Lbr	2017	110,000	208,000	300	50	14	bbu	Jiangsu NYZ JZJ2013 1129
9720952	Ilsabe Oldendorff	Cyp	2016	35,990	64,000	200	32	14	bbu	Qingshan QS64000 1
9720964	Imme Oldendorff	Cyp	2016	35,990	64,000	200	32	14	bbu	Qingshan QS64000 2
9720976	Irene Oldendorff	Cyp	2016	35,990	64,000	200	32	14	bbu	Qingshan QS64000 3
9720988	Ingrid Oldendorff	Cyp	2016	35,990	64,000	200	32	14	bbu	Qingshan QS64000 4
9720990	Ingmar Oldendorff	Cyp	2016	35,990	64,000	200	32	14	bbu	Qingshan QS64000 5
9721009	Isa Oldendorff	Cyp	2016	35,990	64,000	200	32	14	bbu	Qingshan QS64000 6
9721047		Cyp	2016	35,990	64,000	200	32	14	bbu	Qingshan QS64000 7
9721059		Cyp	2016	35,990	64,000	200	32	14	bbu	Qingshan QS64000 8
9721061		Cyp	2017	35,990	64,000	200	32	14	bbu	Qingshan QS64000 9
9721073		Cyp	2017	35,990	64,000	200	32	14	bbu	Qingshan QS64000 10
9721085		Cyp	2017	35,990	64,000	200	32	14	bbu	Qingshan QS64000 11
9721097		Cyp	2017	35,990	64,000	200	32	14	bbu	Qingshan QS64000 12

also operate a large number of time-chartered vessels ++.   Self-dischargers operate in joint Pool with CSL Group Inc., Canada, Marbulk and Klaveness.
* managed by subsidiary Oldendorff Carriers GmbH & Co. KG (formed 2001) and ** managed by Pacific King Shipping Pte Ltd, Singapore.
+ sold and bareboat chartered back (from Laskaridis)
† managed by Oldendorff Carriers GmbH for Investeringsgruppen Danmark A/S, Denmark or ‡ for Buchanan Maritime Corp.

Reederei 'Nord' Klaus E. Oldendorff   Cyprus

funnel: *grey with white 'N' inside white ring on broad blue band or charterers colours.* **hull:** *dark grey with red boot-topping.* **history:** *founded 1964 in Germany, relocated to Cyprus in 1987. Business divided into two operating divisions, one for dry cargo based in Hamburg, the other for tankers based in Amsterdam.* **web:** *www.reederei-nord.com*

Reederei Nord GmbH, Germany

IMO	name	flag	year	gt	dwt	loa	bm	kts	type	comments
9323041	ANL Barega [H]	Cyp	2008	38,332	46,212	247	32	23	ucc	3,586 teu: ex Winter D-14, MOL Winter-13, Winter D.-12, Nordwinter-11
9323039	Autumn E [H]	Cyp	2008	38,332	45,309	247	32	23	ucc	3,586 teu: ex Nordautumn-11
9212694	Elbe [H]	Cyp	2001	40,605	75,259	225	32	14	bbu	ex Nordelbe-11
9224685	Ems [H]	Cyp	2001	40,605	75,253	225	32	14	bbu	ex Nordems-11
9241487	Med [H]	Cyp	2003	25,407	33,900	207	30	22	ucc	2,506 teu: ex MCC Jakarta-12, Normed-10, CMA CGM Intensity-08, Nordmed-04
9057173	MSC Agata	Cyp	1994	16,202	22,450	179	25	19	ucc	1,524 teu: ex Nordlake-13, X-Press Khyber-09, Nordlake-08, YM Okinawa-08, Nordlake-05, CSAV Lonquimay-98, Nordlake-96
9595967	N Discovery [H]	Mlt	2012	24,195	37,019	190	28	13	bbu	ex Emerald-13, Dominator-12
9596026	N Loire [H]	Mlt	2013	24,195	37,211	190	28	13	bbu	
9596038	N Schelde [H]	Mlt	2013	24,195	37,200	190	28	13	bbu	
9241451	NileDutch Impala [H]	Cyp	2003	25,407	33,853	207	30	22	ucc	2,506 teu: ex Atlantic-12, Nordatlantic-11, Libra Niteroi-10, Nordatlantic-05, Cala Palos-04, Nordatlantic-03
9241475	Nordbaltic [H]	Iom	2003	25,407	33,850	207	30	22	ucc	2,506 teu: ex NieDutch Gemsbok-15, Baltic-12, Nordbaltic-11, CMA CGM Romania-08, Nordbaltic-03
9673630	Nordcheetah [H]	Mlt	2014	18,826	23,562	170	28	18	ucc	1,756 teu: l/d Erika E
9744673	Nordclaire	Mlt	2016	18,826	23,800	170	28	18	ucc	1,756 teu
9744661	Nordemilia	Mlt	2016	18,826	23,800	170	28	18	ucc	1,756 teu
9697014	Nordisabella	Cyp	2016	28,316	35,587	195	32	18	ucc	2,500 teu
9626261	Nordleopard [H]	Cyp	2015	18,887	23,576	170	28	18	ucc	1,756 teu
9744685	Nordlily [H]	Mlt	2016	18,826	23,800	170	28	18	ucc	1,756 teu
9625235	Nordlion [H]	Cyp	2014	18,887	23,574	170	28	18	ucc	1,756 teu
9673666	Nordluchs [H]	Cyp	2014	18,826	23,573	170	28	18	ucc	1,756 teu
9673642	Nordocelot [H]	Cyp	2014	18,826	23,552	170	28	18	ucc	1,756 teu: l/d Iris E
9741712	Nordorinoco	Mlt	2015	23,974	37,964	190	28	14	bbu	
9697002	Nordpacific	Cyp	2015	28,237	35,587	195	32	18	ucc	2,500 teu
9673654	Nordpanther [H]	Cyp	2014	18,826	23,520	170	28	18	ucc	1,756 teu
9626259	Nordpuma [H]	Cyp	2015	18,826	23,629	170	28	18	ucc	1,756 teu
9596040	Nordrhone [H]	Mlt	2015	23,975	38,036	190	28	14	bbu	
9763693	Nordrubicon [H]	Mlt	2016	23,974	37,200	190	28	14	bbu	
9596052	Nordseine [H]	Mlt	2015	23,975	37,036	190	28	14	bbu	
9626247	Nordtiger [H]	Cyp	2014	18,887	23,558	170	28	18	ucc	1,756 teu
9741700	Nordtigris	Mlt	2015	23,974	37,964	190	28	14	bbu	
9224702	Nordrhine [H]	Cyp	2001	40,605	75,080	225	32	14	bbu	ex Rhine-15, Nordrhine-11
9744659	Nordviolet	Mlt	2015	18,826	23,519	170	28	18	ucc	1,756 teu
9212709	Nordweser [H]	Cyp	2001	40,605	75,321	225	32	14	bbu	ex Weser-15, Nordweser-11
9294549	Nordwoge [H]	Cyp	2001	26,611	34,704	210	30	22	ucc	2,602 teu: ex Woge-15, Australia Express-13, Nordwoge-11

IMO	name	flag	year	gt	dwt	loa	bm	kts	type	comments
9321897	Spring R [H]	Cyp	2007	38,212	45,230	247	32	23	ucc	3,586 teu: ex MOL Spring-13, Spring R.-12, Nordspring-11
9321902	Summer E. [H]	Cyp	2007	38,332	46,321	247	32	23	ucc	3,586 teu: ex MOL Summer-12, Nordsummer-11, Orange River Bridge-11, Nordsummer-07
9294537	Welle [H]	Cyp	2005	26,611	34,740	210	30	22	ucc	2,602 teu: ex Nordwelle-11
newbuildings:										
9697026		Cyp	2016	28,350	35,000	195	32	18	ucc	2,500 teu Guangzhou Wenchong 452
9724958		Cyp	2016	28,350	35,000	195	32	18	ucc	2,500 teu Guangzhou Wenchong 458
9724960		Cyp	2016	28,350	35,000	195	32	18	ucc	2,500 teu Guangzhou Wenchong 459
9724972		Cyp	2016	28,350	35,000	195	32	18	ucc	2,500 teu Guangzhou Wenchong 460
					38,000	180	32	14	bbu	Jiangsu Hantong
					38,000	180	32	14	bbu	Jiangsu Hantong

[H] managed by Hanseatic Unity Chartering, a j/v set up in 2013 between Bernhard Schulte and Reederei Nord GmbH as O&S Chartering, changing to present name in September 2015 when joined by Borealis Maritime

Reederei Nord b.v., Netherlands

IMO	name	flag	year	gt	dwt	loa	bm	kts	type	comments
9241114	Energy R. +	Cyp	2003	161,306	319,174	333	60	16	tcr	ex Nordenergy-11
9624067	Lotus *	Cyp	2013	57,081	104,280	244	42	14	tcr	ex Nordlotus-13
9319870	Nordbay *	Cyp	2007	62,241	116,104	249	44	15	tcr	
9277761	Merkur O. **	Cyp	2004	42,432	74,999	225	32	14	tco	ex Nordmerkur -11
9277759	N. Mars **	Cyp	2004	42,432	74,999	225	32	14	tco	ex Nordmars-11
9277773	Neptun D **	Cyp	2004	42,432	74,999	225	32	14	tco	ex Nordneptun-11
9624079	Orchid *	Cyp	2013	57,081	104,280	229	42	14	tcr	l/a Nord Orchid
9241102	Power D +	Cyp	2003	161,308	319,012	333	60	16	tcr	ex Nordpower-11
9521435	Rose *	Cyp	2012	56,320	104,583	244	42	14	tcr	ex Nordrose-13
9521447	Tulip *	Cyp	2013	57,081	104,280	244	42	14	tcr	ex Nordtulip-13
9277747	Venus R. **	Cyp	2004	42,432	74,999	225	32	14	tco	ex Nordvenus-11
9334571	Two Million Ways **	Cyp	2008	40,865	73,965	228	32	14	tco	ex Eagle Hope-11

newbuildings: 4 x 112,000 tcr [Sumitomo/Samsung (2017/8)]
* operates in Sigma Tankers Pool ** operates in Straits Product Pool + operates in Tankers International Pool
see also Nordcapital Holding GmbH & Cie KG (ER Schiffahrt GmbH & Cie KG)

D. Oltmann GmbH & Co.   Germany

funnel: *mainly in charterers colours.* **hull:** *dark grey with red boot-topping.* **history:** *founded 1871.* **web:** *www.oltmann.com*

IMO	name	flag	year	gt	dwt	loa	bm	kts	type	comments
9623673	Cap Ferrato	Mlt	2012	52,464	63,007	256	37	21	ucc	4,975 teu: l/a RDO Fortune
9623661	Cap Frio	Mlt	2012	52,464	62,997	256	37	21	ucc	4,975 teu: l/a RDO Favour
9369734	MSC Bremen	Lbr	2007	54,605	67,033	294	32	25	ucc	5,029 teu: l/a RDO Bremen
9232890	MSC England	Lbr	2001	39,812	51,020	258	32	24	ucc	4,132 teu: ex CMA CGM Vega-07, l/a RDO England
9415844	RDO Concert	Lbr	2009	75,604	85,622	304	40	25	ucc	6,969 teu: ex UASC Yanbu-12, l/a RDO Concert
9401283	RDO Concord	Lbr	2009	73,819	85,626	304	40	25	ucc	6,969 teu: ex CMA CGM Flaubert-11, l/a RDO Concord

Rose : Klaus E Oldendorff, Reederei Nord b.v. : *Chris Brooks*

Schiffahrts Oltmann Verwaltung GmbH — Germany

funnel: *mainly in charterers colours.* **hull:** *dark grey with red boot-topping.* **history:** *founded 1962 as Rederei Gerhard Oltmann KG to 1989.* **web:** *www.oltship.de*

IMO	name	flag	year	gt	dwt	loa	bm	kts	type	comments
9138288	Anika Oltmann	Deu	1998	25,361	33,919	207	30	21	ucc	2,470 teu: ex MSC Caracas-13, Montebello-06, Anika Oltmann-99, Montebello-99, Anika Oltmann-98
9220316	JPO Aquarius	Atg	2000	25,361	33,937	207	30	22	ucc	2,470 teu: ex CMA CGM Bahia-12, Libra Buenos Aires-06, CMA CGM Chili-02, JPO Aquarius-01
9220328	JPO Aries	Atg	2001	25,361	33,900	207	30	22	ucc	2,470 teu: ex MOL Dream-12, Trade Rainbow-05, TCL Challenger-02, JPO Aries-01
9631876	JPO Atair	Lbr	2014	48,438	60,149	251	38	22	ucc	4,700 teu: I/a Atair
9495402	JPO Canopus *	Lbr	2005	41,359	52,450	264	32	24	ucc	4,130 teu: ex JPO Cancer-13, Maersk Dabou-12, Seattle Express-07, Maersk Dabou-06, P&O Nedlloyd Cardenas-05, JPO Cancer-05
9495414	JPO Capricornus *	Lbr	2005	41,359	52,786	264	32	24	ucc	4,130 teu: ex Maersk Danville-12, P&O Nedlloyd Cardigan-05, JPO Capricornus-05
9455648	JPO Delphinus	Lbr	2009	32,987	56,819	190	32	14	bbu	
9455650	JPO Dorado	Lbr	2009	32,987	56,686	190	32	14	bbu	
9294020	JPO Gemini	Deu	2005	25,630	33,742	207	30	22	ucc	2,474 teu: ex CSAV Yokohama-10, JPO Gemini-05
9246700	JPO Leo	Lbr	2005	35,881	41,743	220	32	22	ucc	3,091 teu: ex Hyundai Renaissance-09, MOL Renaissance-08, JPO Leo-05
9297840	JPO Libra	Lbr	2006	41,359	52,450	264	32	24	ucc	4,132 teu: ex Maersk Dunbar-13, P&O Nedlloyd Carolinas-06, JPO Libra-05
9297852	JPO Pisces	Lbr	2006	41,359	52,786	264	32	24	ucc	4,132 teu: ex Maersk Duncan-13, P&O Nedlloyd Carthago-06, JPO Pisces-05
9307279	JPO Scorpius **	Lbr	2006	27,100	34,537	210	30	22	ucc	2,582 teu
9400174	JPO Taurus	Mar	2010	42,609	52,300	269	32	24	ucc	4,178 teu: ex UASC Ajman-14, I/a JPO Taurus
9400198	JPO Tucana	Lbr	2009	42,609	52,788	269	32	24	ucc	4,178 teu
9406180	JPO Vela	Lbr	2009	41,225	50,420	265	32	24	ucc	4,254 teu: ex Bunga Raya Sembilan-10, I/a JPO Vela
9430765	JPO Virgo	Lbr	2009	41,225	50,361	265	32	24	ucc	4,254 teu
9430777	JPO Volans	Lbr	2010	41,225	50,041	265	32	24	ucc	4,254 teu
9430789	JPO Vulpecula	Lbr	2010	41,225	50,425	265	32	24	ucc	4,254 teu
9153408	Ute Oltmann	Deu	1998	25,359	33,964	207	30	20	ucc	2,474 teu: ex CP Rangitoto-06, Contship Rangitoto-05, Cielo di San Francisco-05, Ute Oltmann-99

** managed for HCI Capital AG or ** for HCI Hanseatische Schiffstreuhand GmbH.*

Olympic Shipping and Management SA — Greece

funnel: *orange, large white disc containing blue/yellow pennant flag with five interlocking coloured rings above and below.* **hull:** *black with red boot-topping.* **history:** *Founded 1951 as Olympic Maritime SA to 1992.* **web:** *www.olyship.com*

IMO	name	flag	year	gt	dwt	loa	bm	kts	type	comments
9271341	Olympic Flag	Grc	2004	80,591	155,099	274	47	16	tcr	
9271353	Olympic Future	Grc	2004	80,591	155,039	274	47	16	tcr	
9375915	Olympic Galaxy	Mhl	2009	42,751	81,383	225	32	14	bbu	ex Sea of Harvest-14, I/a Star of Kilakarai
9331397	Olympic Gemini	Mhl	2006	42,887	82,992	225	32	14	bbu	ex Grand Challenger-14, Clipper Suffolk-09
9510694	Olympic Glory	Mhl	2011	45,999	84,091	235	32	14	bbu	ex B Max-14
9750828	Olympic Hope	Pan	2016	93,286	182,631	292	45	14	bbu	
9292498	Olympic Leader	Mys	2005	160,046	309,164	333	58	15	tcr	ex Eagle Venice-13
9088689	Olympic Legacy	Mhl	1996	160,129	302,789	332	58	14	tcr	
9238868	Olympic Legend	Grc	2003	160,083	308,500	333	60	15	tcr	
9470040	Olympic Leopard	Grc	2011	172,146	318,869	340	60	15	tcr	ex Camilla T.-15, H Whale-14, (conv. cbo-15)
9233791	Olympic Liberty	Grc	2003	160,083	304,992	333	60	15	tcr	
9424273	Olympic Light	Grc	2011	160,278	317,106	330	60	16	tcr	ex Fortune Elephant -14
9445459	Olympic Lion	Mhl	2010	172,146	319,869	340	60	15	tcr	ex Selma B.-14, D Whale-10, (conv. cbo-15)
9292486	Olympic Loyalty II	Sgp	2005	160,046	306,999	333	58	15	tcr	ex Eagle Valencia-13
9424211	Olympic Luck	Grc	2010	169,955	319,106	340	60	15	tcr	ex B Whale-14, (conv. cbo-15)
9303883	Olympic Peace	Mhl	2006	30,681	55,709	190	32	14	bbu	ex Atlantic Adventure-14, Ikan Mexico-10
9545728	Olympic Pegasus	Mhl	2016	32,983	56,726	190	32	14	bbu	ex Marine King-16
9513830	Olympic Pioneer	Mhl	2012	32,795	55,340	188	32	14	bbu	ex South-14

Olympic Pioneer : Olympic Shg. & Mgmt. : *Mike Rhodes*

Olympic Leader : Olympic Shg. & Mgmt. : *Hans Kraijenbosch*

NYK Hyperion : Orient Overseas Container Line : *Chris Brooks*

IMO	name	flag	year	gt	dwt	loa	bm	kts	type	comments
9303015	Olympic Pride	Mhl	2006	31,279	55,705	190	32	14	bbu	ex Dyna Crane-14
9513854	Olympic Progress	Mhl	2012	32,795	54,439	188	32	14	bbu	ex West-14
9489285	Olympic Sea	Mhl	2008	58,418	104,255	244	42	14	tcr	ex DT Providence-14, Savina Caylyn-1
9489297	Olympic Sky	Mhl	2008	58,418	104,215	244	42	14	tct	ex Enrica Lexie-14
9133587	Olympic Spirit II	Grc	1997	52,197	96,773	232	42	13	tcr	
9468853	Olympic Target	Grc	2011	172,146	319,869	340	60	15	tcr	ex Rosey R-16, G Whale-14, (conv. cbo-16)
9445461	Olympic Trophy	Grc	2010	172,146	319,869	340	60	15	tcr	ex Abby-15, E Whale-14, (conv. cbo-16)
9437177	Olympic Trust	Mhl	2010	172,146	319,869	340	60	15	tcr	ex-Elizabeth M-15, C Whale-14, (conv cbo-15)

vessels owned by Alexander S. Onassis Public Benefit Foundation and managed by subsidiary Springfield Shipping Co. (Panama) SA, Greece.

Orient Overseas International Ltd   Hong Kong (China)

Orient Overseas Container Line Ltd., Hong Kong (China)

funnel: *yellow with red and gold 'plum blossom' symbol.* **hull:** *light grey with red 'OOCL', orange with white 'OOCL' or black with red boot-topping.* **history:** *parent founded in 1946 as C.Y. Tung Group and OOCL formed in 1969. C.Y. Tung acquired Furness, Withy & Co in 1980, but resold to Rudolf A Oetker in 1990.* **web:** *www.oocl.com*

IMO	name	flag	year	gt	dwt	loa	bm	kts	type	comments
9622631	NYK Hermes *	Hkg	2013	141,003	144,342	366	48	23	ucc	13,208 teu
9627980	NYK Hyperion *	Hkg	2013	141,003	144,342	366	48	23	ucc	13,208 teu
9102291	OOCL America	Hkg	1995	66,047	67,741	276	40	24	ucc	5,344 teu
9300790	OOCL Asia	Hkg	2006	89,097	99,602	323	43	25	ucc	8,063 teu
9285005	OOCL Atlanta	Hkg	2005	89,097	99,620	323	43	25	ucc	8,063 teu
9332200	OOCL Australia	Hkg	2006	41,479	52,217	263	32	24	ucc	4,583 teu
9627978	OOCL Bangkok	Hkg	2013	141,003	144,342	366	48	23	ucc	13,208 teu
9477878	OOCL Beijing	Hkg	2011	91,563	101,589	335	43	25	ucc	8,888 teu
9169419	OOCL Belgium	Hkg	1998	39,174	40,972	245	32	21	ucc	2,808 teu
9622605	OOCL Berlin	Hkg	2013	141,003	143,521	366	48	23	ucc	13,208 teu
9445502	OOCL Brisbane	Hkg	2009	40,168	50,575	260	32	24	ucc	4,526 teu
9622590	OOCL Brussels	Hkg	2013	141,003	144,342	366	48	23	ucc	13,208 teu
9329540	OOCL Busan	Hkg	2008	40,168	50,567	260	32	23	ucc	4,526 teu: l/a NYK Busan
9102289	OOCL California	Hkg	1995	66,046	67,765	276	40	24	ucc	5,344 teu
9477880	OOCL Canada	Hkg	2011	91,563	101,412	335	43	25	ucc	8,888 teu
9461790	OOCL Charleston	Hkg	2010	40,168	50,518	260	32	24	ucc	4,526 teu
9199270	OOCL Chicago	Hkg	2000	66,677	67,278	277	40	25	ucc	5,714 teu
9622628	OOCL Chongxing	Hkg	2013	141,003	143,500	366	48	23	ucc	13,208 teu
9445526	OOCL Dalian	Hkg	2009	40,168	50,554	260	32	24	ucc	4,526 teu
9300805	OOCL Europe	Hkg	2006	89,097	99,618	323	43	25	ucc	8,063 teu
9622617	OOCL France	Hkg	2013	141,003	144,342	366	48	23	ucc	13,208 teu ex NYK Hercules-16
9613587	OOCL Genoa	Hkg	2015	90,757	101,115	335	43	25	ucc	8,888 teu
9404869	OOCL Guangzhou	Hkg	2010	40,168	50,486	260	32	24	ucc	4,526 teu
9252008	OOCL Hamburg	Hkg	2004	89,097	99,618	323	43	25	ucc	8,063 teu
9613599	OOCL Ho Chi Minh City	Hkg	2015	90.757	101,046	335	43	25	ucc	8,888 teu
9355757	OOCL Houston	Hkg	2007	40,168	50,585	260	32	23	ucc	4,526 teu
9404883	OOCL Jakarta	Hkg	2010	40,168	50,560	260	32	24	ucc	4,526 teu: ex OOCL Ho Chi Minh-10
9329524	OOCL Kobe	Hkg	2007	40,168	50,554	260	32	23	ucc	4,526 teu
9627792	OOCL Korea	Hkg	2014	141,003	144,342	366	48	24	ucc	13,208 teu
9404857	OOCL Le Havre	Hkg	2010	40,168	50,580	260	32	24	ucc	4,526 teu
9417268	OOCL London	Hkg	2010	89,097	99,636	323	43	25	ucc	8,063 teu
9417270	OOCL Luxembourg	Hkg	2010	89,097	99,654	323	43	25	ucc	8,063 teu
9486075	OOCL Memphis	Hkg	2013	91,563	101,544	335	43	25	ucc	8,888 teu
9477892	OOCL Miami	Hkg	2013	91,563	101,566	335	43	25	ucc	8,888 teu
9253739	OOCL Montreal	Hkg	2003	55,994	47,840	294	32	24	ucc	4,404 teu
9445538	OOCL Nagoya	Hkg	2009	40,168	50,501	260	32	24	ucc	4,526 teu
9445514	OOCL New Zealand	Hkg	2009	40,168	50,554	260	32	24	ucc	4,526 teu
9198109	OOCL New York	Lbr	1999	66,289	67,660	277	40	26	ucc	5,762 teu: l/a E.R. Hong Kong
9256482	OOCL Ningbo	Hkg	2004	89,097	99,500	323	43	25	ucc	8,063 teu
9440045	OOCL Norfolk	Hkg	2009	40,168	50,489	260	32	24	ucc	4,526 teu
9367190	OOCL Oakland †	Pan	2007	66,462	66,940	281	40	25	ucc	5,888 teu
9355769	OOCL Panama	Hkg	2008	40,168	50,633	260	32	24	ucc	4,526 teu
9622588	OOCL Poland	Hkg	2013	141,003	144,342	366	48	23	ucc	13,208 teu: ex NYK Helios-16
9256470	OOCL Qingdao	Hkg	2004	89,097	99,600	323	43	25	ucc	8,063 teu
9251999	OOCL Rotterdam	Hkg	2004	89,097	99,522	323	43	25	ucc	8,063 teu
9199268	OOCL San Francisco	Hkg	2000	66,677	67,286	277	40	25	ucc	5,888 teu
9404871	OOCL Savannah	Hkg	2010	40,168	50,490	260	32	24	ucc	4,526 teu
9417244	OOCL Seoul	Hkg	2010	89,097	99,635	323	43	25	ucc	8,063 teu
9198111	OOCL Shanghai	Lbr	1999	66,289	67,473	277	40	26	ucc	5,762 teu: l/a E.R. Shanghai
9628001	OOCL Singapore	Hkg	2014	141,003	144,342	366	48	23	ucc	13,208 teu
9310240	OOCL Southampton	Hkg	2007	89,097	99,678	323	43	25	ucc	8,063 teu

IMO	name	flag	year	gt	dwt	loa	bm	kts	type	comments
9477907	OOCL Taipei	Hkg	2015	91,499	101,147	335	43	25	ucc	8,888 teu
9329552	OOCL Texas	Hkg	2008	40,168	50,610	260	32	23	ucc	4,526 teu
9285471	OOCL Tianjin	Hkg	2005	89,097	99,500	323	43	25	ucc	8,063 teu
9310238	OOCL Tokyo	Hkg	2007	89,097	99,706	323	43	25	ucc	8,063 teu
9486087	OOCL Utah	Hkg	2015	91,499	101,279	335	43	25	ucc	8,888 teu
9417256	OOCL Washington	Hkg	2010	89,097	99,631	323	43	25	ucc	8,063 teu
9329538	OOCL Yokohama	Hkg	2007	40,168	50,634	260	32	23	ucc	4,526 teu
9332195	OOCL Zhoushan	Hkg	2006	41,479	52,214	263	32	24	ucc	4,583 teu
newbuildings:										
9776171		Hkg	2017	199,000	197,500	400	59		ucc	21,000 teu Samsung 2172 05.2017
9776183		Hkg	2017	199,000	197,500	400	59		ucc	21,000 teu Samsung 2173 06.2017
9776195		Hkg	2017	199,000	197,500	400	59		ucc	21,000 teu Samsung 2174 07.2017
9776200		Hkg	2017	199,000	197,500	400	59		ucc	21,000 teu Samsung 2175 08.2017
9776212		Hkg	2017	199,000	197,500	400	59		ucc	21,000 teu Samsung 2176 10.2017
9776224		Hkg	2017	199,000	197,500	400	59		ucc	21,000 teu Samsung 2177 11.2017

* chartered to Nippon Yusen Kaisha or † on charter from various mainly Japanese owners or finance houses and managed by Anglo-Eastern Shipmanagement, by Fleet Management Ltd, Hong Kong, by Orient Marine Co Ltd or by Bernhard Schulte Shipmanagement (China) Co Ltd.

Grace Ocean Investments Ltd., Hong Kong

IMO	name	flag	year	gt	dwt	loa	bm	kts	type	comments
9444273	MOL Presence	Sgp	2008	71,884	72,712	293	40	25	ucc	6,326 teu
9307023	OOCL Dubai	Sgp	2006	66,462	66,940	281	40	21	ucc	5,888 teu: ex Canada Express-13, OOCL Dubai-10
9367205	OOCL Italy	Hkg	2007	66,462	66,940	281	40	25	ucc	5,888 teu: ex Vietnam Express-13, OOCL Italy-10
9307009	OOCL Kaohsiung	Sgp	2006	66,462	66,940	281	40	25	ucc	5,888 teu
9367176	OOCL Kuala Lumpur	Hkg	2007	66,462	66,940	281	40	25	ucc	5,888 teu
9350989	Star Best	Sgp	2007	14,030	13,191	163	26	22	grf	
9517903	Star Care	Sgp	2009	14,022	13,300	163	26	22	grf	
9517927	Star Endeavour I	Sgp	2010	14,022	12,967	163	26	22	grf	ex Star Endeavour-11
9517939	Star Leader	Sgp	2010	14,022	12,944	163	26	22	grf	
9517915	Star Pride	Sgp	2009	14,022	12,955	163	26	22	grf	
9438494	Star Quality	Sgp	2009	14,030	13,193	163	26	22	grf	
9438482	Star Service I	Spg	2008	14,030	13,207	163	26	22	grf	ex Star Service-11

Baltic Prince : Ost-West Handel - Baltic Reefers : *Chris Brooks*

IMO	name	flag	year	gt	dwt	loa	bm	kts	type	comments
9438509	Star Standard	Sgp	2009	14,030	13,201	163	26	22	grf	
9350991	Star Stratos	Sgp	2007	14,030	13,186	163	26	22	grf	
9438511	Star Trust	Sgp	2009	14,030	13,189	162	26	22	grf	

also owns a number of bulk carriers

Ost-West-Handel und Schiffahrt GmbH   Germany

funnel: *blue with cream panel with blue globe device split with letters OWH.* **hull**: *blue with white 'Baltic Reefers', red boot-topping.* **history**: *founded 1946 as Samband Islenzkra Samvinnufelaga until 1991 and Samband Line to 1994. Ost-West founded 1996 as Ost-West-Handel Bruno Bishoff GmbH until 2000.* **web**: *www.owhbb.de*
Vessels owned by Baltic Reefers, St. Petersburg founded 1999 **web**: *www.baltic-reefers.com*

IMO	name	flag	year	gt	dwt	loa	bm	kts	type	comments
9181144	Baltic Heather	Pan	1998	9,859	10,114	150	22	20	grf	ex Wild Heather-13
9189902	Baltic Hollyhock	Lbr	1999	9,649	11,788	145	22	20	grf	ex Atlantic Hollyhock-12
9181156	Baltic Jasmine	Lbr	1998	9,859	10,114	150	22	19	grf	ex Wild Osprey-13, Wild Jasmine-12
8520501	Baltic Meadow	Vct	1986	10,298	11,044	146	23	18	grf	ex Al Zohal 1-12, Baltic Spirit-00, Baltic Universal-97
8616324	Baltic Merchant	Vct	1988	10,298	11,055	146	23	18	grf	ex Talca-12, Tasman Spirit-00, Tasman Universal-97, Hornwave-93, Tasman Universal-93
8616312	Baltic Mercury	Vct	1987	10,298	11,067	146	23	18	grf	ex Teno-12, Lincoln Spirit-00, Lincoln Universal-98, Hornwind-93, Lincoln Universal-92
8520213	Baltic Moon	Vct	1987	10,298	11,022	146	23	18	grf	ex Amer Annapurna-08, Arctic Spirit-99, Arctic Universal-97
9038488	Baltic Patriot	Ant	1992	10,402	10,621	150	23	20	grf	ex Eagle Bay-13, Ivory Eagle-03
9016674	Baltic Performer	Ant	1992	10,381	10,603	150	23	20	grf	ex Hawk Bay-13, Roman Bay-04, Roman Star-99, Chiquita Sulu-94
9016662	Baltic Pilgrim	Lbr	1992	10,381	10,621	150	23	20	grf	ex Buzzard Bay-13, French Bay-04, Royal Star-99, Chiquita Honshu-94, Royal Star-92
9070137	Baltic Pioneer	Ant	1993	10,374	10,532	150	23	20	grf	ex Falcon Bay-13, Ivory Falcon-02
8819213	Baltic Pride	Lbr	1989	10,368	10,695	150	23	19	grf	ex Ivory Tirupati-08
8921470	Baltic Prime	Vct	1990	10,405	10,742	150	23	20	grf	ex Condor Bay-12, Ivory Nina-03, Ivory Cape-01
8813594	Baltic Prince	Vct	1990	10,394	10,713	150	23	20	grf	ex Ivory Ace-13
8909070	Baltic Spring	Lbr	1991	10,842	12,942	157	23	21	grf	ex Hansa Stockholm-13
8802090	Baltic Summer	Vct	1989	10,842	12,942	157	23	18	grf	ex Hansa Visby-13
8700228	Zenit	Lbr	1987	13,312	12,848	152	25	18	grf	ex Amer Choapa-08, Choapa-96

Cool Carriers AB, Sweden

funnel: *deep red base and broad blue top with blue and red arcs on broad white central band.* **hull**: *red, cream or white with red/blue, red or blue boot-topping.* **history**: *formed September 2014 when NYKCool was purchased by Baltic Reefers. Previously j/v between NYK and LauritzenCool who had purchased Cool Carriers in 2000.* **web**: *www.cool.se*

IMO	name	flag	year	gt	dwt	loa	bm	kts	type	comments
9038335	Autumn Wave +	Bhs	1993	13,077	13,981	158	24	22	grf	ex Dominica-09, Geest Dominica-97
9038323	Autumn Wind +	Bhs	1993	13,077	13,981	158	24	22	grf	ex St. Lucia-08, Geest St. Lucia-97
9128049	Crown Garnet +	Pan	1996	10,519	10,322	152	23	21	grf	
9128051	Crown Jade +	Pan	1997	10,519	10,332	152	23	21	grf	
9128063	Crown Opal ++	Pan	1997	10,519	10,332	152	23	21	grf	
9159103	Crown Ruby ++	Pan	1997	10,519	10,338	152	23	21	grf	
9159115	Crown Sapphire ++	Pan	1997	10,519	10,334	152	23	21	grf	
9191498	Crown Topaz +	Pan	1999	10,527	10,318	152	23	21	grf	
9008732	Ivory Dawn ++	Bhs	1991	10,412	10,713	150	23	20	grf	
9143099	Ivory Girl ++	Vut	1996	11,438	10,432	154	24	21	grf	
8911102	Triton Reefer *	Lbr	1990	8,818	9,683	144	22	18	grf	
9181132	Wild Cosmos +	Pan	1998	9,859	10,097	150	22	20	grf	
9181168	Wild Lotus +	Pan	1998	9,859	10,139	150	22	20	grf	
9191474	Wild Peony +	Pan	1998	9,859	10,110	150	22	20	grf	

chartered from various owners/managers including + Norbulk Shg. UK ++ other owners

Overseas Shipholding Group Inc.   U.S.A.

funnel: *blue with white 'OSG' ('S' having waves in lower part), black top.* **hull**: *black with red boot-topping.* **history**: *formed 1969 Acquired Stelmar Shipping in 2005. Filed for Chapter 11 bankruptcy 2014, refinanced and restructured.* **web**: *www.osg.com*

IMO	name	flag	year	gt	dwt	loa	bm	kts	type	comments
9337705	Al Gattara (st) §	Mhl	2007	136,410	106,898	315	50	19	lng	266,000 m³
9337717	Al Gharrafa (st) §	Mhl	2008	136,410	107,000	315	50	19	lng	266,000 m³
9337743	Al Hamla (st) §	Mhl	2008	136,410	106,983	315	50	19	lng	266,000 m³
9244661	Alaskan Explorer †	Usa	2005	110,693	193,049	287	50	15	tcr	
9244659	Alaskan Frontier †	Usa	2004	110,693	193,049	287	50	15	tcr	
9271432	Alaskan Legend †	Usa	2006	110,693	193,048	287	50	15	tcr	

IMO	name	flag	year	gt	dwt	loa	bm	kts	type	comments
9244673	Alaskan Navigator †	Usa	2005	110,693	193,048	287	50	15	tcr	l/dn Alaskan Adventurer
9275725	Cabo Hellas **	Mhl	2003	40,038	69,636	228	32	14	tco	
9265861	Overseas Alcesmar	Mhl	2004	30,018	46,215	183	32	14	tco	ex Alcesmar-06
9265873	Overseas Alcmar	Mhl	2004	30,018	46,245	183	32	14	tco	ex Alcmar-06
9231626	Overseas Ambermar	Mhl	2002	23,843	35,970	183	27	14	tco	ex Ambermar-05
9353591	Overseas Anacortes *	Usa	2010	29,252	46,666	183	32	15	tco	
9265885	Overseas Andromar	Mhl	2004	30,018	46,195	183	32	14	tco	ex Andromar-06
9271834	Overseas Antigmar	Mhl	2004	30,018	46,168	183	32	14	tco	ex Antigmar-06
9273624	Overseas Ariadmar	Mhl	2004	30,018	46,205	183	32	14	tco	ex Ariadmar-06
9273636	Overseas Atalmar	Mhl	2004	30,018	46,177	183	32	15	tco	ex Atalmar-05
9470260	Overseas Athens	Mhl	2012	30,031	50,342	183	32	14	tco	
9353565	Overseas Boston *	Usa	2009	29,242	46,802	183	32	14	tco	
9475935	Overseas Cascade *	Usa	2009	29,234	46,287	183	32	14	tco	
9432218	Overseas Chinook *	Usa	2010	29,234	46,666	183	32	14	tco	
9400679	Overseas Everest +	Mhl	2010	156,651	296,907	333	60	15	tcr	ex Front Emperor-10
9213313	Overseas Fran *	Mhl	2001	62,385	112,118	250	44	14	tcr	
9239628	Overseas Goldmar **	Mhl	2002	40,343	69,684	228	32	14	tcr	ex Goldmar-05, l/a LMZ Mandi
9351062	Overseas Houston *	Usa	2007	29,242	46,815	183	32	14	tco	
9232606	Overseas Jademar **	Mhl	2002	40,343	69,697	228	32	14	tcr	ex Jademar-05
9213301	Overseas Josefa Camejo *	Mhl	2001	62,385	112,200	250	44	14	tcr	
9563237	Overseas Kilimanjiro +	Mhl	2012	157,048	296,999	330	60	14	tcr	
9384019	Overseas Kimolos	Mhl	2008	30,109	51,218	183	32	14	tco	l/a Aris II
9569841	Overseas Kythnos	Mhl	2010	30,021	50,284	183	32	14	tco	
9246633	Overseas Laura Lynn	Mhl	2002	234,006	441,585	380	68	16	tcr	ex TI Oceania-15, Hellespont Fairfax-04
9470272	Overseas Leyte **	Mhl	2011	42,153	73,944	229	32	14	tco	
9353527	Overseas Long Beach *	Usa	2007	29,242	42,994	183	32	14	tco	
9353530	Overseas Los Angeles *	Usa	2007	29,242	46,817	183	32	14	tco	l/a Overseas San Francisco
9301940	Overseas Luzon	Mhl	2006	42,403	74,908	228	32	14	tco	ex Amalia Jacob-07
9353589	Overseas Martinez *	Usa	2010	29,242	46,666	183	32	14	tco	
9530228	Overseas McKinley +	Mhl	2011	157,048	296,971	330	60	14	tcr	

Overseas Skopelos : Overseas Shipholding Group : *Chris Brooks*

IMO	name	flag	year	gt	dwt	loa	bm	kts	type	comments
9470258	Overseas Milos	Mhl	2011	30,031	50,378	183	32	14	tco	
9230880	Overseas Mulan	Mhl	2002	161,233	319,029	333	60	16	tcr	
9435894	Overseas Mykonos *	Usa	2010	29,433	51,711	183	32	14	tco	
9353541	Overseas New York *	Usa	2008	29,242	46,810	183	32	14	tco	
9353577	Overseas Nikiski *	Usa	2009	29,242	46,666	183	32	14	tco	
9232591	Overseas Pearlmar	Mhl	2002	40,043	69,697	228	32	14	tcr	ex Pearlmar-05
9222170	Overseas Petromar	Mhl	2001	23,740	35,768	183	27	14	tco	ex Petromar-05, I/a Nordafrika
9213325	Overseas Portland *	Mhl	2001	62,385	112,139	250	44	14	tcr	
9197894	Overseas Raphael	Mhl	2000	157,883	308,700	335	58	15	tcr	ex Raphael-10
9607954	Overseas Redwood	Mhl	2013	62,647	112,792	250	44	14	tcr	
9275749	Overseas Reymar *	Mhl	2004	40,038	69,636	228	32	14	tcr	ex Reymar-05
9234666	Overseas Rosalyn	Mhl	2003	161,233	317,972	333	60	15	tcr	
9232620	Overseas Rosemar **	Mhl	2002	40,343	69,697	228	32	14	tcr	ex Rosemar-05
9232618	Overseas Rubymar **	Mhl	2002	40,343	69,697	228	32	14	tcr	ex Rubymar-05
9196618	Overseas Sakura +	Mhl	2001	159,397	298,641	333	60	15	tcr	ex Sakura I-06, Berge Sakura-01
9470284	Overseas Samar **	Mhl	2011	42,153	74,192	229	32	14	tco	
9435909	Overseas Santorini *	Usa	2010	29,433	51,711	183	32	14	tco	
9607966	Overseas Shenandoah *	Mhl	2014	62,715	112,691	250	44	14	tcr	c/a Overseas Mindanao
9213296	Overseas Shirley ++	Mhl	2001	62,385	112,056	250	44	14	tcr	
9239630	Overseas Silvermar **	Mhl	2002	40,343	69,609	228	32	14	tcr	ex Silvermar-05, I/a LMZ Zacvi
9478638	Overseas Skopelos	Mhl	2009	29,826	50,222	183	32	14	tco	I/a Hope I
9353606	Overseas Tampa *	Usa	2011	29,242	46,666	183	32	14	tco	
9196632	Overseas Tanabe +	Mhl	2002	159,383	298,561	333	60	16	tcr	ex Tanabe-07
9353553	Overseas Texas City *	Usa	2008	29,242	46,801	183	32	14	tco	
9301952	Overseas Visayas **	Mhl	2006	42,403	74,933	228	32	14	tco	I/a Carl Jacob
9394947	Overseas Yellowstone *	Mhl	2008	62,775	112,990	250	44	14	tcr	
9394959	Overseas Yosemite *	Mhl	2009	62,775	112,905	250	44	14	tcr	
9337731	Tembek (st) §	Mhl	2007	136,410	107,514	315	50	19	lng	266,000 m³
9165293	Victory *	Mhl	1998	28,400	47,225	183	32	15	tco	ex Overseas Maremar-13, Maremar-05, Alam Belia-02

vessels managed by OSG Ship Management (GR)Ltd, Greece (formerly Stelmar Tankers Management Ltd to 2005)
* managed by OSG Ship Management Inc, USA   ** managed by Cape Tankers Inc., USA
+ managed by Tankers UK Agencies Ltd (vessels operate in Tankers International Poo)
++ managed by Shell Trading and Shipping Co.
† managed by subsidiary Alaska Tanker Co. LLC (formed jointly with Keystone Shipping Co, USA and BP Shipping Ltd, UK)
§ owned by Qatar Gas Transport, managed by OSG Ship Management UK Ltd.
see also Navion ASA (under Teekay) and Tanker International Pool under CMB (Euronav Luxembourg SA), Capital

Paragon Shipping Inc. Greece

funnel: blue with two narrow white bands surrounding broad red band containing two white intertwined diamonds or charterers colours.
hull: maroon or grey with red boot-topping. **history:** founded 2006, commercial management of vessels by All Seas Marine as a development of Eurocarriers S.A (founded 1993). Subsidiary. Box Ships. founded 2010. **web**: www.paragonship.com, www.allseas.gr

IMO	name	flag	year	gt	dwt	loa	bm	kts	type	comments
9305099	Coral Seas	Lbr	2006	40,485	74,476	225	32	14	bbu	ex Anny Petrakis-07
9465796	Dream Seas	Lbr	2009	40,170	75,151	225	32	14	bbu	ex Iorana-10
9394832	Friendly Seas	Lbr	2008	32,415	58,779	190	32	14	bbu	ex Nikolas II-08
9703514	Gentle Seas	Lbr	2014	35,812	63,500	200	32	14	bbu	
9305104	Golden Seas	Lbr	2006	40,485	74,475	225	32	14	bbu	ex Iolcos Destiny-07
9718698	Greek Seas	Lbr	2015	44,127	82,043	229	32	14	bbu	
9491252	Kavala Seas	Lbr	2011	33,044	56,380	190	32	14	bbu	ex Minero Tres-11
9491238	Paros Seas	Lbr	2011	33,044	56,780	189	32	14	bbu	ex Chungo Tres-11
9707584	Peaceful Seas	Lbr	2014	35,812	63,500	200	32	14	bbu	
9737589	Phaedra	Mhl	2015	44,127	82,053	229	32	14	bbu	
9589097	Precious Seas	Lbr	2012	24,196	37,205	190	28	14	bbu	
9590618	Priceless Seas	Lbr	2013	24,196	37,202	190	28	14	bbu	
9589085	Prosperous Seas	Lbr	2012	24,196	37,294	190	28	14	bbu	
9590620	Proud Seas	Lbr	2014	24,196	37,227	190	28	14	bbu	
9221633	Voula Seas	Lbr	2002	17,431	28,495	170	27	14	bbu	ex Destino Dos-12
newbuildings:										
9736157	Divine Seas	Lbr	2016	35,812	63,301	200	32	14	bbu	
9736169	Magic Seas	Lbr	2016	35,812	63,301	200	32	14	bbu	
9737591	Inspiring Seas	Mhl	2016	44,127	82,000	229	32	14	bbu	
9737606	Bright Seas	Mhl	2016	44,127	81,966	229	32	14	bbu	
9737618	World Seas	Mhl	2016	44,127	82,000	229	32	14	bbu	
9736133		Mhl	2016	43,000	81,800	229	32	14	bbu	Jiangsu Yangzijiang 1142 Q1 2016
9736119		Mhl	2016	43,000	81,800	229	32	14	bbu	Jiangsu Yangzijiang 1144 Q1 2016
9736121		Mhl	2016	43,000	81,800	229	32	14	bbu	Jiangsu Yangzijiang 1145 Q1 2016

Priceless Seas : Paragon Shipping Inc. : *Chris Brooks*

Box Queen : Paragon Shipping Inc. - Box Ships : *ARO*

Box Ships Inc., Marshall Islands

IMO	name	flag	year	gt	dwt	loa	bm	kts	type	comments
9108178	Box China	Lbr	1996	66,046	67,625	276	41	24	ucc	5,344 teu: ex OOCL China-15
9275646	Box Emma	Mhl	2003	54,881	68,120	294	32	24	ucc	5,048 teu: ex MSC Emma-15
9706281	Box Endeavour	Lbr	2015	17,674	21,732	172	27	18	ucc	1,714 teu
9733820	Box Endurance	Lbr	2015	17,907	21,667	172	27	18	ucc	1,714 teu
9108166	Box Hong Kong	Lbr	1996	66,046	67,637	276	40	24	ucc	5,344 teu: ex OOCL Hong Kong-15
9330989	Box Marlin	Lbr	2007	54,309	65,949	294	32	25	ucc	5,042 teu: ex CMA CGM Marlin-15
9252096	Box Queen	Lbr	2006	52,701	58,281	292	32	24	ucc	4,546 teu: ex Maersk Diadema-14, MSC Siena-12, Maersk Diadema-08, Charlotte Wulff-06
9423035	Box Trader	Lbr	2010	36,087	42,483	229	32	23	ucc	3,414 teu
9418377	Box Voyager	Lbr	2010	36,087	42,454	229	32	23	ucc	3,414 teu: l/d Buxpower
9330991	CMA CGM Kingfish	Lbr	2007	54,309	65,974	294	32	25	ucc	5,042 teu
9400069	Maule	Lbr	2010	75,752	81,002	306	40	25	ucc	6,589 teu
9706279	Philippos-Michalis *	Cyp	2015	17,907	21,718	172	27	18	ucc	1,714 teu: l/d Box Eminence
newbuildings:										
9590632			2016	47,500	56,300	250	37		ucc	4,800 teu: Zhejiang Ouhua 656
9590644			2016	47,500	56,300	250	37		ucc	4,800 teu: Zhejiang Ouhua 657

Passat Schiffahrtsges.mbH & Co.   Germany

history: *associate company formed 1976 as Hanse Bereederungs GmbH & Co KG to 2005.* **web:** *www.hanse-bereederung.de*

IMO	name	flag	year	gt	dwt	loa	bm	kts	type	comments
9232773	Euro Max	Lbr	2002	32,284	39,350	211	32	22	ucc	2,732 teu: CMA CGM Charcot-11, CSAV Rio Loa-07, Euro Max-04, P&O Nedlloyd Dubai-03, l/a Euro Max
9316335	Passat Summer	Lbr	2005	32,214	39,008	211	32	22	ucc	2,732 teu: ex Passat Breeze-14, CSAV Morumbi-10, Passat Breeze-05

Reederei Stefan Patjens GmbH & Co. KG   Germany

funnel: *charterers colours.* **hull:** *grey with red boot topping.* **history:** *founded 2000 as Reederei Stefan Patjens until 2006.* **web:** *www.reederei-patjens.de*

IMO	name	flag	year	gt	dwt	loa	bm	kts	type	comments
9225407	Alexandria	Lbr	2000	32,322	39,128	211	32	22	ucc	2,732 teu: ex ANL Kiewa-14, Alexandra P-14, Kota Perabu-11, Alexandra P-10, OOCL Keelung-09, Alexandra P-07, Maersk Plymouth-06, Alexandra-00
9320685	Allise P	Lbr	2006	53,481	53,900	294	32	23	ucc	5,040 teu: ex Maersk Dubrovnik-14, l/a Allise P.
9225419	Heike P.	Lbr	2000	32,322	39,128	211	32	22	ucc	2,732 teu: ex Tiger Shark-15, Heike P-14, Kota Perwira-11, Heike P-10, OOCL Bangkok-09, Heike-07, Maersk Pelepas-06, Safmarine Ibhayi-05, Maersk Pelepas-03, Heike-00
9317925	Herma P	Lbr	2006	53,481	53,880	294	32	23	ucc	5,040 teu: ex Maersk Dryden-14, l/a Herma P.
9317937	Kaethe P	Lbr	2006	53,481	53,911	294	32	23	ucc	5,040 teu: ex Maersk Drury-14, l/a Kathe P
9232759	Liwia P	Lbr	2001	32,322	39,128	211	32	22	ucc	2,732 teu: ex OOCL Mumbai-09, Liwia-07, Safmarine Ikapa-06, MSC Canada-03, Liwia-02
9232747	Meta	Lbr	2001	32,322	39,128	211	32	22	ucc	2,732 teu: ex Maersk Perth-06, l/a Meta
9126986	Rothorn *	Atg	1996	12,029	14,587	157	24	18	ucc	1,122 teu: ex MOL Amazonas-02, Guatamala-01, Rothorn-98
9317913	Serena P	Lbr	2006	53,453	54,058	294	32	23	ucc	5,040 teu: ex Maersk Drummond-14, l/a Serena P.
9126974	Weisshorn *	Atg	1996	12,029	14,643	157	24	19	ucc	1,122 teu: ex MSC Ghana-04, Weisshorn-02, DAL East London-01, Weisshorn-00, P&O Nedlloyd Maurttius-99, Weisshorn-98

*also owns 4 container feeder ships : * owned by Contal Shipping Ltd. Switzerland*

Dr. Peters GmbH & Co. KG   Germany

funnel: *light green with white DS on light green square on broad white band or charterers colours.* **hull:** *various former owners or charterers colours.* **history:** *originally KG investment fund founded in 1960 as Dr Peters GmbH to 1999* **web:** *www.dr-peters.de and www.ds-schiffahrt.de and www.ds-tankers.com*

DS Schiffahrts GmbH & Co. KG

IMO	name	flag	year	gt	dwt	loa	bm	kts	type	comments
9148635	Ashna	Mhl	1999	156,417	301,438	330	58	15	tcr	ex Nordbay-04
9546904	DS Charme *	Lbr	2011	92,050	176,000	292	45	14	bbu	

DS Warrior : Dr. Peters - DS Tankers : *Chris Brooks*

Front Symphony : Dr. Peters - DS Tankers : *Chris Brooks*

IMO	name	flag	year	gt	dwt	loa	bm	kts	type	comments
9215854	DS Dominion *	Lbr	2001	74,373	80,550	304	40	26	ucc	6,479 teu: ex CSAV Porvenir-14, Hyundai Dominion-11
9215842	DS National *	Lbr	2001	74,373	80,494	304	40	26	ucc	6,479 teu: ex CSAV Pirque-14, Hyundai National-11
9215866	DS Patriot *	Lbr	2001	74,373	80,551	304	40	26	ucc	6,479 teu: ex CSAV Puyehue-14, Hyundai Patriot-11
9215830	DS Republic *	Lbr	2001	74,373	80,596	304	40	26	ucc	6,479 teu: ex CSAV Petorca-14, Hyundai Republic-11

also operates two feeder containerships Blue Wave *and* Blue Ocean

DS Tankers GmbH & Co. KG

IMO	name	flag	year	gt	dwt	loa	bm	kts	type	comments
9186651	Bahamas Spirit	Bhs	1996	57,947	107,261	247	42	17	tcr	ex Sanko Trader-01
9169691	DS Chief	Bhs	1999	157,863	311,224	334	58	15	tcr	ex Front Chief-12
9174397	DS Commander	Bhs	1999	157,863	311,168	334	58	15	tcr	ex Front Commander-12
9179646	DS Crown	Bhs	1999	157,863	311,176	334	58	15	tcr	ex Front Crown-12, Front President-99
9268904	DS Progress	Lbr	2003	39,272	70,427	229	32	15	tcr	ex Sunlight Venture-12
9252187	DS Promoter	Lbr	2002	39,272	70,392	229	32	15	tcr	ex Venture-12, Sanko Venture-12, Stena Venture-07, l/a Sanko Venture
9108154	DS Vada **	Pan	1997	159,422	309,636	333	58	14	tcr	ex Alfa Glory-15, Apollo Glory-11, C. Bright-07
9205079	DS Valentina	Pan	2000	159,187	308,492	333	58	15	tcr	ex Titan Glory-14, Millenium Maersk-04
9203289	DS Vector	Pan	2001	157,831	298,990	332	58	15	tcr	ex Mercury Glory-14
9522180	DS Venture *	Lbr	2011	157,039	297,345	330	60	15	tcr	
9522178	DS Vision *	Lbr	2011	157,039	297,345	330	60	15	tcr	
9169689	DS Warrior	Bhs	1998	79,669	153,181	269	46	14	tcr	ex Front Warrior-13
9176993	Front Commodore †	Lbr	2000	159,397	298,620	333	60	15	tcr	ex Stena Commodore-01
9249312	Front Melody †	Lbr	2001	79,525	150,500	272	46	14	tcr	
9249324	Front Symphony †	Lbr	2001	79,525	149,995	272	46	14	tcr	
9172868	Front Tina †	Lbr	2000	159,463	298,824	333	60	16	tcr	
9171826	Kiowa Spirit ††	Bhs	1999	62,619	113,334	253	44	14	tcr	ex Bona Valiant-99
9241683	Ridgebury Astari +	Mhl	2002	78,845	149,991	274	48	25	tcr	ex Elisewin-14, Eliomar-07

newbuildings:

* managed for DS Rendite Fonds: vessels managed for previous owners/operators   † Front Line   †† Teekay Shipping (USA) Inc, + Ridgebury Tankers

also see managed vessels under Reederei F Laeisz GmbH and Oskar Wehr KG (GmbH & Co)

Polish Steamship Co. (Polska Żegluga Morska p.p.)   Poland

funnel: *black with red band between two narrow white or yellow bands, interrupted by shield with white letters 'PZM' and trident.* **hull:** *black, blue or yellow (tch), most with white 'POLSTEAM', red boot-topping.* **history:** *state owned company, founded 02 January 1951.* **web:** *www.polsteam.com.pl*

IMO	name	flag	year	gt	dwt	loa	bm	kts	type	comments
9708033	Armia Krajowa	Lbr	2016	25,278	39,071	180	30	14	bbu	
9187497	Aurora	Mhl	2000	16,454	24,558	170	28	14	tms	
9582958	Beskidy	Lbr	2013	43,025	82,138	229	32	14	bbu	
9065912	Daria	Cyp	1995	25,190	41,260	186	30	14	bbu	ex Taria-95
9133769	Diana	Cyp	1997	25,206	41,425	186	30	14	bbu	
9393450	Drawsko	Bhs	2010	20,603	29,978	190	24	14	bbu	
9594248	Gdynia	Bhs	2012	24,145	37,933	190	29	14	bbu	
9452593	Giewont	Bhs	2013	42,868	79,649	229	32	14	bbu	
9521875	Ina	Lbr	2012	13,579	16,622	150	24	14	bbu	
9180396	Irma	Cyp	2000	21,387	34,948	200	24	15	bbu	
9180384	Iryda	Cyp	1999	21,387	34,939	200	24	14	bbu	
9180358	Isa	Cyp	1999	21,387	34,939	200	24	14	bbu	
9180372	Isadora	Cyp	1999	21,387	34,948	200	24	14	bbu	
9180360	Isolda	Cyp	1999	21,959	34,949	200	24	14	bbu	
9465608	Jawor	Bhs	2010	43,506	79,692	229	32	14	bbu	
9422378	Juno	Bhs	2011	20,603	29,707	190	24	14	bbu	
9582506	Karpaty	Lbr	2013	43,025	82,138	229	32	14	bbu	
9436847	Kaszuby	Bhs	2008	24,109	37,965	190	29	14	bbu	
9285029	Kujawy	Bhs	2005	24,109	37,965	190	29	14	bbu	
9423798	Kociewie	Bhs	2009	24,109	38,056	190	29	14	bbu	
9594236	Koszalin	Bhs	2012	23,145	37,884	190	29	14	bbu	
9423786	Kurpie	Bhs	2009	24,109	38,056	190	29	14	bbu	
9441984	Lubie	Bhs	2011	20,603	29,694	190	24	14	bbu	
9496264	Mamry	Bhs	2012	20,603	30,206	190	24	14	bbu	
9386914	Mazowsze	Bhs	2009	24,109	37,695	190	29	14	bbu	
9285122	Mazury	Bhs	2005	24,109	38,056	190	29	14	bbu	
9393448	Miedwie	Bhs	2010	20,603	29,984	190	24	14	bbu	
9154294	Mitrope	Mlt	1999	11,530	15,718	149	23	13	tms	
9521813	Narew	Bhs	2012	13,579	16,573	150	24	14	bbu	

IMO	name	flag	year	gt	dwt	loa	bm	kts	type	comments
9154268	Nogat	Cyp	1999	11,848	17,064	149	23	13	bbu	
9521837	Olza	Lbr	2012	13,579	16,592	150	24	14	bbu	
9386926	Orawa	Bhs	2009	24,109	38,065	190	29	14	bbu	
9154270	Orla	Mlt	1999	11,848	17,064	149	23	14	bbu	
9452610	Ornak	Bhs	2011	43,506	79,677	229	32	14	bbu	
9154282	Pilica	Mlt	1999	11,540	17,064	149	23	14	bbu	
9285134	Podhale	Bhs	2005	24,109	38,056	190	29	14	bbu	
9346811	Podlasie	Bhs	2008	24,109	38,071	190	29	14	bbu	
9488097	Polesie	Bhs	2010	24,055	38,056	190	29	14	bbu	
9346823	Pomorze	Bhs	2008	24,109	38,056	190	29	14	bbu	
9521849	Prosna	Lbr	2012	13,579	16,642	150	24	14	bbu	

Orla : Polish Steamship Co : *ARO*

Raba : Polish Steamship Co : *ARO*

IMO	name	flag	year	gt	dwt	loa	bm	kts	type	comments
9594250	Puck	Bhs	2012	24,245	37,894	190	29	14	bbu	
9521825	Raba	Lbr	2012	13,579	16,593	150	24	14	bbu	
9521758	Regalica	Lbr	2011	13,579	16,006	150	24	14	bbu	
9393462	Resko	Bhs	2010	20,603	29,984	190	24	14	bbu	
9346835	Roztocze	Bhs	2008	24,109	37,965	191	29	14	bbu	
9452622	Rysy	Bhs	2011	43,506	79,602	229	32	14	bbu	
9521851	San	Lbr	2012	13,579	16,620	150	24	14	bbu	
9594224	Szczecin	Bhs	2012	24,145	37,930	190	29	14	bbu	
9521863	Skawa	Lbr	2012	13,579	16,600	150	24	14	bbu	
9496252	Solina	Bhs	2012	20,603	29,691	190	24	14	bbu	
9582518	Sudety	Lbr	2013	43,025	82,138	229	32	14	bbu	
9594224	Szczecin	Bhs	2012	24,145	37,930	190	28	14	bbu	
9582960	Tatry	Lbr	2013	43,025	82,600	229	32	14	bbu	
9488102	Wadowice II	Bhs	2010	24,055	38,061	190	28	14	bbu	
9285146	Warmia	Bhs	2005	24,109	38,056	190	29	14	bbu	
9393474	Wicko	Bhs	2010	20,603	29,903	190	24	14	bbu	
newbuildings:										
9708045	*Szare Szeregi*	Lbr	2016	23,475	38,520	180	30	14	bbu	Yangfan BC38K PZ02, Zhoushan SY
9708057	Legiony Polskie	Lbr	2016	23,475	38,520	180	30	14	bbu	Yangfan BC38K PZ03, Zhoushan SY
9708069	Solidarność	Lbr	2016	23,475	38,520	180	30	14	bbu	Yangfan BC38K PZ04, Zhoushan SY
9727493				23,475	38,520	180	30	14	bbu	Yangfan BC38K PZ05, Zhoushan SY
9727508				23,475	38,520	180	30	14	bbu	Yangfan BC38K PZ06, Zhoushan SY
9727510				23,475	38,520	180	30	14	bbu	Yangfan BC38K PZ07, Zhoushan SY
9727522				23,475	38,520	180	30	14	bbu	Yangfan BC38K PZ08, Zhoushan SY
9750323				23,475	38,520	180	30	14	bbu	Yangfan BC38K PZ09, Zhoushan SY
9750335				23,475	38,520	180	30	14	bbu	Yangfan BC38K PZ10, Zhoushan SY
9750347				23,475	38,520	180	30	14	bbu	Yangfan BC38K PZ11, Zhoushan SY
9750359				23,475	38,520	180	30	14	bbu	Yangfan BC38K PZ12, Zhoushan SY
			2017		36,500				bbu	YZJ 2014-1190
			2017		36,500				bbu	YZJ 2014-1191
			2017		36,500				bbu	YZJ 2014-1192
			2017		36,500				bbu	YZJ 2014-1193
			2017		36,500				bbu	YZJ 2014-1194
			2017		36,500				bbu	YZJ 2014-1195

Projex-Schiffahrts GmbH & Co.   Germany

funnel: *white lower half and dark blue upper part with white 'PX' between narrow pale blue wavy bands or charterers colours.*
hull: *blue with pale blue wavy bands on bows, red boot-topping.* **history:** *formed 1978.* **web:** *www.kg-projex.de*

IMO	name	flag	year	gt	dwt	loa	bm	kts	type	comments
9228540	Bosun	Atg	2001	30,024	35,977	208	32	22	ucc	2,672 teu: ex CSCL Fos-10, l/a Bosun
9350317	Hermes	Atg	2006	27,061	34,365	212	30	22	ucc	2.496 teu
9415296	Penelope	Atg	2008	32,269	38,636	211	32	22	ucc	2,672 teu: ex CSAV Totoral-12, l/a Penelope
9364203	Ulysses *	Atg	2006	27,061	34,393	212	30	22	ucc	2,496 teu: ex Maruba Pampero-10, Ulysses-06

* managed by Hansa Shipping GmbH

Pronav Ship Management GmbH & Co. KG   Germany

funnel: *operators colours.* **hull:** *maroon or black, red boot topping.* **history:** founded Hamburg 1995. **web:** *www.pronav.com*

IMO	name	flag	year	gt	dwt	loa	bm	kts	type	comments
9337987	Al Ghariya [df]	Bhs	2008	137,535	121,730	315	50	19	lng	210,110 m³
9337951	Al Ruwais [df]	Bhs	2007	137,535	121,823	315	50	19	lng	210,110 m³
9337963	Al Safliya [df]	Bhs	2007	137,535	121,963	315	50	19	lng	210,110 m³
9337975	Duhail [df]	Bhs	2008	137,535	121,639	315	50	19	lng	210,110 m³
7390143	LNG Gemini [st] *	Mhl	1978	95,084	72,472	285	44	20	lng	126,340 m³
7390155	LNG Leo [st]	Mhl	1978	95,084	72,555	285	44	20	lng	126,449 m³
7390179	LNG Virgo [st] *	Mhl	1979	95,084	72,629	285	44	20	lng	126,451 m³
9321732	Milaha Qatar [st]	Mlt	2006	96,508	77,803	279	43	20	lng	145,602 m³ ex Maersk Qatar-12
9255854	Milaha Ras Laffan [st]	Mlt	2004	93,226	73,705	279	43	20	lng	138,273 m³ ex Maersk Ras Laffan -12

* laid-up 12:2014

Ray Car Carriers   Israel

funnel: *green with large yellow 'R', narrow black top or charterers colours.* **hull:** *blue with dark green upperworks, red boot-topping.*
history: founded 1992. **web:** *www.raycarcarriers.com or www.stamco.gr*

IMO	name	flag	year	gt	dwt	loa	bm	kts	type	comments
9446881	Adria Ace	Bhs	2009	41,009	12,300	176	31	20	mve	4,900 ceu
9277826	Amber Arrow	Bhs	2004	57,718	21,120	200	32	20	mve	6,700 ceu
9318486	Coral Leader	Bhs	2006	40,986	12,164	176	31	19	mve	4,900 ceu
9391581	CSCC Asia	Bhs	2009	57,692	21,037	200	32	20	mve	6,700 ceu
9391593	CSCC Europe	Bhs	2009	57,692	21,300	200	32	20	mve	6,700 ceu
9361823	CSCC Shanghai	Bhs	2008	41,009	12,300	176	31	19	mve	4,900 ceu

IMO	name	flag	year	gt	dwt	loa	bm	kts	type	comments
9361835	CSCC Tianjin	Bhs	2008	41,009	12,300	176	31	19	mve	4,900 ceu
9210440	Crystal Ray	Bhs	2000	57,772	21,400	200	32	20	mve	6,700 ceu
9316309	Danube Highway	Bhs	2006	23,498	7,788	148	25	18	mve	2,130 ceu
9441506	Dignity Ace	Bhs	2010	58,767	20,589	200	32	19	mve	6,700 ceu
9316282	Elbe Highway	Bhs	2005	23,498	7,750	148	25	18	mve	2,130 ceu
9361811	Emerald Leader	Bhs	2008	40,986	12,300	176	31	19	mve	4,900 ceu
9237307	Galaxy Leader	Bhs	2002	48,710	17,127	189	32	20	mve	5,100 ceu
9357327	Garnet Leader	Bhs	2008	57,692	21,020	200	32	20	mve	6,700 ceu
9672416	Genius Highway	Bhs	2014	58,767	21,000	200	32	20	mve	6,700 ceu
9391567	Gentle Leader	Bhs	2008	57,692	21,122	200	32	20	mve	6,700 ceu
9237319	Global Leader	Bhs	2002	48,710	17,125	199	32	20	mve	5,100 ceu
9357298	Glorious Leader	Bhs	2007	57,692	20,999	200	32	20	mve	6,700 ceu
9441594	Glovis Caravel	Bhs	2012	58,767	20,434	200	32	20	mve	6,700 ceu
9441582	Glovis Clipper	Bhs	2012	58,767	20,434	200	32	20	mve	6,700 ceu
9453107	Glovis Passion	Bhs	2011	36,834	11,196	168	28	20	mve	4,000 ceu
9455715	Glovis Prestige	Bhs	2011	36,834	11,196	168	28	20	mve	4,000 ceu
9736808	Glovis Star	Bhs	2016	71,000	20,950	200	36	20	mve	7,500 ceu
9357315	Goliath Leader	Bhs	2008	57,692	20,958	200	32	20	mve	6,700 ceu
9357303	Graceful Leader	Bhs	2007	57,692	20,986	200	32	20	mve	6,700 ceu
9672404	Gravity Highway	Bhs	2014	58,767	21,000	200	32	20	mve	6,700 ceu
9388716	Guardian Leader	Bhs	2008	57,692	21,182	200	32	20	mve	6,700 ceu
9441568	Harmony Leader	Bhs	2011	58,767	20,434	200	32	19	mve	6,700 ceu
9690523	Harvest Leader	Bhs	2014	71,177	20,941	200	36	19	mve	7,700 ceu
9690547	Helios Highway	Bhs	2015	71,177	20,950	200	36	19	mve	7,700 ceu: l/a Glovis Star
9441556	Heritage Leader	Bhs	2011	58,767	20,434	200	32	19	mve	6,700 ceu
9690535	Hermes Leader	Bhs	2015	71,177	20,941	200	36	19	mve	7,700 ceu
9441570	Heroic Leader	Bhs	2011	58,767	20,434	200	32	19	mve	6,700 ceu
9277814	Höegh Africa	Bhs	2004	57,718	21,214	200	32	20	mve	6,700 ceu: ex Hual Africa-09
9277802	Höegh America	Bhs	2003	57,718	21,182	200	32	20	mve	6,700 ceu: ex Hual America-08
9660798	Höegh Amsterdam	Bhs	2013	58,767	21,200	200	32	20	mve	6,700 ceu
9441623	Höegh Antwerp	Bhs	2013	58,767	20,434	200	32	20	mve	6,700 ceu
9441520	Horizon Leader	Bhs	2010	58,767	20,434	200	32	19	mve	6,700 ceu
9690559	Hyperion Highway	Bhs	2015	71,177	20,950	200	36	19	mve	7,500 ceu
9318503	Istra Ace	Bhs	2007	41,000	12,200	176	31	19	mve	4,900 ceu
9277838	Ivory Arrow	Bhs	2004	57,718	21,300	200	32	20	mve	6,700 ceu

CSCC Europe : Ray Car Carriers : *Mike Rhodes*

Victory Leader : Ray Car Carriers : *ARO*

Hermes Leader : Ray Car Carriers : *Mike Rhodes*

IMO	name	flag	year	gt	dwt	loa	bm	kts	type	comments
9267912	Jasper Arrow	Bhs	2005	57,692	21,040	200	32	20	mve	6,700 ceu
9361809	Lapis Arrow	Bhs	2006	40,500	12,105	176	31	19	mve	4,900 ceu
9285615	Morning Calm	Bhs	2004	57,962	21,005	200	32	20	mve	6,700 ceu: I/a Opal Ray
9285627	Morning Champion	Bhs	2005	57,692	21,106	200	32	20	mve	6,700 ceu
9441609	Morning Classic	Bhs	2013	58,767	21,000	200	32	19	mve	6,700 ceu
9441611	Morning Compass	Bhs	2013	58,767	21,000	200	32	19	mve	6,700 ceu
9285639	Morning Courier	Bhs	2005	57,692	21,053	200	32	20	mve	6,700 ceu
9285641	Morning Crown	Bhs	2005	57,692	21,052	200	32	20	mve	6,700 ceu
9386225	Nordic Ace	Bhs	2007	23,498	7,378	148	25	18	mve	2,130 ceu
9267924	Onyx Arrow	Bhs	2005	57,692	21,087	200	32	20	mve	6,700 ceu
9210438	Platinium Ray	Bhs	2000	57,772	21,000	200	32	20	mve	6,700 ceu
9316311	Seine Highway	Bhs	2007	23,498	8,100	148	25	18	mve	2,130 ceu
9391579	Serenity Ace	Bhs	2008	57,692	21,300	200	32	20	mve	6,700 ceu
9311836	Taipan	Bhs	2006	57,692	21,021	200	32	20	mve	6,700 ceu: I/a Morning Countess
9311854	Talia	Bhs	2006	57,692	21,021	200	32	20	mve	6,700 ceu
9327748	Tarifa	Bhs	2007	57,692	21,120	200	32	20	mve	6,700 ceu: I/a Morning Charisma
9316294	Thames Highway	Bhs	2007	23,498	7,750	148	25	18	mve	2,130 ceu
9395628	Victory Leader	Bhs	2010	49,675	13,363	189	32	19	mve	5,000 ceu
9395630	Violet Ace	Bhs	2011	49,708	13,363	189	32	19	mve	5,000 ceu

newbuildings : 2 x 7,700 ceu [Hyundai Mipo (Q2 2017)}
managed by Stamco Ship Management Co. Ltd, Greece (formed 1993). vessels chartered-out to Eukor Car Carriers Inc. (see under Wallenius-Wilhelmsen), Höegh, Hyundai Glovis, K Line, MOL, NYK, Wallenius-Wilhelmsen and other operators.

Carsten Rehder Schiffsmakler und Reederei GmbH   Germany

funnel: *black with white 'CR' on black diamond between narrow red bands on braod white band or charterers colours.* hull: *black or green with red boot-topping.* history: *founded 1903 as Carsten Rehder to 1982* web: *www.carstenrehder.de*

IMO	name	flag	year	gt	dwt	loa	bm	kts	type	comments
9363144	Baltic Strait	Lbr	2008	18,102	23,840	182	25	20	ucc	1,698 teu
9363156	Barents Strait	Lbr	2008	18,102	23,844	183	25	20	ucc	1,698 teu
9670834	Cap Cortes	Pmd	2013	43,015	51,110	228	37	22	ucc	3,820 teu: c/a Osaka Strait
9139634	AHS St. Georg	Mhl	1998	10,384	12,184	149	23	19	ucc	1,138 teu: ex Clou Ocean-13, Besire Kalkavan-06
9236597	Dover Strait	Mhl	2002	14,241	18,402	159	24	18	ucc	1,118 teu: ex Cape Serrat-04, MOL Sahara-02, Cape Serrat-02
9488580	Eagle Strait	Lbr	2010	33,033	56,800	190	32	14	bbu	
9488592	Emerald Strait	Lbr	2010	33,033	56,830	190	32	14	bbu	
9488578	Endeavour Strait	Lbr	2010	33,033	56,806	190	32	14	bbu	
9488566	Essex Strait	Lbr	2010	33,033	56,872	190	32	14	bbu	
9357547	MCC Kyoto	Pmd	2008	18,123	22,314	175	28	20	ucc	1,713 teu: X-press Dhaulagiri-12, Ocean Spica-09
9357535	MCC Seoul	Pmd	2008	18,123	22,314	175	28	20	ucc	1,713 teu: ex X-press Anapurna-12, Ocean Bird-09
9362736	Melbourne Strait	Atg	2008	21,018	25,849	180	28	20	ucc	1,794 teu
9305001	Munk Strait	Lbr	2004	27,915	37,978	215	30	21	ucc	2,702 teu: ex King Adrian-15,Cosco Sydney-09, I/a Frisia Leipzig
9290426	Nansen Strait	Lbr	2005	54,809	67,310	294	32	25	ucc	4,839 teu: ex Santa Philippa-15. Cap Stephens-12, Maersk Durham-10, P&O Nedlloyd Dover-05, I/a Santa Philippa
9526564	Pacific Trust	Lbr	2010	22,636	34,000	181	30	14	bbu	I/a Labrador Strait
9454242	Sonderborg Strait	Atg	2012	12,297	14,222	158	23	19	ucc	1,085 teu
9454230	Svendborg Strait	Atg	2011	12,514	14,220	158	23	19	ucc	1,085 teu
9351218	Tasman Strait	Lbr	2008	18,123	22,314	175	28	20	ucc	1,713 teu: ex Ocean Emerald-14 I/a Tasman Strait
9357523	Torres Strait	Lbr	2008	18,123	22,314	175	28	20	ucc	1,713 teu: ex Ocean Mermaid14, I/a Torres Strait
9362724	Macao Strait	Lbr	2008	21,028	25,826	180	28	20	ucc	1,794 teu: ex Vento di Ponente-14, Macao Strait-13, NileDutch Qingdao-11, Macao Strait-08
9516777	Wellington Strait	Lbr	2012	18,358	23,368	175	27	20	ucc	1,696 teu
9436068	William Strait	Lbr	2009	18,485	23,707	177	27	20	ucc	1,732 teu: ex Viking Hawk-09
9516789	Winchester Strait	Lbr	2012	18,358	23,295	175	27	20	ucc	1,696 teu

also operates a number of container feeder vessels

Schiffahrtskontor Rendsburg GmbH   Germany

funnel: *blue or charterers colours.* hull: *black or green with red boot-topping.* history: *founded 1971 as Schiffahrtskontor Rendsburg, Peterson, Schluter & Werner.* web: *www.westerships.com*

IMO	name	flag	year	gt	dwt	loa	bm	kts	type	comments
9137674	Westerburg	Lbr	1997	23,896	30,291	188	30	21	ucc	2,064 teu: ex CMA CGM Accra-07, Westerburg-07, Tuscany Bridge-07, Westerburg-03, Lykes Achiever-01, Westerburg-98, Maersk La Plata-98, Westerburg-97

IMO	name	flag	year	gt	dwt	loa	bm	kts	type	comments
9137698	Westerhamm	Deu	1998	23,986	30,259	188	30	21	ucc	2,064 teu: ex Cala Paradiso-08, DAL Karoo-04, Westerhamm-02, Actor-01, Westerhamm-99
9240328	Westerland	Cyp	2002	30,047	35,768	208	32	22	ucc	2,764 teu: ex CSAV Mexico-11, Westerland-05, Alianca Hamburgo-03
9222106	Westermoor	Lbr	2001	30,047	35,653	208	32	22	ucc	2,764 teu: ex NileDutch Springbok-14, Westermoor-12

managed by Hans Peterson & Söhne GmbH & Co KG, Germany (formed 1984).

Rickmers Reederei GmbH & Cie. KG Germany

funnel: *black with houseflag (white 'R' on red over green) on broad white band, or charterers colours.* **hull:** *green or black with white 'RICKMERS', red boot-topping or charterer's colours.* **history:** *founded 1889 as Rickmers Reismuhlen Rhederei & Schiffbau AG, became Reederei Bertram Rickmers GmbH to 1992. Rickmers Linie sold to Hapag Lloyd in 1988 and re-acquired 2000. Acquired CCNI (Deutschland) GmbH (formed 1999) from Compania Chilena de Navegacion Interoceanica in 2004.* **web:** *www.rickmers.com or www.rickmers-linie.de*

IMO	name	flag	year	gt	dwt	loa	bm	kts	type	comments
9289972	Agnes Rickmers	Lbr	2005	54,214	68,017	294	32	24	ucc	5,060 teu: ex Maersk Daesan-13
9152739	Alexandra Rickmers	Lbr	1997	26,131	30,781	195	30	20	ucc	2,226 teu: ex CP London-06, Contship London-05, Alexandra Rickmers-97
9324837	ANL Warringa *	Mhl	2007	39,906	50,629	260	32	24	ucc	4,250 teu: ex Vicki Rickmers-07
9287900	Augusta Kontor	Mhl	2004	54,214	68,187	294	32	24	ucc	5,060 teu: ex Charlotte-14, Charlotte C. Rickmers-14, Maersk Douala-10
9151917	Barrier	Pmd	1998	11,925	14,381	150	23	18	ucc	1,104 teu: ex Marine Rickmers-15, P&O Nedlloyd Mahe-05, Marine Rickmers-02, Fanal Mariner-01, Marine Rickmers-99
9222120	Cap Breton *	Sgp	2001	26,582	33,871	210	30	22	ucc	2,556 teu: ex Spirit of Tokyo-14, MOL Inca-14, Cap Breton-12, Christiane Schulte-07, Elisabeth Schulte-01
9448140	Cary Rickmers +	Mhl	2010	47,090	12,300	183	32	20	mve	4,900 ceu
9236523	Cathrine Rickmers §	Lbr	2002	51,364	58,341	286	32	25	ucc	4,444 teu: ex Norasia Valparaiso-09, Cathrine Rickmers-02
9324851	CMA CGM Azure †	Sgp	2007	39,906	50,629	260	32	24	ucc	3,853 teu
9679892	CMA CGM Congo *	Sgp	2015	102,931	115,682	300	48	24	ucc	9,300 teu: c/a R. C. Rickmers, I/a FD Patrizia d'Amato
9324875	CMA CGM Jade *	Mhl	2007	39,906	50,769	267	32	24	ucc	3,853 teu: I/a Sabine Rickmers
9679907	CMA CGM Mississippi *	Sgp	2015	102,931	115,682	300	48	24	ucc	9,300 teu: c/a Peter Rickmers, I/a FD Umberto d'Amato
9679919	CMA CGM Missouri	Sgp	2016	102,931	115,682	300	48	24	ucc	9,300 teu: I/d FD Jacopo d'Amato
9334143	CMA CGM Onyx *	Sgp	2007	39,906	50,770	267	32	24	ucc	3,853 teu: I/a Erwin Rickmers
9431692	Hanjin Duesseldorf	Mhl	2009	40,542	50,591	261	32	24	ucc	4,250 teu: I/a Tanja Rickmers
9431680	Hanjin Milano	Mhl	2009	40,542	50,506	261	32	24	ucc	4,250 teu: I/a Sui Tai Rickmers
9431707	Hanjin Montevideo	Mhl	2010	40,542	50,497	261	32	24	ucc	4,250 teu: I/a Schliemi Rickmers
9404194	Hanjin Newport	Mhl	2009	40,542	50,574	261	32	24	ucc	4,250 teu: I/a India Rickmers
9308003	Henry Rickmers **	Mhl	2006	36,483	42,822	239	32	23	ucc	3,450 teu: ex Ital Fastosa-14
9469912	Hyundai Antwerp	Mhl	2011	23,265	30,175	193	28	19	ghl	cr: 2(320),1(100): I/a Rickmers Busan
9469900	Hyundai Dubai	Mhl	2011	23,265	30,104	193	28	19	ghl	cr: 2(320),1(100): I/a Rickmers Inchon
9469883	Hyundai Masan	Mhl	2010	23,265	30,135	193	28	19	ghl	cr: 2(320),1(100): I/a Rickmers Masan
9469895	Hyundai Ulsan	Mhl	2011	23,265	30,162	193	28	19	ghl	cr: 2(320),1(100): ex Rickmers Savannah-15, Hyundai Ulsan-13, I/a Rickmers Pohang
9681833	Industrial Glory	Mhl	2015	18,410	19,410	171	25	15	ggc	
9320051	Isao	Lbr	2006	27,971	37,934	222	30	21	ucc	2,700 teu: ex Stadt Weimar-14, CCNI Atlantico-13, Stadt Weimar-12, CCNI Atlantico-12, Stadt Weimar-11
9300166	Jacob Rickmers	Mhl	2006	21,971	24,069	196	28	23	ucc	1,858 teu: ex CMA CGM Anapurna-14, I/a Jacob Rickmers
9300154	John Rickmers	Mhl	2006	21,971	24,084	196	28	23	ucc	1,850 teu: ex CMA CGM Everest-11, I/a John Rickmers
9337028	Jona	Pmd	2007	23,666	28,325	191	29	20	ucc	2,007 teu: ex Rio Stora-13, CMA CGM Togo-12, Rio Stora-07
9289960	Juliette Rickmers	Lbr	2005	54,214	68,187	294	32	24	ucc	5,060 teu: ex Maersk Davao-12
9287912	Kaethe C. Rickmers	*Mhl	2004	54,214	68,282	294	32	24	ucc	5,060 teu: Maersk Djibouti-10, I/a Kaethe C. Rickmers
9330537	Keno	Pmd	2007	28,616	39,462	222	30	21	ucc	2,824 teu: ex Annina Schulte-12 Cap Beatrice-11, Annina Schulte-07
9324863	Laranna Rickmers *	Sgp	2007	39,906	50,629	260	32	24	ucc	4,250 teu: ex ANL Warrain-15, CMA CGM Purple-08
9456757	Maersk Edinburgh	Mhl	2010	141,716	142,105	366	48	24	ucc	13,092 teu: I/d Pearl Rickmers
9458030	Maersk Edmonton	Mhl	2011	141,716	142,105	366	48	24	ucc	13,092 teu
9456771	Maersk Eindhoven	Mhl	2010	141,716	142,105	366	48	24	ucc	13,092 teu: I/d Aqua Rickmers

IMO	name	flag	year	gt	dwt	loa	bm	kts	type	comments
9458078	Maersk Elba	Mhl	2011	141,716	142,105	366	48	24	ucc	13,092 teu
9456769	Maersk Emden	Mhl	2010	141,716	142,105	366	48	24	ucc	13,092 teu: l/d Ruby Rickmers
9456783	Maersk Essen	Mhl	2010	141,716	142,105	366	48	24	ucc	13,092 teu: l/d Cocanee Rickmers
9458092	Maersk Essex	Mhl	2011	141,716	142,105	366	48	24	ucc	13,092 teu
9694567	Maersk Euphrates	Mhl	2014	51,872	65,165	255	37	20	ucc	5,466 teu: l/a Wide Echo
9458080	Maersk Evora	Mhl	2011	141,716	142,105	366	48	24	ucc	13,092 teu
9694555	Maersk Indus	Mhl	2014	51,872	65,157	255	37	20	ucc	5,466 teu: l/a Wide Delta
9694593	Maersk Lomé	Mhl	2014	51,872	62,292	255	37	20	ucc	5,466 teu: l/a Wide Hotel
9698264	Maersk Tema	Mhl	2014	51,872	65,347	255	37	20	ucc	5,466 teu: l/a Wide Juliet
9287924	Margrit Rickmers	Lbr	2005	54,214	68,187	294	32	24	ucc	5,060 teu: ex Maersk Dhaka-10, l/a Margrit Rickmers
9324849	Maja Rickmers *	Mhl	2007	39,906	50,769	260	32	24	ucc	4,250 teu: ex ANL Windarra-16, Maja Rickmers-07
9352391	MOL Dedication **	Mhl	2008	39,906	50,629	260	32	24	ucc	3,853 teu: l/a Sui An Rickmers
9352406	MOL Delight *	Mhl	2008	39,906	50,600	260	32	24	ucc	4,853 teu: l/a Pingel Rickmers
9352418	MOL Destiny **	Lbr	2008	39,906	50,638	260	32	24	ucc	3,853 teu: ex Ebba Rickmers-09
9352420	MOL Devotion **	Mhl	2009	39,906	50,596	260	32	24	ucc	3,853 teu: ex Clan Rickmers-09
9478494	MOL Dominance **	Mhl	2008	39,906	50,629	260	32	24	ucc	3,853 teu: l/a Olympia Rickmers
9308027	Moni Rickmers	Mhl	2007	36,483	42,822	239	32	23	ucc	3,450 teu: ex Ital Fiducia-15, l/a Moni Rickmers
9236547	MSC Florida	Mhl	2005	51,364	58,287	286	32	25	ucc	4,425 teu: l/a Maya Rickmers
9160396	Patricia Rickmers	Pmd	1998	26,131	30,781	196	30	19	ucc	2,226 teu: ex CMA CGM Buenos Aires-13, Patricia Rickmers-06, Contship Auckland-05, l/a Patricia Rickmers
9287895	Pinehurst Kontor	Lbr	2004	54,214	68,187	294	32	24	ucc	5,060 teu: ex Jennifer Rickmers-14, Maersk Durban-10, l/dn Jennifer Rickmers
9308015	Richard Rickmers **	Sgp	2006	36,483	42,822	239	32	23	ucc	3,450 teu: ex Ital Festosa-14
9253143	Rickmers Antwerp §	Mhl	2003	23,119	29,912	193	28	19	ghl	cr: 2(320),1(100) ex Cape Dart-02
9292022	Rickmers Dalian	Lbr	2004	23,119	29,827	193	28	19	ghl	cr: 2(320),1(120),1(100) ex Rickmers Genoa-05
9238818	Rickmers Hamburg §	Mhl	2002	23,119	29,980	193	28	19	ghl	cr: 2(320),1(100)
9292010	Rickmers Jakarta	Mhl	2004	23,119	29,750	193	28	19	ghl	cr: 2(320),1(100) : l/d Genoa
9253155	Rickmers New Orleans	Mhl	2003	23,119	29,878	193	28	19	ghl	cr: 2(320),1(100)
9244556	Rickmers Seoul	Mhl	2003	23,119	30,151	193	28	19	ghl	cr: 2(320),1(100)
9238820	Rickmers Singapore	Mhl	2002	23,119	30,018	193	28	19	ghl	cr: 2(320),1(100)
9244544	Rickmers Shanghai §	Mhl	2003	23,119	30,095	193	28	19	ghl	cr: 2(320),1(100)
9235995	Rickmers Tokyo §	Mhl	2002	23,119	29,827	193	28	19	ghl	cr: 2(320),1(100) ex Cape Delgardo-02
9236444	Robert Rickmers §	Mhl	2003	16,801	23,063	185	25	19	ucc	1,730 teu: ex Ninghai-15, Tasman Campaigner-12, Robert Rickmers-08, E.R. Stettin-03
9220079	Sandy Rickmers *	Mhl	2002	14,290	14,901	159	26	22	ucc	1,216 teu: ex OOCL Moscow-09, Sandy Rickmers-07, l/a Mirko Rickmers
9360752	Spirit of Auckland *	Sgp	2007	41,483	53,125	254	32	21	ucc	3,630 teu: ex Bahia-13
9197349	Spirit of Bangkok *	Mhl	1999	16,986	21,184	168	27	20	ucc	1,620 teu: ex Sean Rickmers-13, Delmas Zambia-09, Sean Rickmers-08, Kindia-04, Indamex Kindia-03, Kindia-02
9178290	Spirit of Cape Town *	Sgp	2000	26,047	30,703	196	30	20	ucc	2262 teu; ex Alva Rickmers-14, AS Asturia-13, CSAV Rio Rapel-09, Asturia-04, Comanche-03, Ocelot Max-02
9178288	Spirit of Colombo *	Sgp	2000	26,044	30,703	196	30	21	ucc	2,262 teu; ex Alina Rickmers-14, Aquitania-13, Maersk Aquitania-03, Corrado-03, Lion Max-02
9391660	Spirit of Hamburg *	Sgp	2007	41,483	53,139	254	32	21	ucc	3,630 teu: ex Bahia Laura-13
9431800	Spirit of Lisbon	Mhl	2010	40,541	50,249	261	32	24	ucc	4,250 teu: ex Joseph Conrad-16, CSAV Llanquihue-15, l/a Joseph Conrad
9204972	Spirit of Manila *	Sgp	2000	26,047	30,554	196	30	20	ucc	2,262 teu; ex Angie Rickmers-14, AS Alicantia-13, Safmarine Illovo-10, Alicantia-05, Commander-03, Jaguar Max-02
9362413	Spirit of Melbourne *	Sgp	2007	41,483	53,176	254	32	21	ucc	3,630 teu: ex Bahia Grande-14

IMO	name	flag	year	gt	dwt	loa	bm	kts	type	comments
9178276	Spirit of Mumbai *	Sgp	1999	26,047	30,703	196	30	20	ucc	2,262 teu; ex Amiko Rickmers-13, Columbus Australia-05, Cherokee-03, Panthermax-02, CanMar Supreme-02, Panther Max-01
9204984	Spirit of Piraeus *	Sgp	2001	26,047	30,703	196	30	20	ucc	2262 teu; ex Akki Rickmers-14, AS Andalusia-13, Marfret Provence-10, AS Andalusia-08, Safmarine Mono-08, Andalusia-04, Centurion-03, Puma Max-02
9362401	Spirit of Shanghai *	Sgp	2007	41,483	53,160	254	32	21	ucc	3,630 teu: ex Bahia Castillo-13
9362396	Spirit of Singapore *	Sgp	2007	41,483	53,094	254	32	21	ucc	3,630 teu: ex Bahia Blanca -13
9391672	Spirit of Sydney *	Sgp	2007	41,483	53,152	254	32	21	ucc	3,630 teu: ex Bahia Negra-13, CCNI Shenzhen-08. c/a Bahia Negra
9448138	Vany Rickmers +	Mhl	2010	47,090	12,300	183	32	20	mve	4,900 ceu
9694529	Wide Alpha	Mhl	2014	51,872	65,152	255	37	20	ucc	5,466 teu
9694531	Wide Bravo	Mhl	2014	51,872	65,347	255	37	20	ucc	5,466 teu
9694543	Wide Charlie	Mhl	2014	51,872	65,193	255	37	20	ucc	5,466 teu
9698252	Wide India	Mhl	2014	51,872	62,292	255	37	20	ucc	5,466 teu
9160413	Willi §‡	Mhl	1998	26,125	30,738	196	30	19	ucc	2,226 teu: ex Willi Rickmers-13, Sea Puma-06, Crowley Lion-01, CSAV Boston-99, l/a Willi Rickmers

Rigel Schiffahrts GmbH & Co. KG　　　　　　　　Germany

funnel: *blue with black 'R' on six-pointed white star on red disc on broad white band.* **hull:** *blue with red boot-topping.* **history:** *formed 1990.* **web:** *www.rigel-hb.com*

IMO	name	flag	year	gt	dwt	loa	bm	kts	type
9053220	Alsterstern　*	Can	1994	11,426	17,080	161	23	15	tco
9053218	Havelstern　*	Can	1994	11,423	17,080	161	23	14	tco
9105140	Isarstern	Iom	1995	11,426	17,078	161	23	14	tco
9411989	Orinoco Star	Iom	2009	23,312	37,872	184	25	14	tco
9183831	Rhonestern	iom	2000	14,400	21,871	162	27	15	tco
9183843	Themsestern	Iom	2000	14,400	21,871	162	27	15	tco
9053206	Travestern	Iom	1993	11,423	17,080	161	23	15	tco
9183829	Weichselstern	Iom	1999	14,331	21,950	162	27	15	tco

Spirit of Hamburg : Rickmers Reederei : *Hans Kraijenbosch*

IMO	name	flag	year	gt	dwt	loa	bm	kts	type	comments
9183817	Wolgastern	Iom	1999	14,331	21,950	162	27	15	tco	
9411991	Yukon Star	Iom	2009	23,312	37,873	184	25	14	tco	
9412000	Zambezi Star	Iom	2010	23,312	37,874	184	25	14	tco	

also operate smaller tankers: * vessels owned by Coastal Shipping Ltd., Canada

RollDock Shipping b.v. Netherlands

funnel: *light blue with narrow black top,* **hull:** *light blue with 'ROLLDOCK' in white, red boot topping* **history:** *founded 2006*
web: *www.rolldock.com*

IMO	name	flag	year	gt	dwt	loa	bm	kts	type	comments
9404704	RollDock Sea	Nld	2011	12,802	6,879	141	24	16	ohl	cr: 2(350)
9656498	RollDock Star	Nld	2013	15,392	9,161	152	25	17	ohl	cr: 2(350)
9656503	RollDock Storm	Nld	2014	15,392	9,161	152	25	17	ohl	cr: 2(350)
9393981	RollDock Sun	Nld	2010	12,802	6,959	141	24	16	ohl	cr: 2(350)

Ernst Russ GmbH & Co. KG Germany

funnel: *black with red 'ER' and 5-pointed star between narrow red bands on broad white band or charterers colours.* **hull:** *black with red boot-topping.* **history:** *formed 1893, trading as Ernst Russ to 1992.* **web:** *www.ernst-russ.de*

IMO	name	flag	year	gt	dwt	loa	bm	kts	type	comments
9477359	Jamila	Lbr	2010	16,137	17,152	161	25	19	ucc	1,350 teu
9477335	Jan	Lbr	2009	16,137	17,121	161	25	19	ucc	1,350 teu
9477347	Jost	Lbr	2010	16,137	17,157	161	25	19	ucc	1,350 teu
9477294	Juliana	Lbr	2009	16,137	17,197	161	25	19	ucc	1,350 teu
9470882	Paul Russ	Atg	2010	16,137	17,230	161	25	19	ucc	1,338 teu
9470894	Tillie Russ	Atg	2010	16,137	17,142	161	25	19	ucc	1,350 teu: ex MCC Davao-13, Tillie Russ-10

also operates ro-ro vessels in European coastal trades.

Saga-Welco A/S Norway

funnel: *black with white outlined dark blue and turquoise 'S' on dark blue above turquoise bands.* **hull:** *orange or grey with black 'SAGA', red boot-topping.* **history:** *pool formed 2014 for the commercial management of a the fleets of Saga Forest Carriers, Attic Forest AS and Masterbulk division of Westfal-Larsen.* **web:** *www.sagafc.com*

Saga Forest Carriers International AS, Norway

funnel: *black with white outlined dark blue and turquoise 'S' on dark blue above turquoise bands.* **hull:** *orange or grey with black 'SAGA', red boot-topping.* **history:** *original pool formed 1991 by NYK with Aaby and Borgestad, who sold to Hesnes Group in 1995. Leif Höegh joined in 2002 but left in 2009 whilst Attic Forest joined the pool in 2009.* **web:** *www.sagafc.com*

Rolldock Star : Rolldock Shipping b.v. : *Roy Fenton*

IMO	name	flag	year	gt	dwt	loa	bm	kts	type	comments
9317406	Saga Adventure	Hkg	2005	29,758	46,627	199	31	15	goh	
9197002	Saga Andorinha **	Gbr	1998	29,729	47,027	199	31	15	goh	ex Andorinha-01
9160798	Saga Beija-Flor	Hkg	1997	29,729	47,029	199	31	14	goh	ex Beija-Flor-03
9014066	Saga Crest ‡	Hkg	1994	29,381	47,069	199	31	15	goh	
9317418	Saga Discovery	Hkg	2006	29,758	46,618	199	31	15	goh	
9343481	Saga Enterprise ‡	Hkg	2006	29,758	46,550	199	31	15	goh	
9343493	Saga Explorer †	Hkg	2006	29,758	46,589	199	31	15	goh	
9613848	Saga Falcon	Hkg	2012	37,499	55,596	200	32	15	goh	
9658953	Saga Fantasy	Hkg	2013	37,441	55,973	200	32	15	goh	
9613862	Saga Fjord	Hkg	2012	37,499	55,596	200	32	15	goh	
9644524	Saga Fortune	Hkg	2012	37,441	56,023	200	32	15	goh	
9613874	Saga Fram	Hkg	2013	37,499	54,940	200	32	15	goh	
9613850	Saga Frigg	Hkg	2013	37,499	55,596	200	32	15	goh	
9343510	Saga Frontier	Hkg	2007	29,758	46,500	199	31	15	goh	
9609457	Saga Fuji ‡	Hkg	2013	37,441	56,023	200	32	15	goh	
9613836	Saga Future	Hkg	2012	37,499	55,596	200	32	15	goh	
9121297	Saga Horizon	Hkg	1995	29,381	47,016	199	31	15	goh	
9200421	Saga Jandaia	Hkg	1998	29,729	47,016	199	31	15	goh	ex Jandaia-01
9363637	Saga Journey	Hkg	2007	29,758	46,652	199	31	15	goh	
9117739	Saga Monal *	Bhs	1996	36,463	49,755	200	32	16	goh	ex Höegh Monal-04, Saga Challenger-02
9117741	Saga Morus *	Bhs	1997	36,463	56,801	200	32	16	goh	ex Höegh Morus-04
9371062	Saga Navigator	Hkg	2007	29,758	46,673	199	31	15	goh	
9401788	Saga Odyssey	Hkg	2008	29,758	46,500	199	31	15	goh	
9380764	Saga Pioneer	Hkg	2008	29,758	46,627	199	31	15	goh	
9144354	Saga Sky	Hkg	1996	29,381	47,053	199	31	15	goh	
9014078	Saga Spray ‡	Hkg	1994	29,381	47,029	199	31	15	goh	
8918277	Saga Tide	Hkg	1991	29,235	57,471	199	31	15	goh	
9160803	Saga Tucano	Hkg	1998	29,729	47,032	199	31	14	goh	ex Tucano-01
9233466	Saga Viking ‡	Hkg	2002	29,867	46,500	199	31	14	goh	
9233454	Saga Voyager †	Hkg	2001	29,872	46,882	199	31	14	goh	
8918289	Saga Wave	Hkg	1991	29,235	47,062	199	31	15	goh	
9074078	Saga Wind	Hkg	1994	29,381	47,053	199	31	15	goh	
newbuildings:										
9502336		Hkg	2017	31,900	52,000				goh	Oshima 10631
9502348		Hkg	2017	31,900	52,000				goh	Oshima 10632

*vessels owned by Saga Shipholding (Norway) AS, † owned by Navire Shg. Co. * owned by Attic Forest AS, Norway (formed 2006) ** by Denholm Line Steamers Ltd, UK (formed 1909, parent J&J Denholm Ltd founded 1866), ‡ owned by NYK companies, vessels managed by Anglo-Eastern Ship Management Ltd, Hong Kong (China),*

Masterbulk Pte. Ltd., Singapore

funnel / hull *as above* **history:** *fomed July 1995 as spin-off from Westfal-Larsen. Vessels operated in open-hatch pool, Saga-Welco AS, formed between Saga Forest Carriers and Westfal-Larsen during 2014* **web:** *www.masterbulk.com.sg*

8507200	Geiranger	Sgp	1986	27,972	43,131	200	29	15	goh	ex Star Geiranger-09
8507212	Grindanger	Sgp	1986	27,972	43,131	201	29	15	goh	ex Star Grindanger-09
9079119	Hardanger	Sgp	1995	34,364	44,251	199	31	16	goh	ex Star Hardanger-09
9079121	Heranger	Sgp	1995	37,150	44,251	199	31	16	goh	ex Star Heranger-08

Saga Discovery : Saga-Welco AS : *Hans Kraijenbosch*

IMO	name	flag	year	gt	dwt	loa	bm	kts	type	comments
9081801	Hosanger	Sgp	1995	37,150	44,251	199	31	16	goh	ex Star Hosanger-08
9100073	Hoyanger	Sgp	1995	34,363	44,251	199	31	16	goh	ex Star Hoyanger-09
9186209	Ikebana	Sgp	1999	30,840	39,751	185	31	16	goh	ex Star Ikebana-09
9186211	Indiana	Sgp	2000	30,745	39,760	185	31	16	goh	ex Star Indiana-09
9186223	Inventana	Sgp	2000	30,745	39,789	185	31	16	goh	ex Star Inventana-09
9186235	Isoldana	Sgp	2000	30,745	39,465	185	31	16	goh	ex Star Isoldana-09
9189938	Mariana	Iom	1998	29,688	50,655	195	32	14	bbu	ex Sanko Spring-11
9189940	Mobilana	Iom	1998	29,688	50,655	195	32	14	bbu	ex Sanko Stream-11
9253868	Okiana	Iom	2003	38,910	54,241	213	32	16	goh	ex Star Okiana-09, (len-14)
9253856	Optimana	Sgp	2003	36,324	48,661	199	32	16	goh	ex Star Optimana-09
9253870	Osakana	Iom	2004	38,910	54,241	213	32	16	goh	ex Star Osakana-09, (len-14)
9249295	Oshimana	Sgp	2003	36,324	48,661	199	32	16	goh	ex Star Oshimana-07
9401805	Panamana	Sgp	2010	39,258	54,694	213	32	15	goh	
9401790	Pelicana	Sgp	2009	39,258	54,694	213	32	15	goh	
9371086	Posidana	Sgp	2008	39,258	54,694	213	32	15	goh	
9380788	Providana	Sgp	2007	39,258	54,694	213	32	15	goh	

Reederei H. Schepers Bereederungs GmbH & Co. KG

Germany

funnel: *black with black 'S' on red diamond on white band, black top.* **hull:** *dark blue with red boot-topping.* **history:** *Formed 1997, formerly trading as Reederei Heinrich und Rudolf Schepers until 1962, late Tim Schepers und Söhne until 1987* : **web:** *www.hschepers.de*

IMO	name	flag	year	gt	dwt	loa	bm	kts	type	comments
9517434	Arian	Atg	2011	16,137	17,159	161	25	18	ucc	1,350 teu: ex Mell Seringat-14, Arian-11
9456238	Christoph S	Atg	2011	32,987	56,770	190	32	14	bbu	
9325441	Constantin S	Atg	2006	27,191	33,216	200	32	22	ucc	2,483 teu
9232400	Harald S	Atg	2002	25,370	33,742	207	30	22	ucc	2,478 teu: ex Libra Salvador-09, Montemar Salvador-04, NYK Pasion-04, Montemar Salvador-03, I/a Harald S
9158513	Heinrich S	Deu	1998	25,624	33,914	207	30	20	ucc	2,478 teu: ex NileDutch Cape Town-15, CCNI Cartagena-11, Heinrich S-06, Zim Singapore I-02, I/a Heinrich S
9349368	Helene S	Atg	2006	27,213	32,878	200	32	22	ucc	2,483 teu
9259381	Jandavid S	Atg	2003	27,227	33,232	200	32	22	ucc	2,483 teu: ex CSAV Shenzhen-06, Jandavid S-03
9153393	Kerstin S	Deu	1997	25,361	33,936	207	30	21	ucc	2,478 teu: ex Valparaiso Express-08, P&O Nedlloyd Pantanal-05, Kerstin S-97
9456173	Kilian S	Atg	2011	32,987	56,793	190	32	14	bbu	
9429326	Maria-Katharina S	Atg	2010	26,435	34,333	209	30	22	ucc	2,500 teu
9517422	Tammo	Atg	2011	16,137	17,192	161	25	19	ucc	1,350 teu: ex Mell Springwood-15,Tammo-11

also operates 5 feeder vessels of around 1,100teu

Reederei Rudolf Schepers GmbH & Co. KG

Germany

funnel: *black with black 'S' on red diamond on white band, black top.* **hull:** *dark blue with red boot-topping.* **history:** *formed 1994, formerly trading as Reederei Heinrich und Rudolf Schepers until 1962, later Tim Schepers und Söhne until 1987.* **web:** *www.reederei-schepers.com*

IMO	name	flag	year	gt	dwt	loa	bm	kts	type	comments
9303766	Adelheid-S	Atg	2006	35,581	44,053	223	32	22	ucc	3,398 teu: ex Emirates Wasl-12, TS Dammam-09, Emirates Wasl-08, Adelheid S-06, Hanjin Pusan-03
9383223	Anna-S	Atg	2008	26,435	34,362	209	30	22	ucc	2,546 teu: ex TS Jakarta-13, Emirates Norika-09, I/a Anna S
9525950	Annette-S	Atg	2014	26,374	34,376	209	30	22	ucc	2,546 teu
9359260	Christopher	Atg	2008	16,023	20,073	170	25	19	ucc	1,440 teu
9418652	Elisabeth-S	Atg	2009	40,541	50,269	261	32	24	ucc	4,256 teu: ex CSAV Lanalhue-14
9456123	Hermann-S	Atg	2009	32,987	56,721	190	32	14	bbu	
9376141	Johannes S.	Atg	2008	26,435	34,331	209	30	22	ucc	2,546 teu: ex TS Pusan-14, I/a Johannes S
9294018	Julius S	Deu	2004	25,630	33,390	207	30	21	ucc	2,478 teu: ex CMA CGM Brasilia-10, I/a Julius S
9219343	Katharina S	Atg	2001	35,645	42,211	220	32	22	ucc	3,108 teu: ex CSAV Paranagua-09, Norasia Everest-06, APL Venezuela-04, I/a Carolina, I/dn Camilla
9525948	Katrin-S.	Atg	2014	26,734	34,409	209	30	22	ucc	2,546 teu
9431757	Lena-S	Atg	2010	40,542	50,246	261	32	24	ucc	4,256 teu: ex APL Indonesia-15
9219381	Louis S	Atg	2003	35,881	41,850	220	32	22	ucc	3,091 teu: ex Libra Santos-12, Patricia-04, Amasia-03, I/a Cyrill

IMO	name	flag	year	gt	dwt	loa	bm	kts	type	comments
9456147	Mia-S	Alt	2010	32,987	56,835	190	32	14	bbu	
9153381	Michaela S	Atg	1997	25,361	33,976	207	30	21	ucc	2,478 teu: ex MSC Cristobal-09, Maersk Nantes-07, Michaela S-04, Contship Spirit-03, Michaela S-97
9431719	Rudolf Schepers	Atg	2009	40,541	50,300	261	32	24	ucc	4,256 teu
9431769	Sri Lanka	Atg	2010	40,541	50,264	261	32	24	ucc	4,256 teu: ex APL Sri Lanka-14, c/a Bernard-S
9232412	Thea S	Atg	2002	25,630	33,501	207	30	22	ucc	2,478 teu: ex NileDutch Shanghai-13, Thea S-10, CSAV Rio Petrohue-09, Safmarine Kei-04, Thea S-02
9303742	Tim-S.	Atg	2005	35,581	44,135	223	32	22	ucc	3,398 teu: ex Emirates Excellence-11, CMA CGM Excellence-09, l/dn Tim S

Schöller Holdings Ltd.   Cyprus

Columbia Shipmanagement Ltd., Cyprus

funnel: buff or white with blue 'CSM' on broad red band edged with narrow blue bands or charteres colours. **hull:** green, red or black with red boot-topping, AAL vessels, green with 'Austral Asia Line' in white. **history:** formed 1978. **web:** www.schoeller-holdings.com

IMO	name	flag	year	gt	dwt	loa	bm	kts	type	comments
9521564	AAL Bangkok **	Sgp	2012	14,053	18,603	149	23	14	ghl	cr: 2(350)
9498341	AAL Brisbane	Mhl	2010	23,930	32,311	194	28	16	ghl	cr: 2(350), 1(100)
9498470	AAL Dalian	Mhl	2013	23,930	31,000	194	28	16	ghl	cr: 2(350), 1(100)
9521540	AAL Dampier **	Sgp	2011	14,053	18,707	149	23	14	ghl	cr: 2(350)
9521095	AAL Fremantle **	Sgp	2011	14,053	18,763	149	23	14	ghl	cr: 2(350): l/a AAL Bali
9498468	AAL Hong Kong	Mhl	2013	23,930	32,124	194	28	16	ghl	cr: 2(350), 1(100)
9498353	AAL Kembla	Mhl	2011	23,930	31,000	194	28	16	ghl	cr: 2(350), 1(100)
9498444	AAL Kobe	Mhl	2012	23,930	32,043	194	28	16	ghl	cr: 2(350), 1(100): ex Hyundai Seoul-14, l/a AAL Kobe
9498456	AAL Melbourne	Mhl	2013	23,930	32,128	194	28	16	ghl	cr: 2(350), 1(100): ex Hyundai Incheon14, l/a AAL Melbourne
9521552	AAL Nanjing **	Sgp	2012	14,053	18,697	149	23	14	ghl	cr: 2(350)
9498482	AAL Newcastle	Mhl	2014	23.930	32,241	194	28	16	ghl	cr: 2(350), 1(100)
9498389	AAL Pusan	Mhl	2012	23,930	32,279	194	28	16	ghl	cr: 2(350), 1(100)
9498377	AAL Shanghai	Mhl	2012	23,930	32,106	194	28	16	ghl	cr: 2(350), 1(100)
9498365	AAL Singapore	Mhl	2011	23,930	32,134	194	28	16	ghl	cr: 2(350), 1(100)
9253909	Astra †	Mhl	2002	79,525	149,995	272	46	15	tcr	
9187239	Cape Balder *	Mhl	2000	81,093	159,998	274	48	15	tcr	ex Hudson-06, Front Sun-03
9347712	Cape Faro	Mhl	2006	15,995	20,316	170	25	19	ucc	1,440 teu
9379363	Cape Fawley	Mhl	2008	15,995	20,358	170	25	19	ucc	1,440 teu
9379375	Cape Felton	Mhl	2008	15,995	20,351	170	25	19	ucc	1,440 teu
9359325	Cape Ferrol	Mhl	2008	15,995	20,346	170	25	19	ucc	1,400 teu
9347724	Cape Flint	Mhl	2006	15,995	20,312	170	25	19	ucc	1,440 teu
9324162	Cape Flores	Mhl	2005	14,308	16,393	155	25	18	ucc	1,221 teu: ex TS Ningbo-08, MOL Assurance-07, Cape Flores-05
9356842	Cape Forby	Mhl	2006	15,995	20,308	170	25	19	ucc	1,440 teu
9359301	Cape Franklin	Mhl	2006	15,995	20,300	170	25	19	ucc	1,400 teu
9359313	Cape Fulmar	Mhl	2007	15,995	20,308	170	25	19	ucc	1,440 teu
9348900	Cape Magnus	Mhl	2008	28,007	37,570	222	30	22	ucc	2,742 teu: ex Salah Al Deen-09, Cape Magnus-08, l/a King Adam
9348857	Cape Mahon	Cyp	2007	28,007	37,570	222	30	22	ucc	2,742 teu: ex CSAV Teno-09, Cape Mahon-07, l/a King Aaron
9440150	Cape Male	Mhl	2009	35,878	41,411	212	32	22	ucc	2,758 teu: ex POS Sydney-11, Cape Male-10
9571313	Cape Manila	Mhl	2011	35,708	41,411	212	32	22	ucc	2,758 teu
9571325	Cape Marin	Mhl	2012	35,878	41,463	212	32	22	ucc	2,758 teu
9360271	Cape Mayor	Mhl	2007	28,007	37,909	222	30	22	ucc	2,742 teu: ex CSAV Tubal-09, Cape Mayor-07, l/a King Andrew
9445916	Cape Moss	Mhl	2011	35,878	41,411	212	32	22	ucc	2,758 teu
9436185	Cape Nabil **	Sgp	2010	18,257	23,550	175	27	20	ucc	1,740 teu
9401697	Cape Nassau **	Sgp	2010	18,326	23,328	175	27	20	ucc	1,740 teu
9401685	Cape Nati **	Sgp	2009	18,326	23,263	175	27	20	ucc	1,740 teu
9436173	Cape Nemo **	Sgp	2010	18,257	23,517	175	27	20	ucc	1,740 teu
9360245	Cape Martin	Cyp	2007	28,007	37,867	222	30	22	ucc	2,742 teu: ex CCNI Aquiles-14, Cape Martin-11, King Arthur-07
9259317	Fedor †	Mhl	2003	41,397	70,156	228	32	14	tco	ex Nidia-04
9360269	Fred	Cyp	2007	28,007	37,938	222	30	22	ucc	2,742 teu: ex King Alfred-12, ANL Birrong-12, King Alfred-10, CMA CGM Kepler-08, King Alfred-07
9299771	Kanpur	Lbr	2005	57,243	106,094	244	42	14	tcr	ex Alhasbar-06
9632818	Oriental Trader	Mhl	2012	33,032	57,000	190	32	14	bbu	
9334480	Vereina	Mhl	2008	16,418	27,112	166	27	14	bbu	ex Casanna-08

IMO	name	flag	year	gt	dwt	loa	bm	kts	type	comments
9253894	Voyager †	Mhl	2002	79,525	149,991	272	46	15	tcr	

newbuildings:
see also König & Cie KG, and associated companies Mercator Navigation and Marenave Schiffahrts AG
vessels managed by subsidiaries Columbia Shipmanagement Ltd., Cyprus (www.columbia.com.cy) or * by Columbia Shipmanagement
(Deutschland) GmbH or ** Columbia Shipmanagement (Singapore) Pte Ltd.
† for Salamon AG, Germany,
Also see Kristian Gerhard Jebsens Skipsrederei AS, Knutsen OAS Shipping AS and Rickmers Reederei GmbH & Cie KG.

United Product Tanker (UPT) pool
funnel: *owners colours.* **hull:** *red with white 'UPT'.* **history:** *product tanker pool comprising Schöller Holdings/Columbia Shipmanagement, Hartmann/Donnelly Tanker Management, Conti Reederei, GEBAB, König & Cie, Salamon AG and Blackstone/Tufton* **web:** *www.uptankers.com*

IMO	name	flag	year	gt	dwt	loa	bm	kts	type	comments
9192741	Andreas	Pan	1999	23,843	35,966	183	27	14	tco	ex Atlantic Liguria-14, AS Liguria-12, Robin-12
9222168	Aikaterini	Pan	2001	23,740	35,769	183	27	14	tco	ex Atlantic Latvia-13, AS Latvia-12, Nordscot-09
9208100	Baltic Captain I	Cyp	2000	23,235	37,389	183	27	14	tco	ex Baltic Captain-02, I/a Androcles
9208124	Baltic Chief I	Cyp	2000	23,235	37,389	183	27	14	tco	ex Baltic Chief-01, Baltic Carrier-01, I/a Armodius
9261396	Baltic Sea I **	Cyp	2003	23,235	37,389	183	27	15	tco	ex Glacier Point-09, Baltic Sea-03
9264283	Cape Bacton	Mhl	2004	25,108	35,156	176	31	14	tco	ex Celebes Wind-05, Chabua Amiredjibi-05
9288928	Cape Beale *	Mhl	2005	25,108	40,327	176	31	14	tco	
9196119	Cape Beira	Mhl	2005	25,400	40,946	176	31	14	tco	ex Sable-05
9260067	Cape Bird *	Mhl	2003	25,108	35,070	176	31	14	tco	
9260055	Cape Bon	Mhl	2003	25,108	35,089	176	31	14	tco	
9264271	Cape Bradley	Mhl	2004	25,108	35,159	176	31	14	tco	ex J. Shartava-05
9302671	Cape Brasilia	Mhl	2006	25,108	40,227	176	32	14	tco	
9401221	Cape Taft	Mhl	2008	42,010	73,711	229	32	14	tco	
9569994	Cape Talara	Mhl	2010	42,010	73,371	229	32	14	tco	
9441154	Cape Tallin	Mhl	2008	42,010	73,711	229	32	14	tco	
9441166	Cape Tampa	Mhl	2009	42,010	73,719	229	32	14	tco	
9441180	Cape Tees	Mhl	2009	42,010	73,614	229	32	14	tco	
9441192	Cape Texel	Mhl	2009	42,010	73,766	229	32	14	tco	
9570008	Cape Troy	Mhl	2011	42,053	73,180	229	32	14	tco	
9311713	FSL Hamburg *	Sgp	2005	28,068	47,496	183	32	14	tco	ex Nika I-10, I/a Victoria I
9470985	Mount Everest ††	Lbr	2010	23,313	37,817	184	27	14	tco	
9470997	Mount Kibo ††	Lbr	2010	23,313	37,843	184	27	14	tco	
9306677	Sloman Themis +	Mhl	2006	22,184	34,628	171	27	14	tco	ex Handytankers Unity-11
9306653	Sloman Thetis +	Mhl	2006	22,184	34,662	171	27	14	tco	ex Handytankers Liberty-11
9550709	Summit Africa ††	Cyp	2009	42,010	73,427	229	32	14	tco	
9260263	SW Julia I	Pan	2003	25,108	40,246	176	31	14	tco	ex Cape Bille-15
9260275	SW Monaco I	Pan	2003	25,108	40,246	176	32	14	tco	ex Cape Bruny-15

Pool operated by Schöller Holdings Ltd. Vessels owned/managed by Schöller Holdings (managed by Columbia Shipmanagement (Deutschland) GmbH) * managed by Columbia Shipmanagement (Singapore), ** Columbia Shipmanagement Ltd., Cyprus or ‡ for 40% owned König & Cie KG, owned by + Sloman Neptun, † NSB/Conti or †† Donnelly Tanker Management Ltd, Cyprus (formed 1995 – www.donnellytanker.com.cy).

The Schulte Group   # Germany
funnel: *green with white 'S' on red disc and black top or charterer's colours.* **hull:** *dark grey with red boot-topping.* **history:** *formed 1937.* **web:** *www.beschulte.de or www.bs-shipmanagement.com*

IMO	name	flag	year	gt	dwt	loa	bm	kts	type	comments
9290529	ALM Crystal [H]	Mhl	2004	54,605	67,022	294	32	24	ucc	5,060 teu: ex Crystal-15, Maxine-14, APL Beijing-11
9282950	ALM Dallas [H]	Mhl	2004	54,592	67,170	294	32	24	ucc	5,060 teu: ex E.R. Dallas-15, Maersk Dallas-12, E.R. Dallas-04
9295359	ALM Vietnam [H]	Mhl	2005	54,605	67,025	294	32	24	ucc	5,060 teu: ex SCT Vietnam-15, ANL Whyalla-14, SCT Vietnam-14, APL Vietnam-12
9302554	ALM Wodonga [H]	Mhl	2006	54,214	68,080	294	32	24	ucc	5,060 teu: ex ANL Wodonga-15, SCT Chile-14, MSC Debra-11
9302580	ALM Zurich [H]	Mhl	2006	54,214	68,135	294	32	24	ucc	5,060 teu: ex SCT Zurich-15,MSC Olga-11
9296822	Angelica Schulte	Lbr	2005	56,163	106,433	243	42	14	tcr	
9398254	Anton Schulte [H]	Sgp	2009	75,582	85,836	304	40	25	ucc	6,966 teu: APL Colorado-14
9398230	Astrid Schulte [H]	Sgp	2009	75,582	85,824	304	40	25	ucc	6,966 teu: ex APL Illinois-14, I/a Astrid Schulte
9398242	Adrian Schulte [H]	Mlt	2009	75,582	85,735	304	40	25	ucc	6,966 teu: ex APL Tennessee-14
9231169	Auguste Schulte [H]	Lbr	2002	27,093	34,662	210	30	22	ucc	2,520 teu: ex CMA CGM Claudel-07, Claudel-02, I/a Alexandria, I/dn Auguste Schulte

IMO	name	flag	year	gt	dwt	loa	bm	kts	type	comments
9302944	Cap Bizerta [H]	Mlt	2006	26,671	34,457	210	30	21	ucc	2,602 teu; ex NileDutch Gazelle-14, Margarete Schulte-12, Cap Bizerta-11, Margarete Schulte-06
9484546	Cap Ines [H]	Hkg	2010	47,877	58,350	264	32	24	ucc	4,600 teu: I/a Bernhard Schulte
9484558	Cap Isabel [H]	Hkg	2010	47,877	58,350	264	32	24	ucc	4,600 teu: I/a Bea Schulte
9665683	Carl Schulte [H]	Sgp	2014	51,872	65,072	255	37	21	ucc	5,400 teu
9302956	Catharina Schulte [H]	Mlt	2006	26.671	34,629	210	30	21	ucc	2,556 teu: ex Cap Bon-12, I/a Catharina Schulte
9665657	Charlotte Schulte [H]	Sgp	2014	51,872	65,128	255	37	21	ucc	5,400 teu
9665669	Christa Schulte [H]	Sgp	2014	51,872	65,099	255	37	21	ucc	5,400 teu
9436458	Circular Quay [H]	Lbr	2009	35,991	42,035	210	30	21	ucc	3,554 teu: ex Gustav Schulte-14
9665671	Clemens Schulte [H]	Sgp	2014	51,872	65,193	255	37	21	ucc	5,400 teu
9439840	Elisabeth Schulte	Iom	2011	11,246	16,371	145	23	14	tch	
9439876	Elisalex Schulte	Sgp	2011	11,246	16,427	145	23	14	tch	
9394519	Emmy Schulte	Gbr	2009	11,233	16,669	145	23	14	tch	
9439864	Erika Schulte	Gbr	2011	11,246	16,427	145	23	14	tch	
9439814	Erin Schulte	Gbr	2009	11,233	16,716	145	23	14	tch	
9439826	Eva Schulte	Sgp	2011	11,233	16,621	145	23	14	tch	
9439838	Everhard Schulte	Sgp	2010	11,233	16,658	145	23	14	tch	
9439852	Edzard Schulte	Iom	2011	11,246	16,371	145	23	14	tch	
9247950	Friedrich Schulte [H]	Lbr	2002	35,589	40,995	232	32	22	ucc	3,277 teu: ex APL Sharjah-15, CMA CGM Chardin-07, Friedrich Schulte-02, CMA CGM Gauguin-02, I/a Friedrich Schulte
9328481	Gerhard Schulte [H]	Hkg	2006	35,991	42,083	231	32	23	ucc	3,554 teu: ex APL Bangkok-14, I/a Gerhard Schulte
9328493	Gottfried Schulte [H]	Hkg	2006	35,697	42,102	231	32	23	ucc	3,554 teu: APL Sydney-14, ex Gottfried Schulte-06
9436434	Guenther Schulte [H]	Hkg	2008	35,991	42,201	231	32	23	ucc	3,554 teu: ex Cap Manuel-13, I/a Guenther Schulte
9308429	Haydn	Pmd	2006	27,786	37,882	222	30	22	ucc	2,742 teu: ex Cape Mollini-14, CMA CGM Jefferson-08, Cape Molloni-06
9130171	Henrietta Schulte [H]	Lbr	1997	16,281	22,352	179	25	19	ucc	1,684 teu: ex Cap Rojo-08, Henriette Schulte-05, P&O Nedlloyd Lome-04, Fesco Voyager-02, Henriette Schulte-00, CSAV Brasilia-98, Henriette Schulte-97
9409314	Immanuel Schulte	Iom	2009	18,311	23,361	160	26	15	lpg	20,600 m³
9410624	Irmgard Schulte	Iom	2009	18,311	23,361	160	26	15	lpg	20,600 m³: ex Churun Meru-14, Irmgard Schulte-10
9155341	Johann Schulte	Iom	1998	15,180	17,914	155	23	16	lpg	16,500 m³
9161481	Joost Schulte [H]	Lbr	1997	26,040	45,874	188	31	14	bbu	ex May Oldendorff-09, Houyu-03
9292125	Konrad Schulte [H]	Cyp	2005	18,334	23,679	175	27	20	ucc	1,740 teu: ex Cap Maleas-09, Konrad Schulte-05, I/a Lambert Schulte
9102497	Lissy Schulte [H]	Lbr	1995	16,800	23,001	185	25	20	ucc	1,728 teu: ex P&O Nedlloyd Takoradi-04, Lissy Schulte-01, CSAV Rubens-98, Lissy Schulte-95
9435674	Louisa Schulte [H]	Sgp	2008	18.321	23,252	176	27	20	ucc	1,740 teu
9435686	Ludwig Schulte [H]	Sgp	2008	18,321	23,175	175	27	20	ucc	1,740 teu
9301938	Maersk Needham [H]	Sgp	2006	26,671	34,704	210	30	22	ucc	2,602 teu; ex Hannah Schulte-08
9301926	Maersk Norwich [H]	Sgp	2006	26,671	34,396	210	30	22	ucc	2,602 teu: I/a Lucie Schulte
9694438	Majestic [H]	Sgp	2015	27,279	30,136	189	30	19	ucc	2,345 teu
9694414	Mariner [H]	Sgp	2015	27,279	30,136	189	30	19	ucc	2,357 teu
9214525	Mary Schulte [H]	Lbr	2000	20,624	25,850	180	28	20	ucc	1,702 teu: ex Hua Yun He-10
9280586	Marylebone *	Mhl	2004	41,503	72,663	228	32	14	tco	ex Abram Schulte-15, I/a Penyu Pulan
9676709	Mathilde Schulte [H]	Sgp	2015	27,279	30,337	189	30	19	ucc	2,345 teu
9676711	Max Schulte [H]	Sgp	2015	27,279	30,235	189	30	19	ucc	2,345 teu
9676723	Melchior Schulte [H]	Sgp	2015	27,279	30,231	189	30	19	ucc	2,345 teu
9694402	Meridian [H]	Sgp	2015	27,279	30,084	189	30	19	ucc	2,345 teu
9676735	Mia Schulte [H]	Sgp	2015	27,279	30,235	189	30	19	ucc	2,345 teu
9694426	Minerva [H]	Sgp	2015	26,287	30,079	189	30	19	ucc	2,345 teu
9535163	MOL Glide [H]	Hkg	2011	59,307	71,339	275	40	23	ucc	5,605 teu: I/a Henrika Schulte
9531909	MOL Globe [H]	Hkg	2011	59,307	71,407	275	40	23	ucc	5,605 teu: I/a Hans Schulte
9535149	MOL Grandeur [H]	Hkg	2011	59,307	71,000	275	40	23	ucc	5,605 teu: I/a Hedwig Schulte
9535187	MOL Gratitude [H]	Hkg	2012	59,307	70,590	275	40	23	ucc	5,605 teu
9535204	MOL Growth [H]	Hkg	2012	59,176	71,339	275	40	23	ucc	5,605 teu
9403619	MOL Proficiency	Mhl	2007	71,777	72,912	293	40	25	ucc	6,350 teu
9605231	MSC Arbatax [H]	Hkg	2013	94,402	111,841	299	48	22	ucc	9,403 teu: I/a Johanna Schulte
9605243	MSC Algeciras [H]	Hkg	2013	94,402	111,000	299	48	22	ucc	9,403 teu: I/a Joseph Schulte
9605152	MSC Antalya [H]	Hkg	2013	94,402	111,862	299	48	22	ucc	9,403 teu: I/a Judith Schulte

IMO	name	flag	year	gt	dwt	loa	bm	kts	type	comments
9619464	MSC Agadir [H]	Hkg	2012	94,017	112,516	299	48	22	ucc	8,752 teu: l/a Joel Schulte
9619476	MSC Antigua [H]	Hkg	2013	94,017	112,516	299	48	22	ucc	8,752 teu: l/a Julius Schulte
9619452	MSC Arica [H]	Hkg	2012	94,017	112,516	299	48	22	ucc	8,752 teu: l/a Jacob Schulte
9034729	Nordic Gas	Sgp	1994	18,360	23,267	160	26	16	lpg	20,682 m³ ex Henriette Maersk-07
9487653	North Quay	Lbr	2010	33,044	57,000	190	32	14	bbu	ex Conti Opal-15
9576753	Rebecca Schulte	Sgp	2011	19,793	25,620	186	32	14	tch	
9576789	Reinhold Schulte	Sgp	2012	19,793	25,583	178	27	14	tch	
9576765	Rudolf Schulte	Sgp	2011	19,793	25,583	186	32	14	tch	
9456965	Schubert	Pmd	2010	41,331	51,687	262	32	24	ucc	4,334 teu: ex Rio Chicago-14
9232632	SFL Europa **	Mhl	2003	16,803	22,900	185	25	20	ucc	1,728 teu: ex Montemar Europa-09
9265756	Sophie Schulte	Hkg	2005	61,991	115,583	241	44	14	tcr	
9186687	Weser Stahl	Cyp	1999	28,564	47,257	192	32	12	bsd	
9155626	Wilhelm Schulte	Iom	1997	15,180	17,900	155	23	16	lpg	16,500 m³
newbuildings:										
	Molly Schulte [H]	Sgp	2016	27,279	30,337	189	30	19	ucc	2,345 teu
	Mandalay [H]	Sgp	2016	27,279	30,337	189	30	19	ucc	2,345 teu
	Mimmi Schulte [H]	Sgp	2016	27,279	30,337	189	30	19	ucc	2,345 teu
	Minstrel [H]	Sgp	2016	27,279	30,337	189	30	19	ucc	2,345 teu

vessels owned or managed by various Bernhard Schulte subsidiaries, also manages vessels for many third party owners
* managed for Union Maritime Ltd, London   ** managed for Ship Finance Intl.
[H] managed by Hanseatic Unity Chartering, a j/v originally set up in 2013 between Bernhard Schulte and Reederei Nord GmbH as O&S Chartering,
changing to present name in September 2015 when joined by Borealis Maritime
also see Allocean Ltd, Cido Shipping (HK) Co Ltd, ER Schiffahrt GmbH (Nordcapital Holding GmbH), Kristian Gerhard Jebsen Skipsrederi AS,
MPC Munchmeyer Petersen & Co GmbH, The National Shipping Company of Saudi Arabia, NileDutch Africa Line and D Oltmann GmbH & Co

Reederei Thomas Schulte GmbH & Co. KG   Germany

funnel: *black with white 'TS' on red diamond on broad green band.* **hull**: *dark green with red boot-topping.* **history**: *founded 1987 by Thomas Schulte having previously worked for family company, Bernhard Schulte, since 1968.* **web**: *www.schulteship.de*

9477610	Balthasar Schulte *	Lbr	2012	40,542	49,857	261	32	24	ucc	4,249 teu
9397585	Beatrice Schulte *	Cyp	2009	40,030	50,700	260	32	24	ucc	4,526 teu: ex UASC Doha-15, Beatrice Schulte-09
9453365	Bella Schulte *	Lbr	2011	40,542	49,892	261	32	24	ucc	4,249 teu
9401063	Benedict Schulte *	Cyp	2009	40,030	50,570	260	32	24	ucc	4,526 teu: ex UASC Jubail-15, Benedict Schulte-09

Balthasar Schulte : Reederei Thomas Schulte GmbH : *Chris Brooks*

IMO	name	flag	year	gt	dwt	loa	bm	kts	type	comments
9401075	Benita Schulte *	Lbr	2009	40,030	50,716	260	32	24	ucc	4,526 teu: ex UASC Samarra-14, l/a Benita Schulte
9537628	Betis *	Lbr	2010	43,506	79,700	229	32	24	bbu	ex Diana Schulte-12
9537898	Boavista *	Lbr	2010	51,239	93,077	229	38	14	bbu	ex Daphne Schulte-13
9461623	Bodo Schulte *	Lbr	2011	40,542	49,836	261	32	24	ucc	4,249 teu
9449120	Chopin *	Cyp	2012	38,364	46,954	240	32	23	ucc	3,635 teu: ex Paula Schulte-14
9537903	David Schulte *	Lbr	2010	51,239	93,039	229	38	14	bbu	
9537630	Dora Schulte *	Lbr	2010	43,506	79,607	229	32	14	bbu	
9305881	Elba Island **	Mhl	2005	25,674	33,651	207	30	20	ucc	2,474 teu: ex Natalie Schulte-14, Maersk Neuchatel-09, l/a Natalie Schulte
9540869	Emma Schulte *	Lbr	2012	64,769	115,156	254	43	14	bbu	
9540871	Evelyn Schulte *	Lbr	2012	64,110	115,150	254	43	14	bbu	
9315886	Hayling Island **	Lbr	2005	28,927	39,200	222	30	23	ucc	2,824 teu: ex CMA CGM Rose-15, E.R. Marseille-05
9539494	Hedda Schulte *	Cyp	2013	39,753	46,000	227	32	23	ucc	3,421 teu: ex NileDutch Hippo-14, l/a Hedda Schulte, l/d Nordic Lüneburg
9263320	Hope Island **	Mhl	2006	35,697	42,106	231	32	23	ucc	3,554 teu: ex Helena Schulte-15, CSAV Itaim-12 l/a Helena Schulte
9448827	Hugo Schulte *	Lbr	2010	38,364	47,028	240	32	23	ucc	3,635 teu
9305879	Kanaga Island **	Mhl	2005	25,674	33,594	207	30	20	ucc	2,474 teu: Isabelle Schulte-14, Maersk Neustadt-12, l/a Isabelle Schulte
9449106	Lilly Schulte *	Lbr	2012	38,364	46,956	240	32	23	ucc	3,635 teu
9309289	Maria Schulte *	Cyp	2006	35,697	42,141	231	32	23	ucc	3,554 teu: ex APL Shenzhen-14, Maria Schulte-06
9449118	Martha Schulte *	Lbr	2012	38,364	46,925	240	32	23	ucc	3,635 teu: ex NileDutch Buffalo-14, Martha Schulte-14
9294173	Moen Island **	Mhl	2005	28,592	39,333	207	30	20	ucc	2,474 teu: ex Tatiana Schulte-14, YM Fuzhou-12, Tatiana Schulte-11
9314997	MS Eagle *	Mhl	2007	28,927	39,276	222	30	20	ucc	2,826 teu: ex OCL Eagle-15, SFL Eagle-12, Horizon Eagle-12
9303819	MS Hawk *	Mhl	2007	28,592	39,418	222	30	20	ucc	2,826 teu: ex Phoenix Hawk-15, SFL Hawk-14, Horizon Hawk-12, l/a Irenes Hawk
9303792	MS Tiger *	Mhl	2006	28,592	39,266	222	30	20	ucc	2,826 teu: ex Phoenix Tiger-15, SR Tiger-15, Horizon Tiger-12, Irenes Respect-07
9509126	Noble Regor *	Cyp	2012	35,887	41,139	213	32	21	ucc	2,782 teu: l/d OS Izmir
9509138	Noble Rigel *	Cyp	2012	35,887	41,130	213	32	21	ucc	2,782 teu: l/d OS Antalya
9294185	Patricia Schulte *	Cyp	2006	28,592	39,418	222	30	22	ucc	2,824 teu
9329629	Philippa Schulte *	Lbr	2006	35,975	42,164	231	32	23	ucc	3,554 teu: ex APL Sokhna-14, MOL Wonder-08, APL Sokhna-08, l/a Philippa Shulte
9315836	Rubina Schulte *	Lbr	2005	28,927	39,275	222	30	23	ucc	2,824 teu: ex Kota Pekarang-13, E.R. Manchester-05
9294159	Sarah Schulte *	Cyp	2005	28,592	39,383	222	30	22	ucc	2,824 teu: ex Ariake-10, l/a Sarah Schulte
9306471	Strauss *	Cyp	2005	25,406	33,900	207	30	22	ucc	2,478 teu: ex Antonia Schulte-14, Maersk Navia-09, P&O Nedlloyd Mariana-05, l/a Antonia Schulte
9315874	Valerie Schulte *	Lbr	2005	28,927	39,200	222	30	23	ucc	2,824 teu: ex Kota Pemimpin-10, l/a E.R. Malta
9312418	Victoria Schulte *	Cyp	2005	25,406	33,900	208	30	22	ucc	2,474 teu: ex NYK Floresta -14, Victoria Schulte-05

*managed by Ocean Shipmanagement GmbH, ** managed by associated Uniqa Marine Management
† managed for Atlanti zur Vermittlung Internationaler Investitionen GmbH & Co or ‡ for Lloyd Fonds AG

Scorpio Group   Monaco

history: *originally founded in 1971 and owned by members of Lollo-Ghetti family, joined in 2003 by the Lauro Brothers. Comprises Scorpio Bulkers, Scorpio Tankers, Scorpio Commercial Management and Scorpio Ship Management* **web:** *scorpiogroup.net*

Scorpio Bulkers Inc.

funnel: *white with 'S' logo in black.* **hull:** *red with red boot-topping.* **history:** *founded March 20th 2013* **web:** *scorpiobulkers.com*

IMO	name	flag	year	gt	dwt	loa	bm	kts	type	comments
9748423	SBI Achilles	Mhl	2016	34,835	61,305	200	32	14	bbu	
9705299	SBI Antares	Mhl	2015	34,447	61,593	200	32	14	bbu	
9704829	SBI Athena	Mhl	2015	36,336	63,500	200	32	14	bbu	
9723631	SBI Bolero	Mhl	2015	44,069	82,000	229	32	14	bbu	
9705287	SBI Bravo	Mhl	2015	34,447	61,587	200	32	14	bbu	
9677375	SBI Cakewalk	Mhl	2014	44,099	81,129	229	32	14	bbu	
9719537	SBI Capoeira	Mhl	2015	43,301	81,253	229	32	14	bbu	

IMO	name	flag	year	gt	dwt	loa	bm	kts	type	comments
9719549	SBI Carioca	Mhl	2015	43,301	81,262	229	32	14	bbu	
9677387	SBI Charleston	Mhl	2014	44,099	81,199	229	32	14	bbu	
9723629	SBI Conga	Mhl	2015	44,069	81,167	229	32	14	bbu	
9714719	SBI Cronos	Mhl	2015	34,835	61,305	200	32	14	bbu	
9714692	SBI Echo	Mhl	2015	34,835	61,258	200	32	14	bbu	
9710567	SBI Electra	Mhl	2015	44,200	81,800	229	32	14	bbu	
9710579	SBI Flamenco	Mhl	2015	44,200	81,800	229	32	14	bbu	
9705342	SBI Hercules	Mhl	2016	36,421	63,500	200	32	14	bbu	
9714721	SBI Hermes	Mhl	2016	34,835	61,272	200	32	14	bbu	
9705316	SBI Hydra	Mhl	2015	34,447	61,115	200	32	14	bbu	
9719551	SBI Lambada	Mhl	2016	43,301	81,272	229	32	14	bbu	
9705146	SBI Leo	Mhl	2015	35,584	61,614	200	32	14	bbu	
9705158	SBI Lyra	Mhl	2015	34,584	61,559	200	32	14	bbu	
9705304	SBI Maia	Mhl	2015	34,447	61,105	200	32	14	bbu	
9705330	SBI Orion	Mhl	2015	36,421	63,328	200	32	14	bbu	
9705328	SBI Pegasus	Mhl	2015	36,421	63,371	200	32	14	bbu	
9712151	SBI Perseus	Lbr	2016	36,336	63,500	200	32	14	bbu	
9723655	SBI Reggae	Lbr	2016	44,069	81,214	229	32	14	bbu	
9710581	SBI Rock	Mhl	2016	44,000	82,057	229	32	14	bbu	
9712498	SBI Rumba	Mhl	2015	45,200	84,867	229	35	14	bbu	
9712486	SBI Samba	Mhl	2015	45,200	84,867	229	35	14	bbu	
9723643	SBI Sousta	Mhl	2016	44,069	82,000	229	32	14	bbu	
9705160	SBI Subaru	Mhl	2015	34,584	61,571	200	32	14	bbu	
9714707	SBI Tango	Mhl	2015	34,835	61,192	200	32	14	bbu	
9704843	SBI Thalia	Mhl	2015	36,336	63,500	200	32	14	bbu	
9705172	SBI Ursa	Mhl	2015	34,584	61,571	200	32	14	bbu	
newbuildings:										
9710593	SBI Twist	Mhl	2016	44,000	82,000	229	32	14	bbu	Yangzijiang Q2 2016
9714678	SBI Samson	Mhl	2016	35,900	63,500	200	32	14	bbu	Chengxi CX0655
9719563	SBI Macarena	Mhl	2016	44,000	82,000	229	32	14	bbu	Hudong Q2 2016
9728629	SBI Zumba	Lbr	2016	44,000	82,000	229	32	14	bbu	Hudong H1726 Q1 2016
9763904	SBI Parapara	Mhl	2016	44,000	82,000	229	32	14	bbu	Hudong Zhonghua Q1 2016
9719715	SBI Swing	Mhl	2017	44,000	82,000	229	32	14	bbu	Hudong

further 60,000 and 82,000dwt bbu to be confirmed [Mitsui and various Chinese yards]

SBI Antares : Scorpio Bulkers : *Hans Kraijenbosch*

IMO	name	flag	year	gt	dwt	loa	bm	kts	type	comments

Scorpio Tankers Inc.

funnel: *black with two white curves at base and logo in white on black top black.* **hull:** *red with red boot-topping.* **history:** *founded 2009* **web:** *www.scorpiotankers.com*

IMO	name	flag	year	gt	dwt	loa	bm	kts	type	comments
9295347	Baltic Ambition	Cyp	2006	23,240	37,343	183	27	14	tco	
9327360	Baltic Faith	Cyp	2006	23,337	37,000	183	27	14	tco	
9327384	Baltic Force	Cyp	2006	23,337	37,039	183	27	14	tco	
9314832	Baltic Marshall	Cyp	2006	23,240	37,289	183	27	14	tco	
9314806	Baltic Merchant	Cyp	2006	23,240	37,311	183	27	14	tco	
9697636	Harrison Bay	Mhl	2015	29,735	50,163	183	32	14	tco	
9346433	Ice Base	Cyp	2008	38,977	63,605	229	32	14	tco	
9717773	Jennings Bay	Mhl	2015	29,735	50,150	183	32	14	tco	
9717785	Lafayette Bay	Mhl	2015	29,735	50,135	183	32	14	tco	
9697648	Saint Albans Bay	Mhl	2015	29,735	50,129	183	32	14	tco	
9696553	STI Acton	Mhl	2014	24,162	38,734	184	27	14	tco	
9696694	STI Alexis	Mhl	2015	62,684	109,999	256	43	14	tco	l/a Flagship Dahlia
9629926	STI Amber	Mhl	2012	29,708	49,990	183	32	14	tco	
9686704	STI Aqua	Mhl	2014	29,735	50,132	183	32	14	tco	
9691723	STI Battersea	Mhl	2014	24,162	38,464	184	27	14	tco	
9688362	STI Battery	Mhl	2014	29,785	49,990	183	32	14	tco	
9681132	STI Benecia	Mhl	2014	29,767	49,990	183	32	14	tco	
9658379	STI Beryl	Mhl	2013	29,708	51,840	183	32	14	tco	
9704453	STI Black Hawk	Mhl	2015	29,785	49,990	183	32	14	tco	
9686869	STI Brixton	Mhl	2014	24,162	38,734	184	27	14	tco	
9690846	STI Broadway	Mhl	2014	64,677	109,999	256	43	14	tco	
9706839	STI Bronx	Mhl	2015	29,735	50,135	183	32	14	tco	
9706841	STI Brooklyn	Mhl	2015	29,735	50,175	183	32	14	tco	
9688386	STI Camden	Mhl	2014	24,162	38,734	183	28	14	tco	
9708564	STI Carnaby	Mhl	2015	63,915	109,990	250	44	14	tco	
9676577	STI Clapham	Mhl	2014	24,162	38,734	183	28	14	tco	
9686857	STI Comandante	Mhl	2014	24,162	38,734	184	27	14	tco	
9690810	STI Condotti	Mhl	2014	64,705	109,999	256	43	15	tco	
9697600	STI Connaught	Mhl	2015	64,705	109,999	256	43	15	tco	
9686716	STI Dama	Mhl	2014	29,735	50,137	183	32	14	tco	
9669938	STI Duchessa	Mhl	2014	29,785	51,840	183	32	14	tco	
9688829	STI Elysees	Mhl	2014	64,705	109,999	256	43	14	tco	
9655913	STI Emerald	Mhl	2013	29,708	51,840	183	32	14	tco	
9696565	STI Finchley	Mhl	2014	24,162	38,734	183	28	14	tco	
9645786	STI Fontvieille	Mhl	2013	29,708	51,622	183	32	14	tco	
9688374	STI Fulham	Mhl	2014	24,162	38,734	183	28	14	tco	
9629952	STI Garnet	Mhl	2012	29,708	49,990	183	32	14	tco	
9686766	STI Gramercy	Mhl	2015	29,735	50,145	183	32	14	tco	
9686883	STI Hackney	Mhl	2014	24,162	38,734	184	27	14	tco	
9706463	STI Hammersmith	Mhl	2015	24,162	38,734	184	27	14	tco	
9712852	STI Kingsway	Mhl	2015	63,915	109,999	250	44	14	tco	l/a Navig8 Swift
9645774	STI Larvotto	Mhl	2013	29,708	51,622	183	32	14	tco	
9696711	STI Lauren	Mhl	2015	64,677	109,999	256	43	14	tco	
9645762	STI Le Rocher	Mhl	2013	29,708	51,622	183	32	14	tco	

STI Acton : Scorpio Tankers : *Roy Fenton*

IMO	name	flag	year	gt	dwt	loa	bm	kts	type	comments
9708150	STI Lombard	Mhl	2015	62,684	109,999	256	43	14	tco	c/a Flagship Juniper
9688831	STI Madison	Mhl	2014	64,705	109,999	256	43	14	tco	
9707261	STI Manhattan	Mhl	2015	29,735	50,156	183	32	14	tco	
9686730	STI Mayfair	Mhl	2014	29,735	50,145	183	32	14	tco	
9681118	STI Meraux	Mhl	2014	27,732	49,990	183	32	14	tco	
9686974	STI Milwaukee	Mhl	2014	29,785	49,990	183	32	14	tco	
9706425	STI Notting Hill	Mhl	2015	29,788	49,990	183	32	14	tco	
9629964	STI Onyx	Mhl	2012	29,708	49,990	183	32	14	tco	
9669940	STI Opera	Mhl	2014	29,785	51,840	183	32	14	tco	
9690834	STI Orchard	Mhl	2014	64,677	109,999	256	43	14	tco	
9707807	STI Osceola	Mhl	2015	29,785	49,990	183	32	14	tco	
9697595	STI Oxford	Mhl	2015	64,705	109,999	256	43	14	tco	
9690793	STI Park	Mhl	2014	64,705	109,999	256	43	14	tco	
9686871	STI Pimlico	Mhl	2014	24,162	38,734	184	27	14	tco	
9704465	STI Pontiac	Mhl	2015	29,785	49,990	183	32	14	tco	
9696589	STI Poplar	Mhl	2014	24,162	38,734	182	28	14	tco	
9707273	STI Queens	Mhl	2015	29,735	50,139	183	32	14	tco	
9686728	STI Regina	Mhl	2014	29,735	50,122	183	32	14	tco	
9696682	STI Rose	Mhl	2015	62,684	109,999	256	43	14	tco	l/d Flagship Rose
9706475	STI Rotherhithe	Mhl	2015	24,162	38,734	184	27	14	tco	
9629940	STI Ruby	Mhl	2012	29,708	49,990	183	32	14	tco	
9681120	STI San Antonio	Mhl	2014	29,732	49,990	183	32	14	tco	

STI Westminster : Scorpio Tankers : *Nico Kemps*

STI Veneto : Scorpio Tankers : *Hans Kraijenbosch*

IMO	name	flag	year	gt	dwt	loa	bm	kts	type	comments
9650573	STI Sapphire	Mhl	2013	29,708	49,990	183	32	14	tco	
9708552	STI Savile Row	Mhl	2015	63,915	109,999	256	43	14	tco	
9704477	STI Seneca	Mhl	2015	29,785	49,990	183	32	14	tco	
9690808	STI Sloane	Mhl	2014	64,705	109,999	256	43	14	tco	
9686754	STI Soho	Mhl	2014	29,735	50,140	183	32	14	tco	
9708148	STI Spiga	Mhl	2015	62,684	109,999	256	43	14	tco	c/a Flagship Jasmine
9681144	STI St. Charles	Mhl	2014	29,767	49,990	183	32	14	tco	
9681106	STI Texas City	Mhl	2014	29,732	49,990	183	32	14	tco	
9629938	STI Topaz	Mhl	2012	29,708	49,990	183	32	14	tco	
9686742	STI Tribeca	Mhl	2015	29,735	50,133	183	32	14	tco	
9681390	STI Venere	Mhl	2014	29,785	49,990	183	32	14	tco	
9690822	STI Veneto	Mhl	2015	64,705	109,999	256	43	15	tco	
9645798	STI Ville	Mhl	2013	29,708	51,622	183	32	14	tco	
9686699	STI Virtus	Mhl	2014	29,735	50,148	183	32	14	tco	
9691735	STI Wembley	Mhl	2014	24,162	38,734	184	27	14	tco	
9706437	STI Westminster	Mhl	2015	29,788	49,687	183	32	14	tco	
9696709	STI Winnie	Mhl	2015	64,677	109,999	256	43	14	tco	
9688350	STI Yorkville	Mhl	2014	29,785	49,990	183	32	14	tco	
newbuildings:										
9722584	STI Grace	Mhl	2016	62,000	114,900	256	43	14	tco	
9722596	STI Jermyn	Mhl	2016	62,000	114,900	256	43	14	tco	

vessels managed by Scorpio Ship Management SAM
4 + 2 x 115,000dwt tco [DSME (2016)] DSME 2 x 114,000dwt tco

Quantum Scorpio Box Inc.
funnel: *charterers colours* **hull:** *charterers colours* **history:** *founded 2012, by Lauro Bros' Scorpio Group with investment from Idal Ofer's Quantum Pacific Group* **web:**

9755933	MSC Diana	Lbr	2016	193,000	197,850	399	58	22	ucc	19,437 teu	Samsung 2138
9755945	MSC Ingy	Lbr	2016	193,000	197,850	399	59	22	ucc	19,437 teu	Samsung 2139
9755957	MSC Eloane	Lbr		193,000	197,850	399	59	22	ucc	19,437 teu	Samsung 2140
9767376									ucc	19,437 teu	Samsung 2156
9767388									ucc	19,437 teu	Samsung 2157
9767390									ucc	19,437 teu	Samsung 2158

vessels for 15 year b/b charter to MSC

COSCO Faith : Seaspan Corp. : *Hans Kraijenbosch*

IMO	name	flag	year	gt	dwt	loa	bm	kts	type	comments

Seaspan Corp.

Canada

funnel: *charterers colours.* hull: *generally charterers colours.* history: *non-operating owner - Seaspan Ship Mgmt. incorporated 04:2000 (Seaspan International Ltd., Canadian subsidiary of Washington Corp. USA)* web: *www.seaspancorp.com*

IMO	name	flag	year	gt	dwt	loa	bm	kts	type	comments
9492713	Berlin Bridge	Hkg	2011	46,444	58,200	270	35	24	ucc	4,526 teu
9492701	Bilbao Bridge	Hkg	2011	46,444	58,200	270	35	24	ucc	4,526 teu
9492696	Brevik Bridge	Hkg	2011	46,444	58,200	270	35	24	ucc	4,526 teu
9486116	Brotonne Bridge	Hkg	2010	46,444	58,200	270	35	24	ucc	4,526 teu
9494280	Budapest Bridge	Hkg	2011	46,444	58,200	270	35	24	ucc	4,526 teu
9435038	Calicanto Bridge	Hkg	2010	26,404	34,195	210	30	24	ucc	4,526 teu
9472139	Cosco Development	Hkg	2012	141,823	140,609	366	48	25	ucc	13,092 teu
9472189	Cosco Excellence	Hkg	2012	141,823	140,146	366	48	25	ucc	13,092 teu
9472141	Cosco Faith	Hkg	2012	141,823	140,609	366	48	25	ucc	13,092 teu
9472127	Cosco Fortune	Hkg	2012	141,823	140,637	366	48	25	ucc	13,092 teu
9403009	Cosco Fuzhou	Hkg	2007	35,988	42,201	231	32	22	ucc	3,534 teu
9466245	Cosco Glory	Hkg	2011	141,823	140,637	366	48	25	ucc	13,092 teu
9472177	Cosco Harmony	Hkg	2012	141,823	140,453	366	48	25	ucc	13,092 teu
9472165	Cosco Hope	Hkg	2012	141,823	140,241	366	48	25	ucc	13,092 teu
9448786	Cosco Indonesia	Hkg	2010	91,051	101,200	334	43	24	ucc	8,208 teu
9448748	Cosco Japan	Hkg	2010	91,051	102,834	334	43	24	ucc	8,208 teu
9448750	Cosco Korea	Hkg	2010	91,051	102,710	334	43	24	ucc	8,208 teu
9448774	Cosco Malaysia	Hkg	2010	91,051	102,834	334	43	24	ucc	8,208 teu
9448762	Cosco Philippines	Hkg	2010	91,051	101,200	334	43	24	ucc	8,208 teu
9472153	Cosco Pride	Hkg	2011	141,823	140,609	366	48	25	ucc	13,092 teu
9448803	Cosco Prince Rupert	Hkg	2011	91,051	102,742	334	43	24	ucc	8,208 teu
9448798	Cosco Thailand	Hkg	2010	91,051	101,200	334	43	24	ucc	8,208 teu
9448815	Cosco Vietnam	Hkg	2011	91,051	102,875	334	43	24	ucc	8,208 teu: ex Alianca Itapoa-13, Cosco Vietnam-12
9403011	Cosco Yingkou	Hkg	2007	35,988	41,500	231	32	22	ucc	3,534 teu
9443487	CSAV Lumaco	Hkg	2010	40,541	50,245	261	32	24	ucc	4,253 teu
9286011	CSCL Africa	Hkg	2005	90,645	101,612	334	43	25	ucc	8,468 teu: ex-CMA CGM Africa-08, CSCL Africa-08
9290139	CSCL Brisbane	Hkg	2005	39,941	50,748	260	32	24	ucc	4,250 teu
9402627	CSCL Callao	Hkg	2009	26,404	34,194	209	30	22	ucc	2,504 teu
9386005	CSCL Lima	Hkg	2008	26,404	34,200	209	30	22	ucc	2,504 teu
9314258	CSCL Long Beach	Hkg	2007	108,069	111,889	337	46	25	ucc	9,580 teu
9402639	CSCL Manzanillo	Hkg	2009	26,404	34,194	209	30	22	ucc	2,504 teu
9290127	CSCL Melbourne	Hkg	2005	39,941	50,796	263	32	24	ucc	4,250 teu
9385984	CSCL Montevideo	Hkg	2008	26,404	34,194	209	30	22	ucc	2,546 teu
9290115	CSCL New York	Hkg	2005	39,941	50,500	263	32	24	ucc	4,250 teu
9385972	CSCL Panama	Hkg	2008	26,404	34,194	209	30	22	ucc	4,051 teu
9402615	CSCL San Jose	Hkg	2008	26,404	33,726	209	30	22	ucc	2,504 teu
9386017	CSCL Santiago	Hkg	2008	26,404	33,725	209	30	22	ucc	2,546 teu
9402615	CSCL San Jose	Hkg	2008	26,404	33,726	209	30	22	ucc	2,546 teu
9385996	CSCL Sao Paulo	Hkg	2008	26,404	34,194	209	30	22	ucc	2,546 teu
9290103	CSCL Sydney	Hkg	2005	39,941	50,869	260	32	24	ucc	4,250 teu
9290098	CSCL Vancouver	Hkg	2005	39,941	50,869	263	32	24	ucc	4,250 teu
9314234	CSCL Zeebrugge	Hkg	2007	108,069	111,889	337	46	25	ucc	9,580 teu

MOL Brightness : Seaspan Corp. : *Chris Brooks*

IMO	name	flag	year	gt	dwt	loa	bm	kts	type	comments
9286009	CSCL Oceania	Cyp	2004	90,645	101,810	334	43	25	ucc	8,468 teu: ex MSC Belgium-09, CSCL Oceania-07
9301782	Dubai Express ‡	Hkg	2006	39,941	50,748	260	32	24	ucc	4,253 teu: ex CP Corbett-06, I/a CP Guerrero, I/dn TMM Guerrero
9402641	Guayaquil Bridge	Hkg	2010	25,320	34,194	209	30	22	ucc	2,546 teu
9630391	Hanjin Ami [G]	Hkg	2014	113,042	115,260	337	48	21	ucc	10,010 teu
9630420	Hanjin Bosal [G]	Hkg	2015	113,042	115,297	337	48	21	ucc	10,010 teu
9630365	Hanjin Buddha	Hkg	2014	113,042	115,177	337	48	21	ucc	10,010 teu
9630418	Hanjin Gwanseum [G]	Hkg	2015	113,042	115,159	337	48	21	ucc	10,010 teu
9630377	Hanjin Jungil [G]	Hkg	2014	113,042	115,304	337	48	21	ucc	10,010 teu
9630389	Hanjin Namu	Hkg	2014	113,042	115,318	337	48	21	ucc	10,010 teu
9630406	Hanjin Tabul	Hkg	2014	113,042	115,086	337	48	21	ucc	10,010 teu
9301794	Jakarta Express ‡	Hkg	2006	39,941	50,869	260	32	24	ucc	4,253 teu: ex CP Dartmoor-06, CP Banyan-06, I/dn Contship Banyan
9301811	Lahore Express ‡	Hkg	2006	39,941	50,869	260	32	24	ucc	4,253 teu: ex CP Morelos-06
9301859	Manila Express ‡	Hkg	2007	39,941	50,869	261	32	23	ucc	4,253 teu
9713375	Maersk Guatemala [G]	Hkg	2015	113,042	119,510	337	48	20	ucc	10,000 teu
9727871	Maersk Guayaquil	Hkg	2015	113,042	119,359	337	48	20	ucc	10,000 teu
9713337	MOL Beacon	Hkg	2015	113,042	119,324	337	48	20	ucc	10,000 teu
9713349	MOL Beauty [G]	Hkg	2015	113,042	119,106	337	48	20	ucc	10,000 teu
9713351	MOL Belief [G]	Hkg	2015	113,042	119,137	337	48	20	ucc	10,000 teu
9713363	MOL Bellwether [G]	Hkg	2015	113,042	119,241	337	48	20	ucc	10,000 teu
9739666	MOL Benefactor	Hkg	2016	115,000	117,000	337	48	22	ucc	10,010 teu
9685322	MOL Bravo	Hkg	2014	113,042	115,231	337	48	20	ucc	10,000 teu
9685358	MOL Breeze	Hkg	2014	113,042	115,396	337	48	20	ucc	10,000 teu
9685346	MOL Brightness	Hkg	2014	113,042	115,308	337	48	20	ucc	10,000 teu
9685334	MOL Brilliance [G]	Hkg	2014	113,042	115,173	337	48	20	ucc	10,000 teu
9251365	MOL Efficiency	Hkg	2003	53,940	63,160	294	32	24	ucc	4,646 teu
9407134	MOL Emerald	Hkg	2009	54,940	67,518	294	33	25	ucc	5,087 teu
9407146	MOL Eminence	Hkg	2010	54,940	67,386	294	33	25	ucc	5,087 teu
9407158	MOL Emissary	Hkg	2010	54,940	67,400	294	33	25	ucc	5,087 teu
9407160	MOL Empire	Hkg	2010	54,940	67,000	294	33	25	ucc	5,087 teu
9251377	MOL Excellence	Hkg	2003	53,822	63,160	294	32	24	ucc	4,636 teu
9251389	MOL Expeditor [G]	Hkg	2003	53,822	63,098	294	32	24	ucc	4,646 teu: ex APL Expeditor-10, MOL Expeditor-08
9251391	MOL Express [G]	Pan	2003	53,822	63,046	294	32	24	ucc	4,646 teu
8618308	MSC Carole	Pan	1989	52,191	60,640	294	32	23	ucc	4,814 teu: ex Maersk Moncton-11, MSC Ancona-10, Maersk Moncton-08, Mathilde Maersk-06
8618310	MSC Leanne	Pan	1989	52,191	60,639	184	25	18	ucc	4,814 teu: ex York-11, Cape York-11, Maersk Marystown-08, Maren Maersk-06
8613322	MSC Manu	Pan	1989	52,191	60,639	294	27	23	ucc	4,814 teu: ex Victor-11, Cap Victor-11, Maersk Matane-09, Margrethe Maersk-06
8618293	MSC Veronique	Pan	1989	52,191	60,900	222	32	23	ucc	4,814 teu: ex Maersk Merritt-11, MSC Sweden-10, Maersk Merritt-07, Mette Maersk-06
9301770	New Delhi Express	Hkg	2005	39,941	50,813	260	32	24	ucc	4,253 teu: ex CP Kanha-06, I/a CP Charger, I/dn Lykes Charger
9301847	Rio de Janeiro Express	Hkg	2007	39,941	50,500	260	32	24	ucc	4,253 teu: ex CP Nuevo Leon-07, TMM Nuevo Leon-05
9301823	Rio Grande Express	Hkg	2006	39,941	50,869	260	32	24	ucc	4,253 teu: ex CP Margosa-06
9301809	Saigon Express	Hkg	2006	39,941	50,869	260	32	24	ucc	4,253 teu: ex CP Jasper-06, CP Trader-06, I/dn Lykes Trader
9227027	Seaspan Dalian	Hkg	2002	39,941	50,789	260	32	24	ucc	4,051 teu: ex CSCL Dalian-12
9224312	Seaspan Chiwan	Hkg	2001	39,941	50,488	260	32	24	ucc	4,051 teu: ex CSCL Chiwan-13
9227039	Seaspan Felixstowe	Hkg	2002	39,941	50,789	260	32	24	ucc	4,051 teu: ex CSCL Felixstowe-12
9224300	Seaspan Hamburg	Hkg	2001	39,941	50,790	260	32	24	ucc	4,051 teu: ex CSAV Licanten, CSCL Hamburg-10
9443463	Seaspan Lebu	Hkg	2010	40,541	50,276	261	32	24	ucc	4,253 teu: ex CSAV Lebu-15
9443475	Seaspan Lingue	Hkg	2010	40,541	50,435	261	32	24	ucc	4,253 teu: ex CSAV Lingue-15
9227015	Seaspan Ningbo	Hkg	2002	39,941	50,789	260	32	24	ucc	4,250 teu: ex CSCL Ningbo-12
9301835	Seaspan Santos	Hkg	2006	39,941	50,869	260	32	24	ucc	4,253 teu: ex Santos Express-16, CP Victor-06, I/dn Lykes Victor
9704647	YM Warmth	Hkg	2015	144,651	145,500	368	51	22	ucc	14,080 teu
9684665	YM Wellhead	Hkg	2015	144,651	145,560	368	51	22	ucc	14,080 teu
9704623	YM Wellness	Hkg	2015	144,651	145,557	368	51	22	ucc	14,080 teu
9704611	YM Wholesome [G]	Hkg	2015	144,651	145,502	368	51	22	ucc	14,080 teu
9684689	YM Winner	Hkg	2015	144,651	145,372	368	51	22	ucc	14,080 teu

YM Wondrous : Seaspan Corp. : *Hans Kraijenbosch*

Magellan Strait : SeaTrade Groningen : *Hans Kraijenbosch*

Pacific Reefer : SeaTrade Groningen : *Hans Kraijenbosch*

IMO	name	flag	year	gt	dwt	loa	bm	kts	type	comments
9684641	YM Wish	Hkg	2015	144,651	145,376	368	51	22	ucc	14,080 teu
9704609	YM Witness	Hkg	2015	144,651	145,388	368	51	22	ucc	14,080 teu
9684677	YM Wondrous [G]	Hkg	2015	144,651	145,368	368	51	22	ucc	14,080 teu
9684653	YM World	Hkg	2015	144,651	145,551	368	51	22	ucc	14,080 teu
9704635	YM Worth [G]	Hkg	2015	144,651	145,401	368	51	22	ucc	14,080 teu
newbuildings:										
9708435	YM Window [G]	Hkg	2016	153,500	145,077	368	51	22	ucc	14,080 teu CSBC Kaohsiung 1036
9708447	YM Width	Hkg	2016	153,500	145,077	368	51	22	ucc	14,080 teu CSBC Kaohsiung 1037
9708459	YM Welcome	Hkg	2016	153,500	145,077	368	51	22	ucc	14,080 teu CSBC Kaohsiung 1038
9708461	YM Wind	Hkg	2016	153,500	145,077	368	51	22	ucc	14,080 teu CSBC Kaohsiung 1039
9708473	YM Wreath	Hkg	2016	153,500	145,077	368	51	22	ucc	14,080 teu CSBC Kaohsiung 1040
			2016		115,177				ucc	10,010 teu Yangzijiang 2013-1104
			2016						ucc	10,010 teu Yangzijiang 2013-1105
9739678	MOL Beyond		2016	115,000	117,500	337	48		ucc	10,010 teu Yangzijiang 2013-1107
			2016						ucc	10,010 teu Yangzijiang 2014-1120
			2016						ucc	10,010 teu Yangzijiang 2014-1121
			2016						ucc	10,010 teu Yangzijiang 2014-1122
			2017						ucc	10,010 teu Yangzijiang 2014-1123
			2017						ucc	10,010 teu Yangzijiang 1168
			2017						ucc	10,010 teu Yangzijiang 1169
	MSC		2017						ucc	11,000 teu HHIC NCP 0145
	MSC		2017						ucc	11,000 teu HHIC NCP 0146
	MSC		2017						ucc	11,000 teu HHIC NCP 0147
	MSC [G]		2017						ucc	11,000 teu HHIC NCP 0148
	MSC [G]		2017						ucc	11,000 teu HHIC NCP 0153

[G] owned by Greater China Intermodal, Hong Kong

Seatrade Groningen B.V.   Netherlands

funnel: *blue with white 'S' and blue 'G' symbol on orange square.* **hull:** *white with blue 'Seatrade' or charterers name, red boot-topping.* **history:** *established in 1951 by five captain-owners as NV Scheepvaarts Groningen to 1973. Acquired Dammers & Van der Heide's Shipping & Trading Co BV (formed 1947) in 1989, Triton Schiffahrts GmbH (formed 1994) in 2000 and United Reefers Chartering Ltd (formed 1994 as Global Reefer Trading Ltd to 2002) in 2005. Acquired reefer fleet of Amer Shipping in 2008.*
web: *www.seatrade.com or www.reedereitriton.de*

IMO	name	flag	year	gt	dwt	loa	bm	kts	type	comments
9019652	Aconcagua Bay	Pan	1992	9,074	11,581	149	21	19	grf	ex United Ice-06, Aconcagua-02
9179397	Aracena Carrier #	Pan	1998	7,637	9,011	139	21	20	grf	ex Humboldt Rex-12
9454761	Atlantic Klipper	Nld	2011	14,091	15,692	165	25	23	grf	
9179256	Atlantic Reefer	Lbr	1998	13,055	17,322	175	23	21	grf	(len-12)
9454759	Baltic Klipper	Lbr	2010	14,091	15,609	165	25	23	grf	
9158549	Benguela Stream ‡	Nld	1998	9,298	11,016	150	22	20	grf	
9164770	Cala Palma +	Ita	2000	14,868	16,024	190	24	20	grf	
9164782	Cala Pedra +	Ita	2000	14,868	16,024	190	24	20	grf	
9164756	Cala Pino +	Ita	1999	14,868	16,024	190	24	20	grf	
9164768	Cala Pula +	Ita	1999	14,868	16,024	190	24	20	grf	
9051791	Cold Stream	Cuw	1994	8,414	10,066	140	22	19	grf	l/a Prince of Streams
9085479	Cool Expreso	Nld	1994	5,471	7,480	126	16	18	grf	ex Cool Express-12
9143740	Discovery Bay	Bhs	1997	8,924	10,100	142	22	21	grf	
8911073	Everest Bay	Lbr	1989	8,739	9,692	141	21	21	grf	ex United Cold-06, E.W. Everest-02
9081679	Frio Hellenic §	Pan	1998	9,997	11,070	148	22	21	grf	
8920141	Fuji Bay	Lbr	1990	9,070	11,540	149	21	17	grf	ex Amer Fuji-08
8907888	Humboldt Bay	Lbr	1990	9,070	11,633	149	21	20	grf	ex Amer Whitney-08, Californian Reefer-98, Humboldt Rex-94
9167796	Klipper Stream *‡	Nld	1998	9,305	10,936	150	22	21	grf	
9179402	Lucena Carrier #	Pan	2000	7,627	9,011	139	21	20	grf	ex Season Trader-12
9267534	Magellan Strait	Cuw	2003	18,931	15,052	186	25	20	grf	ex Cala Paradiso-13, Carmel Eco-Fresh-11, l/a Rio Alexandre
9267546	Messina Strait	Cuw	2004	18,931	15,052	186	25	20	grf	ex Cala Pira-13, Carmel Bio-Top-11, l/a Rio Yarkon
8517358	Nova Stella	Bhs	1987	6,579	7,685	146	19	18	grf	ex Tama Star-15, Bulan-93, Tama Star-92
9179268	Pacific Reefer	Lbr	1999	13,055	17,322	175	23	21	grf	(len-12)
9172959	Royal Klipper *	Nld	2000	11,382	12,906	155	24	21	grf	ex Equator Stream-00
9019640	Runaway Bay	Bhs	1992	9,070	11,579	149	21	17	grf	ex Sun Maria-05, Diamond Reefer-98, Hudson Rex-95
9213777	Santa Catharina	Bhs	2000	8,597	9,259	143	22	19	grf	
9045156	Sea Phoenix †	Lbr	1992	7,303	8,056	134	21	19	grf	ex Amber Cherry-96
9127928	Sierra Queen	Nld	1996	5,918	8,500	134	16	16	grf	ex Pacific-15
8911085	Whitney Bay	Lbr	1990	8,739	9,692	141	21	21	grf	ex United Cool-06, E.W. Whitney-03
newbuildings:										
9690092	Seatrade Orange	Nld	2016	25,175	27,366	180	30	19	ucc	2,259 teu Yangfan Cv22h-Jt-03
9690107	Seatrade Red	Nld	2016	25,175	27,350	180	30	19	ucc	2,259 teu Yangfan Cv22h-Jt-04
	Seatrade White	Nld	2017						ucc	2,259 teu Yangfan Cv22h-Jt-05

IMO	name	flag	year	gt	dwt	loa	bm	kts	type	comments
	Seatrade Blue	Nld	2017						ucc	2,259 teu Yangfan Cv22h-Jt-06
	Seatrade Green	Nld								
	Seatrade Gold	Nld								

newbuildings: 8 x 300,000m³ fish carriers
In addition to the above, the company also operates numerous smaller reefer vessels.
owned by: * Jaczon bv (www.jaczon.nl): † Roswell Navigation Corp, Greece, § Laskaridis Shipping Co Ltd., # by Norbulk Shipping, UK,
+ Cosiarma SpA, Genoa, or ++ other various owners. ‡ operated by Geest Line

Triton Schiffahrts GmbH, Germany

funnel: *as Seatrade or operators colours.* **hull:** *white with blue 'Seatrade' or charterers name, red boot-topping.* **history:** *company established in Leer,1994, acquired by Seatrade 2000.* **web:** *www.reedereitriton.de*

IMO	name	flag	year	gt	dwt	loa	bm	kts	type	comments
9158537	Agulhas Stream †	Cuw	1998	9,298	11,048	150	22	20	grf	
9045936	Atlantic Mermaid	Lbr	1992	9,829	10,464	142	23	19	grf	
9047271	Bay Phoenix	Lbr	1993	7,326	8,041	134	21	19	grf	ex Summer Phoenix-12, Spring Phoenix-01, Windward Phoenix-99
9064229	Caribbean Mermaid	Lbr	1993	9,829	10,464	142	23	19	grf	ex Northern Mermaid-04, Caribbean Mermaid-02
9167801	Comoros Stream *	Lbr	2000	11,382	12,906	155	24	21	grf	
9045948	Coral Mermaid	Lbr	1992	9,829	10,461	142	23	19	grf	ex Arctic Mermaid-06, Maud-04, Coral Mermaid-01
9143752	Eastern Bay *	Lbr	1997	8,917	9,662	143	22	19	grf	ex Eastern Express-05, l/a Frost Express
9175901	Elsebeth *	Lbr	1998	10,519	10,327	152	23	21	grf	
9201869	Elvira *	Lbr	2000	10,532	10,309	152	23	21	grf	
9202857	Emerald *	Lbr	2000	10,532	10,346	152	23	21	grf	
9181170	Esmeralda *	Lbr	1999	10,532	10,358	152	23	21	grf	
9067128	Fortuna Bay	Lbr	1993	10,203	11,585	145	22	19	grf	ex Fortune Bay-03, Uruguayan Reefer-99
9047245	Lagoon Phoenix	Lbr	1993	7,313	8,044	134	21	19	grf	ex River Phoenix-12, Clover Moon-99, Dover Phoenix-97
9204958	Lombok Strait *	Lbr	2002	14,413	13,512	167	25	22	grf	ex Leopard Max-02
9204960	Luzon Strait *	Lbr	2002	14,413	14,413	167	25	22	grf	ex Tiger Max-02
9064839	Mexican Bay	Lbr	1994	10,203	11,575	145	22	20	grf	ex Mexican Reefer-06
9045924	Pacific Mermaid	Pan	1992	9,820	10,466	142	23	19	grf	
9189873	Polarlight *	Lbr	1998	11,417	10,447	154	24	21	grf	ex Polarlicht-04
9189885	Polarsteam *	Lbr	1998	11,417	10,449	154	24	21	grf	ex Polarstern-03
9014444	Prince of Seas	Lbr	1993	6,363	7,387	120	19	17	grf	
9061198	Prince of Tides	Bhs	1993	7,329	5,360	134	21	19	grf	
9066485	Prince of Waves	Bhs	1993	7,329	8,039	134	21	19	grf	
9194921	Santa Lucia *	Lbr	1999	8,507	9,566	143	22	20	grf	l/a Santa Lucia II
9194957	Santa Maria *	Lbr	1999	8,507	9,566	143	22	20	grf	l/a Santa Maria III
9152181	Southern Bay *	Lbr	1997	8,879	9,609	143	22	19	grf	ex Southern Express-05
9045950	Tasman Mermaid	Lbr	1993	9,829	10,457	142	23	19	grf	ex Antarctic Mermaid-06, Skausund-04, Tasman Mermaid-01
9172947	Timor Stream *†	Pan	1998	9,307	11,013	150	22	20	grf	ex Stream Express-05

Tectus : Shell Trading & Shipping Ltd : *ARO*

IMO	name	flag	year	gt	dwt	loa	bm	kts	type	comments
9045168	Water Phoenix	Lbr	1992	7,303	8,075	134	21	19	grf	ex Lake Phoenix-12, Amber Rose-96

* managed by Triton for MPC Münchmeyer Peterson Group qv. † operated by Geest Line (www.geestline.co.uk)

Shell Trading & Shipping Ltd. (STASCO)   U.K.

funnel: *yellow with narrow black top .***hull:** *red, black or grey with red or blue boot-topping.* **history:** *Royal Dutch Shell Gp. formed 1907 on 60:40 basis by Royal Dutch Petroleum Co (founded 1890) and Shell Transport & Trading Co Ltd (founded 1897). Took control of Mexican Eagle Petroleum Co in 1919 and formed Shell-Mex Ltd in 1921, which in 1932 merged with BP to form Shell-Mex & BP Ltd until separated in 1975. STASCO responsible for trading and shipping activities of the group.* **web:** *www.shell.com*

IMO	name	flag	year	gt	dwt	loa	bm	kts	type	comments
9443401	Aamira (df) +	Mhl	2010	163,922	130,026	345	54	19	lng	266,000 m³
9210828	Abadi (st)	Brn	2002	117,461	72,758	290	46	19	lng	135,000 m³
9431147	Al Bahiya (df) +	Mhl	2010	136,980	121,957	315	50	19	lng	216,000 m³
9443683	Al Dafna (df) +	Mhl	2009	163,922	130,157	345	54	19	lng	266,000 m³
9397286	Al Ghashamiya (df) +	Mhl	2010	135,423	108,988	315	50	19	lng	216,000 m³
9372742	Al Ghuwairiya (df)	Mhl	2008	168,189	154,950	345	55	19	lng	261,700 m³
9431123	Al Karaana (df) +	Mhl	2009	136,980	122,052	315	50	19	lng	210,100 m³
9397327	Al Kharaitiyat (df) +	Mhl	2009	136,168	107,153	315	50	19	lng	216,200 m³
9431111	Al Khattiya (df) +	Mhl	2009	136,980	121,946	315	50	19	lng	210,100 m³
9397315	Al Mafyar (df) +	Mhl	2009	163,922	130,441	345	54	19	lng	266,000 m³
9397298	Al Mayeda (df) +	Mhl	2009	163,922	130,298	345	54	19	lng	266,000 m³
9431135	Al Nuaman (df) +	Mhl	2009	136,980	121,910	315	50	19	lng	210,100 m³
9397339	Al Rekayyat (df) +	Mhl	2009	136,168	107,165	315	50	19	lng	216,200 m³
9397341	Al Sadd (df) +	Mhl	2009	136,980	121,913	315	50	19	lng	210,100 m³. I/a Jelieha-09
9388821	Al Samriya (df) +	Mhl	2009	168,189	154,900	345	55	19	lng	261,700 m³
9360831	Al Sheehaniya (df) +	Mhl	2009	136,980	122,006	315	50	19	lng	210,000 m³
9682552	Amadi (df)	Brn	2015	102,585	85,466	288	44	19	lng	154,800 m³
9496317	Amali (df)	Brn	2011	98,490	72,800	284	43	19	lng	147,228 m³
9661869	Amani (df)	Brn	2014	102,585	85,634	288	44	19	lng	154,800 m³
9496305	Arkat (df)	Brn	2011	98,490	72,800	284	43	19	lng	147,228 m³
9364588	Batissa	Hkg	2008	29,733	51,506	183	32	14	tco	ex Torm Esberg-12
7121633	Bebatik (st) *	Brn	1972	48,612	51,579	257	35	18	lng	75,100 m³: ex Gadinia-86
7347768	Belanak (st) *	Brn	1975	48,612	51,579	257	35	18	lng	75,000 m³: ex Gouldia-86
9388833	Bu Samra (df) +	Mhl	2008	163,922	130,442	345	65	19	lng	266,000 m³
9387956	Bursa	Hkg	2008	29,733	51,463	183	32	15	tco	
9216913	Elka Angelique	Iom	2001	27,539	44,881	183	32	16	tco	ex Ficus-09, I/a Elka Angelique
9216925	Elka Eleftheria	Iom	2001	27,539	44,787	183	32	16	tco	ex Fulgur-09, I/a Elka Eleftheria
9216901	Elka Nikolas	Iom	2001	27,542	44,788	183	32	16	tco	ex Fusus-09, Elka Nikolas-01
9310850	Eternal Diligence	Pan	2006	40,954	74,994	229	32	14	tco	
9236614	Galea (st)	Sgp	2002	111,459	72,781	290	46	19	lng	134,425 m³
9236626	Gallina (st)	Sgp	2002	111,459	72,781	290	46	19	lng	134,425 m³
9253222	Gemmata (st)	Sgp	2004	111,459	72,727	290	46	19	lng	137,104 m³
9388819	Lijmiliya +	Mhl	2009	168,189	155,159	335	55	19	lng	261,700 m³
9397303	Mekaines (df) +	Mhl	2009	163,922	130,171	345	54	19	lng	266,000 m³
9337729	Mesaimeer (df) +	Mhl	2009	136,138	107,160	315	50	19	lng	216,200 m³
9337755	Mozah (df) +	Mhl	2009	163,922	128,900	345	54	19	lng	266,000 m³
9406013	Naticina ≠	Mhl	2010	83,805	156,720	274	48	15	tcr	
9399480	Northia ≠	Mhl	2010	83,805	156,719	274	48	15	tcr	
8608872	Northwest Sanderling (st) †	Aus	1989	105,010	66,810	272	47	18	lng	127,000 m³
8913150	Northwest Sandpiper (st) †	Aus	1993	105,010	66,695	272	47	18	lng	127,000 m³
8913174	Northwest Seaeagle (st) †	Bmu	1992	106,283	67,003	272	47	18	lng	127,000 m³
8608705	Northwest Shearwater (st) ††	Bmu	1991	106,283	66,802	272	47	18	lng	127,500 m³
8608884	Northwest Snipe (st) †	Aus	1990	105,010	66,695	272	47	18	lng	127,000 m³
9045132	Northwest Stormpetrel (st) †	Aus	1994	105,010	66,695	272	47	18	lng	127,000 m³
9397353	Onaiza +	Mhl	2009	136,980	121,939	315	50	19	lng	210,150 m³
9248485	Ondina ≠	Tur	2002	156,916	299,157	330	60	16	tcr	ex Front Stratus-06
9480837	Orthis	Mhl	2011	162,203	320,105	333	60	15	tcr	ex Andromeda Glory-12
9196644	Otina ≠	Iom	2002	159,383	298,465	333	60	15	tcr	ex Hakata-04
9372731	Umm Slal (df) +	Mhl	2008	163,922	130,059	345	54	19	lng	266,000 m³
9443413	Rasheeda (df) +	Mhl	2010	163,922	130,208	345	54	19	lng	266,000 m³
9418365	Shagra (df) +	Mhl	2009	163,922	130,102	345	54	19	lng	266,000 m³
9692351	Silver Ebalina	Mhl	2015	29,327	49,635	183	32	14	tco	
9692349	Silver Euplecta	Mhl	2015	29,327	49,635	183	32	14	tco	
9433016	Tectus	Lbr	2009	42,340	74,862	228	32	14	tco	ex FPMC P Duke-09
9448152	Tonna	Lbr	2009	42,340	74,862	228	32	14	tco	ex FPMC P Fortune-09
9266750	Turris	Lbr	2004	39,307	70,426	228	32	14	tco	ex Formosaproduct Alpine-12

IMO	name	flag	year	gt	dwt	loa	bm	kts	type	comments
9431214	Zarga (df) +	Mhl	2010	163,922	130,211	345	54	19	lng	266,000 m³

newbuildings: 5 x 173,400 m³ lng [t/c from Teekay Gas] [Daewoo (2017/18)]

*vessels managed by subsidiary STASCO (Shell Trading & Shipping Co., UK) (formerly Shell International Shipping Ltd to 1995)
for + Qatar Gas Transport,Nakilat * Brunei Shell Tankers Sendirian Berhad (formed 1986 jointly with Government of The State of Brunei,
Diamond Gas Carriers BV acquiring 25% in 2002), ** for AP Moller Singapore Pte Ltd, Singapore, # for Bonny Gas Transport, subsidiary of
Nigeria LNG Ltd (formed 1989 as a joint-venture between Nigerian National Petroleum Corp. (49%), Shell Gas b.v. (25.6%), Total LNG Nigeria
(15%) and Eni Int. (10.4%) or ≠ for Frontline Ltd qv.
† operated by Australian LNG Ship Operating Co Pty Ltd (formed 1989 jointly by Shell Co of Australia Ltd and BHP Petroleum Pty Ltd –
www.alsoc.com.au) and †† owned by International Gas Transportation Co Ltd (formed jointly with Chevron, BHP, BP and other companies) and
managed by BP Shipping Ltd, Bermuda.
‡ owned by Shell Co. of Australia Ltd (founded 1905 as British Imperial Oil Co Ltd to 1937 – www.shell.com.au)
§ owned by Shell Compania Argentina de Petroleo SA (founded 1922 as Diadema Argentina SA de Petroleo to 1960)*

Shoei Kisen Kaisha Ltd.   Japan

funnel: *operator colours.* **hull:** *operators colours* **history:** *compary associated with Imabari Shipbuilding* **web:** *www.shoei-kisen.com*

IMO	name	flag	year	gt	dwt	loa	bm	kts	type	comments
9738870	African Avocet **	Pan	2015	34,769	61,328	200	32	14	bbu	
9748071	African Loon †	Pan	2016	34,769	61,255	200	32	14	bbu	
9470739	Anderson Bridge +	Pan	2008	17,211	21,972	172	28	19	ucc	1,708 teu
9444285	APL Austria +	Lbr	2007	71,867	72,807	295	40	26	ucc	6,350 teu
9288394	APL Germany +	Lbr	2003	66,462	67,109	281	40	25	ucc	5,588 teu
9260902	APL Hong Kong ++	Lbr	2002	66,573	67,009	279	40	25	ucc	5,588 teu
9532800	APL Latvia *	Pan	2013	87,865	90,799	336	46	24	ucc	8,110 teu
9350018	APL Minnesota ++	Lbr	2008	71,787	72,912	293	40	26	ucc	6,350 teu
9350020	APL New Jersey †	Lbr	2008	71,787	72,912	293	40	26	ucc	6,350 teu
9403621	APL Norway *	Lbr	2007	71,867	72,807	293	40	26	ucc	6,350 teu
9532771	APL Turkey ++	Lbr	2009	71,787	72,912	293	40	26	ucc	6,350 teu
9675652	Berge Daisen ††	Pan	2014	107,229	207,872	300	50	15	bbu	ex F.D. Laura d'Amato-15
9682954	Berge Kosciuszko †	Pan	2014	92,732	181,394	292	45	14	bbu	
9448011	Berge Lyngor +	Pan	2009	104,727	206,312	300	50	15	bbu	
9738882	Berge Snowdon	Pan	2015	23,281	37,790	180	30	14	bbu	
9599810	Berge Tsurugi ++	Pan	2012	92,752	181,403	292	45	14	bbu	ex Shoei Prosperity-15
9367188	Bremen Bridge ††	Pan	2007	66,462	66,940	281	40	24	ucc	5,888 teu: ex Bremen Bridge I -13 Thailand Express-13, I/a OOCL Seattle
9633226	Cape Armeria *	Pan	2013	92,758	181,393	292	45	14	bbu	

Millau Bridge : Shoei Kisen Kaisha : *Hans Kraijenbosch*

IMO	name	flag	year	gt	dwt	loa	bm	kts	type	comments
9624263	Cape Emerald †	Pan	2013	92,752	181,366	292	45	14	bbu	
9218117	Cape Hope II *	Pan	2000	85,959	170,761	289	47	14	bbu	ex Cape Hope-14
9346380	Cape Merlin +	Pan	2005	104,727	206,312	300	50	15	bbu	ex Berge Bonde-16
9446570	Catharina Bulker **	Pan	2011	92,752	181,458	292	45	14	bbu	
9247558	Chicago Bridge	Pan	2001	66,332	67,170	279	40	25	ucc	5,570 teu: ex YM Chicago-06, Chicago Bridge-04
9590979	Clipper Bari-Star +	Pan	2011	23,264	38,243	180	30	14	bbu	
9682887	Clipper Bliss	Pan	2014	23,254	38,147	180	30	14	bbu	
9738727	Clipper Brilliance **	Pan	2015	23,281	37,786	180	30	14	bbu	
9550266	Clipper Ichiban +	Pan	2009	17,009	28,319	169	27	14	bbu	
9445136	Clipper Imabari	Pan	2008	16,960	28,397	169	27	14	bbu	
9573799	Clipper Iwagi	Pan	2010	17,009	28,189	169	27	14	bbu	
9550163	Clipper Izumo	Pan	2010	17,002	28,338	169	27	14	bbu	
9633147	CMB Chardonnay ††	Pan	2012	50,626	95,707	235	38	14	bbu	
9442873	Columbia Highway	Pan	2008	59,493	18,930	200	32	20	mve	6,237 ceu
9381249	Cygnus Leader **	Pan	2007	61,775	20,180	200	32	19	mve	5,415 ceu
9442861	Florida Highway **	Pan	2008	59,493	18,930	200	32	20	mve	6,237 ceu
9667344	Fremantle Highway	Pan	2013	59,525	18,549	200	32	19	mve	6,153 ceu
9367542	Haruka +	Lbr	2006	17,518	21,413	172	28	19	ucc	1,577 teu: ex Cala Puma-13
9663269	Ipanema Beach	Pan	2014	23,393	37,503	180	30	14	bbu	
9706748	Manchester Bridge †	Pan	2015	150,709	147,443	366	51	24	ucc	13.870 teu
9350070	Maple Grove	Pan	2006	30,002	53,474	190	32	14	bbu	
9591052	Mercury Ace	Pan	2011	59,409	19,110	200	32	19	mve	6,109 ceu
9650743	Metis Leader	Pan	2013	59,550	18,200	200	32	20	mve	6,153 ceu
9706736	Millau Bridge *	Pan	2015	150,709	147,443	366	51	23	ucc	13,870 teu
9388352	MOL Continuity *	Pan	2008	88,089	90,466	320	46	25	ucc	8,110 teu: ex APL Finland-12
9388340	MOL Cosmos	Pan	2008	88,089	90,466	320	46	25	ucc	8,110 teu
9321017	MOL Pace ††	Pan	2006	71,902	72,968	293	40	25	ucc	6,350 teu
9307047	MOL Paradise *	Pan	2005	71,902	72,968	293	40	25	ucc	6,350 teu: ex APL Paradise-12, MOL Paradise-11
9307035	MOL Partner	Pan	2005	71,902	72,968	293	40	25	ucc	6,350 teu
9236470	MOL Precision *	Pan	2002	71,902	73,063	293	40	25	ucc	6,350 teu: ex APL Precision-12, MOL Precision-11
9321029	MOL Prestige **	Pan	2006	71,902	72,968	293	40	25	ucc	6,359 teu: ex MSC Prestige-08, MOL Prestige-07
9236482	MOL Promise ††	Pan	2002	71,902	73,063	293	40	25	ucc	6,350 teu
9477919	Morning Camilla +	Pan	2009	60,876	22,692	200	32	20	mve	6,502 ceu
9338709	Morning Carina †	Pan	2007	60,876	22,755	200	32	19	mve	6,502 ceu
9338723	Morning Caroline +	Pan	2008	60,876	22,717	200	32	19	mve	6,502 ceu
9338694	Morning Charlotte	Pan	2007	60,876	22,578	200	32	20	mve	6,502 ceu
9675585	Morning Cherry †	Pan	2014	55,925	18,556	200	32	20	mve	6,502 ceu
9519145	Morning Cornelia **	Pan	2010	60,876	22,746	200	32	20	mve	6,502 ceu
9706750	Munchen Bridge +	Pam	2015	150,709	147,443	366	51	23	ucc	13.870 teu
9738820	Nord Bering	Pan	2015	34,778	61,186	200	32	14	bbu	
9701164	Nord Titan ++	Pan	2014	40,937	77,095	225	32	14	bbu	
9307011	OOCL Antwerp	Pan	2006	66,462	66,940	281	40	25	ucc	5,888 teu
9306990	OOCL Vancouver	Pan	2006	66,462	66,940	281	40	25	ucc	5,888 teu: ex Italy Express-13, OOCL Vancouver-10
9177430	Perseus Leader *	Pan	1999	57,449	21,503	200	32	19	mve	5,066 ceu
9213454	Prestige Ace +	Pan	2000	55,878	20,202	200	32	19	mve	5,059 ceu
9650767	Raga	Pan	2013	50,615	95,666	235	38	14	bbu	
9560376	San Diego Bridge *	Pan	2010	71,787	72,912	293	40	25	ucc	6,350 teu
9599810	Shoei Prosperity ++	Pan	2012	92,752	181,403	292	45	15	bbu	
9519092	Sincerity Ace *	Pan	2009	59,408	19,265	200	32	19	mve	6,141 ceu
9377690	Manatee ++	Pan	2006	17,518	21,416	172	28	19	ucc	1,577 teu: ex Vento di Tramontana-15, Manatee-13, Cala Pantera-13
9381237	Volans Leader ††	Pan	2007	61,775	20,168	200	32	20	mve	5,415 ceu
9641833	Wisdom Ace	Pan	2013	59,409	19,227	200	32	20	mve	5,198 ceu
9664897	YM Moderation ++	Pan	2014	71,821	72,370	293	40	25	ucc	6,250 teu
9660011	YM Movement †	Pan	2013	71,821	72,370	293	40	25	ucc	6,250 teu
newbuildings:										
9737462	Ever		2016	150,000	147,500	366	51		ucc	14,000 teu	Imabari 2561
9737474	Ever		2016	150,000	147,500	366	51		ucc	14,000 teu	Imabari 2562
9737486	Ever		2016	150,000	147,500	366	51		ucc	14,000 teu	Imabari 2563
9737498	Ever		2017	150,000	147,500	366	51		ucc	14,000 teu	Imabari 2565
9737503	Ever		2017	150,000	147,500	366	51		ucc	14,000 teu	Imabari 2566
9789958	Ever		2018	190,000	199,500	399	51		ucc	20,000 teu	Imabari
9789960	Ever		2018	190,000	199,500	399	51		ucc	20,000 teu	Imabari
9789972	Ever		2018	190,000	199,500	399	51		ucc	20,000 teu	Imabari 2636
9789984	Ever		2018	190,000	199,500	399	51		ucc	20,000 teu	Imabari 2637
9789996	Ever		2018	100,000	199,500	399	51		ucc	20,000 teu	Imabari 2638

IMO	name	flag	year	gt	dwt	loa	bm	kts	type	comments	
			2019	190,000	199,500	399	51		ucc	20,000 teu	Imabari
			2019	190,000	199,500	399	51		ucc	20,000 teu	Imabari
			2019	190,000	199,500	399	51		ucc	20,000 teu	Imabari
			2019	190,000	199,500	399	51		ucc	20,000 teu	Imabari
			2019	190,000	190,500	399	51		ucc	20,000 teu	Imabari
			2019	190,000	199,500	399	51		ucc	20,000 teu	imabari
	YM		2018						ucc	14,000 teu	Imabari
	YM		2018						ucc	14,000 teu	Imabari
	YM		2018						ucc	14,000 teu	Imabari
	YM		2019						ucc	14,000 teu	Imabari
	YM		2019						ucc	14,000 teu	Imabari

*Vessels owned by associated companies: * Cypress Maritime, ** Pedregal Marine, + La Darien Navegacion S.A., † Paraiso Shipping, ++ Los Halillos Shg., †† Catalina Shg. S.A.. also own a large fleet uf bulkers*

Siem Industries Inc.   Norway

Star Reefers Shipowning

funnel: *white with red Siem logo beneath blue top, or operators colours* **hull:** *lilac grey, white or blue with blue over red boot-topping.*
history: *founded 1909 as Vestey Brothers, renamed Blue Star Line Ltd in 1911. Blue Star Ship Management Ltd. formed 1974. Vestey Group sold container business and Austasia Line subsidiary to P&O in 1998 (later to become Blue Star Holdings) and the reefers in 2001 to Swan Reefer ASA, which was a 1998 amalgamation of Irgens Larsen (formerly Rederiet Helge R Myhre to 1992 and Kvaerner Shipping AS (formed 1955) to 1995) and Swan Shipping A/S (formed 1989) before being renamed in 2001 and acquired by Siem Industries in 2002 . Management company Star Reefers Poland Sp z.oo, Poland, founded 2006. **web:** www.star-reefers.com*

IMO	name	flag	year	gt	dwt	loa	bm	kts	type	comments
8713562	Afric Star	Lbr	1990	11,590	12,683	159	24	18	grf	ex Tundra Consumer-04, Del Monte Consumer-00
8816156	Almeda Star	Bhs	1990	11,658	12,714	159	24	20	grf	ex Tundra King-05, Del Monte Pride-91
8816170	Andalucia Star	Bhs	1991	11,658	12,714	159	24	20	grf	ex Tundra Princess-05, Del Monte Spirit-91
8816168	Avelona Star	Bhs	1991	11,658	12,714	159	24	20	grf	ex Tundra Queen-05, Del Monte Quality-91
8713550	Avila Star	Lbr	1990	11,590	12,519	159	24	18	grf	ex Tundra Trader-04, Del Monte Trader-99
9019119	Cape Town Star *	Bhs	1993	10,614	10,629	150	23	21	grf	ex Caribbean Reef-03, Hornbreeze-98, Geestcrest-95, Hornbreeze-95, Caribbean Universal-94
9150810	Caribbean Star *	Lbr	1997	15,058	14,726	184	24	20	grf	ex Hornsea-00, Caribbean Star-98 (len 13)
9172480	Colombian Star	Pan	1998	15,292	15,000	184	24	21	grf	(len : 14)
9150822	Costa Rican Star *	Lbr	1998	15,058	14,726	184	24	21	grf	ex Hornwind-02, Costa Rican Star-98 (len- 13)
9172478	Cote d'Ivoirian Star	Pan	1998	15,292	15,000	184	24	21	grf	(len : 14)
9038945	Dunedin Star	Bmu	1994	8,665	11,793	151	20	22	grf	ex Chiquita Joy-06, Joy-00, Chiquita Joy-97
9019121	Durban Star *	Bhs	1993	10,614	10,629	150	23	20	grf	ex Coral Reef-03, Horncloud-98, Geesttide-95, Horncloud-94, Coral Universal-94
9053658	Regal Star	Bhs	1993	10,375	10,520	150	23	20	grf	ex Tauu-96, Hornstrait-95, Chiquita Tauu-94
9206061	Solent Star	Lbr	2001	10,804	9,709	150	23	21	grf	
9206059	Southampton Star	Lbr	1999	10,804	9,709	150	23	21	grf	
9330056	Star First	Lbr	2006	14,030	13,202	163	26	22	grf	
9338747	Star Prima	Lbr	2006	14,030	13,189	163	26	22	grf	
8917584	Wellington Star *	Bhs	1992	7,944	11,103	141	20	21	grf	ex Bothnian Reefer-03

*vessels managed by Star Reefers Poland Sp z.oo, Poland   or * Star Reefers UK Ltd.*

Siem Car Carriers AS

funnel: *white with red Siem logo, narrow blue band beneath red top.* **hull:** *grey or blue with blue waterline over red boot topping.*
history: *present name taken 2011. **web:** siemshipping.com*

IMO	name	flag	year	gt	dwt	loa	bm	kts	type	comments
9177040	Dresden *	Pan	2000	37,237	12,743	178	31	20	mve	3,919 ceu
9190858	Verona *	Pan	2000	37,237	12,778	178	31	20	mve	3,919 ceu
newbuildings :										
9762534			2016		16,500	200	32		mve	7,000 ceu: Uljanik 513
9762546			2016		16,500	200	32		mve	7,000 ceu: Uljanik 514
9762558			2017		16,500	200	32		mve	7,000 ceu: Uljanik 515
9785275			2017		16,500	200	32		mve	7,000 ceu: Uljanik 524
9785287			2018		16,500	200	32		mve	7,000 ceu: Uljanik 525

* chartered to van Uden, managed by Star Reefers Poland Sp.z.o.o.

Solvang ASA   Norway

funnel: *brown with blue 'CS' on broad white band.* **hull:** *brown with red boot-topping.* **history:** *amalgamation of Skibs Solvang (founded 1936) and Clipper Shipping A/S in 1992.* **web:** *www.solvangship.no*

IMO	name	flag	year	gt	dwt	loa	bm	kts	type	comments
9173068	Clipper Harald	Nis	1999	10,692	13,779	146	21	17	lpg	12,423 m³
9358670	Clipper Hebe	Nis	2007	13,893	18,110	155	23	17	lpg	17,128 m³
9358682	Clipper Helen	Nis	2007	13,893	18,110	155	23	17	lpg	16,789 m³
9378163	Clipper Hermod	Nis	2008	13,893	18,110	155	23	17	lpg	17,128 m³
9378151	Clipper Hermes	Nis	2008	13,893	18,880	156	23	17	lpg	17,128 m³
9699505	Clipper Jupiter	Nis	2015	37,366	42,543	203	33	17	lpg	60,000 m³
9377078	Clipper Mars	Nis	2008	36,459	43,544	205	32	16	lpg	60,256 m³
9253820	Clipper Moon	Nis	2003	35,012	44,872	205	32	16	lpg	58,201 m³
9372432	Clipper Neptun	Nis	2008	36,459	43,508	205	32	16	lpg	59,058 m³
9292101	Clipper Odin	Nis	2005	25,994	29,216	180	29	16	lpg	38,000 m³.ex Odin-15, BW Odin-11, Berge Odin-07
9372420	Clipper Orion	Nis	2008	36,459	43,475	205	32	16	lpg	60,000 m³
9656747	Clipper Posh	Nis	2013	48,051	55,047	225	37	16	lpg	84,000 m³
9630755	Clipper Quito	Nis	2013	48,051	55,047	225	37	16	lpg	84,000 m³
9699517	Clipper Saturn	Nis	2015	37,366	42,543	203	33	17	lpg	60,000 m³
9379404	Clipper Sirius	Nis	2008	42,897	54,048	227	32	16	lpg	75,000 m³
9277943	Clipper Sky	Nis	2004	35,158	44,617	205	32	16	lpg	58,176 m³
9247807	Clipper Star	Nis	2003	34,970	44,807	205	32	16	lpg	58,154 m³
9347516	Clipper Sun	Bhs	2008	47,173	58,677	225	37	16	lpg	82,000 m³
9731042	Clipper Venus	Nis	2015	37,366	42,543	203	33	17	lpg	60,000 m³
9379399	Clipper Victory	Nis	2009	42,897	54,005	227	32	16	lpg	75,000 m³
9173056	Clipper Viking	Nis	1998	10,692	13,777	146	21	17	lpg	12,409 m³

newbuildings: *2 x 78,700 m³ [Hyundai H.I. (Q2/Q3 2017)]*

OAO 'Sovcomflot'   Russia

funnel: *blue with white 'SCF', black top..* **hull:** *black with white 'SCF' or blue with white 'SCF LPG' or red with red boot-topping.* **history:** *formed 1988 and first former Soviet shipping enterprise with independent capital, but wholly owned within Russian Federation. Merged with Novoship in 2007.* **web:** *www.sovcomflot.com*

IMO	name	flag	year	gt	dwt	loa	bm	kts	type	comments
9316127	Aleksey Kosygin	Lbr	2007	87,146	163,545	281	50	15	tcr	
9451707	Alpine Monique	Sgp	2010	29,130	46,087	183	32	14	tco	

Costa Rican Star : Siem Industries Inc - Star Reefers : *Chris Brooks*

IMO	name	flag	year	gt	dwt	loa	bm	kts	type	comments
9256901	Anichkov Bridge	Lbr	2003	27,829	47,843	183	32	14	tco	
9301392	Captain Kostichev	Cyp	2005	60,434	100,927	247	42	14	tcs	
9610793	Georgy Maslov	Lbr	2012	66,818	122,018	250	46	14	tcr	
9249130	Governor Farkhutdinov	Cyp	2004	58,918	108,078	247	42	15	tcs	
9256913	Hermitage Bridge	Lbr	2003	28,000	47,842	183	32	14	tco	
9372559	Kapitan Gotskiy (2p)	Rus	2008	49,597	71,228	257	34	16	tci	
9333682	Kirill Lavrov (2p)	Cyp	2010	49,866	70,053	257	34	16	tci	
9412347	Leonid Loza	Lbr	2011	83,747	156,630	274	48	14	tcr	
9256066	Ligovsky Prospect	Lbr	2003	62,586	114,639	250	44	15	tcr	
9256078	Liteyny Prospect	Lbr	2003	62,586	104,707	250	44	15	tcr	ex Stena Contender-07, Liteyny Prospect-04
9333670	Mikhail Ulyanov (2p)	Rus	2010	49,866	69,830	257	34	16	tci	
9511521	Moskovsky Prospect	Lbr	2010	62,504	114,100	250	44	14	tcr	
9256925	Narodny Bridge	Lbr	2003	27,829	47,791	183	32	14	tco	
9256054	Nevskiy Prospect	Lbr	2003	62,586	114,598	250	44	15	tcr	
9610781	Nikolay Zuyev	Lbr	2012	66,818	122,039	250	46	14	tcr	
9256937	Okhta Bridge	Lbr	2004	27,829	47,803	182	32	14	tco	
9511387	Olympiysky Prospect	Lbr	2010	62,504	113,905	250	44	14	tcr	
9301380	Pavel Chernysh	Cyp	2005	60,434	103,778	247	42	14	tcr	
9186596	Petrodvorets	Lbr	1999	59,731	105,692	248	43	15	tco	ex Astro Saturn-01
9223344	Petropavlovsk	Lbr	2002	57,683	106,532	241	42	15	tcr	
9254915	Petrovsk	Lbr	2004	57,683	105,900	241	42	15	tcr	
9254903	Petrozavodsk	Lbr	2003	57,683	106,449	241	42	15	tcr	
9630028	Pskov [df]	Cyp	2014	113,876	93,500	300	46	19	lng	170,200 m³
9511533	Primorskiy Prospect	Lbr	2010	62,504	113,860	250	44	14	tcr	
9384435	RN Archangelsk **	Cyp	2008	19,986	30,720	176	30	15	tco	ex Archangelsk-08
9384447	RN Murmansk **	Cyp	2009	19,994	30,720	176	30	15	tco	
9384459	RN Privodino **	Cyp	2009	19,994	30,720	176	30	15	tco	
9249128	Sakhalin Island	Cyp	2004	58,918	108,078	247	42	15	tcs	
9224439	SCF Altai	Lbr	2001	81,085	159,169	274	48	15	tcr	
9577056	SCF Alpine	Lbr	2010	42,208	74,602	228	32	15	tco	
9333436	SCF Amur	Lbr	2007	29,844	47,095	183	32	14	tco	
9422457	SCF Baikal	Lbr	2010	81,339	158,097	274	48	15	tcr	l/a SCF Vankor

Kirill Lavrov : Sovcomflot : *Hans Kraijenbosch*

IMO	name	flag	year	gt	dwt	loa	bm	kts	type	comments
9305568	SCF Baltica	Lbr	2005	65,293	117,153	250	44	15	tcr	
9224441	SCF Caucasus *	Lbr	2002	81,085	159,173	274	48	15	tcr	
9224453	SCF Khibiny	Lbr	2002	81,085	159,156	274	48	15	tcr	
9654878	SCF Melampus [tf]	Lbr	2015	113,876	93,508	300	46	19	lng	170,200 m³
9654880	SCF Mitre [tf]	Lbr	2015	113,876	93,585	300	46	19	lng	170,200 m³
9333400	SCF Neva	Lbr	2006	29,644	47,125	183	32	14	tco	
9577068	SCF Pacifica	Lbr	2011	42,208	74,534	228	32	15	tco	
9577109	SCF Pearl	Lbr	2011	42,208	74,552	228	32	15	tco	
9333424	SCF Pechora	Lbr	2007	29,844	47,218	183	32	14	tco	
9577070	SCF Pioneer	Lbr	2011	42,208	74,552	228	32	15	tco	
9456927	SCF Plymouth	Lbr	2011	42,208	74,606	228	32	15	tco	
9577082	SCF Prime	Lbr	2011	42,208	74,581	228	32	15	tco	
9421960	SCF Primorye	Lbr	2009	84,029	158,070	274	48	16	tcr	
9577111	SCF Progress	Lbr	2012	42,208	74,588	228	32	15	tco	
9577094	SCF Provider	Lbr	2011	42,208	74,548	228	32	15	tco	
9577123	SCF Prudencia	Lbr	2012	42,208	74,565	228	32	15	tco	
9421972	SCT Samotlor	Lbr	2010	84,029	158,070	274	48	16	tcr	
9224465	SCF Sayan	Lbr	2002	81,085	159,184	274	48	15	tcr	
9120322	SCF Suek	Lbr	1998	40,538	69,100	225	32	13	bbu	ex Gianni D-09, St. Nicholas-02, l/a Kiev
9422445	SCF Surgut	Lbr	2009	81,339	158,097	274	48	15	tcr	
9324746	SCF Tobolsk	Lbr	2006	23,003	26,424	174	28	15	lpg	35,000 m³
9326598	SCF Tomsk	Lbr	2007	23,003	26,424	174	28	15	lpg	35,000 m³
9231509	SCF Ural	Lbr	2002	81,085	159,169	274	48	15	tcr	
9333412	SCF Yenisei	Lbr	2007	29,844	47,187	183	32	14	tco	
9655511	Sibur Tobol	Lbr	2013	18,300	22,818	159	26	16	lpg	20,550 m³
9655509	Sibur Voronezh	Lbr	2013	18,425	22,819	159	26	16	lpg	20,550 m³
9522324	Suvorovsky Prospect	Lbr	2011	62,504	113,905	250	44	14	tcr	
9292060	Tavrichesky Bridge	Lbr	2006	27,725	46,697	183	32	14	tco	
9292058	Teatralny Bridge	Lbr	2006	27,725	46,697	183	32	14	tco	
9372561	Timofey Guzhenko (2p)	Rus	2009	49,597	72,722	256	34	16	tci	
9292046	Torgovy Bridge	Lbr	2005	27,725	47,363	183	32	14	tco	
9292034	Tower Bridge	Lbr	2004	27,725	47,363	183	32	14	tco	

Sibur Voronezh : Sovcomflot : *Hans Kraijenbosch*

IMO	name	flag	year	gt	dwt	loa	bm	kts	type	comments
9382798	Transsib Bridge *	Lbr	2008	27,725	46,564	183	32	14	tco	
9258167	Troitskiy Bridge	Lbr	2003	27,725	41,158	183	32	14	tco	
9258179	Tuchkov Bridge	Lbr	2004	27,725	47,199	183	32	14	tco	
9344033	Tverskoy Bridge	Lbr	2007	27,725	46,564	183	32	14	tco	
9372547	Vasily Dinkov (2p)	Rus	2008	49,597	71,254	257	34	16	tci	
9630004	Velikiy Novgorod [df]	Lbr	2014	113,876	93,486	300	46	19	lng	170,200 m³
9301421	Victor Konetsky	Cyp	2005	60,434	101,018	247	42	15	tcs	
9301407	Viktor Titov	Cyp	2005	60,434	100,899	247	42	15	tcs	
9311622	Vladimir Tikhonov	Lbr	2006	87,146	162,397	281	50	15	tcr	
9301419	Yuri Senkevich	Cyp	2005	60,434	100,971	247	42	15	tcs	
9418494	Zaliv Aniva	Cyp	2009	60,325	102,946	247	42	15	tcs	
newbuildings:										
9752084	*Shturman Albanov*		2016		42,000	249	34	14	tci	Samsung 2132
9752096	*Shturman Malygin*		2016		42,000	249	34	14	tci	Samsung 2133
9752101	*Shturman Ovtsyn*		2016		42,000	249	34	14	tci	Samsung 2134
9737187	*SCF Yamal*	Cyp	2017			299	50	19	lng	172,600 m³ Daewoo 2418

vessels managed by SCF Unicom Shipmanagement Singapore Pte. (originally formed in 1991 with Acomarit (30%) whose interest was acquired in 1994 – www.unicom-cy.com), by Unicom Management Services (St. Peterburg) Ltd or ** by Rubio Holdings Ltd. (SCF Mgmt.Services. Dubai)*

SCF Novoship J/S Co. (Novorossiysk Shipping Co), Russia

funnel: *Blue with red and black intertwined ropes between narrow diagonal blue bands on broad diagonal white band.* **hull:** *blue, black, brown or red with red boot-topping.* **history:** *formed 1932 and controlled by the Government of The Russian Federation until privatised in 1993. Merged with Sovcomflot in 2007, but operates as a separate company.* **web:** *www.novoship.ru*

IMO	name	flag	year	gt	dwt	loa	bm	kts	type	comments
9292204	Adygeya	Lbr	2005	57,177	105,926	244	42	14	tcr	l/a Four Stream
9610808	Anatoly Kolodkin	Lbr	2013	66,855	118,147	250	46	14	tco	
9276030	Elbrus	Mlt	2004	29,327	46,655	183	32	14	tco	
9610793	Georgy Maslov	Lbr	2012	66,818	122,018	250	46	14	tcr	
9257993	Kaluga	Lbr	2003	62,395	114,800	250	44	14	tcr	
9258002	Kazan	Lbr	2003	62,395	115,727	250	44	14	tcr	
9270517	Krasnodar	Lbr	2003	62,395	115,605	250	44	14	tcr	
9270529	Krymsk	Lbr	2003	62,395	115,605	250	44	14	tcr	
9180279	Kuban	Lbr	2000	56,076	106,562	243	42	14	tcr	l/a Moscow Glory
9412347	Leonid Loza	Lbr	2011	83,747	156,572	274	48	15	tcr	
9165530	Moscow	Lbr	1998	56,076	106,553	243	42	15	tcr	
9166390	Moscow Kremlin	Lbr	1998	56,076	106,521	243	42	15	tcr	
9165542	Moscow River	Lbr	1999	56,075	106,552	243	42	15	tcr	
9180267	Moscow Stars	Lbr	1999	56,076	106,450	243	42	14	tcr	
9166417	Moscow University	Lbr	1999	56,076	106,521	243	42	15	tcr	
9610781	Nikolay Zuyev	Lbr	2012	66,818	122,039	150	46	14	tcr	
9413573	NS Africa	Lbr	2009	62,372	111,682	250	44	15	tco	
9413547	NS Arctic	Lbr	2009	62,372	111,107	250	44	15	tco	
9413559	NS Antarctic	Lbr	2009	62.372	111,107	250	44	15	tco	
9413561	NS Asia	Lbr	2009	62,372	111,682	250	44	15	tco	
9412335	NS Bora	Lbr	2010	83,747	156,838	274	48	15	tcr	
9412359	NS Bravo	Lbr	2010	83,747	156,694	274	48	15	tcr	
9411020	NS Burgas	Lbr	2009	83,747	156,572	274	48	15	tcr	
9341067	NS Captain	Lbr	2006	57,248	105,926	244	42	14	tcr	
9306782	NS Century	Lbr	2006	57,248	105,926	244	42	14	tcr	
9299680	NS Challenger	Lbr	2005	57,248	105,926	244	42	14	tcr	
9299719	NS Champion	Lbr	2005	57,248	105,926	244	42	14	tcr	
9341081	NS Clipper	Lbr	2006	57,248	105,926	244	42	14	tcr	
9312884	NS Columbus	Lbr	2007	57,248	105,788	244	42	14	tcr	
9306794	NS Commander	Lbr	2006	57,248	105,926	244	42	14	tcr	
9299707	NS Concept	Lbr	2005	57,248	105,926	244	42	14	tcr	
9299692	NS Concord	Lbr	2005	57,248	105,926	244	42	14	tcr	
9341093	NS Consul	Lbr	2006	57,248	105,926	244	42	14	tcr	
9341079	NS Corona	Lbr	2006	57,248	105,926	244	42	14	tcr	
9312896	NS Creation	Lbr	2007	57,248	105,802	244	42	14	tcr	
9609732	NS Energy	Lbr	2013	40,972	74,518	225	32	14	bbu	
9339325	NS Laguna	Lbr	2007	61,449	115,831	250	44	15	tcr	
9339301	NS Leader	Lbr	2007	61,449	115,857	250	44	15	tcr	
9339313	NS Lion	Lbr	2007	61,449	115,831	250	44	15	tcr	
9339337	NS Lotus	Lbr	2008	61,449	115,849	250	44	15	tcr	
9329667	NS Parade	Lbr	2008	25,467	40,119	176	31	15	tco	
9328955	NS Point	Lbr	2008	25,467	40,149	176	31	15	tco	
9322968	NS Power	Lbr	2006	25,467	40,161	176	31	15	tco	
9322956	NS Pride	Lbr	2006	25,467	40,042	176	31	15	tco	
9309576	NS Silver	Lbr	2005	27,357	47,197	176	31	14	tco	
9318553	NS Spirit	Lbr	2006	27,357	46,941	176	31	14	tco	
9309588	NS Stella	Lbr	2005	27,357	47,197	176	31	14	tco	
9318541	NS Stream	Lbr	2006	27,357	46,941	176	31	14	tco	

IMO	name	flag	year	gt	dwt	loa	bm	kts	type	comments
9609744	NS Yakutia	Lbr	2013	40,972	74,559	225	32	14	bbu	
9276028	Pamir	Mlt	2004	29,327	46,654	183	32	14	tco	
9625968	SCF Shanghai	Lbr	2014	167,578	320,701	332	60	16	tcr	
9625956	Svet	Lbr	2013	167,578	321,039	332	60	16	tcr	
9610810	Viktor Bakaev	Lbr	2013	66,855	118,175	250	46	14	tco	

Spar Shipping AS   Norway

funnel: *white with white 'S' on blue spade, narrow black top* **hull:** *black with red boot-topping.* **history:** *established 1990 and commenced ship-owning in 1994.* **web:** *www.sparshipping.com*

IMO	name	flag	year	gt	dwt	loa	bm	kts	type	comments
9734989	Spar Apus	Nis	2015	36,311	63,800	200	32	14	bbu	
9701920	Spar Aries	Nis	2015	36,311	63,800	200	32	14	bbu	
9299290	Spar Canis	Nis	2006	32,474	53,565	190	32	14	bbu	
9490844	Spar Capella *	Nis	2011	32,839	58,000	190	32	14	bbu	
9497830	Spar Corona	Nis	2011	32,839	58,000	190	32	14	bbu	
9490791	Spar Corvus	Nis	2011	32,839	58,000	190	32	14	bbu	
9299305	Spar Draco *	Nis	2006	32,474	53,565	190	32	14	bbu	
9307580	Spar Gemini *	Nis	2007	32,474	53,565	190	32	14	bbu	
9490806	Spar Hydra	Nis	2011	32,839	58,000	190	32	14	bbu	
9734991	Spar Indus	Nis	2016	36,730	64,000	200	32	14	bbu	
9328534	Spar Libra	Nis	2006	32,474	53,565	190	32	14	bbu	ex Bulk Navigator-11, Arya Payk-09, Bulk Navigator-06
9154610	Spar Lupus	Nis	1998	25,982	45,146	186	30	15	bbu	ex Golden Aloe-02
9289025	Spar Lynx *	Nis	2005	32,474	53,565	190	32	14	bbu	
9289013	Spar Lyra *	Nis	2005	32,474	53,565	190	32	14	bbu	
9490727	Spar Mira	Nis	2010	32,839	58,000	190	32	14	bbu	
9077238	Spar Neptun	Nis	1994	36,559	70,101	225	32	15	bbu	ex Apollon-04, Gran Trader-99
9735000	Spar Octans	Nis	2015	36,313	64,000	200	32	14	bbu	
9701932	Spar Pyxis	Nis	2015	36,311	63,800	200	32	14	bbu	
9557111	Spar Rigel	Nis	2010	32,837	58,000	190	32	14	bbu	
9307578	Spar Scorpio *	Nis	2006	32,474	53,565	190	32	14	bbu	
9328522	Spar Spica	Nis	2005	32,474	53,565	190	32	14	bbu	ex Bulk Voyager-11, Arya Payam-09, Bulk Voyager-05, Paracan-05
9299288	Spar Taurus *	Nis	2005	32,474	53,565	190	32	14	bbu	
9490856	Spar Ursa	Nis	2011	32,838	58,000	190	32	14	bbu	
9490870	Spar Vega *	Nis	2011	32,839	58,000	190	32	14	bbu	
9299276	Spar Virgo *	Nis	2005	32,474	53,565	190	32	14	bbu	
newbuildings:										
9735012		Nis	2016	36,313	64,000	200	32	14	bbu	Jiangsu Hantong 215

* operate in the Supra8 Pool, formed June 2011 (www.navig8bulk.com)

Spliethoff's Bevrachtingskantoor B.V.   Netherlands

funnel: *orange with black 'S' on diagonally quartered white/red/orange/blue flag.* **hull:** *brown with white 'Spliethoff', green above red boot-topping.* **history:** *formed 1921.* **web:** *www.spliethoff.nl*

IMO	name	flag	year	gt	dwt	loa	bm	kts	type	comments
9420784	Damgracht	Nld	2009	13,558	18,143	157	23	17	ggc	cr: 3(120)
9420796	Danzigergracht	Nld	2009	13,558	18,143	157	23	17	ggc	cr: 3(120)
9420801	Deltagracht	Nld	2009	13,558	18,143	157	23	17	ggc	cr: 3(120)
9420813	Diamantgracht	Nld	2009	13,706	17,966	157	23	17	ggc	cr: 3(120)
9420772	Dijksgracht	Nld	2008	13,558	17,381	157	23	17	ggc	cr: 3(120)
9420825	Dolfijngracht	Nld	2009	13,706	17,967	157	23	17	ggc	cr: 3(120)
9420837	Donaugracht	Nld	2009	13,706	17,967	157	23	17	ggc	cr: 3(120)
9420849	Dynamogracht	Nld	2008	13,706	17,967	157	23	17	ggc	cr: 3(120)
9571492	Maasgracht	Nld	2011	9,524	11,749	142	19	15	ggc	
9571507	Marsgracht	Nld	2011	9,524	11.759	142	19	15	ggc	
9571519	Merwedegracht	Nld	2011	9,524	11,759	142	19	15	ggc	
9571521	Minervagracht	Nld	2011	9,524	11,759	142	19	15	ggc	
9571533	Molengracht	Nld	2012	9,524	11,744	142	19	15	ggc	
9571545	Muntgracht	Nld	2012	9,524	11,744	142	19	15	ggc	
9288069	Saimaagracht	Nld	2004	18,321	23,660	185	26	19	ggc	
9288071	Sampogracht	Nld	2005	18,321	23,688	185	26	19	ggc	
9202510	Scheldegracht	Nld	2000	16,639	21,250	168	25	19	ggc	
9197363	Schippersgracht	Ant	2000	16,641	21,402	168	25	19	ggc	
9197375	Singelgracht	Nld	2000	16,641	21,402	168	25	19	ggc	
9197947	Slotergracht	Nld	2000	16,641	21,402	168	25	19	ggc	
9202522	Sluisgracht	Nld	2001	16,639	21,250	172	25	19	ggc	
9202546	Snoekgracht	Nld	2000	16,641	21,400	168	25	19	ggc	
9202558	Spaarnegracht	Nld	2000	16,641	21,402	168	25	19	ggc	
9197911	Spiegelgracht	Nld	2000	16,641	21,400	168	25	19	ggc	
9202534	Spuigracht	Nld	2001	16,639	21,349	172	25	19	ggc	
9202508	Stadiongracht	Nld	2000	16,639	21,250	172	25	19	ggc	

Diamantgracht : Spliethoff's : *Mike Rhodes*

Merwedegracht : Spliethoff's : *Hans Kraijenbosch*

IMO	name	flag	year	gt	dwt	loa	bm	kts	type	comments
9288045	Statengracht	Nld	2004	16,676	21,250	173	26	19	ggc	
9288057	Suomigracht	Nld	2004	18,321	23,660	185	26	19	ggc	

also owns Ro-Ro's and smaller vessels operating in coastal trades.

BigLift Shipping b.v., Netherlands
funnel: *yellow with black 'BigLift'.* **hull:** *yellow with blue 'BigLift', red or black boot-topping.* **history:** *formed 1973 by Nedlloyd Groep NV as Mammoet Shipping BV, joint venture as Mammoet-Hansa AG from 1989, Spliethoff's gained full control in 2000 and the company renamed.* **web:** *www.bigliftshipping.com*

IMO	name	flag	year	gt	dwt	loa	bm	kts	type	comments
9153898	Da Fu **	Pan	1998	14,021	16,957	153	23	15	ghl	
9153886	Da Hua **	Pan	1998	14,021	16,957	153	23	15	ghl	
9153903	Da Qiang **	Pan	1998	14,021	16,957	153	23	15	ghl	
9153874	Da Zhong **	Pan	1998	14,021	16,957	153	23	15	ghl	
9148116	Han Yi *	Sgp	1998	10,990	16,069	138	23	15	ghl	ex Enchanter-11, Sailer Jupiter-98
8300389	Happy Buccaneer (2)	Nld	1984	16,341	13,740	146	28	15	ghl	cr: 2(700)
9551935	Happy Delta	Nld	2011	14,784	18,276	157	26	16	ghl	cr: 1(120),2(400)
9551947	Happy Diamond	Nld	2011	14,784	18,148	157	26	16	ghl	cr: 1(120),2(400)
9551959	Happy Dover	Nld	2011	14,784	18,074	157	26	16	ghl	cr: 1(120),2(400)
9551961	Happy Dragon	Nld	2011	14,784	18,103	157	26	16	ghl	cr: 1(120),2(400)
9551973	Happy Dynamic	Nld	2011	14,784	18,043	157	26	16	ghl	cr: 1(120),2(400)
9139311	Happy Ranger	Nld	1997	10,990	12,950	138	23	16	ghl	cr: 2(400)
9139294	Happy River	Nld	1997	10,990	12,950	138	23	16	ghl	cr: 2(400)
9139309	Happy Rover	Nld	1997	10,950	12,950	138	23	16	ghl	cr: 2(400)
9457220	Happy Sky	Nld	2013	15,989	18,680	155	27	17	ghl	cr: 2(900)
9661259	Happy Star	Nld	2014	18,374	9,900	155	27	17	ghl	cr: 2(900)

* owned by Pool member Mitsui OSK Lines Ltd (managed by New Asian Shipping Co. Ltd, Hong Kong) qv or ** by Guangzhou Ocean Shipping (COSCO), China.

BigRoll b.v., Netherlands
funnel: *red with 'BIGROLL' in white* **hull:** *red with red boot topping:* **history:** *j/v formed 2013 between BigLift and RollDock to operate specially designed module carriers* **web:** *www.bigrollshipping.com*

newbuildings:

IMO	name	flag	year	gt	dwt	loa	bm	kts	type	comments
9710464	BigRoll Barentsz		2016	18,000	22,500	173	42	13	urr	Cosco Dalian
9710476	BigRoll Bering		2016	18,000	22,500	173	42	13	urr	Cosco Dalian
9758557	BigRoll Baffin		2016	18,000	22,500	173	43	13	urr	Cosco Dalian
9766841	BigRoll Beaumont		2017	18,000	22,500	173	42	13	urr	Cosco Dalian

DYT Yacht Transport b.v., Netherlands
funnel: *blue with orange and blue DYT on white panel,* **hull:** *light grey with 'YACHT-TRANSPORT.COM' in blue, orange trim and boot topping* **web:** *www.yacht-transport.com*

IMO	name	flag	year	gt	dwt	loa	bm	kts	type	comments
8025343	Super Servant 4 (2)	Cuw	1982	12,642	14,138	140	32	13	urr	
9346029	Yacht Express	Cuw	2007	17,951	12,500	209	32	18	urr	

Splošna Plovidba d.o.o.   Slovenia
funnel: *white with company logo of 3 red mountain peaks over a black anchor over 3 blue waves.* **hull:** *black with red boot-topping.*
history: *founded October 22 1954* **web:** *www.splosnaplovidba.com*

IMO	name	flag	year	gt	dwt	loa	bm	kts	type	comments
9483255	Cas Amares	Lbr	2011	32,672	55,783	188	32	14	bbu	ex E.R. Bern-15
9483190	Cas Avanca	Lbr	2009	32,672	55,561	188	32	14	bbu	ex E.R. Bologna-15
9144299	Lipica	Mlt	1998	24,954	42,556	182	30	14	bbu	ex Annetta-07
9290804	Loa	Lbr	2005	42,382	51,870	268	32	25	ucc	4,043 teu: l/a Adda
9508706	Nova Gorica	Lbr	2008	31,117	53,100	190	32	14	bbu	l/a Chun He 18
9330422	Novo Mesta	Lbr	2005	31,273	53,626	190	32	14	bbu	ex Fructidor-09
9294824	Pohorje	Lbr	2006	42,300	51,870	268	32	25	ucc	4,043 teu: ex Lircay-12, l/dn Ariba
9588536	Portorož	Mlt	2011	33,042	56,633	190	32	14	bbu	
9144031	Postojna	Lbr	1998	25,537	46,570	183	31	14	bbu	ex Tristan-08, Glen Helen-08, Alicahue-04
9456226	Tamar	Mhl	2010	32,987	56,563	190	32	14	bbu	l/a Turandot
9456159	Trenta	Mhl	2010	32,987	56,838	190	32	14	bbu	ex Wiking-11
9144304	Triglav	Lbr	1998	24,954	42,527	182	30	14	bbu	ex Andrea D-07
9144055	Vipava	Lbr	1998	25,537	46,570	183	31	14	bbu	ex Isolde-08, Glen Maye-06, Allipen-05

vessels owned by Genshipping Corp., Slovenia

Starship Constellation Group   Monaco

International Andromeda Shipping SAM, Monaco
funnel: *grey with 5-pointed star (of colour to match name) superimposed on white 'A'.* **hull:** *black with red boot-topping.*
history: *founded 1992.* **web:** *www.andromeda-shipping.com*

IMO	name	flag	year	gt	dwt	loa	bm	kts	type	comments
9151840	Blue Trader	Mlt	1997	79,494	149,775	270	45	14	tcr	
9290830	Emerald Stars	Nis	2005	23,298	37,270	183	27	14	tco	ex Emerald Star-10, Emerald-05

IMO	name	flag	year	gt	dwt	loa	bm	kts	type	comments
9035060	Green Trader	Mhl	1993	88,886	156,105	275	50	15	tcr	
9433597	Orange Stars	Mhl	2011	61,314	115,756	249	44	14	tcr	
9433585	Pink Stars	Mhl	2010	61,314	115,592	249	44	14	tcr	
9131876	Scarlet Trader * (2)	Mhl	1997	76,216	126,646	272	46	14	tcs	ex Kometik-15

Stena AB   Sweden

funnel: white 'S' on wide red band separated from narrow blue top and black base by narrow white bands. **hull:** black or dark blue.
With red boot-topping (Stena C series (†) with Stena Weco' in white, Stena P series with 'Stena Bulk' in white anb P max in red/white or
(Shuttle tankers) red with 'Stena Teekay' in black, red boot-topping: LNG tankers – light blue with 'Stena Bulk LNG' in white and
Dragon's head) **history:** founded 1939 as Sten A Olsson Handels A/B to 1963, then Stena Line A/B to 1977. Concordia Maritime AB
(formed 1984), jointly owned with Neste, took over Universe Tankships (Delaware) LLC in 1996. **web:** www.stena.com

IMO	name	flag	year	gt	dwt	loa	bm	kts	type	comments
9283629	Aspropyrgos	Bhs	2004	40,690	72,854	229	32	14	tcr	ex Stena Callas-14, Aspropyrgos-09
9272199	Contest	Bmu	2005	27,357	47,171	183	32	15	tco	ex Stena Contest-14
9152507	Stena Alexita (2) ‡	Nor	1998	76,836	127,466	263	46	15	tcs	
9305556	Stena Arctica	Gbr	2005	65,293	117,099	250	44	15	tco	
9315393	Stena Blue Sky [st]	Pan	2006	97,754	84,363	285	43	20	lng	145,700 m³; ex Bluesky-11
9282625	Stena Companion	Bhs	2005	40,690	72,825	229	32	14	tcr	ex Stena Chiron-15, Daedalos-08
9413327	Stena Clear Sky (df)	Gbr	2011	109,949	96,811	298	46	20	lng	173,593 m³ l/a Crystal Sky
9383900	Stena Crystal Sky (df)	Gbr	2011	109,949	96,889	298	46	20	lng	173,611 m³ l/a Clear Sky
9206671	Stena Natalita (2) ‡	Bhs	2001	62,393	108,073	250	43	14	tcs	
9299123	Stena Paris *	Bmu	2005	36,064	65,125	290	40	14	tco	
9391476	Stena Penguin *	Bmu	2010	36,168	64,834	290	40	14	tco	
9299159	Stena Performance *	Bmu	2006	36,064	65,125	290	40	14	tco	
9312456	Stena Perros *	Bmu	2007	36,168	65,086	290	40	14	tco	
9390032	Stena Polaris *	Bmu	2010	36,168	64,917	290	40	14	tco	
9413523	Stena Premium *	Bmu	2011	36,168	67,055	290	40	14	tco	
9312444	Stena President *	Bmu	2007	36,168	65,112	290	40	14	tco	
9299147	Stena Primorsk *	Lbr	2006	36,064	65,125	290	40	14	tco	
9390020	Stena Progress *	Bmu	2009	36,064	65,125	290	40	14	tco	
9299135	Stena Provence *	Bmu	2006	36,168	65,125	290	40	14	tco	
9188099	Stena Sirita (2) ‡	Nor	1999	77,410	127,466	263	46	15	tcs	
9579042	Stena Suede	Bmu	2011	81,187	159,158	274	48	14	tcr	
9592214	Stena Sunrise	Bmu	2013	81,187	159,034	274	48	14	tcr	
9579030	Stena Superior	Bmu	2011	81,187	159,236	274	48	14	tcr	
9585895	Stena Supreme	Bmu	2012	81,187	159,031	274	48	14	tcr	

newbuildings: 3 x LNG [Daewoo 2403/4 (2014/5), 2015]]
* operated by affiliate Concordia Maritime AB and managed by Northern Marine Management Ltd, UK (www.nmm-stena.com)
‡ jointly owned with Ugland Marine Services AS and managed by Standard Marine Tønsberg AS, Norway.
also see Neste Oil Corporation

Stena Weco A/S

funnel: white 'S' on wide red band separated from narrow blue top and black base by narrow white bands or Dannebrog markings.
hull: black with red base separated with narrow white stripe, and red and white/yellow and blue swirls and 'STENA WECO' in white at
stern, red or pink boot-topping. **history:** founded 2012 as j/v between Stena Bulk and Weco,a subsidiary of Dannebrog group, mainly
for the transport of sustainable palm oil produced by Golden Agri Resources

IMO	name	flag	year	gt	dwt	loa	bm	kts	type	comments
9258595	Stena Concert	Bmu	2004	27,463	47,288	183	32	14	tco	ex Stena Italica-08

Stenaweco Caterina Corrado : Stena AB - Stenaweco : *Chris Brooks*

IMO	name	flag	year	gt	dwt	loa	bm	kts	type	comments
9252448	Stena Conqueror	Bmu	2003	27,335	47,323	183	32	14	tco	l/a Hellenica
9252436	Stena Conquest	Bmu	2003	27,335	47,136	183	32	14	tco	ex Hispanica-03
9667473	Stena Image *	Bmu	2015	29,666	49,719	183	32	14	tco	
9666077	Stena Imperative *	Bmu	2016	29,666	50,000	183	32	14	tco	
9667485	Stena Imperial *	Gbr	2015	29,666	49,750	183	32	14	tco	
9667497	Stena Important *	Bmu	2015	29,666	49,731	183	32	14	tco	
9667461	Stena Impression *	Gbr	2015	29,666	49,776	183	32	15	tco	
9688415	Stenaweco									
	Andrea Corrado	Bhs	2015	29,846	49,999	183	32	15	tco	
9688427	Stenaweco									
	Caterina Corrado	Bhs	2015	29,846	49,999	183	32	15	tco	
9683984	Stenaweco Energy	Mhl	2014	29,429	49,973	183	32	15	tco	
9687942	Stenaweco Evolution	Mhl	2015	29,429	49,973	183	32	15	tco	
9664720	Stenaweco									
	Gladys W.	Mhl	2013	29,940	49,995	183	32	16	tco	ex Gladys W.-13
9661247	Stenaweco Julia L	Mhl	2013	29,940	49,995	183	32	16	tco	ex Julia L.-13
9661235	Stenaweco									
	Marjorie K.	Mhl	2013	29,940	49,995	183	32	16	tco	ex Marjorie K.-13
newbuildings:										
9685463	Stena Imagination *		2016	29,666	50,000	183	32	14	tco	Guangzhou 12130007
9685475	Stena Immense *		2016	29,666	50,000	183	32	14	tco	Guangzhou 12130008
9693018	Stena Immaculate *		2016	29,666	50,000	183	32	14	tco	Guangzhou 12130009
9693020	Stena Impeccable *		2016	29,666	50,000	183	32	14	tco	Guangzhou 12130010

* vessels jointly owned by Stena Bulk and Golden Agri Resources, Indonesia

Stolt-Nielsen Transportation Group Ltd   U.S.A.

funnel: *white with large white 'S' on red square, narrow black top.* **hull:** *yellow with black 'STOLT TANKERS', red or pink boot-topping.*
history: *founded 1886 as subsidiary of Stolt-Nielsen SA, Luxembourg (founded 1891), B Stolt-Nielsen & Co to 1931, B Stolt-Nielsen & Sonner A/S to 1961, Jacob Stolt-Nielsen A/S to 1970, Stolt-Nielsen Rederi A/S to 1999, when Stolt Tankers BV was relocated from Norway to Netherlands and Stolt-Nielsen Transportation Group BV to 2007.* **web:** *www.stolt-nielsen.com*

IMO	name	flag	year	gt	dwt	loa	bm	kts	type	comments
9124469	Stolt									
	Achievement (me)	Cym	1999	25,427	37,000	177	31	16	tco	
9360934	Stolt Ami #	Pan	2006	11,708	19,963	144	24	14	tco	
9351543	Stolt Basuto ‡	Sgp	2006	16,442	25,196	159	26	15	tco	ex Basuto-13, Stolt Basuto-10
9511167	Stolt Bobcat	Lbr	2009	13,517	23,432	155	25	15	tco	ex Golden Legend-11
9414084	Stolt Breland	Nld	2010	25,841	43,475	183	32	14	tco	
9102124	Stolt Capability (me) *	Lbr	1998	24,625	37,042	177	31	16	tco	
9168647	Stolt Commitment	Cym	2000	23,206	37,438	183	32	16	tco	ex Bow Century-11
9178197	Stolt Concept (me)	Cym	1999	24,495	37,236	177	31	16	tco	
9102071	Stolt Confidence (me)	Cym	1996	24,625	37,015	177	31	16	tco	
9296731	Stolt Courage #	Phl	2004	20,058	32,329	174	28	15	tco	
9102095	Stolt Creativity (me)	Cym	1997	24,625	37,271	177	31	16	tco	
9102112	Stolt Efficiency (me)	Cym	1998	24,625	37,271	177	31	16	tco	
9178202	Stolt Effort (me)	Cym	1999	24,495	37,155	177	31	16	tco	
8309543	Stolt Emerald	Cym	1986	23,964	38,719	177	32	15	tco	
9284697	Stolt Endurance #	Pan	2004	20,058	32,306	174	28	15	tco	
9359363	Stolt Facto +	Cym	2008	26,328	46,011	183	32	14	tco	
9214305	Stolt Focus	Cym	2001	23,190	37,467	183	32	16	tco	ex Bow Favour-11
9311012	Stolt Glory	Lbr	2005	20,059	33,302	174	28	15	tco	ex Glory-13, Stolt Glory-10
9414072	Stolt Groenland	Cym	2009	25,881	43,478	183	32	14	tco	
9359399	Stolt Gulf Mirdif +	Cym	2010	26,329	46,011	183	32	14	tco	
9359387	Stolt Gulf Mishref +	Cym	2010	26,329	46.089	183	32	14	tco	ex Stolt Pluto-10
8819093	Stolt Hill	Cym	1992	22,620	40,159	176	32	14	tco	ex Montana Star-06, Star Sapphire-02
9102059	Stolt Innovation (me)	Cym	1996	24,625	36,896	177	31	16	tco	
9102083	Stolt Inspiration (me)	Cym	1997	24,625	37,205	177	31	16	tco	
9102100	Stolt Invention (me) *	Lbr	1998	24,625	37,271	177	31	16	tco	
9414058	Stolt Island	Cym	2008	25,834	43,593	183	32	14	tco	
8320171	Stolt Jade	Cym	1986	23,964	38,746	177	32	15	tco	
9425980	Stolt Megami #	Mhl	2008	12,099	19,997	148	24	14	tco	
9005390	Stolt Mountain	Cym	1994	22,620	40,024	176	32	14	tco	ex Montana Sun-06, Sun Sapphire-02
9414060	Stolt Norland	Cym	2009	25,841	37,141	183	32	14	tco	
9124471	Stolt									
	Perseverance (me)	Cym	2000	25,196	37,059	177	31	16	tco	
9374521	Stolt Pondo ‡	Pan	2007	19,380	33,232	170	27	14	tco	ex Pondo-12, Stolt Pondo-10
9352200	Stolt Sagaland	Cym	2008	25,841	44,044	183	32	14	tco	
9149495	Stolt Sea (me)	Cym	1999	14,742	22,198	163	24	15	tco	
9359375	Stolt Sisto +	Cym	2010	26,329	46,011	183	32	14	tco	
9352212	Stolt Sneland	Cym	2008	25,841	44,080	183	32	14	tco	
9149524	Stolt Span (me) *	Lbr	1998	14,775	22,273	163	24	15	tco	
9168611	Stolt Spray (me)	Cym	2000	14,180	22,460	163	24	15	tco	

IMO	name	flag	year	gt	dwt	loa	bm	kts	type	comments
9169940	Stolt Stream (me)	Cym	2000	14,180	22,199	163	24	15	tco	
9311024	Stolt Strength	Lbr	2005	20,059	33,209	174	28	15	tco	ex Strength-14, Stolt Strength-10
9149512	Stolt Sun (me)	Cym	2000	14,900	22,210	163	24	15	tco	
9168623	Stolt Surf (me)	Cym	2000	14,900	22,198	163	24	15	tco	
8309555	Stolt Topaz	Cym	1986	23,964	38,818	177	32	15	tco	
9274305	Stolt Vanguard #	Lbr	2004	15,711	25,261	159	26	15	tco	
8911669	Stolt Vestland	Cym	1992	19,034	31,494	175	30	15	tco	
9196711	Stolt Viking (me)	Cym	2001	16,754	26,707	166	27	15	tco	ex Isola Blu-05, l/a Isola Verde
8911657	Stolt Vinland	Cym	1992	19,034	31,434	175	30	15	tco	
9274317	Stolt Virtue #	Sgp	2004	15,715	25,230	159	26	15	tco	
9274329	Stolt Vision #	Sgp	2005	15,976	25,147	159	26	15	tco	
9351531	Stolt Zulu ‡	Sgp	2006	16,442	25,197	159	26	15	tco	
newbuildings:										
9680073			2016		38,000	185	32		tco	Hudong Zhonghua H1707A
9680085			2016		38,000	185	32		tco	Hudong Zhonghua H1708A
9680097			2016		38,000	185	32		tco	Hudong Zhonghua H1709A
9600102			2016		38,000	185	32		tco	Hudong Zhonghua H1710A
9680114			2016		38,000	185	32		tco	Hudong Zhonghua H1711A
9720081			2017		38,000	185	32		tco	Hudong Zhonghua H1712A

*managed by Stolt Tankers BV, Netherlands.   * owned by NYK Stolt Tankers SA (formed jointly in 2000 with NYK, Japan)*
+ Gulf Stolt Tankers, # time chartered by Stolt-Nielsen ‡ time chartered to Unicorn Tankers

Avance Gas Holding Ltd., Norway

history: *Stolt-Nielsen Gas formed 2007, established Avance Gas Holding as it's operating company in 2009. SNG merged its assets with Sungas Holdings Ltd. in 2010 and Transpetrol in 2013. In 2013, Frontline 2012 bought into AGH, each partner has an equal share.*
web: *www.avancegas.com*

IMO	name	flag	year	gt	dwt	loa	bm	kts	type	comments
9238284	Avance *	Mhl	2003	46,393	53,677	227	36	17	lpg	84,270 m³. ex Stolt Avance-14, Althea Gas-10
9674842	Breeze *	Mhl	2015	46,789	53,781	226	37	17	lpg	83,000 m³
9689536	Chinook *	Mhl	2015	46,789	53,660	226	37	17	lpg	83,000 m³
7619575	Gaea [st] +	Bmu	1980	93,619	72,571	285	44	19	lng	126,500 m³. ex LNG Abuja-15, Louisana-99
9364382	Iris Glory	Pan	2008	48,425	54,707	226	37	17	lpg	83,700 m³
9686388	Levant *	Mhl	2015	46,789	53,658	226	37	17	lpg	83,000 m³
9667540	Mistral *	Mhl	2015	46,789	53,854	226	37	17	lpg	83,000 m³
9667564	Monsoon *	Mhl	2015	46,789	53,854	226	37	17	lpg	83,000 m³
9689548	Pampero	Mhl	2015	46,789	53,503	226	37	17	lpg	83,000 m³
9674854	Passat	Mhl	2015	46,789	53,701	226	37	17	lpg	83,000 m³
9387750	Progress	Cym	2009	47,266	58,560	225	37	17	lpg	80,793 m³
9354935	Promise	Mlt	2009	47,276	54,984	226	37	17	lpg	83,800 m³. ex Maran Gas Knossos-12, l/d Knossos Gas
9387762	Prospect	Cym	2009	47,266	58,551	225	37	17	lpg	80,797 m³
9350599	Providence	Mlt	2008	47,276	54,784	226	37	17	lpg	83,800 m³. ex Maran Gas Vergina-12, l/a Vergina Gas
9686376	Sirocco *	Mhl	2015	46,789	53,558	226	37	17	lpg	83,000 m³
9364394	Thetis Glory	Pan	2008	48,425	54,707	226	37	17	lpg	83,700 m³
9393682	Venus Glory	Pan	2008	48,654	54,474	226	37	17	lpg	83,700 m³

* managed by Exmar Shipmanagement n.v., Belgium : also operates smaller vessels, + laid-up 25:04:2015

Suisse-Atlantique Soc. de Nav. Maritime S.A.   Switzerland

funnel: *light blue with yellow houseflag interrupting two yellow bands surmounted by 5 yellow stars. Narrow black top.* **hull:** *black or grey with red boot-topping.* **history:** *founded 1941 as Société de Navigation Maritime Suisse-Atlantique to 1956, then Soc d'Armement Maritime Suisse-Atlantique to 1986.* **web:** *www.suisat.com*

IMO	name	flag	year	gt	dwt	loa	bm	kts	type	comments
9423580	Bernina	Che	2011	32,309	57,991	190	32	14	bbu	ex Thunderbird Bulker-14
9176759	Celerina	Che	1999	39,161	73,035	225	32	14	bbu	
9583706	Charmey	Che	2011	22,697	34,275	181	30	14	bbu	
9176747	Corviglia	Che	1999	39,161	73,035	225	32	14	bbu	
9694933	Diavolezza	Che	2016	51,147	87,000	240	38	14	bbu	
9423592	Engiadina	Che	2011	32,309	57,991	190	32	14	bbu	ex Toucan Bulker-14
9177648	General Guisan	Che	1999	39,161	73,035	225	32	14	bbu	
9542817	Lavaux	Che	2010	22,697	34,000	181	30	14	bbu	
9542831	Moleson	Che	2010	22,697	34,266	181	30	14	bbu	
9177650	Nyon	Che	1999	39,161	73,035	225	32	14	bbu	
9542829	Romandie	Che	2010	22,697	34,348	181	30	14	bbu	
9276743	Silvaplana	Che	2003	17,951	29,721	171	27	14	bbu	ex F.D. Clara d'Amato-07, Benedetta d'Amato-06
9276779	Silvretta	Che	2003	17,951	29,721	171	27	14	bbu	ex F.D. Umberto d'Amato-07, Umberto d'Amato-07
9694921	Tzoumaz	Che	2015	51,147	87,665	240	38	14	bbu	
9583691	Vully	Che	2011	22,697	34,000	181	30	14	bbu	

IMO	name	flag	year	gt	dwt	loa	bm	kts	type	comments
newbuildings:										
9694945	Bregaglia	Che	2016	51,147	87,000	240	38	14	bbu	Hyundai Mipo-Vinashin

John Swire & Sons Ltd. U.K.

The China Navigation Co. Ltd., Hong Kong

funnel: black with diagonally quartered houseflag (white top/bottom, red sides, central vertical blue line). **hull:** black some with white 'INDOTRANS', red, grey or pink boot-topping. **history:** parent founded 1816 and China Navigation formed 1872.
web: www.swire.com or www.cnco.com.hk

IMO	name	flag	year	gt	dwt	loa	bm	kts	type	comments
9007374	Chenan	Hkg	1992	18,391	25,554	185	28	18	ggc	ex Pacific Discoverer-12, Tasman Chief-07, Chenan-05, Andes Challenger-99
9007362	Chengtu	Hkg	1991	18,391	25,661	185	28	18	ggc	ex Pacific Explorer-11, Chengtu-05, Asian Challenger-99
9681871	Eredine	Sgp	2014	24,785	39,855	180	30	14	bbu	
9681883	Erradale	Sgp	2014	24,785	39,757	180	30	14	bbu	
9681895	Erisort	Sgp	2014	24,785	39,763	180	30	14	bbu	
9681900	Eriskay	Sgp	2015	24,785	39,810	180	30	14	bbu	
9690884	Fengning	Sgp	2015	24,785	39,836	180	30	14	bbu	
9690896	Fengtien	Sgp	2015	24,785	39,809	180	30	14	bbu	
9690901	Foochow	Sgp	2015	24,785	39,758	180	30	14	bbu	
9690913	Funing	Sgp	2015	24,785	39,784	180	30	14	bbu	
9103116	Kwangsi	Hkg	1995	18,468	23,783	185	28	19	ggc	ex Tasman Mariner-11, PacificPathfinder-09, Tasman Mariner-09, Delmas Blosseville-04, Tropical Challenger-03, Delmas Blosseville-02, Tropical Challenger-99
9070709	Kwangtung	Hkg	1994	18,451	23,683	185	28	19	ggc	ex Tasman Provider-11, Meridian Challenger-03, Delmas Forbin-02, Meridian Challenger-00
9103104	Kweilin	Hkg	1995	18,468	23,586	185	28	19	ggc	ex Tasman Commander-11, Oceanic Challenger-04, Delmas Joinville-02, Oceanic Challenger-01,
9070694	Kweichow	Hkg	1994	18,451	23,000	185	28	19	ggc	ex Tasman Endeavour-11, Caribbean Challenger-03
9715191	Liangchow	Hkg	2015	24,785	39,685	180	30	14	bbu	
9715206	Lintan	Hkg	2015	24,785	39,641	180	30	14	bbu	
9715218	Luchow	Hkg	2015	24,785	39,728	180	30	14	bbu	
9715220	Luenho	Hkg	2016	24,785	39,752	180	30	14	bbu	
9721554	Pakhoi	Hkg	2016	24,785	39,777	180	30	14	bbu	
9657844	Wuchang	Sgp	2013	24,785	39,128	180	30	14	bbu	
9657856	Wuchow	Sgp	2013	24,785	39,090	180	30	14	bbu	
9657868	Wuhu	Sgp	2014	24,785	39,182	180	30	14	bbu	
9657870	Wulin	Sgp	2014	24,785	39,049	180	30	14	bbu	
newbuildings:										
9714228	Hanyang		2016	24,785	39,100	180	30	14	bbu	Chengxi 0353
9714238	Hoihow		2016	24,785	39,100	180	30	14	bbu	Chengxi 0354
9714252	Hunan		2016	24,785	39,100	180	30	14	bbu	Chengxi 0355
9714264	Hupei		2016	24,785	39,100	180	30	14	bbu	Chengxi 0356
9721566	Pekin	Hkg	2016	24,785	39,000	180	30	14	bbu	Zhejiang Ouhua 673
9721578	Poyan	Hkg	2016	24,785	39,000	180	30	14	bbu	Zhejiang Ouhua 674
9721580	Powan	Hkg	2016	24,785	39,000	180	30	14	bbu	Zhejiang Ouhua 675

newbuildings: 8 more x 39,500 bbu B-delta 37 'W-class' [Chengxi SY (2017)]:
also owns a fleet of small container ships operating in the Asia-Pacific region

Swiss Chemical Carriers A.G. Switzerland

funnel: black with white square with MCT and blue and green wave device. **hull:** blue, red boot topping: **history:** founded as Mega Chemical Carriers in 2004, merged with Enzian Ship Management in 2014 and new entity formed. **web:** www.mega-chemicals.ch

IMO	name	flag	year	gt	dwt	loa	bm	kts	type	comments
9298375	MCT Breithorn	Che	2007	12,776	20,635	164	27	15	tco	l/a HLL Celtic
9298351	SCT Matterhorn	Che	2006	12,776	20,677	164	23	15	tco	ex MCT Matterhorn-15, l/a HLL Arctic
9298363	SCT Monte Rosa	Che	2007	12,776	20,718	164	27	15	tco	ex MCT Monte Rosa-15
9298387	MCT Stockhorn	Che	2008	12,776	20,610	164	23	15	tco	l/a HLL Caspian

vessels operated by Mega Chemical Schiffahrts

Team Tankers International Ltd. Bermuda

funnel: dark blue with green and white 'T' inside white shield over 'TEAM' in white. **hull:** red with white 'TEAM' red boot-topping. Superstructure has bold light green band. **history:** Team Tankers established 1968 in Norway, transferred to Bermuda in 2014 and acquired Eitzen Chemical Tankers through share exchange in early 2015. ECT founded 1883 and traded as Tschudi & Eitzen from 1936 until joint venture terminated in 2003. Sichem Shipping merged with Blystad's Songa Shipholding in 2006 to form Eitzen Chemical, which acquired Mosvold Chemical AS in 2007. **web:** www.teamtankers.com

IMO	name	flag	year	gt	dwt	loa	bm	kts	type	comments
9416020	Sichem Contester	Bmu	2007	11,757	19,822	147	24	14	tco	
9358632	Sichem Defender	Pan	2006	11,660	19,999	144	24	14	tco	
9388704	Sichem Eagle	Mhl	2008	17,789	25,421	170	26	14	tco	
9396012	Sichem Falcon	Mlt	2009	17,822	25,419	170	26	14	tco	
9396000	Sichem Hawk	Mlt	2008	17,789	25,385	170	26	14	tco	
9396024	Sichem Osprey	Mlt	2009	17,822	25,432	170	26	14	tco	
9326914	Siteam Adventurer	Bmu	2007	26,751	46,190	183	32	14	tco	
9111058	Siteam Anja	Mhl	1997	28,027	44,640	183	32	14	tco	ex Team Anja-07, Simunye-05, Engen Simunye-00
9326938	Siteam Discoverer	Bmu	2008	26,571	46,005	183	32	14	tco	
9326902	Siteam Explorer	Bmu	2007	27,199	46,190	183	32	14	tco	
9343194	Siteam Leader	Bmu	2009	27,139	46,190	183	32	14	tco	
9326926	Siteam Voyager	Bmu	2008	27,139	46,190	183	32	14	tco	

also operates a large number of smaller tankers

Technomar Shipping Inc. Greece

funnel: *light blue with two yellow parallel horizontal lines and capital 'T' or charterer's colours* **hull:** *black with red boot-topping or charterer's colours.* **history:** *company founded 1994 in Greece by George Youroukos* **web:** *no web-site found*

IMO	name	flag	year	gt	dwt	loa	bm	kts	type	comments
9349605	Agios Dimitrios *	Grc	2011	74,175	85,701	299	40	25	ucc	6,572 teu: l/a Fourth Ocean
9155389	Anthea	Pan	2000	18,335	23,577	176	27	20	ucc	1,740 teu: ex YM Dalian-13, Anthea-12, YM Dalian-12, Anthea-11, Hansa Sonderburg-10, CP Kestrel-06, Direct Kestrel-05, Hansa Sonderburg-01
9710244	Anthea Y	Lbr	2015	94,416	111,884	300	48	23	ucc	9,000 teu
9477787	Argos	Lbr	2012	40,542	49,842	261	32	24	ucc	4,249 teu: ex Bruno Schulte-14
9275361	Athena *	Pan	2003	34,610	43,093	235	32	22	ucc	2,762 teu: ex OOCL Xiamen-11
9102318	Britain *	Mhl	1996	66,046	67,958	276	40	24	ucc	5,344 teu: ex OOCL Britain-15
9594597	Cepheus	Mhl	2012	32,987	56,539	190	32	14	bbu	
9331921	Christina B	Mhl	2007	31,236	56,071	190	32	14	bbu	ex Bright Moon-14
9280641	CMA CGM Strauss	Lbr	2004	65,247	73,235	277	40	24	ucc	5,770 teu
9280653	CMA CGM Verdi	Lbr	2004	65,247	73,235	277	40	24	ucc	5,770 teu
9623647	Darleakay	Mhl	2012	32,839	58,000	190	32	14	bbu	ex Crown Esmeralda-14
9189354	Dimitris Y *	Gbr	2000	66,526	67,515	278	40	24	ucc	5,618 teu: ex Nedlloyd Hudson-15 P&O Nedlloyd Houston-06
9318125	Dolphin II *	Pan	2007	54,309	65,980	294	33	25	ucc	5,040 teu: ex CMA CGM Dolphin-13
9129823	Eleni I	Lbr	1996	16,165	22,250	168	27	21	ucc	1,608 teu: ex Warnow Trader-12, MOL Agility-09, Warnow Trader-06, CMA CGM Springbok-06, Warnow Trader-03, Libra Valencia-99, Warnow Trader-96
9189495	Fleur	Lbr	2000	66,526	67,712	278	40	25	ucc	5,618 teu: ex Nedlloyd Mercator-15, P&O Nedlloyd Mercator-06
9436769	Friederike	Mhl	2011	33,302	57,696	190	32	14	bbu	ex Blue Ocean-14
9189500	Ian M	Gbr	2000	66,590	67,712	278	40	25	ucc	5,618 teu: ex Nedlloyd Drake-15, P&O Nedlloyd Drake-06 sold 07;15
9102306	Japan *	Hkg	1996	66,046	67,752	276	40	24	ucc	5,344 teu; ex OOCL Japan-11

Safmarine Highveld : Technomar Shg. : *Chris Brooks*

IMO	name	flag	year	gt	dwt	loa	bm	kts	type	comments
9420277	Kacey	Mhl	2009	30,816	55,522	190	32	14	bbu	ex Komatsushima Star-14
9630729	Lindsaylou	Mhl	2012	32,839	58,018	190	32	14	bbu	ex Crown Mina-14
9641223	Maersk Grabouw *	Mhl	2013	71,021	80,277	270	43	24	ucc	6,673 teu: ex Kristina-15
9203502	Maira	Pan	2000	25,294	32,308	207	30	22	ucc	2,506 teu: ex Santa Annabella-10, P&O Nedlloyd Agulhas-05, MOL Paraguay-02, P&O Nedlloyd Agulhas-01, Santa Annabella-00
9710232	Maira XL *	Lbr	2015	94,416	111,884	300	48	23	ucc	9,000 teu
9121259	Mamitsa *	Lbr	1996	31,131	38,650	210	32	22	ucc	2,682 teu: ex Potsdam-12, Kota Pelangi-11, Potsdam-10, Kota Pelangi-09, Potsdam-02, Ipex Emperor-99, Sea Elegance-97, Potsdam-96
9189366	Marco R	Nld	2000	66,526	67,785	278	40	25	ucc	5,618 teu: ex Nedlloyd Barentsz-15, P&O Nedlloyd Barentsz-05
9635664	Mary *	Mhl	2013	71,021	80,274	270	42	22	ucc	6,673 teu
9623881	Melinda	Mhl	2012	32,839	58,018	190	32	14	bbu	ex Crown Alexandra-14, Crown Isis-12
9209104	Newyorker *	Pan	2001	25,294	32,299	207	30	22	ucc	2,506 teu: ex Santa Alina-10, P&O Nedlloyd Apapa-05, MOL Santos-02, P&O Nedlloyd Apapa-01, I/a Santa Alina
9203526	Nikolas *	Lbr	2000	25,294	32,391	207	30	22	ucc	2,506 teu: ex Santa Alexandra-09, CMA CGM Okume-09, Santa Alexandra-08, P&O Nedlloyd Abidjan-05, MOL San Paulo-02, P&O Nedlloyd Abidjan-01, Santa Alexandra-00
9318113	Orca I *	Pan	2006	54,309	65,890	294	33	25	ucc	5,040 teu: ex CMA CGM Orca-14
9440980	Queen Jhansi	Mhl	2007	32,415	58,758	185	32	14	bbu	ex Verdi-15, GL Primera-13
9635676	Safmarine Boland	Mhl	2013	71,021	80,350	270	42	22	ucc	6,673 teu: ex Alexandra-14
9641235	Safmarine Highveld	Mhl	2013	71,021	80,295	270	42	22	ucc	6,673 teu: ex Katherine-14
9189342	Tasman *	Mhl	1999	66,526	67,902	278	40	24	ucc	5,618 teu: ex Nedlloyd Tasman-15, P&O Nedlloyd Tasman-06
9710220	UASC Al Khor	Lbr	2015	94,416	111,029	300	48	23	ucc	9,000 teu
9686900	UASC Bubiyan	Mhl	2015	70,704	79,274	270	43	22	ucc	6,882 teu: I/a Alexis
9686912	UASC Yas	Mhl	2015	70,704	79,274	270	43	22	ucc	6,882 teu: I/a Olivia

* owned by associated company, Poseidon Container Holdings: also managed handy size bulkers for third parties

Teekay Corporation

Bahamas

funnel: *white with blue edged red 'TK' symbol, narrow black top.* **hull:** *black with red boot-topping.* **history:** *founded 1973 by Torben Karlshoej, as Teekay Shipping Co Inc, Canada to 1990, then Western Marine Agencies to 1991. Formed Teekay Shipping (Australia) Pty Ltd in 1998 on acquisition of Caltex Petroleum's Australian Tankships Pty Ltd (formed by 1996 merger of Ampol Ltd (founded 1936 as Australian Motorists Petrol Co Ltd to 1949, formerly Ampol Petroleum Ltd to 1982) and Caltex Tanker Co (Australia) Pty Ltd (formed 1972 as Botany Bay Tanker Co (Australia) Pty Ltd to 1985). Teekay Marine Services GmbH, Germany formed 2003. Acquired Naviera F Tapias SA in 2004, which had been a Spanish subsidiary of AP Moller to 1991 (formed 1988). In 2007 acquired 50% of OMI (founded 1962 as Ogden Marine Inc and spun-off from Ogden Corp. in 1984 as OMI Corp, subsidiary being formed in 1998).*
web: *www.teekay.com*

IMO	name	flag	year	gt	dwt	loa	bm	kts	type	comments
9250737	African Spirit *	Bhs	2003	79,668	151,736	269	46	15	tcr	
9325697	Al Areesh (st)	Bhs	2007	99,106	90,617	288	43	20	lng	151,700 m³
9325702	Al Daayen (st)	Bhs	2007	99,106	90,617	288	43	20	lng	151,700 m³
9360879	Al Huwaila (st)	Bhs	2008	135,848	109,503	315	50	20	lng	217,000 m³
9360881	Al Kharsaah (st)	Bhs	2008	135,848	109,484	315	50	20	lng	217,000 m³
9360908	Al Khuwair (st)	Bhs	2008	135,848	109,555	315	50	20	lng	217,000 m³
9325685	Al Marrouna (st)	Bhs	2007	99,106	90,617	288	43	20	lng	151,700 m³
9360893	Al Shamal (st)	Bhs	2008	135,848	107,500	315	50	20	lng	217,000 m³
9326524	Alexander Spirit ***	Bhs	2007	25,382	40,083	175	31	14	tco	ex Miss Marina-09
9247443	Americas Spirit *	Bhs	2003	63,213	111,920	256	45	14	tcr	I/dn Limerick Spirit
9438858	Amundsen Spirit	Bhs	2010	66,563	109,290	249	44	14	tcs	
9001784	Arctic Spirit (st)	Bhs	1993	55,174	48,857	239	40	18	lng	89,880 m³: ex Arctic Sun-07
9247431	Asian Spirit *	Bhs	2004	79,668	151,693	269	46	15	tcr	
9239484	Ashkini Spirit *	Bhs	2003	84,789	165,010	274	50	15	tcr	ex Ingeborg-07, Aegean Lady-04
9427627	Aspen Spirit [T]	Bhs	2009	83,545	157,048	275	48	14	tcr	ex Vadela-15
9594793	Athens Spirit *	Bhs	2012	81,326	158,529	274	48	15	tcr	ex Princimar Integrity-15
9578646	Atlanta Spirit *	Bhs	2011	81,509	158,650	274	48	15	tcr	ex Princimar Hope-15, Costas P-11
9247455	Australian Spirit *	Bhs	2004	63,213	111,942	256	45	15	tcr	
9282041	Axel Spirit *	Bhs	2004	62,929	115,392	250	44	15	tcr	
9408073	Baker Spirit [T]	Bhs	2009	83,695	156,929	275	48	14	tcr	ex Toska-15, I/a Tosca
9578634	Barcelona Spirit *	Bhs	2011	81,509	158,482	274	48	15	tcr	ex Princimar Grace-15, ex Pola P.-11
9418597	Beijing Spirit *	Bhs	2010	83,850	156,493	274	48	15	tcr	ex Princimar Joy-15, I/a Orient Pride
9411226	Bermuda Spirit *	Bhs	2009	81,384	158,769	274	48	14	tcr	
9417335	Blackcomb Spirit	Bhs	2009	60,185	108,914	243	42	15	tcr	ex Valdarno-14
9637703	Bossa Nova Spirit	Bhs	2013	83,882	154,199	282	49	15	tcs	
9399492	Cascade Spirit [T]	Bhs	2009	83,545	156,853	280	45	14	tcr	ex Kamari-15

IMO	name	flag	year	gt	dwt	loa	bm	kts	type	comments
9236420	Catalunya Spirit (st)	Cni	2003	90,835	72,204	284	43	19	lng	138,000 m³: ex Inigo Tapias-04
9191333	Constitution Spirit *	Mhl	1999	58,288	104,623	243	42	14	tcr	ex Constitution-08
9427639	Copper Spirit [T]	Bhs	2010	83,545	156,827	280	45	14	tcr	ex Matala-15
9681687	Creole Spirit (df)	Bhs	2016	113,263	83,400	295	46	19	lng	174,000 m³
9390628	Dilong Spirit *	Bhs	2009	85,037	159,021	275	45	15	tcr	
9312846	Donegal Spirit *	Bhs	2006	57,325	105,611	244	42	14	tco	
9422085	Emerald Spirit *	Bhs	2009	60,185	109,060	243	42	14	tcr	ex Valconca-14
9292515	Erik Spirit *	Bhs	2005	63,500	114,780	250	44	15	tcr	
9282053	Esther Spirit *	Bhs	2004	62,929	115,444	250	44	15	tcr	
9247429	European Spirit *	Bhs	2003	79,668	151,848	269	46	15	tcr	ex Cork Spirit-03
9281009	Everest Spirit *	Bhs	2004	62,845	115,048	250	44	14	tcr	
9247364	Galicia Spirit (st)	Cni	2004	94,822	79,166	280	43	19	lng	138,000 m³ ex Elvira Tapias-04
9312858	Galway Spirit *	Bhs	2006	57,325	105,559	244	42	14	tco	
9230517	Ganges Spirit *	Bhs	2002	81,270	159,452	274	48	15	tcr	ex Delaware-07
9422835	Garibaldi Spirit *	Bhs	2009	60,185	109,039	243	42	15	tcr	ex Valbrenta-14
9286229	Godavari Spirit *	Mlt	2004	81,074	159,106	274	48	15	tcr	ex Angelica-07, Athenian Glory-04
9146730	Goonyella Trader ***	Lbr	1996	85,437	170,873	289	45	14	bbu	
9411238	Hamilton Spirit *	Bhs	2009	81,384	158,769	274	48	15	tcr	
9292503	Helga Spirit *	Bhs	2005	62,929	115,444	250	44	15	tcr	
9230048	Hispania Spirit *	Cni	2004	94,822	79,363	280	43	19	lng	138,000 m³: ex Fernando Tapias-04
9596997	Hovden Spirit	Mhl	2012	57,244	105,276	244	42	15	tcr	ex Neches-14
9236353	Iskmati Spirit *	Mhl	2003	84,789	165,000	274	50	15	tcr	ex Arlene-07, Aegean Eagle-04
9379208	Jiaolong Spirit *	Bhs	2009	85,030	159,021	271	47	15	tcr	
9192337	Kanata Spirit *	Bhs	1999	62,685	113,021	249	44	14	tcr	
9192349	Kareela Spirit *	Bhs	1999	62,685	113,021	249	44	14	tcr	
9286281	Kaveri Spirit *	Bhs	2004	81,074	159,100	274	48	15	tcr	ex Janet-07, Athenian Olympics-04
9171840	Kyeema Spirit *	Bhs	1999	62,619	113,357	253	44	14	tcr	l/a Bona Vigour
9637698	Lambada Spirit	Bhs	2013	83,882	154,036	282	49	15	tcs	
9484089	Leyte Spirit	Mhl	2011	60,193	109,676	243	42	15	tco	ex Cape Endurance-15
9312860	Limerick Spirit *	Bhs	2007	57,325	105,547	244	42	14	tcr	
9490961	Lobito ++	Bhs	2011	110,723	82,929	285	43	19	lng	160,400 m³
9594779	London Spirit *	Bhs	2011	81,326	158,510	274	48	15	tcr	ex Princimar Promise-15
9318072	Los Angeles Spirit *	Bhs	2007	81,339	159,233	274	48	15	tcr	ex Princimar Truth-15, Leni P.-10
9572276	Luzon Spirit	Mhl	2011	60,193	109,581	243	42	15	tco	ex Cape Enterprise-15
9259276	Madrid Spirit (st)	Cni	2004	90,835	77,213	284	43	19	lng	138,000 m³ ex Ivan Tapias-04
9291262	Matterhorn Spirit *	Bhs	2005	63,694	114,834	254	44	14	tcr	
9296389	Montreal Spirit *	Bhs	2006	78,845	149,997	274	48	15	tcr	ex Princimar Confidence-15, Equator-13
9418602	Moscow Spirit	Bhs	2010	83,850	156,480	274	48	15	tcr	ex Princimar Strength-15, l/a Orient Pioneer
9438860	Nansen Spirit	Bhs	2010	66,563	109,239	249	44	14	tcs	
9269075	Narmada Spirit *	Bhs	2003	81,074	159,199	274	48	15	tcr	ex Adair-07, Athenian Victory-04
9313498	Navigator Spirit *	Bhs	2008	57,657	105,773	241	42	15	tcr	ex SPT Navigator-14
9197715	Navion Bergen ††	Nis	1999	56,207	105,641	239	42	14	tcs	ex Bergitta-07, (conv tcr-07)
9063079	Navion Europa ** (me2)	Nor	1995	73,637	130,596	265	43	15	tcs	ex Jorunn Knutsen-98
9308077	Navion Gothenburg ††	Bhs	2006	82,647	152,244	274	48	15	tcs	ex Roviken-07, (conv tcr-07)
9168922	Navion Hispania (2)	Can	1999	72,132	126,749	265	43	14	tcs	
9274525	Nordic Rio ††	Bhs	2004	83,120	151,294	277	48	14	tcs	(conv tcr-05)
9514171	Peak Spirit *	Bhs	2011	56,326	104,621	228	42	14	tcr	ex Pacific Poppy-14
9466130	Peary Spirit	Bhs	2010	66,563	109,325	249	44	15	tcs	
9385192	Pinnacle Spirit *	Bhs	2008	81,732	160,391	274	48	15	tcr	
9001772	Polar Spirit (st)	Bhs	1993	66,174	48,817	239	40	18	lng	89,880 m³: ex Polar Eagle-08
9419565	Rio Spirit *	Bhs	2013	81,394	158,368	274	48	15	tcr	ex Princimar Courage-15, l/a Four Tide
9637686	Samba Spirit	Bhs	2013	83,882	154,107	282	49	15	tcs	
9466142	Scott Spirit	Bhs	2010	66,563	109,334	249	44	15	tcs	
9572264	Sebarok Spirit	Mhl	2011	60,193	109,554	243	42	15	tco	ex Cape Endless-15
9484077	Seletar Spirit	Mhl	2010	60,193	109,001	243	42	15	tco	ex Cape Endeavour-15
9191345	Sentinal Spirit *	Mhl	1999	58,288	104,601	244	42	14	tcr	ex Sentinel-08
9248409	Seoul Spirit *	Bhs	2005	83,616	159,966	274	48	15	tcr	ex Princimar Faith-15, Popi P.-10
9637715	Sertanejo Spirit	Bhs	2013	83,882	154,233	282	49	15	tcs	
9422615	Shoshone Spirit	Mhl	2011	161,969	314,000	333	60	15	tcr	ex C Elephant-14
9475208	Soyo ++	Bhs	2011	110,723	82,858	285	43	19	lng	160,400 m³
9313486	SPT Explorer *	Bhs	2008	57,657	105,804	241	42	15	tcr	
9208033	Stena Spirit †	Bhs	2001	83,120	152,244	274	48	15	tcs	ex Erviken-01 (conv tcr-02)
9404833	Summit Spirit *	Bhs	2008	81,732	160,400	274	48	15	tcr	
9594781	Sydney Spirit *	Bhs	2012	81,326	158,542	274	48	15	tcr	ex Princimar Pride-15
9427641	Tahoe Spirit *	Bhs	2010	83,545	156,831	280	45	14	tcr	ex Karekare-15
9333632	Tangguh Hiri (df)	Bhs	2008	101,957	84,467	282	44	19	lng	155,000 m³
9361990	Tangguh Sago (df)	Bhs	2009	101,957	84,484	282	44	19	lng	155,000 m³
9408322	Tarbet Spirit	Sgp	2009	60,205	107,529	244	42	14	tcr	ex Phoenix Ambition-14

Scott Spirit : Teekay Corp. : *Hans Kraijenbosch*

Magellan Spirit : Teekay - MALT LNG Tspt : *ARO*

IMO	name	flag	year	gt	dwt	loa	bm	kts	type	comments
9283241	Teide Spirit *	Mlt	2004	83,594	159,426	274	48	15	tcr	
9378369	Tianlong Spirit *	Bhs	2009	85,037	159,021	273	47	15	tcr	
9296277	Tokyo Spirit *	Bhs	2006	78,845	149,996	274	48	15	tcr	ex Princimar Loyalty-15, Navigator-13
9288899	Toledo Spirit § *	Esp	2005	83,724	159,342	274	48	15	tcr	
9593414	Trysil Spirit	Mhl	2012	57,244	105,276	244	42	14	tcr	ex Guadalupe-14
9399478	Vail Spirit [T]	Bhs	2009	83,545	157,048	275	48	14	tcr	ex Taipan-15
9417323	Whistler Spirit *	Bhs	2010	60,185	109,060	243	42	14	tcr	ex Valpiave-14
9414503	Yamato Spirit	Bhs	2008	60,379	107,617	244	42	15	tco	ex Diamond Aspire-15
9230505	Yamuna Spirit *	Bhs	2002	81,270	159,435	274	48	15	tcr	ex Dakota-07
9404845	Zenith Spirit *	Bhs	2009	81,732	160,510	272	48	15	tcr	
newbuildings:										
9705641		Bhs	2017	113,000	83,400	291	46	19	lng	173,400 m³ Daewoo H2416
9705653		Bhs	2017	113,000	83,400	291	46	19	lng	173,400 m³ Daewoo H2417
9770921		Bhs	2018	111,000	85,000	295	46	19	lng	173,400 m³ Daewoo H2453
9770933		Bhs	2018	111,000	85,000	295	46	19	lng	173,400 m³ Daewoo H2454
9770945		Bhs	2018	111,000	85,000	295	46	19	lng	173,400 m³ Daewoo H2455
9771080		Bhs	2018	111,000	85,000	295	46	19	lng	173,400 m³ Daewoo H2461

vessels managed by TeeKay Shipping Glasgow Ltd.
all vessels are dual fuel diesel electric propulsion (df)

Teekay Navion Offshore Loading, Singapore

funnel: *white with blue edged red 'TK' symbol, narrow black top.* **hull:** *black with red boot-topping*

IMO	name	flag	year	gt	dwt	loa	bm	kts	type	comments
9281011	Kilimanjaro Spirit *	Bhs	2004	62,845	115,048	250	44	14	tcr	
9204752	Navion Anglia † (2)	Bhs	1999	72,449	126,749	265	43	15	tcs	
9145188	Navion Britannia ** (2)	Bhs	1998	72,110	124,821	265	43	15	tcs	
9200926	Navion Marita †	Bhs	1999	58,117	103,894	246	42	14	tcs	ex Nordic Marita-07
9168946	Navion Oceania (2)	Bhs	1999	72,132	126,749	265	43	14	tcs	
9209130	Navion Oslo	Bhs	2001	55,796	100,257	238	42	14	tcs	ex Bertora-08
9168934	Navion Scandia (2)	Bhs	1998	72,132	126,749	265	43	14	tcs	
9248435	Navion Stavanger ††	Bhs	2003	80,691	148,729	277	46	14	tcs	ex Nordic Stavanger-04, Nordic Liberita-03
9274513	Nordic Brasilia ††	Bhs	2004	83,119	150,939	275	48	14	tcs	l/a Roviken (conv tcr-09)
9208045	Nordic Spirit †	Bhs	2001	83,120	152,292	274	48	15	tcs	ex Storviken-02 (conv tcr-02)
9233818	Petroatlantic	Bhs	2003	54,865	92,968	235	42	14	tcs	
9233806	Petronordic	Bhs	2002	54,885	92,995	234	42	14	tcs	

*vessels owned by Teekay Navion Offshore Loading, managed by Teekay Shipping Norway AS   * managed by Teekay Marine Singapore*
† managed by Petroleo Brasiliero SA, Brazil (www2.petrobras.com.br) †† managed by Transpetro, Brazil (www.transpetro.com.br)

MALT LNG Transport ApS, Norway

funnel: *white with blue edged red 'TK' symbol, narrow black top.* **hull:** *black with red boot-topping.* **history:** *joint venture between Teekay LNG Operating LLC and Marubeni Corporation, Japan incorporated 2009. Acquired all shares of Maersk LNG A/S in late 2011*

IMO	name	flag	year	gt	dwt	loa	bm	kts	type	comments
9339260	Arwa Spirit	Mhl	2008	104.169	82,187	286	43	19	lng	165,500 m³ ex Maersk Arwa-12
9342487	Magellan Spirit	Dnk	2009	104,169	82,265	286	43	19	lng	165,500 m³ ex Maersk Magellan-12
9336737	Methane Spirit	Sgp	2008	104,169	82,115	286	43	19	lng	163,195 m³ ex Maersk Methane-12
9336749	Marib Spirit	Mhl	2008	104,169	82,114	285	43	19	lng	165,500 m³ ex Maersk Marib-12
9369904	Meridian Spirit	Dnk	2010	104,169	81,929	285	43	19	lng	165,772 m³ ex Maersk Meridian-12
9369899	Woodside Donaldson	Sgp	2009	104,169	82,085	285	43	19	lng	165,936 m³
newbuildings:										
			2017						lng	173,400 m³ Daewoo H2416
									lng	173,400 m³ Daewoo H2417
									lng	173,400 m³ Daewoo H2453
									lng	173,400 m³ Daewoo H2454
									lng	173,400 m³ Daewoo H2455
									lng	173,400 m³ Daewoo H2461

vessels managed by TeeKay Shipping Glasgow Ltd.
all vessels are dual fuel diesel electric propulsion (df)

Thenamaris Ships Management   Greece

funnel: *dark blue with broad white band* **hull:** *dark blue with red or green boot topping.* **history:** *founded 1970.*
web: *www.thenamaris.com*

IMO	name	flag	year	gt	dwt	loa	bm	kts	type	comments
9291286	Athina	Bhs	2005	161,382	318,658	333	60	13	tcr	
9640023	Cool Explorer [tf]	Mlt	2014	102,097	81,893	281	43	19	lng: 160,000 m³
9636797	Cool Runner [tf]	Mlt	2014	102,097	81,891	281	43	19	lng: 160,000 m³
9636785	Cool Voyager [tf]	Mlt	2013	102,097	81,890	281	43	19	lng: 160,000 m³
9398668	Ellina	Mlt	2008	43,158	82,612	229	32	14	bbu	
9337597	Galani	Mlt	2006	18,480	23,690	177	27	20	ucc	1,740 teu: ex HS Schubert, Viking Osprey-09
9241255	Globetrotter	Mlt	2001	27,198	48,911	188	31	14	bbu	ex Nantor-07

Seaboni : Thenamaris Ship Management : *Chris Brooks*

Seaempress : Thenamaris Ship Management : *Chris Brooks*

IMO	name	flag	year	gt	dwt	loa	bm	kts	type	comments
9255672	Isabella	Mlt	2004	57,301	105,330	244	42	14	tcr	
9407457	Matilda	Mlt	2009	62,775	112,931	250	44	14	tcr	ex King Conrad-09
9229362	Saint Nicholas	Mlt	2002	57,301	105,541	244	42	14	tcr	
9698941	Seabee	Mlt	2015	35,884	62,770	200	32	14	bbu	
9688647	Seaboni	Mlt	2015	35,884	62,675	200	32	14	bbu	
9288746	Seaborn	Mlt	2005	57,296	105,042	244	42	14	tcr	
9288332	Seaboss	Mlt	2004	30,936	55,426	189	32	14	bbu	
9436070	Seaboxer III	Mlt	2010	18,485	23,696	177	27	20	ucc	1,732 teu: I/a Viking Kestrel
9288734	Seabravery	Mlt	2005	57,296	105,042	244	42	14	tcr	
9343986	Seabreeze	Mlt	2007	31,433	53,714	186	32	14	tco	ex Freja Fionia-12
9314088	Seachance	Mlt	2004	58,136	107,081	247	42	14	tcr	
9297890	Seacross	Bhs	2006	84,601	163,288	274	50	14	tcr	
9248801	Seacrown I	Mlt	2003	25,287	40,039	176	31	14	tco	ex Seacrown-11
9297888	Seadancer	Bhs	2006	84,601	163,288	274	50	14	tcr	
9632832	Seadream	Mlt	2014	52,467	52,340	255	37	21	ucc	5,071 teu
9236755	Seaempress	Mlt	2002	23,241	39,443	183	27	14	tco	
9248796	Seaexplorer	Mlt	2003	25,287	39,975	176	31	14	tco	
9344019	Seaexpress	Mlt	2007	28,069	45,976	180	33	14	tco	
9185279	Seafaith II	Mlt	2000	57,951	109,280	245	42	14	tcr	I/a Stavanger Solveig
9231212	Seafalcon	Mlt	2002	62,247	112,661	250	44	14	tcr	ex Dubai Legend-11, Oinoussian Spirit-06, I/a Golden Sea
9686314	Seafarer	Mlt	2014	94,542	181,110	292	45	14	bbu	
9686326	Seafighter	Mlt	2015	94,542	181,068	292	45	14	bbu	
9685487	Seaforce	Mlt	2015	94,542	181,098	292	45	14	bbu	
9629574	Seafriend	Mlt	2013	29,925	50,909	183	32	14	tco	
9688635	Seaharmony	Mlt	2014	35,884	62,770	200	32	14	bbu	
9315642	Seahero	Pan	2006	157,844	306,507	332	58	15	tcr	ex DS Vidonia-15, Artemis Glory-14
9486013	Seahope II	Mlt	2010	33,036	56,894	190	32	14	bbu	
9292187	Seaking	Bhs	2005	161,382	318,656	333	60	14	tcr	
9488853	Sealink	Mlt	2010	93,565	180,116	292	45	14	bbu	ex Blue Everest-15
9302970	Sealoyalty	Mlt	2005	56,146	106,468	243	42	14	tcr	ex Garden City River-14
9288344	Sealuck II	Mlt	2004	30,936	55,452	189	32	14	bbu	
9317949	Seamagic	Mlt	2007	67,032	116,995	250	44	14	tco	ex Polar Merchant-08
9304825	Seamaster IV	Hkg	2006	60,208	109,266	243	42	14	tcr	ex Seamaster-14

Thorco Isabella : Thorco Shipping AS : *Chris Brooks*

IMO	name	flag	year	gt	dwt	loa	bm	kts	type	comments
9585572	Seamate	Mlt	2010	91,373	177,775	292	45	14	bbu	ex Faustina -16
9260005	Seamercury	Mlt	2003	23,235	37,197	183	27	14	tco	ex Baltic Adonia I-13, Arctic Point-09, I/a Baltic Adonia
9247481	Seamerit	Mlt	2002	23,236	39,441	183	27	14	tco	
9382700	Seamuse	Mlt	2007	28,799	48,673	180	32	14	tco	ex Belaia-14
9407445	Seamusic	Mlt	2007	62,775	112,931	250	44	14	tco	
9290361	Seaoath	Mlt	2005	57,162	105,472	244	42	14	tcr	
9486025	Seapace	Mlt	2010	33,036	56,894	190	32	14	bbu	
9629562	Seapride	Mlt	2013	29,925	50,909	183	32	14	tco	
9241607	Seaprince	Grc	2002	84,598	149,078	274	50	14	tcr	
9373668	Seaprincess	Mlt	2008	61,248	115,949	250	44	14	tcr	
9247479	Seapromise	Mlt	2002	23,236	39,480	183	27	14	tco	
9288863	Seaqueen	Mlt	2004	62,796	115,639	250	44	14	tcr	ex Neverland Soul-08, HS Norma-06
9227443	Searacer	Mlt	2002	84,598	149,830	274	50	14	tcr	
9236743	Searambler	Mlt	2001	23,236	37,135	183	27	14	tco	
9698953	Searider	Mlt	2015	35,884	62,770	200	32	14	bbu	
9629550	Seasalvia	Mlt	2013	29,925	50,900	183	32	14	tco	
9255660	Seascout	Mlt	2004	57,301	105,330	244	42	14	tcr	
9632820	Seasmile	Mlt	2013	52,467	51,020	255	37	21	ucc:	5,071 teu
9290438	Seasong	Mlt	2005	57,162	105,472	244	42	14	tcr	
9711468	Seasprite	Mlt	2015	62,394	113,998	250	44	15	tcr	
9373656	Seastar	Mlt	2008	61,248	115,639	249	44	14	tcr	
9629548	Seatreasure	Mlt	2013	29,925	50,900	183	32	14	tco	
9227455	Seatriumph	Mlt	2002	84,598	149,953	274	50	14	tcr	
9315783	Seavictory	Mlt	2007	29,348	46,702	183	32	14	tco	
9318096	Seavoyager	Mlt	2007	81,339	159,233	274	48	14	tcr	
9229350	St. Helen	Mlt	2002	57,301	105,661	244	42	14	tcr	
newbuildings:										
9783722		Mlt	2017		300,000	333	60		tcr	Hyundai HI 2869
9784734		Mlt	2017		300,000	333	60		tcr	Hyundai HI 2870
9774185		Mlt	2016		158,734	274	48		tcr	Hyundai Samho S837
9790971		Mlt	2017		158,580	274	48		tcr	Hyundai Samho S885
9790983		Mlt	2017		158,580	274	48		tcr	Hyundai Samho S886
9759795		Mlt	2017		115,000	250	44		tco	Sungdong S3110
9759800		Mlt	2017		115,000	250	44		tco	Sungdong S3111
9765017		Mt	2017		115,000	250	44		tco	Sungdong S3112
9765029		Mlt	2017		115,000	250	44		tco	Sungdong S3113
9773753		Mlt	2017		112,000	237	44		tcr	Daewoo 1389
9773765		Mlt	2018		112,000	237	44		tcr	Daewoo 1390
9763033		Mlt	2017		28,100				lpg	38,000 m³ Hyundai Mipo 8188
9763045		Mlt	2017		28,100				lpg	38,000 m³ Hyundai Mipo 8189
9787340		Mlt	2017		28,100				lpg	38,000 m³ Hyundai Mipo 8201
9787352		Mlt	2017		28,100				lpg	38,000 m³ Hyundai Mipo 8202

Thorco Shipping A/S   Denmark

funnel: black with broad white band with stylised 'T' on light blue square **hull:** black with 'WWW.THORCOSHIPPING.COM' in white, red boot topping **history:** Thorco Shipping was established in 2003. In June 2013 the company merged with Clipper Projects Pool, a j/v set up in 2012 between Clipper Gp., Enzian Ship Management, Switzerland and Freese Shipping, Germany **web:** www.thorcoshipping.com

IMO	name	flag	year	gt	dwt	loa	bm	kts	type	comments
9614696	Clipper Helvetia +	Che	2013	14,941	17,551	162	25	15	ggc	I/a SCL Helvetia
9368326	Clipper Macau **	Bhs	2008	11,864	17,110	143	22	15	ggc	ex Gabrielle Scan-12, BBC Rio Grande-11, Beluga Gravitation-08
9232462	Clipper Magdalena *	Bhs	2001	11,894	17,520	143	22	15	ggc	ex Magdalena Green-12
9187045	Clipper Makiri *	Bhs	1999	11,894	17,539	143	22	16	ggc	ex Makiri Green-12
9208198	Clipper Marinus *	Bhs	2000	11,894	17,539	143	22	16	ggc	ex Marinus Green-12
9208203	Clipper Marissa *	Bhs	2000	11,894	17,539	143	22	16	ggc	ex Marissa Green-12
9247405	Clipper Marlene	Bhs	2001	11,894	17,539	143	22	16	ggc	ex Marlene Green-12
9366110	Clipper Miami **	Bhs	2008	11,864	17,110	143	22	15	ggc	ex Amanda-13, Gisele Scan-12, BBC Orinoco-11, Beluga Generation-08
9473224	Clipper Nassau	Bhs	2011	12,795	17,257	144	23	16	ghl	cr: 2(150)
9473236	Clipper Newark	Bhs	2011	12,795	17,273	144	23	16	ghl	cr. 2(150)
9473248	Clipper Newhaven	Bhs	2011	12,795	17,299	144	23	16	ghl	cr. 2(150)
9473250	Clipper New York	Bhs	2012	12,795	17,287	144	23	16	ghl	cr: 2(150)
9469780	Thorco Isabella	Mhl	2011	13,816	19,638	148	23	16	ghl	cr: 2(240): ex Maersk Texas-14
9469778	Thorco Isadora	Mhl	2011	13,816	19,600	148	23	16	ghl	cr: 2(240): ex Maersk Illinois-14
9742390	Thorco Lanner	Phl	2015	13,110	16,963	132	23	15	ggc	
9673173	Thorco Legacy	Pan	2014	13,110	16,954	132	23	15	ggc	
9660152	Thorco Legend	Hkg	2013	13,110	16,956	132	23	15	ggc	
9699969	Thorco Legion	Pan	2015	13,110	16,957	132	32	15	ggc	
9673197	Thorco Lineage	Pan	2014	13,150	16,500	132	23	15	ggc	
9643623	Thorco Liva	Hkg	2012	13,110	16,901	132	23	15	ggc	

IMO	name	flag	year	gt	dwt	loa	bm	kts	type	comments
9742417	Thorco Logic +	Pan	2016	13,110	16,956	132	23	15	ggc	
9742405	Thorco Logos +	Pan	2015	13,110	16,970	132	23	15	ggc	
9742429	Thorco Lohas +	Pan	2015	13,150	16,500	132	23	15	ggc	
9699957	Thorco Luna	Phl	2014	13,110	16,953	132	23	15	ggc	
9538880	Thorco Raffles	Hkg	2011	14,859	17,884	162	25	17	ggc	ex Safmarine Sahara-16
9423516	Thorco Ranger	Hkg	2010	14,859	18,019	162	25	17	ggc	ex Safmarine Sumba-16
9539365	Thorco Reef	Hkg	2011	14,859	17,954	162	25	17	ggc	ex Safmarine Sahel-16
9430222	Thorco Rio	Hkg	2012	14,859	18,010	162	25	17	ggc	ex Safmarine Shaba-16
9539389	Thorco Royal	Hkg	2012	14,859	17,907	162	25	17	ggc	ex Safmarine Suguta-16

owned by * Greenfleet Ltd/Clipper Gp.., ** Freese Shipping GmbH, + Franbo Lines Corp., TWN
also operates a large number of smaller vessels,

A/S Dampskibsselskabet Torm   Denmark

funnel: *black with blue 'T' on white band between two red bands.* **hull:** *black or grey with house flag and 'TORM' in white, red boot-topping.* **history:** *formed 1889 and 30% owned by Beltest Shipping Co. Ltd., Cyprus. Owns 32% of Dampskibsselskabet 'Norden' A/S, Denmark   q.v.. In 2007 acquired 50% of OMI (founded 1962 as Ogden Marine Inc and spun-off from Ogden Corp in 1984 as OMI Corp). In 2008 acquired 50% of FR8, Singapore (formed 2003). In a financial restructuring plan, some vessels were sold in 2015 to Oaktree Capital.* **web:** *www.torm.com*

IMO	name	flag	year	gt	dwt	loa	bm	kts	type	comments
9465992	Torm Agnes [O]	Sgp	2011	30,241	50,274	183	32	14	tco	
9466013	Torm Agnete [O]	Sgp	2010	30,241	50,247	183	32	14	tco	
9466001	Torm Alexandra [O]	Sgp	2010	30,241	50,216	183	32	14	tco	
9465966	Torm Alice [O] †	Sgp	2010	30,241	50,216	183	32	14	tco	
9465980	Torm Almena [O]	Sgp	2010	30,241	50,247	183	32	14	tco	
9466025	Torm Amalie [O]	Sgp	2012	30,241	50,273	183	32	14	tco	
9251028	Torm Amazon	Pan	2002	28,539	47,275	183	32	14	tco	ex Amazon-07
9543550	Torm Anabel [O]	Sgp	2012	30,241	49,999	183	32	14	tco	
9180982	Torm Anne [O]	Sgp	1999	28,932	45,507	180	32	14	tco	.
9543548	Torm Arawa [O]	Sgp	2012	30,241	49,999	183	32	14	tco	
9465978	Torm Aslaug [O]	Sgp	2010	30,241	50,263	183	32	14	tco	
9510682	Torm Astrid *	Sgp	2012	30,400	50,243	183	32	14	tco	ex Maxwell Bay-15, l/a Meriom Lily
9433509	Torm Atlantic *	Sgp	2010	30,221	50,308	183	32	14	tco	ex Maersk Malta-15, Giacinta-15
9263693	Torm Camilla	Dis	2003	30,024	44,990	183	32	14	tco	ex Gron Falk-05
9263708	Torm Carina	Dis	2003	30,024	46,219	183	32	14	tco	
9262091	Torm Caroline	Dis	2002	28,381	46,414	183	32	14	tco	ex Vit Falk-05, High Vit Falk-03
9215103	Torm Cecilie	Dis	2001	28,381	46,414	183	32	14	tco	ex Rod Falk-05, High Rod Falk-03
9230854	Torm Charente †	Dis	2001	23,740	35,751	183	27	14	tco	ex Charente-08
9215098	Torm Clara	Dis	2000	28,381	45,999	183	32	14	tco	ex Svart Falk-05, High Svart Falk-03
9277785	Torm Emilie	Dis	2004	42,493	74,999	228	32	16	tco	
9277723	Torm Estrid	Dis	2004	42,432	74,999	225	32	14	tco	
9302114	Torm Fox	Dis	2004	23,246	37,025	183	27	14	tco	ex Fox-08
9250490	Torm Freya [O]	Sgp	2003	30,058	46,342	183	32	14	tco	
9288930	Torm Garonne	Dis	2004	23,346	37,178	183	27	14	tco	ex Garonne-08
9240897	Torm Gerd [O]	Sgp	2002	30,058	46,300	183	32	14	tco	
9240885	Torm Gertrud	Sgp	2002	30,058	46,362	183	32	14	tco	
9199127	Torm Gudrun †	Dis	2000	57,031	99,965	244	42	14	tco	
9172193	Torm Gunhild	Sgp	1999	28,909	45,457	181	32	14	tco	
9425502	Torm Gyda †	Dis	2009	23,332	36,207	184	27	14	tco	

Torm Arawa : A/S Dampskibsselskabet Torm : *ARO*

IMO	name	flag	year	gt	dwt	loa	bm	kts	type	comments
9344007	Torm Hardrada [O]	Sgp	2007	28,069	45,983	183	32	14	tco	ex Njord Hardrada-15, Seaeden-13, Seamercury-12
9143532	Torm Helene [O]	Sgp	1997	57,031	99,999	244	42	14	tco	
9288021	Torm Helvig	Sgp	2005	30,018	46,187	183	32	14	tco	
9283710	Torm Horizon	Dis	2004	29,242	46,955	183	32	14	tco	ex Horizon-08, Athenian Horizon-04
9243320	Torm Ingeborg [O]	Sgp	2003	57,095	99,900	244	42	14	tco	
9277797	Torm Ismini	Dis	2004	42,432	74,999	228	32	15	tco	
9290646	Torm Kansas	Dis	2006	29,242	46,922	184	32	14	tco	ex Kansas-08
9169512	Torm Kristina †	Dis	1999	57,080	105,002	244	42	14	tco	
9375616	Torm Laura	Dis	2008	29,283	53,160	183	32	14	tco	
9390769	Torm Lene	Dis	2008	29,283	53,160	183	32	14	tco	
9392470	Torm Lilly	Dis	2009	29,283	53,160	183	32	14	tco	
9282986	Torm Loire	Dis	2004	23,246	37,106	183	27	14	tco	ex Loire-08
9301914	Torm Loke *	Sgp	2007	29,683	51,371	183	32	14	tco	ex Halsted Bay-15, Mare di Napoli-12
9392468	Torm Lotte	Dis	2009	29,293	53,160	183	32	14	tco	
9392482	Torm Louise	Dis	2009	29,283	53,160	183	32	14	tco	
9212383	Torm Madison	Dis	2000	23,842	35,833	183	27	14	tco	ex Madison-08, Nina-01
9358400	Torm Maren	Dis	2008	61,724	109,672	245	42	15	tco	
9299343	Torm Margrethe	Sgp	2006	61,724	109,637	245	42	15	tcr	
9299355	Torm Marie	Sgp	2006	61,724	109,637	245	42	15	tcr	
9319698	Torm Marina	Dis	2007	61,724	109,672	245	42	15	tcr	
9246798	Torm Mary [O]	Sgp	2002	30,058	46,634	183	32	14	tco	
9358412	Torm Mathilde	Dis	2008	61,724	109,672	245	42	14	tco	
9254240	Torm Moselle	Dis	2003	28,567	47,038	183	32	14	tco	ex Moselle-08
9221671	Torm Neches	Sgp	2000	28,539	47,052	183	32	14	tco	ex Neches-08, Alam Bayu-00
9234678	Torm Ohio †	Dis	2001	23,235	37,278	183	27	14	tco	ex Ohio-08, l/a Borak
9290660	Torm Platte	Dis	2006	29,242	46,955	183	32	14	tco	ex Platte-07
9290579	Torm Ragnhild [O]	Sgp	2005	30,018	46,187	183	32	14	tco	
9290658	Torm Republican	Dis	2006	29,242	46,955	183	32	14	tco	ex Republican-08
9304588	Torm Resilience [O]	Sgp	2005	30,068	51,218	183	32	14	tco	ex Njord Thyra-15, St..Michaelis-13
9215086	Torm Rhone †	Dis	2000	23,740	35,769	183	27	14	tco	ex Rhone-08, Prospero-01
9254070	Torm Rosetta	Dis	2003	28,567	47,038	183	32	14	tco	ex Rosetta-08
9247778	Torm San Jacinto	Dis	2002	28,539	47,038	183	32	15	tco	ex San Jacinto-08
9295323	Torm Saone	Dis	2004	23,246	36,986	183	27	14	tco	ex Saone-07

TransOsprey : Rederi AB Transatlantic : *Nico Kemps*

IMO	name	flag	year	gt	dwt	loa	bm	kts	type	comments
9273260	Torm Sara	Sgp	2003	41,690	72,718	228	32	15	tco	ex Penyu Agar-05
9290957	Torm Signe	Sgp	2005	41,503	72,718	228	32	15	tco	ex Penyu Siski-05
9295086	Torm Sofia	Sgp	2005	41,503	72,650	228	32	15	tco	ex Penyu Daun-05
9302126	Torm Tevere †	Dis	2005	23,246	36,990	183	28	14	tco	ex Tevere-08, Tiber-05
9318333	Torm Thames	Dis	2005	29,214	47,036	184	32	14	tco	ex Thames-08
9712292	Torm Thor [B]	Sgp	2015	29,484	49,757	183	32	14	tco	
9712307	Torm Thunder [B]	Sgp	2015	29,484	49,842	183	32	14	tco	
9250488	Torm Thyra [O]	Sgp	2003	30,058	46,308	183	32	14	tco	
9726487	Torm Timothy [B]	Sgp	2015	29,484	49,757	183	32	14	tco	
9712319	Torm Titan *	Sgp	2016	29,484	49,757	183	32	14	tco	
9712321	Torm Torino *	Sgp	2016	29,484	49,768	183	32	14	tco	
9212395	Torm Trinity	Dis	2000	23,842	35,833	183	27	14	tco	ex Trinity-08, Snipe-01
9726475	Torm Troilus [O]	Sgp	2016	29,484	49,842	183	32	14	tco	
9243318	Torm Valborg [O]	Sgp	2003	57,095	99,999	244	42	14	tcr	
9307798	Torm Venture	Nis	2007	42,048	73,701	229	32	14	tco	
9246803	Torm Vita [O]	Sgp	2002	30,058	46,308	183	32	14	tco	

* owned by Torm Singapore (Pte.) Ltd (formed 1979),
† managed by Torm Shipping India Pvt. Ltd.
 [B] owned by Breakwater Capital, London,   [O] owned by Oaktree Capital management
company operates about 115 vessels in the Torm LR1, Torm LR2, Torm MR and Torm Handy product tanker pools.

Rederi AB Transatlantic   Sweden

funnel: *yellow with blue 'TA' symbol within blue ring, narrow blue base and top.* **hull:** *grey or white with red boot-topping.*
history: *Transatlantic (originally founded 1904) was acquired by Bilspedition AB in 1988, which also acquired Cool Carriers (1987), Gorthon (1988), Incotrans (1988), Atlantic Container Line (1988-90) and Swedish Orient (1991). All were later sold, Gorthon Lines AB (formed 1915) to B&N Bylock & Nordsjofrakt AB in 1990, before being spun-off in 1997, acquiring the associated Sea Partner AB management company in 2000, which was renamed Gorthon Fleet Services AB. In 2004 a Gorthon-B&N Transatlantic joint venture was formed and in 2005 B&N Nordsjofrakt merged with Gorthon Lines as Transatlantic.* **web:** *www.rabt.se*

IMO	name	flag	year	gt	dwt	loa	bm	kts	type	comments
9216626	Transfighter	Swe	2001	20,851	18,972	179	26	17	urr	ex Finnfighter-09, (len-06)
9213088	Transeagle	Nld	2002	13,340	16,612	142	22	15	ggc	ex Nordon-09
9248552	Transhawk	Gib	2004	13,340	16,558	142	22	15	ggc	ex Sandon-08
9213090	Transosprey	Gib	2003	16,037	20,396	174	22	16	ggc	ex Prinsenborg-10 (len-08)
8515893	Transreel	Swe	1987	18,773	10,917	166	23	20	urr	ex Viola Gorthon-09

managed by Transatlantic Fleet Services AB (formed 1992). Also operates Ro-Ro vessels on Baltic routes.

Transeste Schiffahrt GmbH   Germany

funnel: *mainly in charterers colours.* **hull:** *black, dark grey, blue or red with red boot-topping.* **history:** *formed 1956.*
web: *www.transeste.de*

IMO	name	flag	year	gt	dwt	loa	bm	kts	type	comments
9568562	Harm	Lbr	2011	51,225	93,183	229	38	14	bbu	
9333371	Helle Ritscher *	Lbr	2006	17,360	22,254	179	28	21	ucc	1,719 teu: ex DAL East London-09, Helle Ritscher-06
9179828	Jan Ritscher *	Lbr	1999	25,705	33,843	208	30	22	ucc	2,468 teu: ex MOL Satisfaction-12, Trade Zale-05, TPL Eagle-02, TMM San Antonio-01, Jan Ritscher-99
9333383	Jonni Ritscher *	Lbr	2006	17,189	22,243	179	28	21	ucc	1,719 teu: ex CMA CGM Caribbean-08, Jonni Ritscher-06

Alpine Confidence : Transpetrol : *Nico Kemps*

IMO	name	flag	year	gt	dwt	loa	bm	kts	type	comments
9568574	Piet	Lbr	2011	51,225	93,200	229	38	14	bbu	
9656137	Tommi Rischer	Pmd	2014	48,338	58,000	255	37	22	ucc	4,785 teu
9252735	Widukind *	Lbr	2006	35,881	42,200	221	32	22	ucc	3,104 teu: ex SCI Diya-08, Widukind-07, Hera-06
9654464	Wieland	Pmd	2014	48,385	56,054	255	37	22	ucc	4,785 teu: l/a Tommi Ritscher

*managed for owning partner companies Reederei Gerd Ritscher KG (founded 1956 www.ritschership.com) or * Reederei Dietrich Tamke KG (founded 1970), both Germany*

TransPetrol Ltd.   Bermuda

funnel: *black with white 'tp' above white wavy lines.* **hull:** *black or brown with red or grey boot-topping.* **history:** *formed 1979 as TransPetrol Maritime Services NV until 2005.* **web:** *www.transpetrol.com*

IMO	name	flag	year	gt	dwt	loa	bm	kts	type	comments
9289788	Advance II *	Sgp	2006	30,032	46,101	183	32	14	tco	
9389978	Alpine Confidence	Sgp	2010	60,205	107,600	244	42	14	tco	
9430272	Alpine Eternity	Sgp	2009	29,130	46,105	183	32	14	tco	
9430284	Alpine Loyalty	Sgp	2010	29,130	46,151	183	32	14	tco	
9430296	Alpine Venture	Sgp	2010	29,130	46,046	183	32	14	tco	
9273650	Endeavour	Sgp	2004	30,032	46,101	183	32	14	tco	
9479840	Luctor	Pan	2011	29,419	50,383	183	32	14	tco	
9730139	Perseverance V	Sgp	2015	47,306	54,637	225	36	19	lpg	84,000 m³
9289764	Reliance II *	Sgp	2006	30,032	46,101	183	32	14	tco	
9273246	Resolve	Sgp	2004	30,032	46,048	183	32	14	tco	
9418482	Stride	Sgp	2009	60,325	103,023	244	42	14	tcs	ex Zaliv Anadyr-13
9479838	Turmoil	Pan	2011	29,419	50,358	183	32	14	tco	

newbuildings: *2 x 115,000 dwt tcr [Hyundai Heavy Inds., (Q4 2016)]*
*operated by subsidiary TransPetrol Maritime Services Ltd, Belgium and * owned by TransPetrol TMAS, Norway.*
also see Stolt-Nielsen/Avance Gas

Tsakos Shipping & Trading S.A.   Greece

funnel: *yellow with red 'T' on broad white band edged with narrow blue bands, narrow black top.* **hull:** *black * with white 'TEN', red boot-topping.* **history:** *founded in Piraeus, 1970.* **web:** *www.tsakos.net or www.tenn.gr*

IMO	name	flag	year	gt	dwt	loa	bm	kts	type	comments
9315800	Aegeas *	Grc	2007	23,325	39,378	183	27	14	tco	
9292620	Afrodite *	Bhs	2005	30,053	52,700	186	32	14	tco	ex Western Antarctic-06
9289518	Ajax *	Bhs	2005	30,053	52,700	186	32	14	tco	ex Western Baltic-06
9302607	Alaska *	Grc	2006	85,421	163,250	274	50	15	tcr	
9314882	Amphitrite *	Grc	2006	23,325	36,660	183	27	14	tco	ex Antares-09
9265366	Andes *	Grc	2003	39,085	68,439	229	32	14	tco	
9315795	Andromeda *	Grc	2007	23,325	39,378	183	27	14	tco	
9315185	Antarctic *	Lbr	2007	85,421	163,216	274	50	14	tcr	
9289532	Apollon *	Bhs	2005	30,053	53,148	186	32	14	tco	ex Western Pacific-06
9302592	Archangel *	Grc	2006	85,421	163,216	274	50	15	tcr	
9315173	Arctic *	Grc	2007	85,431	163,152	274	50	15	tcr	
9292967	Ariadne *	Bhs	2005	30,053	52,700	186	32	14	tco	ex Western Icelandic-06
9314894	Arion *	Grc	2006	23,325	39,478	183	27	14	tco	
9289520	Aris *	Bhs	2005	30,053	53,106	186	32	14	tco	ex Western Atlantic-06
9291640	Artemis *	Bhs	2005	30,053	53,039	186	32	14	tco	ex Western Arctic-06
9411197	Asahi Princess *	Lbr	2009	55,909	105,361	229	42	14	tcr	

Euro : Tsakos Shipping & Trading : *Chris Brooks*

IMO	name	flag	year	gt	dwt	loa	bm	kts	type	comments
9253258	Baltic	Mhl	2003	23,217	37,237	183	27	14	tco	ex Kuldiga -13, Coral Star-04
9442744	Beijing 2008	Lbr	2007	43,158	82,561	229	32	14	bbu	
9253234	Berenike	Mhl	2003	23,217	37,261	183	27	14	tco	ex Kaltene-13, Pink Star-04
9315903	Bosporos *	Grc	2007	23,310	39,589	183	27	14	tco	
9623879	Brasil 2014	Grc	2013	83,078	155,709	264	48	14	tcs	
9290828	Byron *	Mhl	2005	23,298	37,252	183	27	14	tco	ex Scarlet Star-15
9315898	Byzantion *	Grc	2007	23,310	39,589	183	27	14	tco	
9227273	Cap Talbot	Lbr	2001	40,085	51,060	257	32	23	ucc	3,739 teu: ex Cap San Antonio-12
9382982	Chantal *	Lbr	2009	41,676	74,329	228	32	14	tco	
9462926	Decathlon	Mhl	2012	81,493	158,475	274	48	14	tcr	ex Yasa Orion-16
9283796	Delphi *	Grc	2004	25,124	37,432	176	31	15	tco	
9288772	Didimon *	Grc	2004	25,124	37,432	176	31	15	tco	ex Dodoni-05
9565950	Dimitris P. *	Lbr	2011	81,314	157,740	274	48	14	tcr	
9221657	El Junior PNT	Mhl	2001	39,085	68,467	229	32	14	tco	ex Riga-14, Aztec-01
9567702	Euro	Bhs	2012	81,314	157,539	274	48	14	tcr	
9299666	Eurochampion 2004 *	Grc	2005	85,431	164,808	274	50	15	tcr	
9299678	Euronike *	Grc	2005	85,431	164,565	274	50	15	tcr	ex Euroniki-05
9567697	Eurovision	Bhs	2013	81,314	157,803	274	48	14	tcr	
9434773	Ian M.	Grc	2010	93,916	179,700	292	45	15	bbu	
9256028	Inca *	Cyp	2003	39,085	68,439	229	32	14	tco	
9346354	Irene II *	Mhl	2006	90,091	180,184	289	45	14	bbu	ex F.D. Luigi d'Amato-14
9123922	Irenes Logos	Pan	1995	18,716	24,370	194	28	20	ucc	1,611 teu: ex CCNI Mejillones-10, CMA CGM Limon-08, Irenes Logos-06, Ise-02
9303780	Irenes Rainbow	Grc	2006	28,592	39,382	222	30	23	ucc	2,824 teu: ex Kota Segar-10, I/a Irenes Rainbow
9315862	Irenes Reliance	Grc	2005	28,592	39,396	222	30	23	ucc	2,824 teu
9315850	Irenes Remedy	Grc	2005	28,592	39,382	222	30	23	ucc	2,824 teu
9238791	Irenes Wisdom	Lbr	2003	39,941	50,900	264	32	24	ucc	4,253 teu: ex E.R. Yantian-15, CMA CGM Yantian-11, I/a E.R. Yantian
9411185	Ise Princess *	Lbr	2009	55,909	105,361	229	42	14	tcr	
9330472	Izumo Princess *	Grc	2007	55,909	105,374	229	42	14	tcr	
9031650	La Paz ‡	Pan	1995	158,475	299,700	344	56	14	tcr	ex Evelyn Maersk-03
9442756	London 2012	Lbr	2007	43,158	82,562	229	32	14	bbu	
9394753	Manousos P	Lbr	2008	43,158	82,549	229	32	14	bbu	
9380661	Maria Princess *	Lbr	2008	55,909	105,346	229	42	14	tcr	
9256016	Maya *	Grc	2003	39,085	68,439	229	32	14	tco	
9158903	Millennium ‡	Pan	1998	156,692	301,171	331	58	15	tcr	
9324277	Neo Energy (st) ‡	Lbr	2007	100,253	85,602	288	44	19	lng	149,700 m³
9380673	Nippon Princess *	Grc	2008	55,909	105,392	229	42	14	tcr	
9187435	Olympia I	Lbr	1999	57,925	107,181	247	42	14	tcr	ex Atlas Valor-14
9438406	Pentathlon	Mhl	2009	81,493	158,475	274	50	14	tcr	ex Yasa Polaris-15
9305611	Promitheas *	Grc	2006	66,919	117,055	250	44	15	tco	I/a Western Asia
9305623	Propontis *	Grc	2006	66,919	116,610	250	44	15	tco	
9305609	Proteas *	Grc	2006	66,919	117,055	250	44	15	tco	
9623867	Rio 2016	Grc	2013	83,078	155,709	264	48	14	tcs	
9358541	Sakura Princess *	Grc	2007	55,909	105,385	229	42	14	tcr	
9382968	Salamina *	Lbr	2009	41,676	74,251	228	32	14	tco	
9439199	Sapporo Princess *	Grc	2010	55,909	105,354	229	42	14	tcr	
9382956	Selini *	Lbr	2009	41,676	74,296	228	32	14	tco	
9390692	Socrates *	Lbr	2008	41,676	74,327	228	32	14	tco	
9565948	Spyros K. *	Lbr	2011	81,314	157,647	274	48	15	tcr	
9388297	Selecao *	Lbr	2008	41,676	74,296	228	32	15	tco	
9229374	Silia T *	Lbr	2002	84,586	164,286	274	50	15	tcr	
9390692	Socrates *	Lbr	2008	41,676	74,327	228	32	14	tco	
9434785	Stella	Lbr	2009	93,916	179,700	292	45	14	bbu	
9233222	Triathlon *	Lbr	2002	84,586	164,445	274	50	14	tcr	
9439204	Uraga Princess *	Grc	2010	55,909	105,344	229	42	15	tcr	
9382970	World Harmony *	Lbr	2009	41,676	74,471	228	32	14	tco	
9394765	Yiannis B. *	Lbr	2008	43,158	82,591	229	32	14	bbu	
newbuildings:										
9724075	Elias Tsakos	Grc	2016	62,000	112,700	250	44	15	tcr	Daewoo Mangalia 5010 Q2 2016
9723124	Hercules I	Mhl	2016	160,000	300,000	333	60	15	tcr	Hyundai Samho ex Scorpio
9765158	Lisboa City		2017		157,000	279	48	14	tcs	Sungdong 7004 02:2017
9659725	Maria Energy [tf]	Mhl	2016	105,600	93,613	290	46	19	lng	162,000 m³
9761944	Sunray		2016	41,500	74,000	228	32	14	tco	Sungdong 3116 H2 2016
9761956	Sunrise		2016	41,500	74,000	228	32	14	tco	Sungdong 3117 H1 2016
9723112	Ulysses	Mhl	2016	160,000	300,000	333	60	15	tcr	Hyundai Samho ex Scorpio
9724087			2016	62,000	112,700	250	44	15	tcr	Daewoo Mangalia 5011 Q2 2016
9724336			2016	62,000	112,700	250	44	15	tcr	Daewoo Mangalia 5012 Q3 2016
9724348			2016	62,000	112,700	250	44	15	tcr	Daewoo Mangalia 5013 Q4 2016
9724350			2017	62,000	112,700	250	44	15	tcr	Daewoo Mangalia 5014 Q1 2017

IMO	name	flag	year	gt	dwt	loa	bm	kts	type	comments
9737371			2017	62,000	112,700	250	44	15	tcr	Daewoo Mangalia 5015 Q1 2017
9737383			2017	62,000	112,700	250	44	15	tcr	Daewoo Mangalia 5016 Q2 2017
9737395			2017	62,000	112,700	250	44	15	tcr	Daewoo Mangalia 5017 Q2 2017
9737400			2017	62,000	112,700	250	44	15	tcr	Daewoo Mangalia 5018 Q3 2017
			2017		158,000				tcr	Sungdong 12:2017
			2018		158,000				tcr	Sungdong 02:2018

*managed by Tsakos Colombia Shipmanagement (TCM) SA, (formed 2010 as j/v with Schoeller Holdings) web. www.tcsm.gr vessels operated by * Tsakos Energy Navigation Ltd (TEN) (formed 1993 as Maritime Investment Fund Ltd to 1996) or ‡ by Hyundai Merchant Marine Co Ltd.*

A/S Uglands Rederi   Norway

funnel: *yellow with white 'U' on broad red band below black top.* **hull:** *grey, blue or orange with black or white 'UGLAND', green or red boot-topping.* **history:** *formed 1930.* **web:** *www.jjuc.no*

IMO	name	flag	year	gt	dwt	loa	bm	kts	type	comments
9494060	Bonita	Nis	2010	32,315	58,105	190	32	14	bbu	
9403176	Carmencita	Nis	2009	32,379	58,773	190	32	14	bbu	
9685633	Ellenita	Nis	2015	32,402	57,501	190	32	14	bbu	
9298519	Favorita	Nis	2005	30,078	52,292	190	32	14	bbu	
9223992	Fermita	Nis	2001	30,053	52,380	190	32	14	bbu	
9493975	Isabelita	Nis	2010	32,297	58,470	190	32	14	bbu	
9131876	Kometik *	Can	1997	76,216	126,646	272	46	14	tcs	
9520936	Kristinita	Nis	2011	32,315	58,105	190	32	14	bbu	
9685621	Lunita	Nis	2014	32,402	57,807	190	32	14	bbu	
9131888	Mattea * (2)	Can	1997	76,216	126,380	272	46	15	tcs	
9281724	Rosita	Nis	2004	30,076	52,292	190	32	14	bbu	
9384540	Senorita	Nor	2008	32,379	58,300	190	32	14	bbu	
9583134	Star Norita	Nis	2012	32,371	58,470	190	32	14	bbu	
9223980	Tamarita	Nis	2001	30,053	52,292	190	32	14	bbu	
9216389	Vinland * (2)	Nis	2000	76,567	125,827	272	46	14	tcs	
newbuildings:										
9762845			2016		60,000				bbu	Sanoyas 1343
9762857			2017		60,000				bbu	Sanoyas 1344
			2017		63,000				bbu	Imabari S-K095
			2017		63,000				bbu	Imabari S-K096

*owned or managed by subsidiaries Ugland Marine Services AS (formed 1996) and Ugland Shipping A/S (formed 1964) managed * by Canship Ugland Ltd. (formed jointly with Canship Ltd). Also see Stena AB and Teekay Corp.*

United Arab Shipping Co. (SAG)   Kuwait

funnel: *black, broad white band with red/purple bands above and black/green bands below black 6-spoked wheel containing black crossed anchors on blue centre disc.* **hull:** *light grey with black 'UASC', green band over red boot-topping.* **history:** *founded 1976 as Kuwait Shipping Co (SAK) to 1977. Formed jointly by The Governments of the United Arab Emirates, the States of Bahrain, Kuwait and Qatar, the Kingdom of Saudi Arabia and the Republic of Iraq.* **web:** *www.uasc.net*

IMO	name	flag	year	gt	dwt	loa	bm	kts	type	comments
9525869	Ain Snan	Mlt	2012	141,077	145,274	366	48	26	ucc	13,296 teu
9349514	Al Bahia	Are	2008	75,579	85,517	306	40	25	ucc	6,921 teu
9708825	Al Dahna	Mlt	2016	195,636	199,900	400	59	24	ucc	19,870 teu
9732307	Al Dhail	Mhl	2016	153,148	150,000	368	51	24	ucc	14.993 teu
9349552	Al Hilal	Qat	2008	75,579	79,030	306	40	25	ucc	6,921 teu
9349538	Al Manamah	Bhr	2008	75,579	85,517	306	40	25	ucc	6,921 teu
9732319	Al Mashrab	Mhl	2016	153,148	150,000	368	51	24	ucc	14,883 teu

Star Norita : Uglands Rederi, A/S : *Mike Lennon*

IMO	name	flag	year	gt	dwt	loa	bm	kts	type	comments
9708837	Al Murabba	Mhl	2015	153,148	134,300	368	51	24	ucc	14,993 teu
9708863	Al Muraykh	Mlt	2015	195,636	199,744	400	59	24	ucc	19,870 teu
9708849	Al Nasriyah	Mhl	2015	153,148	149,360	368	51	24	ucc	14,993 teu
9708813	Al Nefud	Mlt	2016	195,636	199,744	400	59	24	ucc	19,870 teu
9525924	Al Qibla	Kwt	2012	141,077	145,237	366	48	26	ucc	13,296 teu
9152272	Al Rain	Sau	1998	48,154	49,844	277	32	24	ucc	4,101 teu: ex Al-Mutanabbi-13
9349564	Al Rawdah	Mhl	2008	75,579	85,226	306	40	25	ucc	6,921 teu
9525912	Al Riffa	Mlt	2012	141,077	145,534	366	48	26	ucc	13,296 teu
9349497	Al Safat	Kwt	2008	75,579	85,437	306	40	25	ucc	6,921 teu
9154543	Al-Abdali	Sau	1998	48,154	49,844	277	32	24	ucc	4,101 teu
9149756	Al-Farahidi	Sau	1998	48,154	50,004	277	32	24	ucc	4,101 teu
9708875	Al Zubara	Mlt	2015	195,636	199,744	400	59	24	ucc	19,870 teu
9525883	Alula	Mlt	2012	141,077	145,528	366	48	26	ucc	13,296 teu
9154531	Asir	Sau	1998	48,154	49,856	277	32	24	ucc	4,101 teu
9708851	Barzan	Mlt	2015	195,636	199,744	400	59	24	ucc	19,870 teu
9149768	Deira	Sau	1998	48,154	49,993	277	32	24	ucc	4,101 teu
9152260	Fowairet	Sau	1998	48,154	49,993	277	32	24	ucc	4,101 teu
9349502	Hatta	Are	2008	75,579	85,614	306	40	25	ucc	6,921 teu
9349540	Jazan	Sau	2008	75,579	85,463	306	40	25	ucc	6,921 teu
9525936	Jebel Ali	Mlt	2012	141,077	145,149	366	48	26	ucc	13,296 teu
9708801	Linah	Mhl	2015	153,148	134,300	368	51	22	ucc	14,993 teu
9525900	Malik al Ashtar	Mlt	2012	141,077	145,527	366	48	26	ucc	13,296 teu
9349526	Mayssan	Bhr	2008	75,579	85,517	306	40	25	ucc	6,921 teu
9149744	Najran	Sau	1998	48,154	49,993	277	32	24	ucc	4,101 teu
9154529	Sabya	Sau	1998	48,154	49,848	277	32	24	ucc	4,101 teu: ex Al-Sabahia-13
9708784	Sajir	Mhl	2014	153,148	134,300	368	51	22	ucc	14,993 teu
9152258	Sakaka	Sau	1998	48,154	49,844	277	32	24	ucc	4,101 teu: ex Abu Dhabi-13
9708796	Salahuddin	Mhl	2015	153,148	134,300	368	51	22	ucc	14,993 teu
9149770	Sudair	Sau	1998	48,154	49,993	277	32	24	ucc	4,101 teu: ex Al Noof-13
9525895	Tayma	Mlt	2012	141,077	145,451	366	48	26	ucc	13,296 teu
9736107	Tihama	Mlt	2016	195,636	199,900	400	59	24	ucc	19,870 teu
9525857	Umm Salal	Mlt	2011	141,077	145,327	366	48	26	ucc	13,296 teu
9525871	Unayzah	Mlt	2012	141,077	145,520	366	48	26	ucc	13,296 teu
newbuildings :										
9723112	Ulysses	Mhl	2016	160,000	300,000	333	60	15	tcr	Hyundai Samho ex Scorpio
9723124		Mhl	2016	160,000	300,000	333	60	15	tcr	Hyundai Samho ex Scorpio
	Al Jasrah		2016	150,800	149,000	368	51	24	ucc	15,000 teu Hyundai Samho S741
9732333	Umm Qarn		2016	150,800	149,000	368	51	24	ucc	15,000 teu Hyundai Samho S742
9732345	Afif		2016	150,800	149,000	368	51	24	ucc	15,000 teu Hyundai Samho S743
9732357	Al Jmeliyah		2016	150,800	149,000	368	51	24	ucc	15,000 teu Hyundai Samho S744

newbuildings: further 11 x 14,993teu reported

United Arab Chemical Carriers LLC, Dubai

funnel: black, broad white band with 'UACC' in black and blue & green logo. **hull:** black some with 'U.A.C.C.' in white, red boot topping,
history: formed 2007, largest shareholder is UASC with Arabian Chemical Carriers of Saudia Arabia. Vessels managed by UASC,
web: uacc.ae

IMO	name	flag	year	gt	dwt	loa	bm	kts	type	comments
9254939	UACC Al Medina	Pan	2003	28,059	45,987	180	32	14	tco	ex Nord Sea-08
9296585	UACC Consensus	Pan	2005	28,059	45,896	180	32	14	tco	ex High Consensus-09

Barzan : United Arab Shipping Co. : *Hans Kraijenbosch*

IMO	name	flag	year	gt	dwt	loa	bm	kts	type	comments
9458808	UACC Doha	Mhl	2010	29,124	45,553	183	32	14	tco	ex Bunga Bakawali-14
9288289	UACC Harmony	Pan	2005	28,059	45,913	180	32	14	tco	ex High Harmony-09
9254927	UACC Ibn Al Atheer	Pan	2003	28,059	45,994	180	32	14	tco	ex Pacific Sunshine-08
9458822	UACC Manama	Mys	2010	29,124	45,612	183	32	14	tco	ex Bunga Balsam-14
9489089	UACC Mansouria	Mhl	2013	28,279	45,293	183	32	15	tco	
9489091	UACC Marah	Mhl	2013	29,279	45,293	183	32	15	tco	
9489065	UACC Masafi	Mhl	2012	29,279	45,352	183	32	15	tco	
9489077	UACC Messila	Mhl	2012	29,168	45,352	183	32	15	tco	
9402794	UACC Mirdif	Mhl	2010	26,916	47,366	183	32	15	tco	ex Ocean Leo-14
9480162	UACC Muharraq	Pan	2014	29,168	45,562	183	32	14	tco	ex TRF Oslo-16, NCC Bader-14
9425511	UACC Ras Laffan	Lbr	2010	29,563	49,999	183	32	14	tct	ex Eships Falcon-15
9425318	UACC Ras Tanura	Lbr	2010	29,563	49,999	183	32	14	tco	ex Eships Maya-15, l/a SLS Land
9458834	UACC Riyadh	Mys	2011	29,124	45,444	183	32	14	tco	ex Bunga Banyan-14
9458858	UACC Shamiya	Mys	2011	29,124	45,444	183	32	14	tco	ex Bunga Begonia-14
9428360	UACC Shams	Lbr	2009	30,006	50,138	183	32	14	tco	ex Tyrrhenian Wave-11, Indiana-09
9428358	UACC Sila	Lbr	2009	30,006	50,105	183	32	14	tco	ex Ionian Wave-11, l/a Banksy
9272395	UACC Sound	Pan	2003	28,059	45,975	180	32	14	tco	ex Nord Sound-09
9272400	UACC Strait	Pan	2004	28,059	45,934	180	32	14	tco	ex Nord Strait-09
reported acquisitions:										
9692246			2015	29,531	49,126	183	32	14	tco	ex TRF Bergen-16

see also Hafnia Tankers Straits Pool

Linah : United Arab Shipping Co. : *Hans Kraijenbosch*

UACC Shamiya : United Arab Shipping Co. - United Chemical Carriers : *Hans Kraijenbosch*

IMO	name	flag	year	gt	dwt	loa	bm	kts	type	comments

Viken Shipping AS · Norway

funnel: *cream with narrow blue band on white band on broad red band beneath black top.* **hull:** *dark green with white 'Viken' with red boot-topping.* **history:** *formed 1993 and de-merged from joint venture with Mowinckel in 2002. Acquired Wallem Group jointly with Clearwater Investments in 2006.* **web:** *www.vikenshipping.com*

IMO	name	flag	year	gt	dwt	loa	bm	kts	type	comments
9492000	Angra Dos Reis	Bhs	2012	62,753	105,185	248	42	14	tcs	
9587192	Dolviken	Nis	2012	81,453	159,058	274	48	14	tcr	
9274812	Erviken	Nis	2004	82,647	152,146	275	48	14	tcr	
9321677	Kronviken	Nis	2006	61,653	113,450	249	44	14	tcr	
9492050	Madre de Deus	Bhs	2012	62,221	109,250	248	42	14	tcs	
9492062	Rio Grande	Bhs	2012	62,753	105,190	248	42	14	tcs	
9492139	Sao Luiz	Bhs	2013	62,753	105,213	248	42	14	tcs	
9492127	Sao Sebastiao	Bhs	2013	62,753	105,190	248	42	14	tcs	
9321689	Solviken	Nis	2007	61,653	114,523	249	44	14	tcr	
9308065	Storviken	Nis	2006	82,647	152,013	274	48	14	tcr	
9285835	Telleviken	Iom	2005	62,806	115,340	250	44	15	tco	ex Tanea-11, Ganstar-05
9285847	Tofteviken	Iom	2005	62,806	115,340	250	44	15	tco	ex Torinia-11, Gansky-05
9285859	Troviken	Iom	2006	62,806	115,345	250	44	15	tco	ex Trochus-11, l/a Gansea

managed by subsidiary Wallem Shipmanagement Norway AS (renamed from Viken Ship Management AS in 2006)

F. A. Vinnen & Co. (GmbH & Co.) · Germany

funnel: *black with black 'M' on broad white band, white with blue 'V' or charterers colours.* **hull:** *black with red boot-topping.* **history:** *formed 1918 as E.C. Schramm & Co to 1920.* **web:** *www.vinnen.com*

IMO	name	flag	year	gt	dwt	loa	bm	kts	type	comments
9620607	Cap Cleveland	Mlt	2013	42,564	52,068	228	37	20	ucc	3,868 teu: ex Kota Pelangi-16, Cap Cleveland-14, l/a Merkur Fjord
9620619	Cap Coral	Mlt	2013	42,564	52,084	228	37	20	ucc	3,868 teu: l/a Merkur Ocean
9301469	CMA CGM l'Etoile	Mlt	2005	26,626	34,500	210	30	21	ucc	2,556 teu: ex E.R. Camargue-05
9135925	Merkur Cloud	Lbr	1996	15,929	22,026	168	27	21	ucc	1,608 teu: ex Kota Molek-07, Merkur Cloud-04, Calapalos-02, l/a Merkur Cloud
9456991	Merkur Harbour	Lbr	2012	50,885	61,983	249	37	24	ucc	4,532 teu: ex CCNI Arauco-14, l/a Merkur Harbour
9162368	Merkur Tide	Lbr	1998	15,929	22,026	168	27	21	ucc	1,708 teu: ex MOL Heritage-11, Merkur Tide-08, YM Dubai-07, Merkur Tide-04, Calaparana-03, Merkur Tide-01, Atlantico-01, l/a Merkur Tide
9456989	Zim Istanbul	Lbr	2009	41,331	51,602	262	32	24	ucc	4,255 teu: ex Cap Hatteras-14, Zim Istanbul-13, Merkur Horizon-10, Rio Canberra-09

*also see Jungerhans Reederei, * managed for Hansa Treuhand Schiffs GmbH & Co KG, Germany qv*

H. Vogemann GmbH · Germany

funnel: *yellow with white 'V' on broad red band.* **hull:** *black with red boot-topping.* **history:** *founded 1886.* **web:** *www.vogemann.de*

IMO	name	flag	year	gt	dwt	loa	bm	kts	type	comments
9154866	Paul †	Lbr	1998	14,762	23,494	156	26	15	bbu	ex Voge Paul-15, Clipper Bounteous-07, Joint Spirit-03, Sea Harvest-98

Kronviken : Viken Shipping AS : *ARO*

IMO	name	flag	year	gt	dwt	loa	bm	kts	type	comments
9420851	Voge Dignity +	Lbr	2009	24,066	38,334	183	27	14	tco	
9464948	Voge Emma *	Lbr	2011	22,683	36,839	187	28	14	bbu	ex A Handy-14
9541318	Voge Enterprise *	Lbr	2011	43,692	79,409	229	32	15	bbu	
9168154	Voge Fiesta *	Lbr	1997	19,354	29,516	181	26	14	ggc	ex Fiesta-13, DS Fiesta-06, Clipper Fiesta-01
9175913	Voge Lena *	Lbr	1998	14,446	23,612	151	26	14	bbu	ex Blue Aries-09
9339181	Voge Master *	Deu	2006	88,930	174,093	289	45	14	bbu	ex Avore-07
9464950	Voge Mia *	Lbr	2011	22,683	36,866	187	28	14	bbu	ex B Handy-14
9154854	Voge Renate *	Lbr	1997	14,762	23,407	154	26	15	bbu	ex Clipper Breeze-07, Joint Bright-03, Sea Splendor-98
9420863	Voge Trust	Lbr	2009	24,066	38,349	183	27	14	tco	
9475301	Vogerunner *	Deu	2009	89,603	176,838	289	45	16	bbu	

managed by TSC The Shipmanagement Co. GmbH (j/v between Voge, Roth and HJH Shipmanagement founded 2013), + managed by Chemikalien Seetransport GmbH   † owned by Jens & Waller : see also König & Co.

Vroon b.v.   Netherlands

funnel: *white with three wavy blue lines at base of blue 'V', narrow blue or black top* **hull:** *red with large white 'V', red boot-topping.*
history: *formed 1890* **web:** *www.vroon.nl or www.iverships.com*

IMO	name	flag	year	gt	dwt	loa	bm	kts	type	comments
9298715	Acadian	Can	2005	23,356	37,515	183	27	14	tco	
9138161	Aegean Express	Pan	1997	15,095	18,581	169	27	18	ucc	1,439 teu: ex YM Bangkok-02, Kuo Ting-01
9148532	Arabian Express	Pan	1997	15,095	18,300	169	27	18	ucc	1,439 teu: ex Kuo Yang-03
9426324	Bahamian Express	Gib	2010	21,018	25,937	180	28	20	ucc	1,795 teu
9501772	Belgian Express	Gib	2010	21,018	25,774	180	28	20	ucc	1,795 teu
9321471	Caledonian Express	Gib	2006	27,915	38,133	215	30	21	ucc	2,100 teu: ex Nona-14, YM Mundra-12, ANL Bindara-11, Nona-10
9298703	East Coast	Can	2005	23,356	37,515	183	27	14	tco	ex Nor'easter-14
9298739	Great Eastern	Mhl	2005	23,356	37,515	183	27	14	tco	
9474383	Istrian Express	Gib	2011	12,514	14,233	158	25	19	ucc	1,084 teu
9474395	Italian Express	Gib	2012	12,514	14,213	158	25	19	ucc	1,084 teu
9207982	Iver Exact	Nld	2007	29,456	46,575	183	32	14	tco	
9307994	Iver Example	Nld	2007	29,456	46,784	183	32	14	tco	
9207716	Iver Experience	Nld	2000	29,289	45,650	183	32	15	tco	

Voge Dignity : H. Vogemann GmbH : *Chris Brooks*

IMO	name	flag	year	gt	dwt	loa	bm	kts	type	comments
9207728	Iver Exporter	Nld	2000	29,289	45,683	183	32	15	tco	.
9314208	Iver Express	Nld	2007	29,456	46,825	183	32	14	tco	
9350642	Iver Progress	Mhl	2007	23,421	37,412	184	27	14	tco	
9351921	Iver Prosperity	Mhl	2007	23,421	37,456	184	27	14	tco	
9442122	Le Mans Express	Gib	2010	36,711	11,215	168	28	19	mve	3,693 ceu
9451719	Monza Express	Gib	2009	36,711	11,174	168	28	19	mve	3,693 ceu
9298727	New England	Mhl	2005	23,356	37,515	183	27	14	tco	
9553218	Peruvian Express	Mhl	2012	43,692	79,252	229	32	14	bbu	
9487873	Scandinavian Express	Gib	2010	51,209	93,038	230	38	14	bbu	
9487885	Scotian Express	Gib	2011	51,209	93,019	230	38	14	bbu	
9434321	Sebring Express	Phl	2009	43,810	15,154	180	30	19	mve	3,930 ceu
9448061	Sepang Express	Phl	2009	43,810	15,154	180	30	19	mve	3,930 ceu
9498717	Siberian Express	Gib	2012	51,209	92,974	230	38	14	bbu	
9498729	Sicilian Express	Gib	2013	51,209	93,076	230	38	14	bbu	
9434319	Silverstone Express	Phl	2009	43,810	15,154	180	30	19	mve	3,930 ceu
9448073	Suzuka Express	Phl	2010	43,810	15,154	180	30	19	mve	3,930 ceu

tankers operated by wholly owned subsidiary Iver Ships b.v.   also owns smaller tankers and container feeder ships
NB: the company also operates a fleet of 14 livestock carriers with 2 more scheduled for 2016 delivery generally trading between Australasia and the Middle East

Sicilian Express : Vroon b.v. : *Hans Kraijenbosch*

Avonborg : Wagenborg b.v. : *Chris Brooks*

IMO	name	flag	year	gt	dwt	loa	bm	kts	type	comments

Wagenborg Shipping b.v.   Netherlands

funnel: *black with two narrow white bands.* **hull:** *light grey with broad red band interrupted by two diagonal white stripes and white 'WAGENBORG', black boot-topping.* **history:** *founded 1898 as E. Wagenborg's Scheepvaart Expeditiebedrijf NV to 1972 and Wagenborg Scheepvaart BV to 1987.* **web:** *www.wagenborg.com*

IMO	name	flag	year	gt	dwt	loa	bm	kts	type	comments
9546497	Adriaticborg	Nld	2011	11,885	17,294	143	22	17	ggc	ex CCNI Topocalma-12, Adriaticborg-11
9365661	Africaborg	Nld	2008	11,894	17,356	143	22	17	ggc	ex CCNI Topocalma-11, Tianshan-09, Africaborg-08
9466348	Alamosborg	Nld	2011	11,885	17,294	143	22	17	ggc	
9466374	Alaskaborg	Nld	2012	11,894	17,350	143	22	17	ggc	
9466300	Albanyborg	Nld	2010	11,885	17,294	143	22	17	ggc	ex CCNI Tolten-12, Albanyborg-11
9333541	Amazoneborg	Nld	2007	11,894	17,355	143	22	17	ggc	
9365659	Americaborg	Nld	2007	11,894	17,356	143	22	17	ggc	
9333527	Amstelborg	Nld	2006	11,894	17,356	143	22	17	ggc	
9466336	Amurborg	Nld	2011	11,885	17,294	143	22	17	ggc	
9466324	Andesborg	Nld	2011	11,885	17,284	143	22	17	ggc	
9466312	Aragonborg	Nld	2010	11,885	17,294	143	22	17	ggc	
9333539	Arneborg *	Nld	2006	11,894	17,356	143	22	17	ggc	
9466295	Arubaborg	Nld	2010	11,864	17,407	143	22	17	ggc	
9466350	Atlanticborg	Nld	2012	11,885	17,294	143	22	17	ggc	
9466362	Avonborg	Nld	2012	11,864	17,300	143	22	17	ggc	
9466051	Azoresborg	Nld	2010	11,864	17,407	143	22	17	ggc	
9248564	Nassauborg	Nld	2005	16,037	16,615	143	22	16	ggc	
9232797	Oranjeborg	Nld	2004	18,293	15,126	159	26	17	urr	l/a Finnbirch
9592563	Reestborg	Nld	2013	14,141	23,249	170	20	13	ggc	
9592575	Reggeborg	Nld	2014	14,141	23,249	170	20	13	ggc	
9355812	Rijnborg	Nld	2007	16,523	18,450	176	24	21	ucc	1,712 teu: ex Katharina-08, Rijnborg-07
9592599	Roerborg	Nld	2014	14,224	23,249	170	20	13	ggc	l/d Rudderborg
9546461	Taagborg	Nld	2013	14,695	21,338	172	22	15	ggc	ex CCNI Bilbao-15, Taagborg-14
9546459	Thamesborg	Nld	2013	14,695	21,359	172	22	15	ggc	
9546473	Tiberborg	Nld	2013	14,695	21,301	172	22	15	ggc	
9546485	Trinityborg	Nld	2013	14,695	21,277	172	22	15	ggc	

the company also operates ro-ro vessels on northern European routes and numerous smaller vessels.

Wallenius Wilhelmsen Logistics   Norway/Sweden

Wallenius Lines AB, Sweden

funnel: *yellow with yellow 'OW' on broad green band.* **hull:** *green with green 'WALLENIUS WILHELMSEN' on white upperworks, green or red boot-topping.* **history:** *founded 1934 as Rederi AB Soya. Wallenius and Wilhelmsen merged operations in 1999 but fleets retain original identities.* **web:** *www.walleniuslines.com*

IMO	name	flag	year	gt	dwt	loa	bm	kts	type	comments
8202367	Aegean Breeze **	Sgp	1983	29,874	12,527	164	28	18	mve	3,100 ceu: (rbt-10)
9377494	Aniara	Swe	2008	71,673	30,089	232	32	19	mve	7,600 ceu
8202355	Arabian Breeze **	Sgp	1983	29,874	12,577	164	28	18	mve	3,100 ceu: (rbt-10)
8202381	Asian Breeze **	Sgp	1983	29,874	12,562	164	28	18	mve	3,100 ceu: (rbt-10)
8312590	Baltic Breeze **	Sgp	1983	29,979	12,466	164	28	18	mve	3,100 ceu: (rbt-10)
9531715	Bess †	Pan	2010	58,750	18,013	200	32	20	mve	6,284 ceu
9176565	Boheme ††	Sgp	1999	67,264	28,360	228	32	20	mve	7,194 ceu: (len-05)
9505027	Carmen	Swe	2011	74,258	30,140	232	32	19	mve	7,934 ceu
9122655	Don Carlos	Sgp	1997	67,141	28,142	228	32	20	mve	7,200 ceu: (len-06)
9182934	Don Juan	Sgp	1995	55,598	22,514	199	32	20	mve	5,846 ceu
9138513	Don Pasquale	Sgp	1997	67,141	28,142	228	32	20	mve	7,200 ceu: (len-07)
9138525	Don Quijote	Sgp	1998	67,141	28,142	228	32	20	mve	7,200 ceu: (len-06)
9176577	Elektra	Sgp	1999	67,264	22,588	228	32	20	mve	7,194 ceu: (len-05)
8320767	Falstaff	Swe	1985	51,858	28,529	200	32	20	mve	5,406 ceu
9332925	Faust	Swe	2007	71,583	30,383	228	32	19	mve	7,500 ceu
9332949	Fedora	Swe	2008	71,583	30,386	228	32	19	mve	7,500 ceu
9332937	Fidelio	Swe	2008	71,583	30,137	228	32	19	mve	7,934 ceu
9505041	Figaro	Swe	2011	74,258	30,140	232	32	19	mve	7,934 ceu
8321325	Isolde	Swe	1985	51,071	28,396	200	32	19	mve	5,293 ceu
9179725	Manon	Swe	1999	67,264	14,863	228	32	20	mve	7,194 ceu: (len-05)
8016550	Medea	Sgp	1982	50,681	28,566	200	32	19	mve	5,234 ceu
9189251	Mignon	Swe	1999	67,264	28,127	228	32	20	mve	7,194 ceu: (len-05)
9312834	Morning Chorus +	Sgp	2007	57,536	21,500	200	32	20	mve	6,645 ceu
9377509	Oberon	Swe	2008	71,673	24,600	232	32	19	mve	7,620 ceu
9316141	Otello	Swe	2006	60,942	30,134	199	32	19	mve	6,700 ceu
9515395	Parsifal	Sgp	2011	75,251	43,878	265	32	19	urr	6,004 ceu
9409338	Porgy †	Pan	2009	58,752	18,009	200	32	19	mve	6,284 ceu
9515412	Salome	Sgp	2012	75,251	43,878	265	32	19	urr	6,004 ceu

Tosca : Wallenius Lines : *Mike Rhodes*

Thermopylae : Wilhelmsen Ship Management : *ARO*

IMO	name	flag	year	gt	dwt	loa	bm	kts	type	comments
9605798	Tosca	Sgp	2013	61,106	22,585	200	32	20	mve	6,459 ceu
9070450	Turandot	Sgp	1995	55,598	22,815	199	32	20	mve	5,846 ceu
9240160	Undine	Swe	2003	67,264	22,616	228	32	20	mve	7,194 ceu: (len-06)
newbuildings:										
9700512			2016	72,400	21,500	200	37		mve	8,000 ceu Tianjin Xingang NB005 01
9700524			2016	72,400	21,500	200	37		mve	8,000 ceu Tianjin Xingang NB005 02
9731640			2016	72,400	21,500	200	37		mve	8,000 ceu Tianjin Xingang NB005 03
9731652			2016	72,400	21,500	200	37		mve	8,000 ceu Tianjin Xingang NB005 04

*vessels owned by subsidiaries of Wallenius Marine AB, ** operated by United European Car Carriers*
vessels chartered from: † Sedona Car Lines, Panama or †† SSC Shipmanagement : + chartered to Eukor Car Carriers

Wilhelmsen Ship Management, Norway

funnel: *black with two narrow light blue bands.* **hull:** *red with white 'WALLENIUS WILHELMSEN', red boot-topping.* **history:** *founded 1861 as Wilh. Wilhelmsen Enterprises A/S to 1985. Wallenius Wilhelmsen merged operations in 1999 but fleets retain separate identity.* **web:** *www.walleniusmarine.com, www.wilh-wilhelmsen.com, www.ww-group.com or www.2wglobal.com*

IMO	name	flag	year	gt	dwt	loa	bm	kts	type	comments
9312822	Morning Concert +	Gbr	2006	57,415	21,500	200	32	20	mve	5,400 ceu
9460887	Morning Clara †	Sgp	2009	60,213	18,638	200	32	20	mve	6,340 ceu: ex Queen Sapphire-14
9191319	Talisman	Nis	2000	67,140	38,500	241	32	20	mve	5,496 ceu
9218648	Tamerlane *	Nis	2001	67,140	38,500	241	32	20	mve	5,496 ceu
9191307	Tamesis *	Nis	2000	67,140	39,516	241	32	20	mve	5,496 ceu
9191321	Tarago *	Nis	2000	67,140	39,516	241	32	20	mve	7,400 ceu
9702455	Thalatta	Mlt	2015	75,283	23,786	200	37	20	mve	8,000 ceu
9722302	Theban	Sgp	2016	75,283	23,786	200	37	20	mve	7,930 ceu
9702443	Thermopylae	Mlt	2015	75,283	23,786	200	37	20	mve	8,000 ceu
9505039	Tiger	Mlt	2011	74,255	30,140	228	32	19	mve	7,945 ceu
9377511	Tijuca	Nis	2008	71,673	30,089	232	32	19	mve	7,620 ceu
9377523	Tirranna	Nis	2009	71,673	29,936	232	32	19	mve	7,620 ceu
9505053	Titania	Mlt	2011	74,255	30,907	228	32	20	mve	7,934 ceu
9293624	Toledo *	Gbr	2005	61,321	19,628	200	32	20	mve	6,354 ceu
9375264	Tomar *	Nis	2006	61,328	22,144	200	32	20	mve	6,354 ceu
9319753	Tombarra *	Gbr	2006	61,321	19,628	200	32	20	mve	6,354 ceu
9605786	Tongala	Mlt	2012	61,106	22,585	200	32	20	mve	6,459 ceu
9515383	Tønsberg	Mlt	2011	74,682	41,820	265	32	19	urr	5,990 ceu
9310109	Topeka *	Gbr	2006	61,321	19,600	200	32	20	mve	6,354 ceu
9398321	Torino	Gbr	2009	61,328	22,160	200	32	20	mve	6,354 ceu
9302205	Toronto *	Gbr	2005	61,321	19,628	200	32	20	mve	6,354 ceu
9293612	Torrens *	Gbr	2004	61,321	14,512	200	32	20	mve	6,354 ceu
9319765	Tortugas *	Gbr	2006	61,321	14,512	200	32	20	mve	6,354 ceu
9398333	Toscana	Gbr	2009	61,328	22,250	200	32	20	mve	6.354 ceu
9505065	Tugela	Mlt	2011	72,295	28,837	230	32	19	mve	7,880 ceu
9505089	Tulane	Mlt	2012	72,295	28,818	230	32	19	mve	7,880 ceu
9515402	Tysla	Mlt	2012	75,251	43,878	265	33	19	urr	5,990 ceu
newbuildings:										
9722314			2016	74,500	23,780	200	37	20	mve	7,930 ceu: Hyundai Samho S726

* managed by Wilhelmsen Ship Management AS, (www.wilhelmsen.com),   † chartered from MMS Co., Japan,   See also Paal Wilson & Co. and Dockwise NV
+ chartered to Eukor Car Carriers

American Roll-on Roll-off Carrier Inc., USA

funnel: *white with USA national flag and 'ARC' houseflag either side of black anchor, narrow black top.* **hull:** *blue with blue 'ARC' on white superstructure* **history:** *founded 1990, an ASL Group company* **web:** *www.arrcnet.com*

IMO	name	flag	year	gt	dwt	loa	bm	kts	type	comments
9316139	Aida	Usa	2006	60,942	22,564	199	32	19	mve	6,700 ceu
9121273	Endurance	Nis	1996	72,708	48,988	265	32	20	mve	4,923 ceu: ex Taronga-10 (conv urc-06)
9129706	Freedom	Usa	1997	49,821	19,884	190	32	19	mve	4,635 ceu: ex Takamine-03
9126297	Honor	Usa	1996	49,821	19,844	190	32	19	mve	4,635 ceu: ex Takasago-05
9070448	Independence II	Usa	1994	55,598	22,862	199	32	20	mve	5,846 ceu: ex Titus-08
8919934	Integrity	Usa	1992	52,479	29,152	203	32	20	mve	5,800 ceu: ex Otello-05
9080297	Resolve	Usa	1994	49,443	20,082	190	32	19	mve	4,635 ceu: ex Tanabata-03, Nosac Tanabata-96

Eukor Car Carriers Inc., South Korea

funnel: *cream with white curved cross on blue globe or owners colours.* **hull:** *light blue most with 'EUKOR' on cream superstructure, or owners colours.* **history:** *Founded 2002 by Walleniusrederierna AB (40%), Wilhelmsen ASA (40%), Hyundai Motor Group (10%) and Kia Motor Corp. (10%)* **web:** *www.eukor.com*

IMO	name	flag	year	gt	dwt	loa	bm	kts	type	comments
9158616	Asian Captain	Pan	1998	71,383	25,765	229	32	20	mve	7,916 ceu: (len-06)
9203588	Asian Dynasty *	Kor	1999	55,719	21,224	200	32	20	mve	6,480 ceu
9176606	Asian Empire	Pan	1998	71,383	25,765	229	32	20	mve	7,916 ceu: (len-06)
9203576	Asian Majesty	Kor	1999	71,383	25,818	229	32	20	mve	7,916 ceu: (len-06)

IMO	name	flag	year	gt	dwt	loa	bm	kts	type	comments
9122954	Asian Parade	Sgp	1996	67,010	21,407	229	32	20	mve	8,086 ceu: (len-07)
9203590	Asian Trust	Sgp	2000	55,729	21,321	200	32	20	mve	6,677 ceu
9122966	Asian Vision	Sgp	1997	55,680	21,421	200	32	20	mve	6,246 ceu
9638430	Morning Calypso *	Pan	2013	59,432	18,200	200	32	20	mve	6,500 ceu
9663295	Morning Capo	Pan	2013	59,615	20,139	200	32	19	mve	6,645 ceu
9574092	Morning Cara *	Pan	2011	59,454	18,907	200	32	19	mve	6,502 ceu
9336086	Morning Carol	Pan	2008	57,542	21,044	200	32	20	mve	6,645 ceu
9338711	Morning Catherine *	Pan	2008	60,876	22,678	200	32	19	mve	6,502 ceu
9477830	Morning Cecilie *	Pan	2008	60,876	22,699	200	32	20	mve	6,502 ceu
9336062	Morning Celesta	Pan	2008	57,542	20,500	200	32	20	mve	6,645 ceu
9519133	Morning Celine *	Pan	2009	60,799	22,641	200	32	20	mve	6,502 ceu
9329461	Morning Cello *	Pan	2007	57,542	21,059	200	32	20	mve	6,645 ceu
9663300	Morning Chant	Mhl	2014	59,615	20,190	200	32	20	mve	6,645 ceu
9574054	Morning Christina *	Pan	2010	59,454	18,922	200	32	20	mve	6,502 ceu
9633185	Morning Cindy *	Pan	2013	59,432	18,954	200	32	20	mve	6,500 ceu
9620683	Morning Claire *	Pan	2012	60,825	16,722	200	32	20	mve	6,502 ceu
9336074	Morning Composer	Pan	2008	57,542	21,052	200	32	20	mve	6,645 ceu
9336050	Morning Conductor	Pan	2008	57,542	20,500	200	32	20	mve	6,645 ceu
9329473	Morning Cornet *	Sgp	2007	57,542	20,500	200	32	20	mve	6,645 ceu
9574080	Morning Crystal *	Pan	2011	59,524	18,918	200	32	20	mve	6,502 ceu
9445980	Morning Lady	Pan	2010	70,687	27,343	232	32	19	mve	8,011 ceu
9445992	Morning Laura	Pan	2010	70,687	27,297	232	32	19	mve	8,011 ceu
9446001	Morning Lena	Pan	2010	70,687	27,297	232	32	19	mve	8,011 ceu
9446013	Morning Lily	Pan	2011	70,687	27,283	232	32	19	mve	8,011 ceu
9383106	Morning Linda	Pan	2008	68,701	28,061	232	32	20	mve	8,011 ceu
9383417	Morning Lisa	Pan	2008	68,701	28,084	232	32	20	mve	8,011 ceu
9383431	Morning Lucy	Pan	2009	68,701	28,000	232	32	20	mve	8,011 ceu
9383429	Morning Lynn	Pan	2009	68,701	28,000	232	32	20	mve	8,011 ceu
9367580	Morning Margareta *	Sgp	2008	51,917	17,386	180	32	19	mve	5,340 ceu
9318515	Morning Menad *	Bhs	2007	41,192	12,300	176	31	19	mve	4,750 ceu
9367592	Morning Ninni *	Sgp	2008	51,917	17,372	180	32	19	mve	5,340 ceu
9669031	Morning Pilot	Mhl	2014	65,276	22,675	200	35	19	mve	7,200 ceu
9669029	Morning Post	Mhl	2014	65,276	22,675	200	35	19	mve	7,200 ceu
9681431	Morning Pride	Mhl	2014	65,276	22,675	200	35	19	mve	7,200 ceu

managed mainly by Eukor Car Carriers Inc, South Korea, Eukor Shipowning Singapore Pte Ltd, or by Wilhelmsen Shipmanagement Singapore Pte Ltd or Wilhelmsen Ship Management (Korea) Ltd
* chartered from various owners,.
also see chartered vessels under Cido Shipping, Ray Shipping, Vroon and Zodiac (Ofer Bros).

Warwick & Esplen Ltd.   U.K.

The Hadley Shipping Co. Ltd.
funnel: *yellow with black 'HSC' inside white diamond, black top.* **hull:** *black with red boot-topping.* **history:** *formed 1926.*
web: *www.angloeasterngroup.com*

IMO	name	flag	year	gt	dwt	loa	bm	kts	type	comments
9596301	Cerinthus	Gbr	2013	18,485	23,600	176	27	14	ucc	1,740 teu
9305087	Cerafina	Gbr	2005	40,524	74,759	225	32	13	bbu	ex Clare-12, Golden Gunn-07
9307657	Clymene	Gbr	2006	40,244	73,600	225	32	14	bbu	ex Ming Mei-06
9223198	Cymbeline	Iom	2001	38,299	73,060	225	32	14	bbu	

managed by Anglo-Eastern (UK) Ltd., UK.

Oskar Wehr KG (GmbH & Co.)   Germany
funnel: *black with blue 'W' in blue ring over two blue bands in centre and towards top of broad yellow band or charterers colours.*
hull: *blue or grey with diagonal yellow stripe and blue or red boot-topping.* **history:** *formed 1945.* **web:** *www.wehrship.de*

IMO	name	flag	year	gt	dwt	loa	bm	kts	type	comments
9397860	Anni Selmer	Mhl	2009	31,222	56,000	190	32	14	bbu	
9435064	Charlotte Selmer	Mhl	2011	92,079	176,000	292	45	14	bbu	
9434711	Frederike Selmer	Mhl	2009	32,957	56,847	190	32	14	bbu	
9290866	Frieda Selmer	Mhl	2004	31,218	55,718	190	32	14	bbu	
9435076	Greta Selmer	Mhl	2011	92,079	175,181	292	45	14	bbu	
9290878	Helene Selmer	Mhl	2005	31,218	55,741	190	32	14	bbu	
9434448	Hugo Selmer	Mhl	2010	92,079	175,401	292	45	14	bbu	
9500584	Ingwar Selmer	Mhl	2011	31,784	55,733	190	32	14	bbu	
9476642	Klara Selmer	Mhl	2012	92,079	175,247	292	45	14	bbu	
9435052	Lene Selmer	Mhl	2010	92,079	175,401	292	45	14	bbu	
9324083	Mimi Selmer	Mhl	2005	31,500	55,711	190	32	14	bbu	
9331866	Therese Selmer	Mhl	2006	31,500	56,000	190	32	14	bbu	
9476630	Tom Selmer	Mhl	2011	92,079	175,154	292	45	14	bbu	
9232383	Wehr Alster	Mhl	2002	25,630	33,767	207	30	21	ucc	2,546 teu: ex CSAV Rio Baker-09, CCNI Arica-04, Wehr Alster-02

IMO	name	flag	year	gt	dwt	loa	bm	kts	type	comments
9232395	Wehr Bille	Mhl	2002	25,624	33,739	208	30	21	ucc	2,474 teu: ex NileDutch Singapore-12, Wehr Bille-10, NYK Estrela-09, CSAV Rio Cochamo-05, Wehr Bille-04, CCNI Antartico-03, Wehr Bille-02
9236688	Wehr Elbe *	Mhl	2001	25,703	33,795	203	30	22	ucc	2,524 teu: ex CSAV Callao-08, I/a Wehr Elbe
9252981	Wehr Havel	Mhl	2002	25,703	33,795	208	30	21	ucc	2,524 teu: ex CCNI Andes-11, Wehr Havel-10, CSAV Rio Tolten-09, Wehr Havel-04
9301330	Wehr Hong Kong	Mhl	2006	54,193	67,470	294	32	24	ucc	5,089 teu: ex Maersk Dellys-14, Wehr Singapore-06
9144134	Wehr Koblenz *	Mhl	1997	16,801	23,051	184	25	20	ucc	1,726 teu: ex CCNI Bilboa-09, Wehr Koblenz-08, MOL Springbok-06, P&O Nedlloyd Portbury-06, P&O Nedlloyd Calypso-05, Costa Rica-02, Wehr Koblenz-01, Panamerican-01, CSAV Rio Amazonas-99, I/a Wehr Koblenz
9252993	Wehr Oste	Mhl	2002	25,703	33,670	208	30	21	ucc	2,524 teu: ex CCNI Concepcion-11, Wehr Oste-10, Callao Express-10, P&O Nedlloyd Yarra Valley-06, Wehr Oste-03
9149897	Wehr Schulau *	Mhl	1999	16,177	23,026	184	26	19	ucc	1,730 teu: ex Elqui -14, I/a Wehr Schulau
9301328	Wehr Singapore	Deu	2005	54,193	67,470	294	32	24	ucc	5,089 teu: ex Maersk Derince-14, Wehr Hongkong-06
9243239	Wehr Trave	Mhl	2002	25,705	33,795	207	30	21	ucc	2,524 teu: ex CSAV Valparaiso-11, Wehr Trave-10 CSAV Rio Puelo-09, CCNI Aysen-04, I/a Wehr Trave
9243241	Wehr Warnow	Mhl	2002	25,705	33,793	208	30	21	ucc	2,524 teu: ex CCNI Constitucion-11, Wehr Warnow-10, CSAV Rio Maule-09, Columbus China-04, Wehr Warnow-02
9236690	Wehr Weser *	Mhl	2001	25,703	33,795	203	30	22	ucc	2,524 teu: ex Libra New York-09, I/a Wehr Weser

* managed for Lloyd Fonds AG, Germany.

Westfal-Larsen & Co. AS   Norway

funnel: *yellow with two narrow black bands, narrow black top.* **hull:** *dark blue with 'WESTFAL-LARSEN' in white, red boot topping.*
history: *family owned company, formed 1905.* **web:** *www.wlco.no*

IMO	name	flag	year	gt	dwt	loa	bm	kts	type	comments
9387695	Falkanger	Nis	2009	29,644	46,239	183	32	14	tco	
9387700	Fauskanger	Nis	2009	29,644	46,195	183	32	14	tco	
9387712	Finnanger	Nis	2009	29,644	46,251	183	32	14	tco	
9387724	Fjellanger	Nis	2010	29,644	46,287	183	32	14	tco	
9524762	Taranger	Nis	2011	29,712	45,870	183	32	14	tco	
9524774	Torvanger	Nis	2012	29,712	45,318	183	32	14	tco	
newbuildings:										
9725299	Lindanger (df) **	Nis	2016	29,700	49,962	183	32	14	tco	Hyundai Mipo 2503
9725304	(df) **		2016	29,700	50,000	183	32	14	tco	Hyundai Mipo 2505

** chartered to Waterfront Shipping, Canada, subsidiary of Methanex Corp.

Anders Wilhelmsen & Co. AS   Norway

funnel: *black with white 'W' on red over black divided diamond between two narrow red bands on broad white band.* **hull:** *red with red boot-topping or dark blue with 2 diagonal white stripes, red boot topping* **history:** *formed 1939 as A Wilhelmsen to 1964 and sometime 47% owner of Euronav. Awilco LNG founded 2011* **web:** *www.awilco.no*

IMO	name	flag	year	gt	dwt	loa	bm	kts	type	comments
8014409	WilEnergy [st] *	Mhl	1983	102,390	67,055	283	45	19	lng	125,556 m³ ex Banshu Maru-11
9627954	WilForce [df] *	Nis	2013	102,315	87,750	290	44	20	lng	155,900 m³
9627966	WilPride [df] *	Nis	2013	102,315	87,677	290	44	20	lng	155,900 m³ I/d Wilpower
8125832	WilGas [st] *	Nis	1984	102,376	67,552	283	45	19	lng	125,631 m³ ex Dewa Maru-11
newbuildings:										
9734109		Nis		170,000	320,000				tcr	Daewoo 5409
9734111		Nis		170,000	320,000				tcr	Daewoo 5410

managed by Wilhelmsen Marine Services AS. * operated by Awilco LNG ASA

Reederei Gebruder Winter GmbH & Co. KG   Germany

funnel: *mainly charterers colours.* **hull:** *grey, blue or red with red boot-topping.* **history:** *founded in 1900 and shipowners since 1970 as Schiffahrtskontor Reederei Gebruder Winter to 1999.* **web:** *www.winter-ship.de*

IMO	name	flag	year	gt	dwt	loa	bm	kts	type	comments
9487237	Aurelia K	Mlt	2009	31,117	53,100	190	32	14	bbu	ex Cloud-14, Clear-14
9445887	Calandra *	Atg	2010	35,878	41,411	213	32	22	ucc	2,758 teu: ex Pos Melbourne-11, Calandra-10

IMO	name	flag	year	gt	dwt	loa	bm	kts	type	comments
9445899	Calidris *	Mhl	2012	35,878	41,108	213	32	22	ucc	2,758 teu
9143245	Classica	Deu	1998	23,297	30,241	188	30	21	ucc	2,048 teu: ex Adelaide Express-09, Classica-06, Safmarine Mtata-05, Maersk Dakar-04, Classica-02, Libra Buenos Aires-02, Classica-01, CMA Djakarta-00, Jolly Ocra-99, Classica-98
9488188	Feliz N	Mlt	2010	33,005	57,000	190	32	14	bbu	ex Vega Ares-15
9487225	Marie S	Mlt	2008	31,117	53,100	190	32	14	bbu	ex Spark-15, Spot-14
9430868	Mell Solomon	Atg	2009	18,326	23,294	175	27	19	ucc	1,740 teu: ex Catena-09

*also operates smaller feeder container ships : * managed for Buss Capital, Hamburg*

Reederei Hermann Wulff   Germany

funnel: *yellow with green 'W' on white diamond, black top or charterers colours.* **hull:** *black or green with red boot-topping.*
history: *formed 1960 by fifth generation of Wulff family.* **web:** *www.reederei-wulff.de*

IMO	name	flag	year	gt	dwt	loa	bm	kts	type	comments
9316373	Hermann Wulff *	Deu	2006	32,322	39,340	211	32	22	ucc	2,732 eu: ex Ibn Khallikan-12, OOCL Energy-08, Hermann Wulff-06
9401271	Ilse Wulff	Lbr	2009	75,604	85,622	304	40	27	ucc	6,500 teu: ex Al Khor-12, l/a Ilse Wulff
9498896	Johannes Wulff	Lbr	2010	50,697	93,272	229	38	14	bbu	
9498901	John Wulff	Lbr	2010	50,729	93,282	229	38	14	bbu	
9252101	Viktoria Wulff	Lbr	2006	51,350	58,260	292	32	24	ucc	4,546 teu: ex MSC Firenze-14, Maersk Duesseldorf-08, Hijaz-08, Maersk Diadem-06, Viktoria Wulff-06
9537379	Suse	Lbr	2011	32,987	56,925	190	32	14	bbu	

* managed for Ship Invest Emissionshaus AG, Germany.

XT Management Ltd.   Israel

funnel: *blue or charterers colours.* **hull:** *various colours.* **history:** *founded 1957 as Mediterranean Seaways Ltd to 1967 and Mediterranean Lines Ltd to 1970. Formerly Ofer Brothers Holdings Ltd., restyled XT Management, 2010.* **web:** *www.oferg.com*

IMO	name	flag	year	gt	dwt	loa	bm	kts	type	comments
9231793	ANL Woolamai	Lbr	2002	53,453	62,740	294	32	24	ucc	4,839 teu: ex California-15, Zim California-14
9275373	Bellatrix I	Lbr	2003	34,610	43,093	235	32	22	ucc	2,762 teu: ex Leo Osaka-15, OOCL Osaka-11
9649835	Cap Capricorn	Lbr	2013	42,814	51,931	228	37	21	ucc	3,765 teu
9545168	Cape Miron	Lbr	2009	90,399	180,274	289	45	14	bbu	ex Aurora Venus-15, Orient Venus-12
9189249	Cape Tavor	Lbr	1999	87,363	172,515	289	45	15	bbu	ex Cape Lowlands-06, La Selva-04
9051820	Car Star	Lbr	1993	41,931	17,189	196	29	18	mve	4,513 ceu: ex Bujin-10,
9631101	Hanjin California	Lbr	2013	40,855	48,997	228	37	21	ucc	3,614 teu
9631125	Hanjin Florida	Lbr	2013	40,855	51,100	228	37	21	ucc	3,614 teu
9626558	Kestrel	Lbr	2013	16,770	22,071	172	27	21	ucc	1,805 teu
9644990	Kota Ekspres	Lbr	2013	43,015	51,599	228	37	21	ucc	3,765 teu: ex Cap Campbell-16
9311763	Lorraine	Lbr	2006	27,786	37,800	222	30	22	ucc	2,742 teu: ex Cape Mayor-06
9619438	MSC Albany	Lbr	2012	94,017	112,516	299	48	22	ucc	8,752 teu
9619426	MSC Altamira	Lbr	2012	94,017	112,516	299	48	22	ucc	8,752 teu
9619440	MSC Anchorage	Lbr	2013	94,017	112,516	299	48	22	ucc	8,752 teu
9231779	OOCL Mexico	Lbr	2002	53,453	62,686	294	32	24	ucc	4,839 teu: ex Zim Mediterranean-14
9626560	Pelican	Lbr	2013	16,770	22,071	172	27	21	ucc	1,805 teu
9184859	Treasure	Bhs	1999	58,684	21,199	200	32	19	mve	6,500 ceu: ex Höegh Treasure-14, Hual Treasure-06, Hual Carolita-00
9471202	Zim Constanza	Isl	2010	40,542	50,107	261	32	24	ucc	4,253 teu
9318187	Zim Genova	Lbr	2007	39,906	50,532	261	32	24	ucc	4,253 teu
9318175	Zim Livorno	Lbr	2006	39,906	50,689	261	32	24	ucc	4,253 teu
9322322	Zim Shekou	Lbr	2007	39,906	50,629	260	32	24	ucc	4,253 teu
9471214	Zim Tarragona	Isl	2010	40,542	50,088	261	32	24	ucc	4,253 teu
9322334	Zim Vancouver	Lbr	2007	39,906	50,532	261	32	24	ucc	4,253 teu: ex Pearl River I-12, Zim Vancouver-07

newbuildings:

IMO	name	flag	year	gt	dwt	loa	bm	kts	type	comments
9623532			2016	45,054	82,000				bbu	Jinhae J0127 L - 30.08:2013
9623568			2016	45,054	82,000				bbu	Jinhae J0130 L - 28:10:2013

*vessels owned by Ofer (Ships Holdings) Ltd., * owned by subsidiary Kotani Shipmanagement Ltd, Cyprus (founded jointly with Zodiac Maritime Agencies Ltd in 1999,)*

Zodiac Maritime Agencies Ltd., U.K.

funnel: *blue with blue 'Z' on white disc with globe outline.some with black top or charterers colours.* **hull:** *black, grey, red or white with red boot-topping.* **history:** *formed 1976, acquired 50% P&O share of Associated Bulk Carriers in 2000 and balance in 2003. In 2013 following the death of Sammy Ofer, company split between brothers Eyal who retained Zodiac and Idal who set up Eastern Pacific Shipping Singapore.* **web:** *www.zodiac-maritime.com*

IMO	name	flag	year	gt	dwt	loa	bm	kts	type	comments
9594884	Abbey Road	Lbr	2013	42,392	74,435	228	32	14	tco	l/d Emerald Success
9281891	Amber Sun	Lbr	2003	58,100	107,198	247	42	14	tcr	Baltic Sea-13, Diamond Champ-12, Stena Conductor-07

IMO	name	flag	year	gt	dwt	loa	bm	kts	type	comments
9321847	Aries Sun	Lbr	2006	59,158	115,567	244	42	14	bbu	ex Forward Venture-14
9070474	Asian Glory ++	Gbr	1994	44,818	13,363	184	31	18	mve	4,363 ceu
9573701	Bastille Street	Lbr	2011	28,778	47,906	180	32	14	tco	ex Pacific Sapphire-14
9255983	Battersea Park	Lbr	2002	11,590	19,949	146	24	14	tch	ex Chemstar Moon-11
9192260	Blue Sun	Lbr	2000	57,680	105,856	248	43	14	tcr	ex Arafura Sea-14
9332846	Brighton *	Gbr	2008	71,786	72,982	293	40	25	ucc	6,350 teu: ex Zim London-15, APL London-13
9143489	Brother Glory	Gbr	1998	27,105	46,211	190	31	13	bbu	
9729192	Buccleuch	Lbr	2016	93,488	179,519	292	45	14	bbu	l/a SBI Aroma
9539561	Canal Street	Lbr	2012	28,426	50,013	183	32	14	tco	ex Pacific Topaz-14
9629445	Cap Andreas	Lbr	2013	69,809	80,547	271	43	24	ucc	6,612 teu
9446623	Cape Buzzard	Lbr	2011	92,746	181,399	292	45	14	bbu	
624469	Cape Eagle	Lbr	2012	92,758	181,529	292	45	14	bbu	ex Grand Future-16
9344289	Cape Flamingo	Gbr	2005	90,092	180,201	290	45	14	bbu	
9300582	Cape Hawk	Lbr	2006	89,603	176,996	289	45	14	bbu	ex Ocean Cygnus-16
9304540	Cape Heron	Gbr	2005	88,494	177,656	290	45	14	bbu	
9165516	Cape Osprey	Gbr	1999	87,522	171,850	289	45	14	bbu	ex Ocean Ceres-16, Charles L.D.-04
9484807	Cape Stork	Gbr	2011	92,050	175,611	292	45	14	bbu	ex C. Prosperity-15
9333785	Capricorn Sun	Lbr	2007	59,164	115,577	244	42	14	tcr	ex Pacific Condor-13
9629457	Cardiff	Lbr	2014	69,809	80,550	271	43	22	ucc	6,612 teu: ex Cap Aguilar-14, l/d Cardiff
9432880	Carrera	Gbr	2008	46,800	12,296	183	32	20	mve	4,902 ceu
9460318	Castlegate	Gbr	2008	29,923	53,503	190	32	15	bbu	
9725823	Central Park	Lbr	2015	12,145	19,998	146	24	15	tch	
9409170	CMA CGM Corneille	Lbr	2009	73,339	85,408	299	40	24	ucc	6,500 teu
9729180	Cotswold	Mhl	2016	93,488	179,611	292	45	14	bbu	l/a SBI Montecristo
9271585	Crescent Moon	Lbr	2004	78,896	150,581	274	38	14	tcr	ex Archway-13, Monte Granada-12
9308807	CSAV Rio Grande *	Gbr	2007	46,800	12,315	183	32	20	mve	4,902 ceu
9325180	CSAV Rio Nevado *	Gbr	2007	46,800	12,322	183	32	20	mve	4,902 ceu
9627899	CSAV Toconao	Lbr	2013	96,628	116,079	300	48	21	ucc	8,600 teu
9627904	CSAV Traiguen	Lbr	2013	96,628	116,384	300	48	21	ucc	8,600 teu
9627928	CSAV Tyndall	Lbr	2014	96,628	116,058	300	48	21	ucc	8,600 teu
9470088	Dorset	Gbr	2011	45,812	53,076	226	37	18	lpg	80,204 m³
9478468	Eastgate	Lbr	2010	21,483	33,174	176	28	14	ggc	ex Sinfonia-15
9403877	Essex	Lbr	2009	22,914	26,533	174	28	18	lpg	35,556 m³

Kings Road : Zodiac Maritime : *Chris Brooks*

IMO	name	flag	year	gt	dwt	loa	bm	kts	type	comments
9640126	Forest Park	Gbr	2013	11,733	19,803	146	24	14	tch	
9615042	Friendly Islands	Lbr	2012	17,033	28,387	169	27	14	bbu	
9594901	Fulham Road	Lbr	2013	42,411	74,986	228	32	14	tco	l/d Emerald Supreme
9343340	Gemini Sun	Lbr	2008	59,164	115,577	244	42	15	tcr	ex Pacific Empire-13
9253325	Gold Sun	Lbr	2004	57,680	105,666	248	43	15	tcr	ex Ceram Sea
9493145	Goldengate Park	Lbr	2013	11,733	19,801	146	24	14	tch	
9701140	Goodwood	Lbr	2014	59,516	18,770	200	32	19	mve	6,203 ceu
9505998	Greenwich Park	Lbr	2011	11,987	19,991	146	24	14	tch	ex Sanko Neptune-11
9053579	Guofeng Enterprise	Lbr	1993	149,323	260,995	330	59	15	bor	ex Silver Jewel-10, Grand Mountain-08, Mitsumine-04, (conv tcr-10)
9115690	Guofeng First	Sgp	1996	108,083	211,320	312	50	14	bbu	ex Kildare-09, SGC Express-98
9082312	Handan Steel	Lbr	1994	147,580	264,932	333	60	15	bor	ex Golden Jewel-09, Han-Ei-07 (conv tcr-08)
9631137	Hanjin Louisiana	Lbr	2013	40,855	52,023	228	37	21	ucc	3,600 teu
9233856	Holsatia	Gbr	2003	39,941	50,913	260	32	24	ucc	4,253 teu: ex Holsatia Express-12, CP Provider-06, Lykes Provider-05
9725110	Hyundai Earth	Lbr	2016	110,632	124,092	324	48	22	ucc	10,055 teu
9393022	Hyundai Global	Gbr	2009	94,511	99,086	340	46	27	ucc	8,562 teu
9725122	Hyundai Mars	Lbr	2016	110,632	124,000	324	48	22	ucc	10,055 teu
8608157	Hyundai No.106 ++	Lbr	1987	42,469	12,848	184	31	18	mve	4,795 ceu
8608169	Hyundai No.107 ++	Lbr	1987	42,469	12,989	184	31	18	mve	4,795 ceu
9725134	Hyundai Jupiter	Lbr	2016	110,632	118,000	324	48	22	ucc	10,055 teu Daewoo 4292
9385013	Hyundai Oakland	Gbr	2009	71,786	72,982	293	40	26	ucc	6,350 teu
9393321	Hyundai Splendor	Gbr	2009	94,511	98,968	340	46	26	ucc	8,562 teu
9463085	Hyundai Vancouver	Gbr	2010	71,821	71,987	293	40	26	ucc	6,350 teu
9626675	Indian Goodwill	Lbr	2014	42,576	75,398	225	32	14	bbu	
9521409	Indian Partnership	Lbr	2014	95,009	181,125	292	45	14	bbu	
9402770	Ipanema Street	Lbr	2010	26,916	47,378	180	32	14	tco	ex Pacific Citrine-13, Sanko Libra-11
9332834	Jupiter Sun	Lbr	2007	59,164	115,577	244	42	14	tcr	ex Forward Bright-14
9267637	K Pegasus	Pan	2003	76,199	80,270	300	40	25	ucc	6,586 teu: ex NYK Pegasus-14
9267649	K Phoenix	Pan	2003	76,199	80,270	300	40	25	ucc	6,586 teu: ex NYK Phoenix-14
9594872	Kings Road	Lbr	2012	42,411	74,986	228	32	14	tco	ex Emerald Splendor-13
9384887	Kyoto Tower	Gbr	2007	17,229	21,975	172	28	19	ucc	1,708 teu
8808068	Laiwu Steel Harmonious	Lbr	1989	150,454	270,857	337	58	16	bor	ex Eastern Jewel-08, T.S. Asclepius-02 (conv tcr-09)

Portman Square : Zodiac Maritime : *F. de Vries*

IMO	name	flag	year	gt	dwt	loa	bm	kts	type	comments
9457608	Leo Sun	Lbr	2011	59,180	114,531	244	42	14	tcr	ex Sunda Sea-14
9402316	Libra Sun	Lbr	2010	59,180	115,123	244	42	15	tcr	ex Celtic Sea-14
9640097	Lincoln Park	Gbr	2012	11,733	19,801	146	24	14	tch	
9640114	Lumphini Park	Gbr	2012	11,733	19,801	146	24	14	tch	
9463011	Maersk Edison	Gbr	2011	141,649	141,448	366	48	25	ucc	13,092 teu
9463023	Maersk Erving	Gbr	2011	141,649	141,377	366	48	25	ucc	13,092 teu: ex CMA CGM Erving-14, Maersk Erving-12
9332781	Mars Sun	Lbr	2006	59,158	115,536	244	42	14	tcr	ex Forward Flair-14
9539585	Mercer Street	Lbr	2013	28,426	50,007	183	32	14	tco	ex Pacific Lapis-14
9532197	Morning Cloud	Lbr	2011	40,325	74,962	225	32	14	bbu	ex Sanko Frontier-12
9289910	Morning Midas + #	Gbr	2006	46,800	12,672	183	32	20	mve	4,902 ceu
9618276	MSC Agrigento	Pan	2013	95,390	110,875	300	48	22	ucc	8,827 teu
9618288	MSC Alghero	Pan	2013	95,390	110,875	300	48	22	ucc	8,827 teu
9606338	MSC Amsterdam	Lbr	2015	176,490	186,649	399	54	23	ucc	16,652 teu
9647461	MSC Hamburg	Lbr	2015	176,490	186,650	399	54	23	ucc	16,652 teu
9110389	MSC Katyayni	Pan	1996	64,054	68,539	275	40	25	ucc	5,711 teu: ex Hyundai Liberty-13, MOL Infinity-12, APL Liberty-11, Hyundai Liberty-07
9606302	MSC London	Lbr	2014	176,490	186,649	399	54	23	ucc	16,652 teu
9606314	MSC New York	Lbr	2014	176,490	186,649	399	54	23	ucc	16,652 teu
9231781	MSC Panama	Gbr	2002	53,453	66,686	294	32	24	ucc	4,992 teu: ex Zim Panama-14
9233844	Nagoya Tower	Gbr	2003	39,941	50,841	260	32	24	ucc	4,253 teu: ex Saxonia Express-11, CP Monterrey-06, TMM Monterrey-05
9493365	Noble Ace	Gbr	2011	59,515	18,946	200	32	19	mve	6,203 ceu
9384564	North Sea	Lbr	2008	59,177	115,325	244	42	14	tcr	
9280859	OOCL Halifax *	Gbr	2004	53,453	62,740	294	32	24	ucc	4,992 teu: Zim Shenzhen-14
9698989	Ormond	Lbr	2015	94,385	180,986	292	45	15	bbu	l/a SBI Maduro
9264570	Portman Square	Lbr	2002	56,358	105,965	241	42	14	tco	ex Song Lin Wan - 14
9233832	Qingdao Tower	Lbr	2003	39,941	50,886	260	32	24	ucc	4,253 teu: ex Westfalia Express-10, CP Deliverer-06, Lykes Deliverer-05
9119141	Quorn	Bmu	1996	92,194	179,869	290	46	14	bbu	ex SG China-98
9590307	Red Moon	Lbr	2012	83,824	160,024	274	48	14	tcr	ex Crossway-13
9384564	Red Sun	Lbr	2008	59,177	115,325	244	42	14	tcr	ex North Sea-13
9367839	Seoul Tower	Gbr	2009	26,688	34,325	212	30	22	ucc	2,578 teu
9521980	Shagang Faith	Lbr	2013	152,306	298,085	327	55	15	bor	
9002738	Shagang Giant	Lbr	1993	157,402	306,902	332	60	24	bor	ex Starlight Jewel-08, Front Tartar-01
9519573	Shagang Volition	Lbr	2012	152,306	298,004	327	55	14	bor	
9230971	Silver Sun	Lbr	2001	56,346	105,322	239	42	15	tcr	ex SC Sara-14, Nordatlantic-07
9112313	Snowdon	Bmu	1998	85,848	170,079	292	46	14	bbu	l/a SG Creation
9363845	Stanley Park	Gbr	2008	11,590	19,994	146	24	14	tch	
9521980	Shagang Faith	Lbr	2013	152.306	298,085	327	55	14	bor	
9002738	Shagang Giant	Lbr	1993	155,359	308,902	332	60	14	bor	ex Starlight Jewel-08, Front Tartar-01, Tartar-00 (conv. tcr-08)
9682930	Silvergate	Lbr	2014	40,937	77,239	225	32	14	bbu	ex PRT Future-16
9629469	Swansea	Lbr	2014	69,809	80,550	271	43	22	ucc	6,612 teu: ex CCNI Austral-15, l/a Swansea
9332822	Taurus Sun	Lbr	2007	59,164	115,677	244	42	15	tcr	ex Pacific Brave-13
9432907	Tokyo Car	Gbr	2008	46,800	12,352	183	32	20	mve	4,902 ceu
9384875	Tokyo Tower †	Gbr	2007	17,229	21,975	172	28	19	ucc	1,708 teu
9573672	Vendome Street	Lbr	2011	28,778	47,879	180	32	14	tco	ex Pacific Garnet-13
9332810	Virgo Sun	Lbr	2007	59,164	115,577	244	42	14	tcr	ex Pacific Apollo-13
9698965	Waterford	Mhl	2015	94,385	181,060	292	45	15	bbu	l/a SBI Puro
9588148	White Moon	Lbr	2012	83,824	160,152	274	48	14	tcr	ex Broadway-13
9493236	Woodgate	Gbr	2011	17,025	28,219	169	27	14	bbu	
9085352	Wugang Atlantic	Lbr	1995	156,281	281,226	328	57	14	bor	ex Atlantic Jewel-08, C. Trust-07, C. Achiever-03, Yukong Achiever-97 (conv tcr-09)
9510486	Wugang Caifu	Lbr	2012	153,604	299,382	327	55	14	bor	
9510474	Wugang Haoyun	Gbr	2011	153,604	297,980	327	55	14	bor	
9664885	YM Modesty	Lbr	2013	71,821	72,370	293	40	23	ucc	6,250 teu
9698977	York	Lbr	2015	94,385	181,060	292	45	15	bbu	l/a SBI Valrico
9689172	Yorkgate	Lbr	2014	34,570	61,556	200	32	14	bbu	
9384932	Zenith Leader	Gbr	2007	62,080	22,602	200	32	20	mve	6,501 ceu
9318151	Zim Xiamen *	Gbr	2006	39,906	50,689	261	32	24	ucc	4,253 teu
newbuildings:										
9725146	Hyundai Saturn	Lbr	2016	110,632	118,000	324	48	22	ucc	10,055 teu Daewoo 4293
9725158	Hyundai Neptune			110,632	118,000	324	48	22	ucc	10,055 teu Daewoo 4294
9725160	Hyundai Pluto			110,632	118,000	324	48	22	ucc	10,055 teu Daewoo 4295
9725847				12,200	19,950				tco	Kitanihon 610

also reported 10 x 5,000 teu boxboats [STX]
* owned by Lombard Corporate December 3

† manged for various Japanese owners or * for Unique Shipping (HK) Ltd, Hong Kong (China)
+ chartered to EUKOR Car Carriers ++ chartered to Hyundai Glovis

Zim Integrated Shipping Services Ltd., Israel

funnel: white with blue 'ZIM' below seven gold stars (four above three). **hull:** white or grey with green boot-topping, or black with white 'ZIM' and red boot-topping. **history:** founded 1945 as Zim Israel Navigation Co Ltd with 48% government share and 49% owned by Israel Corp (57.3% owned by Ofer Bros). Government share acquired in 2004 and company renamed. **web:** www.zim.com

IMO	name	flag	year	gt	dwt	loa	bm	kts	type	comments
9426790	Aeneas	Hkg	2010	54,182	63,059	294	32	25	ucc	5,086 teu: ex RHL Felicitas-15
9473626	GSL Africa *	Lbr	2010	27,213	32,906	200	32	22	ucc	2,553 teu: l/a Seared
9398448	Zim Antwerp	Lbr	2009	114,044	116,294	349	46	25	ucc	10,070 teu
9280835	Zim Barcelona	Isr	2004	53,450	54,740	294	32	24	ucc	4,814 teu
9288904	Zim Haifa	Isr	2004	54,626	66,938	254	32	24	ucc	5,040 teu
9401776	Zim Moskva	Lbr	2009	40,741	52,316	259	32	24	ucc	4,308 teu
9398400	Zim Ningbo	Lbr	2009	91,158	108,427	349	46	25	ucc	8,208 teu
9318163	Zim Qingdao	Lbr	2006	39,906	50,689	261	32	24	ucc	4,250 teu
9398450	Zim Rotterdam	Lbr	2010	114,044	116,499	349	46	25	ucc	10,070 teu
9398412	Zim San Diego	Lbr	2010	91,158	108,464	334	43	25	ucc	8,208 teu
9403396	Zim Ukrayina	Lbr	2009	40,741	52,316	259	32	24	ucc	4,308 teu
9231808	Zim Virginia	Isr	2002	53,453	62,740	294	32	24	ucc	4,839 teu
9322346	Zim Yokohama	Lbr	2007	39,906	50.532	261	32	24	ucc	4,253 teu: ex Yokohama-12, Zim Yokohama-09

* owned by Fortune Line Inc., Israel

Yangming Marine Transport Corp.   Taiwan

funnel: black with yellow band on broad red band interupted by white square containing blue 'Y' on white 'M' symbol within red outline. **hull:** black with white 'YANG MING', red boot-topping. **history:** government controlled and formed 1973. **web:** www.yml.com.tw

IMO	name	flag	year	gt	dwt	loa	bm	kts	type	comments
9485007	YM Masculinity *	Lbr	2012	76,787	81,145	306	40	25	ucc	6,600 teu
9484998	YM Milestone *	Lbr	2011	76,787	81,145	306	40	25	ucc	6,600 teu
9457737	YM Mobility *	Lbr	2011	76,787	81,145	306	40	25	ucc	6,600 teu
9455870	YM Mutuality *	Lbr	2011	76,787	81,145	306	40	25	ucc	6,600 teu
9337444	YM Uberty	Lbr	2008	90,507	103,614	333	43	25	ucc	8,236 teu
9462706	YM Ubiquity *	Twn	2012	90,532	103,600	333	43	25	ucc	8,236 teu
9462718	YM Unanimity	Lbr	2012	90,532	103,600	333	43	25	ucc	8,236 teu
9462732	YM Unicorn *	Lbr	2013	90,532	103,235	333	43	25	ucc	8,626 teu
9337482	YM Uniform	Lbr	2009	90,507	103,614	333	43	25	ucc	8,236 teu
9462691	YM Uniformity *	Twn	2012	90,532	103,235	333	43	25	ucc	8,236 teu
9462720	YM Upsurgence *	Lbr	2012	90,532	103,235	333	43	25	ucc	8,236 teu
9337468	YM Upward	Lbr	2008	90,507	103,607	333	43	25	ucc	8,236 teu
9337470	YM Utility	Lbr	2009	90,507	103,614	333	43	25	ucc	8,236 teu
9337456	YM Utopia	Lbr	2008	90,507	103,614	333	43	25	ucc	8,236 teu

* chartered from All Oceans Transportation. Also operates smaller container ships on Far Eastern services and manages five tankers owned by associated Government controlled Chinese Petroleum Corp (formed 1959 - wwwcpc.com.tw). Also see other chartered ships with 'YM' prefix in index.

Reederei Horst Zeppenfeld GmbH & Co. KG   Germany

funnel: cream with black 'Z' between narrow black band and narrow black top. **hull:** black with red boot-topping. **history:** founded 1971. **web:** www.zeppenfeld.com

IMO	name	flag	year	gt	dwt	loa	bm	kts	type	comments
9301990	Aldebaran	Lbr	2008	32,903	37,274	207	32	22	ucc	2,785 teu: ex MSC Andes-10, Cala Pigafetta-09
9339612	Algol *	Sgp	2008	16,162	17,350	161	25	19	ucc	1,345 teu: ex USL Condor-09, Algol-06
9339600	Alioth *	Sgp	2006	16,162	17,219	161	25	19	ucc	1,345 teu
9295505	Mizar	Lbr	2005	16,162	17,350	161	25	19	ucc	1,347 teu

* owned by associated Reederei Navylloyd AG, Switzerland (founded 1981)

Index

Anthem of the Seas : Royal Caribbean Intl : *ARO*

Ships by IMO Number

IMO	No.	IMO	No.	IMO	No.	IMO	No.	IMO	No.
5124162	33	8130681	153	8509181	34	8710857	21	8822583	131
5142657	23	8130899	98	8509375	176	8711344	10	8822595	131
5383304	16	8131893	170	8509387	179	8711356	10	8837928	170
5424562	21	8131934	170	8512279	99	8712178	29	8843446	27
6409351	10	8201480	24	8512281	27	8712324	185	8900323	104
6417097	16	8201624	177	8512891	175	8712324	211	8900335	104
6419057	33	8201636	178	8512906	174	8713550	272	8900517	230
6602898	21	8201648	176	8512956	153	8713562	272	8900529	230
6611863	33	8201674	178	8512982	153	8714190	174	8902371	59
6821080	16	8202355	303	8513467	104	8714205	180	8902424	56
7032997	34	8202367	303	8513479	104	8714994	159	8902541	160
7108930	23	8202381	303	8515893	294	8715546	159	8902565	160
7118404	34	8203438	34	8517358	267	8715857	180	8902955	99
7121633	269	8203440	34	8517891	176	8715869	176	8902967	99
7211074	33	8209729	179	8520213	237	8715871	179	8903167	68
7214715	33	8214164	133	8520501	237	8716502	12	8903923	29
7217395	23	8214176	133	8521220	15	8716899	27	8903935	29
7225910	33	8215481	133	8521232	15	8766296	98	8905426	210
7304314	24	8217881	16	8521397	176	8800195	33	8905878	180
7325629	30	8218706	170	8521402	174	8800286	56	8906731	87
7342469	153	8300365	68	8602476	228	8800511	129	8906743	87
7347536	34	8300377	68	8602828	156	8801814	44	8906822	67
7347768	269	8300389	279	8603509	30	8802002	145	8906975	44
7357452	118	8308159	153	8607749	210	8802014	145	8907216	34
7358573	33	8309543	281	8608078	146	8802088	145	8907424	30
7361934	122	8309555	282	8608080	146	8802090	237	8907876	69
7382732	122	8309567	129	8608157	310	8802868	33	8907888	267
7390143	245	8309830	131	8608169	310	8802870	22	8907931	88
7390155	245	8311106	173	8608200	178	8802882	23	8908193	44
7390179	245	8311118	173	8608705	269	8802894	23	8909068	145
7390181	187	8311120	173	8608872	269	8803410	108	8909070	237
7390208	187	8311132	173	8608884	269	8804529	131	8909082	114
7391214	148	8312590	303	8610526	185	8804531	131	8911073	267
7391422	30	8313685	153	8610887	170	8804543	129	8911085	267
7413232	148	8313702	153	8611398	15	8804555	129	8911102	237
7422881	39	8314122	21	8612134	21	8804567	129	8911657	282
7432044	34	8314134	33	8612251	156	8804579	131	8911669	282
7500401	170	8314471	56	8612263	157	8804725	118	8912120	129
7517507	118	8316704	153	8612316	156	8806204	23	8912132	131
7619575	282	8319718	156	8613308	88	8806747	29	8912144	131
7625811	30	8320119	281	8613310	88	8807088	27	8912156	129
7721225	170	8320767	303	8613322	265	8807650	108	8912182	60
7721237	169	8321325	303	8614194	86	8807997	30	8912297	39
7721249	170	8406705	170	8616312	237	8808068	310	8912302	39
7721263	170	8406729	170	8616324	237	8812667	37	8913150	269
7724306	79	8407735	30	8616520	178	8813594	237	8913162	24
7822457	27	8407814	69	8616556	50	8814744	30	8913174	269
7827213	16	8408818	176	8616568	50	8814768	60	8913411	180
7902295	21	8408832	175	8616958	156	8816156	272	8913423	180
7915096	34	8408882	104	8617938	99	8816168	272	8913447	175
7915278	50	8408894	104	8617940	99	8816170	272	8913514	210
7927984	16	8413019	69	8618293	265	8817631	21	8913916	30
7931454	50	8413875	176	8618308	265	8818843	118	8915433	29
8000214	27	8413887	178	8618310	265	8819093	281	8915445	29
8000977	99	8419702	179	8619467	162	8819213	237	8915794	170
8001000	98	8420787	131	8619479	162	8819299	129	8916267	210
8007808	230	8420799	131	8636740	98	8819304	129	8917534	145
8014409	307	8420804	56	8700228	237	8819500	27	8917546	68
8016550	303	8420878	30	8700230	68	8819512	24	8917560	69
8019356	33	8420892	176	8700280	13	8819926	68	8917572	69
8019368	21	8420907	177	8700474	21	8819938	68	8917584	272
8024014	30	8434254	16	8700773	10	8819976	189	8917778	176
8025331	98	8502468	209	8700785	33	8819988	189	8918057	177
8025343	279	8502717	177	8705266	16	8819990	189	8918136	27
8026799	151	8505836	177	8705278	21	8820004	189	8918215	153
8027298	30	8506294	23	8705618	67	8820016	187	8918227	154
8106056	151	8506373	16	8706777	173	8820195	193	8918239	154
8106068	151	8507200	253	8706789	170	8821046	12	8918277	253
8112914	224	8507212	253	8707343	30	8821929	73	8918289	253
8113554	98	8507652	146	8708672	34	8821931	73	8918930	99
8113566	99	8507664	146	8709573	10	8821943	73	8918942	98
8125832	307	8508369	94	8709640	179	8821955	73	8918954	179

8918966	178	9019119	272	9053878	10	9079119	253	9106170	191
8918978	180	9019121	272	9054119	209	9079121	253	9106182	193
8918980	177	9019640	267	9055448	114	9079157	219	9106194	191
8919001	114	9019652	267	9055486	211	9079169	219	9106209	191
8919037	224	9021332	210	9055709	145	9080297	305	9106297	29
8919049	224	9021423	210	9056296	210	9080493	67	9106302	29
8919051	224	9030137	96	9057123	42	9081679	267	9106479	178
8919245	15	9030149	96	9057173	231	9081801	254	9107306	154
8919257	13	9030852	132	9057446	230	9082312	310	9107318	153
8919269	15	9030864	132	9059602	110	9082336	207	9107772	21
8919934	305	9031650	296	9059614	110	9082348	207	9107784	21
8920141	267	9031961	110	9059616	110	9082350	36	9107796	21
8920995	129	9032496	50	9059638	110	9083287	68	9107887	87
8921470	237	9034729	258	9059640	110	9083964	56	9108037	154
9000168	30	9035060	280	9060637	179	9084190	61	9108128	139
9000259	15	9035060	70	9060649	179	9084607	179	9108130	140
9000352	56	9035450	56	9061198	268	9085352	311	9108154	243
9000493	176	9036002	69	9062960	177	9085479	267	9108166	241
9000687	33	9036442	56	9062984	69	9085522	87	9108178	241
9000699	23	9036454	56	9062996	69	9085534	103	9108221	168
9000742	69	9038323	237	9063079	286	9085546	103	9108233	168
9000986	37	9038335	237	9064126	19	9085558	103	9108398	129
9000998	56	9038488	237	9064229	268	9085560	87	9109031	12
9001772	286	9038907	69	9064267	189	9087013	224	9110107	185
9001784	285	9038945	272	9064279	189	9087025	43	9110183	106
9002738	311	9039119	21	9064334	94	9088237	146	9110377	108
9002738	311	9039250	177	9064396	187	9088249	146	9110389	311
9002776	61	9040429	21	9064401	187	9088689	233	9110391	108
9004176	201	9041057	159	9064684	189	9100073	254	9110896	119
9004401	131	9041253	10	9064748	178	9100085	205	9110913	119
9004786	37	9042063	38	9064750	176	9101493	114	9110925	119
9005053	162	9043055	131	9064839	268	9101730	181	9110975	177
9005065	162	9043689	157	9065443	180	9102069	281	9111058	284
9005390	281	9043691	148	9065912	243	9102071	281	9111319	23
9007362	283	9043756	176	9066485	268	9102083	281	9111474	167
9007374	283	9044700	201	9066667	16	9102095	281	9111486	88
9007489	68	9045132	269	9067128	268	9102100	281	9111620	183
9007491	34	9045156	267	9070058	10	9102112	281	9111632	183
9007532	153	9045168	269	9070137	237	9102124	281	9111644	183
9007544	154	9045780	131	9070163	168	9102203	118	9111802	24
9007817	88	9045792	129	9070448	305	9102239	43	9112090	56
9007829	88	9045807	118	9070450	305	9102241	42	9112117	67
9007831	88	9045924	268	9070474	309	9102253	43	9112272	129
9008419	21	9045936	268	9070620	24	9102265	42	9112296	139
9008421	21	9045948	268	9070632	30	9102277	43	9112313	311
9008574	180	9045950	268	9070694	283	9102289	235	9112789	10
9008598	30	9046328	104	9070709	283	9102291	235	9113147	67
9008603	174	9046502	104	9071272	88	9102306	284	9113446	105
9008706	152	9046514	104	9071557	132	9102318	284	9114165	148
9008732	237	9046526	104	9071569	132	9102485	199	9114177	148
9009023	60	9047245	268	9072094	78	9102497	257	9114232	224
9011038	129	9047271	268	9072111	77	9102710	179	9114244	222
9011492	131	9047491	224	9072173	205	9102722	176	9114608	105
9012041	145	9047506	43	9073050	38	9102746	176	9115690	310
9014066	253	9047518	224	9073062	180	9102928	222	9116369	69
9014078	253	9047752	43	9073438	56	9102930	219	9116577	117
9014444	268	9047764	224	9073701	211	9102978	24	9116589	117
9014755	68	9047996	185	9074042	108	9102992	13	9116591	117
9014767	68	9048914	21	9074078	253	9103104	283	9116606	117
9014808	185	9050137	15	9074389	206	9103116	283	9116618	117
9014810	185	9051375	184	9074391	206	9103128	131	9116864	24
9015187	96	9051478	177	9074535	206	9103130	131	9116876	24
9015199	96	9051492	179	9074547	207	9103180	184	9116890	191
9015204	96	9051507	177	9074585	110	9103685	175	9116955	155
9015216	96	9051791	267	9075709	146	9103996	15	9117181	88
9015656	201	9051806	185	9075711	146	9104005	15	9117313	113
9015785	131	9051818	185	9077070	153	9104811	201	9117325	113
9016662	237	9051820	308	9077082	153	9105023	154	9117739	253
9016674	237	9053206	251	9077123	207	9105035	153	9117741	253
9017264	44	9053218	251	9077238	277	9105085	67	9117900	132
9017276	44	9053220	251	9077276	207	9105102	67	9118135	119
9018008	182	9053505	210	9077836	74	9105114	67	9118147	119
9018646	120	9053579	310	9078830	157	9105140	251	9118458	106
9018658	120	9053658	272	9078842	155	9105932	190	9118628	118

9118630	70	9129885	179	9141405	159	9149861	93	9155341	257
9118721	10	9129952	69	9141778	228	9149873	91	9155365	166
9119141	311	9130121	55	9141780	228	9149897	307	9155377	166
9120322	275	9130171	257	9141792	90	9149902	169	9155389	284
9120334	230	9130937	132	9141807	33	9150183	86	9155391	165
9120841	189	9130949	133	9142150	118	9150195	85	9155626	258
9120853	189	9130951	132	9142942	87	9150200	86	9155767	67
9120865	189	9131125	183	9143001	193	9150212	85	9155808	120
9120877	10	9131137	219	9143013	191	9150303	74	9156462	19
9121003	68	9131149	219	9143025	193	9150315	224	9156474	19
9121259	285	9131151	219	9143037	193	9150339	184	9156515	13
9121273	305	9131357	159	9143051	98	9150341	185	9156527	13
9121297	253	9131369	70	9143099	237	9150810	272	9157478	202
9121730	126	9131876	280	9143207	224	9150822	272	9157698	87
9121742	126	9131876	297	9143219	222	9150834	120	9157703	88
9122045	90	9131888	297	9143245	308	9150913	15	9157715	219
9122394	102	9132480	200	9143321	224	9151527	103	9157727	219
9122435	94	9132492	200	9143489	309	9151723	75	9158147	82
9122447	94	9132507	201	9143518	102	9151814	154	9158159	200
9122552	13	9132789	118	9143532	293	9151826	154	9158276	209
9122590	56	9133410	73	9143544	139	9151840	279	9158288	151
9122655	303	9133422	73	9143556	139	9151864	166	9158496	55
9122916	37	9133446	155	9143568	139	9151905	170	9158513	254
9122928	155	9133458	154	9143697	67	9151917	249	9158537	268
9122930	148	9133460	155	9143702	132	9152181	268	9158549	267
9122942	148	9133587	235	9143740	267	9152258	298	9158551	170
9122954	305	9133769	243	9143752	268	9152260	298	9158563	93
9122966	306	9133848	106	9143879	90	9152272	298	9158575	93
9123154	177	9134165	118	9144031	279	9152284	210	9158587	93
9123166	174	9134490	129	9144055	279	9152296	108	9158604	148
9123192	183	9134593	40	9144134	307	9152296	210	9158616	305
9123221	68	9134608	138	9144194	70	9152466	145	9158874	67
9123740	113	9134646	76	9144196	10	9152478	145	9158903	296
9123922	296	9135638	91	9144299	279	9152507	280	9159103	237
9124146	45	9135913	199	9144304	279	9152583	88	9159115	237
9124366	69	9135925	300	9144354	253	9152595	165	9159672	217
9124378	137	9136046	183	9144392	153	9152600	166	9159684	219
9124380	138	9136931	201	9144407	154	9152739	249	9159830	23
9124392	113	9137521	168	9144756	206	9152856	69	9160011	33
9124469	281	9137674	248	9144768	206	9152959	30	9160205	219
9124471	281	9137698	249	9144926	70	9153381	255	9160229	82
9124512	68	9138109	230	9145188	288	9153393	254	9160396	250
9124524	137	9138123	170	9145229	201	9153408	233	9160413	251
9125736	70	9138135	170	9145231	201	9153513	121	9160425	47
9125906	125	9138161	301	9146302	113	9153549	185	9160437	47
9126003	45	9138288	233	9146314	114	9153551	212	9160619	159
9126297	305	9138290	55	9146455	189	9153563	184	9160798	253
9126481	228	9138317	54	9146467	189	9153612	165	9160803	253
9126807	16	9138329	30	9146479	189	9153783	146	9161182	54
9126819	16	9138381	132	9146730	286	9153850	190	9161259	183
9126974	241	9138393	132	9147071	180	9153862	193	9161273	154
9126986	241	9138410	132	9148025	91	9153874	279	9161285	155
9127150	61	9138422	132	9148116	279	9153886	279	9161297	179
9127502	40	9138446	51	9148532	301	9153898	279	9161314	106
9127514	40	9138458	50	9148635	241	9153903	279	9161481	257
9127526	40	9138513	303	9149304	102	9154191	179	9161508	56
9127538	40	9138525	303	9149316	160	9154206	177	9161675	205
9127540	177	9138850	10	9149328	69	9154220	68	9161716	24
9127667	67	9139294	279	9149380	126	9154232	170	9161728	24
9127784	40	9139309	279	9149392	125	9154268	244	9162215	190
9127796	40	9139311	279	9149495	281	9154270	244	9162227	189
9127801	40	9139490	162	9149512	282	9154282	244	9162253	228
9127928	267	9139505	179	9149524	281	9154294	243	9162265	228
9128025	114	9139634	248	9149653	50	9154529	298	9162277	91
9128037	145	9139713	206	9149665	50	9154531	298	9162368	300
9128049	237	9139725	206	9149744	298	9154543	298	9162485	108
9128051	237	9139737	207	9149756	298	9154610	277	9162485	210
9128063	237	9139749	206	9149768	298	9154854	301	9162497	106
9128130	136	9140530	44	9149770	298	9154866	300	9162497	210
9128283	82	9141065	19	9149794	162	9155107	178	9162631	175
9128532	19	9141077	21	9149823	93	9155119	190	9162643	178
9129706	305	9141273	162	9149835	93	9155121	193	9162875	162
9129823	284	9141297	180	9149847	93	9155133	193	9162887	162
9129873	174	9141302	162	9149859	93	9155303	153	9163192	69

9163207	69	9169512	293	9177569	202	9184392	108	9189926	199
9164017	103	9169524	15	9177571	202	9184536	44	9189938	254
9164029	103	9169550	15	9177583	202	9184548	44	9189940	254
9164184	56	9169603	36	9177648	282	9184859	308	9190080	144
9164201	152	9169615	159	9177650	282	9184914	126	9190092	151
9164225	188	9169627	159	9177806	118	9184940	74	9190107	144
9164237	187	9169689	243	9177961	145	9185047	212	9190119	144
9164245	190	9169691	243	9177973	145	9185279	290	9190505	160
9164249	190	9169706	183	9177985	51	9185281	104	9190731	187
9164251	193	9169718	183	9178197	281	9185293	104	9190743	187
9164275	190	9169940	282	9178202	281	9185451	146	9190755	187
9164756	267	9170640	45	9178276	251	9185463	146	9190767	187
9164768	267	9171280	146	9178288	250	9185499	67	9190779	187
9164770	267	9171292	27	9178290	250	9185504	69	9190781	188
9164782	267	9171448	37	9178317	67	9185516	69	9190858	272
9165011	122	9171503	194	9178331	183	9185528	127	9191034	126
9165293	239	9171826	243	9178343	183	9185530	127	9191307	305
9165358	139	9171840	286	9178537	114	9185736	65	9191319	305
9165360	140	9172193	292	9179218	114	9185774	36	9191321	305
9165516	211	9172478	272	9179256	267	9186209	254	9191333	285
9165516	309	9172480	272	9179268	267	9186211	254	9191345	286
9165530	276	9172648	10	9179397	267	9186223	254	9191474	237
9165542	276	9172650	154	9179402	267	9186235	254	9191498	237
9166390	276	9172662	154	9179593	36	9186302	146	9191876	146
9166417	276	9172777	12	9179622	152	9186326	98	9192167	29
9166649	92	9172856	121	9179646	243	9186338	98	9192179	29
9166651	129	9172868	121	9179725	303	9186596	274	9192228	121
9166675	120	9172868	243	9179816	87	9186651	243	9192258	106
9166704	146	9172870	159	9179828	294	9186687	258	9192260	106
9166742	121	9172947	268	9180267	276	9187033	103	9192260	309
9166778	189	9172959	267	9180279	276	9187045	291	9192337	286
9166780	189	9173056	273	9180358	243	9187239	255	9192349	286
9166792	189	9173068	273	9180360	243	9187435	296	9192351	15
9166895	211	9173135	91	9180372	243	9187489	10	9192363	15
9167150	193	9173721	68	9180384	243	9187497	243	9192387	26
9167162	45	9173733	67	9180396	243	9187796	12	9192399	26
9167174	69	9173757	127	9180786	65	9187863	174	9192428	77
9167186	69	9174218	38	9180968	180	9187875	174	9192430	78
9167198	219	9174220	38	9180982	292	9187887	15	9192442	189
9167227	24	9174282	209	9181132	237	9187899	19	9192454	189
9167796	267	9174397	243	9181144	237	9188037	13	9192466	189
9167801	268	9174490	210	9181156	237	9188099	280	9192478	189
9168154	301	9174660	38	9181168	237	9188154	117	9192741	256
9168180	192	9175781	190	9181170	268	9188219	228	9193226	139
9168192	192	9175793	190	9181376	151	9188647	10	9193238	139
9168207	192	9175808	190	9181479	74	9188788	152	9193240	193
9168219	192	9175901	268	9181493	51	9188790	50	9193252	193
9168221	192	9175913	301	9181558	210	9188805	74	9193264	193
9168611	281	9175925	212	9181560	151	9188817	50	9193276	191
9168623	282	9175975	102	9181649	59	9188829	74	9193288	139
9168635	224	9176022	183	9181651	177	9188908	201	9193290	140
9168647	281	9176034	183	9181663	179	9189081	36	9193305	140
9168831	117	9176395	146	9181675	180	9189093	36	9193317	140
9168843	117	9176565	303	9182277	209	9189108	36	9193551	84
9168855	117	9176577	303	9182289	211	9189122	183	9193563	84
9168867	117	9176606	305	9182356	184	9189134	152	9193680	69
9168879	117	9176632	221	9182368	184	9189160	77	9193719	69
9168922	286	9176644	36	9182667	69	9189249	308	9193733	59
9168934	288	9176682	160	9182710	98	9189251	303	9194127	38
9168946	288	9176711	125	9182746	127	9189342	285	9194139	170
9169029	176	9176747	282	9182930	183	9189354	284	9194866	129
9169031	179	9176759	282	9182934	303	9189366	285	9194878	129
9169043	175	9176761	110	9182942	183	9189419	26	9194921	268
9169055	174	9176773	110	9182954	131	9189421	26	9194957	268
9169067	179	9176929	159	9182966	132	9189495	284	9194969	210
9169122	68	9176993	243	9182978	132	9189500	284	9194983	165
9169134	139	9177026	221	9183518	16	9189665	173	9194995	165
9169158	117	9177038	221	9183609	159	9189677	173	9195157	19
9169160	117	9177040	272	9183776	228	9189768	89	9195169	16
9169249	113	9177052	185	9183817	252	9189782	65	9195195	24
9169316	74	9177428	151	9183829	251	9189873	268	9195200	24
9169328	74	9177430	271	9183831	251	9189885	268	9196119	256
9169378	98	9177545	202	9183843	251	9189897	68	9196606	120
9169419	235	9177557	202	9183855	30	9189902	237	9196618	239

9196632	239	9202481	99	9209271	185	9215115	216	9220316	233
9196644	121	9202508	277	9209324	152	9215165	187	9220328	233
9196644	269	9202510	277	9209336	152	9215177	187	9220615	132
9196711	282	9202522	277	9209506	185	9215189	187	9220627	132
9196838	88	9202534	277	9209518	185	9215191	187	9220706	54
9196840	87	9202546	277	9209934	49	9215256	224	9220718	54
9196852	88	9202558	277	9210050	128	9215268	224	9220847	79
9196864	88	9202649	176	9210062	128	9215270	224	9220859	79
9196890	213	9202651	179	9210074	92	9215282	224	9220861	79
9196905	212	9202663	176	9210086	129	9215295	224	9220885	189
9196955	117	9202716	95	9210098	129	9215309	224	9220897	189
9196967	117	9202857	268	9210139	19	9215311	193	9220914	202
9196979	117	9203289	243	9210141	21	9215323	193	9220926	202
9196981	117	9203291	221	9210153	21	9215347	153	9220938	203
9196993	117	9203502	285	9210218	24	9215490	15	9220940	202
9197002	253	9203514	114	9210220	15	9215634	86	9220952	42
9197284	224	9203526	285	9210438	248	9215646	86	9220964	43
9197296	224	9203538	114	9210440	246	9215672	96	9220976	145
9197349	250	9203576	305	9210828	269	9215830	243	9220988	145
9197351	140	9203588	305	9210907	195	9215842	243	9220990	36
9197363	277	9203590	306	9211121	54	9215854	243	9221009	36
9197375	277	9203904	175	9211133	205	9215866	243	9221059	165
9197545	88	9203942	174	9211145	205	9215878	192	9221061	160
9197715	286	9203965	180	9211169	47	9215880	192	9221114	204
9197739	167	9204477	114	9211482	190	9215892	168	9221205	113
9197894	239	9204489	51	9211494	190	9215907	192	9221217	113
9197909	167	9204752	288	9211585	65	9215919	192	9221279	13
9197911	277	9204764	128	9211597	65	9216092	88	9221281	13
9197935	126	9204776	128	9212058	36	9216248	67	9221554	12
9197947	277	9204958	268	9212383	293	9216365	212	9221566	10
9198082	183	9204960	268	9212395	294	9216389	297	9221633	239
9198094	181	9204972	250	9212589	196	9216391	65	9221657	296
9198109	235	9204984	251	9212694	231	9216406	65	9221671	293
9198111	235	9205079	243	9212709	231	9216494	68	9221815	85
9198123	133	9205081	127	9213088	294	9216547	162	9221827	85
9198135	133	9205093	127	9213090	294	9216559	160	9221839	150
9198355	10	9205885	119	9213105	55	9216626	294	9221853	36
9198367	10	9205897	120	9213117	55	9216705	38	9221865	36
9198563	224	9205902	119	9213129	33	9216717	37	9221889	36
9198575	187	9205916	120	9213131	33	9216729	198	9221906	56
9198587	187	9205938	119	9213143	205	9216901	269	9221918	59
9199127	292	9205964	157	9213272	138	9216913	269	9221970	137
9199268	235	9205976	155	9213284	138	9216925	269	9222091	137
9199270	235	9205988	157	9213296	239	9216987	199	9222106	249
9199783	78	9206011	156	9213301	238	9216999	199	9222118	192
9199830	126	9206023	157	9213313	238	9217022	137	9222120	249
9199842	125	9206059	272	9213325	239	9217034	137	9222132	167
9200330	119	9206061	272	9213375	36	9217553	99	9222168	256
9200366	125	9206114	84	9213454	271	9217565	99	9222170	239
9200378	125	9206396	210	9213571	46	9217929	68	9222273	86
9200380	125	9206671	280	9213583	47	9218117	271	9222285	86
9200392	126	9207120	184	9213777	267	9218131	19	9222297	76
9200407	126	9207417	69	9213806	211	9218404	119	9222302	150
9200419	118	9207443	114	9213818	211	9218416	120	9222467	87
9200421	253	9207716	301	9214068	205	9218648	305	9222974	47
9200445	119	9207728	302	9214123	65	9218650	206	9222986	47
9200562	65	9207730	114	9214135	157	9218662	207	9223198	306
9200677	85	9207754	211	9214147	157	9218674	206	9223318	127
9200689	85	9207982	301	9214202	47	9218686	206	9223344	274
9200691	86	9208021	47	9214214	47	9218777	84	9223485	113
9200706	86	9208033	286	9214226	47	9218789	68	9223497	65
9200718	86	9208045	288	9214305	281	9219264	194	9223564	205
9200809	88	9208100	256	9214317	224	9219276	194	9223590	56
9200811	88	9208112	216	9214525	257	9219331	34	9223825	45
9200823	87	9208124	256	9214551	103	9219343	254	9223887	43
9200926	288	9208198	291	9214563	103	9219355	100	9223904	144
9200938	19	9208203	291	9214745	69	9219367	99	9223954	10
9200940	24	9208227	59	9214757	196	9219379	103	9223980	297
9200952	40	9208239	59	9214898	187	9219381	254	9223992	297
9200964	40	9208473	221	9214903	187	9219393	103	9224049	180
9201695	56	9208833	65	9215050	197	9219408	103	9224051	180
9201869	268	9209104	285	9215086	293	9219795	187	9224271	127
9202041	54	9209130	288	9215098	292	9219800	187	9224283	219
9202053	173	9209221	19	9215103	292	9220079	250	9224300	265

9224312	265	9228370	40	9231779	308	9235086	139	9238325	221
9224439	274	9228514	137	9231781	311	9235098	86	9238519	156
9224441	275	9228526	137	9231793	308	9235103	86	9238521	157
9224453	275	9228538	137	9231808	312	9235141	154	9238686	155
9224465	275	9228540	245	9231810	88	9235244	37	9238739	180
9224532	113	9228564	94	9231822	88	9235256	82	9238741	178
9224544	156	9228576	94	9231951	21	9235268	82	9238753	106
9224685	231	9228655	152	9232084	163	9235359	221	9238765	109
9224702	231	9228801	216	9232096	106	9235402	52	9238777	109
9224726	10	9228813	216	9232096	108	9235531	193	9238789	80
9224740	80	9228837	160	9232113	163	9235543	189	9238791	296
9224946	76	9229295	82	9232383	306	9235555	189	9238806	48
9224958	77	9229300	93	9232395	307	9235567	188	9238818	250
9225079	138	9229302	93	9232400	254	9235579	189	9238820	250
9225342	210	9229324	211	9232412	255	9235701	167	9238856	121
9225407	241	9229336	211	9232448	110	9235713	39	9238868	233
9225419	241	9229348	211	9232450	110	9235725	39	9239484	285
9225421	40	9229350	291	9232462	291	9235816	85	9239616	118
9225433	198	9229362	290	9232503	60	9235828	85	9239628	238
9225615	86	9229374	296	9232515	59	9235880	208	9239630	239
9225641	86	9229386	219	9232565	139	9235892	208	9239733	167
9225653	86	9229659	15	9232577	139	9235995	250	9239783	12
9225665	178	9229829	139	9232589	139	9236004	82	9239795	12
9225677	178	9229831	140	9232591	239	9236016	82	9239848	165
9225770	79	9229843	140	9232606	238	9236078	145	9239850	79
9225782	79	9229855	139	9232618	239	9236080	145	9239862	79
9225794	197	9229972	120	9232620	239	9236171	65	9239874	79
9226322	45	9229984	119	9232632	258	9236195	65	9239886	129
9226396	181	9229996	119	9232747	241	9236212	166	9239898	47
9226413	167	9230000	119	9232759	241	9236224	166	9239903	47
9226425	92	9230048	286	9232761	100	9236248	182	9240160	305
9226530	36	9230050	118	9232773	241	9236250	127	9240328	249
9226815	87	9230062	60	9232797	303	9236353	286	9240433	154
9226891	13	9230074	213	9232802	153	9236389	10	9240445	154
9226906	15	9230086	213	9232814	154	9236420	285	9240512	38
9226918	179	9230098	181	9232876	40	9236432	159	9240809	228
9226920	179	9230115	13	9232888	40	9236444	250	9240873	51
9226932	175	9230309	157	9232890	232	9236470	271	9240885	292
9226968	62	9230311	93	9232929	160	9236482	271	9240897	292
9226970	170	9230402	15	9232931	154	9236523	249	9241102	232
9227003	83	9230488	179	9233210	219	9236535	102	9241114	232
9227015	265	9230490	178	9233222	296	9236547	250	9241190	199
9227027	265	9230505	288	9233234	182	9236557	248	9241205	198
9227039	265	9230517	286	9233258	21	9236614	269	9241255	288
9227194	68	9230775	167	9233313	127	9236626	269	9241358	206
9227273	296	9230787	105	9233337	56	9236652	174	9241449	166
9227285	96	9230854	292	9233454	253	9236688	307	9241475	231
9227297	174	9230878	184	9233466	253	9236690	307	9241475	231
9227302	177	9230880	239	9233703	36	9236743	291	9241487	231
9227314	180	9230892	219	9233741	152	9236755	290	9241607	291
9227326	180	9230907	82	9233765	219	9236975	197	9241683	243
9227338	177	9230969	82	9233777	151	9236987	195	9241695	216
9227340	180	9230971	311	9233791	233	9236999	195	9241798	70
9227443	291	9230995	120	9233806	288	9237008	196	9241803	89
9227455	291	9231092	170	9233818	288	9237072	39	9241815	91
9227479	38	9231119	170	9233832	311	9237137	205	9241827	168
9227481	68	9231121	222	9233844	311	9237151	176	9242089	120
9227508	24	9231133	222	9233856	310	9237307	246	9242091	164
9227510	24	9231157	93	9234068	120	9237319	246	9242118	138
9227912	132	9231169	256	9234070	120	9237345	12	9242120	137
9227924	132	9231212	290	9234109	206	9237357	10	9242156	106
9227948	59	9231236	47	9234111	206	9237503	157	9242625	52
9228045	157	9231248	47	9234123	207	9237620	39	9242637	51
9228057	157	9231250	47	9234135	206	9237632	38	9242649	52
9228069	166	9231262	47	9234214	125	9237747	118	9242651	68
9228071	131	9231298	65	9234616	55	9237761	43	9243148	60
9228144	131	9231470	192	9234628	55	9237773	42	9243162	139
9228174	64	9231482	114	9234654	183	9237785	43	9243174	140
9228186	15	9231494	114	9234666	239	9237797	42	9243186	140
9228198	15	9231509	275	9234678	293	9238038	52	9243198	140
9228306	74	9231511	167	9235000	183	9238040	52	9243203	140
9228344	24	9231626	238	9235050	174	9238052	170	9243239	307
9228356	24	9231688	74	9235062	224	9238284	282	9243241	307
9228368	24	9231705	202	9235074	138	9238313	50	9243306	88

9243318	294	9247792	52	9251573	52	9254654	131	9258595	280
9243320	293	9247807	273	9251614	189	9254721	205	9258600	127
9243394	174	9247819	60	9251626	189	9254733	205	9258612	67
9243409	174	9247924	132	9251638	189	9254850	110	9258624	55
9243461	156	9247936	132	9251640	128	9254862	110	9258868	68
9243473	156	9247950	257	9251652	128	9254903	274	9258870	52
9243502	205	9247974	127	9251664	128	9254915	274	9258882	68
9243590	138	9247986	127	9251688	180	9254927	299	9258894	52
9243605	137	9248083	137	9251690	178	9254939	298	9259276	286
9243617	114	9248095	137	9251705	176	9255050	144	9259317	255
9243667	16	9248112	76	9251717	179	9255062	145	9259329	111
9243837	155	9248124	77	9251846	167	9255244	193	9259379	114
9243849	155	9248136	85	9251999	235	9255268	196	9259381	254
9244063	84	9248148	86	9252008	235	9255270	196	9259599	106
9244219	230	9248150	86	9252072	200	9255282	208	9259886	70
9244221	205	9248162	85	9252096	241	9255294	208	9259991	216
9244257	119	9248409	286	9252101	308	9255488	128	9260005	291
9244544	250	9248423	217	9252187	243	9255490	128	9260017	216
9244556	250	9248435	288	9252204	184	9255517	128	9260029	216
9244659	237	9248447	159	9252216	185	9255660	291	9260055	256
9244661	237	9248473	121	9252228	185	9255672	290	9260067	256
9244673	238	9248485	121	9252242	173	9255684	182	9260122	65
9244867	204	9248485	269	9252254	138	9255696	182	9260158	62
9244881	175	9248497	121	9252266	137	9255854	245	9260263	256
9244922	88	9248526	64	9252292	195	9255880	170	9260275	256
9244934	88	9248538	120	9252307	195	9255933	127	9260419	187
9244946	88	9248540	120	9252333	38	9255945	127	9260421	187
9245029	184	9248552	294	9252371	40	9255983	309	9260433	187
9245598	132	9248564	303	9252436	281	9256016	296	9260445	187
9245744	187	9248667	214	9252448	281	9256028	296	9260457	187
9245756	187	9248679	87	9252539	118	9256054	274	9260469	187
9245768	187	9248796	290	9252541	213	9256066	274	9260627	205
9245770	187	9248801	290	9252553	213	9256078	274	9260823	120
9245794	204	9248813	154	9252565	213	9256200	185	9260902	270
9246102	21	9248825	160	9252577	213	9256212	93	9260914	88
9246322	48	9248930	162	9252735	295	9256224	93	9261360	65
9246346	47	9248942	160	9252981	307	9256298	196	9261396	256
9246578	159	9249128	274	9252993	307	9256315	54	9261401	216
9246580	132	9249130	274	9253002	91			9261449	150
9246592	132	9249178	70	9253014	199	9256365	173	9261451	150
9246607	132	9249180	70	9253026	198	9256377	166	9261657	93
9246621	118	9249257	168	9253038	198	9256389	166	9261712	94
9246633	238	9249271	91	9253064	183	9256406	166	9261724	94
9246683	103	9249295	254	9253076	183	9256418	166	9261736	94
9246695	103	9249312	243	9253105	122	9256468	70	9261748	94
9246700	233	9249324	243	9253143	250	9256470	235	9261815	167
9246712	101	9250191	52	9253155	250	9256482	235	9261818	167
9246798	293	9250220	157	9253181	214	9256535	86	9261889	76
9246803	294	9250232	156	9253193	214	9256597	59	9261891	76
9247144	21	9250464	21	9253208	132	9256602	187	9261906	76
9247168	159	9250488	294	9253210	132	9256755	179	9261918	76
9247182	42	9250490	292	9253222	269	9256755	88	9262091	292
9247285	166	9250531	110	9253234	296	9256793	124	9262522	142
9247364	286	9250543	110	9253258	296	9256901	274	9262546	45
9247405	291	9250660	84	9253296	212	9256913	274	9262558	45
9247429	286	9250725	70	9253301	212	9256925	274	9262560	45
9247431	285	9250737	285	9253313	106	9256937	274	9262572	45
9247443	285	9250751	224	9253325	310	9257010	217	9262704	210
9247455	285	9250892	183	9253715	122	9257022	217	9262716	210
9247479	291	9250907	183	9253727	140	9257046	98	9262728	210
9247481	291	9250971	93	9253739	235	9257058	98	9262900	182
9247493	70	9250983	176	9253741	139	9257137	38	9262948	110
9247508	70	9250995	93	9253818	60	9257149	37	9263186	134
9247546	87	9251028	292	9253820	273	9257498	152	9263198	134
9247558	271	9251274	42	9253856	254	9257503	152	9263203	133
9247560	150	9251286	216	9253868	254	9257802	183	9263320	259
9247572	74	9251365	265	9253870	254	9257993	276	9263332	175
9247584	74	9251377	265	9253894	256	9258002	276	9263344	175
9247728	21	9251389	265	9253909	255	9258167	276	9263643	197
9247730	210	9251391	265	9254070	293	9258179	276	9263693	292
9247742	210	9251406	196	9254082	127	9258466	199	9263708	292
9247754	210	9251547	202	9254240	293	9258519	59	9264271	256
9247778	293	9251559	203	9254458	168	9258521	58	9264283	256
9247786	210	9251561	52	9254642	131			9264570	311

9264790	80	9272383	80	9276585	182	9282479	52	9285689	48
9265366	295	9272391	91	9276597	182	9282481	52	9285691	48
9265407	195	9272395	299	9276743	282	9282493	52	9285706	52
9265500	185	9272400	299	9276779	282	9282508	52	9285718	52
9265548	118	9272668	224	9277400	105	9282558	91	9285720	52
9265756	258	9272888	156	9277723	292	9282625	282	9285732	52
9265861	238	9272890	157	9277735	110	9282730	153	9285744	52
9265873	238	9272929	91	9277747	232	9282792	181	9285756	52
9265885	238	9272967	163	9277759	232	9282950	256	9285823	110
9266205	54	9273064	159	9277761	232	9282974	80	9285835	300
9266231	224	9273076	33	9277773	232	9282986	293	9285847	300
9266243	224	9273076	34	9277785	292	9282998	110	9285859	300
9266267	224	9273210	48	9277797	293	9283019	152	9285861	182
9266750	269	9273246	295	9277802	246	9283021	152	9285976	73
9266841	52	9273260	294	9277814	246	9283033	152	9285988	92
9266853	52	9273337	183	9277826	245	9283186	226	9285990	92
9266865	52	9273375	113	9277838	246	9283198	226	9286009	265
9266877	52	9273557	159	9277858	52	9283203	226	9286011	264
9266956	113	9273624	238	9277943	273	9283215	226	9286023	110
9266982	61	9273636	238	9278052	111	9283227	226	9286047	216
9266994	60	9273650	295	9278064	111	9283239	226	9286059	216
9267003	61	9273791	103	9278105	92	9283241	288	9286229	286
9267015	60	9273806	103	9278117	92	9283289	197	9286231	85
9267027	160	9273818	91	9278143	176	9283291	197	9286243	86
9267156	97	9273894	211	9278155	179	9283306	67	9286255	85
9267209	119	9273909	209	9278181	10	9283629	280	9286267	174
9267405	205	9273923	226	9278492	193	9283643	70	9286281	286
9267431	205	9273947	100	9278519	133	9283681	80	9286657	106
9267534	267	9273959	100	9278739	45	9283693	199	9286774	199
9267546	267	9273961	226	9278791	119	9283708	199	9286786	199
9267637	310	9274094	59	9279329	74	9283710	293	9286798	37
9267649	310	9274305	282	9279331	74	9283722	217	9286803	37
9267651	92	9274317	282	9279513	65	9283784	216	9286865	205
9267663	74	9274329	282	9279549	89	9283796	296	9286956	166
9267687	185	9274434	82	9279812	221	9283837	75	9287168	89
9267699	185	9274446	82	9279965	176	9283863	209	9287170	114
9267912	248	9274513	288	9279977	179	9283875	211	9287340	145
9267924	248	9274525	286	9279989	180	9283887	211	9287417	132
9268904	243	9274616	111	9280354	105	9284192	148	9287429	125
9268992	64	9274628	195	9280366	105	9284362	98	9287895	250
9269063	98	9274630	194	9280386	182	9284489	45	9287900	249
9269075	286	9274642	195	9280586	257	9284491	214	9287912	249
9269245	58	9274654	194	9280598	76	9284570	65	9287924	250
9269257	58	9274678	195	9280603	76	9284582	183	9288021	293
9269960	61	9274800	111	9280615	77	9284594	183	9288045	279
9270488	69	9274812	300	9280627	77	9284697	281	9288057	279
9270490	69	9275024	46	9280637	77	9284702	119	9288069	277
9270517	276	9275036	51	9280641	284	9284738	211	9288071	277
9270529	276	9275048	47	9280653	284	9284740	209	9288265	111
9270646	152	9275050	52	9280665	102	9284752	210	9288289	299
9270658	152	9275062	46	9280809	80	9284764	74	9288291	119
9270684	152	9275103	142	9280811	94	9284776	74	9288332	290
9270696	152	9275115	142	9280835	312	9284879	114	9288344	290
9270737	74	9275359	65	9280847	88	9284893	204	9288356	111
9270749	74	9275361	284	9280859	311	9284926	68	9288394	270
9270919	164	9275373	308	9280861	109	9285005	235	9288409	207
9271248	148	9275634	88	9280873	39	9285029	243	9288693	95
9271339	98	9275646	241	9280885	39	9285122	243	9288708	95
9271341	233	9275658	111	9281009	286	9285134	244	9288710	94
9271353	233	9275660	111	9281011	288	9285146	245	9288722	95
9271391	56	9275725	238	9281151	39	9285354	145	9288734	290
9271406	181	9275749	239	9281267	179	9285407	75	9288746	290
9271432	237	9275957	64	9281279	178	9285419	61	9288760	52
9271511	119	9275969	166	9281425	133	9285471	236	9288772	296
9271585	309	9275971	179	9281437	68	9285483	146	9288813	52
9271614	84	9276004	134	9281724	297	9285495	146	9288825	52
9271834	238	9276004	160	9281853	110	9285500	193	9288837	52
9271925	74	9276016	183	9281891	308	9285615	248	9288849	52
9272199	282	9276028	277	9281920	111	9285627	248	9288851	138
9272204	127	9276030	276	9281932	111	9285639	248	9288863	291
9272216	73	9276250	109	9282041	285	9285641	248	9288875	70
9272228	73	9276262	108	9282053	286	9285653	48	9288887	219
9272230	73	9276561	182	9282259	176	9285665	47	9288899	288
9272345	64	9276573	181	9282261	174	9285677	48	9288904	312

321

9288928	256	9290921	167	9293777	86	9296406	106	9299628	77
9288930	292	9290933	165	9293789	86	9296585	298	9299630	77
9288942	202	9290945	101	9293791	86	9296731	281	9299642	76
9289013	277	9290957	294	9293806	86	9296822	256	9299654	77
9289025	277	9291119	166	9293818	86	9297321	181	9299666	296
9289051	157	9291133	209	9293820	86	9297333	181	9299678	296
9289063	163	9291236	67	9293894	185	9297345	52	9299680	276
9289087	227	9291248	68	9293909	148	9297369	52	9299692	276
9289099	227	9291262	286	9293911	185	9297371	52	9299707	276
9289104	178	9291286	288	9293923	119	9297412	133	9299719	276
9289116	180	9291406	230	9293947	217	9297436	105	9299771	255
9289128	178	9291640	295	9294018	254	9297474	168	9299795	76
9289180	193	9291987	45	9294020	233	9297503	219	9299800	77
9289192	193	9292010	250	9294109	65	9297515	219	9299812	77
9289207	193	9292022	250	9294159	259	9297541	65	9299862	216
9289491	70	9292034	275	9294161	191	9297553	67	9299874	43
9289518	295	9292046	275	9294173	259	9297840	233	9299886	43
9289520	295	9292058	275	9294185	259	9297852	233	9299898	95
9289532	295	9292060	275	9294343	157	9297864	209	9299903	94
9289544	94	9292101	273	9294367	156	9297876	209	9299927	48
9289738	91	9292113	118	9294379	187	9297888	290	9299939	48
9289740	91	9292125	257	9294381	190	9297890	290	9300154	249
9289764	295	9292137	192	9294393	194	9297987	184	9300166	249
9289788	295	9292149	168	9294408	113	9298181	128	9300192	61
9289908	108	9292151	167	9294501	113	9298193	128	9300386	116
9289910	311	9292163	121	9294513	198	9298313	69	9300398	116
9289922	48	9292187	290	9294525	198	9298325	70	9300403	116
9289934	48	9292204	276	9294537	232	9298351	283	9300415	116
9289946	48	9292216	163	9294549	231	9298363	283	9300427	117
9289958	48	9292242	80	9294666	167	9298375	283	9300439	116
9289960	249	9292254	80	9294678	167	9298387	283	9300441	116
9289972	249	9292278	202	9294812	101	9298507	181	9300453	117
9290086	82	9292357	91	9294824	279	9298519	297	9300465	116
9290098	264	9292486	233	9294836	140	9298636	100	9300477	116
9290103	264	9292498	233	9294989	213	9298648	100	9300491	54
9290115	264	9292503	286	9294991	212	9298650	181	9300582	211
9290127	264	9292515	286	9295000	70	9298662	133	9300582	309
9290139	264	9292565	80	9295012	36	9298674	133	9300594	108
9290165	101	9292606	111	9295036	59	9298686	193	9300752	145
9290177	101	9292620	295	9295086	294	9298698	193	9300764	145
9290282	179	9292632	183	9295165	168	9298703	301	9300790	235
9290323	40	9292761	118	9295177	212	9298715	301	9300805	235
9290335	40	9292826	42	9295206	94	9298727	302	9300972	138
9290347	82	9292838	42	9295218	86	9298739	301	9300984	138
9290361	291	9292840	203	9295220	86	9298741	95	9300996	91
9290414	168	9292967	295	9295244	139	9298753	94	9301005	91
9290426	248	9292979	183	9295256	139	9298765	95	9301043	89
9290438	291	9293117	160	9295268	139	9298818	70	9301055	205
9290440	94	9293129	160	9295270	43	9298820	196	9301122	54
9290452	94	9293131	160	9295282	43	9298997	97	9301134	54
9290464	86	9293143	160	9295311	202	9299020	142	9301328	307
9290476	86	9293155	108	9295323	293	9299032	142	9301330	307
9290488	86	9293167	80	9295335	160	9299044	142	9301380	274
9290490	160	9293179	80	9295347	261	9299123	282	9301392	274
9290529	256	9293272	132	9295359	256	9299135	280	9301407	276
9290531	179	9293272	133	9295361	227	9299147	280	9301419	276
9290543	180	9293399	15	9295373	227	9299159	280	9301421	276
9290555	227	9293430	162	9295385	179	9299276	277	9301433	47
9290567	227	9293442	157	9295397	176	9299288	277	9301445	47
9290579	293	9293454	157	9295505	312	9299290	277	9301457	129
9290608	67	9293466	80	9295579	98	9299305	277	9301469	300
9290646	293	9293519	185	9295830	146	9299343	293	9301471	103
9290658	293	9293521	185	9295842	160	9299355	293	9301483	103
9290660	293	9293571	185	9295945	99	9299422	196	9301495	103
9290775	39	9293583	148	9295957	140	9299434	194	9301524	154
9290787	101	9293595	185	9295969	77	9299446	196	9301536	154
9290799	101	9293612	305	9295971	75	9299458	194	9301720	126
9290804	279	9293624	305	9296195	182	9299460	119	9301732	106
9290816	139	9293636	156	9296200	69	9299472	119	9301744	106
9290828	296	9293648	185	9296212	108	9299525	227	9301770	265
9290830	279	9293650	185	9296277	288	9299537	227	9301782	265
9290866	306	9293662	185	9296377	106	9299549	177	9301794	265
9290878	306	9293753	86	9296389	105	9299551	180	9301809	265
9290919	167	9293765	86	9296389	286	9299604	65	9301811	265

9301823	265	9303754	206	9306172	97	9308792	108	9312456	280
9301835	265	9303766	254	9306184	100	9308807	309	9312470	146
9301847	265	9303778	206	9306196	140	9308821	67	9312482	146
9301859	265	9303780	296	9306201	99	9308857	65	9312494	82
9301914	293	9303792	259	9306213	101	9308869	64	9312509	82
9301926	257	9303819	259	9306225	100	9308883	209	9312511	82
9301938	257	9303845	84	9306237	101	9308895	209	9312652	138
9301940	238	9303883	233	9306287	100	9308948	197	9312755	136
9301952	239	9304033	24	9306471	259	9308950	197	9312767	136
9301964	204	9304045	19	9306483	227	9309021	80	9312779	136
9301976	204	9304057	16	9306548	60	9309289	259	9312781	211
9301988	114	9304067	157	9306550	48	9309409	197	9312793	211
9301990	312	9304095	118	9306562	110	9309411	203	9312808	211
9302073	156	9304239	84	9306574	110	9309423	182	9312810	211
9302085	156	9304241	113	9306639	197	9309435	181	9312822	305
9302097	156	9304253	205	9306641	45	9309447	179	9312834	303
9302102	156	9304289	83	9306653	256	9309459	180	9312846	286
9302114	292	9304411	176	9306665	45	9309461	180	9312858	286
9302126	294	9304423	178	9306677	256	9309473	177	9312860	286
9302138	156	9304435	177	9306782	276	9309514	45	9312884	276
9302140	156	9304447	227	9306794	276	9309526	45	9312896	276
9302152	156	9304459	227	9306809	43	9309576	276	9312913	62
9302164	156	9304540	309	9306811	43	9309588	276	9312925	62
9302176	156	9304588	293	9306938	196	9309978	217	9312937	136
9302205	305	9304605	182	9306940	196	9309980	217	9312949	136
9302437	142	9304617	181	9306990	271	9310109	305	9312975	211
9302449	142	9304693	213	9307009	236	9310238	236	9312987	211
9302499	39	9304708	213	9307011	271	9310240	235	9312999	211
9302554	256	9304746	167	9307023	236	9310288	204	9313008	211
9302580	256	9304758	40	9307035	271	9310408	65	9313096	196
9302592	295	9304760	40	9307047	271	9310410	197	9313101	196
9302607	295	9304825	290	9307059	184	9310513	131	9313113	196
9302619	206	9304966	213	9307176	185	9310537	214	9313125	196
9302621	206	9304978	214	9307188	124	9310599	164	9313199	135
9302633	174	9305001	248	9307190	124	9310642	89	9313204	135
9302645	174	9305051	166	9307205	124	9310707	48	9313216	135
9302657	133	9305087	306	9307217	73	9310812	91	9313228	135
9302669	134	9305099	239	9307229	92	9310848	135	9313242	174
9302671	256	9305104	239	9307231	73	9310850	269	9313486	286
9302762	206	9305178	142	9307243	92	9311012	281	9313498	286
9302774	89	9305180	142	9307267	176	9311024	282	9313527	159
9302877	187	9305300	193	9307279	233	9311177	36	9313905	194
9302889	187	9305312	193	9307346	44	9311440	108	9313917	194
9302891	187	9305465	47	9307578	277	9311521	109	9313929	188
9302944	257	9305477	46	9307580	277	9311567	61	9313931	188
9302956	257	9305489	46	9307657	306	9311579	61	9313943	194
9302968	183	9305491	46	9307736	59	9311581	60	9313955	194
9302970	290	9305506	46	9307748	52	9311593	169	9313967	194
9302982	127	9305532	160	9307750	52	9311608	169	9314064	80
9302994	127	9305556	280	9307762	52	9311610	63	9314088	290
9303015	235	9305568	275	9307786	58	9311622	276	9314090	80
9303106	166	9305570	87	9307798	294	9311696	190	9314105	48
9303156	74	9305582	87	9307815	214	9311701	190	9314208	302
9303168	74	9305594	87	9307827	182	9311713	256	9314210	190
9303170	74	9305609	296	9307994	301	9311751	196	9314222	73
9303182	74	9305611	296	9308003	249	9311763	308	9314234	264
9303194	74	9305623	296	9308015	250	9311775	225	9314246	73
9303209	74	9305635	80	9308027	250	9311787	226	9314258	264
9303211	74	9305647	203	9308065	300	9311799	225	9314806	261
9303223	74	9305659	203	9308077	286	9311816	203	9314818	216
9303247	165	9305661	203	9308247	120	9311830	142	9314820	216
9303302	53	9305673	203	9308390	160	9311836	248	9314832	261
9303314	54	9305685	203	9308405	160	9311842	142	9314844	164
9303364	98	9305702	178	9308417	101	9311854	248	9314856	164
9303522	48	9305714	177	9308429	257	9311880	101	9314868	164
9303528	113	9305855	182	9308431	39	9312078	142	9314870	164
9303534	48	9305867	182	9308493	59	9312080	142	9314882	295
9303546	193	9305879	259	9308508	87	9312092	132	9314894	295
9303558	193	9305881	259	9308510	87	9312092	133	9314911	196
9303560	122	9306029	181	9308546	196	9312133	95	9314923	173
9303651	224	9306067	100	9308558	196	9312145	95	9314923	76
9303728	217	9306079	99	9308637	48	9312418	259	9314935	173
9303730	217	9306158	97	9308649	48	9312432	174	9314947	173
9303742	255	9306160	101	9308728	157	9312444	280	9314959	173

323

9314961	46	9317119	63	9320427	86	9323326	164	9326718	154
9314973	46	9317406	253	9320439	178	9323338	164	9326720	154
9314985	47	9317418	253	9320441	86	9323340	164	9326770	76
9314997	259	9317494	206	9320453	180	9323352	164	9326782	97
9315056	196	9317547	119	9320556	13	9323364	164	9326794	227
9315068	217	9317559	84	9320685	241	9323376	164	9326809	40
9315070	58	9317717	106	9320697	140	9323388	164	9326811	40
9315082	58	9317767	98	9320702	140	9323390	164	9326823	102
9315173	295	9317860	224	9320738	59	9323405	164	9326835	102
9315185	295	9317913	241	9320740	59	9323481	166	9326861	135
9315197	192	9317925	241	9320752	60	9323493	212	9326873	135
9315202	192	9317937	241	9320764	60	9323508	148	9326885	135
9315214	192	9317949	290	9321017	271	9323510	148	9326897	135
9315226	192	9317951	182	9321029	271	9323522	148	9326902	284
9315238	192	9317963	76	9321160	135	9323560	70	9326914	284
9315240	192	9317975	78	9321172	135	9323584	196	9326926	284
9315252	192	9317987	59	9321191	135	9323596	42	9326938	284
9315343	137	9318010	182	9321201	135	9323675	210	9327097	56
9315355	137	9318034	214	9321237	184	9323780	156	9327102	56
9315367	111	9318046	46	9321249	184	9323819	196	9327114	183
9315379	62	9318058	46	9321251	184	9323821	154	9327360	261
9315381	62	9318060	46	9321263	184	9323936	82	9327372	216
9315393	280	9318072	286	9321471	301	9323948	82	9327384	261
9315446	196	9318096	291	9321483	187	9323986	182	9327396	216
9315458	197	9318101	46	9321495	187	9324083	306	9327401	216
9315537	119	9318113	285	9321500	187	9324150	120	9327413	62
9315642	290	9318125	284	9321512	187	9324162	255	9327437	62
9315680	104	9318151	311	9321524	187	9324174	142	9327449	63
9315707	210	9318163	312	9321536	187	9324277	296	9327451	62
9315719	210	9318175	308	9321548	187	9324289	58	9327463	62
9315745	62	9318187	308	9321550	187	9324291	58	9327554	183
9315757	62	9318319	190	9321677	300	9324306	58	9327669	100
9315769	62	9318321	118	9321689	300	9324318	58	9327671	100
9315783	291	9318333	294	9321691	82	9324320	59	9327748	248
9315795	295	9318462	49	9321706	82	9324435	39	9327798	167
9315800	295	9318474	146	9321718	82	9324497	42	9327803	167
9315812	198	9318486	209	9321720	82	9324710	125	9328132	133
9315836	259	9318486	245	9321732	245	9324734	106	9328144	133
9315850	296	9318498	211	9321744	124	9324746	275	9328168	162
9315862	296	9318503	246	9321756	124	9324837	249	9328170	162
9315874	259	9318515	306	9321768	124	9324849	250	9328285	63
9315886	259	9318527	132	9321770	124	9324851	249	9328297	62
9315898	296	9318541	276	9321847	309	9324863	249	9328481	257
9315903	296	9318553	276	9321897	232	9324875	249	9328493	257
9315915	117	9319404	157	9321902	232	9325013	205	9328522	277
9315939	62	9319480	222	9321938	217	9325025	64	9328534	277
9315941	62	9319545	110	9321940	217	9325063	68	9328558	205
9315953	117	9319674	197	9322255	118	9325178	106	9328560	205
9315965	117	9319686	196	9322267	68	9325180	309	9328572	205
9316036	69	9319698	293	9322279	127	9325221	74	9328900	152
9316115	159	9319703	197	9322281	127	9325233	74	9328955	276
9316127	273	9319753	305	9322293	82	9325324	91	9329459	36
9316139	305	9319765	305	9322322	308	9325336	204	9329461	306
9316141	303	9319870	232	9322334	308	9325350	205	9329473	306
9316153	126	9320001	142	9322346	312	9325439	157	9329526	235
9316165	126	9320013	142	9322358	109	9325441	254	9329538	236
9316220	126	9320025	162	9322463	209	9325609	217	9329540	235
9316232	138	9320037	160	9322475	209	9325611	217	9329552	236
9316282	246	9320049	199	9322487	209	9325685	285	9329629	259
9316294	248	9320051	249	9322499	209	9325697	285	9329631	212
9316309	246	9320087	21	9322504	222	9325702	285	9329643	212
9316311	248	9320099	21	9322516	222	9325764	156	9329667	276
9316323	102	9320142	174	9322695	196	9325776	157	9329693	162
9316335	241	9320233	187	9322700	196	9325788	74	9329708	162
9316347	177	9320245	187	9322712	196	9325790	74	9329710	162
9316359	51	9320257	187	9322827	181	9325831	182	9329722	162
9316361	176	9320295	61	9322839	181	9325908	170	9329784	162
9316373	308	9320300	75	9322956	276	9326055	165	9330032	24
9316593	94	9320312	75	9322968	276	9326067	165	9330056	272
9316608	196	9320348	75	9323015	137	9326524	285	9330068	228
9316672	68	9320374	122	9323027	137	9326536	205	9330070	227
9316854	79	9320386	39	9323039	231	9326598	275	9330317	205
9316866	205	9320398	86	9323041	231	9326603	159	9330343	70
9316927	131	9320403	178	9323314	164	9326706	174	9330355	70

9330422	279	9333412	275	9336517	135	9339296	175	9344631	52
9330472	296	9333424	275	9336737	288	9339301	276	9344643	227
9330501	117	9333436	274	9336749	288	9339313	276	9344655	52
9330513	228	9333527	303	9336763	164	9339325	276	9344667	227
9330525	51	9333539	303	9336945	80	9339337	276	9344679	52
9330537	249	9333541	303	9336971	127	9339480	89	9344681	227
9330549	162	9333591	52	9336983	127	9339545	76	9344693	227
9330563	38	9333606	52	9337004	62	9339583	101	9344708	213
9330599	70	9333618	52	9337016	62	9339595	100	9344710	101
9330604	70	9333620	52	9337028	249	9339600	312	9344722	101
9330616	146	9333632	286	9337107	108	9339612	312	9345366	80
9330698	42	9333656	106	9337133	183	9339662	184	9345403	71
9330745	157	9333670	274	9337250	142	9339806	74	9345415	71
9330812	126	9333682	274	9337262	142	9339818	151	9345427	70
9330874	82	9333785	309	9337274	48	9339820	156	9345439	70
9330989	241	9333826	184	9337327	200	9339832	157	9345441	40
9330991	241	9333838	184	9337406	106	9339844	74	9345609	108
9331000	78	9333840	184	9337444	312	9339868	203	9345611	83
9331012	78	9333852	184	9337456	312	9339959	120	9345623	209
9331048	39	9334143	249	9337468	312	9340104	221	9345764	37
9331397	233	9334155	75	9337470	312	9340128	221	9345818	125
9331555	126	9334167	75	9337482	312	9340439	198	9345958	138
9331866	306	9334234	74	9337511	96	9340489	198	9345960	138
9331921	284	9334246	74	9337523	96	9340491	89	9345972	138
9332054	210	9334349	203	9337597	288	9340570	74	9345984	212
9332157	182	9334351	114	9337614	211	9340582	194	9345996	213
9332195	236	9334375	101	9337626	211	9340594	196	9346005	212
9332200	235	9334387	209	9337638	211	9340623	196	9346017	212
9332212	126	9334480	255	9337640	211	9341067	276	9346029	279
9332250	138	9334519	163	9337652	211	9341079	276	9346160	166
9332303	214	9334521	163	9337664	211	9341081	276	9346172	206
9332315	216	9334571	232	9337676	211	9341093	276	9346304	148
9332511	192	9334662	192	9337688	211	9341146	67	9346354	296
9332523	37	9334674	192	9337705	237	9341433	194	9346380	270
9332535	43	9334686	192	9337717	237	9341445	196	9346433	261
9332547	193	9334715	120	9337729	269	9341512	89	9346445	203
9332614	135	9334789	214	9337731	239	9341940	59	9346457	203
9332626	135	9334818	166	9337743	237	9342176	193	9346524	152
9332640	135	9334820	165	9337755	269	9342205	146	9346546	152
9332781	311	9334832	135	9337913	73	9342217	59	9346558	152
9332810	311	9334844	135	9337925	73	9342281	19	9346720	40
9332810	74	9334856	10	9337937	73	9342487	288	9346756	64
9332822	311	9334868	10	9337949	73	9342499	191	9346768	64
9332834	310	9334882	61	9337951	245	9342504	191	9346811	244
9332846	309	9334923	71	9337963	245	9342516	191	9346823	244
9332858	97	9334935	73	9337975	245	9342528	191	9346835	245
9332860	97	9335032	43	9337987	245	9342580	40	9346859	39
9332872	109	9335044	43	9338058	144	9342815	204	9346873	120
9332884	108	9335056	43	9338084	227	9342865	206	9346885	120
9332925	303	9335068	43	9338266	185	9342906	209	9347035	54
9332937	303	9335094	133	9338620	185	9343118	108	9347047	54
9332949	303	9335109	133	9338632	157	9343132	12	9347059	54
9332951	37	9335123	133	9338694	271	9343156	132	9347061	54
9332975	193	9335135	133	9338709	271	9343168	132	9347176	37
9332987	193	9335147	133	9338711	306	9343170	132	9347255	52
9332999	193	9335197	75	9338723	271	9343194	284	9347267	227
9333008	193	9335202	76	9338747	272	9343266	159	9347279	52
9333010	193	9335953	209	9338797	159	9343340	310	9347281	228
9333022	193	9335965	211	9338814	217	9343481	253	9347293	52
9333034	193	9336048	180	9338826	185	9343493	253	9347308	228
9333046	222	9336050	306	9338838	185	9343510	253	9347425	136
9333058	160	9336062	306	9338840	185	9343613	98	9347437	136
9333060	199	9336074	306	9338852	185	9343716	139	9347449	136
9333072	222	9336086	306	9338864	185	9343728	139	9347504	104
9333149	10	9336165	103	9338876	185	9343730	139	9347516	273
9333151	15	9336177	102	9338888	211	9343986	290	9347542	148
9333163	10	9336189	103	9338905	40	9344007	293	9347554	148
9333175	15	9336191	103	9338917	40	9344019	290	9347566	148
9333187	217	9336397	44	9338937	114	9344033	276	9347712	255
9333369	102	9336402	44	9338955	210	9344289	309	9347724	255
9333371	294	9336414	44	9339181	301	9344423	142	9347856	160
9333383	294	9336426	44	9339260	288	9344435	196	9347877	126
9333395	101	9336490	135	9339272	179	9344552	168	9348053	226
9333400	275	9336505	135	9339284	176	9344564	168	9348065	226

9348077	226	9351452	145	9355563	71	9360142	76	9364277	204
9348089	226	9351531	282	9355575	71	9360154	75	9364382	282
9348091	226	9351543	281	9355604	124	9360245	255	9364394	282
9348106	226	9351581	177	9355733	16	9360257	206	9364588	269
9348156	191	9351593	174	9355757	235	9360269	255	9364796	205
9348168	191	9351634	204	9355769	235	9360271	255	9364992	227
9348170	191	9351737	97	9355812	303	9360324	216	9365001	58
9348297	142	9351919	104	9356074	193	9360336	96	9365477	142
9348302	196	9351921	302	9356086	191	9360415	133	9365489	142
9348431	213	9352004	189	9356098	190	9360427	134	9365623	128
9348443	213	9352016	189	9356103	190	9360439	134	9365635	128
9348455	213	9352028	189	9356115	191	9360441	133	9365659	303
9348467	213	9352030	189	9356127	189	9360453	183	9365661	303
9348479	40	9352042	189	9356139	189	9360465	183	9365788	227
9348493	101	9352195	217	9356141	193	9360568	74	9365790	227
9348649	193	9352200	281	9356153	193	9360697	100	9365805	227
9348651	193	9352212	281	9356165	193	9360752	250	9365817	91
9348663	222	9352298	128	9356294	78	9360764	199	9366110	291
9348675	222	9352303	128	9356309	76	9360805	187	9366263	216
9348687	222	9352315	128	9356311	77	9360817	185	9366275	216
9348699	222	9352391	250	9356610	196	9360831	269	9366287	96
9348704	76	9352406	250	9356696	211	9360879	285	9366299	96
9348857	255	9352418	250	9356701	211	9360881	285	9367176	236
9348900	255	9352420	250	9356713	211	9360893	285	9367188	270
9349368	254	9352561	181	9356842	255	9360908	285	9367190	235
9349497	298	9352860	124	9357080	86	9360910	93	9367205	236
9349502	298	9353084	228	9357092	85	9360922	187	9367542	271
9349514	297	9353096	228	9357107	167	9360934	281	9367578	210
9349526	298	9353101	228	9357119	85	9361079	118	9367580	306
9349538	297	9353113	228	9357121	167	9361249	125	9367592	306
9349540	298	9353125	228	9357298	246	9361251	125	9367607	209
9349552	297	9353137	228	9357303	246	9361445	118	9367671	182
9349564	298	9353149	228	9357315	246	9361639	187	9367683	133
9349576	152	9353228	212	9357327	246	9361809	248	9367748	217
9349590	152	9353230	213	9357523	248	9361811	209	9367750	195
9349605	284	9353242	60	9357535	248	9361811	246	9367815	108
9349617	117	9353527	238	9357547	248	9361823	245	9367827	106
9349629	117	9353530	238	9357846	135	9361835	246	9367839	311
9349631	217	9353541	239	9357858	166	9361990	286	9368302	60
9349681	24	9353553	239	9357860	166	9362267	156	9368314	60
9349796	86	9353565	238	9357872	212	9362322	76	9368326	291
9349801	86	9353577	239	9357949	226	9362334	173	9368730	138
9349813	176	9353589	238	9357951	226	9362396	251	9368742	137
9349825	179	9353591	238	9357963	226	9362401	251	9368871	125
9349875	163	9353606	239	9357975	226	9362413	250	9368895	146
9349887	163	9353620	64	9358280	82	9362437	77	9368900	146
9350018	270	9353797	121	9358292	82	9362449	199	9368912	146
9350020	270	9353802	121	9358400	293	9362530	26	9369734	232
9350032	206	9354167	211	9358412	293	9362542	10	9369758	176
9350070	271	9354648	62	9358436	102	9362712	199	9369899	288
9350094	125	9354662	61	9358541	296	9362724	248	9369904	288
9350288	60	9354674	61	9358632	284	9362736	248	9370018	21
9350290	60	9354791	200	9358670	273	9363015	64	9370537	59
9350317	245	9354894	216	9358682	273	9363027	64	9371062	253
9350381	75	9354909	96	9358838	230	9363039	64	9371086	254
9350393	76	9354911	96	9358888	222	9363041	64	9371579	155
9350422	60	9354923	85	9358890	46	9363053	64	9371581	155
9350599	282	9354935	282	9358905	47	9363065	64	9371608	204
9350604	60	9355161	64	9359002	187	9363144	248	9372315	212
9350642	302	9355185	185	9359014	187	9363156	248	9372327	212
9350850	214	9355197	185	9359026	187	9363364	93	9372420	273
9350862	214	9355202	209	9359038	187	9363376	93	9372432	273
9350927	157	9355214	211	9359040	187	9363479	182	9372456	26
9350989	236	9355226	210	9359052	187	9363481	224	9372470	177
9350991	237	9355238	74	9359260	254	9363493	224	9372482	179
9351062	238	9355240	74	9359301	255	9363637	253	9372494	180
9351127	76	9355252	74	9359313	255	9363819	198	9372547	276
9351139	78	9355288	191	9359325	255	9363821	198	9372559	274
9351141	77	9355331	191	9359363	281	9363845	311	9372561	275
9351159	156	9355343	191	9359375	281	9363857	108	9372731	269
9351218	248	9355355	190	9359387	281	9363948	185	9372742	269
9351414	145	9355367	190	9359399	281	9363950	184	9372860	174
9351426	145	9355513	132	9359791	21	9364203	245	9372872	174
9351438	145	9355551	71	9359806	22	9364215	108	9373462	166

326

9373474	165	9378876	106	9383962	216	9387346	126	9391402	86
9373486	135	9379155	200	9383974	74	9387358	126	9391414	86
9373498	135	9379208	286	9384019	238	9387360	126	9391426	214
9373622	142	9379301	128	9384021	62	9387566	106	9391438	96
9373644	142	9379313	204	9384033	63	9387578	105	9391440	96
9373656	291	9379363	255	9384069	67	9387580	202	9391476	280
9373668	291	9379375	255	9384095	160	9387671	43	9391488	202
9374040	80	9379399	273	9384100	203	9387683	43	9391490	203
9374088	61	9379404	273	9384112	202	9387700	307	9391505	203
9374208	203	9379612	67	9384124	202	9387712	307	9391567	246
9374272	74	9379624	68	9384136	203	9387724	307	9391579	248
9374301	96	9379674	165	9384198	43	9387750	282	9391581	245
9374428	196	9379894	224	9384203	43	9387762	282	9391593	245
9374521	281	9379909	224	9384215	42	9387918	95	9391610	51
9374571	174	9379911	224	9384227	42	9387920	95	9391660	250
9374583	174	9379961	128	9384239	42	9387932	96	9391672	251
9374595	174	9380063	181	9384370	181	9387956	269	9391787	212
9374844	160	9380075	182	9384435	274	9387970	111	9391799	213
9375264	305	9380350	217	9384447	274	9388003	111	9392341	211
9375305	136	9380398	181	9384459	274	9388015	111	9392353	210
9375496	136	9380477	128	9384540	297	9388027	113	9392420	205
9375501	136	9380489	128	9384564	311	9388273	43	9392468	293
9375513	136	9380506	95	9384564	311	9388297	296	9392470	293
9375575	133	9380518	214	9384590	121	9388302	224	9392482	293
9375604	133	9380526	214	9384605	121	9388314	224	9392559	137
9375616	293	9380661	296	9384617	204	9388340	271	9392561	138
9375721	185	9380673	296	9384875	311	9388352	271	9392781	216
9375915	233	9380738	82	9384887	310	9388704	284	9392793	95
9375953	75	9380740	82	9384932	311	9388716	246	9392799	96
9376000	145	9380764	253	9384954	80	9388819	269	9392808	96
9376012	102	9380788	254	9385001	108	9388821	269	9392925	191
9376141	254	9380805	145	9385013	310	9388833	269	9393022	310
9376751	204	9380817	90	9385025	108	9389019	38	9393084	59
9376816	217	9380829	90	9385037	59	9389021	106	9393096	59
9376828	217	9380831	182	9385087	164	9389033	106	9393101	59
9376892	51	9381134	118	9385178	203	9389071	67	9393307	108
9377078	273	9381172	68	9385192	286	9389083	65	9393319	108
9377133	85	9381237	271	9385477	153	9389095	67	9393321	310
9377145	85	9381249	271	9385489	154	9389100	67	9393448	243
9377224	61	9381392	137	9385491	153	9389253	39	9393450	243
9377236	61	9381562	133	9385506	153	9389265	39	9393462	245
9377248	61	9381665	157	9385611	97	9389382	136	9393474	245
9377406	61	9381677	185	9385673	148	9389394	136	9393539	144
9377418	62	9381756	96	9385843	59	9389409	136	9393553	144
9377420	82	9381768	96	9385879	170	9389411	136	9393577	144
9377470	132	9381823	133	9385972	264	9389564	105	9393589	144
9377482	132	9381835	133	9385984	264	9389643	118	9393682	282
9377494	303	9381847	133	9385996	264	9389681	93	9393981	252
9377509	303	9381861	201	9386005	264	9389693	93	9394040	217
9377511	305	9381873	201	9386017	264	9389708	93	9394519	257
9377523	305	9382097	222	9386225	248	9389813	122	9394753	296
9377559	101	9382396	146	9386299	61	9389825	197	9394765	296
9377561	55	9382700	291	9386304	61	9389837	133	9394832	239
9377573	55	9382750	182	9386471	97	9389849	133	9394870	191
9377664	217	9382762	182	9386483	97	9389851	133	9394882	191
9377688	89	9382798	276	9386495	97	9389863	133	9394894	191
9377690	271	9382956	296	9386512	64	9389899	62	9394947	239
9377779	67	9382968	296	9386914	243	9389978	295	9394959	239
9377781	59	9382970	296	9386926	244	9390020	282	9395020	198
9378151	273	9382982	296	9386938	42	9390032	282	9395044	173
9378163	273	9383106	306	9386940	42	9390185	124	9395056	199
9378321	48	9383223	254	9386952	42	9390628	286	9395068	198
9378369	288	9383235	104	9386964	42	9390680	148	9395070	173
9378448	13	9383247	103	9386976	54	9390692	296	9395082	173
9378450	13	9383259	103	9386988	54	9390692	296	9395094	199
9378462	15	9383261	103	9387009	42	9390769	293	9395109	198
9378474	10	9383417	306	9387073	21	9390920	106	9395111	198
9378486	10	9383429	306	9387085	21	9390939	106	9395123	173
9378498	12	9383431	306	9387097	97	9391268	93	9395135	199
9378541	42	9383857	122	9387102	97	9391361	85	9395147	156
9378618	74	9383869	67	9387138	96	9391373	85	9395161	156
9378620	74	9383900	280	9387279	111	9391385	85	9395214	144
9378632	74	9383936	24	9387281	111	9391397	86	9395226	144
9378834	106	9383948	24	9387334	126				

9395238	144	9398888	10	9402029	191	9405540	110	9409053	155
9395240	144	9398905	12	9402316	311	9405552	110	9409118	108
9395252	144	9398917	12	9402328	108	9405564	110	9409170	309
9395264	144	9399002	176	9402562	144	9406001	121	9409182	64
9395290	74	9399014	175	9402562	86	9406013	121	9409194	76
9395305	65	9399026	177	9402574	144	9406013	269	9409209	77
9395317	67	9399038	175	9402574	86	9406024	75	9409261	159
9395329	65	9399040	177	9402586	142	9406037	75	9409273	159
9395331	65	9399052	176	9402598	142	9406049	50	9409314	257
9395379	108	9399193	76	9402615	264	9406051	75	9409326	212
9395525	101	9399208	76	9402615	264	9406063	50	9409338	303
9395628	248	9399210	77	9402627	264	9406075	75	9409340	156
9395630	248	9399222	78	9402639	264	9406087	61	9409352	191
9395927	221	9399260	43	9402641	265	9406099	75	9409481	185
9395939	221	9399272	43	9402706	209	9406104	61	9409510	48
9395941	221	9399478	288	9402718	209	9406116	75	9409522	48
9395953	221	9399480	121	9402756	210	9406128	61	9410002	151
9396000	284	9399480	269	9402770	310	9406180	233	9410014	62
9396012	284	9399492	285	9402782	109	9406269	110	9410179	182
9396024	284	9399507	38	9402794	299	9406544	56	9410181	95
9396139	131	9399739	221	9402809	217	9406611	92	9410208	106
9396141	131	9399741	221	9402902	38	9406623	92	9410210	106
9396153	131	9399753	102	9402914	38	9406635	92	9410222	106
9396373	217	9399765	221	9402926	38	9406647	92	9410301	74
9396385	217	9399777	221	9403009	264	9406659	68	9410569	16
9396634	40	9399789	221	9403011	264	9406673	95	9410624	257
9396725	200	9399791	221	9403059	98	9406685	95	9410648	86
9397080	60	9399806	221	9403102	206	9406738	136	9410650	86
9397236	126	9399868	217	9403114	214	9406910	105	9410727	75
9397248	126	9399923	204	9403164	91	9407093	59	9410741	75
9397286	269	9399935	204	9403176	297	9407122	61	9410753	76
9397298	269	9400069	241	9403205	153	9407134	265	9410765	76
9397303	269	9400071	101	9403217	210	9407146	265	9410777	76
9397315	269	9400083	140	9403229	93	9407158	265	9410789	76
9397327	269	9400095	101	9403279	210	9407160	265	9410791	76
9397339	269	9400100	140	9403281	184	9407251	160	9410806	77
9397341	269	9400112	86	9403396	222	9407263	160	9410882	151
9397353	269	9400136	86	9403396	312	9407275	160	9410894	152
9397357	52	9400174	233	9403413	114	9407287	160	9410909	182
9397585	258	9400186	102	9403504	113	9407328	202	9410959	126
9397602	97	9400198	233	9403530	113	9407330	202	9410997	121
9397614	97	9400203	103	9403542	106	9407354	145	9411020	276
9397860	306	9400215	99	9403554	106	9407366	145	9411032	127
9397913	99	9400289	88	9403619	257	9407380	145	9411082	108
9397999	184	9400473	142	9403621	270	9407392	145	9411135	206
9398072	62	9400485	142	9403762	201	9407407	145	9411185	296
9398084	82	9400679	238	9403777	201	9407445	291	9411197	295
9398096	61	9400681	120	9403877	309	9407457	290	9411226	285
9398175	61	9400916	83	9404194	136	9407495	205	9411238	286
9398230	256	9401051	103	9404194	249	9407665	49	9411317	43
9398242	256	9401063	258	9404209	212	9407677	49	9411329	43
9398254	256	9401075	259	9404223	145	9407689	50	9411367	192
9398321	305	9401099	92	9404314	26	9407823	106	9411379	192
9398333	305	9401104	180	9404429	201	9407835	106	9411381	192
9398371	177	9401116	176	9404431	200	9407847	106	9411733	110
9398383	178	9401130	176	9404443	101	9407885	100	9411939	182
9398395	104	9401141	176	9404649	176	9408073	285	9411941	182
9398400	312	9401166	97	9404651	176	9408085	64	9411989	251
9398412	312	9401178	97	9404663	180	9408100	121	9411991	252
9398424	104	9401221	256	9404675	179	9408205	121	9412000	252
9398432	205	9401271	308	9404704	252	9408217	120	9412036	184
9398436	104	9401283	232	9404780	202	9408322	286	9412062	110
9398448	312	9401295	159	9404792	202	9408463	95	9412074	110
9398450	312	9401362	122	9404807	202	9408475	95	9412086	110
9398462	222	9401661	166	9404819	202	9408695	120	9412098	39
9398668	288	9401673	166	9404833	286	9408774	51	9412103	39
9398682	111	9401685	255	9404845	288	9408841	136	9412177	181
9398694	111	9401697	255	9404857	235	9408853	136	9412335	276
9398709	111	9401776	222	9404869	235	9408865	136	9412347	274
9398711	111	9401776	312	9404871	235	9408877	136	9412347	276
9398735	113	9401788	253	9404883	235	9408956	192	9412359	276
9398747	113	9401790	254	9405033	213	9409027	155	9412581	219
9398759	113	9401805	254	9405423	68	9409039	155	9412880	124
9398876	50	9401879	154	9405538	110	9409041	155	9412995	183

9413004	183	9419254	221	9424912	184	9431288	196	9435258	166
9413327	280	9419474	181	9424924	184	9431290	196	9435648	122
9413418	197	9419541	43	9424936	184	9431305	196	9435674	257
9413420	122	9419565	286	9425277	124	9431317	196	9435686	257
9413523	280	9419644	168	9425318	299	9431360	173	9435753	136
9413547	276	9419668	167	9425382	226	9431680	249	9435765	137
9413559	276	9419723	133	9425497	217	9431692	249	9435856	54
9413561	276	9419735	134	9425502	292	9431707	249	9435868	54
9413573	276	9419747	148	9425511	299	9431719	255	9435894	239
9413690	65	9419759	148	9425552	216	9431757	254	9435909	239
9413717	80	9419773	222	9425758	153	9431769	255	9436006	67
9413779	96	9419785	222	9425875	214	9431800	250	9436068	248
9413834	39	9419797	221	9425980	281	9431812	212	9436070	290
9414022	37	9420045	146	9426207	113	9431824	212	9436082	166
9414034	38	9420057	146	9426245	151	9431836	146	9436094	166
9414058	281	9420277	285	9426283	134	9431848	146	9436173	255
9414060	281	9420772	277	9426312	154	9431850	146	9436185	255
9414072	281	9420784	277	9426324	301	9431862	146	9436329	54
9414084	281	9420796	277	9426350	209	9432036	106	9436331	53
9414278	217	9420801	277	9426362	209	9432048	105	9436355	92
9414292	133	9420813	277	9426374	211	9432050	106	9436367	92
9414503	288	9420825	277	9426386	185	9432062	105	9436379	92
9414632	159	9420837	277	9426594	106	9432115	73	9436422	167
9414876	148	9420849	277	9426790	312	9432139	73	9436434	257
9414931	106	9420851	301	9426867	145	9432141	73	9436446	219
9415155	173	9420863	301	9426881	145	9432147	73	9436458	257
9415167	173	9421061	13	9427376	62	9432153	73	9436460	151
9415296	245	9421247	38	9427380	50	9432165	73	9436472	138
9415727	184	9421415	42	9427392	50	9432206	181	9436484	138
9415844	232	9421831	65	9427550	74	9432218	238	9436678	217
9416020	284	9421843	160	9427562	74	9432828	142	9436769	284
9416109	48	9421843	160	9427627	285	9432880	309	9436847	243
9416692	82	9421960	275	9427639	286	9432892	109	9437048	101
9416707	145	9421972	275	9427641	286	9432907	311	9437050	100
9416719	145	9422067	125	9427926	162	9432919	108	9437062	101
9416721	145	9422079	125	9427938	162	9433016	269	9437115	199
9416733	82	9422081	125	9427940	162	9433054	203	9437127	173
9416848	80	9422085	286	9427952	162	9433066	203	9437139	55
9416965	211	9422196	183	9427964	162	9433262	136	9437141	173
9416977	211	9422201	183	9428358	299	9433274	137	9437177	235
9416989	211	9422328	162	9428360	299	9433509	292	9437189	55
9416991	211	9422378	243	9428463	36	9433585	282	9437191	198
9417000	183	9422445	275	9428499	170	9433597	280	9437696	122
9417012	183	9422457	274	9428970	154	9433793	92	9437866	29
9417024	183	9422615	286	9428982	154	9433901	228	9437907	132
9417086	15	9422639	221	9428994	154	9434204	228	9437919	132
9417098	15	9422641	221	9429003	154	9434216	228	9437921	132
9417244	235	9422835	286	9429015	95	9434228	228	9437933	132
9417256	236	9423035	241	9429027	95	9434230	228	9437945	132
9417268	235	9423255	164	9429314	206	9434319	302	9438016	129
9417270	235	9423449	128	9429326	254	9434321	302	9438054	111
9417309	202	9423516	292	9430038	125	9434369	36	9438066	19
9417311	203	9423566	222	9430222	292	9434371	37	9438078	19
9417323	288	9423580	282	9430272	295	9434383	36	9438406	296
9417335	285	9423592	282	9430284	295	9434395	37	9438418	219
9417892	183	9423645	48	9430296	295	9434400	37	9438482	236
9418119	145	9423712	194	9430363	226	9434412	36	9438494	236
9418133	200	9423762	36	9430375	226	9434448	306	9438509	237
9418145	200	9423774	36	9430387	226	9434539	154	9438511	237
9418157	95	9423786	243	9430399	226	9434553	68	9438523	93
9418365	269	9423798	243	9430519	221	9434565	68	9438535	93
9418377	241	9423918	36	9430765	233	9434711	306	9438614	122
9418482	295	9423920	36	9430777	233	9434773	296	9438626	122
9418494	276	9424089	165	9430789	233	9434785	296	9438638	122
9418597	285	9424120	164	9430844	153	9434905	80	9438858	285
9418602	286	9424132	164	9430868	308	9434917	80	9438860	286
9418614	120	9424211	233	9430870	166	9434929	80	9439060	37
9418640	222	9424273	233	9430935	199	9434931	80	9439072	37
9418652	254	9424546	137	9431111	269	9434943	80	9439113	56
9418987	137	9424558	137	9431123	269	9435038	264	9439199	296
9418999	54	9424649	91	9431135	269	9435052	306	9439204	296
9419008	137	9424651	91	9431147	269	9435064	306	9439412	122
9419230	221	9424883	15	9431214	270	9435076	306	9439498	80
9419242	222	9424900	184	9431276	196	9435246	166	9439539	124

9439541	124	9443683	269	9448310	217	9451719	302	9456927	275
9439773	217	9443918	153	9448322	217	9451898	148	9456953	198
9439785	217	9443920	154	9448346	137	9451905	75	9456965	258
9439797	217	9444261	184	9448358	137	9451927	75	9456977	155
9439802	217	9444273	236	9448360	136	9451939	75	9456989	300
9439814	257	9444285	270	9448372	137	9451965	75	9456991	300
9439826	257	9444417	97	9448384	137	9452593	243	9457000	155
9439838	257	9444455	48	9448554	124	9452610	244	9457012	36
9439840	257	9444467	48	9448669	47	9452622	245	9457024	204
9439852	257	9444479	48	9448671	47	9452634	85	9457218	193
9439864	257	9444649	118	9448683	47	9452646	48	9457220	279
9439876	257	9444716	226	9448695	47	9452658	85	9457309	79
9440045	235	9444728	226	9448700	42	9452660	85	9457402	122
9440150	255	9444730	226	9448712	217	9452854	214	9457543	82
9440306	199	9444742	226	9448724	217	9453107	246	9457593	109
9440320	36	9444819	125	9448748	264	9453212	198	9457608	311
9440332	37	9444845	226	9448750	264	9453224	198	9457737	312
9440526	181	9445136	271	9448762	264	9453236	198	9457749	204
9440772	227	9445409	148	9448774	264	9453248	219	9457892	120
9440784	80	9445459	233	9448786	264	9453250	198	9457952	82
9440796	227	9445461	235	9448798	264	9453262	198	9458016	95
9440801	80	9445502	235	9448803	264	9453298	176	9458030	249
9440813	227	9445514	235	9448815	264	9453365	258	9458078	250
9440825	227	9445526	235	9448827	259	9453559	76	9458080	250
9440837	227	9445538	235	9449106	259	9453793	94	9458092	250
9440980	285	9445576	228	9449118	259	9453963	113	9458494	166
9441001	179	9445588	227	9449120	259	9453975	113	9458590	37
9441154	256	9445590	16	9449405	120	9453987	113	9458688	37
9441166	256	9445887	307	9449780	51	9453999	113	9458808	299
9441180	256	9445899	308	9449792	51	9454230	248	9458822	299
9441192	256	9445904	199	9449819	76	9454242	248	9458834	299
9441506	246	9445916	255	9449821	198	9454280	205	9458858	299
9441520	246	9445980	306	9449833	173	9454395	75	9458999	156
9441556	246	9445992	306	9449845	198	9454400	76	9459008	43
9441568	246	9446001	306	9449857	173	9454412	76	9459010	43
9441570	246	9446013	306	9449869	198	9454424	77	9459022	43
9441582	246	9446104	80	9450296	213	9454436	77	9459034	43
9441594	246	9446116	108	9450301	213	9454448	75	9459060	204
9441609	248	9446374	120	9450313	213	9454450	76	9459072	204
9441611	248	9446570	271	9450325	213	9454711	73	9459084	204
9441623	246	9446582	36	9450337	213	9454723	73	9459096	204
9441855	217	9446623	309	9450349	213	9454759	267	9459151	164
9441867	148	9446635	108	9450351	213	9454761	267	9459239	217
9441984	243	9446635	108	9450363	213	9455040	36	9459278	199
9442017	109	9446881	245	9450375	228	9455052	74	9459400	165
9442122	302	9446996	205	9450387	228	9455533	36	9459412	166
9442172	97	9447005	205	9450399	140	9455545	37	9459424	165
9442249	159	9447017	68	9450404	140	9455557	37	9459436	165
9442641	198	9447536	56	9450416	140	9455569	37	9460033	205
9442744	296	9447548	56	9450428	139	9455648	233	9460136	128 / 196
9442756	296	9447550	56	9450430	139	9455650	233	9460318	309
9442859	204	9447562	56	9450442	139	9455662	59	9460356	227
9442861	271	9447732	196	9450600	76	9455686	182	9460459	48
9442873	271	9447768	196	9450612	76	9455703	91	9460461	48
9442885	155	9447847	101	9450624	76	9455715	246	9460887	305
9443011	92	9447861	101	9450636	78	9455739	67	9460899	221
9443023	92	9447873	140	9450648	75	9455820	91	9461051	139
9443035	92	9447885	101	9450703	126	9455870	312	9461142	69
9443047	92	9447897	140	9450715	125	9455973	181	9461154	83
9443059	92	9447902	101	9450727	126	9456123	254	9461173	174
9443073	156	9447914	140	9450739	126	9456147	255	9461386	227
9443140	228	9448011	270	9450741	126	9456159	279	9461398	180
9443152	228	9448023	214	9450753	125	9456173	254	9461403	227
9443164	228	9448035	214	9450765	125	9456226	279	9461415	176
9443401	269	9448047	214	9450777	126	9456238	254	9461427	227
9443413	269	9448059	214	9450911	199	9456367	129	9461439	180
9443425	216	9448061	302	9450923	199	9456379	129	9461441	227
9443463	265	9448073	302	9450935	198	9456678	80	9461465	136
9443475	265	9448138	251	9450947	198	9456680	80	9461477	136
9443487	264	9448140	249	9451094	26	9456692	205	9461489	136
9443592	122	9448152	269	9451264	62	9456757	249	9461491	136
9443607	122	9448243	153	9451276	205	9456769	250	9461505	136
9443619	124	9448255	152	9451484	155	9456771	249	9461623	259
9443669	137	9448308	137	9451707	273	9456783	250	9461659	134

9461661	133	9465608	243	9469895	249	9475624	184	9481233	205
9461673	134	9465708	64	9469900	249	9475636	184	9481245	205
9461685	134	9465710	64	9469912	249	9475648	184	9481257	205
9461697	133	9465796	239	9470040	233	9475650	184	9481295	205
9461702	134	9465801	65	9470088	309	9475674	93	9481312	205
9461714	48	9465966	292	9470258	239	9475686	93	9481348	205
9461764	127	9465978	292	9470260	238	9475698	93	9481439	122
9461776	127	9465980	292	9470272	238	9475703	93	9481441	122
9461790	235	9465992	292	9470284	239	9475715	230	9481453	122
9461831	154	9466001	292	9470375	122	9475935	238	9481465	122
9461843	154	9466013	292	9470387	122	9476525	85	9481520	163
9461855	154	9466025	292	9470739	270	9476537	85	9481532	103
9461867	206	9466051	303	9470820	164	9476630	306	9482299	70
9461879	206	9466130	286	9470882	252	9476642	306	9482304	70
9461881	206	9466142	286	9470894	252	9476654	105	9482550	164
9461893	207	9466245	264	9470923	36	9476721	148	9482562	164
9462017	207	9466295	303	9470961	142	9476733	211	9482574	202
9462029	207	9466300	303	9470973	142	9476745	210	9482586	202
9462031	207	9466312	303	9470985	256	9476757	185	9482653	48
9462043	206	9466324	303	9470997	256	9476812	133	9482665	48
9462366	144	9466336	303	9471018	142	9476824	134	9482847	152
9462691	312	9466348	303	9471032	142	9476977	120	9482859	152
9462706	312	9466350	303	9471123	144	9477294	101	9482861	152
9462718	312	9466362	303	9471202	308	9477294	252	9482873	152
9462720	312	9466374	303	9471214	308	9477309	102	9483126	15
9462732	312	9466867	73	9471408	227	9477311	102	9483138	124
9462811	36	9466960	213	9471678	165	9477323	102	9483188	47
9462897	134	9466972	213	9472086	129	9477335	101	9483190	279
9462926	296	9466984	213	9472098	129	9477335	252	9483205	47
9463011	311	9466996	136	9472103	129	9477347	101	9483217	46
9463023	311	9467005	136	9472127	264	9477347	252	9483229	47
9463035	108	9467017	137	9472139	264	9477359	101	9483231	46
9463047	108	9467043	213	9472141	264	9477359	252	9483243	46
9463059	108	9467055	213	9472153	264	9477385	103	9483255	279
9463085	310	9467251	73	9472165	264	9477438	13	9483267	47
9463205	209	9467263	73	9472177	264	9477593	159	9483451	50
9463267	156	9467265	73	9472189	264	9477610	258	9483516	159
9463281	156	9467287	73	9472206	74	9477787	284	9483669	219
9463293	156	9467299	73	9472529	159	9477799	138	9483671	219
9463310	156	9467304	73	9473028	92	9477804	137	9483683	219
9463346	156	9467316	73	9473224	291	9477830	306	9483695	219
9463633	144	9467392	209	9473236	291	9477878	235	9484077	286
9463645	144	9467407	178	9473248	291	9477880	235	9484089	286
9463657	144	9467419	178	9473250	291	9477892	235	9484429	176
9463669	144	9467421	179	9473274	85	9477907	236	9484431	227
9463671	144	9467433	176	9473315	85	9477919	271	9484443	175
9464247	97	9467445	177	9473327	52	9477921	209	9484455	227
9464376	216	9467457	177	9473341	85	9478468	309	9484467	180
9464388	155	9467548	151	9473626	312	9478494	250	9484479	227
9464455	209	9467550	151	9473731	93	9478638	239	9484481	175
9464546	46	9467562	151	9473913	48	9478743	75	9484493	68
9464560	74	9467574	151	9473925	48	9479046	214	9484510	198
9464572	151	9467586	151	9473937	48	9479163	61	9484522	173
9464584	151	9467598	152	9474137	80	9479369	61	9484534	173
9464596	151	9467603	152	9474199	79	9479838	295	9484546	257
9464663	151	9467627	151	9474216	79	9479840	295	9484558	257
9464675	151	9467794	135	9474228	79	9479852	12	9484560	225
9464948	301	9467809	135	9474230	79	9479864	12	9484572	225
9464950	301	9467811	135	9474242	79	9479929	59	9484704	222
9465095	213	9468293	210	9474254	79	9479979	59	9484716	43
9465241	204	9468308	210	9474266	79	9480150	43	9484728	42
9465253	48	9468671	95	9474278	79	9480162	299	9484730	43
9465265	48	9468853	235	9474280	79	9480174	227	9484742	42
9465277	48	9469259	126	9474383	301	9480186	227	9484807	309
9465289	176	9469560	180	9474395	301	9480198	227	9484924	92
9465291	179	9469560	227	9474618	85	9480203	227	9484936	92
9465306	48	9469572	227	9474620	85	9480215	227	9484948	92
9465318	48	9469687	128	9474632	85	9480227	227	9484998	312
9465370	132	9469687	128 / 196	9474644	85	9480526	64	9485007	312
9465382	132	9469778	291	9474785	125	9480538	64	9485629	135
9465394	94	9469780	291	9475208	286	9480837	269	9485631	135
9465411	170	9469869	182	9475258	227	9481049	49	9485887	198
9465423	170	9469871	183	9475301	301	9481051	50	9485899	198
9465435	170	9469883	249	9475600	70	9481075	50	9486013	290

9486025	291	9492062	300	9498810	222	9507881	47	9515931	206
9486075	235	9492074	68	9498834	222	9507893	46	9516105	82
9486087	236	9492086	68	9498846	222	9508304	54	9516117	82
9486116	264	9492127	300	9498896	308	9508316	54	9516129	124
9486726	122	9492139	300	9498901	308	9508380	54	9516404	71
9487225	308	9492335	126	9498937	79	9508392	80	9516416	71
9487237	307	9492402	101	9499450	131	9508706	279	9516428	71
9487469	204	9492696	264	9499876	159	9508859	106	9516430	71
9487471	204	9492701	264	9499888	159	9509011	106	9516442	71
9487483	204	9492713	264	9500039	153	9509023	106	9516454	71
9487653	258	9493016	64	9500584	306	9509126	203	9516466	71
9487873	302	9493028	64	9500637	205	9509126	259	9516478	71
9487885	302	9493133	109	9500675	151	9509138	203	9516739	165
9487944	96	9493145	310	9500986	205	9509138	259	9516741	166
9488047	94	9493200	106	9501239	101	9509140	219	9516753	166
9488059	94	9493212	109	9501332	139	9509152	219	9516765	166
9488061	94	9493224	109	9501344	139	9509164	219	9516777	248
9488097	244	9493236	311	9501356	139	9509176	204	9516789	248
9488102	245	9493365	311	9501368	140	9509401	212	9516959	65
9488188	308	9493652	111	9501370	139	9509449	164	9517422	254
9488413	221	9493664	113	9501772	301	9509607	55	9517434	254
9488566	248	9493676	113	9501863	142	9509619	173	9517903	236
9488578	248	9493690	113	9502312	170	9509621	55	9517915	236
9488580	248	9493755	108	9502336	253	9509633	173	9517927	236
9488592	248	9493767	106	9502348	253	9509645	55	9517939	236
9488803	206	9493779	106	9502506	24	9509671	55	9518115	205
9488853	290	9493975	297	9502518	24	9509683	54	9518892	183
9489065	299	9494060	297	9502867	101	9509695	173	9518907	183
9489077	299	9494230	122	9502908	101	9509700	55	9519066	46
9489089	299	9494280	264	9502910	101	9509712	173	9519078	47
9489091	299	9494905	106	9502946	101	9509774	198	9519092	271
9489106	204	9495040	207	9502958	101	9509786	173	9519107	156
9489118	204	9495402	233	9502960	101	9509803	173	9519119	156
9489209	67	9495414	233	9502972	101	9510151	156	9519121	185
9489211	230	9495765	135	9503275	85	9510187	165	9519133	306
9489285	235	9495777	135	9503287	85	9510199	165	9519145	271
9489297	235	9496226	205	9503732	101	9510371	51	9519195	46
9489845	80	9496252	245	9504592	157	9510474	311	9519286	84
9489974	173	9496264	243	9504607	157	9510486	311	9519298	84
9489986	173	9496305	269	9504724	53	9510682	292	9519303	84
9490040	12	9496317	269	9504736	53	9510694	233	9519315	85
9490052	10	9496329	151	9504748	53	9511167	281	9519339	85
9490105	181	9496331	151	9504750	54	9511387	274	9519341	85
9490442	160	9496678	70	9504786	54	9511521	274	9519482	42
9490454	160	9496680	70	9504798	54	9511533	274	9519494	38
9490466	206	9497165	165	9504803	54	9511820	125	9519573	311
9490612	203	9497177	164	9504815	54	9511832	126	9519717	42
9490624	125	9497323	105	9505027	303	9512381	142	9519767	80
9490636	125	9497335	105	9505039	305	9512747	91	9519779	80
9490648	44	9497414	219	9505041	303	9512939	108	9520376	124
9490662	125	9497426	135	9505053	305	9513438	159	9520675	84
9490686	125	9497830	277	9505065	305	9513440	159	9520936	297
9490698	125	9497880	131	9505089	305	9513763	204	9521095	255
9490703	44	9498248	201	9505510	142	9513830	233	9521394	108
9490727	277	9498250	201	9505819	133	9513854	235	9521409	310
9490791	277	9498262	200	9505821	133	9514171	286	9521435	232
9490806	277	9498274	201	9505833	47	9514377	54	9521447	232
9490818	44	9498341	255	9505900	212	9514389	91	9521540	255
9490832	126	9498353	255	9505936	224	9514559	204	9521552	255
9490844	277	9498365	255	9505986	108	9514561	204	9521564	255
9490856	277	9498377	255	9505998	310	9514755	219	9521758	245
9490870	277	9498389	255	9506069	59	9514987	50	9521813	243
9490959	210	9498444	255	9506382	51	9514999	50	9521825	245
9490961	286	9498456	255	9506394	157	9515008	50	9521837	244
9491238	239	9498468	255	9506459	26	9515101	119	9521849	244
9491252	239	9498470	255	9506710	156	9515228	153	9521851	245
9491587	84	9498482	255	9506734	155	9515383	305	9521863	245
9491812	209	9498597	211	9506746	155	9515395	303	9521875	243
9491836	80	9498602	209	9506758	155	9515400	305	9521980	311
9491874	162	9498626	205	9507519	47	9515412	303	9521980	311
9491886	162	9498717	302	9507520	46	9515474	185	9522087	228
9491898	162	9498723	113	9507544	47	9515682	45	9522099	228
9492000	300	9498729	302	9507788	47	9515747	102	9522128	65
9492050	300	9498781	205	9507790	47	9515759	102	9522178	243

332

ID	Val	ID	Val	ID	Val	ID	Val	ID	Val
9522180	243	9528201	79	9538907	142	9551375	75	9567441	203
9522324	275	9529280	154	9538945	106	9551674	85	9567453	206
9522635	228	9529293	67	9539169	209	9551686	85	9567697	296
9522647	228	9529451	219	9539171	209	9551698	85	9567702	296
9522881	151	9529463	219	9539183	185	9551703	85	9567740	154
9522893	151	9529475	67	9539212	185	9551923	170	9568031	217
9522908	151	9529487	65	9539224	184	9551935	279	9568043	217
9523512	69	9529499	65	9539236	185	9551947	279	9568562	294
9524205	170	9529504	214	9539274	90	9551959	279	9568574	295
9524542	75	9529530	153	9539286	90	9551961	279	9569841	238
9524762	307	9529578	119	9539365	292	9551973	279	9569932	61
9524774	307	9529592	153	9539389	292	9552276	205	9569944	61
9524970	43	9529956	82	9539482	221	9552886	153	9569970	140
9524982	196	9529968	82	9539494	259	9552898	154	9569994	256
9524994	196	9530228	238	9539561	309	9553103	211	9570008	256
9525285	191	9530890	82	9539573	109	9553115	211	9570838	94
9525297	191	9530905	82	9539585	311	9553218	302	9570840	94
9525302	191	9531454	203	9539597	109	9553488	211	9570852	94
9525314	191	9531466	202	9539664	135	9554200	185	9571038	135
9525326	191	9531478	202	9539688	135	9555292	217	9571296	167
9525338	191	9531507	202	9540716	210	9555319	196	9571301	167
9525340	191	9531519	202	9540807	134	9555723	10	9571313	255
9525352	191	9531636	154	9540819	133	9556181	200	9571325	255
9525364	190	9531648	154	9540821	217	9557111	277	9571375	54
9525376	190	9531715	303	9540833	217	9557123	125	9571387	54
9525388	190	9531739	209	9540869	259	9558713	79	9571399	53
9525390	191	9531741	209	9540871	259	9558892	205	9571416	62
9525405	191	9531753	210	9541306	217	9559690	79	9571492	277
9525455	190	9531882	56	9541318	301	9559705	79	9571507	277
9525467	190	9531909	257	9541380	82	9560352	157	9571519	277
9525479	188	9532197	311	9541813	165	9560364	157	9571521	277
9525479	190	9532757	68	9541825	165	9560376	271	9571533	277
9525481	190	9532771	270	9541837	165	9561253	185	9571545	277
9525493	188	9532783	207	9541849	165	9561265	184	9572264	286
9525857	298	9532795	206	9542283	184	9561277	185	9572276	286
9525869	297	9532800	270	9542520	61	9561289	185	9573660	109
9525871	298	9534779	162	9542532	61	9561368	217	9573672	311
9525883	298	9534781	162	9542544	61	9561370	216	9573684	91
9525895	298	9534793	162	9542817	282	9561382	217	9573696	109
9525900	298	9534808	162	9542829	282	9561485	191	9573701	309
9525912	298	9535096	166	9542831	282	9561497	191	9573799	271
9525924	298	9535101	166	9543251	214	9561954	209	9574042	50
9525936	298	9535137	101	9543548	292	9563237	238	9574054	306
9525948	254	9535149	257	9543550	292	9563380	221	9574066	156
9525950	254	9535151	101	9544138	165	9563392	219	9574078	156
9526461	106	9535163	257	9544140	165	9563407	219	9574080	306
9526502	138	9535175	101	9544152	164	9563706	53	9574092	306
9526564	248	9535187	257	9544164	164	9563720	53	9574107	156
9526875	189	9535199	101	9544592	196	9563732	54	9574612	184
9526887	189	9535204	257	9544607	216	9563744	54	9574858	154
9526899	189	9535216	101	9544736	214	9564138	201	9574860	153
9526904	190	9536363	202	9544748	214	9564384	40	9575436	201
9526916	190	9536375	202	9544750	214	9564671	135	9575527	200
9526928	190	9536818	210	9544762	214	9565140	201	9575668	80
9526930	190	9536820	217	9544918	184	9565338	138	9575943	105
9526942	192	9536909	211	9544920	184	9565340	219	9575955	106
9526954	192	9536959	156	9545168	308	9565546	156	9576014	200
9526966	192	9536961	156	9545728	233	9565558	156	9576753	258
9526978	190	9537264	54	9546459	303	9565560	156	9576765	258
9527025	190	9537276	54	9546461	303	9565948	296	9576789	258
9527037	190	9537379	308	9546473	303	9565950	296	9577032	108
9527049	190	9537628	259	9546485	303	9566382	156	9577044	106
9527051	190	9537630	259	9546497	303	9566394	156	9577056	274
9527063	190	9537745	82	9546904	241	9566564	214	9577068	275
9527180	164	9537757	82	9547506	217	9566605	154	9577070	275
9527192	164	9537769	82	9548823	45	9566617	153	9577082	275
9527295	38	9537771	82	9548835	45	9566629	210	9577094	275
9527855	65	9537898	259	9549281	170	9567025	80	9577109	275
9527910	36	9537903	259	9549463	24	9567063	56	9577111	275
9527996	165	9537915	203	9550163	271	9567403	160	9577123	275
9528017	165	9537927	65	9550266	271	9567415	160	9577410	129
9528031	67	9538658	138	9550682	135	9567427	160	9577422	129
9528043	65	9538880	292	9550694	135	9567439	160	9577886	214
9528196	79	9538892	142	9550709	256			9577898	214

9578634	285	9589839	205	9595321	21	9600932	121	9609457	253
9578646	285	9589932	204	9595436	116	9600944	121	9609653	84
9578995	201	9589944	204	9595448	116	9601132	12	9609665	83
9579030	280	9590072	205	9595450	116	9601314	206	9609732	276
9579042	280	9590084	205	9595462	116	9601902	45	9609744	277
9579391	165	9590307	311	9595474	116	9602174	164	9610157	80
9579573	95	9590319	108	9595486	116	9602186	164	9610169	80
9579864	94	9590589	148	9595498	116	9602473	70	9610389	135
9580015	164	9590591	148	9595503	116	9602679	219	9610391	185
9580376	64	9590618	239	9595515	116	9602710	224	9610406	185
9580405	204	9590620	239	9595527	116	9602722	224	9610418	185
9580417	204	9590632	241	9595632	135	9602875	226	9610420	185
9581203	70	9590644	241	9595632	224	9603219	226	9610432	184
9581239	36	9590709	36	9595644	43	9603221	226	9610444	185
9581241	36	9590747	122	9595888	119	9603233	226	9610456	119
9581681	36	9590759	122	9595890	119	9603594	157	9610468	119
9581693	203	9590826	84	9595905	119	9603609	157	9610638	165
9581708	37	9590979	271	9595917	119	9603611	157	9610767	70
9581758	84	9591052	271	9595967	231	9603790	132	9610779	70
9582506	243	9592214	282	9596026	231	9603805	132	9610781	274
9582518	245	9592563	303	9596038	231	9604081	116	9610781	276
9582958	243	9592575	303	9596040	231	9604093	116	9610793	274
9582960	245	9592599	303	9596052	231	9604108	116	9610793	276
9583005	203	9592680	224	9596301	306	9604110	116	9610808	276
9583134	297	9592692	224	9596573	96	9604122	116	9610810	277
9583691	282	9592848	98	9596947	106	9604134	116	9611278	45
9583706	282	9592850	98	9596985	96	9604146	116	9611280	45
9583720	70	9593191	38	9596997	286	9604158	116	9612143	98
9583732	70	9593218	36	9597006	106	9604160	116	9612246	113
9584059	185	9593220	37	9597018	105	9604172	116	9612284	214
9584499	65	9593402	113	9597185	61	9604938	156	9612296	214
9584504	65	9593414	288	9597197	61	9604938	156	9612313	214
9584712	15	9593426	96	9597202	36	9604940	211	9612325	214
9584724	15	9593438	96	9597214	36	9605023	165	9612765	209
9585285	21	9593452	126	9597226	36	9605073	75	9612777	140
9585338	219	9593464	126	9597238	36	9605102	75	9612789	139
9585572	291	9593743	96	9597240	183	9605152	257	9612791	209
9585651	89	9593854	132	9597252	183	9605231	257	9612870	140
9585663	89	9593866	132	9597264	52	9605243	257	9612882	140
9585895	280	9593878	132	9597276	52	9605255	88	9612997	139
9586722	145	9593880	132	9597472	207	9605267	87	9613006	139
9586734	145	9593892	132	9597484	207	9605279	87	9613018	139
9586801	84	9593907	132	9597496	206	9605700	36	9613020	140
9586813	84	9594224	245	9597501	207	9605786	305	9613135	187
9587166	230	9594224	245	9597513	207	9605798	305	9613147	187
9587192	300	9594236	243	9597525	206	9605853	113	9613159	185
9587207	197	9594248	243	9597537	206	9605865	113	9613161	187
9587245	65	9594250	245	9597549	206	9606053	119	9613587	235
9587257	64	9594470	55	9597551	206	9606302	311	9613599	235
9587269	64	9594482	173	9597563	207	9606314	311	9613836	253
9587453	129	9594494	173	9597812	68	9606326	108	9613848	253
9588079	156	9594509	173	9597977	79	9606338	311	9613850	253
9588081	156	9594597	284	9597989	79	9606479	185	9613862	253
9588093	156	9594731	96	9597991	79	9606754	37	9613874	253
9588146	106	9594755	96	9598012	184	9606766	37	9614036	15
9588148	311	9594767	96	9598127	205	9606821	119	9614141	15
9588299	70	9594779	286	9598256	183	9606833	119	9614696	291
9588392	82	9594781	286	9598268	183	9606912	16	9614842	142
9588419	79	9594793	285	9598335	79	9606924	16	9614858	142
9588445	219	9594822	183	9598995	214	9606948	70	9614880	205
9588469	219	9594834	183	9599004	214	9606950	70	9614892	80
9588536	279	9594846	183	9599016	214	9607083	154	9614969	205
9588603	113	9594858	183	9599755	165	9607095	154	9615042	310
9589085	239	9594872	310	9599779	98	9607174	58	9615119	75
9589097	239	9594884	308	9599810	270	9607186	58	9615171	79
9589140	113	9594896	108	9599810	271	9607198	58	9615183	79
9589152	113	9594901	310	9600102	282	9607203	58	9616230	30
9589621	100	9595008	162	9600425	230	9607447	113	9616838	132
9589633	101	9595010	162	9600528	124	9607459	113	9616840	132
9589683	69	9595149	90	9600530	124	9607954	239	9617519	169
9589748	145	9595151	90	9600619	68	9607966	239	9617521	169
9589750	145	9595216	105	9600865	67	9608697	45	9617648	224
9589815	135	9595228	105	9600877	67	9608702	45	9617650	224
9589827	205	9595254	214	9600889	67	9608867	135	9617959	134

9618006	169	9624263	271	9629550	291	9634086	124	9641833	271
9618018	169	9624275	136	9629562	291	9634098	124	9642019	129
9618264	108	9624287	136	9629574	290	9634165	155	9642083	118
9618276	311	9624299	136	9629691	216	9634701	65	9642095	118
9618288	311	9624328	45	9629706	217	9634713	65	9642370	230
9618290	174	9624469	134	9629718	221	9634969	129	9643623	291
9618305	87	9624914	122	9629902	184	9635315	122	9644483	119
9618317	87	9624926	122	9629914	184	9635377	153	9644495	119
9618587	138	9624938	122	9629926	261	9635389	153	9644524	253
9618599	138	9625235	231	9629938	263	9635456	61	9644990	308
9618783	98	9625384	226	9629940	262	9635468	61	9645736	187
9619385	101	9625396	226	9629952	261	9635640	150	9645748	187
9619402	101	9625528	63	9629964	262	9635652	150	9645762	261
9619426	308	9625530	63	9630004	276	9635664	285	9645774	261
9619438	308	9625542	63	9630028	274	9635676	285	9645786	261
9619440	308	9625554	63	9630030	159	9635688	150	9645798	263
9619452	258	9625932	178	9630365	265	9635755	164	9645853	73
9619464	258	9625944	209	9630377	265	9635767	164	9645865	73
9619476	258	9625956	277	9630389	265	9635779	164	9645877	73
9619555	181	9625968	277	9630391	265	9635781	164	9645889	73
9619907	189	9625970	174	9630406	265	9635808	59	9645891	73
9619919	189	9626027	122	9630418	265	9635810	59	9645906	73
9619921	189	9626039	122	9630420	265	9635822	58	9645918	73
9619933	189	9626041	80	9630729	285	9635846	59	9645920	73
9619945	188	9626053	80	9630755	273	9635858	58	9646699	50
9619957	189	9626118	45	9631101	308	9636450	75	9646704	50
9619969	189	9626120	45	9631113	108	9636462	75	9646716	50
9619971	189	9626247	231	9631125	308	9636632	196	9646728	50
9619983	189	9626259	231	9631137	310	9636644	196	9646730	50
9619995	189	9626261	231	9631876	233	9636711	65	9646895	169
9620295	212	9626273	124	9631955	207	9636723	65	9646900	169
9620607	300	9626285	124	9631967	207	9636735	65	9647289	219
9620619	300	9626522	42	9631979	207	9636747	65	9647291	219
9620683	306	9626534	42	9631981	206	9636785	288	9647461	311
9620944	42	9626558	308	9631993	207	9636797	288	9647473	108
9620956	42	9626560	308	9632002	207	9636888	12	9648295	36
9620968	42	9626651	108	9632014	206	9636955	10	9648893	230
9620970	42	9626663	108	9632026	207	9636967	12	9648908	230
9621077	210	9626675	310	9632038	207	9637155	63	9649031	98
9621596	67	9627485	39	9632040	207	9637222	148	9649043	98
9621601	67	9627497	39	9632064	189	9637234	148	9649225	159
9622007	103	9627502	39	9632090	189	9637246	148	9649536	40
9622019	102	9627792	235	9632105	189	9637258	148	9649548	40
9622203	226	9627899	309	9632117	189	9637260	148	9649835	308
9622215	225	9627904	309	9632129	189	9637325	122	9650042	39
9622227	225	9627916	106	9632131	189	9637686	286	9650054	39
9622239	225	9627928	309	9632143	189	9637698	286	9650418	30
9622241	225	9627954	307	9632155	189	9637703	285	9650573	263
9622253	226	9627966	307	9632167	189	9637715	286	9650585	155
9622588	235	9627978	235	9632179	189	9637777	70	9650743	271
9622590	235	9627980	235	9632208	206	9638044	230	9650767	271
9622605	235	9628001	235	9632210	206	9638056	230	9650937	98
9622617	235	9628154	88	9632480	136	9638135	91	9651101	148
9622628	235	9628166	88	9632492	136	9638147	90	9651113	148
9622631	235	9628178	88	9632507	136	9638159	90	9653408	162
9622916	222	9628180	88	9632765	136	9638430	306	9653410	162
9623532	308	9628192	88	9632789	221	9638525	118	9653422	162
9623568	308	9628300	159	9632818	255	9638551	204	9653434	162
9623635	159	9629031	116	9632820	291	9638563	204	9653446	162
9623647	284	9629043	116	9632832	290	9638903	124	9654464	295
9623661	232	9629055	116	9633147	271	9638915	124	9654555	120
9623673	232	9629067	116	9633161	39	9639517	230	9654567	120
9623685	106	9629079	116	9633173	39	9640023	288	9654579	121
9623740	214	9629081	116	9633185	306	9640097	311	9654581	121
9623752	214	9629093	116	9633226	270	9640102	108	9654696	122
9623843	103	9629108	116	9633422	39	9640114	311	9654701	122
9623855	174	9629110	116	9633434	39	9640126	310	9654775	121
9623867	296	9629122	116	9633446	106	9640437	60	9654787	121
9623879	296	9629380	106	9633458	106	9640465	61	9654878	275
9623881	285	9629445	309	9633501	62	9640645	60	9654880	275
9624029	221	9629457	309	9633939	111	9641223	285	9655042	122
9624067	232	9629469	311	9633941	111	9641235	285	9655212	50
9624079	232	9629495	221	9633953	111	9641675	24	9655509	275
9624237	185	9629548	291	9633965	111	9641730	29	9655511	275

9655808	122	9664897	271	9673642	231	9681687	286	9686388	282
9655913	261	9665592	111	9673654	231	9681833	249	9686637	120
9655975	196	9665607	111	9673666	231	9681845	91	9686699	263
9655987	196	9665619	111	9673850	120	9681857	91	9686704	261
9656022	162	9665621	111	9674165	148	9681871	283	9686716	261
9656034	162	9665633	111	9674177	148	9681883	283	9686728	262
9656046	162	9665645	111	9674189	148	9681895	283	9686730	262
9656058	162	9665657	257	9674517	76	9681900	283	9686742	263
9656084	168	9665669	257	9674529	76	9681950	230	9686754	263
9656096	168	9665671	257	9674531	76	9681962	230	9686766	261
9656101	24	9665683	257	9674543	77	9682239	59	9686857	261
9656137	295	9665736	70	9674555	78	9682241	59	9686869	261
9656498	252	9665748	70	9674567	78	9682552	269	9686871	262
9656503	252	9666077	281	9674713	91	9682576	39	9686883	261
9656747	273	9666089	94	9674725	91	9682588	39	9686900	285
9657038	204	9667150	111	9674787	165	9682590	39	9686912	285
9657052	204	9667162	111	9674799	164	9682605	39	9686974	262
9657844	283	9667174	111	9674842	282	9682760	98	9687019	124
9657856	283	9667186	111	9674854	282	9682772	98	9687021	124
9657868	283	9667344	271	9675391	40	9682875	24	9687083	153
9657870	283	9667447	75	9675406	40	9682887	271	9687095	153
9658238	39	9667461	281	9675494	58	9682930	311	9687162	153
9658240	39	9667473	281	9675509	59	9682942	205	9687174	154
9658379	261	9667485	281	9675573	156	9682954	270	9687186	214
9658446	167	9667497	281	9675585	271	9682967	53	9687227	219
9658458	167	9667540	282	9675638	108	9682980	53	9687239	219
9658898	120	9667564	282	9675652	270	9682992	53	9687306	94
9658903	120	9667576	219	9675937	56	9683001	52	9687485	118
9658953	253	9667588	219	9675949	56	9683013	52	9687497	118
9658965	214	9667722	164	9676101	165	9683025	53	9687502	118
9658977	120	9668063	119	9676125	183	9683037	53	9687514	118
9659103	118	9668908	165	9676137	183	9683049	53	9687526	140
9659115	118	9668910	164	9676577	261	9683051	53	9687538	140
9659127	118	9669029	306	9676591	230	9683063	53	9687547	140
9659139	118	9669031	306	9676606	230	9683075	53	9687552	140
9659725	296	9669653	91	9676618	230	9683087	53	9687564	140
9659919	205	9669665	91	9676709	257	9683099	53	9687576	140
9660011	271	9669873	224	9676711	257	9683245	124	9687588	140
9660061	61	9669884	224	9676723	257	9683257	124	9687837	154
9660085	75	9669897	224	9676735	257	9683269	124	9687849	154
9660097	83	9669902	224	9676840	211	9683271	124	9687851	154
9660152	291	9669938	261	9676852	211	9683843	221	9687942	281
9660358	167	9669940	262	9676864	209	9683867	221	9688336	43
9660360	167	9670016	156	9676876	211	9683984	281	9688348	43
9660516	43	9670224	98	9677026	150	9684102	135	9688350	263
9660528	43	9670573	133	9677076	16	9684469	230	9688362	261
9660530	43	9670585	133	9677375	259	9684471	230	9688377	261
9660542	43	9670597	133	9677387	260	9684641	267	9688386	261
9660554	43	9670602	133	9678329	205	9684653	267	9688415	281
9660592	89	9670614	133	9678408	29	9684665	265	9688427	281
9660607	89	9670822	100	9678795	230	9684677	267	9688635	290
9660657	129	9670834	248	9678800	230	9684689	265	9688647	290
9660798	246	9670937	217	9678812	230	9684976	146	9688829	261
9661235	281	9670949	217	9678824	230	9684988	146	9688831	262
9661247	281	9671058	120	9679555	150	9684990	146	9689134	91
9661259	279	9671060	120	9679567	150	9685190	43	9689146	91
9661558	201	9671072	120	9679593	183	9685205	43	9689172	311
9661807	201	9671084	120	9679892	249	9685322	265	9689184	108
9661869	269	9671096	119	9679907	249	9685334	265	9689536	282
9662409	183	9671101	119	9679919	249	9685346	265	9689548	282
9663116	75	9671216	202	9680073	282	9685358	265	9689562	219
9663128	75	9671228	202	9680085	282	9685396	159	9689574	221
9663269	271	9672088	132	9680097	282	9685425	114	9689603	156
9663295	306	9672090	132	9680114	282	9685437	114	9689615	156
9663300	306	9672105	132	9680712	132	9685449	116	9689627	157
9663740	90	9672404	246	9680724	132	9685451	114	9689639	157
9663776	90	9672416	246	9681106	263	9685463	281	9689641	157
9664720	281	9673018	49	9681118	262	9685475	281	9689914	104
9664770	121	9673020	50	9681120	262	9685487	290	9689926	104
9664782	121	9673173	291	9681132	261	9685621	297	9690078	113
9664794	121	9673197	291	9681144	263	9685633	297	9690080	113
9664809	121	9673379	146	9681390	263	9686314	290	9690092	267
9664873	205	9673381	146	9681405	43	9686326	290	9690107	267
9664885	311	9673630	231	9681431	306	9686376	282	9690523	246

9690535	246	9695640	90	9700316	230	9703796	19	9707742	90
9690547	246	9696242	91	9700342	62	9703837	104	9707807	262
9690559	246	9696553	261	9700469	62	9704130	24	9707833	164
9690614	200	9696565	261	9700471	62	9704453	261	9708033	243
9690626	200	9696589	262	9700483	62	9704465	262	9708045	245
9690793	262	9696682	262	9700512	305	9704477	263	9708057	245
9690808	263	9696694	261	9700524	305	9704491	202	9708069	245
9690810	261	9696709	263	9700550	211	9704506	201	9708071	58
9690822	263	9696711	261	9700691	95	9704518	201	9708083	59
9690834	262	9696761	170	9700706	95	9704520	202	9708148	263
9690846	261	9696773	170	9700794	98	9704532	202	9708150	262
9690884	283	9696826	102	9701140	310	9704609	267	9708435	267
9690896	283	9696838	102	9701164	271	9704611	265	9708447	267
9690901	283	9696905	228	9701190	79	9704623	265	9708459	267
9690913	283	9696917	228	9701205	98	9704635	267	9708461	267
9691034	169	9697002	231	9701217	39	9704647	265	9708473	267
9691046	169	9697014	231	9701229	39	9704829	259	9708552	263
9691632	50	9697416	222	9701255	98	9704843	260	9708564	261
9691723	261	9697428	222	9701267	98	9704960	178	9708576	200
9691735	263	9697430	204	9701279	168	9704972	176	9708588	200
9691929	230	9697442	204	9701281	168	9704984	179	9708617	197
9691931	230	9697595	262	9701293	167	9704996	177	9708629	197
9691943	230	9697600	261	9701322	122	9705005	176	9708679	179
9691955	230	9697636	261	9701334	122	9705055	76	9708681	180
9692129	217	9697648	261	9701346	122	9705067	78	9708693	176
9692131	217	9697753	24	9701360	167	9705079	78	9708746	89
9692143	217	9697806	118	9701372	167	9705081	78	9708784	298
9692155	217	9697818	118	9701786	59	9705134	83	9708796	298
9692246	299	9697820	118	9701798	59	9705134	84	9708801	298
9692349	269	9697832	119	9701920	277	9705146	260	9708813	298
9692351	269	9697844	119	9701932	277	9705158	260	9708825	297
9692557	13	9697856	119	9702003	104	9705160	260	9708837	298
9692569	10	9697909	217	9702015	104	9705172	260	9708849	298
9692662	122	9698185	44	9702027	104	9705287	259	9708851	298
9692674	122	9698197	44	9702039	104	9705299	259	9708863	298
9692686	228	9698252	251	9702041	104	9705304	260	9708875	298
9692698	228	9698264	250	9702065	178	9705316	260	9709075	82
9692777	98	9698628	226	9702077	179	9705328	260	9709087	82
9692789	98	9698630	226	9702089	180	9705330	260	9709192	76
9693018	281	9698642	226	9702091	180	9705342	260	9709207	77
9693020	281	9698654	226	9702106	175	9705641	288	9709219	77
9693206	70	9698941	290	9702132	76	9705653	288	9709489	39
9693290	101	9698953	291	9702144	76	9706061	59	9709491	39
9693329	101	9698965	311	9702156	76	9706073	59	9709506	56
9693331	102	9698977	311	9702261	180	9706190	88	9709518	56
9693745	63	9698989	311	9702273	175	9706205	89	9709520	56
9693812	48	9699036	85	9702405	148	9706279	241	9709532	56
9693824	49	9699115	94	9702417	148	9706281	241	9709776	133
9694402	257	9699127	94	9702429	148	9706308	62	9709788	135
9694414	257	9699165	91	9702431	148	9706310	63	9710139	154
9694426	257	9699177	90	9702443	305	9706425	262	9710141	154
9694438	257	9699189	226	9702455	305	9706437	263	9710177	73
9694464	59	9699191	226	9702479	122	9706463	261	9710189	74
9694476	58	9699206	226	9702596	230	9706475	262	9710220	285
9694529	251	9699270	122	9702601	230	9706487	104	9710232	285
9694531	251	9699282	122	9702613	230	9706499	104	9710244	284
9694543	251	9699294	124	9702625	230	9706504	104	9710426	175
9694555	250	9699311	85	9702637	230	9706516	104	9710438	176
9694567	250	9699323	85	9702687	36	9706736	271	9710464	279
9694579	191	9699335	85	9702699	37	9706748	271	9710476	279
9694581	191	9699347	85	9703007	60	9706750	271	9710488	63
9694593	250	9699359	85	9703019	60	9706839	261	9710490	63
9694921	282	9699361	85	9703057	104	9706841	261	9710567	260
9694933	282	9699373	85	9703069	104	9706889	78	9710579	260
9694945	283	9699505	273	9703071	104	9706891	76	9710581	260
9694995	165	9699517	273	9703150	21	9706906	78	9710593	260
9695004	164	9699634	230	9703198	206	9706918	146	9710737	146
9695016	150	9699957	292	9703203	206	9706994	148	9710749	146
9695028	150	9699969	291	9703239	37	9707003	148	9710787	214
9695121	73	9700122	167	9703241	37	9707015	148	9710799	214
9695133	73	9700134	168	9703291	179	9707027	148	9710892	230
9695145	73	9700196	167	9703306	179	9707261	262	9711133	114
9695157	73	9700287	98	9703318	180	9707273	262	9711145	157
9695169	73	9700299	98	9703514	239	9707584	239	9711456	68

9711468	291	9714721	260	9720201	176	9723526	124	9726607	135
9711494	110	9715191	283	9720287	179	9723538	124	9726619	134
9711509	110	9715206	283	9720457	180	9723540	124	9726621	135
9711511	110	9715218	283	9720471	181	9723629	260	9726669	222
9711523	110	9715220	283	9720483	181	9723631	259	9726671	222
9711535	110	9716004	58	9720495	181	9723643	260	9726695	156
9711547	200	9716016	59	9720500	181	9723655	260	9726700	157
9711559	199	9717101	200	9720512	181	9724049	63	9726774	98
9711561	200	9717113	200	9720524	181	9724075	296	9727003	127
9711573	200	9717125	200	9720952	231	9724087	296	9727015	128
9711705	173	9717137	200	9720964	231	9724087	296	9727027	128
9711717	173	9717204	225	9720976	231	9724180	205	9727039	128
9711937	214	9717216	225	9720988	231	9724192	84	9727065	214
9712151	260	9717228	226	9720990	231	9724336	296	9727118	219
9712292	294	9717266	91	9721009	231	9724348	296	9727120	219
9712307	294	9717656	230	9721011	37	9724350	296	9727326	75
9712319	294	9717668	230	9721023	37	9724532	53	9727352	80
9712321	294	9717670	230	9721035	37	9724544	53	9727364	108
9712486	260	9717773	261	9721047	231	9724556	53	9727405	98
9712498	260	9717785	261	9721059	231	9724568	53	9727493	245
9712553	224	9718064	197	9721061	231	9724570	53	9727508	245
9712565	224	9718076	197	9721073	231	9724582	53	9727510	245
9712577	224	9718088	197	9721085	231	9724594	53	9727522	245
9712589	224	9718090	197	9721097	231	9724609	53	9727534	199
9712632	156	9718105	222	9721487	122	9724611	63	9727546	199
9712644	156	9718117	222	9721499	122	9724623	63	9727558	200
9712840	200	9718351	230	9721554	283	9724635	65	9727560	200
9712852	261	9718363	230	9721566	283	9724647	65	9727572	199
9712864	200	9718375	230	9721578	283	9724659	65	9727584	199
9712876	200	9718387	230	9721580	283	9724661	65	9727596	230
9713040	230	9718442	50	9721724	159	9724673	53	9727601	230
9713052	230	9718454	50	9721736	159	9724685	53	9727613	89
9713064	231	9718698	239	9721932	126	9724697	53	9727625	89
9713076	231	9718935	221	9721982	124	9724702	53	9727871	265
9713167	56	9718947	222	9721994	124	9724714	53	9728069	156
9713179	56	9718959	222	9722015	126	9724726	53	9728071	157
9713181	56	9719238	225	9722170	200	9724738	132	9728083	157
9713193	56	9719240	225	9722182	200	9724958	232	9728095	157
9713208	56	9719252	225	9722302	305	9724960	232	9728136	83
9713210	58	9719264	225	9722314	305	9724972	232	9728174	214
9713222	58	9719276	118	9722338	230	9725110	310	9728253	189
9713337	265	9719288	118	9722364	36	9725122	310	9728485	98
9713349	265	9719290	118	9722376	36	9725134	310	9728497	98
9713351	265	9719305	118	9722388	36	9725146	311	9728629	260
9713363	265	9719434	199	9722417	122	9725158	311	9728693	128
9713375	265	9719446	199	9722429	122	9725160	311	9728708	128
9713428	75	9719458	199	9722584	263	9725299	307	9728710	128
9713480	75	9719460	199	9722596	263	9725304	307	9728722	128
9713492	206	9719496	60	9722651	76	9725421	30	9728851	50
9713820	164	9719501	60	9722663	76	9725433	30	9728863	50
9713844	59	9719537	259	9722675	77	9725433	30	9728916	88
9713856	59	9719549	260	9722687	77	9725445	120	9728928	88
9713882	108	9719551	260	9722699	77	9725457	214	9728930	88
9713894	209	9719563	260	9722704	78	9725469	214	9728942	88
9713911	214	9719692	200	9722716	76	9725512	102	9728954	88
9713959	164	9719707	200	9722792	104	9725524	102	9729166	37
9714056	199	9719715	260	9722807	104	9725574	153	9729178	36
9714068	199	9719719	200	9722924	82	9725586	153	9729180	309
9714228	283	9719721	200	9722936	82	9725603	133	9729192	309
9714238	283	9719745	199	9723045	114	9725615	134	9729271	134
9714240	230	9719757	200	9723057	114	9725627	134	9729283	135
9714252	283	9719769	199	9723069	127	9725639	134	9729477	126
9714264	283	9719771	200	9723071	127	9725706	222	9729489	126
9714381	104	9719903	124	9723083	127	9725718	222	9729738	159
9714393	104	9719915	124	9723095	127	9725744	230	9729740	159
9714501	199	9719927	124	9723100	127	9725823	309	9729764	159
9714513	199	9719939	124	9723112	296	9725847	311	9730139	295
9714630	110	9719941	124	9723203	169	9725859	109	9730361	96
9714642	110	9720043	152	9723215	169	9726451	197	9730373	96
9714654	110	9720055	153	9723289	182	9726463	197	9730816	54
9714678	260	9720067	153	9723291	182	9726475	294	9731042	273
9714692	260	9720079	153	9723306	200	9726487	294	9731171	15
9714707	260	9720081	282	9723502	124	9726580	121	9731377	74
9714719	260	9720196	177	9723514	124	9726592	121	9731389	74

9731573	230	9736107	298	9742417	292	9755191	181	9774185	291
9731585	230	9736119	239	9742429	292	9755217	59	9774525	59
9731597	231	9736121	239	9742742	110	9755737	98	9774537	59
9731602	230	9736133	239	9742754	110	9755933	263	9776171	236
9731614	230	9736157	239	9742895	109	9755945	263	9776183	236
9731640	305	9736169	239	9742900	109	9755957	263	9776195	236
9731652	305	9736341	205	9742912	109	9756743	206	9776200	236
9731705	226	9736418	164	9744001	24	9757838	80	9776212	236
9731808	165	9736420	164	9744374	56	9758557	279	9776224	236
9731822	154	9736808	246	9744386	56	9759795	291	9776418	79
9731834	154	9736925	98	9744398	56	9759800	291	9776420	79
9731846	154	9736949	98	9744659	231	9760213	200	9776432	79
9731913	73	9737046	98	9744661	231	9760225	200	9776731	67
9731925	73	9737187	276	9744673	231	9760495	109	9776743	67
9731937	73	9737371	297	9744685	231	9760500	109	9776755	67
9731949	73	9737383	297	9744752	164	9760512	22	9776767	67
9731951	73	9737395	297	9744893	225	9760524	22	9777589	140
9732151	119	9737400	297	9744908	225	9761449	63	9777606	140
9732163	119	9737462	271	9745366	22	9761889	219	9777618	140
9732307	297	9737474	271	9745378	22	9761944	296	9777620	140
9732319	297	9737486	271	9745598	122	9761956	297	9777632	140
9732321	298	9737498	271	9746243	164	9762326	181	9777931	67
9732333	298	9737503	271	9746255	203	9762338	181	9777943	67
9732345	298	9737515	225	9746267	164	9762340	181	9778791	189
9732357	298	9737527	225	9747948	203	9762534	272	9778806	190
9732369	39	9737565	79	9747950	205	9762546	272	9778818	190
9732371	39	9737589	239	9748071	270	9762558	272	9778820	190
9732589	174	9737591	239	9748095	80	9762845	297	9778832	190
9732591	189	9737606	239	9748100	80	9762857	297	9778844	190
9732606	174	9737618	239	9748409	61	9762871	129	9779587	167
9732682	135	9737747	200	9748423	259	9762883	129	9779800	43
9732694	135	9737759	200	9748679	219	9762895	129	9779812	43
9732709	135	9737840	108	9748681	219	9762912	129	9779824	43
9732929	197	9737888	219	9749568	148	9763033	291	9779836	43
9732931	197	9738208	131	9749570	148	9763045	291	9779848	43
9733105	16	9738210	131	9749582	148	9763693	231	9780283	190
9733117	16	9738727	271	9749594	148	9763710	80	9780445	190
9733258	169	9738753	97	9749685	59	9763722	82	9780457	190
9733260	169	9738777	209	9750323	245	9763904	260	9780469	190
9733272	169	9738789	75	9750335	245	9764491	225	9780471	190
9733284	169	9738818	205	9750347	245	9764506	225	9780653	82
9733806	62	9738820	271	9750359	245	9764958	15	9780665	82
9733818	63	9738832	108	9750402	230	9765017	291	9780847	78
9733820	241	9738868	56	9750414	230	9765029	291	9780859	78
9734109	307	9738870	270	9750828	233	9765158	297	9780861	79
9734111	307	9738882	270	9750919	56	9765706	54	9780873	79
9734288	53	9738947	83	9750921	58	9766190	59	9780885	79
9734642	127	9739240	36	9750933	58	9766205	59	9780897	79
9734654	127	9739501	128	9750945	58	9766229	59	9783722	291
9734678	104	9739513	128	9751509	19	9766841	279	9784350	29
9734680	104	9739666	265	9751511	19	9767091	10	9784734	291
9734692	104	9739678	267	9752084	276	9767376	263	9785275	272
9734989	277	9740366	231	9752096	276	9767388	263	9785287	272
9734991	277	9740457	189	9752101	276	9767390	263	9787340	291
9735000	277	9740770	59	9752993	38	9769271	184	9787352	291
9735012	277	9740782	59	9753002	38	9769283	184	9789958	271
9735452	90	9741372	210	9753014	38	9769295	184	9789960	271
9735464	90	9741384	211	9753026	38	9769300	184	9789972	271
9735476	90	9741396	211	9753193	29	9770921	288	9789984	271
9735488	90	9741401	211	9753208	29	9770933	288	9789996	271
9735579	200	9741413	211	9753674	200	9770945	288	9790971	291
9735581	200	9741425	211	9753686	200	9771080	288	9790983	291
9735593	200	9741437	211	9753698	200	9771652	169	9793545	29
9735608	200	9741449	211	9753703	200	9771664	169	9797508	124
9735610	200	9741700	231	9754903	201	9772113	167	9797510	124
9735622	200	9741712	231	9754915	201	9772125	167		
9735634	200	9742168	222	9754927	201	9773478	65		
9735646	200	9742170	222	9754939	201	9773521	65		
9735658	61	9742390	291	9754953	181	9773753	291		
9735660	61	9742405	292	9754965	181	9773765	291		

Ships by Name

Name	Pg	Name	Pg	Name	Pg	Name	Pg	Name	Pg
50 Let Pobedy	30	Aegean Wave	95	Ain Snan	297	Al-Abdali	298	Alpha Dignity	36
A. Idefix	61	Aegeas	295	Ainazi	164	Al-Farahidi	298	Alpha Effort	36
A. Obelix	61	Aeneas	312	Aison	63	Alameda	64	Alpha Era	36
A. P. Møller	187	Afales	181	Aisopos	174	Alamosborg	303	Alpha Faith	36
AAL Bangkok	255	Afif 298		Ajax	295	Alaska	295	Alpha Flame	36
AAL Brisbane	255	Afric Star	272	Akeraios	62	Alaskaborg	303	Alpha Freedom	36
AAL Dalian	255	Africaborg	303	Akinada Bridge	113	Alaskan Explorer	237	Alpha Happiness	36
AAL Dampier	255	African Avocet	270	Aktea	67	Alaskan Frontier	237	Alpha Harmony	36
AAL Fremantle	255	African Baza	97	Al Aamriya	185	Alaskan Legend	237	Alpha Honesty	36
AAL Hong Kong	255	African Blue Crane	97	Al Areesh	285	Alaskan Navigator	238	Alpha Hope	36
AAL Kembla	255	African Bulker	164	Al Bahia	297	Albanyborg	303	Alpha Liberty	36
AAL Kobe	255	African Dove	98	Al Bahiya	269	Albatros	24	Alpha Loyalty	36
AAL Melbourne	255	African Eagle	98	Al Daayen	285	Albatross	50	Alpha Melody	36
AAL Nanjing	255	African Falcon	98	Al Dafna	269	Albemarle Island	110	Alpha Millennium	36
AAL Newcastle	255	African Goshawk	98	Al Dahna	297	Albert Maersk	187	Alpha Optimism	36
AAL Pusan	255	African Griffon	98	Al Dasma	162	Aldebaran	312	Alpha Progress	36
AAL Shanghai	255	African Grouse	98	Al Deebel	185	Aleksandr Suvorov	169	Alpha Prudence	36
AAL Singapore	255	African Halcyon	98	Al Derwazah	162	Aleksey Kosygin	273	Alpha Vision	36
Aamira	269	African Harrier	98	Al Dhail	297	Alentejo	45	Alpine Amalia	128
Abadi	269	African Hawk	98	AL Encore	94	Alex	82	Alpine Aquilina	128
Abbey Road	308	African Hornbill	98	AL Endeavor	94	Alexander Maersk	187	Alpine Confidence	295
Aberdeen	70	African Ibis	98	AL Enterprise	94	Alexander Spirit	285	Alpine Eternity	295
Abigail N	61	African Jay	98	Al Funtas	162	Alexander the Great	62	Alpine Loyalty	295
Abqaiq	42	African Kite	98	Al Gattara	237	Alexandra		Alpine Madeleine	214
Abtenauer	50	African Lark	98	Al Ghariya	245	Rickmers	249	Alpine Magic	95
Abyssinian	50	African Loon	270	Al Gharrafa	237	Alexandria	241	Alpine Mathilde	214
Acadian	301	African Merlin	98	Al Ghashamiya	269	Alexandria Bridge	155	Alpine Mathilde	95
Acapulco	167	African Osprey	98	Al Ghuwairiya	269	Alexandrit	84	Alpine Maya	96
Acer Arrow	152	African Owl	98	Al Hamla	237	Alexandros II	62	Alpine Melina	96
Achat	84	African Pelican	98	Al Hilal	297	Alexandros P.	114	Alpine Mia	214
Achilleas	166	African Piper	98	Al Huwaila	285	Alexia	167	Alpine Minute	96
Achilleas	62	African Raptor	98	Al Jabriyah II	162	Alexia 2	67	Alpine Moment	96
Aconcagua Bay	267	African Raven	98	Al Jasrah	298	Alfa Baltica	170	Alpine Monique	273
Acrux N	203	African Robin	98	Al Jassasiya	39	Alfa Britannia	170	Alpine Mystery	96
Active	62	African Rook	98	Al Jmeliyah	298	Alfa Germania	170	Alpine Penelope	128
Adam Asnyk	73	African Sanderling	98	Al Karaana	269	Alfa Italia	170	Alpine Persephone	128
Adelheid-S	254	African Spirit	285	Al Kharaitiyat	269	Alfred Oldendorff	228	Alpine Venture	295
Adelina D.	99	African Swan	98	Al Kharsaah	285	Algarrobo	221	Alsace	82
Admiral	55	African Tern	98	Al Khattiya	269	Algol	312	Alsterstern	251
Admiral Bulker	164	African Wagtail	98	Al Khuwair	285	Aliakmon	166	Altair Leader	209
Adonia	15	African Weaver	98	Al Kout	162	Alianca Manaus	226	Altantic Hawk	166
Adria Ace	245	Afrodite	295	Al Mafyar	269	Alianca Santa Fé	137	Alterego II	62
Adrian Maersk	187	Agamemnon	62	Al Manamah	297	Alianca Santos	226	Althea	67
Adrian Schulte	256	Agathonissos	110	Al Marrouna	285	Alicante	65	Altonia	99
Adriana	34	Aggeliki P	113	Al Mashrab	297	Alice	82	Alula	298
Adriatic Highway	155	Agios Dimitrios	284	Al Mayeda	269	Alice Oldendorff	228	Alwine Oldendorff	228
Adriatic Wave	95	Agios Minas	150	Al Murabba	298	Alidra	99	Amadea	24
Adriaticborg	303	Agisilaos	62	Al Muraykh	298	Alioth	312	Amadeus	62
Advance II	295	Agistri	105	Al Nabila 5	67	Alkaios	63	Amadi	269
Advance Victoria	135	Aglaia	99	Al Nasriyah	298	Alkiviadis	62	Amalfi	65
Adventure		Agnes Rickmers	249	Al Nefud	298	Allegoria	99	Amali	269
of the Seas	24	Agon	63	Al Nuaman	269	Alliance Fairfax	193	Amalia C	92
Adygeya	276	Agrari	65	Al Qibla	298	Alliance Norfolk	193	Amalienborg	93
Aegea	67	Agulhas Stream	268	Al Rain	298	Alliance Richmond	193	Amalthea	181
Aegean Angel	40	AHS St. Georg	248	Al Rawdah	298	Alliance St. Louis	193	Amalthea	99
Aegean Blue	40	Aias	62	Al Rekayyat	269	Allise P	241	Amanda D	99
Aegean Breeze	303	Aida	305	Al Riffa	298	Allure of the Seas	24	Amani	269
Aegean Dignity	40	AIDAaura	10	Al Riqqa	162	ALM Crystal	256	Amazon	105
Aegean Express	301	AIDAbella	10	Al Ruwais	245	ALM Dallas	256	Amazon Beauty	166
Aegean Faith	40	AIDAblu	10	Al Sadd	269	ALM Vietnam	256	Amazon Brilliance	167
Aegean Freedom	40	AIDAcara	10	Al Safat	298	ALM Wodonga	256	Amazon Explorer	167
Aegean Harmony	40	AIDAdiva	10	Al Safliya	245	ALM Zurich	256	Amazon Gladiator	167
Aegean Highway	155	AIDAluna	10	Al Salam II	162	Almandin	84	Amazon Guardian	167
Aegean Horizon	40	AIDAmar	10	Al Salheia	162	Almeda Star	272	Amazon Victory	167
Aegean Leader	209	AIDAperla	12	Al Salmi	162	Alona	64	Amazon Virtue	167
Aegean Legend	40	AIDAprima	10	Al Samriya	269	Alonissos	110	Amazoneborg	303
Aegean Myth	40	AIDAsol	12	Al Shamal	285	Alpha Afovos	36	Amazonit	85
Aegean Navigator	40	AIDAstella	12	Al Sheehaniya	269	Alpha Bravery	36	Ambassador Bridge	155
Aegean Nobility	40	AIDAvita	12	Al Shegaya	162	Alpha Bulker	164	Amber Arrow	245
Aegean Odyssey	33	Aifanourios	68	Al Soor II	162	Alpha Century	36	Amber Lagoon	170
Aegean Power	40	Aigeorgis	68	Al Yarmouk	162	Alpha Confidence	36	Amber Sun	308
Aegean Pride	40	Aikaterini	256	Al Zubara	298	Alpha Cosmos	36	Amelie	219

Americaborg	303	Anatoly Kolodkin	276	Anvil Point	120	Apollonas	62	Artemis Leader	209
American Bulker	164	Ance	164	Apatura	55	Apolytares	181	Artenos	152
American Highway	155	Andalucia	219	Aphrodite Leader	209	Apostolos	62	Arthur Maersk	187
Americas Spirit	285	Andalucia Star	272	APL Agate	206	Apostolos II	62	Artois	82
Américo Vespúcio	226	Andama	64	APL Antwerp	206	Appaloosa	50	Arubaborg	303
Amethyst	85	Andaman Sea	106	APL Austria	270	Apulia	102	Arundel Castle	199
Amethyst Ace	184	Anderson Bridge	270	APL Barcelona	206	Aquamarin	85	Arwa Spirit	288
Ametrin	85	Andes	221	APL Belgium	206	Aquamarine Ace	184	AS Amalia	197
Amfitrion	63	Andes	133	APL Boston	206	Aquarius Ace	184	AS Aries	40
Amine Bulker	164	Andes	295	APL Cairo	206	Aquarius Leader	209	AS Carelia	197
Amira	67	Andesborg	303	APL Changi	206	Aquarius Voyager	70	AS Carinthia	198
Amoenitas	142	Andino	221	APL Charleston	206	Aquitania	54	AS Castor	40
Amor	62	Andreas	256	APL China	206	Aquitania	45	AS Cypria	198
Amore Mio II	62	Andromeda	181	APL Chongxing	206	Arabella	167	AS Elbia	198
Amorea	68	Andromeda	295	APL Columbus	206	Arabian Breeze	303	AS Elenia	198
Amorgos	50	Andromeda Leader	209	APL Coral	206	Arabian Express	301	AS Fabiana	198
Amoureux	62	Andromeda Spirit	212	APL Cyprine	206	Arabiyah	162	AS Fatima	198
Amphitrite	181	Andromeda Voyager	70	APL Dalian	206	Aracari Arrow	152	AS Federica	198
Amphitrite	295	Andronikos	174	APL Denver	138	Aracena Carrier	267	AS Felicia	198
Amstelborg	303	Anemos I	62	APL Detroit	206	Aragonborg	303	AS Fiorella	198
Amsterdam	13	Angeles	221	APL Dublin	206	Aragonit	85	AS Magnolia	198
Amundsen Spirit	285	Angelica Schulte	256	APL Egypt	212	Aral Sea	106	AS Mariana	198
Amurborg	303	Angistri	110	APL England	206	Arcadia	15	AS Mariella	198
Anafi	110	Angol	221	APL Florida	206	Arcadia Highway	155	AS Mars	40
Anangel Argonaut	36	Angra Dos Reis	300	APL Germany	270	Archangel	295	AS Morgana	198
Anangel Aspiration	36	Aniara	303	APL Gwangyang	206	Archimidis	62	AS Olivia	198
Anangel Astronomer	36	Anichkov Bridge	274	APL Holland	206	Archon	63	AS Omaria	198
Anangel Conqueror	36	Anika Oltmann	233	APL Hong Kong	270	Arctic	118	AS Ophelia	198
Anangel Courage	36	Anikitos	63	APL Houston	206	Arctic	295	AS Orelia	198
Anangel Dawn	36	Anja Kirk	133	APL Iolite	206	Arctic Bay	214	AS Palatia	198
Anangel Destiny	36	Anke	99	APL Iris	206	Arctic Blizzard	214	AS Patria	198
Anangel Dynasty	36	ANL Barega	231	APL Japan	206	Arctic Breeze	214	AS Ragna	198
Anangel Elegance	36	ANL Barwon	221	APL Jeddah	206	Arctic Bridge	214	AS Riccarda	198
Anangel Eternity	36	ANL Bindaree	137	APL Korea	206	Arctic Lady	148	AS Romina	198
Anangel Explorer	36	ANL Echuca	165	APL Latvia	270	Arctic Princess	148	AS Rosalia	198
Anangel Fortune	36	ANL Elanora	165	APL Le Havre	206	Arctic Spirit	285	AS Savonia	198
Anangel Future	36	ANL Elinga	203	APL Merlion	206	Arcturus Voyager	70	AS Valdivia	198
Anangel Glory	36	ANL Wangaratta	75	APL Mexico City	206	Ardennes	50	AS Valentia	198
Anangel Grace	36	ANL Waratah	227	APL Miami	206	Ardennes Venture	82	AS Varesia	198
Anangel Guardian	36	ANL Warringa	249	APL Minnesota	270	Areopolis	87	AS Vega	198
Anangel Haili	36	ANL Woolamai	308	APL New Jersey	270	Aretea	68	AS Venus	40
Anangel Happiness	36	ANL Wyong	75	APL New York	207	Argos	284	AS Victoria	198
Anangel Harmony	36	Anna Maersk	187	APL Ningbo	207	Ariadne	295	AS Vincentia	198
Anangel Hero	36	Anna Oldendorff	228	APL Norway	270	Arian	254	AS Virginia	198
Anangel Hope	36	Anna-S	254	APL Oakland	138	Ariana	100	Asahi Bulker	164
Anangel Horizon	37	Annaba	99	APL Oregon	207	Arica	221	Asahi Princess	295
Anangel Innovation	37	Anne Mette Bulker	164	APL Pearl	207	Arica	221	Ashkini Spirit	285
Anangel Mariner	37	Anneleen Knutsen	159	APL Philippines	207	Arica Bridge	155	Ashna	241
Anangel Merchant	37	Annette-S	254	APL Phoenix	207	Arica Express	209	Asia Endeavour	70
Anangel Nobility	37	Anni Selmer	306	APL Pusan	207	Aries Leader	209	Asia Energy	70
Anangel Ocean	37	Antarctic	295	APL Qingdao	207	Aries Sun	309	Asia Excellence	70
Anangel Odyssey	37	Antares Leader	209	APL Raffles	207	Aries Voyager	70	Asia Vision	70
Anangel Progress	37	Antares Voyager	70	APL Salalah	207	Arion	295	Asian Breeze	303
Anangel Prosperity	37	Anthea	284	APL Santiago	207	Arionas	62	Asian Bulker	165
Anangel Sailor	37	Anthea Y	284	APL Savannah	207	Aris	295	Asian Captain	305
Anangel Seafarer	37	Anthem of the Seas	24	APL Scotland	207	Aristaios	63	Asian Dynasty	305
Anangel Shagang	37	Antigone	82	APL Sentosa	207	Aristidis	62	Asian Emperor	221
Anangel Sky	37	Antikeros	110	APL Singapore	207	Aristoklis	63	Asian Empire	305
Anangel Spirit	37	Antimilos	110	APL Southampton	207	Aristomenis II	63	Asian Glory	309
Anangel Sun	37	Antiparos	110	APL Spain	207	Aristos II	62	Asian King	221
Anangel Transporter	37	Antofagasta	221	APL Temasek	207	Aristotelis	62	Asian Majesty	305
Anangel Trust	37	Antofagasta Express	139	APL Thailand	207	Arkadia	87	Asian Parade	305
Anangel Unity	37	Anton Schulte	256	APL Tourmaline	207	Arkat	269	Asian Spirit	285
Anangel Venture	37	Antonia	50	APL Turkey	270	Arklow Spirit	40	Asian Trust	306
Anangel Victory	37	Antonie Oldendorff	228	APL Turquoise	207	Arklow Spray	40	Asian Vision	306
Anangel Vigour	37	Antonis Angelicoussis	36	APL Vancouver	207	Armia Krajowa	243	Asiatic	165
Anangel Virtue	37	Antonis I. Angelicoussis	37	APL Vanda	207	Arneborg *	303	Asir	298
Anangel Vision	37	Antwerp	190	APL Yangshan	207	Arnold Maersk	187	Asklipios II	63
Anangel Voyager	37	Antwerp Trader	167	Apollo	105	Arosia	100	Aspasia Luck	113
Anangel Wisdom	37	Antwerpen	118	Apollo	55	Arsan	42	Aspen Spirit	285
Anangel Zenith	37	Antwerpen Express	139	Apollo Bulker	164	Arsos	173	Aspropyrgos	280
Anangel Zhongte	37			Apollon	295	Artania	24	Asteria Leader	209
Anastasia	174			Apollon D	100	Artemis	100	Astipalea	110
Anastasia K	68			Apollon Leader	209	Artemis	295	Astor	16

344

Name	Page
CMB Charlotte	79
CMB Chikako	79
CMB Coralie	79
CMB Edouard	79
CMB Giulia	79
CMB Julliette	79
CMB Kristine	79
CMB Liliane	79
CMB Maé	79
CMB Medoc	79
CMB Mistral	79
CMB Pauillac	79
CMB Paule	79
CMB Pomerol	79
CMB Sakura	79
CMB Virginie	79
CMB Weihei	79
CMB Yasmine	79
Cobra	104
Cochrane	140
Cohiba	64
Cold Stream	267
Colette	100
Colombian Star	272
Colombo Express	139
Colorado	96
Colorado Highway	156
Colossus	111
Columbia	173
Columbia Highway	271
Columbine Maersk	187
Combi Dock I	142
Combi Dock III	142
Comet	104
Comet Ace	184
Commander	104
Commander	105
Commodore	104
Comoros Stream	268
Compass	59
Compassion	59
Concept	127
Concord	127
Concorde	104
Condor Arrow	153
Confidence	105
Confignon	98
Connecticut Trader	169
Conquistador	65
Constantin S	254
Constantinos	105
Constellation	104
Constitution	104
Constitution Spirit	285
Contest	282
Conti Agulhas	85
Conti Annapurna	85
Conti Arabella	85
Conti Basel	85
Conti Benguela	85
Conti Canberra	85
Conti Darwin	85
Conti Elektra	85
Conti Emden	174
Conti Equator	85
Conti Everest	85
Conti Flint	85
Conti Fuchsit	85
Conti Gothenburg	86
Conti Greenland	86
Conti Guinea	86
Conti Helsinki	86
Conti Humboldt	86
Conti Jade	85
Conti Japsis	85
Conti Lapislazuli	85
Conti Larimar	85
Conti Lyon	86
Conti Madrid	86
Conti Melbourne	86
Conti Paris	86
Conti Peridot	85
Conti Salome	86
Conti Saphir	85
Conti Selenit	85
Conti Spinell	85
Conti Stockholm	86
Continental	104
Continental Highway	156
Cool Explorer	288
Cool Expreso	267
Cool Runner	288
Cool Voyager	288
Copernicus	104
Copernicus N	203
Copiapo	140
Copper Spirit	286
Coral Leader	245
Coral Leader	209
Coral Mermaid	268
Coral Princess	15
Coral Sea	106
Coral Seas	239
Corcovado	140
Corcovado LNG	65
Cordelia	199
Cordula Jacob	152
Corella Arrow	153
Corinthiakos	97
Cornavin	98
Cornelia Maersk	187
Cornelius Maersk	187
Corona J	155
Coronado	65
Corossol	65
Corrientes	221
Corsair	104
Corvette	104
Corviglia	282
Cosco Achievement	71
Cosco Africa	70
Cosco America	70
Cosco Asia	71
Cosco Beijing	87
Cosco Belgium	71
Cosco Creation	71
Cosco Denmark	71
Cosco Development	264
Cosco Endeavour	71
Cosco England	71
Cosco Europe	71
Cosco Excellence	264
Cosco Explorer	71
Cosco Faith	264
Cosco Fortune	264
Cosco France	71
Cosco Fuzhou	264
Cosco Germany	46
Cosco Glory	264
Cosco Grand	71
Cosco Guangzhou	87
Cosco Happiness	71
Cosco Harmony	264
Cosco Hellas	87
Cosco Hope	264
Cosco Indonesia	264
Cosco Italy	71
Cosco Japan	264
Cosco Kaohsiung	71
Cosco Korea	264
Cosco Legend	71
Cosco Luck	71
Cosco Magnificence	71
Cosco Malaysia	264
Cosco Napoli	46
Cosco Netherlands	71
Cosco Ningbo	87
Cosco Oceania	71
Cosco Pacific	71
Cosco Philippines	264
Cosco Portugal	71
Cosco Pride	264
Cosco Prince Rupert	264
Cosco Shengshi	73
Cosco Spain	71
Cosco Taicang	71
Cosco Tengfei	73
Cosco Thailand	264
Cosco Valiance	71
Cosco Vietnam	264
Cosco Wisdom	71
Cosco Yantian	87
Cosco Yingkou	264
Cosmic	165
Cosmos Ace	184
Costa Atlantica	12
Costa Deliziosa	12
Costa Diadema	12
Costa Fascinosa	12
Costa Favolosa	12
Costa Fortuna	12
Costa Luminosa	12
Costa Magica	12
Costa Mediterranea	12
Costa neoClassica	12
Costa neoRiviera	12
Costa neoRomantica	12
Costa Pacifica	12
Costa Rican Star	272
Costa Serena	12
Costa Victoria	12
Cote d'Ivoirian Star	272
Cotinga Arrow	153
Cotswold	309
Cougar	104
Cougar Ace	184
Courageous Ace	184
Courcheville	118
Coyhaique	140
CPO America	228
CPO Asia	228
CPO Australia	228
CPO China	228
CPO England	228
CPO Europe	228
CPO Finland	228
CPO France	228
CPO Germany	228
CPO India	228
CPO Italy	228
CPO Japan	228
CPO Korea	228
CPO Malaysia	228
CPO Miami	227
CPO New York	227
CPO New Zealand	228
CPO Norfolk	227
CPO Norway	228
CPO Oceana	228
CPO Russia	228
CPO Singapore	228
CPO Sweden	228
Cragside	193
Cratis	104
Crawford	167
Creole Spirit	286
Crescent Moon	309
Cresques	104
Cristina Star	129
Cronus Leader	209
Crown Emma	145
Crown Garnet	237
Crown Jade	237
Crown Opal	237
Crown Princess	15
Crown Princess	63
Crown Ruby	237
Crown Sapphire	237
Crown Topaz	237
Crystal Ace	184
Crystal Esprit	16
Crystal Exclusive	16
Crystal Ray	246
Crystal Reefer	44
Crystal Serenity	16
Crystal Symphony	16
Crystalgate	106
CS Calla	61
CS Calvina	61
CS Candy	61
CS Caprice	61
CS Caroline	61
CS Chara	61
CS Crystal	61
CS Discovery	100
CS Jaden	61
CS Jenna	61
CS Salina	61
CS Sarafina	61
CS Satira	61
CS Sonoma	61
CS Soraya	61
CS Vanguard	61
CSAV Lumaco	264
CSAV Rio Aysen	106
CSAV Rio Grande	309
CSAV Rio Grey	106
CSAV Rio Nevado	309
CSAV Toconao	309
CSAV Traiguen	309
CSAV Trancura	106
CSAV Tyndall	309
CSCC Asia	245
CSCC Europe	245
CSCC Shanghai	245
CSCC Tianjin	246
CSCL Africa	264
CSCL America	92
CSCL Arctic Ocean	73
CSCL Asia	73
CSCL Atlantic Ocean	73
CSCL Autumn	73
CSCL Bohai Sea	73
CSCL Brisbane	264
CSCL Callao	264
CSCL East China Sea	73
CSCL Europe	92
CSCL Globe	73
CSCL Indian Ocean	73
CSCL Jupiter	73
CSCL Le Havre	92
CSCL Lima	264
CSCL Long Beach	264
CSCL Manzanillo	264
CSCL Mars	73
CSCL Melbourne	264
CSCL Mercury	73
CSCL Montevideo	264
CSCL Neptune	73
CSCL New York	264
CSCL Oceania	265
CSCL Pacific Ocean	73
CSCL Panama	264
CSCL Pusan	92
CSCL San Jose	264
CSCL San Jose	264
CSCL Santiago	264
CSCL Sao Paulo	264
CSCL Saturn	73
CSCL South China Sea	73
CSCL Spring	73
CSCL Star	73
CSCL Summer	73
CSCL Sydney	264
CSCL Uranus	73
CSCL Vancouver	264
CSCL Venus	73
CSCL Winter	73
CSCL Yellow Sea	73
CSCL Zeebrugge	264
Cubal	209
Cuckoo Hunter	80
Cumbria	108
Cygnus Leader	271
Cygnus Voyager	70
Cymbeline	306
Cypress Arrow	153
D. Skalkeas	129
Da Fu	279
Da Hua	279
Da Qiang	279
Da Zhong	279
DACC Egeo	90
DACC Tirreno	91
Daedalus Leader	209
Dahlia	173
Daio Southern Cross	210
Daiwan Fortune	164
DAL Karoo	150
Dalarna	45
Dali	222
Dalian	105
Dalian Express	139
Dalian Highway	156
Dallas Express	139
Dalmatia	45
Damgracht	277
Dan Cisne	159
Dan Eagle	159
Dan Sabia	159
Danae C.	92
Daniel N	61
Danship Bulker	45
Danube Highway	246
Danubia	199
Danzigergracht	277
Daphne	100
Dar Salwa	162
Daria	243
Darleakay	284
David Schulte	259
Davis Sea	108
Dawn Princess	15
Daytona	65

Name	Page
Decathlon	296
Deep Blue	94
Deira	298
Delaware Trader	169
Delhi Highway	156
Delmas Keta	79
Delmas Swala	78
Delphi	296
Delphi Ranger	111
Delphin	34
Delphinus Leader	209
Delphis Bothnia	80
Delphis Finland	82
Delphis Gdansk	82
Delphis Riga	82
Delta Captain	94
Delta Commander	95
Delta Harmony	95
Delta Hellas	95
Delta Ios	95
Delta Kanaris	95
Delta Maria	95
Delta Mariner	95
Delta Millennium	95
Delta Ocean	95
Delta Pioneer	95
Delta Poseidon	95
Delta Sailor	95
Delta Sky	95
Delta Star	95
Delta Tolmi	95
Delta Victory	95
Deltagracht	277
Delya Eurydice	95
Demeter	100
Demeter Leader	209
Demetrios	105
Deneb Leader	209
Derby D.	92
Desimi	65
Deutschland	33
Deva	92
Devon	82
Devongate	108
Dhonoussa	110
Diamantgracht	277
Diamantis P.	114
Diamond	230
Diamond Highway	156
Diamond Jubilee	54
Diamond Land	45
Diamond Princess	15
Diamondway	109
Diana	243
Diana Bolten	50
Diane	68
Diaporos	150
Diavolezza	282
Didimon	296
Dignity Ace	246
Dijksgracht	277
Dilam	42
Dilong Spirit	286
Dilos	110
Dimitris C	92
Dimitris P.	296
Dimitris Y	284
Dione Leader	209
Dionysus Leader	209
Discovery Bay	267
Disney Dream	16
Disney Fantasy	16
Disney Magic	16
Disney Wonder	16
Ditlev Reefer	68
Divine Ace	184
Divine Seas	239
Divinus	111
Dockwise Vanguard	98
Dockwise White Marlin	98
Dole Africa	104
Dole America	104
Dole Asia	104
Dole Atlantic	104
Dole California	104
Dole Caribbean	104
Dole Chile	104
Dole Colombia	104
Dole Costa Rica	104
Dole Ecuador	104
Dole Europa	104
Dole Honduras	104
Dole Pacific	104
Dolfijngracht	277
Dolphin II	284
Dolviken	300
Don Carlos	303
Don Juan	303
Don Pasquale	303
Don Quijote	303
Dona Bibi	68
Dona Tara	68
Donaugracht	277
Donegal Spirit	286
Dong-A Glaucos	148
Dong-A Metis	148
Dora Oldendorff	230
Dora Schulte	259
Dorado Leader	209
Doric	165
Dorothea Oldendorff	230
Dorra	42
Dorset	309
Dover Highway	156
Dover Strait	248
Dragongate	109
Drawsko	243
Dream Angel	74
Dream Beauty	74
Dream Canary	203
Dream Coral	203
Dream Diamond	74
Dream Diva	74
Dream Jasmine	74
Dream Orchid	74
Dream Seas	239
Dresden	272
Drive Green Highway	156
DS Charme	241
DS Chief	243
DS Commander	243
DS Crown	243
DS Dominion	243
DS National	243
DS Patriot	243
DS Progress	243
DS Promoter	243
DS Republic	243
DS Vada	243
DS Valentina	243
DS Vector	243
DS Venture	243
DS Vision	243
DS Warrior	243
Dubai Express	265
Dublin Express	139
Duck Hunter	80
Duhail	245
Dukhan	216
Dukhan	185
Duncan Island	110
Dunedin Star	272
Durande	173
Durban Highway	156
Durban Star	272
Düsseldorf Express	139
Dynamic Striker	111
Dynamogracht	277
E. Oldendorff	230
E.R. Amsterdam	46
E.R. Barcelona	46
E.R. Basel	46
E.R. Bavaria	46
E.R. Bayern	46
E.R. Bayonne	46
E.R. Bergamo	47
E.R. Berlin	47
E.R. Bilbao	47
E.R. Bordeaux	47
E.R. Borneo	47
E.R. Bornholm	47
E.R. Boston	47
E.R. Bourgogne	47
E.R. Brandenburg	47
E.R. Brighton	47
E.R. Bristol	47
E.R. Buenos Aires	47
E.R. Caen	47
E.R. Calais	47
E.R. Canada	47
E.R. Cape Town	47
E.R. Cuxhaven	47
E.R. Denmark	47
E.R. Elsfleth	47
E.R. Felixstowe	47
E.R. France	47
E.R. Hamburg	47
E.R. Helgoland	47
E.R. India	47
E.R. Kobe	47
E.R. London	47
E.R. Los Angeles	47
E.R. Martinique	47
E.R. Pusan	47
E.R. Riga	47
E.R. Santiago	47
E.R. Seoul	47
E.R. Sweden	47
E.R. Tallinn	47
E.R. Tianan	47
E.R. Turku	47
E.R. Visby	47
E.R. Yokohama	47
Eagle	50
Eagle Anaheim	183
Eagle Arrow	153
Eagle Atlanta	183
Eagle Augusta	183
Eagle Austin	183
Eagle Baltimore	183
Eagle Barents	183
Eagle Bay	118
Eagle Beaumont	183
Eagle Bergen	183
Eagle Birmingham	183
Eagle Boston	183
Eagle Columbus	183
Eagle Kangar	183
Eagle Kinabalu	183
Eagle Kinarut	183
Eagle Klang	183
Eagle Kuantan	183
Eagle Kuching	183
Eagle Louisiana	183
Eagle Paraiba	183
Eagle Parana	183
Eagle Phoenix	183
Eagle San Antonio	183
Eagle San Diego	183
Eagle San Juan	183
Eagle San Pedro	183
Eagle Seville	183
Eagle Stavanger	183
Eagle Stealth	183
Eagle Strait	248
Eagle Sydney	183
Eagle Tacoma	183
Eagle Tampa	183
Eagle Texas	183
Eagle Toledo	183
Eagle Torrance	183
Eagle Trenton	183
Eagle Tucson	183
Eagle Turin	183
Eagle Vancouver	183
Eagle Varna	183
Eagle Vermont	183
Eagle Virginia	184
East Coast	301
Easter Island	100
Eastern Bay	268
Eastern Highway	156
Eastgate	309
Ebba Maersk	187
Ebony Ray	108
Eckert Oldendorff	230
Ecola	65
Eddystone	120
Edgar	100
Edith Kirk	133
Edith Maersk	187
Edward N	61
Edward Oldendorff	230
Edwine Oldendorff	230
Edzard Schulte	257
Eibe Oldendorff	230
Eilbek	135
Eirini P.	114
Eishun	49
EIT Palmina	142
EIT Paloma	142
El Junior PNT	296
El Pipila	63
Elafonisos	87
Elandra Oak	164
Elandra Palm	164
Elandra Spruce	164
Elba Island	259
Elbe	231
Elbe Highway	246
Elbrus	276
Elegant Ace	184
Elektra	303
Eleni	105
Eleni D.	129
Eleni I	284
Eleni P.	114
Eleonora Maersk	187
Eli Knutsen	159
Elias Tsakos	296
Elisa Delmas	79
Elisabeth Knutsen	159
Elisabeth Oldendorff	230
Elisabeth Schulte	257
Elisabeth-S	254
Elisalex Schulte	257
Eliza	105
Elizabeth I. A.	37
Elka Angelique	269
Elka Eleftheria	269
Elka Nikolas	269
Ellenita	297
Ellensborg	94
Ellina	288
Ellinis	68
Elly Maersk	187
Elsa Oldendorff	230
Elsborg	94
Elsebeth	268
Elversele	118
Elvia	94
Elvira	268
Elvira Bulker	164
EM Andros	114
EM Astoria	114
EM Athens	114
EM Chios	114
EM Corfu	114
EM Hydra	114
EM Ithaki	114
EM Kea	114
EM Spetses	114
Emden	156
Emerald	268
Emerald Ace	185
Emerald Leader	246
Emerald Leader	209
Emerald Princess	15
Emerald Spirit	286
Emerald Stars	279
Emerald Strait	248
Emerald Summit	108
Emilie Bulker	164
Eminent Ace	185
Emirates Dana	100
Emirates Sana	100
Emirates Wafa	101
Emma Bulker	164
Emma Maersk	187
Emma Oldendorff	230
Emma Schulte	259
Emma Victory	67
Emmy Schulte	257
Empress	27
Ems	231
Ems Trader	55
Emu Arrow	153
Enchantment of the Seas	24
Endeavour	295
Endeavour Strait	248
Endurance	305
Energy Centaur	111
Energy Centurion	111
Energy Century	111
Energy Challenger	111
Energy Champion	111
Energy Chancellor	111
Energy Commander	111
Energy Conqueror	111
Energy Enterprise	151
Energy Panther	111
Energy Patriot	111
Energy Pioneer	111
Energy Power	111
Energy Pride	111
Energy Progress	111

Future	36	Genco Commodus	125	GenMar Zeus	127	Glovis Passion	246	Golden Taurus	124
Fuwairit	185	Genco Constantine	125	Genoa	92	Glovis Phoenix	148	Golden Virgo	124
Gaea	282	Genco Explorer	125	Genting Dream	16	Glovis Prestige	246	Golden Zhejiang	124
Gaia Leader	210	Genco Hadrian	125	Gentle Leader	246	Glovis Prime	148	Golden Zhoushan	124
Galani	288	Genco Hunter	125	Gentle Seas	239	Glovis Sirius	148	Goldengate Park	310
Galaxy Ace	185	Genco Knight	125	Genuine Ace	185	Glovis Solomon	148	Goldway	109
Galaxy Leader	246	Genco Languedoc	125	Georg Jacob	152	Glovis Spirit	148	Goliath Leader	246
Galaxy River	156	Genco Leader	125	Georg Maersk	187	Glovis Splendor	148	Good Hope Max	113
Galea	269	Genco Loire	125	Georg Oldendorff	230	Glovis Star	246	Goodwood	310
Galicia Spirit	286	Genco London	125	George N.	61	Glovis Stella	148	Goonyella Trader	286
Gallina	269	Genco Lorraine	125	George Washington		Glovis Summit	148	Gotland Aliya	133
Galveston Highway	156	Genco Mare	125	Bridge	156	Glovis Sun	148	Gotland Carolina	133
Galway Spirit	286	Genco Marine	125	Georgia Highway	156	Glovis Sunrise	148	Gotland Marieann	133
Gandhi	70	Genco Maximus	125	Georgia Trader	167	Glovis Superior	148	Gotland Sofia	133
Gandria	122	Genco Muse	125	Georgios	106	Glovis Supreme	148	Gottfried Schulte	257
Ganges Spirit	286	Genco Normandy	126	Georgy Maslov	274	Glovis Symphony	148	Governor	
Garibaldi Spirit	286	Genco Ocean	126	Georgy Maslov	276	Godavari Spirit	286	Farkhutdinov	274
Garnet Leader	246	Genco Picardy	126	Gerd Knutsen	159	Golar Arctic	122	Goya	197
Gas Al Kuwait II	162	Genco Pioneer	126	Gerd Maersk	187	Golar Bear	122	Grace Acacia	210
Gas Al Mutlaa	162	Genco Predator	126	Gerda Maersk	187	Golar Celsius	122	Grace Barleria	210
Gas Al-Gurain	162	Genco Progress	126	Gerdt Oldendorff	230	Golar Crystal	122	Grace Cosmos	210
Gas Al-Negeh	162	Genco Prosperity	126	Gerhard Schulte	257	Golar Frost	122	Grace Dahlia	210
Gas Diana	210	Genco Provence	126	Gerner Maersk	187	Golar Glacier	122	Grace Victoria	135
Gas Taurus	210	Genco Pyrenees	126	Gertrude		Golar Grand	122	Graceful Leader	246
Gaschem Adriatic	142	Genco Raptor	126	Oldendorff	230	Golar Ice	122	Graig Cardiff	164
Gaschem Antarctic	142	Genco Reliance	126	Ghawar	42	Golar Kelvin	122	Graig Rotterdam	164
Gaschem Bremen	142	Genco Rhone	126	Ghazal	42	Golar Maria	122	Gral. Manuel	
Gaschem Hamburg	142	Genco Spirit	126	Ghinah	42	Golar Mazo	122	Belgrano	222
Gaschem Nordsee	144	Genco Success	126	Giannis	106	Golar Penguin	122	Gran Bretagna	132
Gaschem Nordsee	86	Genco Sugar	126	Giannutri	216	Golar Seal	122	Grand Aniva	210
Gaschem Pacific	144	Genco Surprise	126	Giewont	243	Golar Snow	122	Grand Benelux	132
Gaschem Pacific	86	Genco Thunder	126	Gigira Laitebo	187	Golar Tundra	122	Grand Celebration	33
Gaschem Stade	144	Genco Tiberius	126	Gijon Knutsen	159	Golbon	152	Grand Champion	74
GasLog Chelsea	124	Genco Tiger	126	Gimi	122	Gold Sun	310	Grand Choice	74
GasLog Glasgow	124	Genco Titus	126	Gingko Arrow	153	Golden Aries	122	Grand Cosmo	74
GasLog Greece	124	Genco Vigour	126	Gisela Oldendorff	230	Golden Aso	122	Grand Dahlia	74
GasLog Salem	124	Genco Warrior	126	Giulia I	91	Golden Barnet	122	Grand Diamond	74
GasLog Santiago	124	Genco Wisdom	126	Gjertrud Maersk	187	Golden Beijing	122	Grand Dolphin	74
GasLog Saratoga	124	Gener8 Apollo	127	Gladiator	106	Golden Bexley	122	Grand Duke	74
GasLog Savannah	124	Gener8 Ares	127	Gladiator	113	Golden Brilliant	122	Grand Eagle	74
GasLog Seattle	124	Gener8 Argus	127	Glasgow Express	139	Golden Bull	122	Grand Elena	210
GasLog Shanghai	124	Gener8 Athena	127	Glen Canyon Bridge	156	Golden Cathrine	122	Grand Hero	74
GasLog Singapore	124	Gener8 Atlas	127	Global Highway	156	Golden Cecilie	122	Grand Legacy	74
GasLog Skagen	124	Gener8 Companion	127	Global Leader	246	Golden Daisy	122	Grand Mark	74
GasLog Sydney	124	Gener8 Daphne	127	Globetrotter	288	Golden Diamond	122	Grand Mercury	74
GDF Suez		Gener8 Defiance	127	Gloria	105	Golden Eminence	122	Grand Neptune	74
Cape Ann	148	Gener8 Elektra	127	Gloriana	54	Golden Empress	122	Grand Orion	74
GDF Suez Neptune	148	Gener8 George T.	127	Gloric	165	Golden Endeavour	122	Grand Pace	74
GDF Suez		Gener8 Harriet G.	127	Glorious Ace	185	Golden Endurer	122	Grand Pavo	74
Point Fortin	185	Gener8 Hera	127	Glorious Express	210	Golden Feng	122	Grand Pearl	74
Gdynia	243	Gener8 Hercules	127	Glorious Leader	246	Golden Finsbury	122	Grand Phoenix	74
Gdynia Trader	167	Gener8 Horn	127	Glory	137	Golden Future	122	Grand Pioneer	74
Gebe Oldendorff	230	Gener8 Kara G.	127	Glorycrown	121	Golden Gemini	122	Grand Princess	15
Geiranger	253	Gener8 Maniate	127	Glovis Captain	148	Golden Hawk	122	Grand Quest	74
Gemini	33	Gener8 Nautilus	128	Glovis Caravel	246	Golden Heiwa	203	Grand Race	74
Gemini Leader	210	Gener8 Neptune	127	Glovis Cardinal	148	Golden Ice	122	Grand Ruby	74
Gemini Sun	310	Gener8 Orion	127	Glovis Century	148	Golden Iris	33	Grand Sapphire	74
Gemmata	269	Gener8 Pericles	127	Glovis Challenge	148	Golden Karoo	170	Grand Uranus	74
Genco Acheron	125	Gener8 Phoenix	127	Glovis Champion	148	Golden Kathrine	122	Grand Vega	74
Genco Aquitaine	125	Gener8 Poseidon	127	Glovis Chorus	148	Golden Leo	124	Grand Venus	74
Genco Ardennes	125	Gener8 Spartiate	127	Glovis Clipper	246	Golden Magnum	122	Grand Victory	74
Genco Augustus	125	Gener8 Spyridon	127	Glovis Comet	148	Golden Opportunity	122	Grande Abidjan	132
Genco Auvegne	125	Gener8 St. Nikolas	127	Glovis Companion	221	Golden Opus	122	Grande Africa	133
Genco Avra	125	Gener8 Strength	127	Glovis Composer	148	Golden Pearl	122	Grande Amburgo	132
Genco Bay	125	Gener8 Success	127	Glovis Condor	148	Golden Princess	15	Grande America	132
Genco Beauty	125	Gener8 Supreme	127	Glovis Conductor	148	Golden Ray	108	Grande Angola	132
Genco Bourgogne	125	Gener8 Ulysses	127	Glovis Corona	148	Golden Rose	122	Grande Anversa	132
Genco Brittany	125	General Guisan	282	Glovis Cosmos	148	Golden Saguenay	122	Grande Argentina	133
Genco Carrier	125	Generous	113	Glovis Cougar	148	Golden Scape	122	Grande Atlantico	132
Genco Cavalier	125	Genius	113	Glovis Countess	148	Golden Seas	239	Grande Benin	132
Genco Challenger	125	Genius Highway	246	Glovis Courage	148	Golden Shui	122	Grande Brasile	133
Genco Champion	125	GenMar Compatriot	127	Glovis Crown	148	Golden Strength	122	Grande	
Genco Charger	125	GenMar Victory	127	Glovis Crystal	148	Golden Suek	122	Buenos Aires	132
Genco Claudius	125	GenMar Vision	127	Glovis Pacific	148	Golden Surabaya	124	Grande Cameroon	132

Grande Colonia 132
Grande Congo 132
Grande Costa d'Avorio 132
Grande Cotonou 132
Grande Dakar 132
Grande Detroit 132
Grande Detroit 133
Grande Ellade 132
Grande Europa 132
Grande Francia 132
Grande Gabon 132
Grande Ghana 132
Grande Guinea 132
Grande Italia 132
Grande Lagos 132
Grande Luanda 132
Grande Marocco 132
Grande Mediterraneo 132
Grande Napoli 132
Grande Nigeria 132
Grande Portogallo 132
Grande Roma 132
Grande San Paolo 132
Grande Scandinavia 132
Grande Senegal 132
Grande Sicilia 132
Grande Sicilia 133
Grande Sierra Leone 132
Grande Spagna 132
Grande Tema 132
Grande Togo 132
Grandeur of the Seas 24
Grasmere Maersk 191
Gravity Highway 246
Great 97
Great Eastern 301
Grebe Arrow 153
Greek Seas 239
Green Austevoll 129
Green Bay 151
Green Bodo 129
Green Brazil 129
Green Chile 129
Green Concordia 129
Green Cooler 129
Green Costa Rica 129
Green Cove 151
Green Crystal 129
Green Dale 151
Green Egersund 129
Green Freezer 129
Green Glacier 131
Green Guatemala 131
Green Honduras 131
Green Italia 131
Green Karmoy 131
Green Lake 151
Green Magic 131
Green Magnific 131
Green Maloy 131
Green Maveric 131
Green Mountain 170
Green Music 131
Green Point 70
Green Ray 108
Green Ridge 151
Green Selje 131
Green Toledo 131
Green Trader 280

Greenwich Bridge 156
Greenwich Park 310
Grena Knutsen 159
Greta Selmer 306
Grete Maersk 187
Gretke Oldendorff 230
Grey Fox 170
Grimstad 44
Grindanger 253
Grouse Arrow 153
Grouse Hunter 80
Grumant 170
GSL Africa 312
Guang Dong Bridge 156
Guangzhou Highway 156
Guardian Leader 246
Guayaquil Bridge 265
Gudrun Maersk 187
Guenther Schulte 257
Gulf Baynunah 133
Gulf Castle 133
Gulf Coast 133
Gulf Cobalt 133
Gulf Coral 133
Gulf Crystal 133
Gulf Elan 133
Gulf Esprit 133
Gulf Horizon 133
Gulf Jumeirah 133
Gulf Mews 133
Gulf Mist 133
Gulf Moon 133
Gulf Muttrah 133
Gulf Pearl 133
Gulf Rastaq 133
Gulf Stream 133
Gulf Valour 133
Gulf Vision 133
Gunde Maersk 187
Gunhild Kirk 133
Gunhilde Maersk 187
Gunvor Maersk 187
Guofeng Enterprise 310
Guofeng First 310
Gustav Maersk 187
Guthorm Maersk 187
Habari 42
Hadiyah 162
Hafnia Adamello 133
Hafnia Africa 135
Hafnia America 135
Hafnia Andromeda 133
Hafnia Ane 133
Hafnia Arctic 135
Hafnia Asia 135
Hafnia Atlantic 133
Hafnia Australia 135
Hafnia Bering 133
Hafnia Crux 133
Hafnia Daisy 135
Hafnia Europe 135
Hafnia Green 133
Hafnia Hope 133
Hafnia Karava 134
Hafnia Kirsten 135
Hafnia Lene 134
Hafnia Leo 134
Hafnia Libra 134
Hafnia Lise 135
Hafnia Lotte 135
Hafnia Lupus 134
Hafnia Magellan 134
Hafnia Malacca 134

Hafnia Mikala 135
Hafnia Nordica 134
Hafnia Pegasus 134
Hafnia Phoenix 134
Hafnia Rainier 134
Hafnia Robson 134
Hafnia Soya 134
Hafnia Sunda 134
Hafnia Taurus 134
Hafnia Torres 135
Hafnia Victoria 134
Hakata 82
Hakone 82
Halifax Express 87
Halki 110
Hamburg 97
Hamburg 30
Hamburg Bridge 156
Hamburg Express 139
Hamburg Highway 156
Hamburg Star 70
Hamilton Spirit 286
Hammersmith Bridge 156
Hammonia America 102
Hammonia Bavaria 102
Hammonia Berolina 102
Hammonia Calabria 102
Hammonia Emden 102
Hammonia Galicia 102
Hammonia Gallicum 102
Hammonia Grenada 102
Hammonia Husum 102
Hammonia Internum 102
Hammonia Ionium 102
Hammonia Istra 102
Hammonia Jutlandia 102
Hammonia Korsika 102
Hammonia Malta 102
Hammonia Massilia 103
Hammonia Palatium 103
Hammonia Pescara 103
Hammonia Roma 103
Hammonia Sapphire 103
Hammonia Teutonica 103
Hammonia Thracium 103
Hammonia Toscana 103
Hammonia Venetia 103
Hammonia Virginia 103
Han Yi 279
Handan Steel 310
Hanfia Henriette 135
Hangzhou Bay Bridge 156
Hanjin Africa 101
Hanjin Algeciras 92
Hanjin America 101
Hanjin Ami 265
Hanjin Aqua 136
Hanjin Argentina 136
Hanjin Asia 101
Hanjin Atlanta 136
Hanjin Baltimore 86
Hanjin Blue Ocean 101
Hanjin Bosal 265
Hanjin Boston 86
Hanjin Bremerhaven 136
Hanjin Budapest 136
Hanjin Buddha 265

Hanjin Buenos Aires 92
Hanjin California 308
Hanjin China 136
Hanjin Chongqing 136
Hanjin Constantza 92
Hanjin Dallas 86
Hanjin Duesseldorf 249
Hanjin Durban 136
Hanjin Europe 101
Hanjin Florida 308
Hanjin Gdynia 136
Hanjin Geneva 86
Hanjin Germany 92
Hanjin Gold 101
Hanjin Greece 92
Hanjin Green Earth 101
Hanjin Gwanseum 265
Hanjin Haiphong 162
Hanjin Hamburg 136
Hanjin Harmony 101
Hanjin Indigo 136
Hanjin Italy 92
Hanjin Jungil 265
Hanjin Kingston 136
Hanjin Korea 136
Hanjin Long Beach 136
Hanjin Los Angeles 136
Hanjin Louisiana 310
Hanjin Mar 136
Hanjin Marine 136
Hanjin Miami 86
Hanjin Milano 249
Hanjin Monaco 136
Hanjin Montevideo 249
Hanjin Mumbai 136
Hanjin Mundra 162
Hanjin Namu 265
Hanjin Netherlands 136
Hanjin New Jersey 108
Hanjin New York 136
Hanjin Newport 136
Hanjin Newport 249
Hanjin Norfolk 136
Hanjin Piraeus 136
Hanjin Port Kelang 136
Hanjin Rio de Janiero 136
Hanjin Rotterdam 136
Hanjin San Diego 162
Hanjin Santos 92
Hanjin Scarlet 136
Hanjin Seattle 136
Hanjin Shenzhen 136
Hanjin Sooho 101
Hanjin Spain 136
Hanjin Tabul 265
Hanjin Tianjin 136
Hanjin United Kingdom 136
Hanjin Versailles 92
Hanjin Vienna 86
Hanjin White 136
Hanjin Xiamen 136
Hanjin Yantian 136
Hanna Oldendorff 230
Hannes Oldendorff 230
Hannover Bridge 156
Hanoi Bridge 156
Hanover Express 139
Hans Oldendorff 231
Hans Scholl 70
Hansa Altenburg 165
Hansa America 165
Hansa Arendal 165

Hansa Asia 165
Hansa Augsburg 165
Hansa Australia 165
Hansa Bremen 145
Hansa Calypso 165
Hansa Castella 165
Hansa Centurion 166
Hansa Cloppenburg 166
Hansa Constitution 137
Hansa Duburg 166
Hansa Europe 166
Hansa Flensburg 166
Hansa Fresenburg 166
Hansa Freyburg 166
Hansa Fyn 166
Hansa Homburg 166
Hansa Kirkenes 166
Hansa Langeland 166
Hansa Liberty 137
Hansa Limburg 166
Hansa Lübeck 145
Hansa Ludswigsburg 166
Hansa Magdeburg 166
Hansa Marburg 166
Hansa Meersburg 166
Hansa Narvik 166
Hansa Neuberg 166
Hansa Nordburg 166
Hansa Offenburg 166
Hansa Oldenburg 166
Hansa Papenburg 166
Hansa Ravensburg 166
Hansa Reggensburg 166
Hansa Rendsburg 166
Hansa Ronneburg 166
Hansa Rotenburg 166
Hansa Salzburg 166
Hansa Siegburg 166
Hansa Steinburg 166
Hansa Victory 137
Hanseatic 30
Hanyang 283
Happy Buccaneer 279
Happy Delta 279
Happy Diamond 279
Happy Dover 279
Happy Dragon 279
Happy Dynamic 279
Happy Ranger 279
Happy River 279
Happy Rover 279
Happy Sky 279
Happy Star 279
Harad 42
Harald S 254
Harbour Bridge 156
Hardanger 253
Harefield 153
Harm 294
Harmen Oldendorff 230
Harmony Ace 185
Harmony Leader 246
Harmony N 203
Harmony of the Seas 24
Harriette N 61
Harrison Bay 261
Hartland Point 120
Haruka 271
Harvest Leader 246
Hatsu Courage 86
Hatsu Crystal 86
Hatta 298
Hauke Oldendorff 230

Name	No.	Name	No.	Name	No.	Name	No.	Name	No.
Ingrid	82	Ivar Reefer	68	John Wulff	308	Kandava	164	Knokke	118
Ingrid Knutsen	159	Iver Exact	301	Joie N	203	Kanpur	255	Knud Reefer	68
Ingrid Oldendorff	231	Iver Example	301	Jona	249	Kapitan Danilkin	170	Kobe Express	139
Ingwar Selmer	306	Iver Experience	301	Jonathan Swift	212	Kapitan Gotskiy	274	Kociewie	243
Insignia	19	Iver Exporter	302	Jonni Ritscher	294	Kapitan Sviridov	170	Kom	200
Inspiring Seas	239	Iver Express	302	Joost Schulte	257	Kaprijk	118	Kometik	297
Insurgentes	63	Iver Progress	302	Jorgen Reefer	68	Kara Sea	108	Komi	167
Integrity	305	Iver Prosperity	302	Josephine Maersk	187	Karan	42	Kong Harald	21
Inventana	254	Ivory Arrow	246	Jost	101	Kareela Spirit	286	Koningsdam	13
Ioanna	106	Ivory Dawn	237	Jost	252	Karen Knutsen	159	Konrad Schulte	257
Ioanna D.	129	Ivory Girl	237	JPO Aquarius	233	Karen Maersk	194	Konstantin Jacob	152
Ioannis Zafirakis	166	Ivory Ray	108	JPO Aries	233	Karine Bulker	164	Kontich	118
Ionic	165	Izumo Princess	296	JPO Atair	233	Karmen	87	Koro Sea	108
Ipanema Beach	271	Jacamar Arrow	153	JPO Canopus	233	Karoline N	61	Kortrijk	118
Ipanema Street	310	Jack London	212	JPO Capricornus	233	Karolos	106	Koszalin	243
Iran Kashan	152	Jacob Rickmers	249	JPO Delphinus	233	Karpaty	243	Kota Ekspres	308
Irene II	296	Jacques Jacob	152	JPO Dorado	233	Kashi Arrow	153	Koznitza	201
Irene Oldendorff	231	Jadrana	101	JPO Gemini	233	Kastos	110	Kraslava	164
Irene SL	110	Jaeger Arrow	153	JPO Leo	233	Kaszuby	243	Kraszewski	73
Irenes Logos	296	Jaguar Max	113	JPO Libra	233	Katharina	174	Krisjanis Valdemars	164
Irenes Rainbow	296	Jaham	42	JPO Pisces	233	Katharina S	254	Kristin Knutsen	159
Irenes Reliance	296	Jakarta Express	265	JPO Scorpius	233	Katrin-S.	254	Kristinita	297
Irenes Remedy	296	Jakarta Tower	108	JPO Taurus	233	Kavala Seas	239	Kronborg	94
Irenes Wisdom	296	Jaladi	42	JPO Tucana	233	Kaveri Spirit	286	Kronviken	300
Iris	82	James Cook	216	JPO Vela	233	Kaya	162	Krymsk	276
Iris Ace	185	Jamila	101	JPO Virgo	233	Kaya Manx	164	KSL China	124
Iris Glory	282	Jamila	252	JPO Volans	233	Kazan	276	KSL Sakura	124
Iris Oldendorff	230	Jan	101	JPO Vulpecula	233	Kazdanga	164	KSL Salvador	124
Iris Victoria	135	Jan	252	JS Ineos Ingenuity	114	Kazimah II	162	KSL San Francisco	124
Irma	243	Jan Ritscher	294	JS Ineos Insight	114	Kea 150		KSL Santiago	124
Irmgard Schulte	257	Jana	42	JS Ineos Inspiration	114	Kea Trader	168	KSL Santos	124
Iron Baron	113	Jandavid S	254	JS Ineos Intrepid	116	Kefalonia	51	KSL Sapporo	124
Irongate	108	Janice N	61	Judith Borchard	212	Keno	249	KSL Savannah	124
Iryda	243	Japan	284	Juist Trader	55	Kent	108	KSL Seattle	124
Isa	243	Japin Arrow	153	Jules Verne	212	Kerala	106	KSL Seoul	124
Isa Oldendorff	231	Jasmine Knutsen	159	Julia N	61	Kerel	216	KSL Seville	124
Isabelita	297	Jasper Arrow	248	Julia Oldendorff	230	Keros	110	KSL Singapore	124
Isabella	290	Jawor	243	Julian	48	Kerstin S	254	KSL Stockholm	124
Isadora	243	Jazan	298	Juliana	101	Kestrel	308	KSL Sydney	124
Isao	249	Jean LD	169	Juliana	252	Khafji	42	Kuala Lumpur	
Isarstern	251	Jebel Ali	298	Julie Delmas	79	Khatanga	170	Express	139
Ise Princess	296	Jeju Island	101	Juliette Rickmers	249	Khuzama	42	Kuban	276
Iskmati Spirit	286	Jennings Bay	261	Julius S	254	Kidan	42	Kujawy	243
Island Princess	15	Jenny N	61	Jumbo Javelin	155	Kiel Trader	167	Kuljak Arrow	153
Island Sky	23	Jens Maersk	187	Jumbo Jubilee	155	Kilian S	254	Kumasi	79
Isodora	174	Jepperson Maersk	187	Jumbo Kinetic	155	Kilimanjaro Spirit	288	Kumul	187
Isolda	243	Jewel of the Seas	24	Jümme Trader	55	Kimolos	110	Kumul Arrow	153
Isoldana	254	Jia Xing	73	Juno	243	Kimolos Trader	167	Kuo Hsiung	114
Isolde	303	Jiaolong Spirit	286	Jupiter Leader	210	Kinaros	110	Kurpie	243
Isolde	174	Jill Jacob	152	Jupiter N	203	King Daniel	160	Kurt Paul	54
Istra Ace	246	Jingu	210	Jupiter Spirit	212	King Darius	160	Kuzma Minin	170
Istria	45	Jinsei Maru	210	Jupiter Sun	310	King Darwin	160	Kwangsi	283
Istrian Express	301	Jo Acer	224	Jurkalne	164	King Dorian	160	Kwangtung	283
Ital Contessa	86	Jo Alm	222	Justice Victoria	135	King Douglas	160	Kweichow	283
Ital Fulgida	117	Jo Betula	224	K Pegasus	310	King Duncan	160	Kweilin	283
Ital Laguna	209	Jo Ilex	224	K Phoenix	310	King Edward	160	Kyeema Spirit	286
Ital Libera	209	Jo Kashi	224	Kacey	285	King Emerald	160	Kyoto Express	139
Ital Lirica	209	Jo Kiri	224	Kaethe		King Ernest	160	Kyoto Tower	310
Ital Lunare	209	Jo Larix	224	C. Rickmers	249	King Everest	160	L'Austral	24
Ital Massima	117	Jo Lotus	224	Kaethe P	241	King Hadley	160	La Briantais	169
Ital Mattina	117	Jo Pinari	224	Kahla	42	King Ore	203	La Chambordais	169
Ital Melodia	117	Jo Provel	224	Kaifan	162	King Robert	160	La Chesnais	169
Ital Milione	117	Jo Redwood	224	Kaijin	210	King Robert	160	La Guimorais	169
Ital Moderna	117	Jo Rowan	224	Kalahari	151	Kingbird Arrow	153	La Landriais	169
Ital Oriente	144	Jobst Oldendorff	230	Kalamata Trader	167	Kings Road	310	La Mancha Knutsen	159
Ital Unica	117	Jogela	101	Kalamoti Trader	168	Kiowa Spirit	243	La Partenais	169
Ital Universo	117	Johann Jacob	152	Kalliopi	106	Kirill Lavrov	274	La Paz	296
Ital Usodimare	117	Johann Oldendorff	230	Kalliopi R.C.	160	Kita LNG	65	La Richardais	169
Italia Reefer	96	Johann Schulte	257	Kaluga	276	Kite Arrow	153	La Sauternais	169
Italian Express	301	Johanna Oldendorff	230	Kambos	167	Kithnos	110	La Sillonais	169
Itea	87	Johannes Maersk	187	Kamenitza	200	Klara Selmer	306	La Solognais	169
Ithaki	106	Johannes S.	254	Kamome Victoria	135	Klipper Stream	267	Lacerta	67
Ithaki	50	Johannes Wulff	308	Kanaga Island	259	Kmarin Jasmine	164	Laconic	165
Ivan Papanin	170	John Rickmers	249	Kanata Spirit	286	Kmarin Mugungwha	165		

Name	Page	Name	Page	Name	Page	Name	Page	Name	Page
Maersk Michigan	193	Maersk Stepnica	189	Manon	303	Mare Lycium	139	Martha Schulte	259
Maersk Mississippi	196	Maersk Stockholm	189	Manousos P	296	Mare Nostrum	120	Marvellous	36
Maersk Missouri	193	Maersk Stralsund	48	Maple Ace II	185	Mare Oriens	120	Marvelous Ace	185
Maersk Montana	193	Maersk Sydney	48	Maple Grove	271	Mare Pacific	162	Mary	285
Maersk Needham	257	Maersk Tacoma	197	Mapocho	140	Mare Phoenicium	139	Mary Maersk	189
Maersk Nejmegen	80	Maersk Taikung	192	Maran Apollo	38	Mare Picenum	120	Mary Schulte	257
Maersk Newbury	192	Maersk Tampa	197	Maran Artemis	38	Mare Siculum	120	Marylebone	54
Maersk Newcastle	192	Maersk Tangier	197	Maran Atlas	37	Mare Siculum	139	Marylebone	257
Maersk Newhaven	192	Maersk Tanjong	192	Maran Callisto	37	Mare Tirrenum	120	Mastera	208
Maersk Newport	189	Maersk Taurus	192	Maran Canopus	38	Mare Tracer	160	Mataquito	101
Maersk Niagara	80	Maersk Teesport	197	Maran Capella	38	Mare Trader	160	Matar N	204
Maersk Niamey	80	Maersk Tema	250	Maran Capricorn	38	Mare Transporter	160	Mathilde Maersk	189
Maersk Nienburg	80	Maersk Tianjin	197	Maran Carina	38	Mare Traveller	160	Mathilde Oldendorff	230
Maersk Nimes	80	Maersk Tokyo	197	Maran Cassiopeia	38	Maren Maersk	189	Mathilde Schulte	257
Maersk Niteroi	80	Maersk Torshavn	197	Maran Castor	38	Mareta	65	Mathraki	110
Maersk Norfolk	189	Maersk Tukang	192	Maran Centaurus	38	Marete Maersk	189	Matilda	290
Maersk Northampton	192	Maersk Utah	193	Maran Cleo	38	Marfret Guyane	173	Matsu Arrow	153
Maersk Northwood	192	Maersk Vallvik	192	Maran Corona	38	Marfret Marajo	173	Mattea	297
Maersk Norwich	257	Maersk Varna	192	Maran Cygnus	38	Margarita	106	Matterhorn Spirit	286
Maersk Nottingham	52	Maersk Vilnius	192	Maran Gas Achilles	39	Margret Oldendorff	230	Matthew	148
Maersk Ohio	193	Maersk Virginia	193	Maran Gas Agamemnon	39	Margrethe Maersk	189	Matz Maersk	189
Maersk Palermo	192	Maersk Visby	192	Maran Gas Alexandria	39	Margrit Rickmers	250	Maule	241
Maersk Patras	192	Maersk Volta	192	Maran Gas Amphipolis	39	Marguerite Ace	185	Maullin	101
Maersk Pearl	196	Maersk Wisconsin	193	Maran Gas Apollonia	39	Mari Ugland	135	Max Jacob	152
Maersk Peary	193	Maersk Wolgast	74	Maran Gas Asclepius	39	Maria	129	Max Oldendorff	230
Maersk Pelican	196	Maersk Wyoming	190	Maran Gas Coronis	39	Maria	82	Max Schulte	257
Maersk Pembroke	192	Maestro Diamond	173	Maran Gas Delphi	39	Maria A. Angelicoussi	36	May Oldendorff	230
Maersk Penang	192	Maestro Lion	173	Maran Gas Efessos	39	Maria A. Angelicoussis	38	Maya	296
Maersk Penguin	197	Maestro Pearl	173	Maran Gas Lindos	39	Maria Energy	296	Mayssan	298
Maersk Petrel	197	Maestro Tiger	173	Maran Gas Mystras	39	Maria Princess	296	Mayview Maersk	189
Maersk Phoenix	197	Maganari	65	Maran Gas Pericles	39	Maria Schulte	259	Mazowsze	243
Maersk Phuket	192	Magdalena Oldendorff	230	Maran Gas Posidonia	39	Maria-Katharina S	254	Mazury	243
Maersk Piper	197	Magelby Maersk	189	Maran Gas Sparta	39	Mariana	254	MCC Kyoto	248
Maersk Pittsburg	193	Magellan	16	Maran Gas Troy	39	Mariann	135	MCC Mergui	189
Maersk Princess	197	Magellan Spirit	288	Maran Gas Vergina	39	Marianne	192	MCC Seoul	248
Maersk Privilege	197	Magellan Strait	267	Maran Gemini	38	Marianne Kirk	134	MCT Breithorn	283
Maersk Producer	197	Magic Seas	239	Maran Lyra	38	Marib Spirit	288	MCT Stockhorn	283
Maersk Progress	197	Magic Striker	113	Maran Penelope	38	Maribel	135	Meandros	167
Maersk Promise	197	Magic Victoria	135	Maran Plato	38	Maribella	68	Med	231
Maersk Prosper	197	Magnavia	94	Maran Poseidon	38	Maribo Maersk	189	Medea	303
Maersk Rapier	193	Magnus Oldendorff	230	Maran Pythia	38	Marichristina	68	Medi Baltimore	89
Maersk Remlin	195	Main Trader	55	Maran Regulus	38	Marie Delmas	79	Medi Bangkok	89
Maersk Rhode Island	197	Maine Trader	167	Maran Sagitta	38	Marie Kirk	134	Medi Cagliari	89
Maersk Riesa	195	Maipo	140	Maran Taurus	38	Marie Maersk	189	Medi Hakata	89
Maersk Rosyth	195	Maira	285	Maran Thaleia	38	Marie S	308	Medi Hong Kong	89
Maersk Saigon	48	Maira XL	285	Maran Thetis	38	Marielle Bolten	50	Medi Lausanne	89
Maersk Salalah	189	Maistros	106	Maran Triton	38	Marietta	68	Medi Lisbon	89
Maersk Salina	189	Maitaca Arrow	153	Maratha	40	Marijeannie	68	Medi Manila	89
Maersk Saltoro	222	Maja Rickmers	250	Marbacan	173	Marika	135	Medi Nagasaki	91
Maersk Sana	48	Majestic	165	Marbella	65	Marilee	135	Medi Okinawa	91
Maersk Santana	48	Majestic	257	Marbioko	173	Mariloula	68	Medi Segesta	91
Maersk Sarat	189	Majestic Maersk	189	MarCarolina	173	Marina	106	Medi Tokyo	89
Maersk Sarnia	48	Majestic Princess	15	March	97	Marina	19	Medi Valencia	89
Maersk Savannah	189	Majesty of the Seas	24	Marchen Maersk	189	Marina	87	Medi Venezia	89
Maersk Sebarok	192	Majorca	65	MarChicora	173	Marina Ace	185	Medi Vitoria	91
Maersk Seletar	192	Makronissos	110	Marco Polo	16	Mariner	257	Medi Yokohama	89
Maersk Semakau	192	Malanje	210	Marco R	285	Mariner of the Seas	24	Mediterranean Highway	157
Maersk Semarang	227	Maliakos	97	MarColorado	173	Marinicki	68	Medontario	199
Maersk Sembawang	192	Malik al Ashtar	298	Mare Action	160	Marinor	135	Megalonissos	110
Maersk Senang	192	Malindi	64	Mare Ambassador	160	Mariperla	68	Meganisi	110
Maersk Sentosa	192	Malleco	101	Mare Arcticum	138	Marit Maersk	189	MegaStar Aries	21
Maersk Seoul	48	Mamitsa	285	Mare Atlantic	160	Maritime Jewel	108	Mehuin	140
Maersk Serangoon	192	Mamry	243	Mare Atlanticum	138	Maritina	135	Mein Schiff 1	29
Maersk Seville	48	Manasota	64	Mare Baltic	160	Marivia	94	Mein Schiff 2	29
Maersk Shams	222	Manatee	271	Mare Britannicum	138	Marivictoria	68	Mein Schiff 3	29
Maersk Sheerness	48	Manchester Bridge	271	Mare Caribbean	134	Marjan	43	Mein Schiff 4	29
Maersk Shivling	189	Mandalay	258	Mare Caribbean	160	Marlene Oldendorff	230	Mein Schiff 5	29
Maersk Singapore	48	Mandarin Arrow	153	Mare Caribicum	139	Marmara Sea	108	Mein Schiff 6	29
Maersk Sirac	222	Manhattan Bridge	156	Mare Doricum	120	Mars Sun	311	Mein Schiff 7	29
Maersk Skarstind	189	Manifah	43	Mare Fox	160	Marselisborg	94	Mein Schiff 8	29
Maersk Sofia	48	Manila Express	265	Mare Frio	162	Marsgracht	277	Mekaines	269
Maersk Stadelhorn	222	Manitoba	109			Marstal Maersk	189	Melbourne Strait	248
		Manolis P.	114			Martha Oldendorff	230	Melchior Schulte	257

Melinda	285	Milau Bulker	165	Minerva Nike	182	MOL Gateway	101	Morning Caroline	271
Mell Solomon	308	Millau Bridge	271	Minerva Nounou	182	MOL Generosity	101	Morning Catherine	306
Melody	21	Millennium	296	Minerva Oceania	182	MOL Genesis	101	Morning Cecilie	306
Meltemi	106	Milos	129	Minerva Pacifica	182	MOL Glide	257	Morning Celesta	306
Meltemi	95	Milos	51	Minerva Pisces	182	MOL Globe	257	Morning Celine	306
Memphis	222	Miltiadis Junior	63	Minerva Rita	182	MOL Grandeur	257	Morning Cello	306
Mendocino	65	Miltiadis M II	63	Minerva Roxanne	182	MOL Gratitude	257	Morning Champion	248
Mercer Street	311	Mimi Selmer	306	Minerva Sophia	182	MOL Growth	257	Morning Chant	306
Mercosul Manaus	193	Mimmi Schulte	258	Minerva Symphony	182	MOL Guardian	101	Morning Charlotte	271
Mercosul Santos	193	Mina Oldendorff	230	Minerva Tychi	182	MOL Maestro	184	Morning Cherry	271
Mercosul Suape	193	Mindoro	67	Minerva Vaso	182	MOL Magnificence	184	Morning Chorus	303
Mercury Ace	271	Mineral Antwerpen	80	Minerva Vera	182	MOL Majesty	184	Morning Christina	306
Mercury Leader	210	Mineral Beijing	80	Minerva Virgo	182	MOL Maneuver	184	Morning Cindy	306
Meridian	257	Mineral Belgium	80	Minerva Xanthe	182	MOL Marvel	184	Morning Claire	306
Meridian Ace	185	Mineral China	80	Minerva Zen	182	MOL Matrix	184	Morning Clara	305
Meridian Spirit	288	Mineral Dalian	80	Minerva Zenia	182	MOL Maxim	184	Morning Classic	248
Merkur Cloud	300	Mineral Dragon	80	Minerva Zoe	182	MOL Mission	184	Morning Cloud	311
Merkur Harbour	300	Mineral Edo	80	Minervagracht	277	MOL Modern	184	Morning Compass	248
Merkur O.	232	Mineral Energy	80	Minna	101	MOL Motivator	184	Morning Composer	306
Merkur Planet	155	Mineral Faith	80	Minstrel	258	MOL Nabila	80	Morning Concert	305
Merkur Tide	300	Mineral Haiku	80	Miraculous Ace	185	MOL Naima	80	Morning Conductor	306
Merlin Arrow	153	Mineral Hokkaido	80	Miramarin	64	MOL Naja	80	Morning Cornelia	271
Mermaid Ace	185	Mineral Hokusai	80	Misago Arrow	153	MOL Nala	80	Morning Cornet	306
Merwedegracht	277	Mineral Honshu	80	Miss Benedetta	217	MOL Pace	271	Morning Courier	248
Mesaimeer	269	Mineral Hope	80	Mississauga		MOL Paradise	271	Morning Crown	248
Messina Strait	267	Mineral Kyoto	80	Express	139	MOL Paramount	184	Morning Crystal	306
Messini	87	Mineral Kyushu	80	Mississippi Voyager	70	MOL Partner	271	Morning Glory	106
Meta	241	Mineral New York	80	Mistral	282	MOL Precision	271	Morning Lady	306
Methane		Mineral Ningbo	80	Mitrope	243	MOL Premium	184	Morning Laura	306
Alison Victoria	124	Mineral Nippon	80	Mizar	312	MOL Presence	236	Morning Lena	306
Methane		Mineral Noble	80	Mobilana	254	MOL Prestige	271	Morning Lily	306
Becki Anne	124	Mineral Oak	80	Modern Express	74	MOL Proficiency	257	Morning Linda	306
Methane		Mineral Shikoku	80	Modern Link	74	MOL Promise	271	Morning Lisa	306
Heather Sally	124	Mineral Stonehenge	80	Modern Peak	74	MOL Quartz	207	Morning Lucy	306
Methane		Mineral Subic	80	Moen Island	259	MOL Quasar	207	Morning Lynn	306
Jane Elizabeth	124	Mineral Tianjin	80	Mogens Maersk	189	MOL Quest	207	Morning Margareta	306
Methane		Mineral Utamaro	80	MOL Beacon	265	MOL Quintet	207	Morning Menad	306
Julia Louise	124	Mineral Yarden	80	MOL Beauty	265	MOL Solution	184	Morning Mercator	146
Methane Kari Elin	124	Minerva	174	MOL Belief	265	Molengracht	277	Morning Midas	311
Methane		Minerva	10	MOL Bellwether	265	Moleson	282	Morning Miracle	108
Lydon Volney	124	Minerva	257	MOL Benefactor	265	Molly Schulte	258	Morning Ninni	306
Methane		Minerva Alexandra	181	MOL Beyond	267	Momi Arrow	153	Morning Pilot	306
Mickie Harper	124	Minerva Alice	181	MOL Bravo	265	Monarch	27	Morning Post	306
Methane Nile Eagle	124	Minerva Anna	181	MOL Breeze	265	Monemvasia	182	Morning Pride	306
Methane Patricia		Minerva Antarctica	181	MOL Brightness	265	Mongoose Hunter	80	Morten Maersk	189
Camila	124	Minerva Antonia	181	MOL Brilliance	265	Moni Rickmers	250	Moscow	276
Methane Princess	122	Minerva Aries	181	MOL Celebration	184	Monica P.	114	Moscow Kremlin	276
Methane		Minerva Astra	181	MOL Charisma	184	Monsoon	282	Moscow River	276
Rita Andrea	124	Minerva Atlantica	181	MOL Commitment	184	Monte Aconcagua	226	Moscow Spirit	286
Methane Shirley		Minerva Clara	181	MOL Competence	184	Monte Alegre	226	Moscow Stars	276
Elisabeth	124	Minerva Concert	181	MOL Continuity	271	Monte Azul	226	Moscow University	276
Methane Spirit	288	Minerva Doxa	181	MOL Contribution	184	Monte Cervantes	226	Mosel Ace	185
Methania	118	Minerva Eleonora	181	MOL Cosmos	271	Monte Olivia	226	Mosel Trader	55
Metis Leader	271	Minerva Ellie	181	MOL Courage	184	Monte Pascoal	226	Moskovsky	
Mette Maersk	189	Minerva Elpida	181	MOL Creation	184	Monte Rosa	226	Prospect	274
Mexican Bay	268	Minerva Emily	181	MOL Dedication	250	Monte Sarmiento	226	Mount Apo	108
Mia Schulte	257	Minerva Emma	182	MOL Delight	250	Monte Tamaro	226	Mount Austin	108
Mia-S	255	Minerva Georgia	182	MOL Destiny	250	Monte Verde	226	Mount Bolivar	108
Miami Trader	167	Minerva Gloria	182	MOL Devotion	250	Montecristo	64	Mount Bolivar	109
Michaela S	255	Minerva Grace	182	MOL Dominance	250	Montego	67	Mount Dampier	108
Michigan Highway	157	Minerva Helen	182	MOL Earnest	184	Monterey	67	Mount Everest	256
Michigan Trader	55	Minerva Indiana	182	MOL Efficiency	265	Montreal	222	Mount Faber	108
Midjur	201	Minerva Iris	182	MOL Emerald	265	Montreal Express	139	Mount Fuji	106
Midnatsol	21	Minerva Joanna	182	MOL Eminence	265	Montreal Spirit	286	Mount Hedland	108
Miedwie	243	Minerva Joy	182	MOL Emissary	265	Monza Express	302	Mount Hermon	108
Mighty Servant	98	Minerva Julie	182	MOL Empire	265	Moose Hunter	80	Mount Kibo	256
Mignon	303	Minerva Leo	182	MOL Endowment	184	Moritz Oldendorff	230	Mount Kinabalu	108
Mikhail Kutuzov	170	Minerva Libra	182	MOL Endurance	94	Morning Calm	248	Mount Nevis	108
Mikhail Ulyanov	274	Minerva Lisa	182	MOL Excellence	265	Morning Calypso	306	Mount Ophir	108
Milagro	64	Minerva Lydia	182	MOL Expeditor	265	Morning Camilla	271	Mount Rainier	108
Milaha Qatar	245	Minerva Marina	182	MOL Experience	184	Morning Capo	306	Mount Sinai	108
Milaha Ras Laffan	245	Minerva Maya	182	MOL Explorer	184	Morning Cara	306	Mount Uluru	108
Milan Express	139	Minerva		MOL Express	265	Morning Carina	271	Mozah	269
Milan Trader	167	Mediterranea	182	MOL Garland	101	Morning Carol	306	Mozambique	108

Name	Pg	Name	Pg	Name	Pg	Name	Pg	Name	Pg
Mozart	48	MSC Brianna	175	MSC Francesca	176	MSC Lisbon	227	MSC Pamela	179
Mozu Arrow	154	MSC Brunella	175	MSC Gabriella	176	MSC Livorno	227	MSC Panama	311
MS Eagle	259	MSC Bruxelles	227	MSC Gaia	176	MSC London	311	MSC Paola	179
MS Hawk	259	MSC Busan	227	MSC Geneva	86	MSC Lorena	178	MSC Paris	103
MS Simon	70	MSC Cadiz	227	MSC Genova	227	MSC Loretta	178	MSC Patricia	86
MS Sophie	70	MSC Caitlin	175	MSC Gianna	69	MSC Los Angeles	138	MSC Perle	179
MS Tiger	259	MSC Camille	176	MSC Gina	176	MSC Lucia	178	MSC Pilar	179
MSC Abidjan	108	MSC Canberra	176	MSC Giorgia	176	MSC Luciana	178	MSC Pina	179
MSC Adelaide	174	MSC Candice	176	MSC Giovanna	177	MSC Lucy	178	MSC Poesia	21
MSC Adele	174	MSC Capella	176	MSC Giselle	177	MSC Ludovica	178	MSC Poh Lin	179
MSC Adriana	174	MSC Capri	68	MSC Grace	177	MSC Luisa	178	MSC Positano	179
MSC Agadir	258	MSC Carina	209	MSC Hamburg	311	MSC Madeleine	178	MSC Prague	212
MSC Agata	231	MSC Carla 3	68	MSC Hannah	177	MSC Madrid	227	MSC Preziosa	21
MSC Agrigento	311	MSC Carmen	176	MSC Heidi	177	MSC Maeva	178	MSC Pylos	88
MSC Ajaccio	87	MSC Carole	265	MSC Himanshi	177	MSC Magali	178	MSC Rachele	179
MSC Alabama	174	MSC Carolina	176	MSC Hina	69	MSC Magnifica	21	MSC Rafaela	179
MSC Albany	308	MSC Carouge	86	MSC Ilona	86	MSC Malin	178	MSC Rania	179
MSC Alessia	86	MSC Caterina	176	MSC Imma	69	MSC Mandraki	88	MSC Rapallo	227
MSC Alexa	174	MSC Celine	176	MSC Immacolata	209	MSC Mandy	178	MSC Ravenna	227
MSC Alexandra	174	MSC Channe	176	MSC Ines	177	MSC Manu	265	MSC Rebecca	179
MSC Algeciras	257	MSC Charleston	227	MSC Ingrid	177	MSC Margarita	178	MSC Regina	179
MSC Alghero	311	MSC Chiara	176	MSC Ingy	263	MSC Margrit	48	MSC Regulus	179
MSC Alicante	227	MSC Chicago	227	MSC Irene	177	MSC Maria Elena	178	MSC Renee	48
MSC Alice	174	MSC Chloe	181	MSC Iris	177	MSC Maria Laura	178	MSC Reunion	88
MSC Altair	48	MSC Clara	176	MSC Ishyka	177	MSC Maria Pia	178	MSC Rhiannon	180
MSC Altamira	308	MSC Claudia	108	MSC Istanbul	108	MSC Maria Saveria	179	MSC Rita	180
MSC Alyssa	174	MSC Clorinda	176	MSC Ivana	177	MSC Marianna	179	MSC Roberta	69
MSC Amalfi	87	MSC Cordoba	86	MSC Jade	181	MSC Marina	179	MSC Rochelle	180
MSC America	174	MSC Corinna	176	MSC Japan	177	MSC Marta	179	MSC Roma	227
MSC Amsterdam	311	MSC Coruna	227	MSC Jasmine	177	MSC Martina	179	MSC Romanos	88
MSC Amy	68	MSC Cristiana	176	MSC Jeanne	91	MSC Marylena	179	MSC Ronit	180
MSC Anahita	91	MSC Cristina	204	MSC Jemima	177	MSC Matilde	179	MSC Rosa M	180
MSC Anchorage	308	MSC Damla	176	MSC Jenny	69	MSC Maureen	179	MSC Rosaria	180
MSC Angela	174	MSC Daniela	176	MSC Jeongmin	181	MSC Maxine	179	MSC Rossella	180
MSC Aniello	174	MSC Danit	176	MSC Jilhan	177	MSC Maya	179	MSC Sabrina	180
MSC Anisha R	174	MSC Deila	176	MSC Joanna	177	MSC Mediterranean	179	MSC Samantha	108
MSC Annamaria	174	MSC Denisse	176	MSC Jordan	177	MSC Melatilde	179	MSC Sandra	180
MSC Annick	68	MSC Dhahran	222	MSC Joy	177	MSC Meline	179	MSC Santhya	180
MSC Ans	174	MSC Diana	263	MSC Judith	177	MSC Melissa	179	MSC Sao Paulo	180
MSC Antalya	257	MSC Didem	176	MSC Julia R.	177	MSC Meraviglia	22	MSC Sara Elena	180
MSC Antigua	258	MSC Diego	176	MSC Julie	177	MSC Messina	108	MSC Sarah	180
MSC Antonella	175	MSC Divina	21	MSC Kalamata	88	MSC Methoni	179	MSC Sariska	180
MSC Antonia	175	MSC Domitille	176	MSC Kalina	177	MSC Methoni	88	MSC Sasha	181
MSC Anya	209	MSC Don Giovanni	176	MSC Karlskrona	103	MSC Mia Summer	179	MSC Savona	227
MSC Anzu	175	MSC Donata	176	MSC Katie	177	MSC Michaela	179	MSC Seaside	22
MSC Arbatax	257	MSC Dymphna	108	MSC Katrina	177	MSC Mila 3	69	MSC Seattle	48
MSC Ariane	175	MSC Edith	176	MSC Katya R.	177	MSC Mirella	179	MSC Sena	69
MSC Arica	258	MSC Ela	176	MSC Katyayni	311	MSC Mirja	181	MSC Shanghai	227
MSC Armonia	21	MSC Eleni	176	MSC Kerry	177	MSC Monica	179	MSC Shannon	180
MSC Arushi R.	175	MSC Eleonora	176	MSC Kim	177	MSC Monterey	86	MSC Shaula	69
MSC Asli	175	MSC Eloane	263	MSC Kingston	88	MSC Musica	21	MSC Sheila	180
MSC Astrid	175	MSC Elodie	176	MSC Kleven	103	MSC Mykonos	88	MSC Shenzen	48
MSC Asya	175	MSC Eloise	176	MSC Kolkata	88	MSC Nadriely	69	MSC Shirley	180
MSC Athens	87	MSC Elsa 3	68	MSC Korea	177	MSC Namibia II	88	MSC Sierra II	88
MSC Athos	87	MSC Emanuela	176	MSC Koroni	88	MSC Naomi	179	MSC Silvana	180
Mozu Atlanta	138	MSC England	232	MSC Krittika	177	MSC Natalia	86	MSC Silvia	180
MSC Atlantic	175	MSC Erminia	176	MSC Krystal	177	MSC Nederland	179	MSC Sindy	180
MSC Augusta	175	MSC Esthi	176	MSC La Spezia	227	MSC Nerissa	179	MSC Sinfonia	21
MSC Aurora	175	MSC Eugenia	176	MSC Lana	69	MSC New York	311	MSC Sofia Celeste	180
MSC Azov	88	MSC Eva	176	MSC Lara	178	MSC Nicole	179	MSC Sola	180
MSC Banu	175	MSC Eyra	176	MSC Laura	178	MSC Nilgun	179	MSC Sonia	180
MSC Barbara	175	MSC Fabienne	176	MSC Lauren	178	MSC Ningbo	48	MSC Sophie	180
MSC Barcelona	227	MSC Fabiola	101	MSC Laurence	178	MSC Nita	179	MSC Soraya	180
MSC Bari	227	MSC Fantasia	21	MSC Lausanne	86	MSC Noa	179	MSC Splendida	22
MSC Beatrice	175	MSC Faustina	101	MSC Lea	178	MSC Nora	69	MSC Stella	180
MSC Beijing	227	MSC Federica	176	MSC Leanne	265	MSC Nuria	179	MSC Suez	180
MSC Belle	175	MSC Fiammetta	176	MSC Leigh	178	MSC Oliver	179	MSC Susanna	180
MSC Benedetta	48	MSC Fillippa	101	MSC Leila	178	MSC Opera	21	MSC Sveva	180
MSC Beryl	209	MSC Filomena	101	MSC Letizia	178	MSC Orchestra	21	MSC Taranto	227
MSC Bettina	175	MSC Flaminia	86	MSC Levina	178	MSC Oriane	179	MSC Tasmania	180
MSC Bhavya	209	MSC Flavia	176	MSC Lieselotte	178	MSC Ornella	179	MSC Teresa	180
MSC Bilbao	103	MSC Florentina	176	MSC Lily	178	MSC Oscar	179	MSC Teresa	227
MSC Branka	181	MSC Floriana	176	MSC Lirica	21	MSC Paloma	179	MSC Texas	86
MSC Bremen	232	MSC Florida	250	MSC Lisa	178			MSC Tia	69

MSC Tokyo	227
MSC Tomoko	180
MSC Toronto	227
MSC Trieste	227
MSC Ulsan	88
MSC Uma	69
MSC Vaishnavi R.	180
MSC Valencia	103
MSC Valeria	180
MSC Vancouver	48
MSC Vandya	180
MSC Vanessa	180
MSC Vega	48
MSC Venice	108
MSC Veronique	265
MSC Vidhi	180
MSC Vidisha R.	180
MSC Vienna	212
MSC Vigo	227
MSC Vita	180
MSC Vittoria	180
MSC Zebra	93
MSC Zlata R.	180
MSC Zoe	180
Munchen Bridge	271
Munk Strait	248
Munkebo Maersk	189
Muntgracht	277
Murgash	201
Murwab	187
Mutriba	162
Myrtos	67
Mystic	65
N Amalthia	204
N Bonanza	204
N Discovery	231
N Loire	231
N Schelde	231
N. Mars	232
Nadir	40
Nagoya Express	139
Nagoya Tower	311
Najade	174
Najran	298
Nala Delmas	79
Nandu Arrow	154
Nansen Spirit	286
Nansen Strait	248
Nantucket	67
Narew	243
Narmada Spirit	286
Narodny Bridge	274
Nasca	45
Nassauborg	303
Natal	222
Nataly	170
Naticina	269
National Geographic Endeavour	33
National Geographic Explorer	33
National Geographic Orion	33
Nautic	82
Nautica	19
Nautical Elizabeth	85
Nautical Hilary	85
Nautical Jennifer	85
Nautical Loredana	85
Nautical Lucia	85
Nautical Marie	85
Nautical Runi	85
Nautical Sif	85
Nautilus	95

Nautilus	82
Navarin	82
Navarino	88
Navarra	45
Nave Alderamin	204
Nave Andromeda	204
Nave Aquila	204
Nave Ariadne	204
Nave Atria	204
Nave Atropos	204
Nave Bellatrix	204
Nave Buena Suerte	204
Nave Capella	204
Nave Cassiopeia	204
Nave Cetus	204
Nave Cielo	204
Nave Constellation	204
Nave Cosmos	204
Nave Dorado	204
Nave Electron	204
Nave Equator	204
Nave Equinox	204
Nave Estella	204
Nave Galactic	204
Nave Jupiter	204
Nave Neutrino	204
Nave Orbit	204
Nave Orion	204
Nave Photon	204
Nave Polaris	204
Nave Pulsar	204
Nave Pyxis	204
Nave Quasar	204
Nave Rigel	204
Nave Sextans	204
Nave Spherical	204
Nave Synergy	204
Nave Titan	204
Nave Universe	204
Nave Velocity	204
Navig8 Achroite	199
Navig8 Adamite	199
Navig8 Alabaster	199
Navig8 Almandine	199
Navig8 Amazonite	199
Navig8 Amber	199
Navig8 Amessi	199
Navig8 Amethyst	199
Navig8 Ametrine	199
Navig8 Ammolite	199
Navig8 Andesine	199
Navig8 Aquamarine	200
Navig8 Aragonite	200
Navig8 Aronaldo	200
Navig8 Aventurine	200
Navig8 Axinite	200
Navig8 Azotic	200
Navig8 Azurite	200
Navig8 Exceed	200
Navig8 Excel	200
Navig8 Excellence	200
Navig8 Excelsior	200
Navig8 Executive	200
Navig8 Expedite	200
Navig8 Experience	200
Navig8 Express	200
Navig8 Faith	200
Navig8 Gallantry	200
Navig8 Gauntlet	200
Navig8 Gladiator	200
Navig8 Goal	200
Navig8 Grace	200
Navig8 Gratitude	200
Navig8 Guard	200

Navig8 Guide	200
Navig8 Honor	200
Navig8 Precision	200
Navig8 Prestige	200
Navig8 Pride	200
Navig8 Providence	200
Navig8 Saiph	200
Navig8 Sanctity	200
Navig8 Sirius	200
Navig8 Sky	200
Navig8 Sol	200
Navig8 Solace	200
Navig8 Solidarity	200
Navig8 Spark	200
Navig8 Spectrum	200
Navig8 Spica	200
Navig8 Spirit	200
Navig8 Stability	200
Navig8 Steadfast	200
Navig8 Stealth	200
Navig8 Stealth S.V.	200
Navig8 Stellar	200
Navig8 Strength	200
Navig8 Success	200
Navig8 Supreme	200
Navig8 Symphony	200
Navig8 Tanzanite	200
Navig8 Topaz	200
Navig8 Tourmaline	200
Navig8 Turquoise	200
Navig8 Victoria	200
Navig8 Violette	200
Navigator	106
Navigator Aries	201
Navigator Atlas	201
Navigator Capricorn	201
Navigator Centauri	201
Navigator Ceres	201
Navigator Ceto	202
Navigator Copernico	202
Navigator Europa	201
Navigator Galaxy	202
Navigator Gemini	202
Navigator Genesis	202
Navigator Global	202
Navigator Glory	202
Navigator Grace	202
Navigator Gusto	202
Navigator Leo	202
Navigator Libra	202
Navigator Magellan	202
Navigator Mars	202
Navigator Neptune	202
Navigator Oberon	202
Navigator of the Seas	24
Navigator Pegasus	202
Navigator Phoenix	202
Navigator Pluto	202
Navigator Saturn	202
Navigator Scorpio	202
Navigator Spirit	286
Navigator Taurus	202
Navigator Triton	202
Navigator Umbrio	202
Navigator Venus	202
Navigator Virgo	202
Navion Anglia	288
Navion Bergen	286
Navion Britannia	288
Navion Europa	286
Navion Gothenburg	286
Navion Hispania	286
Navion Marita	288

Navion Oceania	288
Navion Oslo	288
Navion Scandia	288
Navion Stavanger	288
Navios Achilles	204
Navios Aldebaran	204
Navios Alegria	204
Navios Altair	204
Navios Altamira	205
Navios Amber	205
Navios Amitié	205
Navios Antares	205
Navios Apollon	205
Navios Arc	205
Navios Armonia	205
Navios Asteriks	205
Navios Astra	205
Navios Aurora II	205
Navios Avior	205
Navios Azimuth	205
Navios Bonavis	205
Navios Bonheur	205
Navios Buena Ventura	205
Navios Celestial	205
Navios Centaurus	205
Navios Coral	206
Navios Etoile	205
Navios Fantastiks	205
Navios Felicity	205
Navios Felix	206
Navios Fulvia	205
Navios Galaxy I	205
Navios Galileo	205
Navios Gem	205
Navios Gemini S	205
Navios Happiness	205
Navios Harmony	205
Navios Helios	205
Navios Herakles	205
Navios Hios	205
Navios Hope	205
Navios Horizon	205
Navios Hyperion	205
Navios Ionian	205
Navios Joy	205
Navios Koyo	205
Navios Kypros	205
Navios La Paix	205
Navios Libra II	205
Navios Lumen	205
Navios Luz	205
Navios Lyra	205
Navios Magellan	205
Navios Marco Polo	205
Navios Mars	205
Navios Melodia	205
Navios Mercator	205
Navios Mercury	205
Navios Meridian	205
Navios Northern Star	205
Navios Obeliks	205
Navios Orbiter	205
Navios Oriana	205
Navios Phoenix	205
Navios Pollux	205
Navios Primavera	205
Navios Prosperity	205
Navios Ray	205
Navios Sagittarius	205
Navios Serenity	205
Navios Sky	205
Navios Soleil	205

Navios Southern Star	205
Navios Sphera	205
Navios Star	205
Navios Stellar	205
Navios Sun	206
Navios Taurus	206
Navios Ulysses	206
Navios Vector	206
Navios Vega	206
Navios Venus	206
NCC Abha	43
NCC Amal	43
NCC Dammam	43
NCC Danah	43
NCC Fajr	43
NCC Haiel	43
NCC Hijaz	43
NCC Huda	43
NCC Jood	43
NCC Maha	43
NCC Masa	43
NCC Najd	43
NCC Najem	43
NCC Nasma	43
NCC Noor	43
NCC Qamar	43
NCC Qassim	43
NCC Rabigh	43
NCC Reem	43
NCC Safa	43
NCC Sama	43
NCC Shams	43
NCC Sudair	43
NCC Tabuk	43
NCC Tihama	43
NCC Wafa	43
Nectar	82
Nectar Sea	108
Nederland Reefer	96
Negonego	65
Nele Maersk	189
Nell Jacob	152
Nelson	222
Neo Energy	296
Neptun	82
Neptun D	232
Neptune Ace	185
Neptune Pioneer	120
Neptune Voyager	70
Neste	208
Neva River	157
NevadaTrader	169
Nevskiy Prospect	274
New Breeze	217
New Delhi Express	265
New England	302
New Hampshire Trader	167
New Nada	210
New York Express	139
New York Star	70
Newark	222
Newton	82
Newyorker	285
Nexø Maersk	189
Nexus Victoria	135
Niban	43
Nicolai Maersk	189
Nicolas Delmas	79
Nicoline Bulker	165
Nicoline Maersk	189
Nieuw Amsterdam	13
Nikolas	285

RT Dagr	160	Saga Sky	253
RT Odin	160	Saga Spray	253
Rubena N	206	Saga Tide	253
Rubina	102	Saga Tucano	253
Rubina Schulte	259	Saga Viking	253
Ruby Ace	185	Saga Voyager	253
Ruby Princess	15	Saga Wave	253
Ruby Star	69	Saga Wind	253
Rudolf Schepers	255	Sagitta	97
Rudolf Schulte	258	Sagittaurus Leader	211
Ruen	201	Sahba	43
Runaway Bay	267	Saigon Express	265
Rysy	245	Saimaagracht	277
Ryujin	211	Saint Albans Bay	261
S/R American		Saint Laurent	33
Progress	118	Saint Nicholas	290
SA Altius	113	Saint Roch	79
SA Fortius	113	Sajir	298
Sabine	96	Sakaka	298
Sabya	298	Sakar	201
Saetta	67	Sakhalin Island	274
Safaniyah	43	Sakura Princess	296
Safmarine Bayete	190	Salacgriva	164
Safmarine Benguela	190	Salahuddin	298
Safmarine Boland	285	Salamina	296
Safmarine		Saldanha	64
Cameroun	193	Salford Quay	48
Safmarine Chachai	190	Sallie Knutsen	159
Safmarine Chambal	190	Sally Maersk	189
Safmarine Chilka	190	Salome	303
Safmarine Highveld	285	Salta	222
Safmarine Kuramo	193	Salvia Ace	185
Safmarine Mafadi	190	Samatan	65
Safmarine Makutu	190	Samba Spirit	286
Safmarine Meru	190	Sampogracht	277
Safmarine Mulanje	190	Samurai	106
Safmarine Nakuru	190	San	245
Safmarine Ngami	193	San Adriano	52
Safmarine Nile	190	San Alessio	52
Safmarine Nimba	193	San Alvaro	227
Safmarine		San Amerigo	227
Nokwanda	194	San Andres	52
Safmarine		San Antonio	227
Nomazwe	190	San Antonio	
Safmarine Nuba	191	Express	140
Safmarine Nyassa	191	San Aurelio	228
Safwa	43	San Christobal	226
Saga	67	San Clemente	226
Saga Adventure	253	San Diego Bridge	271
Saga Andorinha	253	San Felipe	226
Saga Beija-Flor	253	San Felix	226
Saga Crest	253	San Fernando	226
Saga Discovery	253	San Francisca	226
Saga Enterprise	253	San Francisco	
Saga Explorer	253	Bridge	157
Saga Falcon	253	San Marino Trader	55
Saga Fantasy	253	San Rafael	222
Saga Fjord	253	San Saba	96
Saga Fortune	253	San Vicente	226
Saga Fram	253	San Vicente	209
Saga Frigg	253	Sana	152
Saga Frontier	253	Sanderling Ace	185
Saga Fuji	253	Sandnes	181
Saga Future	253	Sandra	82
Saga Horizon	253	Sandy Rickmers	250
Saga Jandaia	253	Santa Barbara	226
Saga Journey	253	Santa Bettina	227
Saga Monal	253	Santa Catarina	226
Saga Morus	253	Santa Catharina	267
Saga Navigator	253	Santa Clara	226
Saga Odyssey	253	Santa Cruz	114
Saga Pearl II	27	Santa Cruz	226
Saga Pioneer	253	Santa Fe	222
Saga Sapphire	27	Santa Fiorenza	228

Santa Francesca	228	SCF Baikal	274
Santa Giannina	228	SCF Baltica	275
Santa Giuliana	228	SCF Caucasus	275
Santa Giulietta	228	SCF Khibiny	275
Santa Ines	226	SCF Melampus	275
Santa Isabel	226	SCF Mitre	275
Santa Laura	228	SCF Neva	275
Santa Lucia	268	SCF Pacifica	275
Santa Maria	268	SCF Pearl	275
Santa Rita	226	SCF Pechora	275
Santa Rosa	226	SCF Pioneer	275
Santa Teresa	226	SCF Plymouth	275
Santa Ursula	226	SCF Prime	275
Santiago	144	SCF Primorye	275
Sao Luiz	300	SCF Progress	275
Sao Sebastiao	300	SCF Provider	275
Sapienza	183	SCF Prudencia	275
Sapphire Ace	185	SCF Sayan	275
Sapphire Princess	15	SCF Shanghai	277
Sapporo Princess	296	SCF Suek	275
Sara	82	SCF Surgut	275
Sarah Schulte	259	SCF Tobolsk	275
Sarasota	67	SCF Tomsk	275
Sarpen	170	SCF Ural	275
Satie	228	SCF Yamal	276
Saturn	40	SCF Yenisei	275
Saxonia	103	Scheldegracht	277
SBI Achilles	259	Schinousa	183
SBI Antares	259	Schippersgracht	277
SBI Athena	259	Schubert	258
SBI Bolero	259	Schweiz Reefer	96
SBI Bravo	259	Scirocco	106
SBI Cakewalk	259	Scorpio	67
SBI Capoeira	259	Scotian Express	302
SBI Carioca	260	Scott Spirit	286
SBI Charleston	260	SCT Matterhorn	283
SBI Conga	260	SCT Monte Rosa	283
SBI Cronos	260	SCT Samotlor	275
SBI Echo	260	Sea Adventurer	30
SBI Electra	260	Sea Bay	124
SBI Flamenco	260	Sea Behike	122
SBI Hercules	260	Sea Cloud	27
SBI Hermes	260	Sea Cloud II	27
SBI Hydra	260	Sea Discoverer	33
SBI Lambada	260	Sea Falcon	39
SBI Leo	260	Sea Hope	124
SBI Lyra	260	Sea Land	
SBI Macarena	260	Champion	191
SBI Maia	260	Sea Lion	39
SBI Orion	260	Sea Lynx	39
SBI Parapara	260	Sea Monterrey	122
SBI Pegasus	260	Sea Phoenix	267
SBI Perseus	260	Sea Princess	15
SBI Reggae	260	Sea Spirit	33
SBI Rock	260	Sea-Land Charger	193
SBI Rumba	260	Sea-Land Comet	193
SBI Samba	260	Sea-Land Eagle	191
SBI Samson	260	Sea-Land Intrepid	193
SBI Sousta	260	Sea-Land Lightning	193
SBI Subaru	260	Sea-Land Mercury	191
SBI Swing	260	Sea-Land Meteor	191
SBI Tango	260	Sea-Land Racer	191
SBI Thalia	260	Seabass	128
SBI Twist	260	Seabee	290
SBI Ursa	260	Seaboard America	144
SBI Zumba	260	Seaboard Pacific	144
Scandinavian	69	Seaboard Peru	144
Scandinavian		Seaboard	
Express	302	Valparaiso	144
Scarlet Ray	109	Seaboni	290
Scarlet Trader	280	Seaborn	290
SCF Alpine	274	Seaboss	290
SCF Altai	274	Seabourn Encore	15
SCF Amur	274	Seabourn Odyssey	15

Seabourn Ovation	15
Seabourn Quest	15
Seabourn Sojourn	15
Seaboxer III	290
Seabravery	290
Seabreeze	290
Seachance	290
Seacod	128
Seaconger	128
Seacross	290
Seacrown I	290
Seadancer	290
Seadream	290
SeaDream I	34
SeaDream II	34
Seaempress	290
Seaexplorer	290
Seaexpress	290
Seafaith II	290
Seafalcon	290
Seafarer	290
Seafighter	290
Seaforce	290
Seafriend	290
Seago Antwerp	194
Seago	
Bremerhaven	194
Seago Felixstowe	194
Seago Istanbul	194
Seago Piraeus	194
Seahake	128
Seaharmony	290
Seahero	290
Seahope II	290
Seaking	290
Sealand Illinois	88
Sealand Michigan	88
Sealand New York	88
Sealand Washington	88
Sealing	128
Sealink	290
Sealoyalty	290
Sealuck II	290
Seamagic	290
Seamarlin	128
Seamaster IV	290
Seamate	291
Seamax Stamford	174
Seamercury	291
Seameridian	134
Seamerit	291
Seamullet	128
Seamuse	291
Seamusic	291
Seaoath	291
Seapace	291
Seapike	128
Seapride	291
Seaprince	291
Seaprincess	291
Seapromise	291
Seaqueen	291
Searacer	291
Searambler	291
Searay	128
Searider	291
Seasalvia	291
Seascout	291
Seashark	128
Seasmile	291
Seasong	291
Seaspan Chiwan	265
Seaspan Dalian	265
Seaspan Felixstowe	265

Star Kilimanjaro 131
Star Kinn 131
Star Kirkenes 131
Star Kvarven 131
Star Laguna 132
Star Leader 236
Star Legend 30
Star Lima 132
Star Lindesnes 132
Star Livorno 132
Star Loen 132
Star Lofoten 132
Star Louisiana 132
Star Luster 132
Star Lygra 132
Star Lysefjord 132
Star Merlin 217
Star Minerva 132
Star N 206
Star Norita 297
Star Osprey 217
Star Pisces 21
Star Planet 69
Star Pride 236
Star Pride 30
Star Prima 272
Star Princess 15
Star Princess 69
Star Quality 236
Star Service I 236
Star Standard 237
Star Stratos 237
Star Trader 69
Star Trust 237
Stara Planina 201
Stargate 109
Statengracht 279
Stavronisi 110
Stealth Skyros 184
Stella 296
Stellar Voyager 70
Stena Alexita 280
Stena Arctica 280
Stena Blue Sky 280
Stena Clear Sky 280
Stena Companion 282
Stena Concert 280
Stena Conqueror 281
Stena Conquest 281
Stena Crystal Sky 280
Stena Image 281
Stena Imagination 281
Stena Immaculate 281
Stena Immense 281
Stena Impeccable 281
Stena Imperative 281
Stena Imperial 281
Stena Important 281
Stena Impression 281
Stena Natalita 280
Stena Paris 282
Stena Penguin 280
Stena Performance 280
Stena Perros 280
Stena Polaris 282
Stena Premium 280
Stena President 280
Stena Primorsk 280
Stena Progress 282
Stena Provence 280
Stena Sirita 280
Stena Spirit 286
Stena Suede 280
Stena Sunrise 282
Stena Superior 280
Stena Supreme 280
Stenaweco Andrea Corrado 281
Stenaweco Caterina Corrado 281
Stenaweco Energy 281
Stenaweco Evolution 281
Stenaweco Gladys W. 281
Stenaweco Impulse 94
Stenaweco Julia L 281
Stenaweco Marjorie K. 281
Stenaweco Spirit 129
Stenaweco Venture 129
Steven N 61
STI Acton 261
STI Alexis 261
STI Amber 261
STI Aqua 261
STI Battersea 261
STI Battery 261
STI Benecia 261
STI Beryl 261
STI Black Hawk 261
STI Brixton 261
STI Broadway 261
STI Bronx 261
STI Brooklyn 261
STI Camden 261
STI Carnaby 261
STI Clapham 261
STI Comandante 261
STI Condotti 261
STI Connaught 261
STI Dama 261
STI Duchessa 261
STI Elysees 261
STI Emerald 261
STI Finchley 261
STI Fontvieille 261
STI Fulham 261
STI Garnet 261
STI Grace 263
STI Gramercy 261
STI Hackney 261
STI Hammersmith 261
STI Jermyn 263
STI Kingsway 261
STI Larvotto 261
STI Lauren 261
STI Le Rocher 261
STI Lombard 262
STI Madison 262
STI Manhattan 262
STI Mayfair 262
STI Meraux 262
STI Milwaukee 262
STI Notting Hill 262
STI Onyx 262
STI Opera 262
STI Orchard 262
STI Osceola 262
STI Oxford 262
STI Park 262
STI Pimlico 262
STI Pontiac 262
STI Poplar 262
STI Queens 262
STI Regina 262
STI Rose 262
STI Rotherhithe 262
STI Ruby 262
STI San Antonio 262
STI Sapphire 263
STI Savile Row 263
STI Seneca 263
STI Sloane 263
STI Soho 263
STI Spiga 263
STI St. Charles 263
STI Texas City 263
STI Topaz 263
STI Tribeca 263
STI Venere 263
STI Veneto 263
STI Ville 263
STI Virtus 263
STI Wembley 263
STI Westminster 263
STI Winnie 263
STI Yorkville 263
Stjerneborg 94
Stolt Achievement 281
Stolt Ami 281
Stolt Basuto 281
Stolt Bobcat 281
Stolt Breland 281
Stolt Capability 281
Stolt Commitment 281
Stolt Concept 281
Stolt Confidence 281
Stolt Courage 281
Stolt Creativity 281
Stolt Efficiency 281
Stolt Effort 281
Stolt Emerald 281
Stolt Endurance 281
Stolt Facto 281
Stolt Focus 281
Stolt Glory 281
Stolt Groenland 281
Stolt Gulf Mirdif 281
Stolt Gulf Mishref 281
Stolt Hill 281
Stolt Innovation 281
Stolt Inspiration 281
Stolt Invention 281
Stolt Island 281
Stolt Jade 281
Stolt Megami 281
Stolt Mountain 281
Stolt Norland 281
Stolt Perseverance 281
Stolt Pondo 281
Stolt Sagaland 281
Stolt Sea 281
Stolt Sisto 281
Stolt Sneland 281
Stolt Span 281
Stolt Spray 281
Stolt Stream 282
Stolt Strength 282
Stolt Sun 282
Stolt Surf 282
Stolt Topaz 282
Stolt Vanguard 282
Stolt Vestland 282
Stolt Viking 282
Stolt Vinland 282
Stolt Virtue 282
Stolt Vision 282
Stolt Zulu 282
Stones 181
Storviken 300
Strandja 201
Strauss 259
Stride 295
Striggla 64
Strofades 110
Strymon 167
Sudair 298
Süderoog 54
Sudety 245
Suez Canal 93
Sulu Sea 109
Summer E. 232
Summer Flower 69
Summer Meadow 69
Summit Africa 256
Summit Spirit 286
Sun Princess 15
Sunbird Arrow 154
Sunlight Ace 185
Sunray 296
Sunrise 296
Sunrise Ace 185
Sunshine Ace 185
Suomigracht 279
Super Challenge 44
Super Servant 3 98
Super Servant 4 279
SuperStar Aquarius 21
SuperStar Gemini 21
SuperStar Libra 21
SuperStar Virgo 21
Supreme Ace 185
Surfer Rosa 183
Susan Maersk 189
Susanne Victory 67
Suse 308
Suvorovsky Prospect 275
Suzuka Express 302
Svend Maersk 189
Svendborg Maersk 189
Svendborg Strait 248
Svet 277
SW Julia I 256
SW Monaco I 256
Swakop 113
Swallow Ace 185
Swan 98
Swan Ace 185
Swan Chacabuco 69
Swansea 311
Swedish Reefer 96
Swift 98
Swift Ace 185
Swift Arrow 154
Sycamore 224
Sydney Spirit 286
Sydney Trader 168
Symi 110
Symphonic 165
Sypress 224
Szare Szeregi 245
Szczecin 245
Szczecin 245
Szczecin Trader 55
Szymanowski 73
Taagborg 303
Tabea 101
Tahiti 67
Tahoe Spirit 286
Taipan 248
Tajimare 106
Tala 51
Talassa 101
Talia 248
Talisman 305
Talisman 98
Tamar 279
Tamara 67
Tamarita 297
Tamerlane 305
Tamesis 305
Tamina 101
Tammo 254
Tampa 64
Tana Sea 222
Tanchou Arrow 154
Tangguh Hiri 286
Tangguh Sago 286
Tango Sea 222
Tansanit 85
Tanya Jacob 152
Tarago 305
Taranger 307
Tarbet Spirit 286
Targale 164
Target 99
Tarifa 248
Tâsinge Maersk 189
Tasman 285
Tasman Castle 214
Tasman Mermaid 268
Tasman Strait 248
Tataki 106
Tatry 245
Tauros 88
Taurus 113
Taurus 40
Taurus Leader 211
Taurus Sun 311
Tavrichesky Bridge 275
Tawa Arrow 154
Tayma 298
Teal 99
Teal Bulker 165
Teatralny Bridge 275
Tectus 269
Teesta Spirit 217
Teide Spirit 288
Telendos 110
Telleviken 300
Tembek 239
Tempanos 140
Tempera 208
Temse 118
Tenca Arrow 154
Tere Moana 23
Tern 99
Tern Bulker 165
Tessa 101
Texas 106
Texas Highway 157
Texas Trader 168
TG Aphrodite 129
TG Athena 129
TG Nike 129
TG Poseidon 129
Thalassa Avra 111
Thalassa Axia 111
Thalassa Doxa 111
Thalassa Elpida 111
Thalassa Hellas 111
Thalassa Mana 111
Thalassa Niki 111
Thalassa Patris 111
Thalassa Pistis 111
Thalassa Tyhi 111
Thalatta 305
Thalos 88

Company Names